INTRODUCTION TO

STATISTICAL

INVESTIGATIONS

Nathan L. Tintle | Ruth E. Carver | Beth L. Chance

George W. Cobb | Allan J. Rossman | Soma Roy

Todd M. Swanson | Jill L. VanderStoep

WILEY

VICE PRESIDENT AND DIRECTOR	Laurie Rosatone
SENIOR ACQUISITIONS EDITOR	Joanna Dingle
PRODUCT DESIGN MANAGER	Tom Kulesa
PRODUCT DESIGNER	Adria Giattino
MARKETING MANAGER	John LaVacca III
DEVELOPMENT ASSISTANT	Kimberly Eskin
SENIOR CONTENT MANAGER	Valerie Zaborski
PHOTO RESEARCH	Billy Ray
SENIOR DESIGNER/COVER DESIGN	Wendy Lai
XML SPECIALIST	Bud Peters
PRODUCTION EDITOR	Ashley Patterson
SENIOR MARKET DEVELOPMENT MANAGER	Robert Johnston
SENIOR MARKET DEVELOPMENT ASSISTANT	Sue DelGatto

This book was set in MinionPro-Regular, HelveticaNeueLTStd, and STIX by Aptara® Inc., and printed and bound by Courier Westford. The cover was printed by Courier Westford.

This book is printed on acid free paper. ∞

Founded in 1807, John Wiley & Sons, Inc. has been a valued source of knowledge and understanding for more than 200 years, helping people around the world meet their needs and fulfill their aspirations. Our company is built on a foundation of principles that include responsibility to the communities we serve and where we live and work. In 2008, we launched a Corporate Citizenship Initiative, a global effort to address the environmental, social, economic, and ethical challenges we face in our business. Among the issues we are addressing are carbon impact, paper specifications and procurement, ethical conduct within our business and among our vendors, and community and charitable support. For more information, please visit our website: www.wiley.com/go/citizenship.

This project has been and is being supported from the National Science Foundation Grant DUE-1140629 and Grant DUE-1323210. Any opinions, findings, and conclusions or recommendations expressed in this materials are those of the authors and do not necessarily reflect the views of the National Science Foundation.

The inside back cover will contain printing identification and country of origin if omitted from this page. In addition, if the ISBN on the back cover differs from the ISBN on this page, the one on the back cover is correct.

ISBN: 978-1-119-50347-7

Printed in the United States of America

10 9 8 7 6 5 4 3 2 1

ABOUT THE AUTHORS

RUTH E. CARVER teaches AP® Statistics at Germantown Academy in Fort Washington, Pennsylvania, where she served as chairperson of the mathematics department from 1996 to 2014 and was the first recipient of the Claire and Jeffrey Black Endowed Chair for Excellence in the Teaching of Mathematics (2013–2016). She has been involved with the Advanced Placement® Statistics program as a reader and table leader and served on the AP® Statistic Test Development Committee from 2008 to 2012. She is co-founder of the Philadelphia Area Statistics Teachers' Association (PASTA) and is a consultant for the Middle States Region of the College Board. She is a recipient of the Siemens Foundation AP® Teacher Award; the Presidential Award for Excellence in Mathematics and Science Teaching; the National Education and Technology Alliance STAR Award and "Best of the Best" Award; the Teachers Teaching with Technology Demana/Waits Vision Award; and the Tandy Technology Prize for Teaching Excellence in Mathematics, Science, and Computer Science.

BETH L. CHANCE is Professor of Statistics at California Polytechnic State University. She is co-author with Allan Rossman of the *Workshop Statistics* series and *Investigating Statistical Concepts, Applications, and Methods*. She has published articles on statistics education in *The American Statistician*, *Journal of Statistics Education*, and the *Statistics Education Research Journal*. She has also collaborated on several chapters and books aimed at enhancing teacher preparation to teach statistics and has been involved for many years with the Advanced Placement Statistics program. She is a Fellow of the American Statistical Association and received the 2002 Waller Education Award for Excellence and Innovation in Teaching Undergraduate Statistics. The Rossman/Chance collection of online applets for exploring statistical concepts was awarded the 2009 CAUSEweb Resource of the Year Award and a 2011 MERLOT Award for Exemplary Learning Materials.

GEORGE W. COBB is Robert L. Rooke Professor Emeritus of Statistics at Mount Holyoke College and has extensive knowledge of statistics education, expertise in developing imaginative and innovative curricular materials, and the honor of having brought the conversation on randomization-based approaches in introductory statistics to the mainstream via his 2005 USCOTS presentation and 2007 paper. He served as the first chair of the Joint Committee on Undergraduate Statistics of the American Mathematical Association and American Statistical Association (1991–98), editing that committee's 1992 report "Teaching Statistics." He served for three years on the National Research Council's Committee on Applied and Theoretical Statistics and served as vice-president of the American Statistical Association. He is a Fellow of the ASA and received the ASA's Founders Award in 2007. He has published/edited a number of books.

ALLAN J. ROSSMAN is Professor and Chair of the Statistics Department at California Polytechnic State University. He earned a Ph.D. in Statistics from Carnegie Mellon University. He is co-author with Beth Chance of the *Workshop Statistics* series and *Investigating Statistical Concepts, Applications, and Methods*, both of which adopt an active learning approach to learning introductory statistics. He served as Program Chair for the 2007 Joint Statistical Meetings, as President of the International Association for Statistical Education from 2007 to 2009, and as Chief Reader for the Advanced Placement program in statistics from 2009 to 2014. He is a Fellow of the American Statistical Association and has received the Mathematical Association of America's Haimo Award for Distinguished College or University Teaching of Mathematics in 2010 and the American Statistical Association's Waller Distinguished Teaching Career Award in 2016.

SOMA ROY is Associate Professor of Statistics at California Polytechnic State University. She is the current editor for the *Journal of Statistics Education* and has presented talks related to the randomization-based curriculum and student learning at national meetings. She has written and reviewed assessment tasks for the Illustrative Mathematics Project, an initiative to support adoption of the K–12 core standards for statistics. She has been serving as a reader for Advanced Placement® exams in statistics since June 2012. She co-leads, with her colleagues at Cal Poly, a teacher-preparation workshop for AP® Statistics teachers. She also has an active research program in health statistics involving undergraduates.

TODD SWANSON is an Associate Professor of Mathematics at Hope College. He is a co-author of *A Spiral Approach to Financial Mathematics*, *Precalculus: A Study of Functions and Their Applications*, *Understanding Our Quantitative World*, *Projects for Precalculus*, which was an INPUT Award winner, and *Introduction to Statistical Investigations*, which was a Most Promising New Textbook Award winner. He has published articles in *Mathematics Teacher*, *Journal of Statistics Education*, *Statistics Education Research Journal*, and *Stats: The Magazine for Students of Statistics*. He has presented at numerous national meetings, workshops, and mini-courses about innovative ways to teach mathematics and statistics that focus on guided-discovery methods and projects.

NATHAN L. TINTLE is a Professor of Statistics at Dordt College. He has led efforts to develop and institutionalize randomization-based curricula at two institutions

(Hope College 2005–2011; Dordt 2011–present), and currently leads the curriculum development project. He has been an invited panelist for a number of statistics education sessions at national meetings, served on the Executive Committee of the Section of Statistical Education of the ASA, received the 2013 Waller Education Award for Teaching and Innovation in Introductory Statistics, the 2017 Robert V. Hogg Award for Excellence in Teaching Introductory Statistics, and served as a member of a national advisory committee to the ASA President on training the next generation of statisticians. He has co-authored multiple articles on student learning using the randomization curriculum, one of which recently won an award for best paper of the year from the *Journal of Statistics Education.*

JILL L. VANDERSTOEP is an Adjunct Assistant Professor of Mathematics at Hope College. She has participated in efforts to develop and implement simulation/randomization-based curricula at Hope College since 2005. She has presented on the curriculum and assessment results at national conferences and has co-led workshops on introducing and implementing the simulation/randomization-based curriculum. She has co-authored articles published in the *Journal of Statistics Education, Statistics Education Research Journal,* and *The American Statistician.*

PREFACE

This book leads students to learn about the process of conducting statistical investigations from data collection, to exploring data, to statistical inference, to drawing appropriate conclusions. We focus on genuine research studies, active learning, and effective use of technology. In particular, we use simulation and randomization tests to introduce students to statistical inference, yielding a strong conceptual foundation that bridges students to theory-based inference approaches, which are presented throughout the book. This approach allows students to see the logic and scope of inference in the first chapter and to repeatedly cycle through these ideas, too often lost to introductory statistics students, throughout the course. Our implementation follows the GAISE recommendations endorsed by the American Statistical Association.

APPROACH

We adopt several distinctive features:

1. **Spiral approach to statistical process.** We introduce the six-step process of conducting statistical investigations in the very first section (see Figure 1).

We introduce this process in its entirety beginning in the Preliminaries chapter. Then we present a complete implementation in Chapter 1, involving research questions focused on a process probability. This relatively simple scenario enables us to introduce students to the fundamental concept of statistical significance, along with some issues related to collecting data and drawing conclusions, early in the course.

Our goal is for students to begin to develop an understanding of important and challenging concepts such as the p-value from the beginning, and then deepen their understanding as they encounter such ideas repeatedly in new scenarios:

- Single binary variable (inference for a population proportion)

FIGURE 1 The six-step statistical investigation method.

- Single quantitative variable
- Comparing a binary variable between two groups (inference for 2 × 2 table)
- Comparing a quantitative variable between two groups
- Comparing a categorical variable across multiple groups
- Comparing a quantitative variable across multiple groups
- Association between two quantitative variables

With each of these scenarios, students reconsider and apply the six-step statistical investigation method. Students also revisit, at deeper and deeper levels each time, the core ideas of statistical inference. They learn that the fundamental reasoning process of statistical inference remains the same in all scenarios that they study.

¹http://www.amstat.org/education/gaise/

2. **Randomization-based introduction to statistical inference.** A randomization-based approach to statistical inference is key to its successful early introduction. For every scenario that students encounter in this book, they first learn how to make inferences using simulations of chance models. Then we introduce students to theory-based procedures for statistical inference, based on the normal distribution and its derivatives, as an alternative approximation to the randomization-based methods. Some of the advantages for starting with the randomization-based approach, as spelled out by Cobb (2007), include:

- More intuitive for students to understand
- Easily generalizable to other situations and statistics
- Takes advantage of modern computing
- Closer to what founders of statistical inference (e.g., R. A. Fisher) envisioned

3. **Focus on logic and scope of inference.** For virtually every study we present, we ask students to consider two questions related to the *logic* of inference and two questions related to *scope* of inference:

- Are the study's results unlikely to have arisen by chance alone, indicating that the difference between the observed data and the hypothesized model is **statistically significant**?
- How large do you estimate the difference/effect to be, and how **confident** can you be in this estimate?
- To what group can a conclusion from the study reasonably be **generalized**?
- Can a **cause-and-effect** conclusion be legitimately drawn between the variables? (This applies to studies involving at least two variables, starting in Chapter 4.)

The first pair of questions addresses the two key issues of statistical inference: significance and confidence. Answering the second pair depends on examining how subjects were selected for the study and how the groups were formed, determining whether random sampling or random assignment (or both) was used.

4. **Integration of exposition, examples, and explorations.** Every section includes at least one example that illustrates the ideas and methods presented, and at least one exploration that students work through to learn about and gain experience with applying the topic. We offer much flexibility for instructors to decide on the order in which they will present these components, and what they will ask students to do in class vs. outside of class. *To facilitate this flexibility, examples and explorations within a section are written so that neither depends on the other,* allowing the instructor to present either one first. The only exception appears in the Preliminaries, where there are two examples and one exploration, each of which introduces new concepts. We make

this exception to encourage instructors to *finish the Preliminaries in no more than 2–3 class periods,* while still introducing the text's flexibility for use with both lecture-based and activity-based class periods.

5. **Easy-to-use technology integrated throughout.** Rather than ask students to learn to use a statistical software package, we have designed easy-to-use Web-applets that enable students to conduct all of the simulations and perform all of the analyses presented in this book. Instructors may also ask students to use a commercial software package, but this is not required.

6. **Real data from genuine studies.** We utilize real data from genuine research studies throughout the book. These studies are taken from a variety of fields of application and popular culture. Each chapter also includes a detailed investigation and a research article, giving students even more exposure to genuine applications of statistics.

CHANGES IN CONTENT SEQUENCING

Inference. This book puts inferential statistics at the heart of the curriculum. Thus, the course starts with core concepts of inference immediately in the Preliminaries and Chapter 1 and continues focusing on ideas of inference throughout. We introduce students to fundamental ideas such as statistical significance and p-values in Chapter 1. We engage students with thinking about these crucial, and challenging, issues from the very start of the course, setting the stage for revisiting these core concepts repeatedly in new settings throughout the course. With this spiraling approach, we expect students to deepen their understanding of the inferential process each time it is revisited.

Descriptive statistics. We take a case-study approach that focuses on the statistical investigation process as a whole. Thus, descriptive statistics are integrated throughout this curriculum. The curriculum cycles through different types of data and numbers of variables in each chapter, so students are introduced to basic descriptive methods as they are necessary for analysis. By the end of the course, the content covered is very similar to a traditional course, but the content has been introduced in context through genuine applications.

Probability. Students see probability concepts in this book, but in a way that differs substantially from how probability is taught in the traditional curriculum. Specifically, we expect students to explore notions of probability through tactile and computer-based simulations. Students use chance models to obtain approximate sampling and randomization distributions of statistics. These concepts are seen throughout the curriculum and are closely tied to specific research studies. Our approach requires no formal training in formal probability theory or rules. Initially, we choose examples where the simulation procedure is natural and intuitive to students, such as coin flipping. Later we explain how normal-based methods connect to these simulations and randomization tests. At that point, because students already understand the logic of inference, normal-based tests are presented as the long-run behavior of the simulation under certain conditions. With this approach, students can grasp normal-based tests without getting bogged down in the technical cogs of the procedures. At the end of the course, and thus not interrupting the flow of the majority of the course, we present a full-length chapter on probability theory (Chapter 11) in preparation for the AP® exam.

Alignment to the AP® Statistics curriculum. The format of this book is very different from other AP® Statistics textbooks since the logic of inference is not divorced from the data collection process. However, throughout the book, AP® Tips and AP®-style exercises are included, as well as one full-length practice exam and an AP® review chapter (Chapter 12). An additional full-length practice exam is available on the Book Companion Site.

You have a lot of flexibility in how you decide to move through the curriculum. The one strategy we would strongly recommend is to start with the Preliminaries and Chapter 1. In the Preliminaries, students are introduced to the process of conducting statistical investigations from data collection, to exploring data, to statistical inference, to drawing appropriate conclusions. Then we present a complete implementation of this in Chapter 1, involving research questions focused on a process probability. This relatively simple scenario enables us to introduce students to the fundamental concept of statistical significance, along with some issues related to collecting data and drawing conclusions, early in the course.

While p-values are first determined using simulation-based techniques in Chapter 1, theoretical models of determining p-values are introduced at the end of this chapter. This process of starting with simulation-based techniques and following with theory-based techniques is continued in subsequent chapters. Because students understand how to simulate a null distribution and how to use it to determine strength of evidence against the null hypothesis (the more abstract concepts of inference), a theory-based model does not seem like the abstraction that it does to most students learning statistics through a traditional curriculum.

In Chapter 11 we provide a complete chapter on formal probability, to supplement the intuitive, simulation-based presentation they have been getting throughout the rest of the course. In Chapter 12 we revisit each of the four major strands of the AP® Statistics curriculum, focusing on how best to prepare for the AP® exam. We also include two full-length practice exams.

Although this approach may be significantly different from how you have previously taught the course, you will quickly see that your students are fully engaged in the learning process from Day 1, and by using the six-step statistical investigation method on each study they encounter, they will have an understanding and appreciation of the usefulness of statistics.

Comparing multiple means using analysis of variance tests is not on the AP Statistics exam. It is a topic, however, that is often included in a college-level statistics course as it

continues exploration of methods to evaluate the association between two variables – one quantitative and one categorical. While that chapter is not included in the printed version of the text, it is included online on the textbook companion site at www.wiley.com/go/highschool.

CHANGES IN PEDAGOGY

Active learning. We have also substantially changed the pedagogical approach from passive (e.g., listening to lectures) to active learning, which engages the full range of students' senses. Each chapter contains a number of explorations for the students to complete, in addition to example-driven exposition of concepts. These materials allow for a variety of instructor-determined approaches to content delivery, including approaches where examples/concepts are presented first by the instructor, then explored by the student or vice versa.

Explorations. Student explorations involve a variety of tactile learning experiences like shuffling decks of cards and flipping coins to estimate their own p-values, using computer-based simulations, using Web-applets, collecting data, running experiments, and (potentially) using computer software to help interpret results. The majority of explorations are flexibly designed to be completed by students working individually, in small or large groups, either inside or outside of class.

Examples and FAQs. Concepts are introduced using compelling examples explained in an easy-to-understand manner that limits technical jargon and focuses on conceptual understanding. In addition to this, we have included Frequently Asked Questions on the Book Companion Site. These "dialogues" help students understand difficult concepts and answer some of their common questions. We have also included Key Idea boxes and Thought Questions to help students understand what they read, identify core concepts, and become engaged readers. Overall, we advocate utilizing a small amount of instructor-led interactive lecture and discussion, but mainly focusing on engaging and strengthening different student learning processes by way of a variety of active, self-discovery learning experiences for students.

Exercises and investigations. Each chapter contains an extensive set of exercises. Almost all of these are based on real studies and real data. We also include an investigation in each chapter, an in-depth exercise exploring the entire six-step statistical investigation method so that the single assignment can assess a variety of concepts.

Each chapter also contains icons directing students to online Research Article exercises on the Book Companion Site. These exercises challenge students to develop their critical reading skills by having them read a research article followed by a series of questions about the article. (*Note:* Some articles are freely accessible to anyone online, while others require a school/library subscription to access; the Research Article Guide on the Book Companion Site notes the status of each article.)

Real data. The GAISE recommendations argue that statistics courses should make use of real data. We go a step further and argue that statistics courses should use real data *that matters*. Statistics should be viewed less as a course in which students see "cute" but impractical illustrations of statistics in use, and more about examples where statistics is used to make decisions that have health, monetary, or other implications impacting hundreds, thousands, or millions of people. Our approach has two-fold benefits, first in improving students' statistical literacy and second by helping students to recognize that statistics is the indispensable, interdisciplinary language of scientific research.

Topic Outline for AP® Statistics From the College Board's AP® Statistics Course Description	Introduction to Statistical Investigations: AP® edition Chapter and Section References
I. Exploring Data: Describing patterns and departures from patterns (20%–30%)	
A. Constructing and interpreting graphical displays of distributions of univariate data (dotplot, stemplot, histogram, cumulative frequency plot)	dotplot 6.1 Part 2; stemplot 6.1 Part 2; histogram 2.1; cumulative frequency plot 6.1 Part 2
1. Center and spread 2. Clusters and gaps 3. Outliers and other unusual features 4. Shape	P.2, 6.1, 6.1 Part 2 P.2, 6.1, 6.1 Part 2 P.2, 6.1, 6.1 Part 2 P.2, 6.1, 6.1 Part 2
B. Summarizing distributions of univariate data	
1. Measuring center: median, mean 2. Measuring spread: range, interquartile range, standard deviation 3. Measuring position: quartiles, percentiles, standardized scores (z-scores) 4. Using boxplots 5. The effect of changing units on summary measures	2.2, 6.1, 6.1 Part 2 6.1, 6.1 Part 2 1.3, 11.7 6.1, 6.1 Part 2 11.5
C. Comparing distributions of univariate data (dotplots, back-to-back stemplots, parallel boxplots)	
1. Comparing center and spread: within group, between group variation 2. Comparing clusters and gaps 3. Comparing outliers and other unusual features 4. Comparing shapes	6.1, 6.1 Part 2, 7.2 6.1, 6.1 Part 2, 7.2 6.1, 6.1 Part 2, 7.2 6.1, 6.1 Part 2, 7.2
D. Exploring bivariate data	
1. Analyzing patterns in scatterplots 2. Correlation and linearity 3. Least squares regression line 4. Residual plots, outliers, and influential points 5. Transformations to achieve linearity: logarithmic and power transformations	10.1, 10.2 10.1, 10.2 10.3, 10.3 Part 2 10.3, 10.3 Part 2 10.3 Part 3
E. Exploring categorical data	
1. Frequency tables and bar charts 2. Marginal and joint frequencies for two-way tables 3. Conditional relative frequencies and association 4. Comparing distributions using bar charts	1.1, 5.1, 5.2, 5.3 5.1, 5.2, 5.3, 8.1, 8.2, 8.3 8.1, 8.2, 8.3 5.1, 5.2, 5.3, 8.1, 8.2, 8.3
II. Sampling and Experimentation: Planning and conducting a study (10%–15%)	
A. Overview of methods of data collection	
1. Census 2. Sample survey 3. Experiment 4. Observational study	2.1 2.1 4.3, 4.3 4.2

AP® is a trademark registered and/or owned by the College Board which was not involved in the production of, and does not endorse this product.

B. Planning and conducting surveys	
1. Characteristics of a well-designed and well-conducted survey	2.1
2. Populations, samples, and random selection	2.1
3. Sources of bias in sampling and surveys	2.1, 2.1 Part 2
4. Sampling methods, including simple random sampling, stratified random sampling, and cluster sampling	2.1, 2.1 Part 2, 2.1 Part 3
C. Planning and conducting experiments	
1. Characteristics of a well-designed and well-conducted experiment	4.1, 4.2, 4.3
2. Treatments, control groups, experimental units, random assignments, and replication	4.1, 4.2, 4.3
3. Sources of bias and confounding, including placebo effect and blinding	4.1, 4.2, 4.3
4. Completely randomized design	4.1, 4.2, 4.3
5. Randomized block design, including matched pairs design	4.4
D. Generalizability of results and types of conclusions that can be drawn from observational studies, experiments, and surveys	4.2
III. Anticipating Patterns: Exploring random phenomena using probability and simulation (20%–30%)	
A. Probability	
1. Interpreting probability, including long-run relative frequency interpretation	P.3, 11.1
2. "Law of Large Numbers" concept	11.1
3. Addition rule, multiplication rule, conditional probability, and independence	11.2, 11.3
4. Discrete random variables and their probability distributions, including binomial and geometric	11.4, 11.6
5. Simulation of random behavior and probability distributions	11.1
6. Mean (expected value) and standard deviation of a random variable, and linear transformation of a random variable	11.5
B. Combining independent random variables	
1. Notion of independence versus dependence	11.5
2. Mean and standard deviation for sums and differences of independent random variables	11.5
C. The normal distribution	
1. Properties of the normal distribution	11.7, 11.8
2. Using tables of the normal distribution	11.7, 11.8
3. The normal distribution as a model for measurements	11.7, 11.8
D. Sampling distributions	
1. Sampling distribution of a sample proportion	1.5, 1.6, 11.8
2. Sampling distribution of a sample mean	2.2, 2.2 Part 2, 11.8
3. Central limit theorem	1.5, 2.2, 2.2 Part 2
4. Sampling distribution of a difference between two independent sample proportions	5.2, 5.3
5. Sampling distribution of a difference between two independent sample means	6.2, 6.3
6. Simulation of sampling distributions	Ch 1, 2, 3, 5–8, 10
7. t-distribution	2.2, 2.2 Part 2
8. Chi-square distribution	8.1, 8.2, 8.3, 8.4

IV. Statistical Inference: Estimating population parameters and testing hypotheses (30%–40%)	
A. Estimation (point estimators and confidence intervals)	
1. Estimating population parameters and margins of error	3.1, 3.2, 3.2 Part 2, 3.3, 3.3 Part 2, 3.4, 3.5
2. Properties of point estimators, including unbiasedness and variability	3.1, 3.2, 3.4, 3.5
3. Logic of confidence intervals, meaning of confidence level and confidence intervals, and properties of confidence intervals	3.1, 3.2, 3.2 Part 2, 3.4, 3.5
4. Large sample confidence interval for a proportion	3.2, 3.2 Part 2
5. Large sample confidence interval for a difference between two proportions	5.3, 5.4
6. Confidence interval for a mean	3.3, 3.3 Part 2
7. Confidence interval for a difference between two means (unpaired and paired)	6.3, 6.4, 7.3, 7.4
8. Confidence interval for the slope of a least squares regression line	10.5, 10.6
B. Tests of significance	
1. Logic of significance testing, null and alternative hypotheses; p-values; one- and two-sided tests; concepts of Type I and Type II errors; concept of power	1.1, 1.4 2.3
2. Large sample test for a proportion	1.5, 1.7
3. Large sample test for a difference between two proportions	5.3, 5.5
4. Test for a mean	2.2, 2.2 Part 3
5. Test for a difference between two means (unpaired and paired)	6.3, 6.4, 7.3, 7.4
6. Chi-square test for goodness of fit, homogeneity of proportions, and independence (one- and two-way tables)	8.2, 8.3, 8.4
7. Test for the slope of a least squares regression line	10.4, 10.5, 10.6

RESOURCES

Resources for students and instructors. The Book Companion Site www.wiley.com/go/highschool contains the following:

- **Data sets** Data sets tied to examples, exercises, explorations, and investigations.
- **Applets** Easy-to-use web applets created by the authors.
- **FAQs** Dialogues between student and instructor that help students understand difficult concepts and answer some of their common questions.
- **Research Article exercises and Research Article guide** Tied to each chapter, Research Article exercises challenge students to develop their critical reading skills by reading a research article and then answering a series of questions about the article.
- **AP® Instructor's Manual** To help AP® instructors with lesson planning, pacing, classroom activities, teaching tips and more.

Explorations and Investigations Workbook All explorations and investigations in the text are collected into a workbook with space for student answers in an assignable, collectible format.

WileyPLUS

The next generation of *WileyPLUS* gives you the freedom and flexibility to tailor curated content and easily manage your course in order to keep students engaged and on track.

- **Customized Content** Using the content editor, you can add videos, documents, pages, or relevant links to keep students motivated.
- **Interactive eTextbook** Students can easily search content, highlight and take notes, access instructor's notes and highlights, and read offline.
- **Drag-and-Drop Customization** Quick reordering of learning objectives and modules lets you match content to your needs.
- **Linear Design and Organization** Customizable modules organized by learning objective include eTextbook content, videos, animations, interactives, and practice questions.
- **Calendar** The drag-and-drop calendar syncs with other features in WileyPLUS—like assignments, syllabus, and grades—so that one change on the calendar shows up in all places.
- **Instructor App** You can modify due dates, monitor assignment submissions, change grades, and communicate with your students all from your phone.

Resources for instructors. Instructor's Solutions Manual with solutions to all exercises.

TO THE STUDENT

We know from decades of experience as teachers of statistics that many students never master the most important but hardest ideas of our subject in their first course. Partly, that's just because the ideas are truly difficult. Partly, it's because learning the formulas of statistics often gets in the way of learning the ideas of statistics. And partly, it's because the hardest and most important ideas are too often saved for the end of the course, when time is running short.

This intro stat book is different. We show you the most important ideas up-front, even though we know they are challenging. We downplay formulas, especially at the start, in order to put the ideas first. This approach asks more of you up-front, but we have become convinced from our own classes that, in the long run, this approach will pay off for you, the reader. Students leave our classes better prepared to use statistical thinking in their science, social science, and business courses, and in their careers after graduation.

At the same time, we also recognize that this approach may put you in an uncomfortable position. We are asking you at the beginning of the term to start working at understanding ideas that may take several weeks of thinking, effort, and practice to become clear. Many of the most important ideas in all subjects are like that. What we ask of you is continued effort and patience. In return, we offer our understanding that some of the goals we have set for you cannot be achieved in just a week or two or three.

ACKNOWLEDGMENTS

This project, which has encompassed many years, has benefited from input from many individuals and groups.

First, we thank the National Science Foundation for two grants (DUE 1140629 and DUE 1323210) that have supported the development and evaluation of this curriculum. We also appreciate funding received to support initial development from the Howard Hughes Medical Institute Undergraduate Science Education Program, the Great Lakes College Association Pathways to Learning Collegium, and the Teagle Foundation.

This book has improved considerably based on very helpful suggestions from class testers who have implemented earlier drafts:

- Karl Beres, *Ripon College*
- Erin Blankenship, *University of Nebraska, Lincoln*
- Julie Clark, *Hollins University*
- Sheryl Cleveland, *Golden Valley High School*
- Linda Brant Collins, *University of Chicago*
- Lacey Echols, *Butler University*
- Tami Elsey, *Olathe High School*
- Kim Gilbert, *University of Georgia*
- Julia Guggenheimer, *Greenwich Academy*
- John Hail, *Olathe High School*
- Tim Hansen, *Highland High School*
- Allen Hibbard, *Central College*
- Chester Ismay, *Ripon College*
- Gary Kader, *Appalachian State University*
- Lisa Kay, *Eastern Kentucky University*
- Dave Klanderman, *Trinity Christian College*
- John Knoester, *Holland Christian High School*
- Lindsay Konell, *William Tennent High School*
- Henry Kramer, *Unity Christian High School*
- Tom Linton, *Central College*
- Vanna McIntosh, *Coffee County High School*
- Paul Meyers, *The Paideia School*
- Mark A. Mills, *Central College*
- Ron Palcic, *Johnson County Community College*
- Tom Pappenhagen, *Middleton High School*
- Bob Peterson, *Mona Shores High School*
- Karen Ray, *River Bluff High School*
- Angel Rodriguez, *G. Holmes Braddock Senior High School*
- Betsi Roelofs, *Holland Christian High School*
- Scott Rifkin, *University of California, San Diego*
- Laura Schultz, *Rowan University*
- Laura Shoup, *Boise High School*
- Sean Simpson, *Westchester Community College*
- Tim Sirois, *Highland Park High School*
- Josh Wilkerson, *Regents School of Austin*
- Michelle Wittler, *Ripon College*

We also thank our departmental colleagues at Dordt College, Hope College, and Cal Poly who have used earlier versions with their students and provided valuable feedback:

- Airat Bekmetjev, *Hope College*
- Aaron Cinzori, *Hope College*
- Dyana Harrelson, *Hope College*
- Vicki-Lynn Holmes, *Hope College*
- Karen McGaughey, *Cal Poly San Luis Obispo*
- Mary Nienhuis, *Hope College*
- Kevin Ross, *Cal Poly San Luis Obispo*
- Paul Pearson, *Hope College*
- Brian Yurk, *Hope College*
- Valorie Zonefeld, *Dordt College*

We thank the following people for permission to adapt their practice AP exam questions.

- Christy Brown, *Clemson University*
- Paul Buckley, *Gonzaga College High School*
- James Bush, *Waynesburg University*
- Ruth Carver, *Germantown Academy*
- Bryan Crissinger, *The University of Delaware*
- Lew Davidson, *Mallard Creek High School*
- Jonathan Duggins, *North Carolina State University*
- Beth Johnson, *George Mason University*
- Sarah Johnson, *Grand Blanc High School*
- Rich Lambert, *University of North Carolina at Charlotte*
- Bob Taylor, *Clemson University*
- Northeast GA RESA AP Stats Professional Learning Community

We also benefited greatly from reviewers of the text:

Ali Arab, *Georgetown University*

K. B. Boomer, *Bucknell University*

Audrey Brock, *Eastern Kentucky University*

Stephanie Casey, *Eastern Michigan University*

Seo-eun Choi, *Arkansas State University*

Kathy Chu, *Eastern Michigan University*

Julie Clark, *Hollins University*

Bob Dobrow, *Carleton College*

Jay Emerson, *Yale University*

John Emerson, *Middlebury College*

Michael Ernst, *St. Cloud State University*

Larry Feldman, *Indiana University of Pennsylvania*

Brian Garant, *Prairie State College*

Chi Giang, *Westchester Community College*

Carla L. Hill, *Marist College*

Tisha Hooks, *Winona State University*

Gary Kader, *Appalachian State University*

Lisa Kay, *Eastern Kentucky University*

Amy Kimbrough, *Virginia Commonwealth University*

Tom Linton, *Central College*

Chris Malone, *Winona State University*

Mark A. Mills, *Central College*

Tony Ng, *Southern Methodist University*

Eric Nordmoe, *Kalamazoo College*

Ron Palcic, *Johnson County Community College*

Scott Rifkin, *University of California, San Diego*

Douglas Ruvolo, *University of Akron*

Jose Sanqui, *Appalachian State University*

Sean Simpson, *Westchester Community College*

Jill Thomley, *Appalachian State University*

We also received valuable help from students Virginia Burroughs, Andrea Eddy, Kayla Lankheet, Brooke Quisenberry, Kyliee Topliff, and Jimmy Wong. Ann Cannon provided invaluable assistance as an accuracy checker. The entire Wiley team, but especially Joanna Dingle, Ken Santor, Anne Scanlan-Rohrer, Ashley Patterson, Adria Giattino, and Tom Kulesa were vital in helping us bring our vision to reality.

Finally, and most importantly, we thank all of our students who have studied with this curriculum as it has evolved. Our students have inspired us to develop curriculum materials and provide a learning environment to support them in the important goal of learning statistical ideas and methods.

CONTENTS

Introduction to Statistical Investigations

Have you ever heard statements like these?

- "Don't get your child vaccinated. I vaccinated my child and now he is autistic."

- "I will never start jogging because my friend's dad jogged his whole life but he died at age 46 of a heart attack."

- "Teenagers shouldn't be allowed to drive. Everyone knows they are too easily distracted."

The people making these statements are using *anecdotal evidence* (personal observations or striking examples) to support broad conclusions. The first person concludes that vaccinations cause autism, based solely on her own child. The second concludes that running is too risky and could lead to heart attacks, based entirely on the experience of one acquaintance. The third uses hearsay to draw a broad conclusion.

Scientific conclusions should not be based on anecdotal evidence or single observations. Science requires evidence from a well-collected data set. *Statistics* is the science of producing useful data to address a research question, analyzing the resulting data, and drawing appropriate conclusions from the data.

For example, suppose you are running for a student government office and have two different campaign slogans in mind. You're curious about whether your fellow students would react more positively to one slogan than the other. Would you ask only for your roommate's opinion or several of your friends? Or could you conduct a more systematic study? What might that look like? The study of Statistics will help you see how to design and carry out such a study, and you will see how Statistics can also help to answer many important research questions from a wide variety of fields of application.

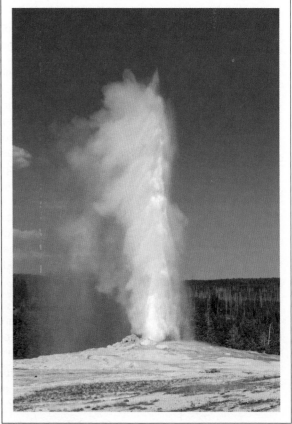

Edward Fielding/Shutterstock

INTRODUCTION TO THE SIX-STEP METHOD

In this section, we will highlight the six steps of a statistical investigation through an example. These six steps are a framework for all statistical investigations and are something you will see throughout this book. We will also use this section to introduce and define some key terms.

Organ Donations

Example P.1

Even though organ donations save lives, recruiting organ donors is difficult. Interestingly, surveys show that about 85% of Americans approve of organ donations in principle and many states offer a simple organ donor registration process when people apply for a driver's license. However, only about 38% of licensed drivers in the United States are registered to be organ donors. Some people prefer not to make an active decision about organ donation because the topic can be unpleasant to think about. But perhaps phrasing the question differently could affect people's willingness to become a donor.

Johnson and Goldstein (2003) recruited 161 participants for a study, published in the journal *Science*, to address the question of organ donor recruitment. The participants were asked to imagine they have moved to a new state and are applying for a driver's license. As part of this application, the participants were to decide whether or not to become an organ donor. Participants were presented with one of three different default choices:

- Some of the participants were forced to make a choice of becoming a donor or not, without being given a default option (the "neutral" group).
- Other participants were told that the default option was *not* to be a donor but that they could choose *to* become a donor if they wished (the "opt-in" group).
- The remaining participants were told that the default option was to *be* a donor but that they could choose *not* to become a donor if they wished (the "opt-out" group).

What did the researchers find? Those given the "opt-in" strategy were much less likely to agree to become donors. Consequently, policy makers have argued that we should employ an "opt-out" strategy instead. Individuals can still choose not to donate but would have to more actively do so rather than accept the default. Based on their results, Johnson and Goldstein stated that their data "suggest changes in defaults could increase donations in the United States of additional thousands of donors a year." In fact, as of 2010, 24 European countries had some form of the opt-out system—which some call "presumed consent"—with Spain, Austria, and Belgium yielding high donor rates.

Why were Johnson and Goldstein able to make such a strong recommendation? Because rather than relying on their own opinions or on anecdotal evidence, they conducted a carefully planned study of the issue using sound principles of science and statistics. These principles can be summarized as the six steps of a statistical investigation, which is in line with the scientific method.

SIX STEPS OF A STATISTICAL INVESTIGATION

- **Step 1: Ask a research question** that can be addressed by collecting data. These questions often involve comparing groups, asking whether something affects something else, or assessing people's opinions.
- **Step 2: Design a study and collect data.** This step involves selecting the people or objects to be studied, deciding how to gather relevant data on them, and carrying out this data collection in a careful, systematic manner.
- **Step 3: Explore the data**, looking for patterns related to your research question as well as unexpected outcomes that might point to additional questions to pursue.

- **Step 4: Draw inferences beyond the data** by determining whether any findings in your data reflect a genuine tendency and estimating the size of that tendency.
- **Step 5: Formulate conclusions** that consider the scope of the inference made in Step 4. To what underlying process or larger group can these conclusions be generalized? Is a cause-and-effect conclusion warranted?
- **Step 6: Look back and ahead** to point out limitations of the study and suggest new studies that could be performed to build on the findings of the study.

Let's see how the organ donation study followed these steps.

P.1.1

STEP 1: Ask a research question. The general question here is whether a method can be found to increase the likelihood that a person agrees to become an organ donor. This question was then sharpened into a more focused one: Does the default option presented to driver's license applicants influence the likelihood of someone becoming an organ donor?

STEP 2: Design a study and collect data. The researchers decided to recruit various participants and ask them to pretend to apply for a new driver's license. The participants did not know in advance that different options were given for the donor question or even that this issue was the main focus of the study. These researchers recruited participants for their study through various general interest discussion forums on the internet. They offered an incentive of $4.00 for completing an online survey. After the results were collected, the researchers removed data arising from multiple responses from the same IP address, surveys completed in less than five seconds, and respondents whose residential address could not be verified.

STEP 3: Explore the data. The results of this study were:

The results of this study were 78.6% agreeing to become donors in the neutral group, 41.8% for the opt-in group, and 82.0% for the opt-out group. The *Science* article displayed a graph of these data similar to Figure P.1.

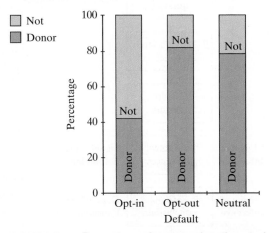

FIGURE P.1 Percentages for organ donation study.

These results indicate that the neutral version of the question, forcing participants to make a choice, and the opt-out option (default organ donor) produced a higher percentage who agreed to become donors than the opt-in option (default not organ donor).

STEP 4: Draw inferences beyond the data. Using methods that you will learn in this course, the researchers analyzed whether the observed differences between the groups were large enough to indicate that the default option had a genuine effect and then estimated the size of that effect. In particular, this study reported strong evidence that the neutral and opt-out versions generally lead to a higher chance of agreeing to become a donor, as compared to the opt-in version currently used in many states. In fact, they could be quite confident that the neutral version increases the chances that a person agrees to become a donor by between 20 and 54 percentage points, a difference large enough to save thousands of lives per year in the United States.

STEP 5: Formulate conclusions.   Furthermore, as we will also discuss later in the book, based on the analysis of the data and the design of the study, it is reasonable for these researchers to conclude that the neutral version *causes* an increase in the proportion who will agree to become donors. But because the participants in the study were volunteers recruited from internet discussion forums, generalizing conclusions beyond these participants is only legitimate if they are representative of a larger group of people.

STEP 6: Look back and ahead.   The organ donation study provides strong evidence that the neutral or opt-out wording could be helpful for improving organ donation proportions. One limitation of the study is that participants were asked to imagine how they would respond, which might not mirror how people would actually respond in such a situation. A new study might look at people's actual responses to questions about organ donation or could monitor donor rates for states that adopt a new policy. Researchers could also examine whether presenting educational material on organ donation might increase people's willingness to donate. Another improvement would be to include participants from wider demographic groups than these volunteers.

Part of looking back also considers how an individual study relates to similar studies that have been conducted previously. Johnson and Goldstein compare their study to two others: one by Gimbel et al. (2003) that found similar results with European countries and one by Caplan (1994) that did not find large differences in the three proportions agreeing to donate.

Figure P.2 displays the six steps of a statistical investigation that we have identified.

FIGURE P.2   Six steps of a statistical investigation.

FOUR PILLARS OF STATISTICAL INFERENCE

Notice from Figure P.2 that Step 4 can be considered as the *logic* of statistical inference and Step 5 as the *scope* of statistical inference. Furthermore, each of these two steps involves two components. The following questions comprise the four pillars of statistical inference:

1. **Significance**: How **strong** is the evidence of an effect?

   You will learn how to provide a measure of the strength of the evidence provided by the data. For example, how strong is the evidence that the neutral and opt-out versions increase the chance of agreeing to become an organ donor, as compared to the opt-in version?

2. **Estimation**: What is the **size** of the effect?

   You will learn how to estimate how different two groups are. For example, how much larger (if at all) are the chances someone agrees to donate organs when asked with the neutral version instead of the opt-in version?

3. **Generalization**: How **broadly** do the conclusions apply?

   You will learn to consider what larger group of individuals you believe your conclusions can be applied to. For example, what are the characteristics of the individuals who participated in the organ donation study, and how are they similar or different than typical drivers?

4. **Causation**: Can we say what **caused** the observed difference?

   You will learn whether you can legitimately identify what caused the observed difference. For example, can you conclude that the way the researchers asked the organ donation question was the cause of the observed differences in proportions of donors?

These four pillars are so important that they should be addressed in virtually all statistical studies. Chapters 1–4 of this book will be devoted to introducing and exploring these four pillars of inference. To begin our study of the six steps of statistical investigation, we now introduce some basic terminology that will be used throughout the text.

 P.1.2

Basic terminology

Before we go any further let's introduce you to a few basic terms that we will use throughout the book.

- **Data** can be thought of as the values measured or categories recorded on individual entities of interest.
- These individual entities on which data are recorded will be called **observational units**.
- The recorded characteristics of the observational units are the **variables** of interest.
  - Some variables are **quantitative**, taking *numerical* values on which ordinary arithmetic operations make sense. For example, height, number of siblings, and age are quantitative variables.
  - Other variables are **categorical**, taking *category* designations. For example, eye color, marital status, and whether or not you voted in the last election are categorical variables.
- The **distribution** of a variable describes the pattern of value/category outcomes.

 P.1.3

 P.1.4

In the organ donation study, the observational units are the participants in the study. The two variables recorded on these participants are (1) the version of the question that the participant received and (2) whether or not the participant agreed to become an organ donor. Both of these are categorical variables. The graph in Figure P.1 displays the distributions of the donation variable for each default option category.

The observational units in a study are not always people. For example, you might take the Reese's Pieces candies in a small bag as your observational units, on which you could record variables such as the color (a categorical variable) and weight (a quantitative variable) of each individual candy. Or you might take all of the Major League Baseball games being played in one week as your observational units, on which you could record data on variables such as the total number of runs scored, whether the home team wins the game, and the attendance at the game.

THINK ABOUT IT

For each of the three variables just mentioned (about Major League Baseball games), identify the type of variable: categorical or quantitative.

The total number of runs scored and attendance at the game are quantitative variables. Whether or not the home team won the game is a categorical variable.

THINK ABOUT IT

Identify the observational units and variable for a recent study (Ackerman, Griskevicius, and Li, 2011) that investigated this research question: Among heterosexual couples in a committed romantic relationship, are men more likely than women to say "I love you" first?

The observational units in this study are the heterosexual couples, and the variable is whether the man or the woman was the first to say "I love you."

SECTION P.2 EXPLORING DATA

In this section, you will look more closely at Step 3 of the six-step statistical investigation method which concerns exploring data to help answer interesting questions and to help make informed decisions. In Example P.2, you will encounter data arising from a natural "data-generating" process that repeats the same "random event" many, many times, which allows us to see a pattern (distribution) in the resulting data.

Old Faithful

Example P.2

EXAMPLE

Millions of people from around the world flock to Yellowstone Park in order to watch eruptions of the Old Faithful geyser. But, just how faithful is this geyser? How predictable is it? How long does a person usually have to wait between eruptions? Suppose the park ranger gives you a prediction for the next eruption time, and then that eruption occurs five minutes after that predicted time. Would you conclude that predictions by the Park Service are not very accurate? We hope not, because that would be using anecdotal evidence. To investigate these questions about the reliability of Old Faithful, it is much better to collect data.

(A live webcam of Old Faithful and surrounding geysers is available at: http://www.nps.gov/features/yell/webcam/oldFaithfulStreaming.html.)

Researchers collected data on 222 eruptions of Old Faithful taken over a number of days in August 1978 and August 1979. Figure P.3 contains a graph (called a *dotplot*) displaying the times until the next eruption (in minutes) for these 222 eruptions. Each dot on the dotplot represents a single eruption.

Edward Fielding/Shutterstock

FIGURE P.3   Times between eruptions of Old Faithful geyser.

> ### THINK ABOUT IT
>
> What are the observational units and variable in this study? Is the variable quantitative or categorical?

The observational units are the 222 geyser eruptions, and the variable is the time until the next eruption, which is a quantitative variable. The dotplot displays the **distribution** of this variable, which means the values taken by the variable and how many eruptions have those values. The dotplot helps us see the patterns in times until the next eruption.

The most obvious point to be seen from this graph is that even Old Faithful is not perfectly predictable! The time until the next eruption varies from eruption to eruption. In fact, **variability** is the most fundamental property in studying Statistics.

We can view the times until the next eruption as observations from a **process**, an endless series of potential observations from which our data constitute a small "snapshot." Our assumption is that these observations give us a representative view of the long-run behavior of the process. Although we don't know in advance how long it will take for the next eruption, in part because there are many factors that determine when that will be (e.g., temperature, season, pressure) and in part because of unavoidable, natural variation, we may be able to see a predictable pattern overall if we record enough inter-eruption times. Statistics helps us to describe, measure, and, often, explain the pattern of variation in these measurements.

Looking more closely at the dotplot, we can notice several things about the distribution of the time until the next eruption:

- The shortest time until the next eruption was 42 minutes, and the longest time was 95 minutes.

- There appear to be two clusters of times, one cluster between roughly 42 and 63 minutes, another between about 66 and 95 minutes.

- The lower cluster of inter-eruption times is centered at approximately 55 minutes, give or take a little, whereas the upper cluster is centered at approximately 80 minutes, give or take a little. Overall, the distribution of times until the next eruption is centered at approximately 75 minutes.

- In the lower cluster, times until next eruption vary between 42 and 63 minutes, with most of the times between 50 and 60 minutes. In the upper cluster, times vary between 66 and 95 minutes, with most between 70 and 85 minutes.

What are some possible explanations for the variability in the times? One thought is that some of the variability in times until the next eruption might be explained by considering the length of the previous eruption. It seems to make sense that after a particularly long eruption Old Faithful might need more time to build enough pressure to produce another eruption. Similarly, after a shorter eruption, Old Faithful might be ready to erupt again sooner without having to wait very long. Fortunately, the researchers recorded a second variable about each eruption: the duration of the eruption, which is another quantitative variable. For simplicity we

P.2.1

can categorize each eruption's duration as short (less than 3.5 minutes) or long (3.5 minutes or longer), a categorical variable. Figure P.4 displays dotplots of the distributions of time until the next eruption for short and long eruptions separately.

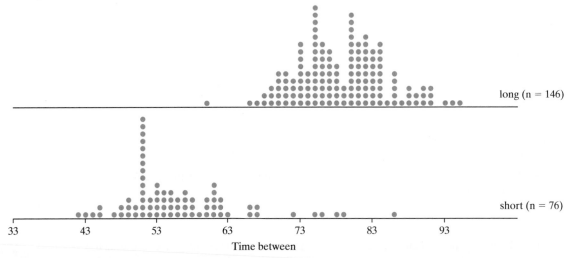

FIGURE P.4   Times between eruptions of Old Faithful geyser, separated by duration of previous eruption (less than 3.5 minutes or at least 3.5 minutes).

We can make several observations about the distributions of times until next eruption, comparing eruptions with short and long durations, from these dotplots:

P.2.2

P.2.3

P.2.4

- The **shapes** of each individual distribution no longer reveal the two distinct clusters (bi-modality) that was apparent in the original distribution before separating by duration length. Each of these distributions seems to have a single peak.
- The **centers** of these two distributions are quite different: After a short eruption, a typical time until the next eruption is between 45 and 60 minutes. In contrast, after a long eruption, a typical time until the next eruption is between 70 and 85 minutes.
- The **variability** in the times until the next eruption is much smaller for each individual distribution (times tend to fall closer to the middle within each duration type) than the variability for the overall distribution, as we have been able to take into account one source of variability in the data. But of course the times still vary, partly due to other factors that we have not yet accounted for and partly due to *natural variability* inherent in all random processes.

One way to measure the center of a distribution is with the average, also called the mean. One way to measure variability is with the **standard deviation**, which can be roughly interpreted as the typical distance (in absolute value) between the data values and the mean of the distribution. Hence, the more varied or spread out a data set is, the larger its standard deviation will be. (See the Calculation Details appendix for details about calculating standard deviation. We will also explore the idea of standard deviation more in Chapter 3 and throughout the book.) These values for the time until next eruption, both for the overall distribution and for short and long eruptions separately, are given in Table P.1 and shown in Figure P.5.

TABLE P.1 Means and standard deviations of inter-eruption times		
	Mean	**Standard deviation**
Overall	71.0 min	12.8 min
After short duration	56.3 min	8.5 min
After long duration	78.7 min	6.3 min

Notice that the standard deviations (SDs) of time until the next eruption are indeed smaller for the separate groups than for the overall data set, as suggested by examining the variability in the dotplots.

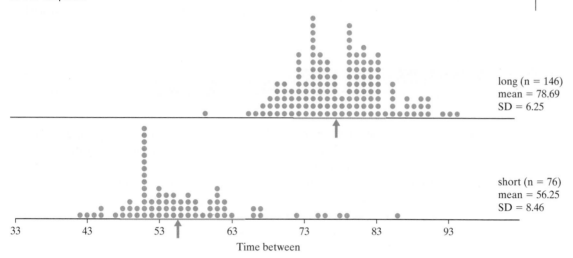

long (n = 146)
mean = 78.69
SD = 6.25

short (n = 76)
mean = 56.25
SD = 8.46

Time between

FIGURE P.5   Times between eruptions of Old Faithful geyser, separated by duration of previous eruption, with mean and standard deviation shown.

So, what can you learn from this analysis? First, you can better predict when Old Faithful will next erupt if you know how long the previous eruption lasted. Second, with that information in hand, Old Faithful is rather reliable, because it often erupts within six to nine minutes of the time you would predict based on the duration of the previous eruption. So if the park ranger's prediction was off by only five minutes, that's pretty good.

Basic terminology

From this example you should have learned that a graph such as a dotplot can display the distribution of a quantitative variable. Some aspects to look for in that distribution are:

- *Shape*: Is the distribution symmetric? Mound shaped? Are there several peaks or clusters?
- *Center*: Where is the distribution centered? What is a typical value?
- *Variability*: How spread out are the data? Are most within a certain range of values?
- **Unusual observations:** Are there **outliers** that deviate markedly from the overall pattern of the other data values? If so, identify them to see whether you can explain why those observations are so different. Are there other unusual features in the distribution?

You have also begun to think about ways to measure the center and variability in a distribution. In particular, the standard deviation is a tool we will use quite often as a measure of variability. At this point, we want you to be comfortable visually comparing the variability among distributions and anticipating which variables you might expect to have more variability than others.

> **THINK ABOUT IT**
>
> Suppose that Mary records the ages of people entering a McDonald's fast-food restaurant near the interstate today, while Colleen records the ages of people entering a snack bar on a college campus. Who would you expect to have the *larger* standard deviation of these ages: Mary (McDonald's) or Colleen (campus snack bar)? Explain briefly.

The customers at McDonald's are likely to include people of all ages, from young children to elderly people. But customers at the campus snack bar are most likely to be college-aged students, with some older people who work on campus and perhaps a few younger people. Therefore the ages of the customers at McDonald's will vary more than the ages of those at the campus snack bar. Mary is therefore more likely to have a larger standard deviation of ages than Colleen.

SECTION P.3 · EXPLORING RANDOM PROCESSES

Work through Exploration P.3 below to discover for yourself how to explore data from a random process (like rolling dice), in order to use that information to make better decisions. Similar to naturally occurring data-generating processes (such as times between eruptions at Old Faithful), we can often generate sufficient outcomes from a random process to help us learn about long-term patterns. In subsequent chapters, you will analyze both data-generating processes and random processes, often with the goal of seeing how well a random process models, or "behaves like," what you find in the data.

EXPLORATION P.3 | Cars or Goats

A popular television game show, *Let's Make a Deal*, from the 1960s and 1970s featured a new car hidden behind one of three doors, selected at random. Behind the other two doors were less appealing prizes (e.g., goats!). When a contestant played the game, he or she was asked to pick one of the three doors. If the contestant picked the correct door, he or she won the car!

1. Suppose you are a contestant on this show. Intuitively, what do you think is the probability that you win the car (i.e., that the door you pick has the car hidden behind it)?

2. Give a one-sentence description of what you think *probability* means in this context.

Assuming there is no set pattern to where the game show puts the car initially, this game is an example of a ***random process***: Although the outcome for an individual game is not known in advance, we expect to see a very predictable pattern in the results if you play this game many, many times. This pattern is called a ***probability distribution***, which is similar to a data distribution like you examined with Old Faithful interruption times. We are interested in features such as how common certain outcomes are—for example are you more likely to win this game (select the door with the car) or lose this game?

To investigate what we mean by the term probability, we ask you to play the game many times. Actually, we will ***simulate*** (artificially re-create) playing the game, keeping track of how often you win the car.

3. Use three playing cards with identical backs but where two of the card suits match and one should differ (e.g., one red and two black). The different card represents the car. Work with a partner (playing the role of game show host), who will shuffle the three cards and then randomly arrange them face down. You pick a card and then reveal whether you have won the car or selected a goat. Play this game a total of 15 times, keeping track of whether you win the car (C) or a goat (G) each time:

Game #	1	2	3	4	5	6	7	8	9	10	11	12	13	14	15
Outcome (car or goat)															

4. In what proportion of these 15 games did you win the car? Is this close to what you expected? Explain.

These 15 "trials," or "repetitions," mimic the behavior of the game show's random process, where you are introducing randomness into the process by shuffling the cards between games. To get a sense of the long-run behavior of this random process, we want to observe many, many more trials. Because it is not realistic to ask you to perform thousands of repetitions with your partner, we will use a computer to generate a large number of outcomes from this random process.

5. Suppose that you were to play this game 1,000 times. In what proportion of those games would you expect to win the car? Explain.

6. Use a website (for example, http://www.grand-illusions.com/simulator/montysim.htm) to simulate playing this version of the game 10 times. Record the proportion of wins in these 10 games. Then simulate another 10 games, and record the <u>overall</u> proportion of wins at this point. Keep doing this in multiples of 10 games until you reach 100 games played. Record the overall proportions of wins after each additional multiple of 10 games in the table below.

Number of games	10	20	30	40	50	60	70	80	90	100
Proportion of wins										

7. What do you notice about how the overall proportion of wins changes as you play more games? Do these proportions appear to be approaching some common value?

8. Now keep adding sets of 100 more games played until you reach a total of 1,000 games played. What percentage of the time did you win a car? Is this close to what you expected in Question 5?

Number of games	100	200	300	400	500	600	700	800	900	1,000
Proportion of wins										

You should see that the proportion of wins generally gets closer and closer to 1/3 (or 0.3333) as you play more and more games. This is what it means to say that the **probability** of winning is 1/3: If you play the game repeatedly under the same conditions, then after a very large number of games, your proportion of wins should be very close to 1/3. For example, when tossing a coin, it is assumed that the probability of heads is equal to 0.50, meaning that we expect heads to occur about 50% of the time if you toss the coin forever!

Figure P.6 displays a graph showing how the proportion of wins changed over time for one simulation of 1,000 games. Notice that the proportion of wins bounces around a lot at first but then gradually settles down and approaches a long-run value of 1/3.

Definition

The **probability** of an event is the long-run proportion of times the event would occur if the random process were repeated indefinitely (under identical conditions).

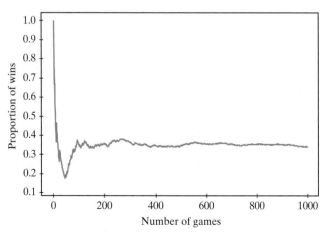

FIGURE P.6 Proportion of wins as more and more games are played.

Now consider a fun twist that the game show host adds to this game: Before revealing what's behind your door, the host will first reveal what's behind a different door that the host *knows* to be a goat. Then the host asks whether you (the contestant) prefer to stay with (keep) the door you picked originally or switch (change) to the remaining door.

9. Prediction: Do you think the probability of winning is different between the "stay" (keep) and "switch" (change) strategies? If so, what do you think the probability of winning with the switch strategy is?

Whether the "stay" or "switch" strategy is better is a famous mathematical question known as the Monty Hall Problem, named for the host of the game show. What makes this problem famous is that the answer is not intuitive for many people! Fortunately for us, we can use simulation to easily estimate the probability and help us decide if one strategy is better than the other in the long run.

10. Investigate the probability of winning with the "switch" strategy by playing with three cards for 15 games. This time your partner should randomly arrange the three cards in his/her hand, making sure that your partner (playing the role of game show host) *knows* where the car is but you do not. You pick a card. Then your partner reveals one of the cards *known* to be a goat but not the card you chose. Play with the "switch" strategy for a total of 15 games, keeping track of the outcome (winning a car or goat) each time:

Repetition	1	2	3	4	5	6	7	8	9	10	11	12	13	14	15
Outcome (car or goat)															

11. In what proportion of these 15 games did you win the car? Is this more or less than (or the same as) when you stayed with the original door? (Question 3)

12. To investigate what would happen in the long run, again use a website (for example, http://www.grand-illusions.com/simulator/montysim.htm). Notice that you can change from "keep" your original choice to "change" your original choice. Clear any previous work and then simulate playing 1,000 games with each strategy, and record the number of times you win/lose with each:

	"Stay" strategy	"Switch" strategy
Wins (cars)		
Losses (goats)		
Total	1,000	1,000

13. Do you believe that the simulation has been run for enough repetitions to declare one strategy as superior? Which strategy is better? Explain how you can tell.

14. Based on the 1,000 simulated repetitions of playing this game, what is your estimate for the probability of winning the game with the "switch" strategy?

15. How could you use simulation to obtain a better estimate of this probability?

16. The probability of winning with the "switch" strategy can be shown mathematically to be 2/3. (One way to see this is to recognize that with the "switch" strategy you only lose when you had picked the correct door in the first place.) Explain what it means to say that the probability of winning equals 2/3.

Extension

17. Suppose that you watch the game show over many years and find that Door 1 hides the car 50% of the time, Door 2 has the car 40% of the time, and Door 3 has the car 10% of the time. What then is your optimal strategy? In other words, which door should you pick initially, and then should you stay or switch? What is your probability of winning with the optimal strategy? Explain.

Basic terminology

Through this exploration you should have learned:

- A *random process* is one that can be repeated a very large number of times (in principle, forever) under identical conditions with the following property:
  - Outcomes for any one instance cannot be known in advance, but the proportion of times that particular outcomes occur in the long run can be predicted.
- The *probability* of an outcome refers to the long-run proportion of times that the outcome would occur if the random process were repeated a very large number of times under identical conditions.
- *Simulation* (artificially re-creating a random process) can be used to estimate a probability.
  - Simulations can be conducted both with tactile (by-hand) methods (e.g., cards) and with computers.
  - Using a larger number of repetitions in a simulation generally produces a better estimate of the probability than a smaller number of repetitions.
- Simulation can be used for making good decisions involving random processes.
  - A "good" decision (in this context) means you can accurately predict which strategy would result in a larger probability of winning. This tells you which strategy to use if you do find yourself on this game show but of course does not guarantee you will win!

PRELIMINARIES Summary

This concludes your study of the preliminary but important ideas necessary to begin studying Statistics. We hope you have learned that:

- Collecting data from carefully designed studies is more dependable than relying on anecdotes for answering questions and making decisions.
- Statistical investigations, which can address interesting and important research questions from a wide variety of fields of application, follow the six steps illustrated in Figure P.2.
- Some data arise from processes that include a mix of systematic elements and natural variation.
- Almost all data display variability. Distributions of quantitative data can be analyzed with dotplots, where we look for shape, center, variability, and unusual observations.
- Standard deviation is a widely used tool for quantifying variability in data.
- Random processes that arise from chance mechanisms display predictable long-run patterns of outcomes. Probability is the language of random processes.
- Using data to draw conclusions and make decisions requires careful planning in collecting and analyzing the data, paying particular attention to issues of variability and randomness.

Beginning in Chapter 1, we will use a known random process to model a data-generating process in order to assess whether the data process appears to behave similarly to the random process.

PRELIMINARIES
GLOSSARY

anecdotal evidence Personal experience or striking example.

categorical variable A variable whose outcomes are category designations.

center A middle or typical value of a quantitative variable.

data The values measured or categories recorded on individual observational units.

distribution   The pattern of outcomes of a variable.

dotplot   A graph with one dot representing the variable outcome for each observational unit.

observational units   The individual entities on which data are recorded.

probability distribution   The pattern of long-run outcomes from a random process.

probability   The long-run proportion of times an outcome from a random process occurs.

process   An endless series of potential observations.

quantitative variable   A variable taking numerical values on which ordinary arithmetic operations make sense.

random process   A repeatable process with unknown individual outcomes but a long-run pattern.

shape   A characteristic of the distribution of a quantitative variable.

simulation   Artificial re-creation of a random process.

six steps of a statistical investigation   A framework for learning from data.

standard deviation   A measure of variability of a quantitative variable.

Statistics   A discipline that guides researchers in collecting, exploring, and drawing conclusions from data.

variability   The spread in observations for a quantitative variable.

variables   Recorded characteristics of the observational units.

PRELIMINARIES
EXERCISES

SECTION P.1

P.1.1*   For each of the following research questions identify the observational units and variable(s).

a. An article in a 2006 issue of the *Journal of Behavioral Decision Making* reports on a study involving 47 undergraduate students at Harvard. All of the participants were given $50, but some (chosen at random) were told that this was a "tuition rebate," while the others were told that this was "bonus income." After one week, the students were contacted again and asked how much of the $50 they had spent and how much they had saved. Researchers wanted to know whether those receiving the "rebate" would tend to save more money than those receiving the "bonus."

b. How much did a typical American consumer spend on Christmas presents in 2012?

c. Do college students who pull all-nighters tend to have lower grade point averages than those who do not pull all-nighters?

d. Is the residence situation of a college student (on-campus, off-campus with parents, off-campus without parents) related to how much alcohol the student consumes in a typical week?

e. Can you predict how far a cat can jump based on factors such as its length?

P.1.2   For each of the following research questions identify the observational units and variable(s).

a. Subjects listened to 10 seconds of the Jackson 5's song "ABC" and then were asked how long they thought the song snippet lasted. Do people tend to overestimate the song length?

b. Are newborns from couples where both parents smoke less likely to be boys than newborns from couples where neither parent smokes?

c. There many different types of diets, but do some work better than others? Is low-fat better than low-carb or is some combination best? Researchers conducted a study involving three popular diets: Atkins (very low carb), Zone (40:30:30 ratio of carbs, protein, fat), and Ornish (low fat). They randomly assigned overweight women to one of the three diets. The 232 women who volunteered for the program were educated on their assigned diet and were observed periodically as they stayed on the diet for a year. At the end of the year, the researchers calculated the changes in body mass index for each woman and compared the results across the three diets.

d. An instructor wants to investigate whether the color of paper (blue or green) on which an exam is printed has an effect on students' exam scores.

e. Statistical evidence was used in the murder trial of Kristen Gilbert, a nurse who was accused of killing patients. More than 1,000 eight-hour shifts were analyzed. Was the proportion of shifts with a death substantially higher for the shifts that Gilbert worked?

P.1.3*   Refer back to exercise P.1.1. For each of the research questions (a)–(e), identify which variables are quantitative and which categorical. Also classify categorical variables according to whether they only have two possible outcomes (sometimes called a binary variable) or more than two possible outcomes.

P.1.4   Refer back to exercise P.1.2. For each of the research questions (a)–(e), identify which variables are quantitative and which categorical. Also classify categorical variables according to whether they only have two possible outcomes (sometimes called a binary variable) or more than two possible outcomes.

P.1.5* Consider the students in your class as the observational units in a study.

a. Identify three quantitative variables that could be recorded on these students.

b. Identify three categorical variables that could be recorded on these students.

P.1.6 Consider all of the countries in the world as the observational units in a study.

a. Identify three quantitative variables that could be recorded on these countries.

b. Identify three categorical variables that could be recorded on these countries.

Expert performance*

P.1.7 A famous study titled "The Effect of Deliberative Practice in the Acquisition of Expert Performance," published in *Psychological Review* (Ericsson, Krampe, and Tesch-Romer, 1993) led to the now-conventional wisdom that 10,000 hours of deliberate practice are necessary to achieve expert performance in skills such as music and sports. The researchers in this study asked violin students at the Music Academy of West Berlin to keep a diary indicating how they spent their time. The researchers also asked the students' professors to indicate which were the top students with the potential for careers as international soloists, which were good violinists but not among the best, and which were studying to become music teachers. Researchers found that those in the top two groups devoted much more time per week to individual practice than did those in the group studying to become music teachers.

a. Identify the observational units in this study.

b. Identify the quantitative variable in this study.

c. Identify the categorical variable in this study.

Spinning racquets

P.1.8 Tennis players often spin a racquet to decide who serves first. The spun racquet can land with the manufacturer's label facing up or down. A reasonable question to investigate is whether a spun tennis racquet is equally likely to land with the label facing up or down. (If the spun racquet is equally likely to land with the label facing in either direction, we say that the spinning process is fair.) Suppose that you gather data by spinning your tennis racquet 100 times, each time recording whether it lands with the label facing up or down.

a. What are the observational units?

b. What is the variable?

c. Is the variable categorical or quantitative?

Tattoos*

P.1.9 Consider the students in your class as the observational units in a statistical study about tattoos. For each of the following, indicate whether it is a categorical variable, a quantitative variable, or a research question and therefore not a variable at all.

a. How many tattoos the student has

b. Whether male students are more likely to have a tattoo than female students

c. Whether or not the student has a tattoo

d. In which subject the student is majoring

e. Whether students majoring in Liberal Arts tend to have more tattoos than students majoring in Engineering

Hand washing

P.1.10 In August of 2005, researchers for the American Society for Microbiology and the Soap and Detergent Association monitored the behavior of more than 6,300 users of public restrooms. They observed people in public venues such as Turner Field in Atlanta and Grand Central Station in New York City. For each person they kept track of the person's sex and whether or not the person washed his or her hands along with the person's location.

a. Identify the observational units in this study.

b. Identify the three variables that were recorded on each observational units.

Consider the following two graphs produced from the resulting data:

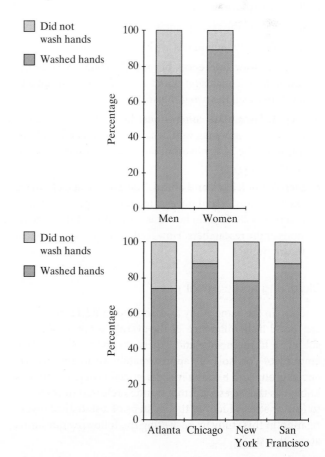

c. For the graph on the left, state a research question that can be addressed with the graph. Then answer the question based on the graph.

d. Repeat part (c) for the graph on the right.

Skydiving and anxiety*

P.1.11   A recent study investigated self-reported anxiety levels immediately before a skydive among 11 first-time skydivers and 13 experienced skydivers (at least 30 jumps) recruited from a parachute center in northern England (Hare et al., 2013). The researchers found that anxiety levels were substantially higher (average anxiety score of 43, higher means more anxiety) among the first-time skydivers as compared to the experienced skydivers (average anxiety score of 27) on a standard test for anxiety (Spielberger State-Trait Anxiety Inventory). Identify the six steps of a statistical investigation in this study by answering the following questions about this study.

a. **Step 1: Ask a research question.** What is the research question being investigated in this study?

b. **Step 2: Design a study and collect data.**

   i. What are the observational units in the study?

   ii. How were the observational units obtained?

   iii. What are the variables in this study? Classify each as categorical or quantitative.

c. **Step 3: Explore the data.**

   i. What are the average anxiety scores in the two groups?

   ii. How many individuals are in each group?

d. **Step 4: Draw inferences beyond the data.** What is the researchers' conclusion about the difference in anxiety levels between the two groups?

e. **Step 5: Formulate conclusions.** In order to make their conclusions more relevant, what are the researchers hoping about the 24 skydivers in this study as compared to all skydivers in general?

f. **Step 6: Look back and ahead.** The average age of novice skydivers was 21 and the average age of experienced skydivers was 28. Explain how this could impact the conclusions of the researchers. How could this be addressed in a future study?

Skydiving and cortisol

P.1.12   In the same study as described in P.1.11, researchers found little difference in the average amount of cortisol levels in the novice and expert skydivers. The average amount of cortisol was approximately 10 in the experienced group and 8 in the inexperienced group. Cortisol is known as the "stress" hormone and is released in response to fear or stress. Identify the six steps of a statistical investigation in this study by answering the following questions about this study.

a. **Step 1: Ask a research question.** What is the research question being investigated in this study?

b. **Step 2: Design a study and collect data.**

   i. What are the observational units in the study?

   ii. How were the observational units obtained?

   iii. What are the variables in this study? Classify each as categorical or quantitative.

c. **Step 3: Explore the data.**

   i. What are the average cortisol scores in the two groups?

   ii. How many individuals are in each group?

d. **Step 4: Draw inferences beyond the data.** What is the researchers' conclusion about the difference in cortisol levels between the two groups?

e. **Step 5: Formulate conclusions.** In order to make their conclusions more relevant, what are the researchers hoping about the 24 skydivers in this study as compared to all skydivers in general?

f. **Step 6: Look back and ahead.** The researchers note that novice skydivers used an automatically deploying parachute, whereas experts deployed their own parachute. Explain the impact this could have on the results of the study and how it could be addressed in future studies.

Your own research study*

P.1.13   Find a research study or article about a study that interests you. After reading the research article, describe how all six steps of the statistical investigation method were applied in the study, as was done in **Example P.1: Organ donations.** Some websites that often report interesting studies are *LiveScience* (www.livescience.com), *Science Daily* (www.sciencedaily.com/), *Yahoo News* (http://news.yahoo.com/), and *USA Today* (www.usatoday.com).

Emergency room patients

P.1.14   Suppose that the observational units in a statistical study are the patients arriving at the emergency room of a particular hospital for one month.

a. Identify two *categorical* variables that could be recorded for these patients.

b. Identify two *quantitative* variables that could be recorded for these patients.

c. State two research questions that hospital administrators might want to investigate with these data.

Online purchasing*

P.1.15   Suppose that the observational units in a statistical study are purchases made on a particular website (think of amazon.com) for one month.

a. Identify two *categorical* variables that could be recorded for these purchases.

b. Identify two *quantitative* variables that could be recorded for these purchases.

c. State two research questions that the company executives might want to investigate with these data.

Online dating service

P.1.16 Suppose that the observational units in a statistical study are people who submit information about themselves to an online dating service (think of match.com).

a. Identify two *categorical* variables that could be recorded for these people.

b. Identify two *quantitative* variables that could be recorded for these people.

c. State two research questions that the dating service managers might want to investigate with these data.

About you*

P.1.17 State a research question relevant to your own life that that you could investigate by collecting data. Also identify the observational units and variables for this statistical study.

SECTION P.2

P.2.1* Suppose that Nellie records the high temperature every day for one year in New York City, while Sandy does the same in San Diego.

a. Who would you expect to have the larger *mean* of these temperatures? Explain.

b. Who would you expect to have the larger *standard deviation* of these temperatures? Explain.

P.2.2 Consider three students with the following distributions of 24 quiz scores:

Amanda: 8, 8, 8, 8, 8, 8, 8, 8, 8, 8, 8, 8, 8, 8, 8, 8, 8, 8, 8, 8, 8, 8, 8, 8

Barney: 5, 6, 6, 6, 6, 7, 7, 7, 7, 7, 7, 7, 8, 8, 8, 8, 8, 8, 8, 9, 9, 9, 9, 10

Charlene: 0, 0, 0, 0, 0, 0, 0, 0, 0, 0, 0, 0, 0, 10, 10, 10, 10, 10, 10, 10, 10, 10, 10, 10

Answer the following without bothering to do any calculations. Explain your choices.

a. Which student has the *smallest* standard deviation of quiz scores?

b. Which student has the *largest* standard deviation of quiz scores?

P.2.3* Consider the following four distributions of quiz scores for a class of 10 students:

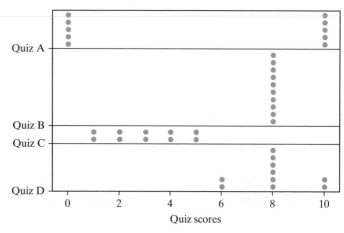

Arrange these in order from smallest standard deviation to largest standard deviation. Also explain how you make your choices.

Grisham books

P.2.4 The P.2.4 dotplot displays the distribution of sentence lengths (number of words in a sentence) for 55 sentences selected from John Grishham's novel *The Confession*. Describe what this graph reveals, paying attention to shape, center, variability, and unusual observations. Write as if you are describing this distribution to someone with no knowledge about sentence lengths.

NFL replacement referees*

P.2.5 In the 2012 National Football League (NFL) season, the first three weeks' games were played with replacement referees because of a labor dispute between the NFL and its regular referees. Many fans and players were concerned with the quality of the replacement referees' performance. We could examine whether data might reveal any differences between the three weeks' games played with replacement referees and the next three weeks' games that were played with regular referees. For example, did games generally take less or more time to play with replacement referees than with regular referees? The pair of P.2.5 dotplots displays data

EXERCISE P.2.4

about the duration of games (in minutes), separated by the type of referees officiating the game.

a. What proportion of the 48 games officiated by replacement referees lasted for at least 3.5 hours (210 minutes)? What proportion of the 43 games officiated by regular referees lasted for this long?

b. What proportion of the 48 games officiated by replacement referees lasted for less than 3 hours (180 minutes)? What proportion of the 43 games officiated by regular referees lasted for this long?

c. Would you say that either type of referee tended to have longer games than the other on average? If so, which type of referee tended to have longer games and by about how much on average?

d. Would you say that either type of referee tended to have more variability in game durations? If so, which type of referee tended to have more variability?

e. Write a paragraph in which you compare the distributions of game durations between the two types of referees. Be sure to comment on shape, center, variability, and unusual observations.

Penalties with replacement refs

P.2.6 Refer to Exercise P.2.5. The pair of P.2.6 dotplots displays data on the total number of penalties called in the game, again separated by the type of referee. Summarize

what these reveal about whether the two types of referees differ with regard to the distributions of this variable.

Weather in San Luis Obispo*

P.2.7 The July 8, 2012, edition of the *San Luis Obispo Tribune* listed predicted high temperatures (in degrees Fahrenheit) for locations throughout San Luis Obispo (SLO; California) county on that date. The P.2.7 dotplot displays the distribution of these temperatures:

a. Write a paragraph describing the distribution of these predicted high temperatures. Be sure to comment on shape, center, variability, and unusual observations.

b. Can you suggest an explanation for the bimodal (two-cluster/peak) nature of this distribution?

Weather in California

P.2.8 Refer to the previous exercise. The newspaper also listed predicted high temperatures for locations throughout the state of California. The P.2.8 dotplots display the two distributions:

Compare and contrast the distributions of predicted high temperatures in the two locations.

Weather throughout the United States

P.2.9* Refer to the previous two exercises. The newspaper also listed predicted high temperatures for locations throughout the United States and for locations

EXERCISE P.2.8

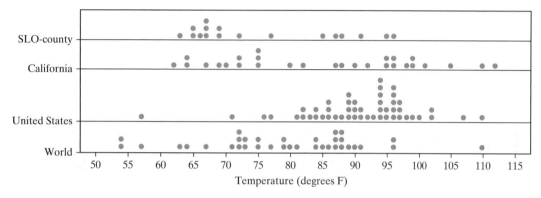

EXERCISE P.2.9

around the world. The P.2.9 dotplots display the four distributions:

a. Without calculating, arrange the four groups from approximately the highest temperature (on average) to the smallest.

b. Without calculating, arrange the four groups from approximately the most variability in temperatures to the least.

c. Suggest an explanation for the low outlier in the distribution of the United States temperatures.

d. Suggest an explanation for the bimodal shape in the distribution of the world temperatures.

SECTION P.3

P.3.1* It has been reported that the probability that a new business closes or changes owners within its first three years is about 0.60. Interpret what this probability means, beginning with: "About 60% of …."

Ice cream shop discount

P.3.2 An ice cream shop offers a discount price on a small ice cream cone—the price is obtained by rolling two dice and then taking the larger number followed by the smaller number to be the price (in cents). So, rolling a 3 and a 2 or a 2 and a 3 would result in a price of 32 cents. If I visit the ice cream shop with only 50 cents in my pocket, the probability that the ice cream cone costs no more than 50 cents is 4/9, which is about 0.444. How would you interpret this probability? (Circle all that apply.)

A. If I go to this ice cream shop a very large number of times with only 50 cents each time, then I will be able to afford the ice cream cone in about 44.4% of all such visits.

B. I will be able to afford the ice cream cone in four of my next nine visits to this shop if I always enter with two quarters.

C. Among all customers who enter this ice cream shop tomorrow, about 4/9 will be able to afford the ice cream cone.

P.3.3* Which of the following numbers *cannot* represent a probability? Circle all that apply.

A. 0.01   **B.** −0.50   **C.** 1.05

D. 88%   **E.** 107%

P.3.4 Explain in your own words what it means to say "the probability of…" for each statement below. Be clear about describing the random process that is repeated over and over again. Do **not** include the words "probability," "chance," "odds," or "likelihood" or any other synonyms of "probability."

a. The probability of getting a red M&M candy is 0.20.

b. The probability of winning at a "daily number" lottery game is 1/1000.

c. The probability of rain tomorrow is 0.30.

d. Pennies can be a nuisance. Suppose 30% of the population of adult Americans want to get rid of the penny. If I randomly select one person from this population, the probability this person wants to get rid of the penny is 0.30.

e. Suppose a polling organization takes a random sample of 100 people from the population of adults in a city, where 30% of this population wants to get rid of the penny. Then the probability is 0.015 that the sample proportion who want to get rid of the penny is less than 0.20.

P.3.5* Suppose that baseball Team A is better than baseball Team B. Team A is enough better that it has a 2/3 probability of beating Team B in any one game, and this probability remains the same for each game, regardless of the outcomes of previous games.

a. Explain what it means to say that Team A has a 2/3 probability of beating Team B in any one game.

b. If Team A plays Team B for 3 games, is Team A guaranteed to win exactly twice?

c. If Team A plays Team B for 30 games, is Team A guaranteed to win exactly 20 times?

d. If Team A plays Team B for 30 games, do you think it's very likely that Team A will win exactly 20 times? Explain.

P.3.6 Reconsider the previous exercise. Continue to assume that Team A has a 2/3 probability of beating Team B in any one game. Now suppose that Team A and Team B play a best-of-three series, meaning that the first team to win two games wins the series.

a. If you are a fan of Team A, would you prefer to play a single game or a best-of-three series or would you have no preference? Explain.

b. Describe how you could use a six-sided die to simulate one repetition of a best-of-three series between Teams A and B.

c. Describe how you could use a six-sided die to approximate the probability that Team A would win the best-of-three series against Team B.

d. It turns out that the probability is 0.741 that Team A would win this best-of-three series against Team B. Interpret what this probability means.

P.3.7* Suppose that a birth is equally likely to be a boy or girl, and the outcome of one birth does not change this probability for future births.

a. Describe how you could use a coin to approximate the probability that a couple with four children would have two boys and two girls.

b. It turns out that the probability is 0.375 that a couple with four children would have two boys and two girls. Interpret what this probability means.

c. Based on the probability given in part (b), what is the probability that a couple with four children does not have two boys and two girls?

d. Explain why it makes sense (at least in hindsight) that a couple with four children is more likely not to have two of each sex than to have two of each sex.

P.3.8 Suppose that there are 50 people in a room. It can be shown (under certain assumptions) that the probability is approximately 0.97 that at least two people in the room have the same birthday (month and date, not necessarily year).

a. Explain what this value 0.97 means, as if to someone who has never studied probability or statistics.

b. Now consider the question of how likely it is that at least one person in the room of 50 matches *your particular* birthday. (Do not attempt to calculate this probability.) Is this event more, less, or equally likely as the event that at least two people share *any* birthday? In other words, do you think this probability will be smaller than 0.97, larger than 0.97, or equal to 0.97? Explain your reasoning.

c. Explain how you could use simulation (imagine you had a hat with 365 slips of paper in it, each with a number from 1 to 365 listed on it) to confirm that the probability is 0.97 in part (a).

d. Repeat part (c), but now use simulation to confirm your answer to part (b).

Four Pillars of Inference: Strength, Size, Breadth, and Cause

The four chapters of this unit are devoted to four core concepts:

LOGIC OF INFERENCE		SCOPE OF INFERENCE	
Significance	**Estimation**	**Generalization**	**Causation**
How **strong** is the evidence of an effect? (Chapter 1)	How **large** is the effect? (Chapter 3)	How **broadly** do the conclusions apply? (Chapter 2)	Can we say what **caused** the observed difference? (Chapter 4)
How **strong** is the evidence that the wording of default options affects recruitment of organ donors?	How **much** will the neutral wording (forced choice) increase the donor pool?	Do the conclusions apply only to that one set of volunteers? To other similar groups of volunteers? To all who apply for driver's licenses?	Can we conclude that it was the **wording of the default option** that was responsible for the increased rate of donor recruitment?

The four concepts have a natural pairing. The first two, significance and estimation, deal with the *logic* of inference. They correspond to Step 4 of our six-step statistical investigation method. The last two concepts, generalization and causation, deal with the *scope* of inference. They correspond to Step 5.

In Unit 1 we present these four core concepts—*strength*, *size*, *breadth*, and *cause*—one chapter at a time, in the simplest possible statistical setting: observed values for a single binary (Yes/No) variable. This setting is mathematically simple enough to study by flipping coins or dealing cards from a shuffled deck of red and black cards. However, even though the coins and cards are simple, they can be used for inference about a variety of interesting situations. Do dolphins communicate? Can dogs detect cancer? Do red-uniformed Olympians win more often? Is the more competent-looking politician more likely to win an election?

① ② ③ ④ ⑤ ⑥ ⑦ ⑧ ⑨ ⑩ ⑪ ⑫

Significance: How Strong Is the Evidence?

CHAPTER OVERVIEW

This chapter is about statistical significance, the first of the four pillars of inference: strength, size, breadth, and cause. *Statistical significance* indicates the **strength** of the evidence. For example, how strong is the evidence that the form of the question about organ donation affects the chance that a person agrees to be a donor? Do we have only a suggestion of an impact or are we overwhelmingly convinced?

The goal of the chapter is to explain how statisticians measure strength of evidence. In the organ donation study, the researchers wanted to determine whether the wording (opt in, versus opt out, versus forced choice) really does make a difference. The data in our study pointed in that direction, but are we convinced? How strong is that evidence? Are there other explanations for the results found in the study? One way to approach our investigation is similar to a criminal trial where innocence is assumed and then evidence is presented to help convince a jury that the assumption of innocence and the actual evidence are at odds. Likewise, we will assume that the wording does *not* make a difference and then see whether the evidence (our data) is dramatic enough to convince us otherwise.

But we know the outcomes for any one study are random in the sense that there is "chance variability." How, then, do we eliminate "they just got lucky" as an explanation? We have to compare our results to what we would expect to see, "by chance," if the wording did not have an effect. If the actual data and this "by chance" explanation are at odds, then which do you believe? Short of a fluke outcome, the actual data trump the chance explanation and we then have strong evidence against the "wording does not have an effect" hypothesis and in favor of our research hypothesis that there is an effect. Understanding this logic is the hardest challenge of the chapter.

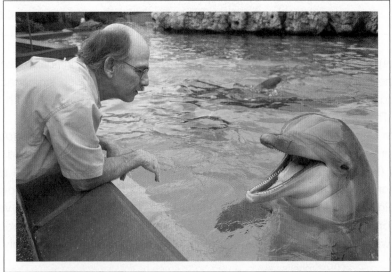

Ben Van Hook/Getty Images, Inc.

INTRODUCTION

A key step in the statistical investigation method is drawing conclusions beyond the observed data. Statisticians often call this "statistical inference." There are four main types of conclusions (inferences) that statisticians can draw from data: significance, estimation, generalization, and causation. In the remainder of this chapter we will focus on *statistical significance*.

If you think back to the organ donor study from the Preliminaries, there were three groups: those in the neutral group were asked to make a yes/no choice about becoming a donor; those in the "opt-in" group were told their default was not to be a donor, but they could choose to become a donor; and those in the "opt-out" group were told their default was they were a donor, but they could choose not to be one if they wished. Let's further examine two of those groups. We saw that 41.8% in the "opt-in" group elected to become donors, compared with 78.6% in the neutral group. A key question here is whether we believe that the 78.6% is far enough away from the 41.8% to be considered *statistically significant*, meaning unlikely to have occurred by random chance alone. True, 78.6% looks very different from 41.8%, but it is at least possible that the wording of the solicitation to donate actually makes no difference and that the difference we observed happened by random chance.

To answer the question "Is our result unlikely to happen by random chance?" our general strategy will be to consider what we expect the results to look like if any differences we are seeing are solely due to random chance. Exploring the random-chance results is critical to our ability to draw meaningful conclusions from data. In this section we will provide a framework for assessing random-chance explanations.

Can Dolphins Communicate?

Example 1.1

A famous study from the 1960s explored whether two dolphins (Doris and Buzz) could communicate abstract ideas. Researchers believed dolphins could communicate simple feelings like "Watch out!" or "I'm happy," but Dr. Jarvis Bastian wanted to explore whether they could also communicate in a more abstract way, much like humans do. To investigate this, Dr. Bastian spent many years training Doris and Buzz and exploring the limits of their communicative ability.

During a training period lasting many months, Dr. Bastian placed buttons underwater on each end of a large pool—two buttons for Doris and two buttons for Buzz. He then used an old automobile headlight as his signal. When he turned on the headlight and let it shine steadily, he intended for this signal to mean "push the button on the right." When he let the headlight blink on and off, this was meant as a signal to "push the button on the left." Every time the dolphins pushed the correct button, Dr. Bastian gave the dolphins a reward of some fish. Over time Doris and Buzz caught on and could earn their fish reward every time.

Then Dr. Bastian made things a bit harder. Now, Buzz had to push his button before Doris. If they didn't push the buttons in the correct order—no fish. After a bit more training, the dolphins caught on again and could earn their fish reward every time. The dolphins were now ready to participate in the real study to examine whether they could communicate *with each other*.

Dr. Bastian placed a large canvas curtain in the middle of the pool. (See Figure 1.1.) Doris was on one side of the curtain and could see the headlight, whereas Buzz was on the other side of the curtain and could not see the headlight. Dr. Bastian turned on the headlight and let it shine steadily. He then watched to see what Doris would do. After looking at the light, Doris swam near the curtain and began to whistle loudly. Shortly after that, Buzz whistled back and then pressed the button on the right—he got it correct and so both dolphins got a fish. But this single attempt was not enough to convince Dr. Bastian that Doris had communicated with Buzz through her whistling. Dr. Bastian repeated the process several times, sometimes having the light blink (so Doris needed to let Buzz know to push the left button) and other times having it glow steadily (so Doris needed to let Buzz know to push the right button). He kept track of how often Buzz pushed the correct button.

EXAMPLE

In this scenario, even if Buzz and Doris can communicate, we don't necessarily expect Buzz to push the correct button every time. We allow for some "randomness" in the process; maybe on one trial Doris was a bit more underwater when she whistled and the signal wasn't as clear for Buzz. Or maybe Buzz and Doris aren't communicating at all and Buzz guesses which button to push every time and just happens to guess correctly once in a while. Our goal is to get an idea of how likely Buzz is to push the correct button in the long run.

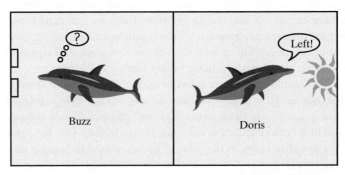

FIGURE 1.1 Depending whether or not the light was blinking or shown steadily, Doris had to communicate to Buzz as to which button to push.

Let's see how Dr. Bastian was applying the six-step statistical investigation method.

STEP 1: Ask a research question. Can dolphins communicate in an abstract manner?

STEP 2: Design a study and collect data. Notice Dr. Bastian took some time to train the dolphins in order to get them to a point where he could test a specific research conjecture. The research conjecture is that Buzz pushes the correct button more often than he would if he and Doris could not communicate. If Buzz and Doris could not communicate, Buzz would just be guessing which button to push. The *observational units* are Buzz's attempts and the *variable* for each attempt is whether or not Buzz pushes the correct button (a *categorical* variable).

STEP 3: Explore the data. In one phase of the study, Dr. Bastian had Buzz attempt to push the correct button a total of 16 different times. In this **sample** of 16 attempts, Buzz pushed the correct button 15 out of 16 times. To summarize these results, we report the **statistic**, a numerical summary of the sample. For this example, we could report either 15, the number of correct pushes, or $15/16 = 0.9375$ as the statistic.

The **sample size** in this example is 16. Note that the word "sample" is used as a noun (the set of observational units being studied), as an adjective, for example to mean "computed from the observed data," as, for example, "sample statistic," and as a verb, for example, "We need to sample 50 people."

STEP 4: Draw inferences beyond the data. These 16 observations are a mere snapshot of Buzz's overall selection process. We will consider this a *random process*. We are interested in Buzz's actual long-run proportion (i.e., probability) of pushing the correct button based on Doris's whistles. This unknown long-run proportion is called a **parameter**.

Note that we are assuming this parameter is not changing over time, at least for the process used by Buzz in this phase of the study. Because we can't observe Buzz pushing the button forever, we need to draw conclusions (possibly incorrect, but hopefully not) about the value of the parameter based only on these 16 attempts. Buzz certainly pushed the correct button most of the time, so we might consider either of the following:

- Buzz is doing something other than just guessing (his probability of a correct button push is larger than 0.50).
- Buzz is just guessing (his probability of a correct button push is 0.50) and he got lucky in these 16 attempts.

Definitions

The set of observational units on which we collect data is called the **sample**. The number of observational units in the sample is the **sample size**. A **statistic** is a number summarizing the results in the sample.

1.1.1

Definition

For a random process, a **parameter** is a long-run numerical property of the process.

These are the two possible explanations to be evaluated. Because we can't collect more data, we have to base our conclusions only on the data we have. It's certainly *possible* that Buzz was just guessing and got lucky! But does this seem like a reasonable explanation to you? How would you argue against someone who thought this was the case?

> ### THINK ABOUT IT
>
> Based on these data, do you think Buzz somehow knew which button to push? Is 15 out of 16 correct pushes convincing to you? Or do you think that Buzz could have just been guessing? How might you justify your answer?

So how are we going to decide between these two possible explanations? One approach is to choose a **model** for the random process (repeated attempts to push the correct button) and then see whether our model is consistent with the observed data. If it is, then we will conclude that we have a reasonable model and we will use that model to answer our questions.

THE CHANCE MODEL

Scientists use models to help understand complicated real-world phenomena. Statisticians often employ **chance models** to generate data from random processes to help them investigate such processes. You did this with the Monty Hall exploration (Section P.3) to investigate properties of the two strategies, switching and staying with your original choice of door. In that exploration it was clear how the underlying chance process worked, even though the probabilities themselves were not obvious. But here we don't know for sure what the underlying real-world process is. We are trying to decide whether the process could be Buzz simply guessing or whether the process is something else, such as Buzz and Doris being able to communicate.

Let us first investigate the "Buzz was simply guessing" process. Because Buzz is choosing between two options, the simplest chance model to consider is a coin flip. We can flip a coin to represent, or *simulate*, Buzz's choice *assuming he is just guessing* which button to push. To generate this artificial data, we can let "heads" represent the outcome that Buzz pushes the correct button and let "tails" be the outcome that Buzz pushes the incorrect button. This gives Buzz a 50% chance of pushing the correct button. This can be used to represent the "Buzz was just guessing" or the "random-chance-alone" explanation. The correspondence between the real study and the physical simulation is shown in Table 1.1.

 1.1.2

TABLE 1.1	Parallels between real study and physical simulation	
Coin flip	=	guess by Buzz
Heads	=	correct guess
Tails	=	wrong guess
Chance of heads	=	1/2, probability of correct button when Buzz is just guessing
One repetition	=	one set of 16 simulated attempts by Buzz

Now that we see how flipping a coin can simulate Buzz guessing, let's flip some coins to simulate Buzz's performance. Imagine that we get heads on the first flip. What does this mean? This would correspond to Buzz pushing the correct button! But, why did he push the correct button? In this chance model, the only reason he pushed the correct button is because he happened to guess correctly—remember the coin is simulating what happens when Buzz is just guessing which button to push.

What if we keep flipping the coin? Each time we flip the coin we are simulating another attempt where Buzz guesses which button to push. Remember that heads represents Buzz guessing correctly and tails represents Buzz guessing incorrectly. How many times do we flip the coin? Sixteen, to match Buzz's 16 attempts in the actual study. After 16 tosses, we obtained the sequence of flips shown in Figure 1.2.

FIGURE 1.2   A sequence of 16 coin flips.

Here we got 11 heads and 5 tails (11 out of 16, or 0.6875, is the simulated statistic). This gives us an idea of what could have happened in the study if Buzz had been randomly guessing which button to push each time.

Will we get this same result every time we flip a coin 16 times? Let's flip our coin another 16 times and see what happens. When we did this, we got 7 heads and 9 tails, as shown in the sequence of coin flips (7 out of 16, or 0.4375, is the simulated statistic) in Figure 1.3.

FIGURE 1.3   Another sequence of 16 coin flips.

So can we learn anything from these coin tosses when the results vary between the sets of 16 tosses?

Using and evaluating the coin flip chance model

Because coin flipping is a random process, we know that we won't obtain the same number of heads with every set of 16 flips. But are some numbers of heads more likely than others? If we continue our repetitions of 16 tosses, we can start to see how the outcomes for the number of heads are distributed. Does the *distribution* of the number of heads that result in 16 flips have a predictable long-run pattern? In particular, how much *variability* is there in our simulated statistics between repetitions (sets of 16 flips) just by random chance?

1.1.3

In order to investigate these questions, we need to continue to flip our coin to get many, many sets of 16 flips (or many repetitions of the 16 choices where we are modeling Buzz simply guessing each time). We did this, and Figure 1.4 shows what we found when we graphed the number of heads from each set of 16 coin flips. Here, the process of flipping a coin 16 times was repeated 100 times in Figure 1.4A (a number small enough so we can see the individual dots) and 1,000 times in Figure 1.4B—a number chosen for convenience but also large enough to give us a fairly accurate sense of the long-run behavior for the number of heads in 16 tosses.

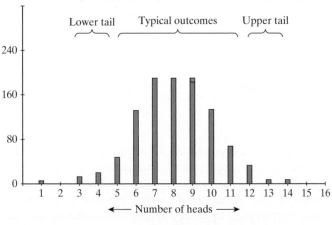

FIGURE 1.4   Dotplots showing (a) 100 repetitions and (b) 1,000 repetitions of flipping a coin 16 times and counting the number of heads.

Let's think carefully about what the graphs in Figure 1.4 show. For these graphs, each dot represents the number of heads in one set of 16 coin tosses. We see that the resulting number of heads follows a clear pattern: 7, 8, and 9 heads happened quite a lot, 10 was pretty common also (though less so than 8), 6 happened some of the time, 1 happened once. But we never got 15 heads in any set of 16 tosses! We might consider any outcome between about 5 and 11 heads to be typical, but getting fewer than 5 heads or more than 11 heads happened rarely enough we can consider it a bit unusual. We refer to these unusual results as being out in the "tails" of the distribution.

> **THINK ABOUT IT**
>
> How does the analysis above help us address the strength of evidence for our research conjecture that Buzz was doing something other than just guessing?

What does this have to do with the dolphin communication study? We said that we would flip a coin to simulate what could happen if Buzz was just guessing each time he pushed the button in 16 attempts. We saw that getting results like 15 heads out of 16 never happened in our 1,000 repetitions. This shows us that 15 is a very unusual outcome—far out in the tail of the distribution of the simulated statistics—if Buzz is just guessing. In short, even though we expect some variability in the results for different sets of 16 tosses, the pattern shown in this distribution indicates that an outcome of 15 heads is outside the typical chance variability we would expect to see when Buzz is simply guessing.

In the actual study, Buzz really did push the correct button 15 times out of 16, an outcome that we just determined would rarely occur if Buzz was just guessing. So, our coin flip chance model tells us that we have very strong evidence that Buzz was not just tossing a coin to make his choices. This means we have strong evidence that Buzz wasn't just guessing. Therefore, we don't believe the "by-chance-alone" explanation is a good one for Buzz. The results mean our evidence is strong enough to be considered **statistically significant**. That is, we don't think our study result (15 out of 16 correct) happened by chance alone, but rather, something other than "random chance" was at play.

 1.1.4

Definition

A result is **statistically significant** if it is unlikely to occur just by random chance.

If our observed result appears to be consistent with the chance model, we say that the chance model is **plausible** or believable.

WHAT NEXT? A GLIMPSE INTO STEPS 5 AND 6

The steps we went through above have helped us evaluate how strong the evidence is that Buzz is not guessing (Step 4 of the statistical investigation method). In this case, the evidence provided by this sample is fairly strong that Buzz isn't guessing. Still, there are some important questions you should be asking right now, such as: If Buzz isn't guessing, what is he doing?

STEP 5: Formulate conclusions. We should also ask ourselves: if Buzz wasn't guessing, does this prove that Buzz and Doris can communicate? And if so, what does this say about other dolphins? As we'll find in later chapters, the answers to these questions hinge mainly on how the study was designed and how we view the 16 attempts that we observed (e.g., we assume Buzz couldn't see the light himself, the light signal displayed each time was chosen randomly so Buzz couldn't figure out a pattern to help him decide which button to push; Buzz's 16 attempts are a good representation of what Buzz would do given many more attempts under identical conditions; but we might still wonder whether Buzz's behavior is representative of dolphin behavior in general or are there key differences among individual dolphins).

STEP 6: Look back and ahead. After completing Steps 1–5 of the statistical investigation method, we need to revisit the big picture of the initial research question. First, we reflect on the limitations of the analysis and think about future studies. In short, we are now stepping back and thinking about the initial research question more than the specific research conjecture being tested in the study. In some ways, this is the most important step of the whole study because it is where we think about the true implications of the scientific study we've conducted. For this study, we would reflect on Dr. Bastian's methods, summarize the results for Buzz, and reflect on ways to improve the study to enhance the conclusions we can draw.

1.1.5

The 3S strategy

Let us summarize the overall approach to assessing *statistical significance* that we have been taking in this section. We observed a sample statistic (e.g., the number of "successes" or the proportion of "successes" in the sample). Then we simulated "could-have-been" outcomes for that statistic under a specific chance model (just guessing). Then we used the information we gained about the random variation in the "by-chance" values of the statistic to help us judge whether the observed value of the statistic is an unusual or a typical outcome. If it is unusual—we say the observed statistic is *statistically significant*—it provides strong evidence that the chance-alone explanation is wrong. If it is typical, we consider the chance model plausible.

You may have noticed that we only simulated results for one specific model. When we saw that the sample statistic observed in the study was not consistent with these simulated results, we rejected the chance-alone explanation. Often, research analyses stop here. Instead of trying to simulate results from other models (in particular we may not really have an initial idea what a more appropriate model might be), we are content to say there is something other than random chance at play here. This might lead the researchers to reformulate their conjectures and collect more data in order to investigate different models.

We will call the process of simulating could-have-been statistics under a specific chance model the *3S strategy*. After forming our research conjecture and collecting the sample data, we will use the 3S strategy to weigh the evidence against the chance model. This 3S strategy will serve as the foundation for addressing the question of statistical significance in Step 4 of the statistical investigation method.

3S Strategy for Measuring Strength of Evidence

1. **Statistic:** Compute the statistic from the observed sample data.

2. **Simulate:** Identify a "by-chance-alone" explanation for the data. Repeatedly simulate values of the statistic that could have happened when the chance model is true.

3. **Strength of evidence:** Consider whether the value of the observed statistic from the research study is unlikely to occur when the chance model is true. If we decide the observed statistic is unlikely to occur by chance alone, then we can conclude that the observed data provide strong evidence against the plausibility of the chance model. If not, then we consider the chance model to be a plausible (believable) explanation for the observed data; in other words what we observed could plausibly have happened just by random chance.

Let's illustrate how we implemented the 3S strategy for the Doris and Buzz example.

1. **Statistic:** Our observed statistic was 15, the number of times Buzz pushed the correct button in 16 attempts.

2. **Simulate:** If Buzz was actually guessing, the parameter (the probability he would push the correct button) would equal 0.50. In other words, he would push the correct button 50% of the time in the long run. We used a coin flip to model what could have happened in 16 attempts when Buzz is just guessing. We flip the coin 16 times and count how many of the 16 flips are heads, meaning how many times Buzz pressed the correct button ("success"). We then repeat this process many more times, each time keeping track of the number of the 16 attempts that Buzz pushed the correct button. We end up with a distribution of could-have-been statistics representing typical values for the number of correct pushes when Buzz is just guessing.

3. **Strength of evidence:** Because 15 successes in 16 attempts rarely happens by chance alone, we conclude that we have strong evidence that, in the long-run, Buzz is not just guessing.

Notice that we have used the result of 15 out of 16 correct attempts to *infer* that Buzz's actual long-run proportion of pushing the correct button was not simply 0.50.

Another Doris and Buzz study

One goal of statistical significance is to rule out random chance as a *plausible* (believable) explanation for what we have observed. We still need to worry about how well the study was conducted. For example, are we absolutely sure Buzz couldn't see the headlight around the curtain? Are we sure there was no pattern to which headlight setting was displayed that he might have detected? And of course we haven't completely ruled out random chance; he may have had an incredibly lucky day. But the chance of his being that lucky is so small that we conclude that other explanations are more plausible or credible.

One option that Dr. Bastian pursued was to redo the study except now he replaced the curtain with a wooden barrier between the two sides of the tank in order to ensure a more complete separation between the dolphins to see whether that would diminish the effectiveness of their communication.

STEP 1: Ask a research question.   The research question remains the same: Can dolphins communicate in a deep abstract manner?

STEP 2: Design a study and collect data.   The study design is similar with some adjustments to the barrier between Doris and Buzz. The canvas curtain is replaced by a plywood board. The research conjecture, observational units, and variable remain the same.

In this case, Buzz pushed the correct button only 16 out of 28 times. The variable is the same (whether or not Buzz pushed the correct button), but the number of observational units (sample size) has changed to 28 (the number of attempts).

> ### THINK ABOUT IT
>
> Based on the results for this phase of the study, do you think that Doris could tell Buzz which button to push, even under these conditions? Or is it believable that Buzz could have just been guessing?

STEP 3: Explore the data.   So our observed statistic is 16 out of 28 correct attempts, which is $16/28 \times 100\% \approx 57.1\%$ of Buzz's attempts. This is again more than half the time, but not much larger than 50%. A simple **bar graph** of these results is shown in Figure 1.5.

STEP 4: Draw inferences.   Is it plausible (believable) that Buzz was simply guessing in this set of attempts? How do we measure how much evidence these results provide against the chance model? Let's use the same chance model as we used earlier to see what could have happened if Buzz was just guessing. We will apply the 3S strategy to this new study.

1. **Statistic:** The new observed sample statistic is 16 out of 28, or about 0.571.

> ### THINK ABOUT IT
>
> Consider again our simulation of the chance model assuming Buzz is guessing. What do we need to change for this new phase of the study?

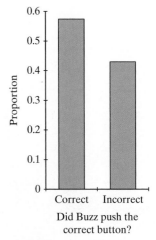

FIGURE 1.5 Bar graph for Buzz's 28 attempts.

2. **Simulation:** This time we need to do repetitions of 28 coin flips, not just 16. A distribution of the number of heads in 1,000 repetitions of 28 coin flips is shown in Figure 1.6. This models 1,000 repetitions of 28 attempts with Buzz randomly pushing one of the buttons (guessing) each time.

FIGURE 1.6 A graph showing 1,000 repetitions of flipping a coin 28 times and counting the number of heads. This models the number of correct pushes in 28 attempts when Buzz is guessing each time.

3. **Strength of evidence:** Now we need to consider the new observed statistic (16 out of 28, or 0.571). We see from the graph that 16 out of 28 is a fairly typical outcome if Buzz is just randomly guessing. What does this tell us? It tells us that the results of this study are something that could easily have happened if Buzz was just randomly guessing. So what can we conclude? We can say his 16 successes are not convincing evidence against the "by-chance-alone" model.

The graph in Figure 1.6 shows what happens for the hypothetical Buzz who just guesses. An actual outcome far out in the tail of that distribution would be strong evidence against the "just guessing" hypothesis. But be careful: The opposite result—an actual outcome near the center—is *not* strong evidence in support of the guessing hypothesis. Yes, the result is *consistent* with that hypothesis, but it is also consistent with many other hypotheses as well.

1.1.6

Bottom line: In this second study we conclude that there is not enough evidence that the "by-chance-alone" model is wrong. That model is still a *plausible* explanation for the statistic we observed in the study (16 out of 28). Based on this set of attempts, we do not have convincing evidence against the possibility that Buzz is just guessing, but other explanations also remain plausible. For example, the results are consistent with very weak communication between the dolphins. All we know from this analysis is that one plausible explanation for the observed data is that Buzz was guessing.

In fact, Dr. Bastian soon discovered that in this set of attempts the equipment malfunctioned and the food dispenser for Doris did not operate and so Doris was not receiving her fish rewards during the study. Because of this malfunction, it's not so surprising that removing the incentive hindered the communication between the dolphins and we cannot refute that Buzz was just guessing for these attempts.

Dr. Bastian fixed the equipment and ran the study again. This time he found convincing evidence that Buzz was not guessing.

For a bit more discussion on processes and parameters, see FAQ 1.1.1.

FAQ 1.1.1   www.wiley.com/college/tintle

What is a random process?

EXPLORATION | Can Dogs Understand Human Cues?
1.1

Dogs have been domesticated for about 14,000 years. In that time, have they been able to develop an understanding of human gestures such as pointing or glancing? How about similar nonhuman cues? Researchers Udell, Giglio, and Wynne tested a small number of dogs in order to answer these questions.

In this exploration, we will first see whether dogs can understand human gestures as well as nonhuman gestures. To test this, the researchers positioned the dogs about 2.5 meters from the experimenter. Two cups were placed, one on each side of the experimenter. The experimenter would perform some sort of gesture (pointing, bowing, looking) toward one of the cups or there would be some other nonhuman gesture (a mechanical arm pointing, a doll pointing, or a stuffed animal looking) toward one of the cups. The researchers would then see whether the dog would go to the cup that was indicated. There were six dogs tested. We will look at one of the dogs in two of his sets of trials. This dog, a four-year-old mixed breed, was named Harley. Each trial involved one gesture and one pair of cups, with a total of 10 trials in a set.

We will start out by looking at one set of trials where the experimenter bowed toward one of the cups to see whether Harley would go to that cup.

STEP 1: State the research question.

1. Based on the description of the study, state the research question.

STEP 2: Design a study and collect data. Harley was tested 10 times and 9 of those times he chose the correct cup.

2. What are the observational units?
3. Identify the variable in the study. What are the possible outcomes of this variable? Is this variable quantitative or categorical?

STEP 3: Explore the data. With categorical data, we typically report the number of "successes" or the proportion of successes as the statistic.

4. What is the number of observational units (sample size) in this study?
5. Determine the observed statistic and produce a simple bar graph of the data (have one bar for the proportion of times Harley picked the correct cup and another for the proportion of times he picked the wrong cup).
6. If the research conjecture is that Harley can understand what the experimenter means when they bow toward an object, is the statistic in the direction suggested by the research conjecture?
7. Could Harley have gotten 9 out of 10 correct even if he really didn't understand the human gesture and so was randomly guessing between the two cups?
8. Do you think it is likely Harley would have gotten 9 out of 10 correct if he was just guessing randomly each time?

STEP 4: Draw inferences beyond the data. There are two possibilities for why Harley chose the correct cup 9 out of 10 times:

- He is merely picking a cup at random and in these 10 trials happened to guess correctly in 9 of them. That is, he got more than half correct just by random chance alone.
- He is doing something other than merely guessing and perhaps understands what the experimenters mean when they bow towards the cup.

The unknown long-run proportion (i.e., probability) that Harley will choose the correct cup is called a *parameter*.

We don't know the value of the parameter, but the two possibilities listed above suggest two different possibilities.

9. What is the value of the parameter if Harley is picking a cup at random? Give a specific value.
10. What is the possible range of values (greater than or less than some value) for the parameter if Harley is not just guessing and instead understands the experimenter?

Definitions

The set of observational units on which we collect data is called the *sample*. The number of observational units in the sample is the *sample size*. A *statistic* is a number summarizing the results in the sample.

Definition

For a random process, a *parameter* is a long-run numerical property of the process.

We will show you how statisticians use simulation to make a statement about the strength of evidence for these two possible statements about the parameter's value.

The chance model

Statisticians often use *chance models* to generate data from random processes to help them investigate the process. In particular, they can see whether the observed statistic is consistent with the values of the statistic simulated by the chance model. If we determine that Harley's results are not consistent with the results from the chance model, we will consider this to be evidence against the chance model and in favor of the research conjecture, that he understands the bowing gesture. In this case, we would say Harley's results are *statistically significant*, meaning unlikely to have occurred by chance alone.

We can't perform the actual study more times in order to assess the second possibility, but we can simulate the behavior of Harley's choices if we were to assume the first possibility (that he is simply guessing every time).

Definition

A result is **statistically significant** if it is unlikely to occur just by random chance. If our observed result appears to be consistent with the chance model, we say that the chance model is **plausible** or believable.

----

11. Explain how you could use a coin toss to represent Harley's choices if he is guessing between the two cups each time. How many times do you have to flip the coin to represent one set of Harley's attempts? What does heads represent?

12. If Harley was guessing randomly each time, on average, how many out of the 10 times would you expect him to choose the correct cup?

13. Simulate one repetition of Harley guessing randomly by flipping a coin 10 times (why 10?) and letting heads represent selecting the correct cup ("success") and tails represent selecting the incorrect cup ("failure"). Count the number of heads in your 10 flips. Combine your results with the rest of the class to create a *dotplot* of the distribution for the number of heads out of 10 flips of a coin.

    a. Where does 9 heads fall in the distribution? Would you consider it an unusual outcome or a fairly typical outcome for the number of heads in 10 flips?

    b. Based on your answer to the previous question, do you think it is plausible (believable) that Harley was just guessing which cup to choose?

Using an applet to simulate flipping a coin many times

To really assess the typical values for the number of heads in 10 coin tosses (number of correct picks by Harley assuming he is guessing at random), we need to simulate many more outcomes of the chance model. Open the **One Proportion** applet from the textbook webpage.

Notice that the probability of heads has been set to be 0.50, representing Harley guessing between the two cups. Set the number of tosses to 10 and press the **Draw Samples** button. What was the resulting number of heads?

Notice that the number of heads in this set of 10 tosses is then displayed by a dot on the graph. Uncheck the **Animate** box and press the **Draw Samples** button 9 more times. This will demonstrate how the number of heads varies randomly across each set of 10 tosses. Nine more dots have been added to your dotplot. Is a pattern starting to emerge?

Now change the **Number of repetitions** from 1 to 990 and press **Draw Samples**. The applet will now show the results for the number of heads in 1,000 different sets of 10 coin tosses. So each dot represents the number of times Harley chooses the correct cup out of 10 attempts assuming he is just guessing.

Remember why we conducted this simulation: to assess whether Harley's result (9 correct in 10 attempts) would be unlikely to occur by chance alone if he were just guessing between the pair of cups for each attempt.

14. Locate the result of getting 9 heads in the dotplot created by the applet. Would you consider this an unlikely result in the tail of the distribution of the number of heads?

15. Based on the results of 1,000 simulated sets of 10 coin flips each, would you conclude that Harley would be very unlikely to have picked the correct cup 9 times in 10 attempts if he

was randomly guessing between the two cups each time? Explain how your answer relates to the applet's dotplot.

16. Do the results of this study appear to be statistically significant?

17. Do the results of this study suggest that Harley just guessing is a plausible explanation for Harley picking the correct cup 9 out of 10 times?

Summarizing your understanding

18. To make sure that you understand the coin-flipping chance model, fill in Table 1.2 indicating what parts of the real study correspond to the physical (coin-flipping) simulation.

TABLE 1.2 Parallels between real study and physical simulation		
Coin flip	=	
Heads	=	
Tails	=	
Chance of heads	=	
One repetition	=	one set of _____ simulated attempts by Harley

The 3S strategy

We will call the process of simulating could-have-been statistics under a specific chance model the **3S strategy**. After forming our research conjecture and collecting the sample data, we will use the 3S strategy to weigh the evidence against the chance model. This 3S strategy will serve as the foundation for addressing the question of statistical significance in Step 4 of the statistical investigation method.

> **3S Strategy for Measuring Strength of Evidence**
>
> 1. **Statistic:** Compute the statistic from the observed sample data.
> 2. **Simulate:** Identify a "by-chance-alone" explanation for the data. Repeatedly simulate values of the statistic that could have happened when the chance model is true.
> 3. **Strength of evidence:** Consider whether the value of the observed statistic from the research study is unlikely to occur if the chance model is true. If we decide the observed statistic is unlikely to occur by chance alone, then we can conclude that the observed data provide strong evidence against the plausibility of the chance model. If not, then we consider the chance model to be a plausible (believable) explanation for the observed data; in other words what we observed could plausibly have happened just by random chance.

Let's review how we have already applied the 3S strategy to this study.

19. **Statistic.** What is the statistic in this study?

20. **Simulate.** Fill in the blanks to describe the simulation. We flipped a coin _____ times and kept track of how many times it came up heads. We then repeated this process _____ more times, each time keeping track of how many heads were obtained in each of the _____ flips.

21. **Strength of evidence.** Fill in the blanks to summarize how we are assessing the strength of evidence for this study. Because we rarely obtained a value of _____ heads when flipping the coin _____ times, this means that it is _____ (believable/unlikely) that Harley is just guessing, because if Harley was just guessing he _____ (rarely/often) would get a value like _____ correct out of _____ attempts.

STEP 5: Formulate conclusions.

22. Based on this analysis, are you convinced that Harley can understand human cues? Why or why not?

Another study

One important step in a statistical investigation is to consider other models and whether the results can be confirmed in other settings.

23. In a different study, the researchers used a mechanical arm (roughly the size of a human arm) to point at one of the two cups. The researchers tested this to see whether dogs understood nonhuman gestures. In 10 trials, Harley chose the correct cup 6 times.

    a. Using the dotplot you obtained when you simulated 1,000 sets of 10 coin flips assuming Harley was just guessing, locate the result of getting 6 heads. Would you consider this an unlikely result in the tail of the distribution?

    b. Based on the results of 1,000 simulated sets of 10 coin flips each, would you conclude that Harley would be very unlikely to have picked the correct cup 6 times in 10 attempts if he was randomly guessing between the two cups each time? Explain how your answer relates to the applet's dotplot.

    c. Is this study's result statistically significant?

    d. Do the results of this study suggest that Harley just guessing is a plausible explanation for Harley picking the correct cup 6 out of 10 times?

    e. Does this study prove that Harley cannot understand the mechanical arm?

STEP 6: Look back and ahead.

24. Compare the analyses between the two studies. How does the unusualness of the observed statistic compare between the two studies? Does this make sense based on the value of the observed statistic in the two studies? Does this make sense based on how the two studies were designed? Explain. (*Hint:* Why might the results differ for human and mechanical arms? Why would this matter?)

25. A single study will not provide all of the information needed to fully understand a broad, complex research question. Thinking back to the original research question, what additional studies would you suggest conducting next?

- -

SECTION 1.1 Summary

The set of observational units on which we collect data is called a **sample**. The number of observational units is the **sample size**. A number computed to summarize the variable measured on a sample is called a **statistic**.

For a chance process, a **parameter** is a long-run numerical property of that process, such as a probability (long-run proportion).

A simulation analysis based on a chance model can assess the strength of evidence provided by sample data against a particular claim about the chance model. The logic of assessing statistical significance employs what we call the **3S strategy**:

- **Statistic:** Compute an observed statistic from the data.
- **Simulate:** Identify a model for the "by-chance-alone" explanation. Repeatedly simulate values of the statistic that could have occurred from that chance model.
- **Strength of evidence:** Examine how unusual the observed value of the statistic would be under repeated application of the chance model.
  - If the observed value of the sample statistic is *unlikely* to have occurred from the chance model, then the data provide *strong* evidence against the chance model as the explanation.

- If the observed value of the sample statistic is *not* unlikely to have occurred from the chance model, then the chance model is a *plausible* explanation for the observed data.

The **chance model** considered in this section involved tossing a fair coin. This chance model allowed for assessing whether an observed number of "successes" in a study provided strong evidence that the two outcomes of a categorical variable were not equally likely. In the next section you will consider other chance models, but the reasoning process will remain the same.

MEASURING THE STRENGTH OF EVIDENCE   SECTION 1.2

INTRODUCTION

In the previous section, we discussed testing whether or not a chance model of *equally choosing between two equally likely options (e.g., flipping a coin)* was plausible (believable) based on some observed sample data. Not all situations call for a coin-flipping model. For example, if you were guessing at the answers to a true-false test, you would expect to have a 50% chance of getting a question correct. However, if you were guessing at the answers to a multiple-choice test where each question had four possible answers, you should expect to have only a 25% chance of guessing a particular question correctly. Other events, as you will soon see, can be a bit more complicated than this. In this section, we will apply the six-step statistical investigation method in the more general setting of an arbitrary probability of "success."

We will also learn helpful terminology (null and alternative hypotheses, p-value) that are commonly used in statistical investigations to describe the process of drawing conclusions from data. These things will both help us formalize the procedure of a **test of significance** and give us some guidelines to help us determine when we have strong enough evidence that our chance model is not correct. We will also introduce some new symbols, for convenience, so try to keep the big picture in mind.

Rock-Paper-Scissors

Example 1.2

Have you ever played rock-paper-scissors (or *Rochambeau*)? It's considered a "fair game" in that the two players are equally likely to win (like a coin toss). Both players simultaneously display one of three hand gestures (rock, paper, or scissors), and the objective is to display a gesture that defeats that of your opponent. Official rules are available from the World RPS Society (www.worldrps.com), but the main gist is that rocks break scissors, scissors cut paper, and paper covers rock.

But is it really a fair game? Do some players exhibit patterns in their behavior that an opponent can exploit? An article published in *College Mathematics Journal* (Eyler, Shalla, Doumaux, and McDevitt, 2009) found that players, particularly novices, tend to not prefer scissors. Suppose you decide to investigate this tendency with a friend of yours who hasn't played the game before. You explain the rules of the game and play 12 rounds. Suppose your friend only shows scissors twice in those 12 plays.

> **THINK ABOUT IT**
>
> - What are the observational units? What is the variable?
> - What is the underlying process from which the researchers (you) gathered their sample data?
> - What is the parameter of interest?
> - What is the observed statistic?

EXAMPLE

A similarity between this study and ones we've looked at previously (e.g., Buzz and Doris) is that we have repeated outcomes from the same random process. In this study, the individual plays of the game are the observational units, and the variable is whether or not the player chooses scissors. This categorical variable has just two outcomes (scissors or not scissors) and so is sometimes called a **binary variable**.

The underlying process here is choosing a hand gesture in each repeated play of the game. The parameter of interest is the long-run proportion that any player picks scissors. The observed statistic is the number of times scissors was chosen in the 12 plays (two) or the proportion of times that scissors was chosen (1/6).

THINK ABOUT IT

What is the research conjecture about the long-run proportion?

We are told that novice players seem to pick scissors less than the other two gestures. This would imply that the long-run proportion for picking scissors is less than 1/3. And in this study, that's what you found. Your friend only chose scissors one-sixth of the time.

But perhaps that was just an unlucky occurrence in this study? Maybe your friend would play scissors one-third of the time if he played the game for a very long time, and, just by chance, you happened to observe less than one-third in the first 12 games? So, again, we have two possible explanations for why our statistic (1/6) is below what we think is the true parameter (1/3) if the random-chance model is correct:

- Novice players, like your friend, pick equally among the three gestures and we just happened to observe fewer scissor choices in this study by chance alone.
- Novice players really do tend to pick scissors less than 1/3 of the time.

We can rewrite these two possible explanations as two competing hypotheses:

Null hypothesis: Novice players pick equally between the three gestures in the long run (picking scissors one-third of the time in the long run).

Alternative hypothesis: Novice players pick scissors less than one-third of the time in the long run.

Notice that the null and alternative hypotheses are statements about the parameter (probability of choosing scissors) and the underlying process (in the long run), not just about what was observed in this study. In fact, we should state the hypotheses prior to conducting the study, before we ever gather any data! Our goal is to use the sample data to estimate the parameter and to infer whether this unknown value is less than 1/3.

USE OF SYMBOLS

We can use mathematical symbols to represent quantities and simplify our writing. Throughout the book we will emphasize written explanations but will also show you mathematical symbols which you are free to use as a short-hand once you are comfortable with the material. The distinction between parameter and statistic is so important that we always use different symbols to refer to them.

We will use the Greek letter for **p**, which is π (pronounced "pie"), to represent a parameter that is a probability. For example, the long-run proportion that a novice player picks scissors can be represented by π. We will then use the symbol $\hat{p}$ (pronounced "**p-hat**") to represent the proportion in the sample. In this example, $\hat{p} = 2/12 \approx 0.167$, the proportion of times that your friend chose scissors. In fact, one way to distinguish between the parameter and the statistic is verb tense! The statistic is the proportion of times that your friend did (past tense, observed) show scissors. The parameter is the long-run proportion he would throw scissors (future tense, unobserved) if he played the game forever.

We can also use symbols for the hypotheses. The null hypothesis is often written as H_0 and the alternative as H_a. Finally, the sample size, which is the same as the number of observational units, also has a symbol: the letter "**n**."

Definition

A **binary variable** is a categorical variable with only two outcomes. Often we convert categorical variables with more than two outcomes (e.g., rock, paper, or scissors) into binary variables (e.g., scissors or not scissors). In this case we also define one outcome to be a "success" and one to be a "failure."

Definitions

- The **null hypothesis** typically represents the "by-random-chance-alone" explanation. The chance model (or "null model") is chosen to reflect this hypothesis.

- The **alternative hypothesis** typically represents the "there is an effect" explanation that contradicts the null hypothesis. Researchers typically hope this hypothesis will be supported by the data they collect.

1.2.1

1.2.2

We can use these symbols to rewrite the null and alternative hypotheses:

$$H_0: \pi = 1/3$$
$$H_a: \pi < 1/3$$

where π represents your friend's true probability of throwing scissors.

Notice that both of these hypothesis statements are claims about the parameter π. When testing a single probability as we are doing in this example, we compare the actual (but unknown) value of the parameter (π) to the same numerical value in both the null and alternative hypotheses. In this case that value is 1/3 (often called the "hypothesized" probability). What differs between the two statements is the inequality symbol. The null hypothesis will always contain an equals sign and the alternative hypothesis will contain a (strictly) greater than sign (as it would have in the Doris and Buzz example from the previous question), a (strictly) less than sign (as it does in this example), or a not equal to sign like we will see in Section 1.4. Which inequality symbol to use in the alternative hypothesis is determined by the research conjecture.

APPLYING THE 3S STRATEGY

Now, let's apply the 3S strategy to evaluate the evidence against the null hypothesis in favor of the alternative hypothesis, that your friend is less likely to choose scissors than the other options.

1. **Statistic:** Your friend showed scissors one-sixth of the time in the first 12 plays.

2. **Simulation:** We will again focus on the chance-alone explanation, to see whether we have strong evidence that your friend chooses scissors less than one-third of the time in the long run. So we will use a chance model that assumes the probability of your friend choosing scissors is 1/3 and then examine the types of results we get for the sample proportion of times he chooses scissors to see whether our observed statistic is consistent with that chance variability.

> **THINK ABOUT IT**
>
> Can we use a coin to represent the chance model specified by the null hypothesis like before? If not, can you suggest a different random device we could use? What needs to be different about our simulation this time?

We cannot directly use a coin to simulate the chance model for this scenario. The key difference is now we want to sample from a process where the probability of "success" is not 0.50 (as with coin tossing) but 1/3. This will model your friend choosing scissors one-third of the time. We could use dice (e.g., rolls of 1 or 2 represent scissors) or cards (like with Monty Hall), or the computer can do this for us with correspondences as outlined in Table 1.3.

TABLE 1.3 Parallels between actual study and simulation

Observational unit	=	One round of the game
Success	=	Plays scissors
Failure	=	Doesn't play scissors
Chance of success	$\pi = 1/3$	Three gestures are equally likely; chance of scissors is one out of three
One repetition	=	A simulated set of 12 rounds of the game

For the first 12 plays of the game, your friend only showed scissors twice. If scissors were chosen as often as the other two options, we would expect 4 of the 12 plays to be scissors, so maybe this is not all that different, especially in the short run. Let's first evaluate how surprising it is for your friend to only play scissors twice, looking at results from a simulation that models your friend choosing scissors one-third of the time in the long run.

1.2.3

In the **One Proportion** applet you can change the probability of success to any number between 0 and 1, and the applet will generate successful attempts at that rate. One way to think about it is as a spinner that will spin and land in one area one-third of the time and the other area two-thirds of the time. So we now have a chance model that generates successes with a long-run proportion equal to the null hypothesis probability of 1/3.

1.2.4

Figure 1.7 shows us the distribution of the simulated sample proportion of scissor choices (successes) that could have happened in 12 rounds of the game assuming this chance model. We can use this distribution to assess the strength of evidence against the one-third chance model. The distributions of simulated statistics we have been looking at represent what could have happened in the study assuming the null hypothesis was true. For that reason, we will now refer to this distribution as the *null distribution*.

FIGURE 1.7   The null distribution of simulated sample proportion of successes in 12 plays assuming scissors is chosen 1/3 (≈0.3333) of the time in the long run.

1.2.5

Notice that we are using the proportion of successes as the statistic instead of the number of successes, but these are equivalent. This distribution is centered around 1/3 and has a very slight skew to the right. But what does the distribution tell us about whether or not your friend tends to avoid scissors?

3. **Strength of evidence:**

THINK ABOUT IT

How do we use this null distribution to evaluate whether the one-third model is appropriate for your friend's scissors selection process?

The key is to see whether the observed statistic (2 out of 12 ≈ 0.167) is consistent with the chance variability in the one-third process. So we need to decide whether or not 0.167 is a typical value or falls in the tail of the distribution. In Figure 1.7, we see that this is a bit of a difficult call. The outcomes at 0.17 are not that far in the tail of the distribution but are not right in the middle either. What we need is a more systematic way of measuring how unusual an outcome of 0.167 is in this null distribution.

We could see how often our observed result occurs in the distribution, but that becomes difficult to compare across different distributions (see FAQ 1.2.1). A more common approach for measuring how unusual an observation is in a distribution is to determine either what proportion of the distribution lies at or above the value or what proportion lies at or below the value. The probability of getting a result at least as extreme in the direction of the alternative hypothesis as the observed statistic, when the null hypothesis is true, is called the *p-value*. We can estimate the p-value from our simulated null distribution by counting how many (and what proportion) of the simulated sample proportions are as extreme or more extreme than the observed sample proportion.

Definition

The *p-value* is the probability of obtaining a value of the statistic at least as extreme as the observed statistic when the null hypothesis is true. We can estimate the *p*-value by finding the proportion of the simulated statistics in the null distribution that are *at least as extreme* (in the direction of the alternative hypothesis) as the value of the statistic actually observed in the research study.

1.2.6

FAQ 1.2.1   www.wiley.com/college/tintle

Why do we need to include "or more extreme" when computing our p-value?

The p-value takes into account the could-have-been outcomes (assuming the null hypothesis is true) that are as extreme or more extreme than the one we observed. This provides a direct measure of our strength of evidence against the "by-chance-alone" or null model and allows for a standard, comparable value for all scientific research studies. Smaller p-values mean the value of the observed statistic, under the null model, is more unlikely by chance alone. Hence, smaller p-values indicate stronger evidence against the null model.

Let's reconsider the distribution from Figure 1.7. In Figure 1.8, we added a vertical line at the observed statistic, 0.167. The "proportion of repetitions" counts how many times 0.167 or smaller occurred under the specified chance model. In this case, we found 173 of the 1,000 samples from a process with $\pi = 1/3$ resulted in a simulated sample proportion $\hat{p}$ of 0.167 or smaller. So 0.173 is our estimate of the study's p-value.

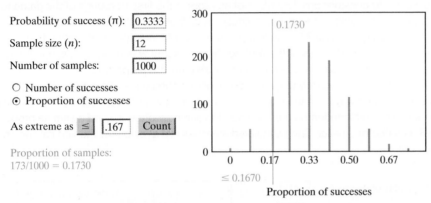

FIGURE 1.8   The null distribution of simulated sample proportion of successes in 12 rounds of rock-paper-scissors for a novice that plays scissors one-third of the time in the long run with the observed proportion (0.167) or even smaller shown to the left of the vertical, yielding an approximate p-value of 0.1730.

Calculating a p-value from a simulation analysis is an approximation. Different simulations will have slightly different p-values based on 1,000 repetitions. Performing more repetitions generally produces more accurate approximations. For our purposes, using 1,000 repetitions is typically good enough to provide reasonable approximations for p-values.

Notice that the approximate p-value of 0.173 in Figure 1.8 is computed as the proportion of the 1,000 simulated samples with a sample proportion of 0.167 *or smaller*. A p-value always computes "more extreme" in the direction of the alternative hypothesis. In this case the alternative hypothesis is "less than 1/3" and so we look at the lower tail to compute "more extreme than" for the p-value.

So how do we *interpret* this 0.173? As a probability; so we can say that in the long run, if we repeatedly generate random sets of 12 rounds of the game under identical conditions with the probability of scissors equal to 1/3, we expect to observe a sample proportion of 0.167 or smaller, by chance alone, in about 17.3% of those repetitions.

But what does 0.173 tell us about the strength of the evidence? As stated earlier, smaller p-values are stronger evidence against the null hypothesis in favor of the alternative hypothesis. Is 0.173 small enough? Although there is no hard-and-fast rule for determining how small is small enough to be convincing, we offer the following guidelines.

Guidelines for evaluating strength of evidence from p-values

0.10 < p-value	not much evidence against null hypothesis; null is plausible
0.05 < p-value ≤ 0.10	moderate evidence against the null hypothesis
0.01 < p-value ≤ 0.05	strong evidence against the null hypothesis
p-value ≤ 0.01	very strong evidence against the null hypothesis

The smaller the p-value, the stronger the evidence against the null hypothesis.

Many researchers consider a p-value ≤ 0.05 to be sufficient to conclude there is convincing evidence against the null hypothesis (see FAQ 1.2.2 for some intuition on that number), but in some situations you may want stronger evidence. For now, just keep in mind that the smaller the p-value, the stronger the evidence against the null hypothesis (chance model is true) and in favor of the alternative hypothesis (typically the research conjecture).

FAQ 1.2.2   www.wiley.com/college/tintle
- -
What p-value should make us suspicious?
- -

So we would consider only two plays of scissors in the first 12 rounds of the game to not be much evidence against the null hypothesis your friend would play scissors one-third of the time in the long run. Why? Because a p-value of 0.173 indicates that getting two or fewer choices of scissors in 12 plays, if the probability of scissors was really 1/3, is *not surprising*. Hence, 1/3 is still a plausible value for your friend's long-run proportion.

What if your friend had only played scissors once? Then our statistic becomes $\hat{p} \approx 0.083$. This is even farther away from the expected 1/3. So what will happen to the p-value? We can use the same null distribution but now we need to see how often we find a sample proportion as small as 0.083 or smaller. Such simulated statistics are at or below the vertical line shown in Figure 1.9.

FIGURE 1.9   The null distribution of simulated sample proportion of successes in 12 rounds of rock-paper-scissors for novices that play scissors one-third of the time in the long run. If the observed proportion would only have been 0.083, we can see the p-value would have been smaller and we would therefore have stronger evidence against the null hypothesis.

The approximate p-value has decreased to 0.077. This makes sense because if the null hypothesis is true ($\pi = 1/3$), it should be more surprising to get a sample proportion farther from 1/3.

KEY IDEA

Values of the statistic that are even farther from the hypothesized parameter result in a smaller p-value and stronger evidence against the null hypothesis.

CONCLUSIONS

So what can we conclude from this study? We approximated a p-value (0.173) for the first 12 plays of the game that was not small and did not provide strong evidence against the null hypothesis. Have we *proven* the null hypothesis is true? No! In fact, we will never get to prove the null hypothesis true because we had to assume it was true to do the analysis. So the results of the simulation can never "support" the null hypothesis. What we can say is that these results are not inconsistent with the type of result we would expect to see when the null hypothesis is true. In other words, the null hypothesis is one plausible (or believable) explanation for the data. If we wanted to investigate the issue more closely, we could have our friend play more games (increase the sample size). A larger sample size would give us a better chance of detecting any tendency that might be there (we'll discuss the issue of sample size more fully in Section 1.4).

Key assumptions: Model vs. reality

Stepping back, we need to keep something in mind about the use of chance models in assessing strength of evidence. Chance models are models and, thus, are not reality. They make key assumptions to which we need to pay careful attention; otherwise we may leap too quickly to an incorrect conclusion.

For example, with the rock-paper-scissors game we simulated data from a chance model with a 1/3 success probability. This means each and every round has exactly the same probability of scissors. But, is that a reasonable assumption? What if your friend changes his strategy part way through? Our chance model ignores these aspects of "reality" and makes the situation much simpler than it really is.

Thus, if we could have said "we have strong evidence against the chance model," are we saying that your friend subconsciously avoids scissors? Well, maybe, but maybe not. All we are saying is we think something else is going on other than your friend picking equally among the three gestures every round. When we think about Steps 4 and 5 of the six-step statistical investigation method, we must be aware about these assumptions we're making—specifically about the ways in which our model does not match reality.

Tasting Water

EXPLORATION 1.2

People spend a lot of money on bottled water. But do they really prefer bottled water to ordinary tap water? Researchers at Longwood University (Lunsford and Dowling Fink, 2010) investigated this question by presenting people who came to a booth at a local festival with four cups of water. Three cups contained different brands of bottled water, and one cup was filled with tap water. Each **subject** (person) was asked which of the four cups of water they most preferred. Researchers kept track of how many people chose tap water in order to see whether tap water was chosen significantly less often than would be expected by random chance.

Definition

A **binary variable** is a categorical variable with only two outcomes. Often we convert categorical variables with more than two outcomes (e.g., four brands of water) into binary variables (e.g., tap water or not). In this case we also define one outcome to be a "success" and one to be a "failure."

STEP 1: Ask a research question.

1. What is the research question that the researchers hoped to answer?

STEP 2: Design a study and collect data.

2. Identify the observational units in this study.
3. Identify the variable. Is the variable quantitative or categorical?
4. Write this as a binary variable.
5. Describe the parameter of interest (in words). (*Hint*: The parameter is the long-run proportion of …?)
6. One possibility here is that subjects have an equal preference among all four waters and so are essentially selecting one of the four cups at random. In this case what is the long-run proportion (i.e., probability) that a subject in this study would select tap water?
7. Another possibility is that the subjects are less likely to prefer tap water than the bottled water brands. In this case what can you say about the long-run proportion that a subject

- The **null hypothesis** typically represents the "by-chance-alone" explanation. The chance model (or "null model") is chosen to reflect this hypothesis.

- The **alternative hypothesis** typically represents the "there is an effect" explanation that contradicts the null hypothesis. Researchers typically hope this hypothesis will be supported by the data they collect.

in this study would select tap water? (*Hint:* You are not to specify a particular value this time; instead indicate a *direction* from a particular value.)

8. Your answers to #6 and #7 should be the null and alternative hypotheses for this study. Which is which?

   The researchers found that 3 of 27 subjects selected tap water.

STEP 3: Explore the data.

9. Calculate the value of the relevant statistic.

Use of symbols

We can use mathematical symbols to represent quantities and simplify our writing. Throughout the book we will emphasize written explanations but will also show you mathematical symbols which you are free to use as a short-hand once you are comfortable with the material. The distinction between parameter and statistic is so important that we always use different symbols to refer to them.

When dealing with a parameter that is a long-run proportion, such as the probability that a (future) subject in this study *would* choose tap water as most preferred, we use the Greek letter π (pronounced "pie"). But when working with a statistic that is the proportion of "successes" in a sample, such as the proportion of subjects in this study who *did* choose tap water as most preferred, we use the symbol $\hat{p}$ (pronounced "p-hat"). Finally, we use the symbol n to represent the sample size.

10. What is the value of $\hat{p}$ in this study?

11. What is the value of n in this study?

12. Hypotheses are always conjectures about the unknown parameter π. You can also use H_0 and H_a as short-hand notation for the null and alternative hypotheses, respectively. A colon, ":", is used to represent the word "is." Restate the null and alternative hypotheses using π.

    H_0:

    H_a:

STEP 4: Draw inferences.

13. Is the sample proportion who selected tap water in this study less than the probability specified in the null hypothesis?

14. Is it *possible* that this proportion could turn out to be this small even if the null hypothesis was true (i.e., even if people did not really dislike the tap water and were essentially selecting at random from among the four cups)?

    As we did with Buzz and Doris in Section 1.1, we will use simulation to investigate how surprising the observed sample result (3 of 27 selecting tap water) would be if in fact subjects did not dislike tap water and so each had a 1/4 probability of selecting tap water. (Note also that our null model assumes the same probability for all subjects.)

> **THINK ABOUT IT**
>
> Can we use a coin to represent the chance model specified by the null hypothesis like before? It not, can you suggest a different random device we could use? What needs to be different about our simulation this time?

15. Explain why we cannot use a simple coin toss to simulate the subjects' choices, as we did with the Buzz/Doris study.

16. We could do the simulation using a set of four playing cards: one black and three red. Explain how the simulation would work in this case.

17. Another option would be to use a spinner like the one shown here 🥧, like you would use when playing a child's board game. Explain how the simulation would work if you were using a spinner. In particular:

    a. What does each region represent?

    b. How many spins of the spinner will you need to do in order to simulate one repetition of the experiment when there is equal preference between the four waters (null hypothesis is true)?

18. We will now use the **One Proportion** applet to conduct this simulation analysis. Notice that the applet will show us what it would be like if we were simulating with spinners.

    a. First enter the **probability of heads/probability of success** value specified in the null hypothesis.

    b. Enter the appropriate **sample size** (number of subjects in this study).

    c. Enter 1 for the number of samples, and press **Draw Samples**. Report the number of "successes" in this simulated sample.

    d. Now, select the radio button for "Proportion of successes." Report the proportion of successes in this simulated sample. Use your answer to "c" to verify how this value is calculated.

    e. Leaving the "Proportion of successes" radio button selected but unchecking the "Animate" box, click on **Draw Samples** four more times. Do you get the same results each time?

    f. Now enter 995 for the number of samples and click on **Draw Samples**, bringing the number of simulated samples to 1,000. Comment on the center, variability, and shape of the resulting distribution of sample proportions.

    This distribution of simulated sample proportions is called the **null distribution**, because it is based on assuming the null hypothesis to be true.

19. Recall that the observed value of the sample proportion who selected tap water in this study was $\hat{p} = 3/27 \approx 0.1111$. Looking at the null distribution you have simulated, is this a very unlikely result when the null hypothesis is true? In other words, is this value far in the tail of the null distribution?

    You might very well find that #19 is a bit of a tough call. The value 0.1111 is not far in the tail of the distribution, but it's also not near the middle of the distribution. To help make a judgment about strength of evidence in this case, we can count how many (and what proportion) of the simulated sample proportions are as extreme or more extreme than the observed value.

20. Use the applet to count how many (and what proportion) of the simulated sample proportions are more extreme than the observed value. To do this, first click on the $\geq$ inequality symbol to change it to $\leq$ (to match the alternative hypothesis). Then enter **0.1111** (the observed sample proportion who chose tap water) in the box to the left of the **Count** button. Then click on the **Count** button. Record the number and proportion of simulated sample proportions that are as extreme or more extreme than the observed value.

    How do we *evaluate* this p-value as a judgment about strength of evidence provided by the sample data against the null hypothesis? One answer is: The smaller the p-value, the stronger the evidence against the null hypothesis and in favor of the alternative hypothesis. But how small is small enough to regard as convincing? There is no definitive answer, but here are some guidelines:

> **Definition**
>
> The **p-value** is estimated as the proportion of simulated statistics in the null distribution that are *at least as extreme* (in the direction of the alternative hypothesis) as the value of the statistic actually observed in the research study.

Guidelines for evaluating strength of evidence from p-values

0.10 < p-value	not much evidence against null hypothesis; null is plausible
0.05 < p-value ≤ 0.10	moderate evidence against the null hypothesis
0.01 < p-value ≤ 0.05	strong evidence against the null hypothesis
p-value ≤ 0.01	very strong evidence against the null hypothesis

The smaller the p-value, the stronger the evidence against the null hypothesis.

21. Is the approximate p-value from your simulation analysis (your answer to #20) small enough to provide much evidence against the null hypothesis that subjects prefer tap water equally to the brands of bottled water? If so, how strong is this evidence? Explain.

22. When computing p-values, "more extreme" is always measured in the direction of the alternative hypothesis. Use this fact to explain why you clicked the ≤ earlier.

STEP 5: Formulate conclusions.

23. Do you consider the observed sample result to be statistically significant? Recall that this means that the observed result is unlikely to have occurred by chance alone.

24. How broadly are you willing to generalize your conclusions? Would you be willing to generalize your conclusions to water drinkers beyond the subjects in this study? How broadly? Explain your reasoning.

STEP 6: Look back and ahead.

25. Suggest a new research question that you might investigate next, building on what you learned in this study.

Alternate analysis

Instead of focusing on the subjects who chose tap water, you could instead analyze the data based on the subjects who chose one of the three bottled waters. Because 3 of 27 subjects chose tap water, we know that 24 of the 27 subjects chose one of the brands of bottled water. Now let the parameter of interest (denoted by π) be the probability that a subject will select one of the *bottled* water cups as most preferred.

26. Conduct a simulation analysis to assess the strength of evidence provided by the sample data.

    a. The research conjecture is that subjects tend to select bottled water (*more* or *less*) often than tap water. (Circle your answer.)

    More   Less

    b. State the null hypothesis in words and in terms of the (newly defined) parameter π.

    c. State the alternative hypothesis in words and in terms of the (new) parameter π.

    d. Calculate the observed value of the relevant statistic.

    e. Before you use the **One Proportion** applet to analyze these data, indicate what values you will input:

    Probability of success:

    Sample size:

    Number of samples:

    f. Use the applet to produce the null distribution of simulated sample proportions. Comment on the center, variability, and shape of this distribution. Be sure to comment on how this null distribution differs from the null distribution in #18(f).

    g. In order to approximate the p-value, you will count how many of the simulated proportions are _____ or (larger or smaller) and then divide by _____.

    h. Estimate the p-value from your simulation results.

    i. *Interpret* this p-value. (*Hint*: This is the probability of what, assuming what?)

    j. *Evaluate* this p-value: How much evidence do the sample data provide against the null hypothesis?

27. Does your analysis based on the number who chose bottled water produce similar conclusions to your previous analysis based on the number who chose tap water? Explain.

You should have found that it does not matter whether you focus on the number/proportion that chose tap water or the number/proportion that chose bottled water. In other words, it does not matter which category you define to be a "success" for the *preferred water* variable. Your findings should be very similar provided that you make the appropriate adjustments in your analysis:

- Using 0.75 instead of 0.25 as the null value of the parameter
- Changing the alternative hypothesis to "$\pi > 0.75$" rather than "$\pi < 0.25$"
- Calculating the p-value as the proportion of samples with $\hat{p} \geq 0.8889$ rather than $\hat{p} \leq 0.1111$

SECTION 1.2   Summary

The 3S strategy for assessing statistical significance also applies to chance models other than a coin toss:

- Other probabilities of success, such as $1/3$, can be analyzed.
- The strategy can assess whether a long-run proportion is *less than* a conjectured value as well as greater than a conjectured value.

Introducing some terminology can help to clarify the 3S strategy when used to conduct a **test of significance**:

- The **null hypothesis** is the "by-chance-alone" explanation.
- The **alternative hypothesis** contradicts the null hypothesis.
- The **null distribution** refers to the simulated values of the statistic generated under the assumption that the null hypothesis ("by-chance-alone" explanation) is true.

Strength of evidence can be assessed numerically by determining how often a simulated statistic as or more extreme than the observed value of the statistic occurs in the null distribution of simulated statistics.

- The **p-value** is estimated by determining the proportion of simulated statistic values in the null distribution that are at least as extreme as the observed value of the statistic.
- The smaller the p-value, the stronger the evidence against the null hypothesis ("by-chance-alone" explanation).

Some guidelines for evaluating **strength of evidence** based on a p-value are:

$0.10 <$ p-value	not much evidence against null hypothesis
$0.05 <$ p-value ≤ 0.10	moderate evidence against the null hypothesis
$0.01 <$ p-value ≤ 0.05	strong evidence against the null hypothesis
p-value ≤ 0.01	very strong evidence against the null hypothesis

NOTATION CHECK

Here is a quick summary of the symbols we've introduced in this section.
- π represents the parameter when it is a probability
- $\hat{p}$ represents the statistic when it is the observed proportion
- H_0 represents the null hypothesis
- H_a represents the alternative hypothesis
- n represents the sample size

SECTION 1.3

ALTERNATIVE MEASURE OF STRENGTH OF EVIDENCE

INTRODUCTION

In the previous section, you learned the formal process of a *test of significance*: make a claim about the parameter of interest (through competing null and alternative hypotheses); gather and explore data; follow the 3S strategy to calculate an observed statistic from the data, simulate a null distribution, and measure the strength of evidence the observed statistic provides against the null hypothesis; draw a conclusion about the null hypothesis. The p-value was introduced as a standard way to measure the strength of evidence against the null hypothesis. We found that the smaller the p-value, the stronger our evidence against the null hypothesis and in favor of the alternative hypothesis. However, if we find strong evidence against the null hypothesis, this does not mean we have proven the alternative hypothesis to be true. Similarly, if we don't have strong evidence against the null hypothesis, this does not mean we have proven the null hypothesis to be true. What we can conclude is whether or not the "by-chance-alone" explanation is reasonable. You also confirmed in the previous section that if an observed result is not as far away from the proportion under the null hypothesis, then it provides less evidence against the null hypothesis, meaning that the null hypothesis is one plausible explanation for the observed data. In this section, you will explore another method often used to measure how far away the observed statistic is from the parameter value conjectured by the null hypothesis.

The key to Step 4 of the statistical investigation method, when we apply the 3S strategy with one categorical variable, has been assuming some claim about the long-run proportion of a particular outcome, π, and then seeing whether or not our observed sample proportion is consistent with that claim. One approach is to create the null distribution (the could-have-been simulated sample proportions assuming the null hypothesis to be true) and then use the p-value to measure how often we find a statistic at least as extreme as that of the actual research study. The p-value gives us a standard way of measuring whether or not our observed statistic fell in the tail of this distribution. In this section you will find that there is another convenient way to measure how far the observed statistic is from the hypothesized value under the null hypothesis.

Heart Transplant Operations

Example 1.3

EXAMPLE

In an article published in the *British Medical Journal* (2004), researchers Poloniecki, Sismanidis, Bland, and Jones reported that heart transplantations at St. George's Hospital in London had been suspended in September 2000 after a sudden spike in mortality rate. Of the last 10 heart transplants, 80% had resulted in deaths within 30 days of the transplant. Newspapers reported that this mortality rate was over five times the national average. Based on historical national data, the researchers used 15% as a reasonable value for comparison.

> **THINK ABOUT IT**
>
> What research question can we ask about these data? Identify the observational units, variable of interest, parameter, and statistic. What is the null hypothesis?

We would like to know whether the current underlying heart transplantation mortality rate at St. George's Hospital exceeds the national rate. So the observational units are the individual heart transplantations (the sample size for the data above is 10) and the variable is whether or not the patient dies within 30 days of the transplant.

When we conduct analyses with binary variables, we often call one of the outcomes a "success" and the other a "failure" and then focus the analysis on the "success" outcome. It is arbitrary which outcome is defined to be a success, but you need to make sure you do so consistently throughout the analysis. In many epidemiological studies, death is the outcome of interest and so "patient did not survive for 30 days postoperation" is called a "success" in this case!

Knowing the "success" outcome allows us to find the observed statistic, which is the number of successes divided by the sample size. In this case, the observed statistic is 8 out of 10, or $\hat{p} = 0.80$, and the parameter is the actual long-run, current probability of a death within 30 days of a heart transplant operation at St. George's. We don't know the actual value of this probability; we have just observed a small sample of data from the heart transplantation operation process; if a different set of 10 people had been operated on, the statistic would mostly likely differ.

The null hypothesis is that the current death rate at St. George's hospital is no different from other hospitals, but the researchers want to know whether these data are convincing evidence that the death rate is actually higher at St. George's. So we will state the hypotheses as follows:

Null hypothesis: Death rate at St. George's is the same as the national rate (0.15).

Alternative hypothesis: Death rate at St. George's is higher than the national rate.

SYMBOLS
You can also write your null and alternative hypotheses like this:

$$H_0: \pi = 0.15$$
$$H_a: \pi > 0.15$$

where π is the actual long-run proportion of deaths after a heart transplant at St. George's.

APPLYING THE 3S STRATEGY
Using the 3S strategy from the previous section, we observed 0.80 as our statistic and now we will simulate 1,000 repetitions from a process where $\pi = 0.15$ (under the null hypothesis). We did this using the **One Proportion** applet as shown in Figure 1.10.

FIGURE 1.10 Null distribution (could-have-been simulated sample proportions) for 1,000 repetitions of drawing samples of 10 "patients" from a process where the probability of death is equal to 0.15. "Success" has been defined to be patient death.

Even though the sample size for this study is quite small ($n = 10$), we can see that 0.80 is not even close to the could-have-been results from the simulation. In fact, the approximate p-value is less than 1/1,000, as we never observed a value of 0.80 or larger by chance in these 1,000 repetitions. This provides very strong evidence against the null hypothesis and in favor of the alternative hypothesis. Of course, it tells us nothing about *why* the death rate from heart transplantations is higher at St. George's, but it is pretty convincing that something other than random chance is at play.

Note that in Figure 1.10 the average of the 1,000 values of the simulated proportions of success is 0.152, which is quite close to 0.15—the probability of deaths if the chance model is correct. This makes sense. Also, notice that the proportions of success vary quite a lot from sample to sample, ranging from 0 to 0.60. In fact, the variability of the distribution as measured by the standard deviation is 0.113. Remember from the Preliminaries that we can think of standard deviation as the distance a typical value in the distribution is away from the mean of the distribution. In this case, 0.113 is the average distance that a simulated value of the statistic (proportion of patients who died) is from 0.152. We'll come back and use the value of the standard deviation in a moment.

DIGGING DEEPER INTO THE ST. GEORGE'S MORTALITY DATA

We might still wonder whether these most recent 10 operations, which caught people's attention, are truly representative of the process as a whole. One approach is to investigate whether there were any major changes at the hospital recently (e.g., new staff, new sterilization protocols). Another is to gather more data over a longer period of time, to better represent the underlying process. So the researchers decided to examine the previous 361 heart transplantations at St. George's Hospital, dating back to 1986. They found that 71 of the patients died within 30 days of the transplant.

THINK ABOUT IT

Now what is the value of the observed statistic? Predict how the simulated null distribution will change for this new situation. Do you think the observed statistic will still be highly statistically significant?

Figure 1.11 shows the results of 1,000 repetitions of drawing samples of size $n = 361$ from a process with $\pi = 0.15$ (still assuming the null hypothesis to be true).

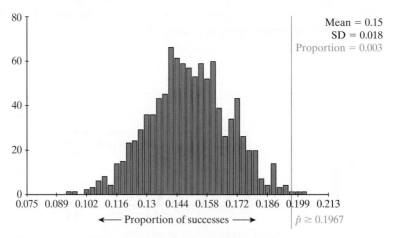

FIGURE 1.11 The null distribution of 1,000 repetitions of drawing "samples" of 361 "patients" from a process where the probability of death is equal to 0.15.

THINK ABOUT IT

Where does $\hat{p} = 0.197$ fall in this distribution? In the tail or among the more typical values? How does the p-value tell us whether the observed statistic is in the tail or not?

First, we note that again the p-value is small (0.003), so we still have strong evidence against the null hypothesis and in favor of the conclusion that the mortality rate at St. George's is above 0.15, but not quite as strong as in the first case. In the first case, all we could say was that the estimated p-value was less than 1 in 1,000, but visually appeared to be much smaller still. Whereas one option to more precisely quantify the p-value would be to increase the number of repetitions (say 10,000 or 100,000), we'll now look at another commonly used option.

AN ALTERNATIVE TO THE P-VALUE: STANDARDIZED VALUE OF A STATISTIC

Using p-values is the most common way of assessing the strength of evidence by indicating the probability, under the null hypothesis, of getting a statistic as extreme as or more extreme than the one observed. Another way to measure strength of evidence is to standardize the observed statistic by measuring how far it is from the mean of the distribution using standard deviation units. (Common notation: z.)

1.3.1

$$\text{Standardized statistic} = z = \frac{\text{statistic} - \text{mean of null distribution}}{\text{standard deviation of null distribution}}$$

Definition

To **standardize** a statistic, compute the distance of the observed statistic from the (hypothesized) mean of the null distribution and divide by the standard deviation of the null distribution.

For the second study, a standardized value of the statistic would result in the following calculation because Figure 1.11 tells us that the standard deviation of the null distribution is 0.018 and we know that the mean of the null distribution is approximately 0.15 (the hypothesized probability):

$$\text{standardized statistic} = z = \frac{0.197 - 0.15}{0.018} = 2.61$$

So we would say that the observed statistic (0.197) falls 2.61 standard deviations above the mean of the distribution (0.15).

KEY IDEA

Observations that fall more than 2 or 3 standard deviations from the mean can be considered in the tail of the distribution.

1.3.2

Because the observed statistic is more than 2 standard deviations above the mean, we can say the statistic is in the tail of the distribution.

We can also apply this approach to the original sample of 10 patients. In that simulation, the standard deviation of the null distribution was 0.113 with a mean of 0.15. Thus, the standardized value of the statistic is computed as:

$$\text{standardized statistic} = z = \frac{0.800 - 0.15}{0.113} = 5.75$$

This means that $\hat{p} = 0.800$ is 5.75 standard deviations above the mean of 0.15. This is another way of saying that 0.800 would be extremely unlikely to happen by chance alone if the true long-run, current mortality rate was 0.150.

There are guidelines for assessing the strength of the evidence against the null hypothesis based on the standardized value, as given next.

Guidelines for evaluating strength of evidence from standardized values of statistics

Standardizing gives us a quick, informal way to evaluate the strength of evidence against the null hypothesis. For standardized statistics:

1.3.3

between −1.5 and 1.5	**little or no** evidence against the null hypothesis
below −1.5 or above 1.5	**moderate** evidence against the null hypothesis
below −2 or above 2	**strong** evidence against the null hypothesis
below −3 or above 3	**very strong** evidence against the null hypothesis

Figure 1.12 illustrates the basis for using a standardized statistic to assess strength of evidence against the null hypothesis for a mound-shaped, symmetric distribution.

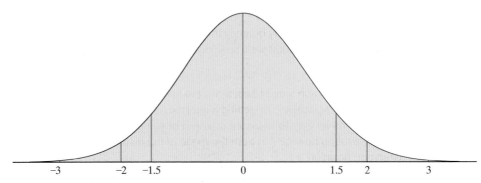

FIGURE 1.12 Positions of standardized statistics for a bell-shaped distribution.

1.3.4

Notice that the farther from zero the standardized statistic is, the stronger the evidence against the null hypothesis. Like the p-value, we can directly compare the standardized values across data sets. We see the stronger evidence from the small data set compared to the larger data set ($5.73 > 2.61$).

EXPLORATION 1.3 | Do People Use Facial Prototyping?

A study in *Psychonomic Bulletin and Review* (Lea, Thomas, Lamkin, and Bell, 2007) presented evidence that "people use facial prototypes when they encounter different names." Participants were given two faces and asked to identify which one was Tim and which one was Bob. The researchers wrote that their participants "overwhelmingly agreed" on which face belonged to Tim and which face belonged to Bob but did not provide the exact results of their study.

STEP 1: Ask a research question. We will gather data from your class to investigate the research question of whether students have a tendency to associate certain facial features with a name.

STEP 2: Design a study and collect data. Each student in your class will be shown the same two pictures of men's faces used in the research study. You will be asked to assign the name Bob to one photo and the name Tim to the other. Each student will then submit the name that he or she assigned to the picture on the left. Then the name that the researchers identify with the face on the left will be revealed.

1. Identify the observational units in this study.
2. Identify the variable. Is the variable categorical or quantitative?

The parameter of interest here is the probability that a student in your class would assign the same name to the face on the left.

3. State the null and alternative hypotheses to be tested when the data are collected. Express these both in words and symbols. (*Hint*: Think about the parameter and the research question of interest here.)

Consider these two photos:

Melissa A. Lea/Robin D. Thomas/Nathan A. Lamkin/Aaron Bell ©Psychonomic Bulletin & Review 2007, 14 (5), 901–907.

4. Do you think the face on the left is Bob or Tim? Collect the responses (data) for all the students in your class.

STEP 3: Explore the data.

5. How many students put Tim as the name on the left? How many students participated in this study (sample size)? What proportion put Tim's name on the left?

When we conduct analyses with binary variables, we often call one of the outcomes a "success" and the other a "failure" and then focus the analysis on the "success" outcome. It is arbitrary which outcome is defined to be a success, but you need to make sure you do so consistently throughout the analysis. In this case we'll call "Tim on left" a success because that's what previous studies have found to be a popular choice.

STEP 4: Draw inferences. You will use the **One Proportion** applet to investigate how surprising the observed class statistic would be if students were just randomly selecting which name to put with which face.

6. Before you use the applet, indicate what you will enter for the following values:
   a. Probability of success:
   b. Sample size:
   c. Number of repetitions:

7. Conduct this simulation analysis. Make sure the **Proportion of heads** button is selected in the applet and not **Number of heads**.
   a. Indicate how to calculate the approximate p-value (count the number of simulated statistics that equal _____ or _____).
   b. Report the approximate p-value.
   c. Use the p-value to evaluate the strength of evidence provided by the sample data against the null hypothesis, in favor of the alternative that students really do tend to assign the name Tim (as the researchers predicted) to the face on the left.

The p-value is the most common way to evaluate strength of evidence against the null hypothesis, but now we will explore a common alternative way to evaluate strength of evidence. The goal of any measure of strength of evidence is to use a number to assess whether the observed statistic falls in the tail of the null distribution (and is therefore surprising when the null hypothesis is true) or among the typical values we see when the null hypothesis is true.

8. Check the **Summary Stats** box in the applet.
   a. Report the mean (average) value of the simulated statistics.
   b. Explain why it makes sense that this mean is close to 0.50.
   c. Report the standard deviation (SD) of the simulated statistics.
   d. Report (again) the observed class value of the statistic. (What proportion of students in your class put Tim's name on the left?)

$$\hat{p} =$$

   e. Calculate how many standard deviations the observed class value of the statistic is from the hypothesized mean of the null distribution, 0.50. In other words, subtract the 0.50 from the observed value and then divide by the standard deviation. In still other words, calculate:

   (observed statistic $(\hat{p})$ − 0.50)/SD of null distribution.

> **Definition**
>
> To **standardize** a statistic, compute the distance of the statistic from the (hypothesized) mean of the null distribution and divide by the standard deviation of the null distribution.

Your calculation in #8e is called "standardizing the statistic." It is telling us how far above the mean the observed statistic is in terms of the "how many standard deviations."

$$\text{standardized statistic} = z = \frac{\text{statistic} - \text{mean of null distribution}}{\text{standard deviation of null distribution}}$$

Once you calculate this value, you interpret it as "how many standard deviations the observed statistic falls from the hypothesized parameter value."

The next question is how to evaluate strength of evidence against the null hypothesis based on a standardized value. Here are some guidelines:

Guidelines for evaluating strength of evidence from standardized values of statistics

Standardizing gives us a quick, informal way to evaluate the strength of evidence against the null hypothesis. For standardized statistics:

Between -1.5 and 1.5	**little or no** evidence against the null hypothesis
Below -1.5 or above 1.5	**moderate** evidence against the null hypothesis
Below -2 or above 2	**strong** evidence against the null hypothesis
Below -3 or above 3	**very strong** evidence against the null hypothesis

The diagram in Figure 1.13 illustrates the basis for using a standardized statistic to assess strength of evidence against the null hypothesis for a mound-shaped, symmetric distribution.

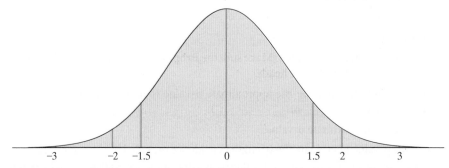

FIGURE 1.13 Positions of standardized statistics for a bell-shaped distribution.

The figure can be summarized by the following key idea.

KEY IDEA

Observations that fall more than 2 or 3 standard deviations from the mean can be considered in the tail of the distribution.

STEP 5: Formulate conclusions.

9. Let's examine the strength of evidence against the null.

   a. Based on the value of the standardized statistic, z, in #8e and the guidelines shown above, how much evidence do the class data provide against the null hypothesis?

   b. How closely does your evaluation of strength of evidence based on the standardized statistic compare to the strength of evidence based on the p-value in #7c?

Now, let's step back a bit further and think about the scope of inference. We have found that in most classes, the observed data provide strong evidence that students do better than random guessing which face is Tim's and which is Bob's. In that case, do you think that most students at your school would agree on which face is Tim's? Do you think this means that most people can agree on which face belongs to Tim? Furthermore, does this mean that all people do ascribe to the same facial prototyping?

STEP 6: Look back and ahead.

10. Based on the limitations of this study, suggest a new research question that you would investigate next.

Extensions

11. In #5 you recorded the proportion of students in your class who put Tim's name with the photo on the left. Imagine that the proportion was actually larger than that (e.g., if your class was 60%, imagine it was 70%).

    a. How would this have affected the p-value:

    Larger   Same   Smaller

    b. How would this have affected the absolute value of the standardized statistic:

    Larger   Same   Smaller

    c. How would this have affected the strength of evidence against the null hypothesis:

    Stronger   Same   Weaker

12. Suppose that less than half of the students in your class had put Tim's name on the left, so your class result was in the opposite direction of the research conjecture and the alternative hypothesis.

    a. What can you say about the standardized value of the statistic in this case? Explain. (*Hint*: You cannot give a value for the standardized statistic, but you can say something specific about its value.)

    b. What can you say about the strength of evidence against the null hypothesis and in favor of the alternative hypothesis in this case?

- -

SECTION 1.3   Summary

In addition to the p-value, a second way to evaluate strength of evidence numerically is to calculate a **standardized statistic**:

$$\text{standardized statistic} = \frac{\text{statistic} - \text{mean of null distribution}}{\text{standard deviation of null distribution}}$$

A standardized statistic provides an alternative to the p-value for measuring how far an observed statistics falls in the tail of the null distribution. More specifically:

- A standardized statistic indicates how many standard deviations the observed value of the statistic is above or below the hypothesized process probability.
- Larger values of the standardized statistic (in absolute value) indicate stronger evidence against the null model.
- Values of a standardized statistic greater than 2 or less than -2 indicate strong evidence against the null model; values greater than 3 or less than -3 indicate very strong evidence against the null model.

- -

WHAT IMPACTS STRENGTH OF EVIDENCE?   SECTION 1.4

INTRODUCTION

When we are conducting a test of significance for a single proportion, we assume the null hypothesis is true (or that the long-run proportion equals some number) and then determine how unlikely it would be to get a sample proportion that is as far away (or farther) from the probability assumed in the null hypothesis. The p-value and standardized scores are measures of how unlikely this is. Small p-values and large standardized scores (in absolute value) give us strong evidence against the null.

In this section we will explore some of the factors that affect the strength of evidence. You should have already seen that as the sample proportion moves farther away from the probability in the null hypothesis, we get more evidence against the null. We will review this factor and explore two more. We will see how sample size and what are called "two-sided tests" affect strength of evidence.

1.4

Example 1.4

EXAMPLE

Predicting Elections from Faces?

Do voters make judgments about a political candidate based on his/her facial appearance? Can you correctly predict the outcome of an election, more often than not, simply by choosing the candidate whose face is judged to be more competent-looking? Researchers investigated this question in a study published in *Science* (Todorov, Mandisodka, Goren, and Hall, 2005). Participants were shown pictures of two candidates and asked who has the more competent-looking face. Researchers then predicted the winner to be the candidate whose face was judged to look more competent by most of the participants. In particular, the researchers predicted the outcomes of the 32 U.S. Senate races in 2004.

> ### THINK ABOUT IT
>
> What are the observational units? What is the variable measured? Is the variable categorical or quantitative? What is the null hypothesis?

The observational units are the 32 Senate races and the variable is whether or not this method correctly predicted the winner—a categorical variable. Because we are looking for evidence that this method works better than guessing we will state:

Null hypothesis: The probability this method predicts the winner between the two candidates equals 0.50 ($\pi = 0.50$).

Alternative hypothesis: The probability this method predicts the winner is greater than 0.50 ($\pi > 0.50$).

The researchers found the competent-face method of predicting election outcomes to be successful in 23 of the 32 Senate races. Thus the observed statistic, or observed proportion of correct predictions, is $23/32 \approx 0.719$, or 71.9%. We can use simulation to investigate whether this provides us with strong enough evidence against the null to conclude the competent-face method is better than randomly choosing the winner. Figure 1.14 displays the results of 1,000 simulated sets of 32 races, assuming that the competent-face method is no better than flipping a coin, using the **One Proportion** applet.

FIGURE 1.14 The results of 1,000 sets of 32 coin tosses from a process with probability 0.50 of success indicating which results are at least as extreme as 23 ($\hat{p} \geq 0.7188$).

Only 9 of these 1,000 simulated sets of 32 races show 23 or more correct predictions (or a proportion of $23/32 = 0.7188$ or more), so the approximate p-value is 0.009. This p-value is small enough to provide strong evidence against the null hypothesis, in favor of concluding that the competent-face method makes the correct prediction more than half the time in the long run. Alternatively, we can compute the standardized value of the statistic as

$$\text{standardized statistic} = \frac{0.7188 - 0.500}{0.09} = 2.43$$

Thus, the observed statistic is 2.43 standard deviations away from the hypothesized parameter value (the mean of that null distribution) specified by the chance model, and so this (being larger than 2), again, confirms the observation is in the tail of the null distribution, so there is strong evidence that the chance model is wrong.

WHAT IMPACTS STRENGTH OF EVIDENCE?

In the previous two sections we've looked at two measures of the strength of evidence: p-value and standardized statistic; however we've not yet formally looked at what factors *impact* the strength of evidence. In other words, why is the strength of evidence (measured by p-value or standardized statistic) sometimes strong and sometimes weak or nonexistent? We will look at three factors that impact the strength of evidence: the difference between the observed statistic ($\hat{p}$) and null hypothesis parameter value, the sample size, and whether we do a one- or two-sided test.

1. **Difference between statistic and null hypothesis parameter value**

1.4.1

> **THINK ABOUT IT**
>
> What if instead of 23 correct predictions out of 32, the researchers had been able to correctly predict 26 elections? Or, what if they only correctly predicted 20 elections? How would the number of correct predictions in the sample impact our strength of evidence against the null hypothesis?

Intuitively, the more extreme the observed statistic, the more evidence there is against the null hypothesis. But, let's be a bit more precise.

If the researchers correctly predicted 26 elections, that is a success rate of $\hat{p} = 26/32 = 0.8125$, which is farther away from what would occur, in the long-run, if they were just guessing (0.50). Back in Figure 1.14 you can see that a value of 0.81 or larger never occurs just by chance, approximating a p-value < 0.001. Similarly, the standardized statistic would be $(0.8125 - 0.50)/0.09 = 3.47$ (meaning 0.8125 is 3.47 standard deviations above the mean of the null distribution). In short, if researchers correctly predict 26 elections, this would be extremely strong evidence against the null hypothesis because the observed statistic is farther out in the tail of the null distribution.

On the other hand, if the researchers correctly predicted only 20 elections, the success rate drops to $\hat{p} = 20/32 = 0.625$. In this case, the observed statistic (0.625) is something that is fairly likely to happen just by chance if the researchers were guessing who would win the election. The p-value increases to 0.115 (there were 115 out of 1,000 times that 62.5% or more correct predictions occurred by chance), and the standardized statistic is closer to zero $[(0.625 - 0.50)/0.09 = 1.39]$, suggesting that if the researchers correctly predicted 20 of the 32 elections, there is little evidence that the researchers' method performs better (in the long run) than guessing.

> **KEY IDEA**
>
> The farther away the observed statistic is from the mean of the null distribution, the more evidence there is against the null hypothesis.

1.4.2

2. Sample size

> **THINK ABOUT IT**
>
> Do you think that increasing the sample size will increase the strength of evidence, decrease the strength of evidence, or have no impact on the strength of evidence against the null hypothesis (assuming that both the value of the observed statistic and the chance model do not change)?

Intuitively, it seems reasonable to think that as we increase the sample size, the strength of evidence against the null hypothesis will increase. Observing Doris and Buzz longer, playing rock-paper-scissors longer, and looking at St. George's heart transplant patients outside of the initial set of 10 patients all intuitively suggest we'll have more knowledge about the truth. Let's dig a bit deeper into this intuition.

In Exploration P.3, we looked at how probability is the long-run proportion of times an outcome occurs. The key there is "long run." We realize that in the short term we expect more chance variability than in the long term. For example, long-term investment strategies are typically good (variability is reduced). Whereas if you flip a coin just three times and get heads each time, you aren't convinced the coin isn't fair because with such a small sample size almost anything can happen.

In terms of statistical inference, our sample size (number of observational units) is what dictates how precise a measure of the parameter we have. In Figure 1.15, we can see how the null distribution changes as we increase the sample size from 32 Senate races to 128 races (4 times as many) or 256 races (8 times as many).

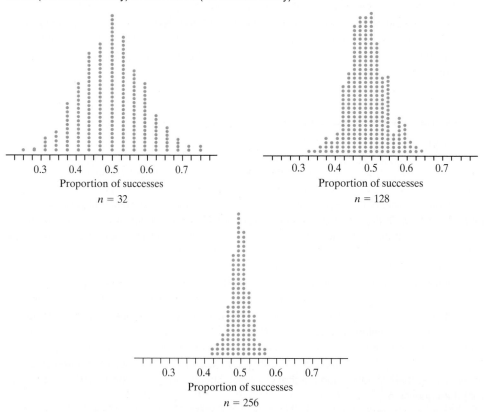

FIGURE 1.15 As the sample size increases, the variability of the null distribution decreases.

In each case the distribution is centered at 0.50, the null hypothesis value. What, then, is changing? What's changing is the variability of the distribution. With 32 races, the variability of the distribution, as measured by the standard deviation, is 0.088; with 128 races, it is 0.043; and with 256 races it is only 0.031. You can see this visually by noting that the distributions are getting squeezed closer and closer to the null hypothesis value. Stated yet another way, there is less sample-to-sample variability in the sample proportions as the sample size gets bigger.

What does this decrease in variability mean in terms of statistical significance? Remember from our observed data that in 71.9% of elections the competent-face method predicted the winning candidate. This is strong evidence (p-value = 0.009; standardized statistic = 2.43) that the competent-face method does better than guessing. But, what if the sample size was 128 elections and the competent-face method correctly predicted 71.9% of the races? Now the p-value would be <0.001 and the standardized statistic would be $z = 5.09$—the strength of evidence against the chance model of just guessing. The strength of evidence against the null hypothesis increases even more if the competent-face method can get 71.9% correct in 256 elections (p-value < 0.001; standardized statistic = 7.06). We are even more convinced that our result was not just a "fluke" outcome.

KEY IDEA

As the sample size increases (and the value of the observed sample statistic stays the same), the strength of evidence against the null hypothesis increases.

Two more quick points: (1) If you are trying to pass a true/false test (let's say get 60% or higher) but know NOTHING about what is going to be on the test, would you rather have more questions or fewer questions on the test? You, the student, would rather have fewer questions. If there was only one question on the test you'd have a 50% chance of passing! The teacher would rather have more questions on the test because the more questions on the test the more likely your outcome on the test will be close to 50% (just guessing!) and the less likely you would be to "get lucky" and pass the test by just guessing; (2) Importantly, we can't automatically assume that if we have Doris and Buzz do more trials or have your friend play more rounds of rock-paper-scissors or collect more data at St. George's Hospital that the strength of evidence will increase (smaller p-value, larger standardized statistic). Why not? Because when we collect more data, our observed statistic will almost always change as well. If we have Doris and Buzz do more trials, they won't always get exactly 93.75% correct, your friend may not always throw scissors in exactly one-sixth of the rounds played, and the other heart transplant patients may not have 80% mortality after 30 days.

3. **One-sided versus two-sided tests.** What if the researchers were wrong, and instead of the more competent looking person being elected more frequently, it was actually the less competent looking person who was more likely to win the election?

 1.4.3

Currently, as we've stated our null and alternative hypotheses, we haven't allowed for this possibility. The null hypothesis says that the competent-face method predicts the winner 50% of the time, the alternative hypothesis says greater than 50%, but less than 50% doesn't appear:

Null hypothesis: The probability this method predicts the winner equals 0.50.

Alternative hypothesis: The probability this method predicts the winner is greater than 0.50.

These hypotheses can be written in symbols as

$$H_0: \pi = 0.50$$
$$H_a: \pi > 0.50$$

where π = the probability this method predicts the correct winner.

This type of alternative hypothesis is called "one-sided" because it only looks at one of the two possible ways that the null hypothesis could be wrong. In this case, it only considers that the null hypothesis could be wrong if the probability is more than 0.50. Many researchers consider this way of formulating the alternative hypothesis to be too narrow and too biased towards assuming the researchers are correct ahead of time. Instead, a more objective approach is to conduct a two-sided test, which can be formulated as follows:

Null hypothesis: The probability this method predicts the winner equals 0.50.

Alternative hypothesis: The probability this method predicts the winner is not 0.50.

These hypotheses can be written in symbols as

$$H_0: \pi = 0.50$$

$$H_a: \pi \neq 0.50$$

In this case, the alternative hypothesis states that the probability the competent-face method predicts the winner is not 0.50—might be more, might be less. This change to the alternative hypothesis, however, has ramifications on the rest of the analysis. Recall that p-values are computed as the probability under the null hypothesis of obtaining a value that is equal to or more extreme than your observed statistic, where more extreme goes in the direction of the alternative hypothesis (greater than **or** less than). In the case of a **two-sided test**, more extreme must go in both directions. The way this is operationalized is that the p-value is computed by finding out how frequently the observed statistic or more extreme occurred in one tail of the distribution and adding that to the corresponding probability of being at least as extreme in the other direction—in the other tail of the null distribution.

For example, how often does 0.7188 or more occur by chance? Because 0.7188 is 0.2188 *above* 0.50, we need to look at what number is 0.2188 *below* 0.50. Calculating $0.50 - 0.2188 = 0.2812$, we need to also look at the proportion of outcomes at or below 0.2812. (See Figure 1.16.)

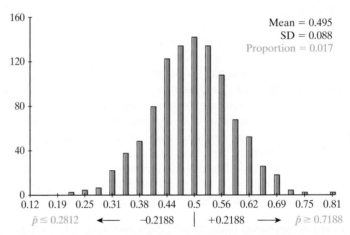

FIGURE 1.16 When determining a two-sided p-value, we can look at outcomes in both tails for the null distribution that are the same distance above or below the mean.

Figure 1.16 illustrates how a two-sided p-value is computed. In this case 0.7188 or greater was obtained nine times by chance, and 0.2812 or less was obtained eight times by chance. Thus, the two-sided p-value is approximately $(8 + 9)/1,000 = 0.017$. Two-sided tests always increase the p-value (approximately doubling it from a one-sided test), and thus, using two-sided tests always decreases the strength of evidence. Two-sided tests are more conservative and are used most of the time in scientific practice. However, because of their objectivity they require even stronger results before the observed statistic will be statistically significant.

KEY IDEA

Because the p-value for a two-sided test is about twice as large as that for a one-sided test, they provide less evidence against the null hypothesis. However two-sided tests are used more often in scientific practice.

Technical note: When the hypothesized probability is something other than 0.50, there are actually a couple of different ways of defining an observation as being more extreme. The **One Proportion** applet determines that an outcome is more extreme if it has a smaller individual probability than that of the observed outcome. In other words, if an observation is more unlikely, then it is considered more extreme. See FAQ 1.4.1 for more on one-sided vs. two-sided p-values.

FAQ 1.4.1   www.wiley.com/college/tintle

When and why do we use two-sided alternative hypotheses?

FOLLOW-UP STUDY

As a way of applying what we just learned, consider the following. The researchers investigating the competent-face method also predicted the outcomes of 279 races for the U.S. House of Representatives in 2004, looking for whether the probability that the competent-face method predicts the correct winner (π) is different from 0.50. In these 279 races, the method correctly predicted the winner in 189 of the races, which is a proportion of $\hat{p} = 189/279 \approx$ 0.677, or 67.7% of the 279 House races. Notice this sample percentage of 67.7% is a bit smaller than the 71.9% correct predictions in 32 Senate races; however, the sample size (279 instead of 32) is larger. We are also now considering a two-sided alternative hypothesis.

THINK ABOUT IT

Do you expect the strength of evidence for the "competent-face" method to be stronger for the House results, weaker for the House results, or essentially the same for the House results as compared to the Senate results? Why?

Let's take the three factors separately:

1. **Distance of the observed statistic to the null hypothesis value.** In the new study the observed statistic is 0.677, whereas in the original study it was 0.719—this is a small change, closer to the hypothesized value of the parameter, which will slightly decrease the strength of evidence against the null hypothesis.
2. **Sample size.** The sample size is almost 10 times as large (279 vs. 32) in the new study, which will have a large impact on the strength of evidence against the null hypothesis. This will increase the strength of evidence quite a bit, because the observed statistic didn't change much.
3. **One- or two-sided test.** When we looked at the Senate races, we obtained a p-value of 0.009 with a one-sided test and 0.017 with a two-sided test. Because we are asked to use a two-sided test here, that means we will obtain a p-value about twice as large as what we would obtain with a one-sided test.

So, what's the p-value? Figure 1.17 shows the null distribution for a sample size of 279 with 0.50 as the probability under the null hypothesis.

FIGURE 1.17   A null distribution for the Senate sample of 279 races.

Notice that a proportion of 0.677 or larger does not occur just by chance in the null distribution. Neither do any values of 0.323 or smaller. (We need to look down there (0.677 − 0.500 ≈ 0.177, 0.500 − 0.177 ≈ 0.323) because this is a two-sided test.) Thus the p-value is approximately zero and the evidence against the null hypothesis in the House of Representatives sample is stronger than in the Senate sample. This is mainly due to the increased sample size and the fact that the observed sample statistic didn't change too much.

Looking at the standardized statistics, for the Senate races, we find z = (0.719 − 0.500)/0.088 ≈ 2.49 and for the House of Representatives we find z = (0.677 − 0.500)/0.03 ≈ 5.90. We see that the numerator is a bit smaller in the second case, but the denominator (the standard deviation of the null distribution) is much smaller, leading to much stronger evidence against the null hypothesis.

EXPLORATION 1.4 | Competitive Advantage to Uniform Colors?

In this exploration, we are going to explore three factors that influence the strength of evidence in a test of significance: (1) the difference between the observed sample statistic and the value of the parameter used in the null hypothesis; (2) the sample size; and (3) one-sided tests versus two-sided tests. To do this we will look at a study conducted by Hill and Barton (*Nature*, 2005) to investigate whether Olympic athletes in certain uniform colors have an advantage over their competitors. They noticed that competitors in the combat sports of boxing, tae kwon do, Greco-Roman wrestling, and freestyle wrestling are randomly assigned red or blue uniforms. For each match in the 2004 Olympics, they recorded the uniform color of the winner.

THINK ABOUT IT

What are the observational units? What is the variable measured? Is the variable categorical or quantitative?

The observational units in this study are the matches, and the variable is whether the match was won by someone wearing red or someone wearing blue—a categorical variable. Let's suppose that going into this study, the researchers wanted to see whether the color red had an advantage over blue. In other words, competitors that wear red uniforms will win a majority of the time.

1. State the null and the alternative hypotheses in words.

2. We will let π represent the probability that a competitor wearing a red uniform wins. Using this, restate the hypotheses using symbols.

3. Researchers Hill and Barton used data collected on the results of 457 matches and found that the competitor wearing red won 248 times, whereas the competitor wearing blue won 209 times. We will carry out a simulation to assess whether or not the observed data provide evidence in support of the research conjecture. This simulation will employ the **3S strategy**: Determine the statistic, simulate could-have-been outcomes of the statistic under the null model, and assess the strength of evidence against the null model by estimating the p-value or the standardized statistic.

   a. What is the statistic we will use? Calculate the observed value of the statistic in this study.

   b. Describe how you could use a coin to develop a null distribution to test our hypothesis.

   c. Use the **One Proportion** applet to test our hypothesis. Based on your simulation, find the p-value and write a conclusion. Also write down the mean and standard deviation from your null distribution when the proportion of successes is used for the variable on the horizontal axis. You will need this later.

One sided vs. two-sided tests

One factor that influences strength of evidence is whether we conduct a two-sided or a one-sided test. Up until now we have only done one-sided tests. In a one-sided test the alternative hypothesis is either > or <. In a two-sided test, the alternative hypothesis is ≠. So, why would you do a two-sided test and what are the implications?

Suppose the researchers did not necessarily think that red would win more often, but they also didn't necessarily think that blue would win more often. They were just interested in whether one color would win more often than the other. A two-sided alternative hypothesis (red wins at a rate other than 50% of the time, or at a rate not equal to 50%) allows the researchers to be less sure of the anticipated value of the parameter than a one-sided test.

4. If we let π equal the probability that a competitor wearing a red uniform wins, state the hypotheses for this study in symbols using a two-sided alternative.

5. Return to the **One Proportion** applet to approximate the p-value for our original overall proportion of red winning 248 times out of 457 matches, but now select the "Two-sided" check box to find the "two-sided p-value."

   a. Describe how the portion of the null distribution that is shaded red is different than our first test done in #3c.

   b. Describe how the p-value is different from the p-value that was obtained in our original test done in #3c.

   c. To find the two-sided p-value, the applet is looking to see how often 0.543 or larger occurs and how often the comparable value on the other side of the null distribution (or smaller) occurs. To find this value, first compute how far 0.543 is from the center of the null distribution and then go that same distance to the left (less than) the center of the null distribution. What is the comparable value?

   d. Complete the following sentence: The two-sided p-value of _____ is the probability of obtaining _____ or larger plus the probability of obtaining _____ or smaller if the _____ is true.

   e. You should have seen that when the alternative hypothesis is *two-sided*, the p-value is computed by looking at how extreme the observed data is in *both* tails on the null distribution. This makes the p-value about twice as large. Because of this, explain how switching from a one-sided to a two-sided test influences the strength of evidence against the null.

> **KEY IDEA**
>
> Because the p-value for a two-sided test is about twice as large as that for a one-sided test, they provide less evidence against the null hypothesis. However, two-sided tests are used more often in scientific practice.

Difference between statistic and null hypothesis parameter value

6. A second factor that influences the strength of evidence against the null is how far apart the observed sample statistic and the value of the parameter specified under the null hypothesis are. For this study the null value was 0.50 and the observed sample statistic was about 0.543 (or 54.3% of the competitors wearing red won their matches). Suppose a larger proportion of competitors wearing red won their matches. If fact, suppose 57% of the 457 matches were won by a competitor wearing red.

   a. Go back to the **One Proportion** applet and approximate the (one-sided) p-value for this situation where again we are testing to see whether the overall probability of winning is more than 0.50.

b. Is your p-value larger or smaller than your original one? Explain why this makes sense.

c. Write a sentence explaining the relationship between the distance between the observed sample statistic and the value of the parameter specified under the null hypothesis to the strength of evidence against the null hypothesis.

> **KEY IDEA**
>
> The farther away the observed statistic is from the average value of the null distribution, the more evidence there is against the null hypothesis.

Sample size

7. The third factor we will look at that influences strength of evidence against the null hypothesis is the sample size. As we said earlier, the data for this study came from four combat sports in the 2004 Olympics. One of those sports was boxing. The researchers found that out of the 272 boxing matches, 150 of them were won by competitors wearing red. This proportion of $150/272 \approx 0.551$ is similar to the overall proportion of times the competitor wearing red won. Let's see what the smaller sample size does to the strength of evidence. Use the **One Proportion** applet to test the same hypotheses as we originally did, but with just the boxing matches as our sample.

a. Compare the null distribution you generate in this case to that generated in #3. In particular, how do the center (mean) and variability (standard deviation) compare?

b. What is your new p-value? Is it larger or smaller than your original p-value from #3c? Explain why this makes sense.

c. Write a sentence explaining the relationship between sample size and the strength of evidence against the null hypothesis.

> **KEY IDEA**
>
> As the sample size increases (and the value of the observed sample statistic stays the same) the strength of evidence against the null hypothesis increases.

SECTION 1.4 Summary

Three factors impact the strength of evidence provided by sample data against a null hypothesis:

- **Two-sided alternatives/tests** are used when the researcher does not have a prior suspicion about the direction that the parameter value is from the hypothesized value.
  - A two-sided test produces a larger p-value than a one-sided test based on the same sample data.
  - Two-sided tests therefore require a higher "standard of proof" to provide convincing evidence against the null hypothesis.
  - The p-value for a two-sided test is generally twice as large as the p-value would have been from a one-sided test on the same sample data.
- The farther away the observed statistic is from the hypothesized value of the parameter, π, in the direction of the alternative hypothesis, the stronger the evidence against the null hypothesis.
- A larger sample size generally produces stronger evidence against the null hypothesis if the observed value of the statistic does not change (and if the observed result is in the direction of the alternative hypothesis).

INFERENCE FOR A SINGLE PROPORTION: THEORY-BASED APPROACH

INTRODUCTION

The focus of this chapter has been on Step 4: Drawing inferences. We have learned that we can draw inferences from data by comparing our observed statistic to a conjecture or claim about a long-run proportion. In order to assess the strength of evidence for the claim, we have always simulated the null distribution. However, simulation takes a lot of computer power, and historically that wasn't always possible. In this section we will see how, in many cases, we can predict what will happen when you simulate, thus avoiding the need to conduct a simulation, but still providing the ability to assess strength of evidence against the null hypothesis. As we'll find out in this and later sections, in addition to being necessary historically, this method (we'll call it a ***theory-based approach***) also gives insights into and advantages in standardization (Section 1.3) and confidence intervals (the theme of Chapter 3).

At the heart of this method is the fact that the null distributions of sample proportions that we have been simulating often exhibit a common and familiar shape. In particular:

1. They often follow, though not always, bell-shaped curves.
2. They are centered at the null hypothesis value for π.
3. Their variability (spread, standard deviation) is influenced by the sample size.

Figure 1.18 shows a few examples of null distributions from this chapter.

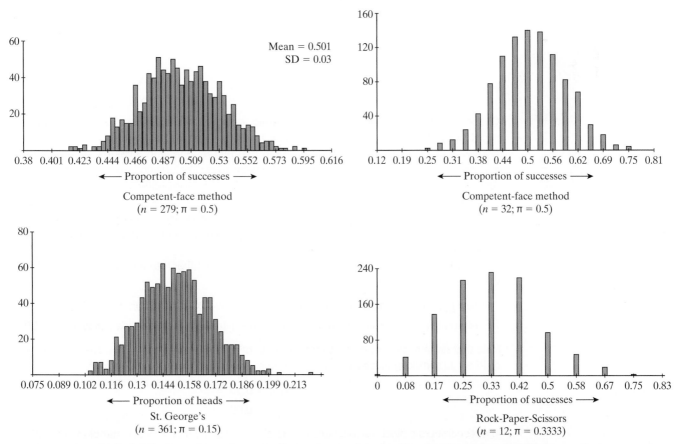

FIGURE 1.18 Null distributions for various studies we've explored so far. A bell-shaped distribution, called a normal distribution, can be used to nicely approximate some of them but will not work well for others.

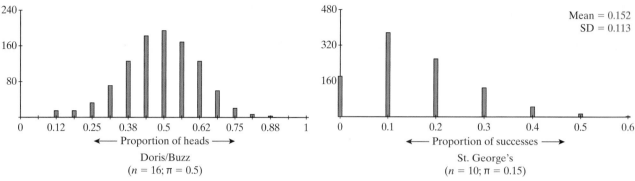

FIGURE 1.18   (*Continued*).

The competent-face method ($n = 279$) and St. George's ($n = 361$) simulations show bell-shaped curves. However, the rock-paper-scissors study and the first sample of St. George's heart patients ($n = 10$) are not bell-shaped curves, in part because the distribution is not symmetric and in part because there are so few values that the sample proportion can be. For the Doris/Buzz dolphin study, even though the distribution of sample proportions is quite symmetric, an approximation based on a bell-shaped curve will not be very good because of the small number of possible values (i.e., because of the extreme discreteness, the gaps between the values) for the sample proportion in those simulations.

As we will learn in this section, in many, but not all, cases we can predict when the simulated distribution is bell-shaped (or ***normally distributed***), where it will be centered, and how variable it will be. All of these predictions can be used to generate p-values and standardized statistics without simulating, in an approach called a *one-proportion z-test*, one example of a theory-based approach to statistical inference.

1.5 Halloween Treats

Example 1.5

EXAMPLE

Concerned over the nation's obesity epidemic, researchers investigated whether children might be as tempted by toys as by candy for Halloween treats. Test households in five Connecticut neighborhoods offered children two plates: one with lollipops or fruit candy and one containing small, inexpensive Halloween toys, like plastic bugs that glow in the dark. The researchers observed the selections of 283 trick-or-treaters between the ages of 3 and 14. They found that 148 of the trick-or-treaters took candy and the other 135 took toys (Schwartz, Chen, and Brownell, 2003). We can focus on either candy or toy to be what we call a success and we choose to focus on candy. Thus our observed sample proportion is $148/283 = 0.523$.

To investigate whether children show a preference for either the candy or the toys, we test the following hypotheses:

Null hypothesis: The probability a trick-or-treater would choose candy is 0.50.

Alternative hypothesis: The probability a trick-or-treater would choose candy is not 0.50.

Note that our null model assumes that the probability of choosing candy (π) is the same for all children. In symbols, these hypotheses translate to

$$H_0: \pi = 0.50$$

$$H_a: \pi \neq 0.50$$

The researchers collect the reactions of 283 children for the study. With a sample size of 283, under our null hypothesis, we simulated the null distribution (using 1,000 simulated samples) shown in Figure 1.19.

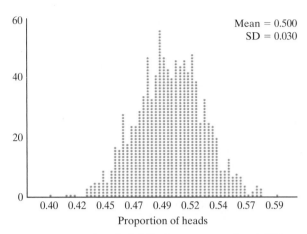

FIGURE 1.19 A null distribution representing 1,000 simulated samples of 283 children where the probability that an individual child would choose candy is 0.50.

We notice that the distribution is quite bell-shaped; the average value is 0.50 (the null hypothesis value for π) and the standard deviation is 0.030. The theory-based approach could have predicted this would happen!

THEORY-BASED APPROACH (ONE PROPORTION Z-TEST)

In the early 1900s, and even earlier, computers weren't available to do simulations, and as people didn't want to sit around and flip coins all day long, they focused their attention on mathematical and probabilistic rules and theories that could predict what would happen if someone did simulate.

They proved the following key result (often called the ***central limit theorem***):

CENTRAL LIMIT THEOREM

If the sample size (n) is large enough, the distribution of sample proportions will be bell-shaped (or normal), centered at the long-run proportion (π), with a standard deviation of $\sqrt{\pi(1-\pi)/n}$.

One bit of ambiguity in the statement is how large is large enough for the sample size? As it turns out, the larger the sample size is, the better the prediction of bell-shaped behavior in the null distribution is, but there is not a sample size where all of a sudden the prediction is good. However, some people have used the convention that you should have at least 10 successes and at least 10 failures in the sample and that is what we will use. Rules like this that must be met in order for theory-based p-values to be valid are what we will call ***validity conditions***.

VALIDITY CONDITIONS

The normal approximation can be thought of as a prediction of what would occur if simulation was done. Many times this prediction is valid, but not always. We will consider the prediction valid when the validity condition (at least 10 successes and at least 10 failures) is met.

Let's see how this prediction compares to what actually happened in the simulation (back in Figure 1.19). With the 283 trick-or-treaters in the researchers' sample, they found that 148 of them took candy (so we have 148 successes) and 135 took toys (so we have 135 failures).

 1.5.1

As both the number of successes and failures are greater than 10, the prediction should work. Looking at Figure 1.19 we see that:

1. The simulated distribution certainly looks bell-shaped.
2. The simulated distribution is centered at 0.50, the hypothesized value of π.
3. The simulated standard deviation of the sample proportions is 0.030, which is very close to the predicted standard deviation of $\sqrt{0.50(1 - 0.50)/283} \approx 0.0297$.

One advantage of using this result is we can determine the standard deviation of the sample proportion without having to conduct the simulation. Knowing the standard deviation allows us to calculate the standardized statistic, z:

$$z = \frac{0.523 - 0.50}{0.0297} = 0.77$$

This tells us that our observed sample proportion (0.523) is 0.77 of a standard deviation above the mean of 0.50. Because this is less than one standard deviation above the mean, it gives us little evidence against the null hypothesis.

To convert this standardized score to a two-sided p-value, we could look at the area under the (standard) normal curve to the right of 0.77 and to the left of −0.77. In the **One Proportion** applet, checking the box for **Normal Approximation** will overlay the theoretical normal curve and give you the p-value from the normal distribution. Figure 1.20 shows the results of this applet for the Halloween treat study where in the sample of 283 trick-or-treaters 148 (52.3%) chose candy and 135 (47.7%) chose toys.

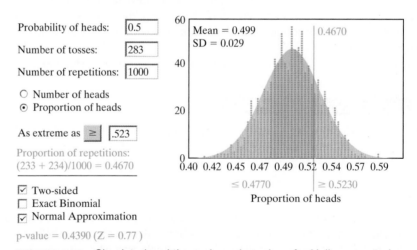

FIGURE 1.20 Simulated and theory-based p-values for Halloween study.

The normal distribution does a nice job of predicting the behavior of the null distribution of sample proportions in this case. The p-value from the theory-based test is 0.4390, compared to 0.4670 from the simulation. We interpret this p-value and draw a conclusion from it as always: If the probability that each trick-or-treater prefers candy to toys is 0.50, then there's about a 44% chance that a random sample of 283 trick-or-treaters would have found 52.3% or more, or 47.7% or fewer, choosing the candy. Because this is not a small p-value, we do not have substantial evidence to suggest that trick-or-treaters prefer either type of treat. This was actually good news to the researchers, to learn that both types of treats are viable and we could probably distribute less candy at Halloween (at least in this Connecticut neighborhood).

The p-value of 0.4390 from the theory-based approach (one-proportion z-test) is very similar to that obtained from the simulation (see Figure 1.20) because the prediction of the shape, center, and variability of the null distribution is very good. [*Note:* We can improve the normal approximation by employing a "continuity correction" that would use a value just below 0.523 and just above 0.477 to include more area right at those cutoff values.]

A situation where a theory-based approach doesn't work

 1.5.3

In Section 1.2, we looked at the rock-paper-scissors game where novice players threw scissors 2 of the 12 rounds played.

THINK ABOUT IT

Why do you think the theory-based (also known as one-proportion *z*-test; normal approximation) approach will not work well for these data?

In this case, the theory-based approach is not expected to work well because the sample size (12) is small. Recall that the validity conditions for the theory-based approach state the need for at least 10 successes and 10 failures. We have 2 scissors and 10 not scissors so this condition is not met.

But, let's see what happens when we use the theory-based approach anyway. The theory-based approach predicts that:

1. The null distribution will be bell-shaped and approximately normal.
2. The null distribution will be centered at 0.333.
3. The standard deviation of the null distribution will be $\sqrt{\dfrac{0.333(1 - 0.333)}{12}} \approx 0.136$.

Figure 1.21 shows a picture of the simulated null distribution with the theory-based normal distribution overlaid.

Figure 1.21 shows that the approximate p-value from the simulation (0.1980) is not all that similar to the theory-based p-value (0.1108). Although both distributions (theoretical and simulation) are centered at nearly 0.3333, with similar standard deviations (0.134 vs. 0.136), the distribution is not "normal" in that it is not "filled in." In other words, the null distribution is too discrete (too much empty space between the possible observations) for it to be well-modeled by a normal distribution.

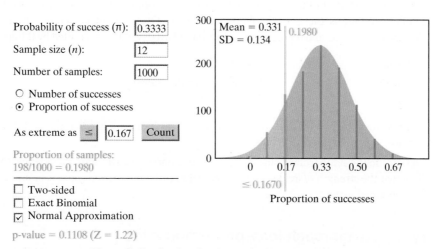

FIGURE 1.21 The null distribution for the rock-paper-scissors example.

With the larger p-value, the simulation-based approach provides a bit less evidence against the null hypothesis. Because these two p-values are not all that similar we would have a bit more faith in the p-value obtained from the simulation. In summary, the theory-based approach should not have been used in this case because the sample size was too small, and, thus, the end result is that the theory suggested that there was more evidence against the null than there was.

When asked to call the outcome of a coin toss, are people equally likely to choose heads or tails? Let's investigate this question by collecting some data from you and your classmates.

1. What would you call: heads or tails?

   Before we even collect data from your classmates, let's think about what we want to test here. Conventional wisdom says that people tend to pick heads more often than tails, so that's the research hypothesis we'll investigate.

2. In the coin toss study with your class:
   a. What are the observational units in this study?
   b. What is the variable that is recorded?
   c. Describe the parameter of interest in words. (Use the symbol π to represent this parameter.)
   d. If people do *not* have a tendency to pick heads more often than tails (or tails more often than heads), what would you expect the numerical value of the parameter to be? Is this the null hypothesis or the alternative hypothesis?
   e. If people *do* have a tendency to pick heads more often than tails, what can you say about the numerical value of the parameter? Is this the null hypothesis or the alternative hypothesis?

3. Including yourself and your classmates, how many people participated in this study? How many picked heads? Calculate the sample proportion that picked heads.

4. To have a larger sample size to analyze, combine your class results with the results from one of the author's classes, in which 54 of 83 students picked heads. Now what are the sample size and the sample proportion that picked heads?

Sample size:	Sample proportion:

5. Use the **One Proportion** applet to test the hypotheses from #2d and #2e.
   a. Describe the shape of the null distribution of sample proportions. Does this shape look familiar? Where is the null distribution centered? Does this make sense? Check the **Summary Stats** box and report the mean and standard deviation as reported by the applet.

Shape:	Familiar?
Center?	Why does this make sense?
Mean:	SD:

   b. Approximate the p-value and summarize the strength of evidence that the sample data provide regarding the research hypothesis.
   c. Determine the standardized statistic, z, and summarize the strength of evidence. Confirm that the strength of evidence obtained using the standardized statistic is similar to that obtained using the p-value.

Theory-based approach (one-proportion z-test)

In Question 5(a), you probably described the shape of the null distribution using words such as bell-shaped, symmetric, or maybe even normal. You have seen many null distributions in this chapter that have had this same basic shape. You should have also noticed that the null distributions have all been centered at the hypothesized value of the long-run proportion used in the null hypotheses. You probably could have predicted that your null distribution was going to be somewhat bell-shaped and centered at 0.50. You probably would have a harder time predicting your null distribution's variability (standard deviation), but this too can be predicted in advance, as we will see shortly.

We can use mathematical models known as normal distributions (bell-shaped curves) to approximate many of the null distributions we have generated so far in this text. When rules and theories are used to predict what the value of the standardized statistic and p-value would be if someone did simulate, we call the approach a ***theory-based approach***. The normal distribution provides a second way, in addition to simulation, to approximate a p-value.

6. Check the box next to **Normal Approximation** in the applet. Does the region shaded in blue seem to be a good description (model) of what we actually got in the simulation?

Validity conditions for theory-based approach

The normal approximation to the null distribution is valid whenever the sample size is reasonably large. One convention is to consider the sample size to be large enough whenever there are at least 10 observations in each category.

7. According to this convention, is the sample size large enough in this study to use the normal approximation and theory-based inference? Justify your answer.

> ### VALIDITY CONDITIONS
>
> The normal approximation can be thought of as a prediction of what would occur if simulation was done. Many times this prediction is valid, but not always. It is only valid when the condition (at least 10 successes and at least 10 failures) is met.

Formulas

The normal approximation will also give you values of the standardized statistic and p-value based on its mathematical predictions. As you learned in Section 1.3, the standardized score is calculated as

$$z = \frac{\text{statistic} - \text{mean of null distribution}}{\text{standard deviation of null distribution}}$$

The mean of the null distribution is the hypothesized value of the long-run proportion (π). The standard deviation can be obtained in two ways:

First, find the standard deviation of the null distribution by simulating.

Second, predict the value of the standard deviation by plugging into this formula: $\sqrt{\pi(1 - \pi)/n}$.

8. Use the formula to determine the (theoretical; predicted) standard deviation of the sample proportion. Then compare this to the SD from your simulated sample proportions, as recorded in #5a. Are they similar?

The predicted value of the standard deviation (using the formula) will be very close to the simulated standard deviation of the null distribution. The validity condition mentioned earlier says the shape will be approximately normal when the sample size is large enough where, a "large enough" sample size means at least 10 successes and at least 10 failures. This mathematical prediction is often called the "central limit theorem."

> ### CENTRAL LIMIT THEOREM
>
> If the sample size (n) is large enough, the distribution of sample proportions will be bell-shaped (or normal), centered at the long-run proportion (π), with a standard deviation of $\sqrt{\pi(1 - \pi)/n}$.

9. Use the predicted value of the standard deviation from #8 to calculate the standardized statistic (z) by hand and confirm that your answer is very close to what you found in #5c when using simulation.

In the applet, see that the predicted value of the standardized statistic, z, is given immediately below the button for "Normal approximation" in parentheses and should match your answer to #9.

10. The theory-based (normal approximation) p-value is also now displayed. Compare this p-value to the one you got from simulation (#5b). Are they similar?

11. Why are the standard deviation (#8), standardized statistic (#9) and p-value (#10) similar when using the theory-based (one-proportion z-test; normal approximation) to what you got in your simulation? When would they be different?

Follow-up analysis #1

In his book *Statistics You Can't Trust*, Steve Campbell claims that people pick heads 70% of the time when they're asked to predict the outcome of a coin toss.

12. Use the theory-based approach to test Campbell's claim based on the sample data used above (your class combined with author's class) using a two-sided alternative. Report the null and alternative hypothesis, standardized statistic, and p-value. Summarize your conclusion and explain the reasoning process by which it follows from your analysis.

Follow-up analysis #2

In a small class of eight students, seven students picked heads when given the choice between heads and tails.

13. Use simulation to generate a two-sided p-value evaluating the strength of evidence that the long-run proportion of students picking heads is different than 50% based on this small class's data alone.

14. Why can't you use the normal approximation in this case?

15. Use the normal approximation anyway. Compare and comment on the p-values obtained from the two methods.

- -

SECTION 1.5 Summary

Most of the null distributions for a sample proportion that we have seen follow a common and familiar shape. This bell-shaped curve, known mathematically as a **normal distribution**, allows us to anticipate what a null distribution will look like and to determine an approximate p-value, without bothering to conduct a simulation analysis.

All normal distributions have a bell-shaped curve, but they can differ with regard to center and variability. When working with the null distribution of a sample proportion:

- The center is described by the mean, which for a null distribution equals the hypothesized value of the long-run proportion π.
- The variability is described by the standard deviation, which is determined primarily by the sample size.
  - The larger the sample size, the smaller the variability in sample proportions.
  - The standard deviation of the sample proportion equals $\sqrt{\pi(1 - \pi)/n}$.

The **theory-based approach** (also known as one-proportion z-test; normal approximation) standardizes the statistic based on the observed value of the statistic (sample proportion) and these theoretical mean and standard deviation values.

- The p-value is calculated by software as the area under the normal curve in the appropriate direction (as specified by the alternative hypothesis) from the standardized statistic.
- The p-value is interpreted and evaluated just as with the simulation-based method.

This theory-based method works well whenever the sample size is large enough for the normal curve to provide a good approximation to the null distribution.

- We consider the theory-based method to be valid when there are at least 10 observations of each category ("success" and "failure") in the sample.
- When this validity condition is not met, and even when it is met, an alternative is simply to use the simulation-based method.

The names, conditions, and applets used for the simulation and theory-based tests are shown in the following table.

Summary of validity conditions and applets for one proportion tests

Type of data	Name of test	Applet	Validity conditions
Single binary variable	Simulation test for a single proportion	One Proportion	—
	Theory-based test for a single proportion (*one-proportion z-test*)	One Proportion or Theory-Based Inference	At least 10 successes and at least 10 failures

---

SAMPLING DISTRIBUTION OF A SAMPLE PROPORTION

SECTION 1.6

INTRODUCTION

In the previous section, you learned a theory-based approach (the one-proportion z-test) to measure the strength of evidence against the null hypothesis without simulating the null distribution. The *sampling distribution of a sample proportion* (that's a mouthful!) can seem like a very abstract concept to most students. Fortunately, throughout Chapter 1, we have been exploring the sampling distribution of the sample proportion ($\hat{p}$) in a more concrete way by using simulation. As we talked about in the last section, the mean of the theoretical distribution is exactly equal to the value of the long-run proportion of success, π, and the standard deviation of the simulated distribution is given by a formula ($\sqrt{\pi(1 - \pi)/n}$). A key difference between a simulated sampling distribution of $\hat{p}$ and a theoretical sampling distribution is that the theoretical distribution is made up of every single possible sample, whereas a simulation only considers some possibilities. We often only simulated 1,000 possibilities and that was enough. Because our simulations did not contain values of $\hat{p}$ from every possible sample of a given size, the mean and standard deviation of the distribution of sample proportions were very, very close to π and $\sqrt{\pi(1 - \pi)/n}$, but not always exact. Also, remember that the shape of the theoretical distribution is dependent upon the sample size.

In this section we will see how to describe a theoretical sampling distribution of a sample proportion (shape, center, variability) without conducting a simulation first. The way we describe the theoretical sampling distribution will be based on the central limit theorem and validity conditions we learned in the previous section. In particular, we will explore how both the long-run process proportion of success, π, and the sample size impact the sample proportion.

1.6 — Color Psychology: Personality Color Orange

Example 1.6

EXAMPLE

According to some proponents of color psychology, the color orange radiates warmth and happiness, combining the physical energy and stimulation of red with the cheerfulness of yellow. According to these proponents, if orange is your favorite color, then you are warm, optimistic, extroverted, and often flamboyant. You are friendly, good-natured, and a generally agreeable person (http://www.empower-yourself-with-color-psychology.com/personality-color-orange.html). Would a warm, optimistic person have a good chance of selecting an orange M&M from a bag of milk chocolate M&Ms?

Suppose your optimistic friend loves the color orange and M&M milk chocolate candies (but only the orange ones!). The manufacturer of M&Ms states that based on "consumer preference tests," on average, the mix of colors for milk chocolate M&Ms follows the following color percentage breakdown:

Color Breakdown for Milk Chocolate M&Ms	
Color	Manufacturer percentage breakdown
Brown	30%
Yellow	20%
Red	20%
Orange	10%
Green	10%
Blue	10%

You are curious what outcomes could happen, and how likely those outcomes will be, if you randomly select a sample of 10 candies from this manufacturing process, and then calculate $\hat{p}$, the proportion of orange candies in your sample.

THINK ABOUT IT

What are the observational units? What's the variable of interest and is it categorical or quantitative? What's the parameter of interest? What is the relevant statistic?

Each candy is an observational unit and the variable of interest is whether or not the candy is orange in color. Thus, the variable is categorical, which makes the parameter of interest the probability of selecting an orange candy (or the long-run proportion of orange candies in the manufacturing process) and the statistic is the sample proportion of orange candies in a sample of 10. If we use notation, this means that π represents the probability of obtaining an orange candy when randomly selecting a milk chocolate M&M (i.e., the long-run proportion of M&M candies that are orange in the production process) and the manufacturer claims that $\pi = 0.10$.

What would the distribution of the sample proportion of orange M&Ms look like if you were to repeatedly take samples of 10 M&M candies? What would the shape of the distribution look like? Where would the distribution of sample proportions be centered? How much variability can we expect in the distribution of our sample proportion of orange M&Ms for samples of size 10? How could you begin to explore the answers to these questions?

To answer these questions, you need to consider the *sampling distribution of the sample proportion* of orange M&Ms in a sample of 10.

As we've done before, we can use simulation to investigate the answers to these questions. Figure 1.22 displays the results of a simulation that randomly selected 1,000 samples of 10 candies each, from the M&Ms manufacturing process, by using the **One Proportion** applet and scrolling to the bottom, selecting the "other colored candies," and changing the probability of orange (0.10), number of candies (10), and number of samples (1,000). Each dot in the simulated sampling distribution represents the proportion of orange candies in a single sample of 10 candies, with the graph showing the results from 1,000 different samples of size 10.

Definition

A *sampling distribution for a sample proportion*, $\hat{p}$, would consist of proportions from all possible samples of the same size, n, from a long-run process (or population) with proportion of success, π.

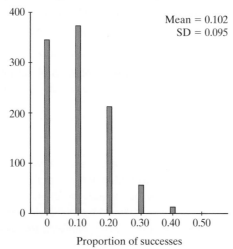

Mean = 0.102
SD = 0.095

Proportion of successes

FIGURE 1.22 Distribution of 1,000 simulated sample proportions of orange M&Ms from samples of size 10, where the probability of an orange candy is 0.10.

Shape: As we saw in the previous section, sometimes the sampling distribution of sample proportions takes the well-known "bell shape." There are different ways to check to see whether our sample size is large enough relative to the process probability to feel fairly certain that the shape of the distribution of sample proportions is bell-shaped. These are not hard and fast rules and thus different guidelines exist. For example, we showed you one set of guidelines (validity conditions) in Section 1.5, but for the AP exam, when doing a hypothesis test for a single proportion, we look at *expected number of successes and failures* using the probability assumed under the null hypothesis.

 1.6.1

Because we assume that the null hypothesis is true when conducting a hypothesis test, we use the parameter value (π) specified by the null as a validity check to determine whether a normal distribution is a reasonable model for the distribution of our sample proportion. On the AP exam, be sure to substitute the actual values of n and π from your problem when checking the expected number of successes and failures.

Definition

The mean of a sampling distribution of sample proportions is the long-run process proportion or probability of success, π.

Definition

The standard deviation of a sampling distribution of sample proportions represents the "typical" or "average" distance between the sample proportions from all possible samples of the same size and the long-run process proportion or probability, π. It can be calculated using the formula $\sqrt{\pi(1-\pi)/n}$.

1.6.2

1.6.3

Center: The distribution of possible sample statistics in our simulated distribution is centered at 0.102, which is very close to 0.10, the probability of success—π. As we saw in the last section, if we continue to simulate more and more sample statistics, the mean of the simulated sampling distribution will get closer and closer to the probability of an orange candy (the parameter), $\pi = 0.10$. Thus, we can say that the mean of the sampling distribution will be the long-run process proportion (probability of success).

Variability: You discovered in Section 1.4 that the size of the sample affects the variability in the distribution of possible sample proportions, and in Section 1.5 you learned that the standard deviation of a null distribution of sample proportions is given by the formula $\sqrt{\pi(1-\pi)/n}$. In this case, because the sample size is $n = 10$ and the long-run proportion of orange candies is 10% we have

$$\text{Standard Deviation of sample proportions} = \sqrt{0.1(1-0.1)/10} \approx 0.095$$

Remember that a small standard deviation indicates that proportions vary little from sample to sample and a large standard deviation indicates the proportions vary greatly from sample to sample. As we saw in Section 1.4, as the sample size increases, the variation in the sampling distribution will decrease.

For this example,

Expected number of orange M&Ms: 10(0.10) = 1

Expected number of non-orange M&Ms: 10(0.90) = 9

In this case, since both 1 and 9 are less than 10, the validity condition is not met for this sample size. This means that the shape of the distribution of sample proportions may not be approximately normal or bell-shaped. Look back at Figure 1.22: it doesn't look very bell-shaped, does it?

> **KEY IDEA**
>
> This validity condition requires that we **expect** there to be at least 10 orange M&Ms (successes) <u>and</u> at least 10 non-orange M&Ms (failures) in the sample. The **expected number of successes** is how many successes we expect to occur, on average, for a given sample size and can be calculated by multiplying the sample size times the process probability of success (that is, $n\pi$). Similarly, the **expected number of failures** is simply $n(1-\pi)$.

Recall from Section 1.3 that in a bell-shaped distribution, almost all the values are within 3 standard deviations on either side of the mean. Because the distribution of orange candies is centered at 0.10 with a standard deviation of about 0.095 and because you cannot have fewer than 0 orange candies in your sample, there is not "enough room" for the distribution of sample proportions to extend 3 standard deviations to the left of the mean of the distribution ($0.1 - 3(0.095) = -0.185$). Thus, the shape of the distribution of sample proportions is skewed to the right (the sample proportions are piled up on the left with the tail of the distribution extending to the right) and so a normal distribution is not a good fit for this sampling distribution. This is what we anticipated by the fact that the expected counts were not large enough.

> **THINK ABOUT IT**
>
> What would the distribution of sample proportions of orange candies look like if we increased the sample size?

Figure 1.23 displays the results of 1,000 simulated sets when randomly selecting 25, 50, and 100 candies from an infinite production process of M&M milk chocolate candies, where 10% of the M&Ms produced are orange.

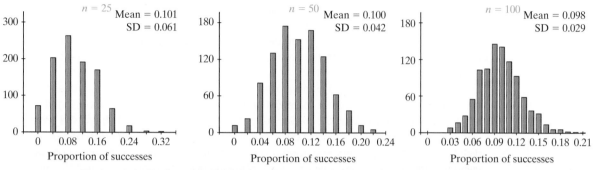

FIGURE 1.23 Each graph displays the distribution of 1,000 simulated sample proportions of orange M&Ms from samples of size 25, 50, and 100, respectively, where the probability of an orange candy is 0.10.

As you would expect, all three simulated distributions of sample proportions are centered at $\pi = 0.10$. As the sample size increases, the sample-to-sample variability decreases (notice that the SD of the simulated sample proportions decreases from 0.061 ($n = 25$) to 0.042 ($n = 50$) to 0.029 ($n = 100$)) and the shape of the distribution of sample proportions becomes more bell-shaped (approximately normal).

Let's look at the validity condition we are using to determine whether our sample size is large enough relative to the probability of 0.10 for samples of 25, 50, and 100.

For $n = 25$, our expected number of orange M&Ms (successes, $n\pi$) is only 2.5, so the validity condition is not met. Our sample size has gotten larger, and although the standard deviation decreased from 0.095 to 0.061, we still do not have enough room to go 3 standard deviations below the mean of 0.10. The shape of the distribution is still somewhat skewed to the right.

For $n = 50$, our expected number of orange M&Ms (successes) is only 5, so the validity condition is not met. Our sample size has gotten large enough so that there is almost enough "room" for the distribution of sample proportions to go 3 standard deviations below the mean of 0.10 ($0.10 - 3 \times 0.042 = -0.026$), so why is this distribution not considered to be bell-shaped enough?

There is another aspect of the normal distribution that we need to consider. The normal distribution (which we will cover in detail in Chapter 11) is more "filled in" (it is a continuous distribution with an infinite number of possible values). The actual sampling distribution is more "discrete" (too much empty space between possible observations). Recall from Section 1.2 when we discussed model vs. reality that chance models make key assumptions that we need to pay careful attention to when assessing strength of evidence or calculating probabilities; otherwise, we may make incorrect conclusions. For example, suppose that we obtained only 3 orange candies in a random sample of 50 M&Ms and are wondering how likely it would be to obtain 3 or fewer orange candies if the advertised proportion of orange is actually 0.10. (Are the M&Ms folks lying to us?) Figure 1.24 shows the simulated distribution of sample proportions for samples of size $n = 50$ shaded for values less than or equal to 0.06.

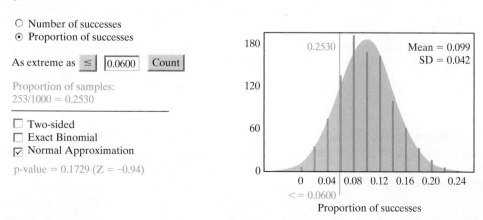

FIGURE 1.24 Simulated distribution of sample proportions for samples of size $n = 50$.

We can see that there is quite a difference between our simulation-based probability of obtaining 3 or fewer orange candies out of 50 (0.2530) and the normal approximation or theory-based probability (0.1729). Remember from the previous section that if our validity condition for sample size is not met, the simulation-based probability will provide a better estimate than the theory-based probability.

For $n = 100$, our expected number of successes is 10 and our expected number of failures is 90, so our validity condition is (barely) met. We can see in Figure 1.25 below that the simulated probability of obtaining 3 or fewer out of 100 orange candies (0.014) and the probability using the normal approximation (0.0098) are quite close now. With samples of size 100, the distribution of possible sample proportions is more "filled in," and the estimated probabilities using the normal model are similar to those obtained using simulation. Figure 1.25 shows the simulated distribution of sample proportions for samples of size $n = 100$ shaded for values less than or equal to 0.03.

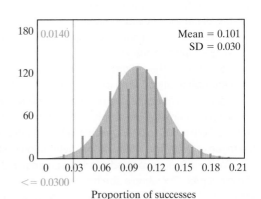

FIGURE 1.25   Simulated distribution of sample proportions for samples of size $n = 100$.

KEY IDEA

The **sampling distribution of a sample statistic** can be described by its shape, center (mean), and variability (standard deviation).

Shape: If the number of expected successes $n\pi$ and failures $n(1 - \pi)$ are both at least 10, then the sampling distribution of sample proportions has an approximately normal distribution.

Center: Mean of $\hat{p}$'s $= \pi$

Variability: Standard Deviation of $\hat{p}$'s $= \sqrt{\pi(1 - \pi)/n}$

The statement about shape in the Key Idea box is often called the Central Limit Theorem, one of the most important results in statistics. You were first introduced to the central limit theorem in Section 1.5 and you will see various versions of the central limit theorem throughout this text.

Spinning Pennies

According to statistician Persi Diaconis, the probability of a penny landing heads when it is spun on its edge is only about 0.20. Let's assume this is true. Suppose you were to spin a coin on its edge 10 times.

1. How many times would you expect it (on average) to land heads? Why?

2. Would you expect it to always land heads the number of times you answered in #1? If so, why? If not, why not?

3. How would you go about investigating how the proportion of heads in a sample of 10 spins varies from sample to sample?

> **Definition**
>
> A *sampling distribution for a sample proportion*, $\hat{p}$, would consist of proportions from all possible samples of the same size, n, from a long-run process (or population) with proportion of success, π.

Of course, what you would like to investigate is the *sampling distribution for a sample proportion* of heads when a penny is spun on its edge 10 times.

Let's use the **One Proportion** applet to further investigate the sampling distribution.

4. Use the **One Proportion** applet to generate a *simulated* sampling distribution of sample proportions of 10 pennies when the probability of landing heads when spinning the penny is 0.20.

   a. Indicate how you would use the **One Proportion** applet by filling in the values below, then run the applet.

   Probability of heads: [   ]
   Number of tosses: [   ]
   Number of repetitions: [   ]
   ☑ Animate
   [Draw Samples]
   Total = 0
   ○ Number of heads
   ⊙ Proportion of heads

> **Definition**
>
> The mean of a sampling distribution of sample proportions is the long-run process proportion or probability of success, π.

   b. Describe the *simulated* sampling distribution you obtained when running the applet. When describing the distribution, be sure to address shape, center, and variability.

   If you spun a coin on its edge 10 times and it landed heads 3 out of the 10 times, would you consider that to be an unusual outcome based on the *simulated* distribution of the null hypothesis? Why or why not?

5. In addition to simulation, you can also use a theory-based approach to answer questions about the sampling distribution. Using the theory-based approach, answer each of the following questions about the sampling distribution of sample proportions for samples of size $n = 10$.

   a. Where will the sampling distribution be centered?

   b. What is the standard deviation of the sampling distribution of sample proportions?

> **Definition**
>
> The standard deviation of a sampling distribution of sample proportions represents the "typical" or "average" distance between the sample proportions from all possible samples of the same size and the long-run process proportion or probability, π. It can be obtained using the formula $\sqrt{\pi(1 - \pi)/n}$.

As we saw in the previous section, sometimes the sampling distribution of sample proportions takes the well-known "bell shape." There are different ways to check to see whether our sample size is large enough relative to the process probability to feel fairly certain that the shape of the distribution of sample proportions is bell-shaped. These are not hard and fast rules and thus different guidelines exist. For example, we showed you one set of guidelines in Section 1.5, but for the AP exam, when doing a hypothesis test for a single proportion, we look at *expected number of successes and failures* using the probability assumed under the null hypothesis.

> **AP TIP**
>
> Because we assume that the null hypothesis is true when conducting a hypothesis test, we use the parameter value (π) specified by the null as a validity check to determine whether a normal distribution is a reasonable model for the distribution of our sample proportion. On the AP exam, be sure to substitute the actual values of n and π from your problem when checking the expected number of successes and failures.

> **KEY IDEA**
>
> The *expected number of successes* is how many successes we expect to occur for a given sample size and can be calculated by multiplying the sample size times the process probability of success (that is, $n\pi$). Similarly, the **expected number of failures** is simply $n(1 - \pi)$.

    c. Based on the expected number of "successes" (heads) and "failures" (tails), will the shape of the sampling distribution be approximately normal? Note: You will need to calculate expected counts of heads spun and expected counts of tails spun. If yes, explain why; if no, explain why not.

    d. If we spun a coin 10 times and got three heads, what is the value of sample proportion? The standardized statistic? Is this an unusual outcome?

In this case, the sample size is fairly small and so the expected number of heads is only 2—well below the 10 required for a sampling distribution to be fairly normal. We would need a larger sample size and/or a large proportion of heads to yield a bell-shaped distribution of sampling proportions. Furthermore, getting 30% heads is not all that unusual in this case. Let's see how this plays out as we increase the sample size.

6. What if we spun the coin 50 times?

    a. Where will the sampling distribution be centered?

    b. What is the standard deviation of the sampling distribution of sample proportions?

    c. Should the shape of the sampling distribution be approximately normal? If yes, explain why; if no, explain why not.

    d. If you spun a coin on its edge 50 times and it landed heads 15 out of the 50 times, what is the value of the sample proportion? The standardized statistic? Is this an unusual outcome?

7. Repeat #6 assuming you spun the coin 100 times and found 30 out of 100 heads.

8. Discuss your responses to Questions 5(d), 6(d), and 7(d) regarding whether a sample proportion of 0.30 would be considered unusual for samples of size 10, 50, and 100. Was your answer the same in all three cases or did it change for different sample sizes? Why or why not? How does this connect with the relationship between sample size and strength of evidence you explored in Section 1.4?

9. Complete the following sentences that summarize the main ideas from this section.

    a. The mean of a sampling distribution of sample proportions will be centered at the probability or long-run proportion of success _____ (define/give symbol) regardless of _____ size.

    b. The sample-to-sample variability in sample proportions, which we measure with _____, will <u>increase/decrease</u> (choose one) as the sample size increases.

    c. The AP guidelines state that a sampling distribution of proportions is approximately normal, when the expected number of _____ and _____ are both at least 10.

> **KEY IDEA**
>
> The **sampling distribution of a sample statistic** can be described by its shape, center (mean), and variability (standard deviation).
>
> **Shape:** If the number of expected successes $n\pi$ and failures $n(1-\pi)$ are both at least 10, then the sampling distribution of sample proportions has an approximately normal distribution.
>
> $SD = \sqrt{\pi(1-\pi)/n}$
>
> $Mean = \pi$
>
> **Center:** Mean of $\hat{p}$'s $= \pi$
>
> **Variability:** Standard Deviation of $\hat{p}$'s $= \sqrt{\pi(1-\pi)/n}$

The statement about shape in the Key Idea box is often called the Central Limit Theorem, one of the most important results in statistics. You were first introduced to the central limit theorem in Section 1.5 and you will see various versions of the central limit theorem throughout this text.

SECTION 1.6 Summary

In this section we explored the distribution of sample proportions (shape, center, variability) using simulations for samples of different sizes drawn from a population with proportion of success π. We saw

- **Central Limit Theorem:** As the sample size increases, the shape of the distribution of sample proportions will become approximately normal, provided that our expected number of successes, $n\pi$, and failures, $n(1-\pi)$, are both at least 10.

- The distribution of sample proportions will be centered at the probability or long-run proportion of success, π.

- The variability in the sampling distribution of sample proportions will decrease as the sample size increases. We can use the theory-based formula $\sqrt{\pi(1-\pi)/n}$ to calculate the variability in the sampling distribution.

ONE-PROPORTION z-TEST FOR A POPULATION PROPORTION

SECTION 1.7

INTRODUCTION

In Section 1.5 you learned an alternative to simulating a sampling distribution in order to assess our strength of evidence against a null hypothesis. We called this approach a "theory-based" approach because it relied on mathematical theory to predict the center, variability, and shape of the null distribution when certain validity conditions were true. You built on this knowledge in Section 1.6, where you took a more in-depth look at the sampling distribution of a sample proportion. You learned that you can use mathematical models known as normal distributions (bell-shaped curves) to approximate many of the null distributions you have seen and generated so far in this course.

You also learned in Section 1.5 that when the variable of interest is a single binary variable (e.g., whether or not Buzz pushes the correct button), then the appropriate theory-based approach is called a **one-proportion z-test**.

On the AP Statistics exam, when a hypothesis test is called for, students must show the following work for full credit:

1. **State the hypotheses either in words or using appropriate symbols.**

   You have had lots of practice stating hypotheses in this chapter. Some things to remember in order to receive full credit for this component of a hypothesis test on the AP Statistics exam:

   - When using symbols, be sure to use the appropriate symbol for the population parameter.

   - Hypotheses are conjectures about some underlying process and not the sample, and so hypotheses should always be statements about the population parameter(s) of interest. Thus, you should <u>never</u> state your hypotheses in terms of $\hat{p}$, your sample proportion, but rather in terms of π, the process probability or long-run proportion of success. For example, to investigate whether Buzz does better than just guessing, we state our hypotheses as Null hypothesis: $\pi = 0.5$ versus Alternative hypothesis: $\pi > 0.5$, where π represents the long-run process probability of Buzz making the correct choice in this selection process.

   - If stating your hypotheses in words, refrain from using the past tense, for example *The proportion of trick-or-treaters who chose the candy over the toy*, makes it sound like your hypotheses are about the sample, not the long-run process. Instead, you could say, *The proportion of students who would <u>favor</u> (note the use of the future tense, as this value has not been observed) abolishing the penny.*

2. **Name the test that will be used.**

   The theory-based approach for inference for a single proportion is a **one-proportion z-test**.

3. **State and verify the validity conditions for the test chosen.**

   There are two main conditions to check for every theory-based hypothesis test.

   - One is the **manner in which the data were collected**. The method used to collect the data will determine to what long-run process the results of our study can be generalized and whether or not we can attribute a cause-and-effect relationship. Earlier in Chapter 1 you looked at data obtained from a random process (e.g., the long-run process probability that Buzz would push the correct button). In this case, the key question is "Are these 16 trials from Buzz a good representation of Buzz's true abilities? Or was he having a particularly good (or bad) day?" For that example, we need to assume that the 16 trials of data we have are a good representation of Buzz's abilities; otherwise, what conclusions can we really make? In Chapter 2 you will examine data obtained from sampling from a finite population and will learn strategies to obtain a representative sample. In each case, we will need to ask whether the method used to collect the data will result in a sample that is representative of the process we are trying to model, or representative of the population we are interested in inferring something about. In Chapter 4 we will look at data obtained from a controlled, randomized experiment and the different kinds of conclusions we can make when our data are produced in this manner.

   - A second validity condition for a theory-based approach is that the **model chosen is a good prediction** for the null distribution. With sample proportions, this means we need to verify whether the sample size is large enough.

     - Recall that in Section 1.6 we saw that the distribution of sample proportions will be bell-shaped (or approximately normal) when the expected count of successes ($n\pi$) and the expected count of failures ($n(1 - \pi)$) are both at least 10. You will need to verify that $n\pi \geq 10$ and $n(1 - \pi) \geq 10$ by substituting the appropriate values into the formula. In a hypothesis test, you will use the hypothesized value of π to perform this check.

4. **Calculate the test statistic (standardized statistic) and corresponding p-value.**

   For a one-proportion z-test, we will calculate a standardized statistic and denote it with a z.

   - Recall that in Section 1.3 we looked at using a standardized statistic (also known as a *test statistic*) as an alternative to the p-value for measuring our strength of evidence against the null hypothesis.

   - For a single proportion, our test statistic is a *z*-statistic:

     $$\text{test statistic (standardized statistic)} = z = \frac{\text{statistic} - \text{mean of null distribution}}{\text{standard deviation of null distribution}}$$

     Note: *The general formula for a test statistic (standardized statistic) on the formula sheet provided on the AP Statistics exam is shown below and is a generalization of what is shown above for a test on a single proportion:*

     $$\text{standardized test statistic} = \frac{\text{statistic} - \text{parameter}}{\text{standard deviation of statistic}}$$

   - Your test statistic will give you a fairly strong indication of the strength of evidence against the null hypothesis, but you should either use one of the tables at the back of the exam or a calculator to convert the test statistic to a p-value.

   CALCULATOR TIPS:

   You can determine the test statistic and p-value using graphing calculators. For example:

   - **TI-84:** STAT → TESTS → 1-PropZTest
   - **TI-Nspire:** Statistics → Stat Tests → 1-Prop *z* Test

   ---

5. **State your conclusion (with appropriate justification based on your p-value and stated significance level) in the context of the research question.**

   You have had lots of practice stating conclusions to hypothesis tests in this chapter. Some things to remember in order to receive full credit for the conclusion component of a hypothesis test on the AP Statistics exam:

   - Your conclusion should always be written in terms of your alternative (research) hypothesis.

     - In the first Buzz and Doris study (he got 15 out of 16 correct), where you rejected the null hypothesis that Buzz's long-run process proportion of pushing the correct button is 0.50, you could conclude

       - *There is sufficient evidence to conclude that in the long run Buzz does better than he would if he was just guessing.*

     - In the second Buzz and Doris study, where you did **not** have enough evidence to reject the null hypothesis (he only got 16 out of 28 correct), you could conclude

       - *There is **not** sufficient evidence to conclude that in the long run Buzz does better than he would if he was just guessing.*

   - You need to state the criteria you used to make your decision. You do this by evaluating the size of the p-value. As we stated earlier (see Section 1.2 for details), if the p-value is less than 0.05, we generally say that is "strong evidence" against the null hypothesis. *Note:* Later in Chapter 2 you'll learn that this value (0.05, and others you could choose) is known as the *significance level* or *α-level*.

> **Definition**
>
> The ***significance level***, often denoted by the Greek letter α ("alpha"), is a value used as a criterion for deciding how small a p-value needs to be to provide convincing evidence to reject the null hypothesis.

For example:

Our p-value of 0.03 is less than our stated significance level, α, of 0.05. There is sufficient evidence to conclude that in the long run Buzz does better than he would if he were just guessing.

Our p-value of 0.16 is greater than our stated significance level, α, of 0.05. There is not sufficient evidence to conclude that in the long run Buzz does better than he would if he were just guessing.

- Your conclusion must always be about the parameter (e.g., long-run process proportion or population proportion) rather than the statistic.
- Your conclusion must always be in context.
- There is <u>always</u> the potential that we made an incorrect decision (more on that in Chapter 2 when we look at Errors and Significance). We can <u>never</u> say that we **proved** our research hypothesis or that we **accept** our null hypothesis as true. A large p-value simply means that the null hypothesis is one plausible explanation for the data—there may be others!

> **AP TIP**
>
> A question requiring a hypothesis test will not typically be phrased as obvious as something like "conduct a hypothesis test." Instead, key phrases to watch for that signal the need to conduct a hypothesis test are statements such as *"Does this provide convincing evidence that...?"* and *"Is there a significant difference...?"*.

1.7 — Halloween Treats Revisited

Example 1.7

1.7.1

EXAMPLE

Inspired by the Halloween treat study described in Example 1.5, a pair of students (Avery & Botts, 2004) conducted their own study of whether trick-or-treaters would be more likely to choose fruit-flavored candy (high in sugar, but not fat) or chocolate candy (high in both sugar and fat). The students gave justification for why they felt the sample they obtained was representative of all trick-or-treaters in their community. Prior to conducting the study, some of the students decided to test whether two-thirds of trick-or-treaters would choose the chocolate candy in the long run.

The students found that 127 of 191 children in the study chose the chocolate candy. Does this provide convincing evidence to suggest that the long-run proportion of trick-or-treaters in this community who would choose the chocolate candy is different from two-thirds?

Let's look at a model solution following the AP Statistics style we discussed in the introduction to this section.

> **THINK ABOUT IT**
>
> What is the parameter of interest? State the hypothesis either in words or using appropriate symbols.

Let the parameter of interest be denoted by π, which represents the probability that a trick-or-treater would choose the chocolate candy. [*Note:* We could just as well define the parameter in terms of the probability of choosing the fruit-flavored candy, as long as we are consistent throughout the analysis.] We want to know whether this long-run proportion differs from two-thirds. On the AP exam you could state the hypotheses either in symbols and/or in words:

$H_0: \pi = 2/3$

$H_a: \pi \neq 2/3$ or in words as

Null hypothesis: In the long run, trick-or-treaters will choose chocolate candy 2/3 of the time.

1.7.2

Alternative hypothesis: In the long run, the probability that a trick-or-treater would choose the chocolate candy differs from 2/3.

> **THINK ABOUT IT**
>
> Identify the theory-based test that will be used to investigate whether the data provide evidence to conclude that the probability of choosing the chocolate candy differs from two-thirds.

We will use a one-proportion *z*-test because we are conducting a test on a single proportion, the proportion of trick-or-treaters that would choose the chocolate candy.

THINK ABOUT IT

What are the validity conditions that need to be met to be able to use this test? Verify the conditions.

Now let's check the validity conditions (from Section 1.6) for a one-proportion z-test.

1. First of all, we need our observations to be representative of the treat-choosing process. This was just one group of trick-or-treaters in one neighborhood and may not be representative of other neighborhoods. [Our analysis will tell us how unusual it is for this many trick-or-treaters to choose the chocolate candy if everyone had a 2/3 chance of choosing the chocolate candy. This model does not account for differences among the trick-or-treaters. You will learn more in Chapter 2 about what population you can reasonably generalize the results from your sample to.]

2. The distribution of sample proportions will be bell-shaped (approximately normal) if the number of successes and failures expected under the null hypothesis are both at least 10 (or $n\pi \geq 10$ and $n(1-\pi) \geq 10$). In our example, the expected number of trick-or-treaters choosing the chocolate candy $n\pi = 191(2/3) \approx 127.33$ and the expected number of trick-or-treaters choosing the fruit-flavored candy $n(1-\pi) = 191(1/3) \approx 63.67$ both exceed 10.

Therefore, a one-proportion z-test is appropriate, with the caveat that we are a bit unsure how representative this sample is of the trick-or-treating process in other locations.

1.7.3

THINK ABOUT IT

Calculate the test statistic (standardized statistic) and corresponding p-value.

By substituting into the appropriate formula, we find the following:
$$\hat{p} = 127/191 \approx 0.6649$$
$$z = \frac{0.6649 - 0.6667}{\sqrt{(2/3)(1/3)/191}} \approx -0.053$$

Note: Answers will vary slightly depending on what decimal representation you use for 2/3 and when you round the z-value, so it's important that it is clear what numbers you are using to find the p-value.

1.7.4

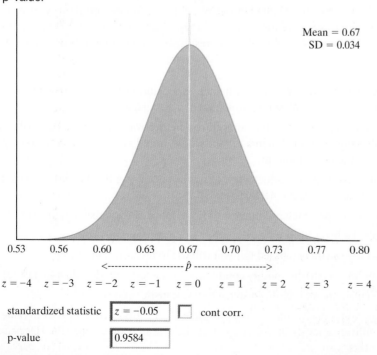

FIGURE 1.26 Output from the Theory-based Inference applet gives us a very large p-value.

With a z-statistic so close to zero, we do not have strong evidence against the null hypothesis. We can also use Table B or a calculator to determine the corresponding p-value. [Figure 1.26 gives the p-value from the **Theory-based Inference** applet.]

> ## THINK ABOUT IT
>
> State your conclusion (with appropriate justification based on your p-value and stated significance level) in the context of the research question.

With such a small test statistic (almost zero) and such a large p-value (0.9584 > 0.05), we do not have sufficient evidence to claim that, in general, the proportion of trick-or-treaters that would prefer chocolate candy to fruit-flavored candy is different from 2/3. In other words, 2/3 appears to be a plausible value for the long-run proportion of times trick-or-treaters will choose the chocolate candy, though we did have some concerns on how generalizable the results were from this sample at one house. It's important also to consider exactly which items were offered to the trick-or-treaters.

1.7.5

> ## AP TIP
>
> Your conclusion for a hypothesis test should include three parts: your decision (we have evidence in favor of the alternative hypothesis or we do not), the criteria you used to make your decision (explicit reference to the test statistic and/or p-value), and context (answer the original research question).

EXPLORATION 1.7 | Retire the Penny?

The *Citizens to Retire the U.S. Penny* group believe that the penny has outlived its usefulness. *New York Times* bestselling author John Green is quoted on their website as saying, "If Abraham Lincoln were alive today, he would say, 'Why is my face on a coin that is worth 1/26 of what a penny was worth when I was president?'" What do you think? Should we abolish the penny?

1. Collect data from your class on whether or not students think we should retain or abolish the penny as the smallest denomination of U.S. currency.

2. Based on your sample result, conjecture whether you think these data will provide convincing evidence that students at your school would vote to abolish the penny more than half the time in the long run.

3. Use the class data to conduct a test of significance using the 0.05 level of significance in a manner that follows the AP Style.

   a. Define the parameter of interest. What symbol can you use to represent this value?

   b. State the hypothesis in words and/or using appropriate symbols.

   c. Identify the theory-based test you will use to test your hypotheses.

   d. State and verify the validity conditions for the test you identified in part (c).

   e. Calculate the standardized statistic (test statistic) and p-value.

   f. State your conclusion (with appropriate justification based on your p-value and stated significance level) in the context of the research question. *Hint*: Decision, criteria, context.

4. Do you have any concerns about how this study was conducted or any advice for how to conduct a similar study in the future?

SECTION 1.7 Summary

In this section we reviewed the work necessary to receive full credit on the AP Statistics examination when a hypothesis test (test of significance) is called for. Specifically, we looked at the validity conditions for a ***one-proportion z-test*** and how to compute a z-statistic (test statistic) and corresponding p-value to measure our strength of evidence against the null hypothesis using a theory-based approach for inference for a single proportion. We saw that all hypothesis tests follow the same basic format:

1. State the hypotheses either in words or using appropriate symbols.
2. Name the test that will be used.
3. State and verify the validity conditions for the test chosen.
4. Calculate the test statistic (standardized statistic) and corresponding p-value.
5. State your conclusion (with appropriate justification based on your p-value and stated significance level) in the context of the research question.

CHAPTER 1 Summary

This chapter has focused on Step 4 of the statistical investigation method: assessing the statistical significance of an observed result against some claim about the long-run proportion of successes. This reasoning will stay the same as we consider other statistics (e.g., sample mean, difference in sample proportions) and other parameters (e.g., a difference in long-run probabilities) in other chapters. The basic approach is the 3S strategy: Decide on an appropriate statistic, simulate values of that statistic under the assumption that the null hypothesis is true, and then assess the strength of evidence against the null hypothesis and in favor of the alternative hypothesis. Keep in mind that the null and alternative hypotheses are competing claims about the parameter value. We expect the observed sample statistic to differ from the parameter by chance. The goal is to see whether the difference observed in the study is larger than can be reasonably expected by chance alone. This unusualness (deciding whether the observed result in the tail of the null distribution) can be measured through the standardized statistic (e.g., ***z-statistic***), which measures the distance between the observed statistic and the hypothesized parameter value in terms of number of standard deviations away, and/or the p-value, which measures how often a statistic at least as extreme would occur when the null hypothesis is true.

In the case of one categorical variable, when the sample size is large (e.g., at least 10 success and at least 10 failures in the sample or at least 10 expected successes and at least 10 expected failures), then we can approximate the p-value using the normal distribution. This theory-based approach is referred to as a one proportion z-test.

You also considered factors that affect the strength of evidence against the null hypothesis:

- How far the observed sample statistic is from the hypothesized parameter value
- Sample size
- One-sided vs. two-sided alternatives.

The relationships you learned in this chapter will also apply in other scenarios as well.

CHAPTER 1
GLOSSARY

3S strategy A framework for evaluating the strength of evidence against the chance model (null hypothesis). The 3S's are statistic, simulate, and strength of evidence.

alternative hypothesis The *not by chance* or *there is an effect* explanation, it is typically our research conjecture.

bar graph A graphical display of the distribution of a categorical variable.

binary variable Categorical variable with only two outcomes.

central limit theorem A mathematical prediction of the behavior of the null distribution when certain validity conditions are met.

chance models A real or computerized process to generate data according to a well-understood set of conditions.

expected number of failures How many failures we expect to occur for a given sample size and can be calculated by multiplying the sample size by one minus the probability of success (that is, $n(1 - \pi)$).

expected number of successes How many successes we expect to occur for a given sample size and can be calculated by multiplying the sample size by the probability of success (that is, $n\pi$).

model A mathematical or probabilistic conceptualization meant to closely match reality but always making assumptions about the reality which may or may not be true.

n A symbol used to indicate the sample size.

normally distributed How the null distribution is described when it takes the shape of a bell.

null distribution Distribution of simulated statistics that represent what could have happened in the study assuming the null hypothesis was true.

null hypothesis The *by chance alone* or *no effect* explanation; a hypothesis that can be modeled by simulation.

one-proportion z-test The theory-based approach for inference for a single proportion.

parameter For a random process a parameter is a long-run numerical property of the process.

pi (π) The Greek letter for *p*, which is pronounced "pie" and is used to represent a parameter that is a probability.

p-hat (p̂) The proportion of observational units that have a particular characteristic based on a measured variable; a statistic.

plausible A term used to indicate that the chance model is a reasonable/believable explanation for the data we observed.

p-value The probability of obtaining a value of the statistic at least as extreme as the observed statistic when the null hypothesis is true.

sample The set of observed values.

sample size The number of observational units in the sample.

sampling distribution of a sample proportion The theoretical distribution of sample proportions from all possible sample of the same size, *n*, from a long-run process (or population) with a population proportion of success of π.

significance level The value used as a criterion for deciding how small a p-value needs to be to provide convincing evidence to reject the null hypothesis.

standardize To standardize an observation, compute the distance of the observation from the mean and divide by the standard deviation of the distribution.

statistic A number computed from the sample.

statistically significant Unlikely to occur just by random chance.

strength How much evidence we have against the null hypothesis.

subjects Study participants that are human.

test of significance A procedure for measuring the strength of evidence against a null hypothesis about the parameter of interest.

theory-based approach Mathematical approach which predicts the shape, center, and variability of the null distribution instead of obtaining a null distribution by simulating.

two-sided test Estimates the p-value by considering results that are at least as extreme as our observed result *in either direction*.

validity conditions Check to see that certain conditions are met that render the theory-based approach valid. Often these conditions deal with sample size and shape and variability of null distributions.

z-statistic Synonymous with standardized sample proportion, also called the standardized statistic.

CHAPTER 1
EXERCISES

SECTION 1.1

Spinning tennis racquet*

Tennis players often spin a racquet to decide who serves first. The spun racquet can land with the manufacturer's label facing up or down. A reasonable question to investigate is whether a spun tennis racquet is equally likely to land with the label facing up or down. (If the spun racquet is equally likely to land with the label facing in either direction, we say that the spinning process is fair.) Suppose that you gather data by spinning your tennis racquet 100 times, each time recording whether it lands with the label facing up or down.

1.1.1

a. Describe the relevant long-run proportion of interest in words.

b. What statistical term is given to the long-run proportion you described in (a)?

c. What value does the chance model assert for the long-run proportion?

d. Suppose that the spun racquet lands with the label facing up 48 times out of 100. Explain, as if to a friend who has not studied statistics, why this result does *not* constitute strong evidence against believing that the spinning process is fair.

e. Is the result in (d) statistically significant evidence that spinning is not fair or is it plausible that the spinning process is fair?

1.1.2

a. Suppose that the spun racquet lands with the label facing up 24 times out of 100. Explain, as if to a friend who has not studied statistics, why this result *does* constitute strong evidence against believing that the spinning process is fair.

b. Is the result in (a) statistically significant evidence that spinning is not fair or is it plausible that the spinning process is fair?

1.1.3 To conduct a simulation analysis of this racquet-spinning study for either **1.1.1** or **1.1.2**, you could flip a coin _____ times and repeat that process _____ times.

A. 100, 1,000

B. 1,000, 100

C. 100, 1

D. 1, 1,000

1.1.4 Which of the following is the most important reason that a simulation analysis would repeat the coin-flipping process many times?

A. To see whether the distribution of sample proportions follows a normal, bell-shaped curve

B. To see whether the distribution of sample proportions is centered at 0.50

C. To see how much variability results in the distribution of sample proportions

Shooting percentage

1.1.5 LeBron James of the Miami Heat hit 765 of his 1354 field goal attempts in the 2012/2013 season for a shooting percentage of 56.5%. Over the lifetime of LeBron's career, can we say he is more likely than not to make a field goal?

a. Describe the parameter of interest.

b. Is 56.5% a parameter or a statistic?

c. What value would the chance model assign to the parameter from (a)?

d. Describe how you would use coin flipping to simulate the 2012/2013 season under the assumption of the chance model.

e. What would be a typical value from a repetition of 1,354 coin flips? Justify your answer.

1.1.6 Dwyane Wade of the Miami Heat hit 569 of his 1,093 field goal attempts in the 2012/2013 season for a shooting percentage of 52.1%. Over the lifetime of Dwyane's career, can we say that Dwyane is more likely than not to make a field goal?

a. Is the long-run proportion of Dwyane making a field goal a parameter or a statistic?

b. Is 52.1% a parameter or a statistic?

c. When simulating possible outcomes assuming the chance model, how many times would you flip a coin for one repetition of the 2012/2013 season?

d. With each repetition, what would you keep track of?

e. What would be a typical value from a repetition of 1093 coin flips? Justify your answer.

1.1.7 If Dwyane Wade of the Miami Heat hits 52 out of his first 100 field goals in the 2013/2014 season, let's see how we might investigate if he is more likely than not to make a field goal?

a. Based on these first 100 field goals, we want to find out what Dwyane's long-run proportion of making a field goal is. Will this value be a statistic or a parameter?

b. Is 52 out of 100 a statistic or a parameter?

c. We can use the **One Proportion** applet to generate 1,000 possible values of Dwyane's last 100 field goals under the chance model that he has a long-run proportion of 50% of making a field goal. Match the aspects of the simulation in **Column A** to their equivalent aspects in the actual study listed in **Column B**.

Column A	Column B
Coin flip	Dwyane misses his field goal
Heads	Long-run proportion of field goals Dwyane makes
Tails	One set of 100 field goal shots by Dwyane
Chance of heads	Dwyane shoots a field goal
One repetition	Dwyane makes his field goal

Minesweeper*

1.1.8 One of the authors sometimes likes to play Minesweeper, and of the last 20 times she played Minesweeper, she won 12 times. That is, she won 60% of the games.

a. Based on these 20 games, we would like to learn about her long-run proportion of winning at Minesweeper. Is this value a parameter or a statistic?

b. Is 60% (12 wins in last 20 games) a parameter or a statistic?

To find out whether her performance on the last 20 games provides convincing evidence that her long-run proportion of winning at Minesweeper is higher than 50%, she used the **One Proportion** applet to generate 100 possible values of what her number of wins could have been if her long-run proportion of winning was *equal to 50%*.

c. In the table below, match the aspects of the simulation performed by the applet as listed in **Column A** to their equivalent aspects in the actual study as listed in **Column B**.

Column A	Column B
Coin flip	Author wins a game
Heads	Long-run proportion of games that the author wins
Tails	One set of 20 Minesweeper games played by author
Chance of heads	Author loses a game
One repetition	Author plays a game of Minesweeper

1.1.9 The dotplot generated below by the **One Proportion** applet assumed the long-run proportion of winning was equal to 50%. Use this dotplot to answer the following questions.

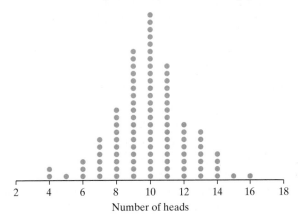

Number of heads

a. How many dots are in the dotplot? (*Hint:* You should reason it out and *not* count the number of dots.)

b. What does each dot represent in terms of Minesweeper games and wins?

c. At what number is the dotplot centered? Could you have anticipated that? Why or why not?

d. Based on 12 wins on the last 20 games and the above dotplot, are you convinced that the author's long-run proportion of winning at Minesweeper is higher than 50%? Explain how you are deciding.

e. Does this analysis prove that the author's long-run proportion of winning at Minesweeper is 50%?

f. Suppose that it so happened that when the author played the last 20 games, she was also watching her favorite TV show. Does this information change your conclusion in part (d)? If yes, how and why? If not, why not?

Buttered toast

1.1.10 If you drop a piece of buttered toast on the floor, is it just as likely to land buttered side up as buttered side down? It sure seems like mine always lands buttered side down! Suppose that 7 of the last 10 times I dropped toast it landed buttered side down. In order to carry out a statistical analysis, the **One Proportion** applet was used to see if my toast fell buttered side down a majority (more than 50%) of the time. Use the dotplot generated by the applet to answer the following questions.

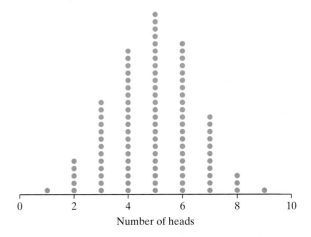

Number of heads

a. How many dots are in the dotplot?

b. What does each dot represent in terms of dropped toast and buttered side down?

c. At what number is the dotplot centered? Could you have determined that before running the applet simulation? Why or why not?

d. Based on 7 of the last 10 slices of toast landing buttered side down and the above dotplot, are you convinced that the long-run proportion of times my toast lands buttered side down is greater than 50%? Explain how you are deciding.

e. Does this prove that my long-run proportion of dropping toast buttered side down is 50%?

Mark's tennis game*

1.1.11 Mark is practicing his tennis serves. He wants to be able to tell newspaper reporters the long-run proportion of getting his first serve in. Mark gets 17 of his first 20 serves in.

a. Is 17 out of 20 = 85% a statistic or a parameter?

b. Is the long-run proportion of Mark's first serve being in a statistic or a parameter?

c. Do you think that 17 out of 20 serves in is a *possible* outcome if Mark is just as likely to get his first serve in as to not get his first serve in?

d. Do you think that 17 out of 20 serves in is a *plausible* outcome if Mark is just as likely to get his first serve in as not to get his first serve in?

Lady tasting tea

A famous (in statistical circles) study involves a woman who claimed to be able to tell whether tea or milk was poured first into a cup. She was presented with eight cups containing a mixture of tea and milk, and she correctly identified which had been poured first for all eight cups.

1.1.12

a. Identify the observational units and variable in this study.

b. Identify the parameter for this study. (*Hint:* The long-run proportion that…)

c. Identify the sample size. Also, identify the observed value of the statistic for this study.

d. Is it *possible* that the woman could get all eight correct if she were randomly guessing with each cup?

e. Is it *unlikely* that the woman could get all eight correct if she were randomly guessing with each cup? (Answer for now based on your intuition, without doing any analysis.)

1.1.13

a. Describe how you can use a coin to address the question "Is it *unlikely* that the woman could get all eight correct if she were randomly guessing with each cup?" Be sure to include details such as how many times you would toss the coin and why; what would "heads" and "tails" stand for; what you would record after each set of coin tosses; how many times you would repeat this process. Also, how is this repeated coin tossing going to help you address the question?

b. Now use an applet simulation to address the question "Is it *unlikely* that the woman could get all eight correct if she were randomly guessing with each cup?" Then explain how your answer follows from your simulation results.

c. Based on your simulation analysis, would you conclude that the woman's result produces strong evidence that she is not guessing as to whether milk or tea was poured first? Also explain the reasoning process behind your answer.

d. Is your result in (c) statistically significant or is it plausible she is just guessing?

1.1.14

Suppose that I try to discern whether tea or milk is poured first for 8 cups and make the correct identification 5 times.

a. I say: "5 out of 8 is more than half, so one must conclude that I'm doing better than random guessing." How would you respond? Use simulation results in your response.

b. With regards to my study on 8 cups of tea and milk, does this prove that I cannot tell whether milk or tea is placed in the cup first? Why or why not?

c. Now suppose that someone gets 14 correct out of 16 cups. Conduct a new simulation analysis to assess whether this result provides strong evidence that the person actually has ability better than random guessing to distinguish which was poured first. Be sure to describe which of the applet inputs needs to change and why. Also summarize your conclusion and explain your justification.

Zwerg*

An Austrian study was completed to determine if untrained sea lions and sea lionesses could follow various experimenter-given cues when given a choice of two objects. One experimenter-given cue was to point at one of the objects. One sea lioness, named Zwerg, successfully chose the pointed-at object 37 times out of 48 trials. Does this result show that Zwerg can correctly follow this type of direction by an experimenter more than 50% of the time?

1.1.15

a. What is the parameter of interest for this study? (*Hint:* The long-run proportion that…)

b. What are two possible explanations for Zwerg's results of choosing the correct object 37 out of 48 times?

c. Which explanation of the two suggested in part (b) do you think is the more plausible, based on Zwerg's results? Explain. *Note:* Provide an explanation based only on your intuition.

d. If Zwerg is just randomly choosing between the objects, what is the chance that she will choose the correct object?

1.1.16

In order to discern whether Zwerg is doing better than just guessing (50% correct), we will employ the 3S strategy:

a. *Statistic:* How many times did Zwerg pick the correct object? Out of how many attempts?

b. *Simulate:* Using an applet, simulate 1,000 repetitions of having Zwerg choose between the two objects if she is doing so randomly.

c. Based on the value of the statistic from part (a), do you think the chance model is wrong? Why or why not?

d. *Strength of evidence:* Based on your answers for (a)–(c), state your conclusions about the research question of whether the data provide convincing evidence that Zwerg can correctly follow this type of direction by an experimenter more than 50% of the time?

e. Are the results of this study statistically significant or is the chance model plausible? How are you deciding?

1.1.17

In a related study, another experimenter-given cue was to place a marker in front of the correct object. Zwerg successfully chose the object with the marker 26 out of 48 times. Does this result show that Zwerg can correctly follow this type of direction by an experimenter more than 50% of the time?

a. What are two possible explanations for Zwerg's results of choosing the correct object 26 out of 48 times?

b. Which explanation of the two suggested in part (a) do you think is the more plausible, based on Zwerg's results? Explain based on your intuition.

c. If Zwerg is just randomly choosing between the objects, what is the chance that she will choose the correct object?

1.1.18 Refer to the data in the previous question where Zwerg successfully chose the object with the marker 26 out of 48 times. In order to discern whether Zwerg is doing better than just guessing (50% correct) we will employ the 3S strategy:

a. *Statistic:* How many times did Zwerg pick the correct object? Out of how many attempts?

b. *Simulate:* Using an applet, simulate 1,000 repetitions of having Zwerg choose between the two objects if she is doing so randomly. Where is the distribution centered?

c. Based on the value of the statistic from part (a), do you think the chance model is wrong? Why or why not?

d. *Strength of evidence:* Based on your answers for (a)–(c), state your conclusions about the research question of whether the data provide convincing evidence that Zwerg can correctly follow this type of direction by an experimenter more than 50% of the time?

e. Are the results of this study statistically significant or is the chance model plausible? How are you deciding?

f. Compare Zwerg's performance in this study to that mentioned in Exercise 1.1.15. Do the results of this study provide more, less, or equally convincing evidence that Zwerg can correctly follow this type of direction by an experimenter more than 50% of the time, compared to the study results in Exercise 1.1.15? Could you have anticipated this? Explain.

g. Does this prove that Zwerg is just guessing when the marker is used to indicate the correct object? Why or why not?

Janine's volleyball game

Janine is an ambidextrous volleyball player. She is practicing "short serves" in volleyball because her team has an upcoming match against an opponent who does not pass short serves very well. Janine must land a majority of her "short serves" in bounds or her coach will not let her use her short serve in the upcoming match. When serving left-handed Janine makes 23 out of 30 serves.

1.1.19

a. What is the parameter in this scenario? (*Hint:* The long-run proportion that …)

b. What are two possible explanations for Janine getting 23 out of 30 left-handed short serves in bounds?

c. Which of the two explanations from part (b) do you think is more plausible? No need to perform an analysis yet; explain your answer using only your intuition.

d. If Janine is just as likely to serve in as she is to not serve in, what is the chance she will serve in?

1.1.20 In order to discern whether or not Janine can land a majority of her short serves in bounds, we will employ the 3S strategy.

a. *Statistic:* How many times did Janine land a short serve in bounds? Out of how many service attempts?

b. *Simulate:* Using an applet, simulate 1,000 repetitions of having Janine serve 30 right-handed short serves if she is just as likely to serve in as she is to not serve in. Where is the distribution centered?

c. Based on the value of the statistic from part (a), do you think the chance model is wrong? Why or why not?

d. *Strength of evidence:* Based on your answers for (a)–(c), state your conclusions about the research question of whether the data provide convincing evidence that Janine can get her short serve in with her left hand more than 50% of the time.

e. Are the results of this study statistically significant or is the chance model plausible? How are you deciding?

1.1.21 Janine serves 30 short serves with her right hand and gets 17 of the 30 in the court.

a. What are two possible explanations for Janine getting 17 out of 30 right-handed short serves in?

b. Which of the two explanations in part (a) do you think is more plausible? No need to perform an analysis yet; explain your answer using only your intuition.

c. If Janine is just as likely to serve in as not, what is the chance she will serve in?

1.1.22 Use the data where Janine serves 17 out of 30 right-handed short serves into the court. In order to discern whether or not Janine can serve a majority of her short serves in, we will employ the 3S strategy.

a. *Statistic:* How many times did Janine get a short serve in? Out of how many service attempts?

b. *Simulate:* Using an applet, simulate 1,000 repetitions of having Janine serve 30 right-handed short serves if she is just as likely to serve in as she is to not serve in.

c. Based on the value of the statistic from part (a), do you think the chance model is wrong? Why or why not?

d. *Strength of evidence:* Based on your answers for (a)–(c), state your conclusions about the research question of whether the data provide convincing evidence that Janine can get her short serve in with her right hand more than 50% of the time?

e. Are the results of this study statistically significant or is the chance model plausible? How are you deciding?

f. Does this mean that Janine can serve a short serve in with her right hand 50% of the time? Explain.

Jerry's tennis game*

Jerry is a tennis player. He is working on a really tough first serve. While practicing his new tough serve, he gets 12 out of 20, or 60%, of his serves in. Jerry wants to know if his long-run proportion of getting his first serve in is greater than 50%.

1.1.23 What values would you enter into the **One Proportion** applet to run an analysis for Jerry?

a. Probability of heads _____

b. Number of tosses _____

c. Number of repetitions _____

d. Use the applet to conduct the simulation study. If Jerry's long-run proportion of getting his new first serve in is truly 50%, is 12 out of 20 a likely value? Is it unlikely? How are you deciding?

1.1.24 Suppose Jerry continues to serve and gets 60 out of 100 serves in. Use the **One Proportion** applet again to test if Jerry's long-run proportion of getting his first serve in is greater than 50%. State the values you would enter into the applet.

a. Probability of heads _____

b. Number of tosses _____

c. Number of repetitions _____

d. If Jerry's long-run proportion of getting his new first serve in is truly 50%, is 60 out of 100 a likely value? Is it unlikely? How are you deciding?

e. Why do you suppose that you found different results in part (d) to this question as compared to part (d) of the previous question even though the sample statistic was 60% in both problems?

1.1.25 If an observed statistic from a study turns out to be a likely value under the chance model, then:

a. We can say we have evidence against the chance model.

b. We can say that the chance model is plausible.

c. We can say that the chance model is true.

d. We can't say anything about the chance model, because it isn't real data.

FAQ

1.1.26 Read FAQ 1.1.1 that describes a random process and answer the following questions.

a. Buzz's section on which button to push can be thought of as a random process as long as we make what two assumptions?

b. What is the parameter of interest in the Buzz and Doris story?

SECTION 1.2

1.2.1* After you conduct a coin-flipping simulation, a graph of the _____ will be centered very close to 0.50. Choose from (A)–(D).

A. Process probability

B. Sample size

C. Number of heads

D. Proportion of heads

1.2.2 The graph of a null distribution will be centered approximately on:

A. The observed proportion

B. The observed count

C. The value of the probability in the null hypothesis

D. The number of repetitions performed

1.2.3* The p-value of a test of significance is:

A. The probability, assuming the null hypothesis is true, that we would get a result at least as extreme as the one that was actually observed

B. The probability, assuming the alternative hypothesis is true, that we would get a result at least as extreme as the one that was actually observed

C. The probability the null hypothesis is true

D. The probability the alternative hypothesis is true

1.2.4 Suppose a researcher is testing to see if a basketball player can make free throws at a rate higher than the NBA average of 75%. The player is tested by shooting 10 free throws and makes 8 of them. In conducting the related test of significance we have a computer applet do an appropriate simulation, with 1,000 repetitions, and produce a null distribution. This distribution represents:

A. Repeated results if the player makes 80% of his shots in the long run

B. Repeated results if the player makes 75% of his shots in the long run

C. Repeated results if the player makes more than 75% of his shots in the long run

D. Repeated results if the player makes more than 80% of his shots in the long run

1.2.5* The simulation (flipping coins or using the applet) done to develop the distribution we use to find our p-values assumes which hypothesis is true?

A. Null hypothesis

B. Alternative hypothesis

C. Both hypotheses

D. Neither hypothesis

1.2.6 When using the coin-flipping chance model, the most important reason you repeat a simulation of the study many times is:

A. To see whether the null distribution follows a symmetric, bell-shaped curve

B. To see whether the null distribution is centered at 0.50

C. To see whether your coin is really fair

D. To see how much variability there is in the null distribution

1.2.7* When we get a p-value that is very large, we may conclude that:

A. The null hypothesis has been proven to be true.

B. There is strong evidence for the alternative hypothesis.

C. The null hypothesis is plausible.

D. The alternative hypothesis has been proven to be false.

1.2.8 When we get a p-value that is very small, we may conclude that:

A. The null hypothesis has been proven to be true.

B. There is strong evidence for the alternative hypothesis.

C. The null hypothesis is plausible.

D. The alternative hypothesis has been proven to be false.

1.2.9* Suppose you are testing the hypotheses $H_0: \pi = 0.25$ and $H_a: \pi < 0.25$ and the observed statistic, $\hat{p}$ is equal to 0.30 with a sample size of 100.

a. If you are using a proportion as your statistic, where do you expect your null distribution to be centered?

b. If you are using a count as your statistic, where do you expect your null distribution to be centered?

1.2.10 Explain the meaning of each of the following symbols.

a. H_0

b. H_a

c. $\hat{p}$

d. π

e. n

1.2.11* What is the difference between $\hat{p}$ and the p-value?

Sarah the chimpanzee

1.2.12 A chimpanzee named Sarah was the subject in a study of whether chimpanzees can solve problems. Sarah was shown 30-second videos of a human actor struggling with one of several problems (for example, not able to reach bananas hanging from the ceiling). Then Sarah was shown two photographs, one that depicted a solution to the problem (like stepping onto a box) and one that did not match that scenario. Researchers watched Sarah select one of the photos, and they kept track of whether Sarah chose the correct photo depicting a solution to the problem. Sarah chose the correct photo in seven of eight scenarios that she was presented.

We want to run a test of significance to determine whether Sarah understands how to solve problems and will

thus pick the photo of the correct solution more often than what would be done by random chance.

a. Describe the parameter of interest in the context of this study and assign a symbol to denote it.

b. What is the observed value of the statistic in this case?

c. Write out the null and alternative hypotheses for this first in words and then in symbols.

d. We conducted a test of significance using the **One Proportion** applet and got the following null distribution for the "number of heads." (*Note*: this null distribution uses only 100 simulated samples and not the usual 1,000 or more.) Based on the null distribution, what is the p-value for the test? How did you calculate it?

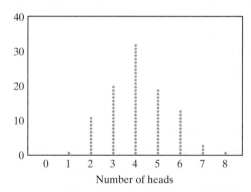

Probability of heads: 0.5
Number of tosses: 8
Number of repetitions: 100
☐ Animate
Toss Coins
Total = 100

e. Based on your p-value, do you have strong evidence that Sarah understands how to solve problems similar to those she was presented? How are you deciding? Justify.

f. Complete this sentence describing what the p-value means: If Sarah doesn't understand how to solve problems and is just guessing at which picture to select, the probability she would …

g. What does a single dot in the null distribution represent in terms of Sarah and the photos?

Hope the dog*

1.2.13 Suppose you are testing to see if your dog, Hope, understands pointing towards an object. You put Hope through 20 trials and 12 times (or 60%) she goes to the correct object when given a choice between two objects. You then conduct a test of significance and generate the following 100 simulations using an applet.

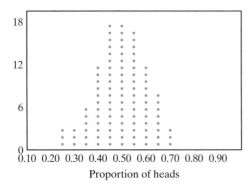

Probability of heads: 0.5

Number of tosses: 20

Number of repetitions: 100

☑ Animate

Toss Coins

Total = 100

a. Write out the null and alternative hypotheses for this study in words.

b. If we let π be the long-run proportion of times Hope will go to the correct object, write out the null and alternative hypotheses for this study in symbols.

c. Based on the null distribution shown, what is the p-value for your test?

d. Based on your p-value, do you have strong evidence that Hope understands pointing?

e. Using the null distribution shown, what is the smallest proportion of times Hope could go toward the correct object so that you would have strong evidence that she understands pointing toward an object?

f. Which of the following best describes what a single dot represents in the null distribution shown?

i. One possible value of the proportion of times Hope goes to the correct object out of 20 if she goes to the correct object 50% of the time in the long run

ii. One possible value of the proportion of times Hope goes to the correct object out of 20 if she goes to the correct object **more than** 50% of the time in the long run

1.2.14 Suppose two researchers are conducting studies about animal behavior, and they both have the same null hypothesis and the same alternative hypothesis as each other. Also, suppose that Researcher A's study results produce a p-value of 0.034, whereas Researcher B's study results produce a p-value of 0.055. Which researcher has found stronger evidence against the null hypothesis and for the alternative hypothesis? Explain how you know.

1.2.15 Suppose you determine that in order to evaluate some data you need to conduct a simulation analysis.

a. In your own words explain how to conduct a simulation using a six-sided die where the sample size is 20 and the null hypothesis probability is 1/6. Be specific.

b. Referring to part (a), explain how you would conduct the simulation using a regular deck of playing cards. Be specific.

c. How would your answer to (a) change if the sample size was 30?

d. How would your answer to (b) change if the sample size was 30?

e. How would your answer to (a) change if the null hypothesis probability is 2/3?

f. How would your answer to (b) change if the null hypothesis probability is 2/3?

Love, first

A recent study (Ackerman, Griskevicius, and Li, 2011) examined expressions of commitment between two partners in a committed romantic relationship. One aspect of the study involved 47 heterosexual couples who are part of an online pool of people willing to participate in surveys. These 47 couples were asked about which person was the first to say "I love you." For 7 of those couples, the two people disagreed about the answer to this question. But both people agreed for the other 40 couples, so those 40 responses were included in the analysis. Previous studies have suggested that males tend to say "I love you" first.

1.2.16

a. Identify the observational units and variable in this study. Also classify the variable as categorical or quantitative.

b. State the appropriate null and alternative hypotheses (in words) for testing whether males are more likely to say "I love you" first.

We can express these hypotheses with symbols as:

Null: $\pi = 0.50$	Alternative: $\pi > 0.50$

c. Describe (in words) what the symbol π stands for here.

It turned out that for 28 of the 40 couples in the sample (after the 7 couples who could not agree were excluded), the man said "I love you" before the woman did.

d. Determine the sample proportion (written as a decimal) of couples for whom the man was the first to say "I love you." What symbol do we use to denote this proportion?

e. Describe how you could use a coin-flipping model to find the p-value for these data.

f. Use an applet to conduct a simulation analysis to assess the strength of evidence against the null hypothesis provided by the sample data. Report the values that you enter into the applet and describe how you approximate the p-value. Also report the value of this (approximate) p-value.

g. Write a sentence or two interpreting this p-value: the probability of _____, assuming _____.

h. Summarize your conclusion from this p-value.

1.2.17 The researchers also interviewed 96 university students that had been or were currently involved in a romantic heterosexual relationship where at least one person said "I love you." The students were asked, "Think about your last or current romantic relationship in which someone confessed their love. In this relationship, who admitted love first?"

a. Identify the observational units and variable in this study. Also classify the variable as categorical or quantitative.

b. State the appropriate null and alternative hypotheses (in words) for testing whether males are more likely to say "I love you" first.

It turned out that for 59 of the 96 responses, the man said "I love you" before the woman did.

c. Determine the sample proportion (written as a decimal) of couples for whom the man was the first to say "I love you." What symbol do we use to denote this proportion?

d. Describe how you could use a coin-flipping model to find the p-value for these data.

e. Use an applet to conduct a simulation analysis to assess the strength of evidence against the null hypothesis provided by the sample data. Report the values that you enter into the applet and describe how you approximate the p-value. Also report the value of this (approximate) p-value.

f. Write a sentence or two interpreting this p-value: the probability of _____, assuming _____.

g. Summarize your conclusion from this p-value.

Rhesus monkeys*

A recent article (Hauser, Glynn, and Wood, 2007) described a study that investigated whether rhesus monkeys have some ability to understand gestures made by humans. In one part of the study, the experimenter approached individual rhesus monkeys and placed two boxes an equal distance from the monkey. The experimenter then placed food in one of the boxes, making sure that the monkey could tell that one of the boxes received food without revealing which one. Finally, the researcher made eye contact with the monkey and then gestured toward the box with the food by jerking his head toward that box. This process was repeated for a total of 40 rhesus monkeys. It turned out that 30 of the monkeys approached the box that the human had gestured toward, and 10 approached the other box. The purpose is to investigate whether rhesus monkeys can interpret the head jerk better than random chance.

1.2.18

a. Identify the observational units and variable in this study. Also classify the variable as categorical or quantitative.

b. Describe in words the parameter of interest for this study and assign a symbol to it.

c. Determine the sample proportion of monkeys who picked the box towards which the human had gestured. Is this value a parameter or a statistic? What is the symbol you should use to denote this proportion?

d. State the appropriate null and alternative hypotheses in the context of this study, first in words and then in symbols.

e. Describe how you could use a coin to conduct a simulation analysis of this study and its result. Give sufficient detail that someone else could implement this simulation analysis based on your description. Be sure to indicate how you would decide whether the observed data provide convincing evidence that rhesus monkeys can interpret human gestures better than random chance.

f. Use an applet to conduct a simulation analysis with at least 1,000 repetitions. Based on the null distribution produced by the applet, explain how you are deciding whether the observed data provide convincing evidence that rhesus monkeys can read human gestures better than random chance. Summarize the conclusion that you would draw about the research question of whether rhesus monkeys have some ability to understand gestures made by humans.

1.2.19 In one part of the study, the experimenter approached individual rhesus monkeys and placed two boxes an equal distance from the monkey. The experimenter then placed food in one of the boxes, making sure that the monkey could tell that one of the boxes received food without revealing which one. Finally, the researcher pointed and looked toward the box that contained the food. This process was repeated for a total of 40 rhesus monkeys. It turned out that 31 of the monkeys approached the box that the human had gestured toward, and 9 approached the other box. The purpose is to investigate whether rhesus monkeys can interpret human gestures better than random chance.

a. Identify the observational units and variable in this study. Also classify the variable as categorical or quantitative.

b. Describe in words the parameter of interest for this study and assign a symbol to it.

c. Determine the sample proportion of monkeys who picked the box towards which the human had gestured. Is this value a parameter or a statistic? What is the symbol you should use to denote this proportion?

d. State the appropriate null and alternative hypotheses in the context of this study, first in words and then in symbols.

e. Describe how you could use a coin to conduct a simulation analysis of this study and its result. Give sufficient detail that someone else could implement this simulation analysis based on your description. Be sure to indicate how you would decide whether the observed data provide convincing evidence that rhesus monkeys can interpret human gestures better than random chance.

f. Use an applet to conduct a simulation analysis with at least 1,000 repetitions. Based on the null distribution produced by the applet, explain how you are deciding whether the observed data provide convincing evidence that rhesus monkeys can read human gestures better than random chance. Summarize the conclusion that you would draw about the research question of whether rhesus monkeys have some ability to understand gestures made by humans.

Minesweeper*

1.2.20 Recall that one of the authors liked to play the game Minesweeper (Exercise 1.1.8) and she won 12 of the last 20 games she played. Now that you know how to calculate p-values, use an applet to find the p-value to investigate whether her results provide convincing evidence that her long-run proportion of winning at Minesweeper is higher than 0.50. Report the p-value and use the p-value to state a conclusion about the strength of evidence.

Spider Solitaire

1.2.21 While the author in the previous question likes to play Minesweeper, another author likes to play Spider Solitaire on the computer. In his last 40 games, he won 24 of them. Use an applet to find the p-value to investigate whether his results provide convincing evidence that his long-run proportion of winning at Spider Solitaire is higher than 0.50. Report the p-value and use the p-value to state a conclusion about the strength of evidence.

Spinning a coin*

1.2.22 It has been stated that spinning a coin on a table will result in it landing heads side up fewer than 50% of the time in the long run. One of the authors tested this by spinning a penny 50 times on a table and it landed heads side up 21 times. A test of significance was then conducted with the following hypotheses.

$$H_0: \pi = 0.50 \qquad H_a: \pi < 0.50$$

a. Describe what the symbol π stands for in this context.

b. Use an applet to conduct a simulation with at least 1,000 repetitions. What is your p-value? Based on your p-value is there strong evidence that the probability the spun coin will land heads up is less than 0.50?

c. Suppose you focused on the proportion of times the coin landed tails up instead of heads up. How would your hypotheses be different? What would you do differently to calculate your p-value?

Flipping a coin

1.2.23 According to Stanford mathematics and statistics professor Persi Diaconis, the probability a flipped coin that starts out heads up will also land heads up is 0.51. Suppose you want to test this. More specifically, you want to test to determine if the probability that a coin that starts out heads up will also land heads up is more than 0.50. Suppose you flip a coin (that starts out heads up) 100 times and find that it lands heads up 53 of those times.

a. If π stands for the probability a coin that starts heads up will also land heads up, write out the hypotheses for this study in symbols.

b. Use an applet to conduct a simulation with at least 1,000 repetitions. What is your p-value? Based on your p-value, is there strong evidence that the probability that a coin that starts heads up will also land heads up is more than 0.50?

c. Even though the coin in the study landed heads up more than 50% of the time, you should not have found strong evidence that it will land heads up more than 50% of the time in the long run. Does this mean that Diaconis is wrong about his assertion that it will land heads up 51% of the time in the long run? Explain.

d. A newspaper article described the 0.51 probability by saying, "This means that if a coin is flipped with its heads side facing up, it will land the same way 51 out of 100 times." What is wrong with this statement?

Free throws*

1.2.24 Suppose your friend says he can shoot free throws as well as someone in the NBA and you don't think he is that good. You know that the NBA average for shooting free throws is 75% and decide to test your friend. You have him shoot 20 free throws and he makes 12 of them. Based on this, do you have strong evidence that he is worse than the average NBA player? Answer this by conducting a simulation and reporting your p-value.

1.2.25 Suppose you retest your friend from the previous question to see if he is a worse free throw shooter than the NBA average of 75%. He shoots 20 more free throws and again makes 12 of them. You combine the data from the two tests together so he made 24 of his 40 attempts. Based on this, do you have strong evidence that he is worse than the average NBA player? Answer this by conducting a simulation and reporting your p-value.

FAQ

1.2.26 Read FAQ 1.2.1 that describes why we need to include "or more extreme" when computing a p-value and, in your own words, describe why we don't just compute the p-value based on the probability of a single outcome, but also include outcomes that are more extreme in that probability.

1.2.27 Read FAQ 1.2.2 that explores how small a p-value needs to be in order for us to have strong evidence against the null hypothesis and answer the following questions.

a. What does Persi Diaconis claim to be able to do?

b. How many heads does Diaconis have to flip in a row in order for the probability of such an outcome to drop below 0.05? Is that the number you would pick for a point where you would start to become convinced that he could flip a coin and get heads every time?

SECTION 1.3

1.3.1* Which standardized statistic (standardized sample proportion) gives you the strongest evidence against the null hypothesis?

A. $z = 1$

B. $z = 0$

C. $z = -3$

D. $z = 1.80$

1.3.2 Consider the output given below that was obtained using the **One Proportion** applet. Use information from the output to find the standardized statistic for a sample proportion value of 0.45.

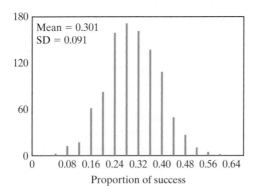

Probability of success (π): 0.30

Sample size (n): 25

Number of samples: 1000

☐ Animate

Draw Samples

Total = 1000

Mean = 0.301
SD = 0.091

Proportion of success

1.3.3* Consider the two null distributions (A and B) given below, both for proportion of successes. For which null distribution will the standardized statistic for a sample proportion value of 0.60 be farther from 0? How are you deciding?

A.

Mean = 0.502
SD = 0.049

Proportion of successes

B.

Mean = 0.497
SD = 0.071

Proportion of successes

1.3.4 Suppose that your hypotheses are $H_0: \pi = 0.25$ and $H_a: \pi < 0.25$. In the context of these hypotheses, which of the following standardized statistics would provide the strongest evidence against the null hypothesis and for the alternative hypothesis? Why?

A. $z = -1$

B. $z = 0$

C. $z = 3$

D. $z = -1.80$

1.3.5* Identify these statements as either true or false.

a. A p-value can be negative.

b. A standardized statistic can be negative.

c. We run tests of significance to determine whether $\hat{p}$ is larger or smaller than some value.

d. As a p-value gets smaller, its corresponding standardized statistic gets closer to zero.

1.3.6 Suppose that a standardized statistic (standardized sample proportion) for a study is calculated to be 2.45. Which of the following is the most appropriate interpretation of this standardized statistic?

A. The observed value of the sample proportion is 2.45 SDs away from the hypothesized parameter value.

B. The observed value of the sample proportion is 2.45 SDs above the hypothesized parameter value.

C. The observed value of the sample proportion is 2.45 times the hypothesized parameter value.

D. The study results are statistically significant.

Rock-paper-scissors*

Refer to Example 1.2, which explored players' choices in the game rock-paper-scissors.

1.3.7 Suppose that you play the game with three different friends separately with the following results:

Friend A chose scissors 100 times out of 400 games.

Friend B chose scissors 20 times out of 120 games.

Friend C chose scissors 65 times out of 300 games.

Suppose that for each friend you want to test whether the long-run proportion that the friend will pick scissors is less than 1/3.

a. Determine the appropriate standardized statistic for each friend's results. (*Hint:* You will need to get the standard deviation of the simulated statistics from the null distribution produced by an applet.)

b. Based on the standardized statistics, which friend's data provides the strongest evidence that the long-run proportion that the friend will choose scissors is less than 1/3? Which friend's data provides the least strong evidence?

1.3.8 Suppose that you play the game, again, with two other friends separately with the following results:

Friend D chose rock 200 times out of 400 games.

Friend E chose rock 20 times out of 40 games.

Suppose that for each friend you want to test whether the long-run proportion that the friend will pick rock is more than 1/3.

a. Even though both of the friends played rock the same proportion of times, one of the two friends' data provide more evidence the null hypothesis is wrong. Which friend's data do you think provides more evidence against the null hypothesis? Why?

b. Based on your answer to (a), which friend's data yields a smaller p-value? Why?

c. Based on your answer to (a), which friend's data yields a larger standardized statistic? Why?

d. Based on your answer to (c), which friend's null distribution has a smaller standard deviation? Why?

1.3.9 Suppose that you play the game, again, with two other friends separately with the following results:

Friend F chose rock 15 times out of 40 games.

Friend G chose rock 30 times out of 40 games.

Suppose that for each friend you want to test whether the long-run proportion that the friend will pick rock is more than 1/3. In which friend's case (F or G) will you find a larger (more extreme) standardized statistic? Explain your reasoning, without actually calculating the standardized statistics.

Minesweeper

1.3.10 Recall that one of the authors likes to play the game Minesweeper (Exercise 1.1.8) and in the last 20 games she played she won 12. Use an applet to conduct appropriate simulations in order to calculate the standardized statistic for these data and investigate whether her results provide convincing evidence that her long-run proportion of winning at Minesweeper is higher than 50%? Report the calculated standardized statistic and use it to state a conclusion about the strength of evidence.

Doris and Buzz*

Refer to Example 1.1 involving two dolphins, Buzz and Doris, where the researcher Dr. Bastian was investigating whether dolphins can communicate.

1.3.11 Recall that in the first study, out of 16 attempts, Buzz pushed the correct button 15 times. Calculate the standardized statistic for these data to investigate whether Buzz's results provide convincing evidence that his long-run proportion of pushing the correct button is higher than 0.50. Report the calculated standardized statistic and use it to state a conclusion about the strength of evidence.

1.3.12 Recall that in the second study mentioned (where they later found out that the fish-delivering equipment had been malfunctioning), out of 28 attempts, Buzz pushed the correct button 16 times. Calculate the standardized statistic for these data to investigate whether Buzz's results provide convincing evidence that his long-run proportion of pushing the correct button is higher than 0.50. Report the calculated standardized statistic and use it to state a conclusion about the strength of evidence.

Right or left

1.3.13 Most people are right-handed, and even the right eye is dominant for most people. Molecular biologists have suggested that late-stage human embryos tend to turn their heads to the right. In a study reported in *Nature* (2003), German bio-psychologist Onur Güntürkün conjectured that this tendency to turn to the right manifests itself in other ways as well, so he studied kissing couples to see which side they tended to lean their heads while kissing. He and his researchers observed kissing couples in public places such as airports, train stations, beaches, and parks. They were careful not to include couples who were holding objects such as luggage that might have affected which direction they turned. For each kissing couple observed, the researchers noted whether the couple leaned their heads to the right or to the left. They observed 124 couples, age 13–70 years. Suppose that we want to use the data from this study to investigate whether kissing couples tend to lean their heads right more often than would happen by random chance.

a. Define the parameter of interest in the context of the study and assign a symbol to it.

b. State the null hypothesis and the alternative hypothesis using the symbol defined in part (a).

c. Of the 124 kissing couples, 80 were observed to lean their heads right. What is the observed proportion of kissing couples who leaned their heads to the right? What symbol should you use to represent this value?

d. Determine the standardized statistic from the data. (*Hint:* You will need to get the standard deviation of the simulated statistics from the null distribution.)

e. Interpret the standardized statistic in the context of the study. (*Hint:* You need to talk about the value of your observed statistic in terms of standard deviations assuming _____ is true.)

f. Based on the standardized statistic, state the conclusion that you would draw about the null and alternative hypotheses.

1.3.14 Suppose that instead of $H_0: \pi = 0.50$ like it was in the previous exercise, our null hypothesis was $H_0: \pi = 0.60$.

a. In the context of this null hypothesis, determine the standardized statistic from the data where 80 of 124 kissing couples leaned their heads right. (*Hint:* You will need to get the standard deviation of the simulated statistics from the null distribution.)

b. How, if at all, does the standardized statistic calculated here differ from that when $H_0: \pi = 0.50$? Explain why this makes sense.

Love, first*

1.3.15 A previous exercise (1.2.16) introduced you to a study of 40 heterosexual couples. In 28 of the 40 couples the male said "I love you" first. The researchers were interested in learning whether these data provided evidence that in significantly more than 50% of couples the male says "I love you" first.

a. State the null hypothesis and the alternative hypothesis in the context of the study.

b. Determine the standardized statistic from the data. (*Hint:* You will need to get the standard deviation of the simulated statistics from the null distribution.)

c. Interpret the standardized statistic in the context of the study. (*Hint:* You need to talk about the value of your observed statistic in terms of standard deviations assuming _____ is true.)

d. Based on the standardized statistic, state the conclusion that you would draw about the research question of whether males are more likely to say "I love you" first.

Rhesus monkeys

Revisit Exercise 1.2.18 about the study on Rhesus monkeys. When given a choice between two boxes, 30 out of 40 monkeys approached the box that the human had gestured toward, and 10 approached the other box. The purpose is to investigate whether rhesus monkeys can interpret human gestures better than random chance.

1.3.16 For this study:

a. State the null hypothesis and the alternative hypothesis in the context of the study.

b. Determine the standardized statistic from the data. (*Hint:* You will need to get the standard deviation of the simulated statistics from the null distribution in an applet.)

c. Interpret the standardized statistic in the context of the study. (*Hint:* You need to talk about the value of your observed statistic in terms of standard deviations assuming _____ is true.)

d. Based on the standardized statistic, state the conclusion that you would draw about the research question of whether rhesus monkeys have some ability to understand gestures made by humans.

Tasting tea*

Revisit Exercise 1.1.12 about the study on a lady tasting tea. When presented with eight cups containing a mixture of milk and tea, she correctly identified whether tea or milk was poured first for all eight cups. Is she doing better than if she were just guessing?

1.3.17 For this study:

a. Define the parameter of interest in the context of the study and assign a symbol to it.

b. State the null hypothesis and the alternative hypothesis using the symbol defined in part (a).

c. What is the observed proportion of times the lady correctly identified what was poured first into the cup? What symbol should you use to represent this value?

d. Suppose that you were to generate the null distribution of the sample proportion of correct answers, that is, the distribution of possible values of sample proportion of correct identifications if the lady always guesses. Where would you anticipate this distribution would center? Also, do you anticipate the SD of the null distribution to be negative, positive, or 0? Why?

e. Use an applet to generate the null distribution of sample proportion of correct identifications and use it to determine the standardized statistic.

f. Interpret the standardized statistic in the context of the study. (*Hint:* You need to talk about the value of your observed statistic in terms of standard deviations assuming _____ is true.)

g. Based on the standardized statistic, state the conclusion that you would draw about the research question of whether the lady does better than randomly guess.

Zwerg

Refer to a previous exercise, 1.1.15, involving Zwerg the sea lioness.

1.3.18 In one study, Zwerg, when given two choices, successfully chose the object pointed at by the experimenter 37 times out of 48 trials. Does this result show that Zwerg can correctly follow this type of direction ("pointing at") by an experimenter more than 50% of the time?

a. Define the parameter of interest in the context of the study and assign a symbol to it.

b. State the null hypothesis and the alternative hypothesis using the symbol defined in part (a).

c. What is the observed proportion of times Zwerg picked the correct object? What symbol should you use to represent this value?

d. Suppose that you were to generate the null distribution of the sample proportion of correct answers, that is, the distribution of possible values of sample proportion of correct identifications if Zwerg always guesses. Where would you anticipate this distribution would center? Also, do you anticipate the SD of the null distribution to be negative, positive, or 0? Why?

e. Use an applet to generate the null distribution of sample proportion of correct answers and use it to determine the standardized statistic.

f. Interpret the standardized statistic in the context of the study. (*Hint:* You need to talk about the value of your observed statistic in terms of standard deviations assuming _____ is true.)

g. Based on the standardized statistic, state the conclusion that you would draw about the research question of whether Zwerg does better than randomly guess when the cue is that the experimenter points at the correct object.

1.3.19 In a related study, Zwerg, when given two choices, successfully chose the object indicated by a "marker" 26 out of 48 times. Does this result show that Zwerg can correctly follow this type of direction ("placing a marker") by an experimenter more than 50% of the time?

a. Define the parameter of interest in the context of the study and assign a symbol to it.

b. State the null hypothesis and the alternative hypothesis using the symbol defined in part (a).

c. What is the observed proportion of times Zwerg picked the correct object? What symbol should you use to represent this value?

d. Suppose that you were to generate the null distribution of the sample proportion of correct answers, that is, the distribution of possible values of sample proportion of correct identifications if Zwerg always guesses. Where would you anticipate this distribution would center? Also, do you anticipate the SD of the null distribution to be negative, positive, or 0? Why?

e. Use an applet to generate the null distribution of sample proportion of correct answers and use it to determine the standardized statistic.

f. Interpret the standardized statistic in the context of the study. (*Hint:* You need to talk about the value of your observed statistic in terms of standard deviations assuming _____ is true.)

g. Based on the standardized statistic, state the conclusion that you would draw about the research question of whether Zwerg does better than randomly guess when the cue is that the experimenter places a marker in front of the correct object.

Helper or hinderer*

Use the following information to answer the next two questions. An investigation reported in the November 2007 issue of *Nature* (Hamlin, Wynn, and Bloom) aimed at assessing whether infants take into account an individual's actions towards others in evaluating that individual as appealing or aversive, perhaps laying the foundation for social interaction. In one component of the study, each of sixteen 10-month-old healthy infants (in New England) were shown a "climber" character (a piece of wood with "google" eyes glued onto it) that could not make it up a hill in two tries. Then they were shown two scenarios for the climber's next try, one where the climber was pushed to the top of the hill by another character ("helper") and one where the climber was pushed back down the hill by another character ("hinderer"). Each infant was alternately shown these two scenarios many times. Then the child was presented with both pieces of wood (the "helper" and the "hinderer") and asked to pick one to play with. In the study 14 out of the 16 babies picked the "helper" toy. Does this provide evidence that such 10-month-old infants have a *genuine preference* for the helper toy?

1.3.20

a. Define the parameter of interest in the context of the study and assign a symbol to it.

b. State the null hypothesis and the alternative hypothesis using the symbol defined in part (a).

c. What is the observed proportion of times the infants picked the helper toy? What symbol should you use to represent this value?

d. Use an applet to generate the null distribution of the proportion of "successes." Determine the standardized statistic for the observed sample proportion of "successes." Show your work.

e. Interpret the standardized statistic in the context of the study. (*Hint:* You need to talk about the value of your observed statistic in terms of standard deviations assuming _____ is true.)

f. Based on the standardized statistic, state the conclusion that you would draw about the research question of whether such 10-month-old infants have a genuine preference for the helper toy.

1.3.21

a. Based on the value of the standardized statistic obtained in the previous question, do you anticipate the p-value to be small? Why or why not?

b. Use an appropriate applet to find and report the p-value. Also, interpret the p-value. (*Hint:* The p-value is the probability of … assuming. …)

c. Based on the p-value, state the conclusion that you would draw about the research question of whether such 10-month-old infants have a genuine preference for the helper toy.

d. Do the p-value and standardized statistic provide similar strength of evidence? Do they both lead you to the same conclusion? Did you anticipate this? Why or why not?

Choosing numbers

Use the following information to answer the next four questions. One of the authors read somewhere that it's been conjectured that when people are asked to choose a number from the choices 1, 2, 3, and 4, they tend to choose "3" more than would be expected by random chance.

To investigate this, she collected data in her class. Here is the table of responses from her students:

Chose 1	Chose 2	Chose 3	Chose 4
10	4	14	5

1.3.22

a. Define the parameter of interest in the context of the study and assign a symbol to it.

b. State the null hypothesis and the alternative hypothesis using the symbol defined in part (a).

c. What is the observed proportion of times students chose the number 3? What symbol should you use to represent this value?

d. Use an applet to generate the null distribution of the proportion of "successes." Report the mean and SD of this null distribution.

e. Determine the standardized statistic for the observed sample proportion of "successes."

f. Interpret the standardized statistic in the context of the study. (*Hint:* You need to talk about the value of your observed statistic in terms of standard deviations assuming _____ is true.)

g. Based on the standardized statistic, state the conclusion that you would draw about the research question of whether students tend to have a genuine preference for the number 3 when given the choices 1, 2, 3, and 4.

1.3.23

a. Based on the value of the standardized statistic obtained in the previous question, do you anticipate the p-value to be small? Why or why not?

b. Use an appropriate applet to find and report the p-value. Also, interpret the p-value. (*Hint:* The p-value is the probability of … assuming. …)

c. Based on the p-value, state the conclusion that you would draw about the research question of whether when people are asked to choose from the numbers 1, 2, 3, and 4, they tend to choose "3" more than would be expected by random chance.

d. Do the p-value and standardized statistic provide similar strength of evidence? Do they both lead you to the same conclusion? Did you anticipate this? Why or why not?

1.3.24 Suppose that you wanted to investigate whether people tend to pick a "big" number (3 or 4) rather than a "small" number (1 or 2).

a. In this context, define the parameter of interest and assign a symbol to it.

b. State the null hypothesis and the alternative hypothesis using the symbol defined in part (a).

c. Recall that, of 33 students, 19 picked a "big" number (that is, 3 or 4). What is the observed proportion of times students picked a "big" number? What symbol should you use to represent this value?

d. Use an applet to generate the null distribution of the proportion of "successes." Report the mean and SD of this null distribution.

e. Determine the standardized statistic for the observed sample proportion of "successes."

f. Based on the standardized statistic, state the conclusion that you would draw about the research question of whether people tend to pick a "big" number.

1.3.25 Suppose that you wanted to investigate whether people tend to pick a "big" number (3 or 4) rather than a "small" number (1 or 2).

a. Based on the value of the standardized statistic obtained in the previous question, do you anticipate the p-value to be small? Why or why not?

b. Use an appropriate applet to find and report the p-value. Also, interpret the p-value. (*Hint:* The p-value is the probability of … assuming. …)

c. Based on the p-value, state the conclusion that you would draw about the research question of whether when people are asked to pick a number from the choices 1, 2, 3, and 4, they tend to pick a "big" number.

d. Do the p-value and standardized statistic provide similar strength of evidence? Do they both lead you to the same conclusion? Did you anticipate this? Why or why not?

SECTION 1.4

Racquet spinning*

Use the following information to answer the following three questions. Reconsider the racquet-spinning Exercise 1.1.1 from earlier. Researchers wanted to investigate whether a spun tennis racquet is equally likely to land with the label facing up or down.

1.4.1 Does this racquet-spinning study call for a one-sided or a two-sided alternative?

A. One-sided, because there is only one variable: how the label lands

B. Two-sided, because there are two possible outcomes: up or down

C. One-sided, because the researchers want to know whether the label is more likely to land face up

D. Two-sided, because the researchers want to know whether the spinning process is fair or biased in either direction

1.4.2 Which of the following will always be true about the standardized statistic for the racquet-spinning study?

A. The standardized statistic increases as the sample proportion that land "up" increases.

B. The standardized statistic decreases as the sample proportion that land "up" increases.

C. The standardized statistic increases as the sample proportion that land "up" gets farther from 0.50.

D. The standardized statistic decreases as the sample proportion that land "up" gets farther from 0.50.

1.4.3 Which of the following will always be true about the p-value for the racquet-spinning study?

A. The p-value increases as the sample proportion that land "up" increases.

B. The p-value decreases as the sample proportion that land "up" increases.

C. The p-value increases as the sample proportion that land "up" gets farther from 0.50.

D. The p-value decreases as the sample proportion that land "up" gets farther from 0.50.

Chess-boxing

Use the following information to answer the following three questions. You have heard that in sports like boxing there might be some competitive advantage to those wearing red uniforms. You want to test this with your new favorite sport of chess-boxing. You randomly assign blue and red uniforms to contestants in 20 matches and find that those wearing red won 14 times (or 70%). You conduct a test of significance using simulation and get the following null distribution. (Note this null distribution uses only 100 simulated samples and not the usual 1,000 or more.)

1.4.4 One-sided or two?

a. Suppose you want to see if competitors wearing red win more than 50% of the matches in the long run, so you test $H_0: \pi = 0.50$ versus $H_a: \pi > 0.50$. What is your p-value based on the above null distribution?

b. Suppose you now want to see if competitors wearing either red or blue have an advantage, so you test $H_0: \pi = 0.50$ versus $H_a: \pi \neq 0.50$. What is your p-value now based on the above null distribution?

1.4.5 Suppose you are testing the hypothesis $H_0: \pi = 0.50$ versus $H_a: \pi > 0.50$. You get a sample proportion of 0.54 and find that your p-value is 0.08. Now suppose you redid your study with each of the following changes. Will your new p-value be larger or smaller than the 0.08 your first obtained?

a. You increase the sample size and still find a sample proportion of 0.54.

b. Keeping the sample size the same, you take a new sample and find a sample proportion of 0.55.

c. With your original sample, you decided to test a two-sided alternative instead of $H_a: \pi > 0.50$.

1.4.6 Identify these statements as either true or false.

a. Using a simulation-based test, the p-value for a two-sided test will be about twice as large as the corresponding p-value for a one-sided test.

b. We run tests of significance to determine if $\hat{p}$ is larger, smaller, or different than some value.

Minesweeper*

1.4.7   Look back to Exercise 1.1.8. Recall that in the last 20 games of Minesweeper she played, the author won 12.

a. What if she had played 20 games and won 18? Would that provide stronger, weaker, or evidence of similar strength compared to 12 wins out of 20, to conclude that her long-run proportion of winning at Minesweeper is higher than 50%? Explain how you are deciding.

b. What if she had played 100 games and won 60? Would that provide stronger, weaker, or evidence of similar strength compared to 12 wins out of 20, to conclude that her long-run proportion of winning at Minesweeper is higher than 50%? Explain how you are deciding.

c. What if she had played 30 games and won 12? Would that provide evidence that her long-run proportion of winning at Minesweeper is higher than 50%? Explain how you are deciding.

Divine providence?

Use the following information to answer the next five questions. Dr. John Arbuthnot (1667–1735) was physician to England's Queen Anne. He was also one of the first scientists to publish a use of p-values and to apply the logic of statistical inference.[1] His goal was to prove the existence of God, and he took as evidence the fact that for 82 years in a row male christenings had outnumbered female christenings. His argument: The p-value is so extremely tiny that the extra male births cannot be due to chance. Therefore the excess males must be due to "Divine Providence." Here is a summary of his data:

Number of male christenings:	484,382
Number of female christenings:	453,841
Total number of christenings:	938,223
Proportion of males:	0.516276

1.4.8   Hypotheses.

a. What was Dr. Arbuthnot's research hypothesis?

b. Let π be Arbuthnot's parameter. Tell in words what π refers to.

c. State in words, and then in symbols, what Dr. Arbuthnot's null hypothesis was.

d. Was Arbuthnot's alternative hypothesis one-sided or two-sided? Give your reasoning.

1.4.9   Based solely on the observed value of $\hat{p}$ and the null value for π, would you expect the evidence against the null hypothesis to be strong or weak? Explain your reasoning.

---

[1]John Arbuthnot (1710), "An argument for Divine Providence, taken from the constant regularity observed in the births of both sexes." *Philosophical Transactions of the Royal Society of London* **27** (325–336): 186–190.

1.4.10   Based solely on the sample size n (ignoring the value of distance $\hat{p} - \pi$), would you expect the evidence against the null hypothesis to be strong or weak? Explain your reasoning.

1.4.11   Suppose (against all historical evidence) Arbuthnot had been an early feminist, equally willing to accept an excess of female births as evidence of "Divine Providence." In that case, his p-value would have been _____ (half, twice) as large.

1.4.12   Summary. For the analysis based on the data above:

a. The distance between $\hat{p}$ and π is _____ (tiny, small, large, huge).

b. The sample size is _____ (tiny, small, large, huge).

c. The alternative hypothesis is _____-sided (one, two).

Buzz and Doris*

Use the following information to answer the next three questions. Refer to Example 1.1. Recall that Buzz pushed the correct lever 15 out of 16 times when given the choice between two levers to push.

1.4.13   Buzz got 15 right out of 16. Suppose the numbers had been exactly double that: 30 right out of 32.

a. Which of the three influences on strength of evidence (distance, sample size, one- or two-sided) would change? Which would stay the same?

b. Overall, the evidence against the null hypothesis would be _____ (stronger, weaker).

1.4.14   In the actual experiment, Buzz got 15 right out of 16. Suppose he had only guessed right 14 times out of 16.

a. Which of the three influences on strength (distance, sample size, one- or two-sided) would change? Which would stay the same?

b. Overall, the evidence against the null hypothesis would be _____ (stronger, weaker).

1.4.15   Just for the sake of this exercise, imagine that the investigators wanted their statistical test to include the possibility that Buzz was a very sadistic dolphin, so malicious that he would willingly give up his own chance at a fish just to deprive Doris.

a. How would this thinking affect the p-value based on the actual data (15 right out of 16): Double it or cut it in half? (Explain your reasoning.)

b. Does this reframing of the alternative hypothesis make the evidence against the null hypothesis stronger or weaker?

Harley

Use the following information to answer the next two questions. Refer to Exploration 1.1. Researchers investigated whether Harley the dog could correctly choose between two objects when a researcher bowed towards one of the cups.

1.4.16 Harley got 9 right out of 10. Suppose instead the numbers had been 18 right out of 20.

a. Which of the three influences on strength of evidence (distance, sample size, one- or two-sided) would change? Which would stay the same?

b. Overall, the evidence against the null hypothesis would be _____ (stronger, weaker).

1.4.17 Suppose that instead of the actual result (9 right out of 10) Harley had only been right 8 times out of 10.

a. Which of the three influences on strength (distance, sample size, one- or two-sided) would change? Which would stay the same?

b. Overall, the evidence against the null hypothesis would be _____ (stronger, weaker).

Krieger*

Can domestic dogs understand human body cues such as bowing, pointing, or glancing? The experimenter presented a body cue toward one of two objects and recorded whether or not the dog being tested correctly chose the object indicated. A four-year-old male pit bull named Krieger participated in this study. He chose the correct object 6 out of 10 times when the experimenter turned and looked towards the correct object.

1.4.18

a. Identify the parameter of interest for this study and assign a symbol to it.

b. If Krieger is just randomly choosing between the two objects, what is the chance that he will choose the correct object?

c. State your null hypothesis and an appropriate one-sided alternative hypothesis.

1.4.19

a. *Statistic:* How many times did Krieger choose the correct object? Out of how many attempts? Thus, what proportion of the time did Krieger choose the correct object?

b. *Simulate:* Using an applet, simulate 1,000 repetitions of having the dog choose between the two objects if he is doing so randomly. Report the mean and standard deviation.

c. Based on the study's result, what is the p-value for this test?

d. *Strength of evidence:* What are your conclusions based on the p-value?

e. How would the evidence change if Krieger got 8 out of 10 correct?

1.4.20

a. Suppose that you decide to use a two-sided alternative hypothesis. What additional values for the parameter will now be part of the alternative?

b. Conjecture how, if at all, the p-value for the two-sided alternative will change compared to that reported in Exercise 1.4.19, part (c) for the one-sided alternative hypothesis. Explain your choice.

   Increase   Stay the same   Decrease

c. Use an applet to find and report the p-value for the two-sided alternative. Did the p-value behave as you had conjectured in (b)?

d. Complete the following: A p-value corresponding to a one-sided alternative hypothesis provides _____ (weaker/the same/stronger) evidence against the null hypothesis, compared to a p-value calculated from the same data, but corresponding to a two-sided alternative hypothesis.

1.4.21 Suppose that we repeated the same study with Krieger, and this time he chose the correct object 12 out of 20 times.

a. Conjecture how, if at all, the p-value would change from that reported in Exercise 1.4.19, part (c) (one-sided alternative).

   Increase   Stay the same   Decrease

b. Using an applet, find this p-value. Did it behave the way you conjectured in (a)?

c. Complete the following: When the sample proportion of successes stays the same, as the sample size gets larger, then the strength of evidence against the null hypothesis gets _____ (weaker/the same/stronger).

1.4.22 In another part of the study, instead of *looking* at the object, the experimenter kept her eyes on the dog and *leaned* toward the object. For this part of the study, Krieger got 9 right out of 10.

a. Identify the parameter of interest for this part of the study and assign a symbol to it.

b. If Krieger is just randomly choosing between the two objects, what is the chance that he will choose the correct object?

c. State your null hypothesis and an appropriate one-sided alternative hypothesis.

d. Conjecture how, if at all, the p-value for these data will change compared to that from the data in Exercises 1.4.18 and 1.4.19 (where Krieger got 6 out of 10 correct). Explain your choice.

   Increase   Stay the same   Decrease

1.4.23 For the "leaning" version of the study from the previous question:

a. *Statistic:* How many times did Krieger choose the correct object? Out of how many attempts? Thus, what proportion of the time did Krieger choose the correct object?

b. *Simulate:* Using an applet, simulate 1,000 repetitions of having the dog choose between the two objects if he is doing so randomly. Report the null and standard deviation.

c. Based on the study's result, what is the p-value for this test?

d. Approximately what proportion of the 10 attempts would Krieger have needed to get correct in order to yield a p-value of approximately 0.05?

1.4.24

a. Based on the study's result, what is the standardized statistic for this test?

b. *Strength of evidence:* What are your conclusions based on the p-value you found in part (d) from the previous exercise? Are the conclusions the same if you base them off the standardized-statistic you found in (a)?

c. Revisit your conjecture in Exercise 1.4.22, part (d). Did the p-value behave the way you had conjectured?

The sign test

So far, the outcome has always been binary—Yes/No, Right/Wrong, Heads/Tails, etc. What if outcomes are quantitative, like heights or percentages? Although there are specialized methods for such data that you will learn in a later chapter, you can also use the methods and logic you have already learned for situations of a very different sort: (1) outcomes are quantitative, (2) you want to compare two conditions A and B, and (3) your data come in pairs, one A and one B in each pair. To apply the coin toss model, you simply ask for each pair, "Is the A value bigger than the B value?" The resulting test is called the "sign test" because the difference $(A - B)$ is either plus or minus. Here's a summary table:

Coin toss	Heads	P(Heads)	Null hypothesis	Statistic
Buzz's guess	Right	$\pi = P\text{(Right)}$	$\pi = 0.50$	$\hat{p}$
Each pair	$A > B$	$\pi = P(A > B)$	$\pi = 0.50$	$\hat{p}$

Divine providence

1.4.25* Refer to Exercises 1.4.8 to 1.4.12. Dr. Arbuthnot's actual analysis was different from the analysis you saw earlier. Instead of using each individual birth as a coin toss, Arbuthnot used a sign test with each of the 82 years as a coin toss, and a year with more male births counted as a "success."

a. Complete the following table of comparisons:

Analysis method	Sample size n	Null value π_0	Value of $\hat{p}$
A: 1.4.8 – 1.4.12	_____	_____	_____
B: 1.4.25	_____	_____	_____

b. For each method of analysis, rate the strength of evidence against the null hypothesis, as one of: inconclusive, weak but suggestive, moderately strong, strong, or overwhelming.

Healthy lungs

1.4.26 Researchers wanted to test the hypothesis that living in the country is better for your lungs than living in a city. To eliminate the possible variation due to genetic differences, they located seven pairs of identical twins with one member of each twin living in the country, the other in a city. For each person, they measured the percentage of inhaled tracer particles remaining in the lungs after one hour: the higher the percentage, the less healthy the lungs. They found that for six of the seven twin pairs the one living in the country had healthier lungs.

a. Is the alternative hypothesis one-sided or two-sided?

b. Based on the sample size and distance between the null value and the observed proportion, estimate the strength of evidence: inconclusive, weak but suggestive, moderately strong, strong, or overwhelming.

c. Here are probabilities for the number of heads in seven tosses of a fair coin:

# Heads	0	1	2	3	4	5	6	7
Probability	0.0078	0.0547	0.1641	0.2734	0.2734	0.1641	0.0547	0.0078

Compute the p-value and state your conclusion.

Bee stings

1.4.27* Scientists gathered data to test the research hypothesis that bees are more likely to sting a target that has already been stung by other bees. On eight separate occasions, they offered a pair of targets to a hive of angry bees; one target in each pair had been previously stung, the other was pristine. On six of the eight occasions, the target that had been previously stung accumulated more new stingers.

a. Is the alternative hypothesis one-sided or two-sided?

b. Based on the sample size and distance between the null value and the observed proportion, estimate the strength of evidence: inconclusive, weak but suggestive, moderately strong, strong, or overwhelming.

c. Here are probabilities for the number of heads in eight tosses of a fair coin:

# Heads	0	1	2	3	4	5	6	7	8
Probability	0.0039	0.0313	0.1094	0.2188	0.2734	0.2188	0.1094	0.0313	0.0039

Compute the p-value and state your conclusion.

Presidential stature

In a race for U.S. president, is the taller candidate more likely to win?

1.4.28 In the first election of the 20th century, Theodore Roosevelt (178 cm) defeated Alton B. Parker (175 cm). There have been 27 additional elections since then, for a total of 28. Of these, 25 elections had only two major party candidates with one taller than the other. In 19 of the 25 elections, the taller candidate won.

a. Let $\pi = P(\text{taller wins})$. State the research hypothesis in words and in symbols.

b. State the null and alternative hypotheses in words and symbols.

c. Compute the appropriate p-value using an applet.

d. If you take the p-value at face value, what do you conclude?

e. Are there reasons not to take the p-value at face value? Is yes, list them.

1.4.29 In this exercise, as in the one before, we eliminate elections with more than two major party candidates as well as elections with two candidates of the same height. In addition, we eliminate the two elections in which George Washington was unopposed and five elections with missing data. Consider four different data sets:

A. Elections from 1960 (Kennedy) to the present: $n = 14$, $\hat{p} = 8/14 = 0.5714$.

B. Elections from Theodore Roosevelt (1904) to the present: $n = 25$, $\hat{p} = 19/25 = 0.76$.

C. Elections from John Adams (1796) through William McKinley (1900): $n = 16$, $\hat{p} = 5/16 = 0.3125$.

D. Elections from John Adams (1796) to the present: $n = 41$, $\hat{p} = 24/41 = 0.5854$.

a. The four p-values, from smallest to largest, are 0.007, 0.174, 0.395, 0.961. Match each data set (A–D) with its p-value.

b. What do you conclude about the hypothesis that taller candidates are more likely to win?

Three features that affect p-values: An abstract summary*

1.4.30 The graph below shows six different curves labeled A–F. Each curve shows the relationship between the p-value (y-axis) and the distance $\hat{p} - \pi$ (x-axis) for testing the null hypothesis $\pi = 0.50$.

Match each curve A–F with one of the descriptions:

Sample size is $n = 25$, alternative hypothesis is right-sided: $\pi > \frac{1}{2}$.

Sample size is $n = 225$, alternative hypothesis is right-sided: $\pi > \frac{1}{2}$.

Sample size is $n = 25$, alternative hypothesis is left-sided: $\pi < \frac{1}{2}$.

Sample size is $n = 225$, alternative hypothesis is left-sided: $\pi < \frac{1}{2}$.

Sample size is $n = 25$, alternative hypothesis is two-sided: $\pi \neq \frac{1}{2}$.

Sample size is $n = 225$, alternative hypothesis is two-sided: $\pi \neq \frac{1}{2}$.

Comment: This is not an easy exercise, but don't let the surface mess of the picture put you off. The purpose of the exercise is to challenge you to think hard about very important issues in a new way and at the same time to challenge you to become more skillful at connecting graphs with ideas. We hope you won't give up and that you'll feel that what you learn from the time you spend is worth it. Give it a shot, see how far you can get, and if you get stuck, skip to the five exercises that come after the graphs, do those, and then come back to this one.

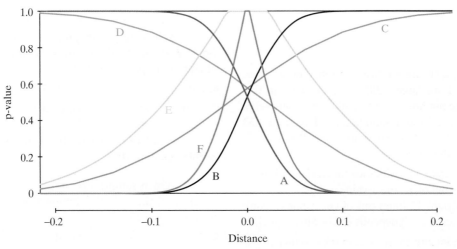

EXERCISE 1.4.30

1.4.31 Notice that there are three basic shapes for the curves: increasing, decreasing, and "up-down." Tell the letters for each shape:

a. Increasing:

b. Decreasing:

c. Up-down:

1.4.32 Notice that the distance $\hat{p} - \pi$ (x-axis) can tell you percent correct. Recall Example 1.1. For Buzz and Doris:

a. A distance of 0.50 means Buzz is right _____% of the time.

b. A distance of 0.00 means Buzz is right _____% of the time.

c. A distance of −0.50 means Buzz is right _____% of the time.

1.4.33 Try to relate the shape of the curve to the alternate hypothesis.

a. Suppose Buzz really wants to earn his fish and tries to guess right. Your alternative hypothesis is that $\pi > 0.50$. The better Buzz does, the _____ (smaller, larger) the p-value. The graph should be _____ (increasing, decreasing, up-down). The graphs that match this alternative are _____.

b. Suppose you are studying sadism in dolphins and your research hypothesis is that Buzz is able to guess right but he wants only to deprive Doris of her fish. Your alternative hypothesis is that $\pi < 0.50$. The better Buzz does, the _____ (smaller, larger) the p-value. The graph should be _____ (increasing, decreasing, up-down). The graphs that match this alternative are _____.

c. You are unsure about whether Buzz is fish-greedy or sadistic. Your more objective alternative hypothesis is that $\pi \neq 0.50$. The graphs that match this alternative are _____ (increasing, decreasing, up-down). Their letters are _____.

d. Complete the following summary table. For "Strongest evidence," choose from among $\hat{p} = 0$, $\hat{p} = 1$, and $\hat{p} = 0$ or 1. For "Shape of curve," choose from among increasing, decreasing, and up-down.

Alternative hypothesis	Strongest evidence	Shape of curve
$\pi > 0.50$		
$\pi < 0.50$		
$\pi \neq 0.50$		

1.4.34 The six graphs are for two different sample sizes: one small (25) and one large (225). Your challenge in this exercise is to figure out how to tell the difference between a small-sample curve and a large-sample curve. Exercise 1.4.33 illustrates that the *form* of the alternative hypothesis determines the *shape* of the curve.

a. Consider two sample sizes with the same distance: If Buzz is right 30 times out of 32, the p-value will be _____ than if Buzz is right 15 times out of 16. (Choose from: higher, lower, can't tell—it depends on the alternative).

b. More generally, for any given value of the distance $\hat{p} - \pi$ (x-axis), the p-value is smaller when the sample size n is _____ (larger, smaller, can't tell—it depends on the alternative).

c. This means that compared to the graph for $n = 225$, the graph for $n = 25$ _____ (always lies above, always lies below, neither: it depends on the alternative hypothesis.).

d. "Above/below" is not a useful comparison. Instead, use the steepness of the curve. Compared to the graph for $n = 225$, the graph for $n = 25$ is _____ (steeper, less steep).

1.4.35 Look at the figure long enough to follow each curve with your eye and recognize its shape and steepness. Keep these two facts in mind—three shapes, two curves of each shape—and try to relate them to the three main influences on p-values: distance, sample size, and one- versus two-sided alternatives. Then fill in the following table indicating which letter (A–F) corresponds to combination of shape descriptions.

	Increasing	Decreasing	Up-Down
Steeper			
Flatter			

Now go back to Exercise 1.4.30 and use your table to do the matching.

FAQ

1.4.36 Read FAQ 1.4.1 about two-sided alternative hypotheses and answer the following questions.

a. Why don't we first take a sample and use the observed sample proportion to help us decide which direction the alternative hypothesis should go? For example if we get a sample proportion greater than 0.50 then we will test to see if the parameter is greater than 0.50.

b. What is a downside of doing a two-sided test?

SECTION 1.5

1.5.1* Which long-run proportion of success, π, gives the largest standard deviation of the null distribution when the sample size is 10?

A. 0.05   B. 0.25

C. 0.50   D. 0.90

1.5.2 Would your answer change in Exercise 1.5.1 if the sample size were 100?

1.5.3* Which sample size, n, gives the smallest standard deviation of the null distribution where the long-run proportion, π, is 0.25?

A. 30   B. 40

C. 50   D. 60

1.5.4 What is calculated using the formula $\sqrt{\pi(1-\pi)/n}$?

1.5.5* What is calculated using the formula (statistic − mean of null distr.)/(SD of null distr.)?

1.5.6 Suppose you are using theory-based techniques (e.g., a one-proportion z-test) to determine p-values. How will a two-sided p-value compare to a one-sided p-value (assuming the one-sided p-value is less than 0.50)?

A. The two-sided p-value will be about the same as the one-sided.

B. The two-sided p-value will be close to twice as large as the one-sided.

C. The two-sided p-value will be exactly twice as large as the one-sided.

D. The two-sided p-value will be half as much as the one-sided.

1.5.7* What is a z-statistic?

1.5.8 Suppose you ride to school with a friend and often arrive at a certain stop light when it is red. One day she states, "It seems like this light is green only 10% of the time when we get here." You think it is more often than 10% and want to test this. You keep track of the color (green/not green) the next 20 times you go to school and find that 4 times (4/20 = 20%) the light is green when you arrive. You wish to see if your sample provides strong evidence that the true proportion of times the light is green is greater than 10%. In other words, you are testing the hypotheses

$$H_0: \pi = 0.10 \text{ versus } H_a: \pi > 0.10$$

where π = the long-run proportion of times the light is green.

Two different approaches were taken in order to yield a p-value and both are shown in the applet output.

- **Option 1.** A simulation-based test was done and found a p-value of **0.148**, showing weak evidence against the null.

- **Option 2.** A one-proportion z-test was conducted and found a p-value of **0.068**, yielding moderate evidence against the null.

a. Which test gives a more valid p-value?

b. Give one or two sentences why you picked the option you did.

1.5.9* According to statistician Persi Diaconis, the probability of a penny landing heads when it is spun on its edge is only about 0.20. Suppose you doubt this claim and think that it should be more than 0.20. To test this, you spin a penny 12 times and it lands heads side up 5 times. You put this information in the **One Proportion** applet and determine a simulation-based p-value of 0.0770, but the one-proportion z-test p-value is 0.0303.

a. Write down the hypotheses for this study.

b. Which p-value would you say is the most valid? Explain.

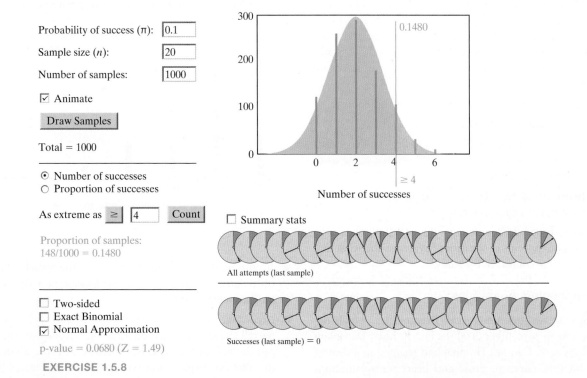

Probability of success (π): 0.1
Sample size (n): 20
Number of samples: 1000

☑ Animate

Draw Samples

Total = 1000

⦿ Number of successes
◯ Proportion of successes

As extreme as ≥ 4 Count

Proportion of samples:
148/1000 = 0.1480

☐ Summary stats

All attempts (last sample)

☐ Two-sided
☐ Exact Binomial
☑ Normal Approximation

p-value = 0.0680 (Z = 1.49)

Successes (last sample) = 0

EXERCISE 1.5.8

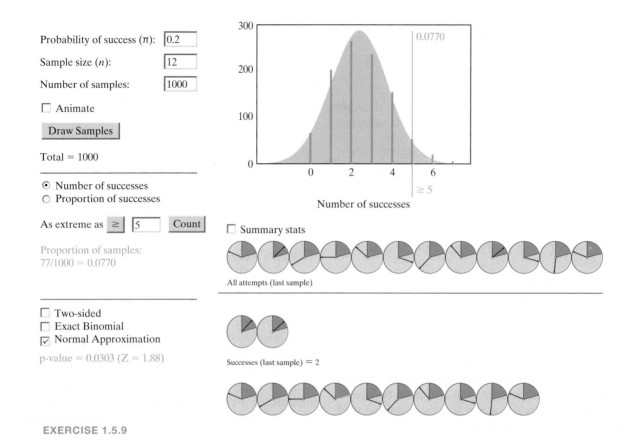

EXERCISE 1.5.9

c. Do you have strong evidence that a spun penny will land heads more that 20% of the time in the long run?

1.5.10 According to researchers, a coin flip may not have a 50% chance of landing heads and a 50% chance of landing tails. In fact, they believe that a coin is more likely to land the same way it started. So if it starts out heads up, it is more likely to land heads up. Suppose someone tests this hypothesis with 1,000 flips of a coin where it starts out heads up each time.

a. Describe what the symbol π stands for in this context.

b. State your null and alternative hypotheses.

c. Suppose 52% of the sample of 1,000 flips landed heads facing up. Verify the validity conditions that allow us to use a theory-based test.

d. A theory-based test reports a standardized statistic of 1.26. Interpret what this means.

e. A theory-based test reports a p-value of 0.1030. State your conclusion in terms of strength of evidence and what that means in the context of the study.

Heart transplant operations*

For the next two questions recall Example 1.3, which describes how in September 2000 the last 10 heart transplant operations at St. George's Hospital had resulted in 8 deaths. Based on this, concerns arose and heart transplantations

were suspended at this hospital. To investigate whether the data provide evidence that the long-run proportion of dying within 30 days of a heart transplant at St. George's is higher than 15%, one can use the **One Proportion** applet to produce the null distribution of sample proportion of deaths as given below:

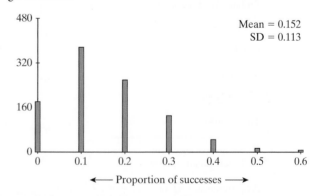

1.5.11

a. According to the dotplot produced by the applet, what is the mean of the null distribution? Explain how you could have anticipated this.

b. According to the dotplot produced by the applet, is the overall shape of the null distribution *bell-shaped*? That is, can the null distribution be described as being a normal distribution? Explain how you could have anticipated this.

1.5.12 Recall that, to explore more deeply, the researchers went on to look at data from the most recent 361 heart transplantations at St. George's and found that 71 had resulted in deaths within 30 days of the heart transplant procedure. Once again, one can use the **One Proportion** applet to produce the null distribution of sample proportion of deaths assuming the long-run proportion of death is 0.15:

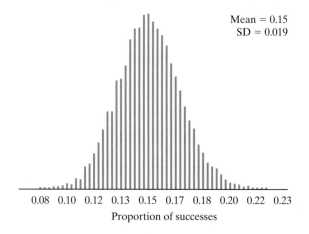

Mean = 0.15
SD = 0.019

0.08 0.10 0.12 0.13 0.15 0.17 0.18 0.20 0.22 0.23
Proportion of successes

a. According to the dotplot produced by the applet, what is the mean of the null distribution? Explain how you could have anticipated this.

b. According to the dotplot produced by the applet, what is the SD of the null distribution? Explain how you could have anticipated this.

c. According to the dotplot produced by the applet, is the overall shape of the null distribution *bell-shaped*? That is, can the null distribution be described as being a normal distribution?

d. Explain why the normal approximation works better in the context of the null distribution in Exercise 1.5.12 compared to the null distribution in Exercise 1.5.11.

Psychic abilities

Use the following information to answer the next two questions. Statistician Jessica Utts has conducted extensive analysis of studies that have investigated psychic functioning. One type of study involves having one person (called the "sender") concentrate on an image while a person in another room (the "receiver") tries to determine which image is being "sent." The receiver is given four images to choose from, one of which is the actual image that the sender is concentrating on. This is a technique called Ganzfeld.

1.5.13

a. Describe what the symbol π stands for in this context.

b. State your null and alternative hypotheses.

c. If the subjects in these studies have no psychic ability, approximately what proportion will identify the correct image? Is this the null hypothesis or the alternative hypothesis?

Utts (1995) cites research from Bem and Honorton (1994) that analyzed 329 Ganzfeld sessions (http://www.ics.uci.edu/~jutts/air.pdf).

d. Use an applet to simulate 1,000 repetitions of this study, assuming the null hypothesis to be true. Sketch a labeled graph of the results.

e. Utts reported that Bem and Honorton found a total of 106 "hits" in the 329 sessions. Does this result provide very strong evidence against the null hypothesis? Use the simulation that you carried out in part (d) to find and report a p-value. Based on this p-value, summarize your conclusion in the context of this study and explain your reasoning for having arrived at this conclusion. Be sure that you have used the 3S strategy for assessing the strength of evidence for the research conjecture.

f. Now carry out the same analysis, only instead of simulating the null, use the theory-based (normal approximation) approach for that null distribution. How does the p-value you found using the theory-based approach compare to the one you found using simulation? Does this surprise you? Why or why not?

1.5.14 In the same research article, Utts (1995) also cites research from Morris et al. (1995) where, out of 97 Ganzfeld sessions, the receiver could correctly identify the image sent 32 times. You would like to know whether these data provide evidence that in Ganzfeld studies receivers will do better than just guess when picking which image is being sent.

a. Find the sample proportion of "hits" in Morris et al.'s study. How does this compare to the sample proportion of "hits" in Bem and Honorton's study: larger, smaller, or about the same?

b. Conjecture whether the p-value for Morris et al.'s study results will be larger, smaller, or about the same compared to that of Bem and Honorton's. Explain your reasoning.

c. Use simulation to find and report a p-value. Based on this p-value, summarize your conclusion in the context of this study and explain your reasoning for having arrived at this conclusion.

d. Now carry out the same analysis, only instead of simulating the null, use the theory-based (normal approximation) approach for that null distribution. How does the p-value you found using the theory-based approach compare to the one you found using simulation? Does this surprise you? Why or why not?

e. Why do the p-values from the simulation versus theory-based approaches in the Bern and Honorton study not differ as much from each other as do the p-values from the simulation versus theory-based approaches as here?

I love you, first*

1.5.15 Recall Exercise 1.2.16, in which researchers asked 40 heterosexual couples which person said "I love you first."

They found that the man said "I love you" in 28 of the 40 couples before the woman did. Since previous research indicated that the man tends to say "I love you" before the woman, we tested to see if the probability a man would say "I love you" before the woman is more than 50%.

a. State the appropriate null and alternative hypotheses (in symbols) for testing whether males are more likely to say "I love you" first.

b. Using an appropriate applet, find the p-value using a theory-based test (one-proportion z-test; normal approximation).

c. Summarize your conclusion from your p-value.

d. What is the z-statistic for the test? What does this number represent in the context of this study?

e. Without using an applet, determine the value of the theory-based (normal approximation) p-value if we used a two-sided alternative hypothesis.

Rhesus monkeys

1.5.16 Recall Exercise 1.2.19, where researchers investigated whether rhesus monkeys have some ability to understand gestures made by humans. In one part of the study, they found that 31 of 40 monkeys correctly went to one of two boxes that researchers pointed towards.

a. State the appropriate null and alternative hypotheses in the context of this study, first in words and then in symbols.

b. Using an appropriate applet, find the p-value using a theory-based test (one-proportion z-test; normal approximation).

c. Summarize your conclusion from your p-value.

d. What is the z-statistic for the test? What does this number represent in the context of this study?

e. Without using an applet, determine the value of the theory-based (normal approximation) p-value if we used a two-sided alternative hypothesis.

Rock-paper-scissors*

Use the following information to answer the next two questions. In Example 1.2, we investigated some results of the game rock-paper-scissors. In the article referenced in the example, the researchers had 119 people play rock-paper-scissors against a computer. They found 66 players (55.5%) started with rock, 39 (32.8%) started with paper, and 14 (11.8%) started with scissors. We want to see if players start with scissors with a long-term probability that is different than 1/3.

1.5.17

a. State the appropriate null and alternative hypotheses in the context of this study, first in words and then in symbols.

b. Using an appropriate applet, find the p-value using a theory-based test (one-proportion z-test; normal approximation).

c. Summarize your conclusion from your p-value.

1.5.18 Based on the statistics from the previous question where people were playing rock-paper-scissors, we want to see if players start with rock with a probability that is different than 1/3.

a. State the appropriate null and alternative hypotheses in the context of this study, first in words and then in symbols.

b. Using an appropriate applet, find the p-value using a theory-based test (one-proportion z-test; normal approximation).

c. Summarize your conclusion from your p-value.

Facial prototyping

1.5.19 Reconsider Exploration 1.3, where we explored whether the long-run proportion that students in a class would correctly assign the names Bob and Tim to the pictures. We tested to see if this long-run proportion is more than 0.50.

a. State the appropriate null and alternative hypotheses in the context of this study.

b. In a class of one of the authors 19 out of 30 students correctly identified that the face on the left belonged to Tim. Using an appropriate applet, find the p-value using a one-proportion z-test (theory-based/normal approximation).

c. Summarize your conclusion from your p-value.

d. What is the z-statistic for the test? What does this number represent in the context of this study?

Predicting elections from faces*

1.5.20 In Example 1.4, we explored whether voters make decisions based on a candidate's facial appearance. The researchers described how they had people determine which of two candidates for the U.S. House of Representatives in 2004 had the more competent face. They then looked to see if the one with the more competent face won the election. We will let π = the probability this method predicts the winner.

a. State the appropriate null and alternative hypotheses in the context of this study.

b. This method predicted the winner in 189 of the 279 House races that year. Based on these results, what are the values of $\hat{p}$ and n?

c. Using an appropriate applet, find the p-value using a theory-based test (one-proportion z-test; normal approximation).

d. Summarize your conclusion from your p-value.

Uniform color

Use the following information to answer the next two questions. Reconsider Exploration 1.4, where we looked to see if an athlete's uniform color affects whether or not they win or lose. The athletes were randomly assigned red or blue uniforms in matches of four combat sports. We want to see if one color has an advantage over the other. If we focus on the red uniform, we can ask if the probability the competitor in the red uniform will win is different than 0.50.

1.5.21 The researchers found that of the 457 matches, the competitor in red won 248 times.

a. State the appropriate null and alternative hypotheses in the context of this study.

b. Using an appropriate applet, find the p-value using a theory-based test (one-proportion z-test; normal approximation).

c. Summarize your conclusion from your p-value.

d. What is the z-statistic for the test? What does this number represent in the context of this study?

1.5.22 The researchers found that of the 272 boxing matches, the competitor in red won 150 times.

a. State the appropriate null and alternative hypotheses in the context of this study.

b. Using an appropriate applet, find the p-value using a theory-based test (one-proportion z-test; normal approximation).

c. Summarize your conclusion from your p-value.

d. What is the z-statistic for the test? What does this number represent in the context of this study?

Yahtzee*

Use the following information to answer the next two questions. One of the authors used to have an electronic Yahtzee game that he played frequently. The game would "roll" five virtual six-sided dice. But were the dice fair?

1.5.23 It seemed to the author that sixes showed up more than what they should if the dice were fair and he wanted to test this. He had the machine roll 500 dice and obtained 92 sixes.

a. Describe what the parameter is in the context of this problem.

b. State the appropriate null and alternative hypotheses in the context of this study.

c. Using an appropriate applet, find the p-value using a theory-based test (one-proportion z-test; normal approximation).

d. Summarize your conclusion from your p-value.

1.5.24 It also seemed to the author that ones showed up less often than what they should if the dice were fair and he wanted to test this. In his 500 dice rolls, 72 resulted in ones.

a. Describe what the parameter is in the context of this problem.

b. State the appropriate null and alternative hypotheses in the context of this study.

c. Using an appropriate applet, find the p-value using a theory-based test (one-proportion z-test; normal approximation).

d. Summarize your conclusion from your p-value.

Mario and Luigi

1.5.25 Suppose two brothers named Mario and Luigi like to compete by playing a certain video game. Mario thinks he is better at this game than Luigi and sets out to prove it by keeping track of who wins. After playing the game 30 times, Mario won 18 of them (or 60%). Mario then declares that this proves he is obviously the better player. Luigi, who just finished Chapter 1 in his statistics class, realizes that perhaps he and his brother are evenly matched and just by chance Mario won 60% of the last 30 games. Luigi is going to test this by running a test of significance.

a. Describe what the parameter is that Luigi should be testing.

b. State the appropriate null and alternative hypotheses in the context of this study. (*Hint:* Luigi likes two-sided tests because he knows that will make it harder to get strong evidence that his brother is better.)

c. Using an appropriate applet, find the p-value using a theory-based test (one-proportion z-test; normal approximation).

d. Summarize your conclusion from your p-value.

e. The p-value you found in part (c) should have been greater than 0.05. Suppose the two brothers continue to compete and Mario continues to win 60% of the games. How many games will they have to play until he gets a p-value less than 0.05 after retesting?

SECTION 1.6

1.6.1* Which combination(s) of population proportion, π, and sample size, n, should yield a sampling distribution that is approximately normal? (Select all that apply.)

A. $\pi = 0.10$, $n = 50$.

B. $\pi = 0.30$, $n = 50$.

C. $\pi = 0.50$, $n = 40$.

D. $\pi = 0.70$, $n = 40$.

E. $\pi = 0.90$, $n = 50$.

1.6. 2 Suppose you are sampling from the students at your large school and are interested in the proportion of students that ride the bus to school. You sample 20 students and your friend samples 40 students. Which distribution of sample proportions will have the larger standard deviation?

A. Your sample of 20.

B. Your friend's sample of 40.

C. Because they are measuring the same variable, both sampling distributions will have the same standard deviation.

D. There is no way to tell until the sample is taken.

1.6.3* In a 2017 study done with Lee University students, 12% of the respondents said they would rather break a bone than lose their phone. Suppose this number is accurate for all students at that university. If we let $\hat{p}$ be the sample proportion who would rather break a bone than lose their phone from a random sample of 130 students at the university, which of the following are the mean and standard deviation for the sampling distribution of $\hat{p}$?

A. mean = 15.6, SD = 3.705

B. mean = 15.6, SD = 0.0285

C. mean = 0.12, SD = 3.705

D. mean = 0.12, SD = 0.325

E. mean = 0.12, SD = 0.0285

1.6.4 Refer to the previous exercise about the survey at Lee University. If the sample size is increased from 130 to 260, how does the new value of the standard deviation of the sampling distribution compare to the old one? To get the new SD, we would have to multiply the old one by:

A. 2

B. 1/2

C. $\sqrt{2}$

D. $1/\sqrt{2}$

E. 0

1.6.5* How does a sampling distribution differ from a simulated null distribution for a single proportion?

1.6.6 What are the mean, standard deviation, and shape of sampling distributions with the following parameters?

a. $\pi = 0.25, n = 30$.

b. $\pi = 0.75, n = 30$.

1.6.7* What are the mean, standard deviation, and shape of a sampling distribution with the following parameters?

a. $\pi = 0.50, n = 20$.

b. $\pi = 0.50, n = 40$.

1.6.8 From the formula for the standard deviation of a sampling distribution for a sample proportion, SD of $\hat{p} = \sqrt{\pi(1 - \pi)/n}$, you can see that the standard deviation of the sample proportion is affected only by the sample size and the population proportion.

a. For the sample population proportion, as the sample size increases, how does the value of SD of $\hat{p}$ change? Does it increase or decrease?

b. What value of π gives the largest value of the SD of $\hat{p}$? What value or values of π give the smallest value of SD of $\hat{p}$?

1.6.9* Suppose that, unknown to you, 60% of the students at your large school typically ride the bus to school. You and a friend are taking random samples of students to estimate this proportion. You take a sample of 30 students and your friend takes a sample of 60 students. Would it be more surprising to have a sample proportion of 0.70 for you or your friend? Explain.

1.6.10 In Example 1.1, you saw that a dolphin named Buzz pushed the correct button 15 out of 16 times. Use the **One Proportion** applet to develop a null distribution for the proportion of times Buzz would choose the correct button if he was just guessing in 16 attempts with at least 10,000 repetitions. Make sure you have Proportion of heads checked.

a. What is the SD of your simulated null distribution?

b. Theoretically, what should be the standard deviation of the null distribution?

1.6.11* In Example 1.3, you saw that 8 out of 10 of the heart transplant patients at St. George's Hospital died. You compared this with the 15% of all heart transplant patients that died shortly after receiving a heart transplant in the United Kingdom. Use the **One Proportion** applet to develop a null distribution for the proportion of heart transplant patients that would die out of 10 if there was a 15% probability that one would die. Make sure you have Proportion of heads checked and use at least 10,000 samples.

a. What is the SD of your simulated null distribution?

b. Theoretically, what should be the standard deviation of the null distribution?

1.6.12 What is the minimum sample size needed for each of the following values of π so that a normal distribution would be appropriate to model a sampling distribution of the sample proportion?

a. $\pi = 0.10$

b. $\pi = 0.30$

c. $\pi = 0.50$

d. $\pi = 0.70$

e. $\pi = 0.90$

1.6.13* An advertisement campaign that ran for years used the slogan, "Four out of five dentists surveyed would recommend Trident® to their patients who chew gum." Suppose it is true that 80% of all dentists would make this recommendation. Also suppose that we randomly sampled 400 dentists and let $\hat{p}$ be the proportion of dentists in our sample that would make this recommendation.

a. What is the mean of the sampling distribution of $\hat{p}$?

b. What is the standard deviation of the sampling distribution of $\hat{p}$?

c. Is the sampling distribution approximately normal? Explain how you made your decision.

1.6.14 Refer to the previous exercise about dentists recommending gum. Use the **One Proportion** applet (and check the box for "normal approximation") to estimate the probability that if you take a random sample of 400 dentists that 75% or fewer would recommend Trident® to their patients who chew gum.

1.6.15* Although we know some animals, like dogs, have a keen sense of smell, what about humans? A woman from Scotland, Joy Milne, claimed that she was able to determine whether someone had Parkinson's disease just based on their smell (Morgan, J. (2016). Joy of super smeller: Sebum clues for PD diagnostics. *The Lancet Neurology, 15*(2), 138–139). Her husband died from the disease and she noticed that he started smelling different prior to his diagnosis. To test this, researchers had six people known to have Parkinson's disease and six people thought not to have the disease wear t-shirts for a day. They collected the shirts and then tested Milne. She correctly identified 11 of the 12 shirts. She was adamant that one of the shirts came from someone with the disease when, in fact, that person had not been diagnosed. However, eight months later, the person she claimed had Parkinson's was given a diagnosis that he had the disease. So she, in fact, got all twelve correct!

a. We will define π as the probability that Joy Milne can correctly determine whether someone has Parkinson's disease. What is the value of π if she is just guessing? What is the range of values for π if she can do better than just guessing?

b. Let's test this scenario by first stating the null hypothesis and the alternative hypothesis in symbols.

c. What is the value of the expected standard deviation of the null distribution in this scenario?

d. What is the value of the standardized statistic (using the theoretical standard deviation) using her initial result (11/12)?

e. Use the **One Proportion** applet to simulate the null distribution. Determine the value of the standardized statistic using a simulated standard deviation.

f. Based on the standardized statistic, state the conclusion you would draw about the null and alternative hypotheses.

g. Is a normal distribution appropriate to model the sampling distribution of the sample proportion in this scenario?

h. Complete a simulation-based test or a theory-based test, whichever is more appropriate. Report your p-value. Does your p-value bring you to the same conclusion you gave in part (f)?

1.6.16 In Exploration 1.3 you were shown two faces, told one was named Bob and one was named Tim, and were asked to identify which was which. One of the authors of this text has two cousins—one named Bob and one named Tim. He wondered whether his students would be more likely than not to correctly match the names to the faces of his cousins just as they had done with the faces in the exploration. He showed the two pictures and asked whether the person on the left was named Bob or Tim. He found that 40 out of 56 students made the correct identification.

a. We will define π as the probability that a student can correctly make the identification as described above. What is the value of π if they are just guessing and are not using any visual cues to make their determination? What is the range of values for π if they are doing something better than just blindly guessing?

b. Let's test this scenario by first stating the null hypothesis and the alternative hypothesis in symbols.

c. What is the value of the expected standard deviation of the null distribution in this scenario?

d. What is the value of the standardized statistic using the theoretical standard deviation?

e. Use the **One Proportion** applet to simulate the null distribution. Determine the value of the standardized statistic based on your simulation.

f. Based on the standardized statistic, state the conclusion that you would draw about the null and alternative hypotheses.

g. Is a normal distribution appropriate to model the sampling distribution of the sample proportion in this scenario?

h. Complete a simulation-based test or a theory-based test, whichever is more appropriate. Report your p-value. Does your p-value bring you to the same conclusion you gave in part (f)?

1.6.17* The Gettysburg Address is a speech given by Abraham Lincoln during the dedication of a cemetery at the site of the Battle of Gettysburg during the Civil War. The address, which contains only 268 words, is one of the most famous speeches in American history. Among those 268 words, 125 of them (about 46.6%) contain an "e." We want to sample from the Gettysburg Address to explore sampling distributions. To do this, open up the **Sampling Words** applet, click on the pulldown box that says Length, and change it to HasE. You should see a graph of the population distribution for the proportion of words that contain an "e."

a. Suppose we take samples of 5 words from our copies of the Gettysburg Address. What do we expect for the mean and standard deviation of the sampling distribution?

b. Go to the applet and change the Sample Size from 10 to 5 and click on Draw Samples. You should see that a random sample of 5 words was taken. What proportion of your 5 words contains an "e"?

c. Now click on Draw Samples a few more times and notice what is happening with the graphs. Each time you click "Draw Samples," a sample distribution is shown, a sample proportion is calculated, and that sample proportion is added to a distribution of sample proportions. Change the Number of Samples to 10,000 and click on Draw Samples.

What are the mean and standard deviation of your distribution of sample proportions? How does that compare to your answers in part (a)?

d. Change the sample size to 10 and generate at least 10,000 samples. What are the mean and standard deviation of the distribution of sample proportions? What should they be theoretically?

1.6.18 Statistician Jessica Utts has conducted an extensive analysis of studies investigating psychic functioning. One type of study involves having one person (called the "sender") concentrate on an image, while a person in another room (the "receiver") tries to determine which image is being "sent." The receiver is given four images to choose from, one of which is the actual image that the sender is concentrating on. This is a technique called Ganzfeld. Utts (1995) cites research from Bem and Honorton (1994) that analyzed 329 Ganzfeld sessions (http://www.ics.uci.edu/~jutts/air.pdf).

Describe what the sampling distribution of sample proportions of correct identifications would look like (center, variability, shape) if the subjects in these 329 studies have no psychic ability and were just guessing.

1.6.19* Type O-negative blood is called the universal donor blood type because it is compatible with any blood type. It is estimated that 7% of the U.S. population has this blood type (http://www.livescience.com/36559-common-blood-type-donation.html).

a. Suppose you decide to take a random sample of 50 people from the U.S. and test to see whether they have type O-negative blood. (You will learn more about random samples in Chapter 2. For now, treat these as random samples from a long-run random process with a constant probability of success.) Describe the sampling distribution of the sample proportion of people with type O-negative blood (be sure to address shape, center, and variability).

b. Suppose you decide to take a random sample of 500 people from the U.S. and test to see whether they have type O-negative blood. Describe the sampling distribution of the sample proportion of people with type O-negative blood (be sure to address shape, center, and variability).

SECTION 1.7

Free throws*

1.7.1 Suppose a friend of yours says she is a 75% free-throw shooter in basketball. You don't think she is that good and want to test her to show that she makes less than 75% in the long run. You have her shoot 40 free throws and she makes 24 (or 60%) of them. Which of the following is an appropriate way to set up the hypotheses, in symbols, for this test?

A. $H_0: \hat{p} = 0.75$, $H_a: \hat{p} < 0.75$

B. $H_0: \pi = 0.75$, $H_a: \pi < 0.75$

C. $H_0: \hat{p} = 0.60$, $H_a: \hat{p} < 0.60$

D. $H_0: \pi = 0.60$, $H_a: \pi < 0.60$

E. $H_0: \pi < 0.75$, $H_a: \pi = 0.75$

1.7.2 Reconsider the scenario in Question 1.7.1 about your friend shooting free throws. Which of the following is the appropriate sample statistic and proper symbol?

A. $\hat{p} = 0.75$

B. $\pi = 0.75$

C. $\hat{p} = 0.60$

D. $\pi = 0.60$

E. $n = 24$

1.7.3 Reconsider the scenario in Question 1.7.1 about your friend shooting free throws. What is the value of the test statistic (i.e., standardized statistic)?

A. $z = 0.60$

B. $z = -0.25$

C. $z = 8.76$

D. $z = -2.19$

E. $z = -0.34$

1.7.4 Reconsider the scenario in Question 1.7.1 about your friend shooting free throws. You run this test and find a p-value of 0.014. At a 5% level of significance, which of the following is the best way to state the conclusion?

A. The obtained p-value of 0.014 is less than the α-level of 0.05; thus, there is not sufficient evidence that your friend is less than a 75% free-throw shooter in the long run.

B. The obtained p-value of 0.014 is less than the α-level of 0.05; thus, there is sufficient evidence that your friend is less than a 75% free-throw shooter in the long run.

C. There is sufficient evidence that your friend is a 75% free-throw shooter in the long run based on the obtained p-value of 0.014, which is less than the α-level of 0.05.

D. There is not sufficient evidence that your friend is less than a 60% free-throw shooter in the long run based on the obtained p-value of 0.014, which is less than the α-level of 0.05.

E. There is sufficient evidence that your friend is a 60% free-throw shooter in the long run based on the obtained p-value of 0.014, which is less than the α-level of 0.05.

1.7.5 Reconsider the scenario in Question 1.7.1 about your friend shooting free throws. Are the validity conditions met for the one-proportion z-test? Explain why or why not.

Coffee consumption

1.7.6 According to the National Coffee Drinking Study from the National Coffee Association, 40 percent of 18- to 24-year-olds in the U.S. regularly drink coffee every day. Suppose this number is accurate. In a sample of 140 students at Hope

College we found that 63 of them (or 45%) regularly drink coffee. We want to test to see whether the daily coffee-drinking habits of students at Hope College differ from the claimed national average of 40%. Which of the following is an appropriate way to set up the hypotheses, in symbols, for this test?

A. $H_0: \hat{p} = 0.40$ $H_a: \hat{p} \neq 0.40$

B. $H_0: \pi = 0.40$ $H_a: \pi \neq 0.40$

C. $H_0: \hat{p} = 0.45$ $H_a: \hat{p} \neq 0.45$

D. $H_0: \pi = 0.45$, $H_a: \pi \neq 0.45$

E. $H_0: \pi = 0.40$, $H_a: \pi > 0.40$

1.7.7 Reconsider the scenario in Question 1.7.6 about coffee consumption. Which of the following is the appropriate sample statistic and proper symbol?

A. $\hat{p} = 0.40$ **B.** $\pi = 0.40$

C. $\hat{p} = 0.45$ **D.** $\pi = 0.45$

E. $n = 1.40$

1.7.8 Reconsider the scenario in Question 1.7.6 about coffee consumption. What is the value of the test statistic (i.e., standardized statistic)?

A. $z = 1.21$ **B.** $z = 0.45$

C. $z = 0.40$ **D.** $z = 10.87$

E. $z = 0.10$

1.7.9 Reconsider the scenario in Question 1.7.6 about coffee consumption. You run this test and find a p-value of 0.23. At a 5% significance level, which of the following is the best way to state the conclusion?

A. The obtained p-value of 0.23 is greater than the α-level of 0.05; thus, there is sufficient evidence that more than 40% of all Hope College students drink coffee every day.

B. The obtained p-value of 0.23 is greater than the α-level of 0.05; thus, there is not sufficient evidence that the proportion of students at Hope College who drink coffee every day is different from 40%.

C. The obtained p-value of 0.23 is greater than the α-level of 0.05; thus, there is sufficient evidence that the proportion of students at Hope College who drink coffee every day is different from 40%.

D. The obtained p-value of 0.23 is greater than the α-level of 0.05; thus, there is not sufficient evidence that the proportion of students at Hope College who drink coffee every day is different from 45%.

E. The obtained p-value of 0.23 is greater than the α-level of 0.05; thus, there is sufficient evidence that the proportion of students at Hope College who drink coffee every day is different from 45%.

1.7.10 Reconsider the scenario in Question 1.7.6 about coffee consumption. Are the validity conditions met for a one-proportion z-test? Explain why or why not.

1.7.11 For each of the following null hypotheses, determine the fewest number of trials (or smallest sample size) needed so the validity conditions are met for completing a one-proportion z-test.

a. $H_0: \pi = 0.50$

b. $H_0: \pi = 0.80$

c. $H_0: \pi = 0.90$

d. $H_0: \pi = 0.10$

Random number?*

1.7.12 Statistics students were asked to randomly pick a whole number between 1 and 10. Sixty-two out of 101 students picked a number greater than 5. If they truly randomly picked their numbers, we would expect about half the students would pick a number greater than 5 in the long run. Do statistics students really randomly choose a number or not? Test as follows: (a) State the hypotheses in words and in symbols. (b) Name the test you will use. (c) State and verify the validity conditions for the test chosen. (d) Calculate the test statistic. (e) Calculate a p-value and state your conclusion in the context of the research question.

Kidney disease

1.7.13 Patients with kidney disease often have a procedure called dialysis done to clean their blood if their kidneys can't do this properly. This procedure is often done three days per week, with Monday, Wednesday, and Friday often being those days. In terms of the dialysis treatments, these days are all the same except for the gap of two off days before the Monday treatment. Does this gap make a difference? Cardiac arrest and sudden death for patients undergoing dialysis for kidney disease are possibilities. In recent years, it has been noted that these types of patients have cardiac arrests on Mondays more often than what would be expected. A study published in *Kidney International* (Karnik, J. et al., 2001) looked at 205 dialysis patients that had cardiac arrests on Monday, Wednesday, or Friday, the same days they had dialysis. They found that 93 of these events happened on a Monday. Do we have convincing evidence of a larger probability of cardiac arrests occurring on Mondays compared to the other two days? Test as follows: (a) State the hypotheses in words and in symbols. (b) Name the test you will use. (c) State and verify the validity conditions for the test chosen. (d) Calculate the test statistic. (e) Calculate a p-value and state your conclusion in the context of the research question.

Counting chimpanzees*

1.7.14 Many types of studies have been done to see whether animals have a sense of numbers. In one study (Beran & Beran, 2004), researchers wanted to see whether chimpanzees could remember how many items were added to a container when they see them added one at a time. To do this, the researchers had two containers set up so the chimpanzees could not see inside them. They randomly added bananas to the containers one at a time and then had the chimpanzees choose the container they wanted. In one set of experiments, they added 3 bananas to one container and 4 to the other and had a chimpanzee named Mercury pick which container he wanted. In 20 trials, he picked the container containing 4 bananas 16 times. Does this show that Mercury is more likely to pick the container with more bananas in it in the long run? Test as follows: (a) State the hypotheses in words and in symbols. (b) Name the test you will use. (c) State and verify the validity conditions for the test chosen. (d) Calculate the test statistic. (e) Calculate a p-value and state your conclusion in the context of the research question.

1.7.15 Recall the previous question on whether chimpanzees are more likely to pick the container containing more bananas. In another set of 20 trials (again with 3 bananas in one container and 4 in the other), a chimpanzee named Panzee picked the one containing 4 bananas 11 times. Does this show that Panzee is more likely to pick the container with more bananas in it in the long run? Test as follows: (a) State the hypotheses in words and in symbols. (b) Name the test you will use. (c) State and verify the validity conditions for the test chosen. (d) Calculate the test statistic. (e) Calculate a p-value and state your conclusion in the context of the research question.

Blindsight

1.7.16 Due to injury or other medical conditions, people can develop blindness on just one side of their vision field. Because of brain damage, a patient whom N. Persaud and colleagues called GY in a *Nature Neuroscience* article was right-side blind, meaning he could not see anything in his right field of vision. (Blindsight is a condition in which people are blind but can still respond to things they cannot consciously see.) Could GY "see" objects in his right field of vision even though he has no conscious perception of the objects? Researchers tested GY on this by having him face a video monitor where they would run trials by sometimes having a square appear on the right side of the monitor and sometimes not. In 200 trials, GY correctly determined whether the square appeared or not 141 times. Is GY more likely than random chance to correctly identify whether or not the square was present? Test as follows: (a) State the hypotheses in words and in symbols. (b) Name the test you will use. (c) State and verify the validity conditions for the test chosen. (d) Calculate the test statistic. (e) Calculate a p-value and state your conclusion in the context of the research question.

1.7.17 Recall the previous exercise about GY and blindsight. To test GY's awareness of whether he correctly identified if the square was present or not, the researchers had him wager on whether or not he thought he was correct after he made his choice. He had to bet either a British pound or half a pound on whether his guess was correct. If he was correct, that amount was added to his earnings, and if he was not correct, that amount was subtracted. So, he should make the high wager when he was more confident in his choice. In the 141 times he correctly identified whether the square was present or not, he made the high wager 67 times. When he has made a correct choice, is GY more likely to make the high wager than the small wager (and thus have some real conscious awareness of the object being present or not)? Test as follows: (a) State the hypotheses in words and in symbols. (b) Name the test you will use. (c) State and verify the validity conditions for the test chosen. (d) Calculate the test statistic. (e) Calculate a p-value and state your conclusion in the context of the research question.

BO and genetics*

1.7.18 Researchers, reporting in *Chemical Senses* (Roberts, S. et al., 2005) and interested in body odor as it relates to genetics, compared body odor between adult identical twins that were not living together. They had the female identical twins follow a complex hygiene regimen and were told not to come in contact with a variety of odors (garlic, smoke, perfume, etc.) 24 hours prior to the collection of their odors. They then attached pads to the upper part of their bodies and covered up with a cotton t-shirt before they went to bed. The pads were collected the next morning. Sniffers were then assigned to sniff a pad and try to match it with one of four pads, where one was from the identical twin and the other three were from non-relatives. The 113 sniffers correctly matched 42 odors to that of the twin. Are the sniffers more likely than random chance to make a correct match? Test as follows: (a) State the hypotheses in words and in symbols. (b) Name the test you will use. (c) State and verify the validity conditions for the test chosen. (d) Calculate the test statistic. (e) Calculate a p-value and state your conclusion in the context of the research question.

1.7.19 Recall the previous question about identical twins and similar body odors. The researchers in this study also ran the same kind of test using non-identical female twins. The 113 sniffers were given a pad to sniff that one of the twins wore. They were then given four other pads, one of which came from the other twin. The 113 sniffers were able to make a correct match 35 times. Are the sniffers more likely than random chance to make a correct match? Test as follows: (a) State the hypotheses in words and in symbols. (b) Name the test you will use. (c) State and verify the validity conditions for the test chosen. (d) Calculate the test statistic. (e) Calculate a p-value and state your conclusion in the context of the research question.

Spinning coins

1.7.20 While flipping a coin should result in 50% heads and 50% tails in the long run, will spinning coins on a table give the same result or not? Test this with a coin of your choice, making sure you have enough trials to meet the validity conditions of a one-proportion z-test. In doing so: (a) State the hypotheses in words and in symbols. (b) State and verify the validity conditions for the one proportion *z*-test. (c) State the sample statistic symbol and its value. (d) Calculate the test statistic. (e) Calculate a p-value and state your conclusion in the context of the research question.

END OF CHAPTER

1.CE.1* A p-value is calculated assuming that which hypothesis is true: null or alternative?

1.CE.2 The standard deviation of a null distribution is calculated using which value: the probability value in the null hypothesis or the observed value of the sample proportion?

Fantasy golf*

1.CE.3 A statistics professor is in a fantasy golf league with four friends. Each week one of the five people in the league is the winner of that week's tournament. During the 2010 season, this particular professor was the winner in 7 of the first 12 weeks of the season. Does this constitute strong evidence that his probability of winning in one week was larger than would be expected if the five competitors were equally likely to win?

a. State the null hypothesis and the alternative hypothesis in the context of the study.

b. Describe how you could use playing cards to conduct a tactile simulation analysis of this study and its result. Give sufficient detail that someone else could implement this simulation analysis based on your description. Be sure to indicate how you would decide whether the observed data provide convincing evidence that the statistics professor's probability of winning in one week was larger than would be expected if the five competitors were equally likely to win?

c. Use an applet to conduct a simulation analysis with at least 1,000 repetitions. Based on the null distribution produced by the applet, explain how you are deciding whether the observed data provide convincing evidence that the statistics professor's probability of winning in one week was larger than would be expected if the five competitors were equally likely to win. Summarize the conclusion that you would draw about the research question of whether the statistics professor's probability of winning in one week was larger than would be expected if the five competitors were equally likely to win.

d. In answering (c), you should have reported a p-value. Interpret this p-value in the context of the study. (*Hint:* The p-value is the probability of what, assuming what?)

e. Explain why it is not advisable to use a one-proportion *z*-test (theory-based approach) to find a p-value for the data from this study.

Mythbusters

1.CE.4 On the television show *Mythbusters*, the hosts Jamie and Adam wanted to investigate which side buttered toast prefers to land on when it falls through the air. To replicate a piece of toast falling through the air, they set up a specially designed rig on the roof of the *Mythbusters'* headquarters. In 48 attempts, 19 pieces of toast fell buttered side down. Do these data provide evidence that buttered toast falling through air has a preference for any specific side (buttered or not buttered) when landing? Write a report describing all six steps of the statistical investigation method as they apply to this question and these data.

Cheating*

Use this information to answer the following two questions. The August 19, 2013, issue of *Sports Illustrated* included a brief article titled "Why Men Cheat," in which the author L. Jon Wertheim argued that Major League Baseball (MLB) players from the United States are less likely than those from poorer countries to take performance-enhancing drugs (PEDs). The article mentioned that 57.3% of all professional baseball players between 2005 and 2013 were from the U.S., and 206 of the 595 (34.6%) players suspended for PED use in these years were from the U.S.

1.CE.5

a. One question is whether 0.346, the observed proportion of PED-suspended players from the U.S., is (statistically) significantly less than 0.573, the proportion of all players from the U.S. Before you attempt to answer this question, explain what the question means (i.e., what statistical significance means) in this context. Write as if to a friend who is a baseball fan but has not studied statistics.

b. Perform a simulation analysis to investigate the question in part (a). Write a paragraph summarizing the results and conclusion that you draw from your simulation analysis, again as if to a friend who is a baseball fan but has not studied statistics.

c. Calculate the value of the standardized statistic (*z*-value) for comparing 34.6% to 57.3% in this context. Interpret what this value means and summarize the conclusion that you can draw from it.

1.CE.6 Additional information supplied in the *Sports Illustrated* article was that 34.6% of all professional baseball players are from Latin-American countries, but 368 of the 595 (61.8%) players suspended for PED use between 2005 and 2013 are from Latin-American countries. Answer parts (a) to (c) of the previous exercise with respect to the question of whether 61.8% is (statistically) significantly greater than 34.6% in this study.

Bob or Tim?

Use the following information to answer the next two questions. Gary Judkins is a teacher in New Zealand who asked his students the question about facial prototyping from Exploration 1.3. Mr. Judkins asked this question of 135 New Zealand students and found that 105 of the students associated the name Tim with the face on the left.

1.CE.7

a. Express the appropriate null and alternative hypotheses, in symbols and in words, for testing whether New Zealand students have a tendency to associate the name Tim with the face on the left.

b. Conduct a simulation analysis to test these hypotheses with data from Mr. Judkins's students. Summarize your conclusion.

c. Is it appropriate to use a theory-based approach with these data? Justify your answer.

d. Implement a theory-based approach to test the hypotheses in part (a). Report the values of the test statistic and p-value. Summarize your conclusion.

1.CE.8 Reconsider the previous exercise. Suppose that you were to define the parameter π, not as the probability that a New Zealand student would associate the name Tim with the face on the left, but as the probability that a New Zealand student would associate the name *Bob* with the face on the left. Re-answer parts (a) to (d) of the previous exercise with this different set-up. Comment on how (if at all) your calculations and conclusions change.

Coin flipping*

1.CE.9 Suppose that Jose and Roberto both collect data to investigate whether people tend to call "heads" more often than "tails" when they are asked to call the result of a coin flip. If Jose uses a larger sample size than Roberto, is Jose guaranteed to have a smaller p-value than Roberto? Explain why or why not.

1.CE.10 Suppose that Sasha and Jayla both collect data to investigate whether people tend to call "heads" more often than "tails" when they are asked to call the result of a coin flip. If Sasha has a smaller p-value than Jayla, which of the following would you conclude? (There may be more than one correct conclusion.)

a. Sasha has stronger evidence than Jayla that people tend to call "heads" more often than "tails."

b. Jayla has stronger evidence than Sasha that people tend to call "heads" more often than "tails."

c. Both Sasha and Jayla have convincing evidence that people tend to call "heads" more often than "tails."

d. Sasha must have used a larger sample size than Jayla.

e. Sasha must have used a smaller sample size than Jayla.

Family structure

1.CE.11 Josephine wants to investigate whether more than one-third of families with two children have one child of each sex, so she collects data for 50 two-child families. Describe how she could use a die to perform a physical (by hand, without using a computer) simulation to approximate the null distribution.

1.CE.12 Alfonso wants to investigate whether fewer than one-fourth of families with two children have two girls, so he collects data for 25 two-child families. Describe how he could use coins to perform a physical (by hand, without using a computer) simulation to approximate the null distribution.

Athletic performance*

1.CE.13 Rick is a basketball player who wants to investigate whether he successfully makes more than 90% of his free throws by shooting with an underhand style.

a. Define (in words) the relevant parameter of interest for Rick.

b. State (in words and in symbols) the appropriate hypotheses to be tested by Rick.

1.CE.14 Lorena is a golfer who wants to investigate whether she successfully makes more than 60% of her 10-foot putts.

a. Define (in words) the relevant parameter of interest for Lorena.

b. State (in words and in symbols) the appropriate hypotheses to be tested by Lorena.

Odd numbers

Use the following information to answer the following two questions. Many studies have investigated the question of whether people tend to think of an odd number when they are asked to think of a single-digit number (0 through 9). Combining results from several studies, Kubovy and Psotka (1976) used a sample size of 1,770 people, of whom 741 thought of an even number and 1,029 thought of an odd number. Consider investigating whether these data provide strong evidence that people have a tendency to think of an odd number rather than an even number in this situation.

1.CE.15

a. Describe the relevant parameter of interest.

b. State the appropriate hypotheses to be tested.

c. Calculate the observed value of the appropriate statistic.

d. Check whether a theory-based approach is appropriate for these data and hypotheses.

e. Calculate the standardized value of the statistic.

f. Determine an approximate p-value.

g. Summarize your conclusion.

1.CE.16 Refer to the previous exercise. The researchers also found that 503 of the 1,770 people thought of the number 7. Do these data provide strong evidence that people have a tendency to select the number 7 disproportionately often? Investigate this question by answering parts (a) to (g) of the previous exercise.

Racket spinning*

1.CE.17 One of the authors once spun his tennis racquet 100 times and found that it landed with the label up for 46 of those 100 spins (0.46). For testing whether the probability (that a spun tennis racquet lands with the label up) differs from 0.50, he calculated the p-value to be 0.484.

a. Summarize the conclusion that you would draw from this study.

b. Explain the reasoning process that leads to your conclusion, as if to someone with no knowledge of statistics.

1.CE.18 Reconsider the previous exercise. Notice that three different decimal numbers appear: 0.46, 0.484, and 0.50. Identify which is the null-hypothesized probability, which is the observed value of the statistic, and which is the p-value.

Your own random process

1.CE.19 Think of a random process of interest to you for which you would be interested in assessing evidence regarding a claim about the value of the long-run proportion associated with the random process.

a. Describe the random process.

b. Describe the parameter of interest.

c. State the null and alternative hypotheses that you would be interested in investigating.

d. Describe how you could collect data to conduct this statistical investigation.

INVESTIGATION: TIRE STORY FALLS FLAT

PART I

A legendary story on college campuses concerns two students who miss a chemistry exam because of excessive partying but blame their absence on a flat tire. The professor allows them to take a make-up exam, and sends them to separate rooms to take it. The first question, worth 5 points, is quite easy. The second question, worth 95 points, asks: Which tire was it?

STEP 1: Ask a research question. Do students pick which tire went flat in equal proportions? It has been conjectured that when students are asked this question and forced to give an answer (left front, left rear, right front, or right rear) off the top of their head, they tend to answer "right front" more than would be expected by random chance.

STEP 2: Design a study and collect data. To test this conjecture about the right front tire, a recent class of 28 students was asked, if they were in this situation, which tire would they say had gone flat. We obtained the following results:

Left front	Left rear	Right front	Right rear
6	4	14	4

1. What are the observational units?
2. What is the variable that is measured/recorded on each observational unit?
3. Describe the parameter of interest in words. (You can use the symbol π to represent this parameter.)
4. State the appropriate null and alternative hypotheses to be tested.

STEP 3: Explore the data

5. What percentage of the students picked the right front tire? Is this more than you would expect if students randomly pick one of the four tires?
6. Is it *possible* that we could observe 14 students from this class of 28 students even if all of the students were just selecting randomly among the four tires?

STEP 4: Draw inferences.   Let's use our 3S strategy to help us investigate how much evidence the sample data provide to support our conjecture that there is something special about the right front tire.

Statistic

7. What is the statistic that you can use to summarize the data collected in the study and what symbol is associated with this statistic?

Simulate

8. Use the **One Proportion** applet to simulate 1,000 repetitions of this study, assuming that every student in class selects randomly (equally) among the four tires. Report what values you input into the applet.

   Probability of success (π)_____

   Sample size (n) _____

   Number of samples _____

9. Using the proportion of successes for the values on the horizontal axis, what is the center of your null distribution? Does it make sense that this is the center? Explain.

Strength of evidence

10. Let's examine the strength of evidence with the three ways we used in Chapter 1.

    a. Determine the p-value from your simulation analysis. Also interpret what this p-value represents (i.e., the probability of what, assuming what?).

    b. Determine the standardized statistic from your simulation analysis. Also interpret what this standardized statistic represents.

    c. Use a theory-based test (or normal approximation) to determine the p-value for this test. Are the validity conditions met for this test? Why or why not?

11. Is there strong evidence against the null hypothesis for all three of the methods used in Question 11? Explain.

STEP 5: Formulate conclusions.

12. Summarize the conclusion that you draw from this study and your simulation analysis. Also explain the reasoning process behind your conclusion.

13. Now, let's step back a bit and think about the scope of our inference. What are the wider implications? Do you think that your conclusion holds true for people in general? (These are extremely important questions that we'll discuss more when we talk about the scope of inference in Chapter 2.)

STEP 5: Look back and ahead.

14. If you were to repeat this study, what improvements might you make? What further research might you propose related to this topic in the future?

PART II

Now suppose another class conducts the same study with exactly half as many students and the proportional breakdown in the four categories is identical to the class of 28. In other words, 7 out of 14 students answered "right front."

15. Before you analyze the data, would you expect to find stronger evidence for the research conjecture (that people pick the right front tire more than one-fourth of the time), weaker evidence, or the same strength of evidence? Explain your thinking.

16. Conduct a simulation analysis to produce a simulated p-value. How does it compare to the p-value from the study of the class with 28 students? Is this what you expected? Explain.

PART III

Suppose we didn't have a preconceived notion that the right front tire would be chosen more often, but just wanted to find out if it was chosen at a rate that was different than 1/4. Let's use our original data where 14 out of 28 chose the right front tire to test this.

17. Write the null and alternative hypotheses for this new question.

18. Use a theory-based test to find the p-value. How does this compare with the p-value you obtained back in Question 11c.

19. Do you have strong evidence that the long-run proportion of times a student will choose the right front tire is different than 1/4?

Research Article   www.wiley.com/college/tintle

Infants prefer to harm those who are different   Read "Not like me = Bad: Infants prefer those who harm dissimilar others" by Hamlin, Mahajan, Liberman, and Wynn (*Psychological Science*, 2013, 24:589)

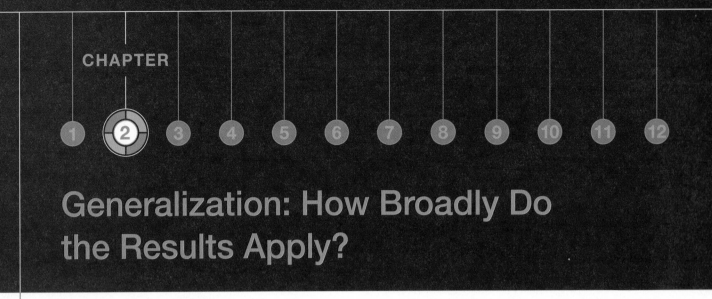
Generalization: How Broadly Do the Results Apply?

CHAPTER OVERVIEW

This chapter is about *generalization*, one of the four pillars of inference: strength, size, *breadth*, and cause. How *broadly* do the conclusions apply?

Polling organizations like Gallup and Harris take weekly polls on various issues. They claim to estimate how all adult Americans think. Have you ever been polled by Gallup? If not, how can Gallup think that your opinion has been represented? When pollsters ask only 1,000 or 1,500 people, can they get useful and reliable information about all Americans?

In Chapter 1, we looked at data from a potentially never-ending random process. For example, Buzz was making choices (e.g., which button to push) that were variable (he didn't always get it right). We set up a chance (null) model for his choices (making the correct choice had the same probability for each trial). In this model, his probability of making a correct choice was 0.50 each time. We repeated the chance process to see how the statistic behaved over the long run and used the could-have-been results to measure the strength of evidence against the null hypothesis that Buzz was just guessing.

So far, so good. But when we look at polling data, we begin to run into a different source of variability—the selection of the observational units. If Gallup chooses a different set of people to interview, each person's opinion won't change, but each different set of people will have its own value for the proportion voting yes. Now the variability is in which group of people are selected, rather than in the response outcomes in repeated trials of a random process.

But our goal in such a study is not only to describe the *sample* that we see, but hopefully to *generalize* characteristics of the sample to a much larger *population* of individuals. We rely on the sample to tell us about the population when the population is too large for us to gather data on each and every individual, or individuals are inaccessible, or

UIG via Getty Images

it is too expensive to gather data on every individual. But this only works when the sample is *representative* of the population.

So now we have two questions:

- How do we obtain a sample that is representative of the larger population?
- How do we model the randomness in the sampling process in order to make inferences about a larger population based only on the sample?

The main goal of this chapter is to explain when and why you can (sometimes) think of choosing your sample as a chance process. When you can, all of the techniques and theoretical results from Chapter 1 apply. When you can't, caution is the order of the day.

In this chapter, you will first learn about how random sampling works in practice and when you can draw inferences in the same way no matter whether you are sampling from a process or from a population. You will also explore different types of random sampling methods. You will also take a closer look at *quantitative data*, learning how random sampling suggests a way to make inferences about a population mean and that the reasoning process from Chapter 1 works for population means also. Finally, you will be reminded that when we make inferences, there is always the chance that we will make the wrong decision, but we have some control over how often this happens.

SAMPLING FROM A FINITE POPULATION   SECTION 2.1

INTRODUCTION

Suppose you want to assess the opinion of students at your school on some issue (e.g., funding of sports teams). The observational units in such an investigation would be the individual students. The *population* of interest would be all students at your school. If you had the time and resources to interview all students at your school, you would be conducting a *census* and you would know exactly what proportion of students at your school agree on the issue (e.g., to increase funding). But what if you don't have such time and resources? If you only interview a subset of the students at your school, this subset is the *sample,* and the proportion or any number you calculate about this sample would again be considered a *statistic* as in Chapter 1. In this case, the corresponding *parameter* of interest can be defined as the proportion of *all* students at your school that agree on the issue. The key question is how can we obtain a statistic that we trust to be reasonably close to the actual (but unknown to us) value of the parameter? And just how close do we think we might be? It turns out that the key is how you select the sample from the population.

Sampling Students

Colleges and universities collect lots of data on their students. We have data from the registrar at a small midwestern college (hereafter known as "College of the Midwest") on all students enrolled at the college in spring 2011. Two of the variables from the registrar are the student's cumulative GPA and whether or not the student is housed on campus. Table 2.1 shows a partial data table for these students.

Notice that whether or not a student is housed on campus is the kind of variable that we focused on in Chapter 1 (specifically, a categorical variable with two categories), whereas cumulative GPA contains numeric data and is a *quantitative* variable, which we first discussed in the Preliminaries.

2.1A

EXAMPLE

Example 2.1A

2.1A.1

Definitions

The **population** is the entire collection of observational units we are interested in, and the **sample** is a subset of the population on which we record data. Numerical summaries about a population are called **parameters**, and numerical summaries calculated from a sample are called **statistics**.

2.1A.2

Definition

A **data table** (or statistical spreadsheet) is a convenient way to store and represent all data values. Typically, in a data table, the rows correspond to observational units, columns represent variables, and the data are the table entries.

2.1A.3

Definition

A **histogram** is a graph that summarizes the distribution of a quantitative variable. Bar heights are used to represent the number of observational units in a particular interval of values.

TABLE 2.1	Data table of College of the Midwest	
Student ID	Cumulative GPA	On campus?
1	3.92	Yes
2	2.80	Yes
3	3.08	Yes
4	2.71	No
5	3.31	Yes
6	3.83	Yes
7	3.80	No
8	3.58	Yes
...	...	...

If we are only interested in students at this college, then we have data for the entire population of 2,919 students. In this case, we can actually examine the distributions of these variables for the entire population (Figure 2.1).

FIGURE 2.1 Population distributions for cumulative GPA (quantitative) and whether or not student lives on campus (categorical).

The figure on the left is called a **histogram**. Like a *dotplot*, it displays the distribution of a quantitative variable. But when you have a large number of observations like this, it may be convenient to "bin" together similar observations into one bar. The height of each bar tells you how many of the values are in each bin (interval of values). The graph still helps us see features of the distribution, like that the GPA values are not symmetric but cluster around 3.30, with most GPAs falling between 2.00 and 4.00 and some falling below 2.00 but none above 4.00.

However, we don't usually have the luxury of having access to the data on every member of the population. Instead, we would like to make inferences about the entire population based only on data from a sample of observational units. Now let's suppose that a researcher does not have access to our data for the population and, in fact, only has time to collect data on a sample of students. Suppose the researcher decides to ask the first 30 students he finds on campus one morning whether he or she lives on campus. This sampling plan is certainly convenient and allows him to select his sample quickly.

THINK ABOUT IT

- For this context, describe the population, sample, parameter, and statistic.
- Do you think this researcher's sampling plan is likely to obtain a sample proportion that live on campus that is close to the population proportion that live on campus?

A sample is only useful to us if the data we collect on our sample are similar to the results we would find in the entire population. In this sense, we say the sample is **representative** of the population. This researcher would like his sample of 30 students to have a similar proportion living on campus (the statistic) as the proportion of all students at this college that live on campus (the parameter). However, it's quite possible to think the first 30 students he sees on campus in the early morning are more likely to be on-campus students than those he might find later in the day. In fact, if he repeatedly applies this method every day, even if he finds different samples of students, we suspect that his samples are likely to consistently overestimate the proportion of students that live on campus. In this sense, we would say his sampling method is *biased*—likely to produce sample statistics that consistently overestimate the population parameter.

Note that bias is a property of a sampling *method*, not a property of an individual sample. Also note that the sampling method must *consistently* produce nonrepresentative results in one direction in order to be considered biased. Sampling bias also depends on what is being measured. One could argue that this sampling method would also be biased in estimating the average (or mean) GPA of students at the college: Students with lower GPAs may be more likely to be sleeping in and not present on campus first thing early in the morning. However, if we look at the proportion of students with black hair, it's hard to imagine why this early morning sampling method would consistently over- or undersample those students compared to the rest of the population. So, one could argue that the early morning sampling method might produce a *representative* sample with regard to hair color but not with respect to living on campus or GPA.

2.1A.4

> **Definition**
>
> A sampling method is **biased** if, under that sampling method, statistics from different samples *consistently* overestimate or consistently underestimate the population parameter of interest.

> **THINK ABOUT IT**
>
> So what can the researcher do instead? What would be a better way of selecting a sample of 30 students from this population to try to obtain a representative sample?

SIMPLE RANDOM SAMPLES

The key to obtaining a representative sample is using some type of *random* mechanism to select the observational units from the population, rather than relying on **convenience samples** or any type of human judgment.

The most common type of random sample is the **simple random sample**.

> **Definition**
>
> A **convenience sample** is a nonrandom sample of a population.

> **KEY IDEA**
>
> A **simple random sample** ensures that every sample of size n is equally likely to be the sample selected from the population. In particular, each observational unit has the same chance of being selected as every other observational unit.

To take a simple random sample you need a list of all individuals (observational units) in the population, called the **sampling frame**. A computer is then used to randomly select some of the individuals in the sampling frame. We note that if the sampling frame is not a list of all individuals in the population of interest, then the resulting random sampling process can still be biased.

To understand the benefits of such an approach, we will see what happens when we take a simple random sample of students from the College of the Midwest. (This is of course a somewhat artificial example because we really do have access to the values for the entire population, so there's no need to examine only a sample. But this exercise of taking several simple random samples will allow us to explore properties of this approach.) Students are represented by ID numbers 1 to 2919, the number of students in the population. The computer then randomly selects numbers between 1 and 2919. Suppose that the computer chooses the number 827. So we find the student whose ID number is 827. He or she is selected for our sample. Then the computer chooses 1,355. This student is also selected for our sample. Table 2.2 shows the IDs of the 30 people selected for our sample, along with their cumulative GPA and residential status.

2.1A.5

2.1A.6

TABLE 2.2   Results for a simple random sample of 30 students

ID	Cumulative GPA	On campus?	ID	Cumulative GPA	On campus?	ID	Cumulative GPA	On campus?
827	3.44	Y	844	3.59	N	825	3.94	Y
1,355	2.15	Y	90	3.30	Y	2,339	3.07	N
1,455	3.08	Y	1,611	3.08	Y	2,064	3.48	Y
2,391	2.91	Y	2,550	3.41	Y	2,604	3.10	Y
575	3.94	Y	2,632	2.61	Y	2,147	2.84	Y
2,049	3.64	N	2,325	3.36	Y	2,590	3.39	Y
895	2.29	N	2,563	3.02	Y	1,718	3.01	Y
1,732	3.17	Y	1,819	3.55	N	168	3.04	Y
2,790	2.88	Y	968	3.86	Y	1,777	3.83	Y
2,237	3.25	Y	566	3.60	N	2,077	3.46	Y

Once we have our sample, we can calculate sample statistics. For example: What is the average cumulative GPA for these 30 students? What proportion of these students live on campus?

In Statistics, we use the symbol $\bar{x}$ ("x-bar") to denote the sample average and the symbol $\hat{p}$ to denote the sample proportion. It is easy enough to calculate $\bar{x} = 3.24$ and $\hat{p} = 0.80$ from these sample data, but how do we know whether these values are at all close to the population values? If we had taken a different sample of 30 students, we would probably have obtained completely different values for these statistics. So, how are these statistics of any use in estimating the population parameter values?

> **NOTE**
>
> Whereas $\bar{x}$ and $\hat{p}$ are common symbols used to denote the sample average and sample proportion, respectively, the corresponding population values are usually denoted by μ and π. Similarly, s is the symbol commonly used to denote the sample standard deviation, with σ the typical symbol used to denote the population standard deviation. The use of Greek letters to denote population parameters helps remind us that the actual values of parameters are typically unknown to us.

> **NOTATION CHECK**
>
> Here is a quick summary of the symbols we've introduced in this section.
>
> | Type of Variable | Quantitative | Categorical |
> |---|---|---|
> | Statistics | $\bar{x}$ = sample mean | $\hat{p}$ = sample proportion |
> | | s = sample standard deviation | |
> | Parameters | μ = population mean | π = population proportion |
> | | σ = population standard deviation | |

In order to understand the behavior of sample statistics calculated from simple random samples, let's take more simple random samples of 30 students from the same population to examine the distribution of the statistics across samples. Table 2.3 shows the values of the two statistics for five different simple random samples of 30 students.

TABLE 2.3 Observed statistics resulting from five different random samples of 30 students					
Random sample	1	2	3	4	5
Sample average GPA ($\bar{x}$)	3.22	3.29	3.40	3.26	3.25
Sample proportion on campus ($\hat{p}$)	0.80	0.83	0.77	0.63	0.83

There are a few interesting things to note about these values. First, each simple random sample gave us different values for the statistics. That is, there is variability from sample to sample (**sampling variability**). This makes sense because the samples are chosen randomly and consist of different students each time, so we expect some differences from sample to sample. You also might notice that despite the variability, the values aren't changing that much: the average GPAs range from 3.22 to 3.40 and the sample proportions range from 0.63 to 0.83. Lastly, we should point out that the population parameters (that is, the true average cumulative GPA among all 2,919 students and the true proportion of the 2,919 students who live on campus) are $\mu = 3.29$ and $\pi \approx 0.776$ (2,265/2,919). (See Figure 2.1.) We can see that the statistics tend to be fairly close to the values of each of the parameters.

Let's see what happens if we take 1,000 different simple random samples. The two histograms in Figure 2.2 show the values of the sample average GPA and the sample proportion of students who live on campus in 1,000 different simple random samples of 30 students.

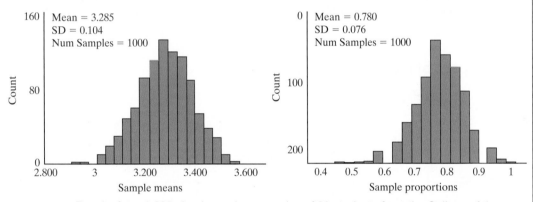

FIGURE 2.2   Results from 1,000 simple random samples of 30 students from the College of the Midwest.

Taking 1,000 random samples helps us see the long-run pattern to these results. In particular, with both statistics (sample mean and sample proportion), the middle of the distribution falls very near the value of the corresponding population parameter. In fact, the average of the 1,000 sample averages on the left turns out to be 3.285, which is almost exactly the same as the population parameter (average GPA among all 2,919 students is $\mu = 3.29$). Similarly, the average of the 1,000 sample proportions turns out to be 0.780, very close to the population proportion of 0.776 (proportion of all 2,919 students who live on campus, π). In fact, if we took all possible random samples of 30 students from this population (rather than just 1,000 samples as shown here), the averages of these statistics would match the parameters exactly.

(Another interesting observation from Figure 2.2 is that both of these distributions have the familiar mound-shaped, symmetric pattern, even though the population distributions did not!)

This example illustrates that sample means and sample proportions computed from simple random samples cluster around the population parameter and the average of those could-have-been statistics equals the value of the population parameter. Thus, simple random sampling would be considered an **unbiased** sampling method because there is no tendency to over- or underestimate the parameter. Whether a sampling method is biased or unbiased

2.1A.7 depends both on the sampling method and on the statistic you chose to calculate from the sample. Luckily, one can show that with simple random sampling the sample average and the sample proportion both have this unbiased property. Although we don't know for sure whether the initially proposed convenience sample of selecting the first 30 people seen on campus provides a reasonable estimate of the parameter, this unbiased property gives us faith that a simple random sample is representative of the population.

> ### KEY IDEA
>
> When we use *simple random sampling*, the average of the sample means from different samples equals the population mean and the average of the sample proportions from different samples equals the population proportion. (This means that these statistics are *unbiased* estimators for the corresponding parameter when we use simple random sampling.)

Although selecting a simple random sample is not always feasible (e.g., what if you don't have a complete sampling frame, what if it is too difficult to track down everyone selected?), it is an example of a broader class of probability sampling methods (e.g., stratified sampling, cluster sampling—see the Stratified and Cluster Sampling Appendix) that also have the same properties. The key is that probability, not human judgment, is responsible for selecting the sample.

Impact of increasing sample size

> ### THINK ABOUT IT
>
> Suppose the researcher at the College of the Midwest decides 30 students may not be enough and decides to sample 75 students using his same early morning sampling method. Do you think this will make his sampling method any less biased?

If the researcher's sampling method tends to oversample students who live on campus, then selecting more students *in the same manner* will not fix this. A larger sample size does not imply our results are more representative or that the sampling method is any less biased. It is actually more effective to select a smaller but truly random sample than a large convenience sample!

2.1A.8 Of course, there are some benefits to using a larger sample size, as you saw in the previous chapter. With a larger sample size, there will be less sample-to-sample variability, and the statistics from different samples will cluster more closely around the center of the distribution (the statistical ball park will be smaller). But the random (unbiased) sampling method is what convinces us that the center of that distribution is in the right place.

Scope of inference: Generalizing results from the sample to the population

Simple random sampling (and probability sampling methods in general) allows us to believe that our sample is representative of the larger population and that the observed sample statistic is "in the ball park" of the population parameter. For this reason, when we use simple random sampling, we will be willing to *generalize* the characteristics of our sample to the entire population. But the next question is "how large is that ballpark?" That is, how far do we think any one observed statistic could be from the parameter? We will investigate that in the next example.

2.1A.9

YOU MAY BE ASKING

> But, what if you don't have a simple random sample? Many people use convenience samples and other sampling designs where the observational units are not randomly selected from the population.

When we have convenience samples, we have no guarantee that the sample is representative of the population. For example, imagine we were trying to learn about how long baseball games take at the major league level. Suppose further that we think of this research question in April and decide to look at all games played within the previous week. Is this a bad idea? Well, this is not a random sample. A random sample would involve making a list of all of the major league baseball games over a certain time frame (e.g., an entire season or several seasons) and randomly choosing a subset of the games. Instead, we've just conveniently looked up the information for the last week's worth of games. But, do games in April really differ with regard to length as compared to games from other times of the year? If they don't, then you might argue that your convenience sample, although not random, is still representative of the population, at least with respect to game lengths. But…maybe the game lengths are different in April. Maybe there are more rain delays or maybe managers use more relief pitchers earlier in the season. That's the problem with convenience samples. They are convenient, but we have no guarantees that they are representative—we're left to try to think about all the ways they might not be representative—a dangerous proposition. Of course, if we were trying to use our sample of games to look at game time temperature, that would probably be a pretty bad idea and lead to some very misleading statistics! Instead, the effort to select a simple random sample may end up saving you time and effort later.

Sampling Words

EXPLORATION 2.1A

1. Select a representative set of 10 words from the passage by circling them with your pen or pencil.

> Four score and seven years ago, our fathers brought forth upon this continent a new nation: conceived in liberty, and dedicated to the proposition that all men are created equal.
>
> Now we are engaged in a great civil war, testing whether that nation, or any nation so conceived and so dedicated, can long endure. We are met on a great battlefield of that war.
>
> We have come to dedicate a portion of that field as a final resting place for those who here gave their lives that that nation might live. It is altogether fitting and proper that we should do this.
>
> But, in a larger sense, we cannot dedicate, we cannot consecrate, we cannot hallow this ground. The brave men, living and dead, who struggled here have consecrated it, far above our poor power to add or detract. The world will little note, nor long remember, what we say here, but it can never forget what they did here.
>
> It is for us the living, rather, to be dedicated here to the unfinished work which they who fought here have thus far so nobly advanced. It is rather for us to be here dedicated to the great task remaining before us, that from these honored dead we take increased devotion to that cause for which they gave the last full measure of devotion, that we here highly resolve that these dead shall not have died in vain, that this nation, under God, shall have a new birth of freedom, and that government of the people, by the people, for the people, shall not perish from the earth.

The authorship of literary works is often a topic for debate. For example, researchers have tried to determine whether some of the works attributed to Shakespeare were actually written by Bacon or Marlow. The field of "literary computing" examines ways of numerically analyzing authors' works, looking at variables such as sentence length and rates of occurrence of specific words.

Definitions

The **population** is the entire collection of observational units we are interested in, and the **sample** is a subset of the population on which we record data. Numerical summaries about a population are called **parameters**, and numerical summaries calculated from a sample are called **statistics**.

The passage is, of course, Lincoln's Gettysburg Address, given November 19, 1863, on the battlefield near Gettysburg, Pennsylvania. We are considering this passage a *population* of words, and the 10 words you selected are considered a *sample* from this population. In most studies, we do not have access to the entire population and can only consider results for a sample from that population, but to learn more about the process of sampling and its implications, we will now deal with a somewhat artificial scenario where we sample from this known population.

2. Record each word from your sample and then indicate the length of the word (number of letters) and whether or not the word contains at least one letter *e*.

Word	Length (no. of letters)	Contains e? (Y or N)
1.		
2.		
3.		
4.		
5.		
6.		
7.		
8.		
9.		
10.		

The table you filled in above is called a data table.

Definition

A **data table** (or statistical spreadsheet) is a convenient way to store and represent all data values. Typically, in a data table, the rows correspond to observational units, columns represent variables, and the data are the table entries.

3. Identify the observational units and the variables you have recorded on those observational units. (Keep in mind that observational units do not have to be people!)

4. Is the variable "length of word" quantitative or categorical?

> **NOTE**
>
> When we are sampling from a finite population (e.g., all 268 words), we can consider the **parameter** to be a numerical summary of the variable in the population. With quantitative variables, we will often be interested in the population mean. With categorical variables, we will often be interested in the population proportion. To distinguish these values from the corresponding statistics, we will use Greek letters, μ for a population mean, σ for the population standard deviation, and π for a population proportion. In contrast, common symbols for sample statistics are $\bar{x}$ for sample mean, s for the sample standard deviation, and $\hat{p}$ for sample proportion.

> **NOTATION CHECK**
>
> Here is a quick summary of the symbols we've introduced in this section.
>
> | Type of Variable | Quantitative | Categorical |
> |---|---|---|
> | Statistics | $\bar{x}$ = sample mean
s = sample standard deviation | $\hat{p}$ = sample proportion |
> | Parameters | μ = population mean
σ = population standard deviation | π = population proportion |

5. Calculate the average length of the 10 words in your sample. Is this number a parameter or a statistic? Explain how you know. What symbol would you use to refer to this value?

6. The average length of the 268 words in the entire speech equals 4.29 letters. Is this number a parameter or a statistic? Explain how you know. What symbol would you use to refer to this value?

7. Calculate the proportion of words in your sample that contain at least one *e*. Is this number a parameter or a statistic? Explain how you know. What symbol would you use to refer to this value?

8. The proportion of all words in the entire speech that contain at least one letter *e* is $125/268 \approx 0.47$. Is this number a parameter or a statistic? Explain how you know. What symbol would you use to refer to this value?

9. Do you think the words you selected are **representative** of the 268 words in this passage? Suggest a method for deciding whether you have a representative sample. (*Hint:* Whereas any one sample may not produce statistics that exactly equal the population parameters, what would we like to be true in general?)

10. Combine your results with your classmates' by producing a dotplot of the distribution of average word lengths in your samples. Be sure to label the axis of this dotplot appropriately.

    a. Explain what each dot on the dotplot represents by filling in the following sentence. Each dot on the dotplot is a single measurement of the value of _____ on a single _____.

    b. Describe the shape, center, and variability of the distribution of average word lengths as revealed in the dotplot.

11. Let's compare your sample statistics to the population parameters.

    a. How many and what proportion of students in your class obtained a sample average word length larger than 4.29 letters, the average word length in the population?

    b. How many and what proportion of students in your class obtained a sample proportion of *e*-words larger than 0.47, the proportion of *e*-words in the population? (You might use a show of hands in class to answer this question.)

Note that bias is a property of a sampling *method*, not a property of an individual sample. Also note that the sampling method must *consistently* produce nonrepresentative results in the same direction in order to be considered biased.

12. What do the answers to #11 tell you about whether the sampling method of asking students to quickly pick 10 representative words is biased or unbiased? If biased, what is the direction of the bias (tendency to overestimate or to underestimate)?

13. Explain why we might have expected this sampling method (asking you to quickly pick 10 representative words) to be biased.

14. Do you think asking each of you to take 20 words instead of 10 words would have helped with this issue? Explain.

Now consider a different sampling method: What if you were to close your eyes and point blindly at the page with a pencil 10 times, taking for your sample the 10 words on which your pencil lands.

15. Do you think this sampling method is likely to be biased? If so, in which direction? Explain.

A sample is only useful to us if the data we collect on our sample are similar to the results we would find in the entire population. In this sense, we say the sample is **representative** of the population.

16. Suggest another technique for selecting 10 words from this population in order for the sample to be representative of the population with regard to word length and *e*-words.

> **Definition**
>
> A sampling method is **biased** if, when using that sampling method, statistics from different samples *consistently* overestimate or consistently underestimate the population parameter of interest.

Taking a Simple Random Sample

> **KEY IDEA**
>
> A **simple random sample** ensures that every sample of size *n* is equally likely to be the sample selected from the population. In particular, each observational unit has the same chance of being selected as every other observational unit.

The key to obtaining a representative sample is using some type of *random* mechanism to select the observational units from the population, rather than relying on **convenience samples** or any type of human judgment. Instead of having you choose "random" words using your own judgment, we will now ask you to take a simple random sample of words and evaluate your results. The first step is to obtain a **sampling frame**—a complete list of every member of the population where each member of the population can be assigned a number. Below is a copy of the Gettysburg Address that includes numbers in front of every word. For example, the 43rd word is *nation*.

17. Go to the **Random Numbers** applet (or http://www.random.org).

Specify that you want 5 **Numbers per replication** in the range from 1 to 268.

Press **Generate** to view the 5 random numbers. Enter the random numbers in the table below:

Generate Random Number

Number of replications:	1
Numbers per replication:	5
Number range: From:	1
To:	268

Randomly generated five ID values from 1 to 268.

Using your randomly generated values, look up the corresponding word from the sampling frame. Fill in the data table below.

	Word	Length (no. of letters)	e-word? (Y or N)
1.			
2.			
3.			
4.			
5.			

Gettysburg address sampling frame

1	Four	11	upon	21	dedicated	31	Now	41	whether	51	dedicated
2	score	12	this	22	to	32	we	42	that	52	can
3	and	13	continent	23	the	33	are	43	nation	53	long
4	seven	14	a	24	proposition	34	engaged	44	or	54	endure
5	years	15	new	25	that	35	in	45	any	55	We
6	ago	16	nation	26	all	36	a	46	nation	56	are
7	our	17	conceived	27	men	37	great	47	so	57	met
8	fathers	18	in	28	are	38	civil	48	conceived	58	on
9	brought	19	liberty	29	created	39	war	49	and	59	a
10	forth	20	and	30	equal	40	testing	50	so	60	great

61	battlefield	96	and	131	far	166	living	201	before	236	died
62	of	97	proper	132	above	167	rather	202	us	237	in
63	that	98	that	133	our	168	to	203	that	238	vain
64	war	99	we	134	poor	169	be	204	from	239	that
65	We	100	should	135	power	170	dedicated	205	these	240	this
66	have	101	do	136	to	171	here	206	honored	241	nation
67	come	102	this	137	add	172	to	207	dead	242	under
68	To	103	But	138	or	173	the	208	we	243	God
69	dedicate	104	in	139	detract	174	unfinished	209	take	244	shall
70	a	105	a	140	The	175	work	210	increased	245	have
71	portion	106	larger	141	world	176	which	211	devotion	246	a
72	of	107	sense	142	will	177	they	212	to	247	new
73	that	108	we	143	little	178	who	213	that	248	birth
74	field	109	cannot	144	note	179	fought	214	cause	249	of
75	as	110	dedicate	145	nor	180	here	215	for	250	freedom
76	a	111	we	146	long	181	have	216	which	251	and
77	final	112	cannot	147	remember	182	thus	217	they	252	that
78	resting	113	consecrate	148	what	183	far	218	gave	253	government
79	place	114	we	149	we	184	so	219	the	254	of
80	for	115	cannot	150	say	185	nobly	220	last	255	the
81	those	116	hallow	151	here	186	advanced	221	full	256	people
82	who	117	this	152	but	187	It	222	measure	257	by
83	here	118	ground	153	it	188	is	223	of	258	the
84	gave	119	The	154	can	189	rather	224	devotion	259	people
85	their	120	brave	155	never	190	for	225	that	260	for
86	lives	121	men	156	forget	191	us	226	we	261	the
87	that	122	living	157	what	192	to	227	here	262	people
88	that	123	and	158	they	193	be	228	highly	263	shall
89	nation	124	dead	159	did	194	here	229	resolve	264	not
90	might	125	who	160	here	195	dedicated	230	that	265	perish
91	live	126	struggled	161	It	196	to	231	these	266	from
92	It	127	here	162	is	197	the	232	dead	267	the
93	Is	128	have	163	for	198	great	233	shall	268	earth
94	altogether	129	consecrated	164	us	199	task	234	not		
95	fitting	130	It	165	the	200	remaining	235	have		

18. Let's examine your sample and those of your classmates.

a. Calculate the average word length and proportion of *e*-words in your random sample.

b. Again produce a dotplot of the distribution of sample average word lengths for yourself and your classmates.

c. Comment on how this distribution compares to the one from #10 based on nonrandom sampling.

Notice that each simple random sample gave us different values for the statistics. That is, there is variability from sample to sample (*sampling variability*). This makes sense because the samples are chosen randomly and consist of different words each time, so we expect some differences from sample to sample.

19. Let's compare your sample statistics to the population parameters.

    a. How many and what proportion of students in your class obtained a sample average word length larger than the population average (4.29 letters)?

    b. How many and what proportion obtained a sample proportion of *e*-words larger than the population proportion (0.47)? (You can use a show of hands.)

    c. What do these answers reveal about whether simple random sampling is an unbiased sampling method? Explain.

You should see that the random samples do a better job of centering around the population parameter value than self-selected samples, *even though* we used a smaller sample size! Thus, simple random sampling would be considered an **unbiased** sampling method because there is no tendency to over- or underestimate the parameter. Whether a sampling method is biased or unbiased depends both on the sampling method and on the statistic you chose to calculate from the sample. Luckily, one can show that with simple random sampling the sample average and the sample proportion both have this unbiased property.

> **KEY IDEA**
>
> When we use **simple random sampling**, the average of the sample means from different samples equals the population mean and the average of the sample proportions from different samples equals the population proportion. (This means that these statistics are **unbiased** estimators for the corresponding parameter when we use simple random sampling.)

Although selecting a simple random sample is not always feasible (e.g., what if you don't have a complete sampling frame, what if it is too difficult to track down everyone selected?), it is an example of a broader class of probability sampling methods (e.g., stratified sampling, cluster sampling; see the Stratified and Cluster Sampling Appendix) that also have the same properties. The key is that probability, not human judgment, is responsible for selecting the sample.

To really see the long-run pattern in these results, let's look at many more random samples from this population.

20. Open the **Sampling Words** applet. You will see three variables measured on all words in the Gettysburg Address: the lengths of the words, whether or not a word contains at least one letter *e*, and whether or not the word is a noun. For now, use the pull-down menu to select the length variable. Before we draw random samples from this population, we want to point out that we often use dotplots to represent a set of quantitative values. Another option is a *histogram* like the one shown below.

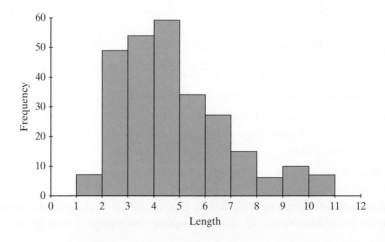

Like a dotplot, a histogram displays the distribution of a quantitative variable. But when you have a large number of observations like this, sometimes it may be convenient to "bin" together similar observations into one bar. The height of each bar tells you how many of the values are in each bin (interval of values). The graph still helps us see features of the distribution, as that the distribution of word lengths is not symmetric but clusters around four to five letters with some shorter words (0-4 letters) but fewer and fewer longer words (9-11 letters).

> **Definition**
>
> A *histogram* is a graph that summarizes the distribution of a quantitative variable. Bars are used to represent the number of observational units in a particular interval of values.

21. Check the **Show Sampling Options** box. Specify 5 in the **Sample Size** box and press the **Draw Samples** button. You will see the five selected words appear in the box below. You will also see five blue dots within the population distribution representing the five lengths that you have sampled. These five lengths are also displayed in a dotplot in the middle panel. The blue triangle indicates the value of this sample's mean, which is then added to the graph on the right. Press **Draw Samples** again. Did you get the same sample this time? Did you get the same sample mean?

You should now see two boxes in the bottom right graph, one for each sample mean (most recent is blue). The mean of these two sample means is displayed in the upper left corner of this panel. Confirm this calculation.

First sample mean:	Second sample mean:	Average:

22. Press the **Draw Samples** button three more times (for a total of five samples). Notice how the samples vary and how the sample mean varies from sample to sample. Now what is the average of your five sample means?

Change the **Number of Samples** to 995 (for a total of 1,000 samples). Press the **Draw Samples** button. (*This should generate a dotplot of 1,000 values of the sample mean for 1,000 different simple random samples, each consisting of 5 words, selected randomly from the population of all 268 words in the Gettysburg Address.*)

23. Describe the resulting distribution of sample means: What are roughly the largest and smallest values? What is the average of the distribution? What is the standard deviation? How does the average of the 1,000 sample means compare to the population mean $\mu = 4.29$?

24. Now change the **Sample Size** from 5 to 20 and the **Number** of **Samples** to 1000. Press the **Draw Samples** button. How do these two distributions compare? Be sure to identify a feature that is similar and a feature that is different.

25. Did changing the sample size change the center of the distribution? If we used a biased sampling method, would increasing the sample size remove the bias? Explain.

You should see that whereas the convenience samples tended to consistently produce samples that overestimate the length of words and even the proportion of words that are *e*-words, the simple random sampling method does not have that tendency. In fact, the average of all the statistics from all possible simple random samples will exactly equal the population parameter value. For this reason, in the real world, where we don't have access to the entire population, when we select a simple random sample, we will be willing to believe that sample is representative of the population. In fact, we would prefer a small random sample over a large convenience sample. That doesn't mean our sample result will match the population result exactly, but we will be able to predict how far off it might be.

Simple random sampling (probability sampling methods in general) allows us to believe that our sample is representative of the larger population and that the observed sample statistic is "in the ball park" of the population parameter. For this reason, when we use simple random sampling, we will be willing to **generalize** the characteristics of our sample to the entire population. But the next question is "how large is that ballpark?" That is, how far do we think any one observed statistic could be from the parameter? We will investigate that in the next example and exploration.

Example 2.1B

EXAMPLE

2.1B — Should Supersize Drinks Be Banned?

In June of 2012, New York City Mayor Michael Bloomberg proposed banning the sale of any regular soda or other sugary drinks in containers larger than 16 oz. Diet drinks and those with more than 70% juice or more than 50% milk would be exempt. Some people saw this as an effort to fight the obesity problem and others saw it as an example of government intrusion.

A poll of 1,093 randomly selected New York City voters conducted by Quinnipiac University taken shortly after the mayor's announcement found that 46% of them supported the ban. Based on this sample proportion, we would like to decide whether less than half of all New York City voters support the ban.

So our parameter, represented by π, is the proportion of all New York City voters that favor the ban. But the poll didn't ask every New Yorker. Our statistic is the sample proportion $\hat{p} = 0.46$. We know that if we had taken a different sample we would likely get a different value for $\hat{p}$. So how can we use this observed $\hat{p}$ to make any conclusions about π?

YOU MIGHT BE THINKING

But didn't we do that in the last chapter?

In the last chapter we focused on the sample-to-sample variability in a sample proportion where the observations came from a never-ending random *process* with a fixed probability of success. We stated a formula for the standard deviation of these sample proportions that helped us measure the amount of sampling variability:

$$\text{SD of } \hat{p} = \sqrt{\pi(1 - \pi)/n}$$

Now, the subtle distinction is that we are looking at the variability in different samples from the same finite *population*.

But recall the distribution of sample proportions we found when we took samples of 30 students from the College of the Midwest (see Figure 2.2). The simulated standard deviation of those 1,000 samples was 0.776, which, remembering that in that case $\pi = 0.776$, is also equal to $\sqrt{0.776(1 - 0.776)/30} \approx 0.076$! It can be shown that when the population is large relative to the size of the sample, the amount of sample-to-sample variability is not impacted by the population size.

KEY IDEA

When sampling from a large population, the standard deviation of sample proportions is estimated by the same formula, $\sqrt{\pi(1 - \pi)/n}$, where π represents the proportion of successes in the population and n represents the sample size. The population is considered large enough when it is more than 20 times that sample size.

This means that the inference methods that you learned in Chapter 1, both simulation-based and theory-based, can be applied to a random sample from a population. In such situations the parameter of interest is the population proportion with the characteristic, rather than the long-run process probability of success. (The population proportion and process probability can be considered to be equivalent if you think of the process as randomly selecting an observational unit from a very large population.)

As of 2009, there were more than 4 million registered voters in New York City. So this population size is definitely large enough for us to treat this as a random sample from an infinite process. This means that we will consider a sample proportion to be far from a hypothesized population proportion if it is more than $2\sqrt{\pi(1-\pi)/n}$ away. So, if 50% of all New Yorkers approve of the ban, a poll of 1,093 New Yorkers should produce a sample proportion within $2\sqrt{0.5(0.5)/1{,}093} \approx 2 \times 0.0151 = 0.0302$ of 0.50. In fact, we can use the **One Proportion** applet exactly as we did before (see Figure 2.3). See Table 2.4 for the mapping of the simulation to the study.

2.1B.10

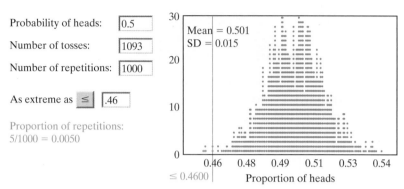

Probability of heads: `0.5`

Number of tosses: `1093`

Number of repetitions: `1000`

As extreme as ≤ `.46`

Proportion of repetitions:
5/1000 = 0.0050

Mean = 0.501
SD = 0.015

≤ 0.4600

Proportion of heads

FIGURE 2.3 Results from 1,000 simple random samples of 1,093 New York City voters, assuming 50% of all New York City voters favor a ban on supersized drinks.

TABLE 2.4 Parallels between real study and simulation		
One repetition	=	A random sample of 1,093 NYC voters
Statistic	=	Sample proportion who favor the ban
Null model	=	Population proportion (π) = 0.50

Our result of 0.46 is more than 2 standard deviations away from 0.50 and a result at least this extreme would be expected to happen in less than 1% of random samples from the population. This gives us convincing evidence that random chance is not a plausible explanation for the lower sample proportion. We have strong evidence that less than half of all New York City voters favor the ban. We feel comfortable generalizing this sample result to the entire population of voters because Quinnipiac University selected a *random* sample from that population. We would not feel comfortable generalizing this result to all New York City residents or to other states because the sampling frame only consisted of registered New York City voters.

2.1B.11

Furthermore, we can also use the theory-based approach to approximate the p-value under the same validity conditions as before, with the addition of the population size consideration.

VALIDITY CONDITIONS

The normal approximation can be used to model the null distribution of random samples from a finite population when the population size is more than 20 times the size of the sample and if there are at least 10 successes and at least 10 failures in the sample.

Our sample size is quite large (503 successes and 590 failures) so we expect the normal approximation to be valid, as shown in Figure 2.4. Read more about these validity conditions in FAQ 2.1.1.

FAQ 2.1.1   www.wiley.com/college/tintle

Should *n* be large or *n* be small?

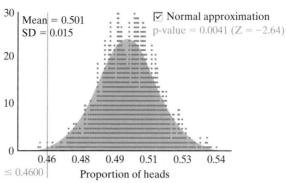

FIGURE 2.4 The theory-based approach to the New York City ban on supersized drinks.

| **Banning Smoking in Cars?**

In Exploration 2.1A about the Gettysburg Address, you saw that values of statistics generated from simple random samples from a finite population follow a predictable pattern. In particular, the center of the distribution of sample statistics is equal to the population parameter we are trying to make inferences about. In this exploration, you will focus on the variability of sample statistics and see how we can use what we learned in Chapter 1 to predict the sample-to-sample variability for samples from finite populations.

In February 2012, a bill was introduced into the Ohio State Senate that would outlaw smoking in vehicles if young children are present. That same month a poll was conducted by Quinnipiac University and asked randomly selected Ohio voters if they thought this bill was a good idea or a bad idea. Of the 1,421 respondents, 55% said it was a good idea. We can use this sample proportion to investigate whether more than half of all Ohio voters in February 2012 thought that this bill was a good idea.

1. Identify the population and sample in this survey.

   Population:

   Sample:

2. Is it reasonable to believe that the sample of 1,421 Ohio voters is representative of the larger population? Explain why or why not.

3. Explain why 55% is a statistic and not a parameter. What symbol would you use to represent it?

4. Describe in words the corresponding parameter for this study. What symbol would you use to represent this value?

5. Is it reasonable to conclude that exactly 55% of Ohio voters agree with the ban on smoking in cars when young children are present? Explain why or why not.

6. Describe how we could conduct a simulation to decide whether a simple random sample from this population could produce a sample proportion like 0.55 if, in fact, only 50% of the population supports ban on smoking in cars when young children are present.

   Each trial represents _____

   Number of trials =

   Probability of success =

7. Some estimates suggest that there are approximately 7.8 million registered voters in Ohio. Suppose 50% of Ohio voters are in favor of this ban. If this is true, what is the probability that a randomly selected voter will be in favor of the ban?

8. If 50% of Ohio voters are in favor of the ban, how many people is this? Report your answer in millions.

9. Suppose I select an Ohio voter from the set of all 7.8 million voters and that voter is in favor of the ban. What is the probability that the next randomly selected voter will also be in favor of the ban?

Your answer to the previous question suggests that when we are sampling from a finite population, without replacement, we technically don't have a constant probability of success like we assumed in Chapter 1. However, if the population size is much much larger than the sample size, then we can treat the probability of success as roughly constant. In other words, we will assume samples from a very large population behave just like samples from an infinite process.

> **KEY IDEA**
>
> When sampling from a large population, the standard deviation of sample proportions is estimated by the same formula, $\sqrt{\pi(1-\pi)/n}$, where π represents the proportion of successes in the population and n represents the sample size since samples from very large populations behave like samples from an infinite process. The population is considered large enough when it is more than 20 times that sample size.

This means that the inference methods that you learned in Chapter 1, both simulation-based and theory-based, can be applied to a random sample from a population. In such situations the parameter of interest is the population proportion with the characteristic, rather than the long-run process probability of success. (The population proportion and process probability can be considered to be equivalent if you think of the process as randomly selecting an observational unit from the population.)

10. Use the **One Proportion** applet to estimate a p-value for testing whether more than 50% of Ohio voters are in favor of the ban for this survey. Begin by stating the null and alternative hypotheses. Be clear how many "coin tosses" you use and how many repetitions you use. Report the p-value you obtain.

11. Write a one-sentence interpretation of your p-value *and* summarize the strength of evidence against the null hypothesis provided by this p-value.

12. Report the standard deviation of the null distribution displayed by the applet. How does this compare to the formula for the standard deviation of a sample proportion discussed in Chapter 1 ($\sqrt{\pi(1-\pi)/n}$) when $\pi = 0.50$?

> **VALIDITY CONDITIONS**
>
> The normal approximation can be used to model the null distribution of the sample proportion for random samples from a finite population when the population size is more than 20 times the size of the sample and if there are at least 10 successes and at least 10 failures in the sample.

13. Are the validity conditions met for using a theory-based method to predict a p-value from this sample? Why or why not?

14. Check the box for **Normal Approximation** in the applet. Report and interpret the value of the standardized statistic.

15. Is the theory-based estimate of the p-value similar to the p-value from the simulation-based method?

SECTION 2.1 Summary

An important question to ask about any statistical study is how broadly the results can be **generalized**. The key to conducting a study that allows us to generalize the results from the sample to a larger population is how the sample is selected from the population.

- Remember that a population is the entire group of interest; a sample is a part of the population on which data are gathered.
  - A parameter is a number that describes a population, typically unknown.
  - A statistic is a number calculated from a sample, often used to estimate the corresponding population parameter.

The primary goal of sampling is to select a sample that is **representative** of the population on all characteristics of interest.

- A sampling method based on **convenience** is often biased and not likely to produce a representative sample.
  - A biased sampling method is one that systematically tends to overrepresent some parts of the population and underrepresent others.
  - A biased sampling method leads to a biased statistic, meaning that the statistic systematically overestimates or underestimates the corresponding population parameter.

The best way to ensure that the sample will be representative is to take a **random sample**.

- A simple random sample gives every possible sample of the desired size the same chance of being the sample selected.
  - In fact, a simple random sample gives each observational unit in the population the same chance of being selected for the sample.
  - With random sampling, the values of sample statistics from different samples (such as proportions and means) center around the corresponding population parameter.
- The sampling variability in sample statistics decreases as sample size increases.
  - But using a larger sample size is not helpful if the sampling method is biased in the first place.
  - The population size does not affect sampling variability as long as the population is at least 20 times larger than the sample.

When a sample is not selected with random sampling, be cautious about generalizing results from the sample to a larger population.

- Depending on the characteristic being studied, generalizing may or may not be advisable.

When a random sample is selected from a population, the simulation- and theory-based approaches from Chapter 1 for determining p-values can be applied to make inferences about the population proportion based on the sample proportion. This is because sample-to-sample variability can be modeled the same way, whether we are taking random samples from finite populations or samples from random processes, provided that the population size is at least 20 times the sample size. More details about assumptions and contrasting a population and a process are provided in FAQ 2.1.2.

FAQ 2.1.2   www.wiley.com/college/tintle

Why should we let random chance dictate our sample selection?

MORE ON SIMPLE RANDOM SAMPLES

POTENTIAL SOURCES OF ERROR IN SAMPLING AND SURVEYS

When we don't have access to the entire population or a random process is ongoing, we often want to infer something about the population or the process using data obtained from a subset of the population or a snapshot of the process: the sample. A well-designed and well-conducted method of measuring the individuals in the sample (e.g., conducting a survey) can provide data that are representative of the population, and you can use these data to calculate statistics that will help you estimate some attributes (parameters) of the population of interest.

 2.1P2.1

THINK ABOUT IT

What are some things that can go wrong when administering a survey to a selected sample of people?

Many things could go wrong: the sampling method could be a poor choice, or the survey could be poorly designed, or the sample may not be representative in spite of a good choice of sampling method. We often group these into two kinds of errors: sampling errors and non-sampling errors.

- *Random sampling errors* are not errors in the everyday sense. These occur as a result of using random chance to select our sample. You know that if you were repeatedly to obtain samples from the same population, using the same sampling method, and calculate the same statistic for each sample, the numeric values of the statistic would most likely not be exactly the same each time. If our sampling method is unbiased, then the mean of the statistics taken from all possible samples will equal the population parameter. However, there will still be "chance variation" in the statistic from sample-to-sample; recall that this variation in the values of the statistic is known as sampling variability. You can reduce sampling variability by increasing your sample size. Random sampling errors are a way to describe sample-to-sample (chance) variability that is accounted for by the margin of error.

- *Non-sampling (systematic) errors* are errors in the everyday sense of the word. These could result from using a nonrandom sampling method such as voluntary response and convenience sampling, or be due to a biased questionnaire design or nonresponse. Non-sampling error is nonrandom error, because it arises due to some systematic source and not from randomness. Let us take a closer look at the following two types of non-sampling errors: response error and nonresponse error.

  - *Response error* can occur for a number of reasons, such as:
    - Wording of a question, which can make people respond differently.
    - Order of questions, which can influence how a person responds.
    - "Social desirability," which can influence how a person responds to a question.
    - The attitude or appearance of the interviewer can affect how someone responds.
    - People sometimes forget or misrepresent the truth.
    - The measurement instrument used may not be accurate or valid or reliable.

  - *Nonresponse error* occurs when:
    - The participants selected to be part of a sample do not respond and the sample is no longer representative. One way to guard against nonresponse errors is to make repeated attempts to contact individuals if they don't respond at first.

 2.1P2.2

2.1P2.3

In Chapter 3 we explore these types of error in greater detail.

2.1.2 — Methods for Choosing a Simple Random Sample

Example 2.1.2

EXAMPLE

Suppose your friend would like to survey students at her high school about the upcoming student government elections. She decides to choose a random sample of 10 students from all 875 students at her school, and asks for your assistance in selecting the sample. How would you go about actually figuring out whom to select? That is, how would you design the sampling plan?

> **AP TIP**
>
> For the AP Statistics exam, your instructions for selecting a sample should be such that another knowledgeable user of statistics would collect the sample in the same manner, using only your instructions (and perhaps a brief example). *Note:* This does not mean that your friend would obtain exactly the same sample, just that the method implemented would be the same.

Definition

A random number table (RNT) is a list of numbers, composed of the digits 0, 1, 2, 3, 4, 5, 6, 7, 8, 9, and arranged so that each digit has no predictable relationship to the digits that preceded it or to the digits that follow it. Each set of digits chosen from the RNT must have the same length in order to have equal probability of being selected (e.g., if we want to select 1,000 people to survey, we would assign them numbers 000 through 999 so that each person has an equal probability of being selected). To use a RNT, begin at a random spot in the table and count off by the specified number of digits moving from right to left. The gaps between every five numbers in the RNT are there to help you keep track of your place in the table. Ignore the gaps and generate the random numbers as if they are not present.

Here are the steps your friend should take.

STEP 1: Create the sampling frame.   Recall that the sampling frame is a list of all individuals in the population of interest. In this case, this means getting a list of all 875 students at the high school and then assigning each student at the high school a **unique** number from 1 to 875.

STEP 2: Use a random mechanism (calculator/computer, random number table, "paper bag" method) to randomly select a sample of size *n* from the sampling frame.   There are a few different ways to describe how to use a random mechanism to choose the random sample. We illustrate each of those options now.

> **AP TIP**
>
> You may choose any of the three methods here. On the exam, you only need to explain one method, not multiple methods.

- *Technology:* Use the random number generator on your calculator, or use a computer, to randomly select 10 *unique* values from 1 and 875. If any value is selected more than once, delete the repeat occurrence and select again. *Note:* You do not need to explain the keystrokes you would use on your calculator or computer. Furthermore, although the TI calculator may randomly choose a number more than once, other more sophisticated computer programs (e.g., www.random.org, as we showed you in Exploration 2.1) are programmed not to choose the same value more than once. Whether you use a calculator or computer applet, you need to make it clear to the reader whether the method you are using ignores repeated values.

- *Random number table:* Typically, on the AP Exam you will be given a few lines from a random number table, which is another way to illustrate that you understand the process of choosing a random sample.

Example lines from a random number table

```
6 5 2 8 5    9 7 1 9 8    8 2 1 3 8    5 3 0 1 0    9 4 6 0 1    1 5 1 3 8
3 8 1 0 9    3 4 9 7 6    6 5 6 9 2    9 8 5 6 2    9 5 5 0 9    5 6 3 9 2
```

Because, in this case, we have less than one thousand individuals in the sampling frame, we can count off 3-digit numbers until we have 10 unique values between 001 and 875. Any values larger than 875 (876–999), as well as the value 000, will be ignored.

Here is what that would look like:

```
    1      2      3      X      4      5      6      7      8      X
 6 5 2|8 5 9|7 1 9|8 8 2|1 3 8|5 3 0|1 0 9|4 6 0|1 1 5|1 3 8
    9     10
 3 8 1|0 9 3|4 9 7 6 6 5 6 9 2 9 8 5 6 6 2 9 5 5 0 9 5 6 3 9
```

Thus, person number 652 is the first person in our sample, 859 is the second, etc.

- *"Paper bag" method:*
  1. Write each student's name on same-sized slips of paper.
  2. Place all of the slips of paper in a bag and mix well.
  3. Randomly select 10 slips of paper from the hat. Do not replace the chosen slips of paper.

THINK ABOUT IT

Why would it be incorrect to choose a slip of paper from the hat, write the name down, and put it back in the bag before choosing another one?

Once a student is chosen to be in our sample, we do not want to pick him or her a second time to complete the survey. For this reason, we do not return the slip of paper to the bag after choosing it.

AP TIP

Notice in each case we clarified how we would handle repeats and values not in the range of the assigned labels, as well as how the 3-digit values would have equal probability of being selected. In particular, with the random number table, each set of digits must have the same length.

STEP 3: Select the observational units from the population. For the first two methods, we still need to match the 10 randomly generated numbers with the students on the list corresponding to those numbers. Those students will be given the survey.

 2.1P2.4

AP TIP

When asked to demonstrate how to choose a simple random sample, make sure each of the steps below is addressed in the context of the research question.

1. Assign each member of the population a unique label.
2. Choose a random mechanism (computer/calculator, random number table, "paper bag" method) to randomly select a sample of size *n* from your population of size *N*. Explain how you will select your sample using the chosen method. Be sure to address how repeats and values that are not in the range of the assigned labels will be handled.
3. Explain what to do with the labels selected by the random mechanism (e.g., match each number selected with the corresponding person in the population and include those people in your sample).

EXPLORATION | **Methods for Choosing a Simple Random Sample**
2.1.2

Suppose that you would like to select a simple random sample of five (5) words from the Gettysburg Address (which you can find in Exploration 2.1A). Recall that in this scenario the population is made up of 268 words. How would you design the sampling plan?

> **AP TIP**
>
> For the AP Statistics exam, your instructions for selecting a sample should be such that another knowledgeable user of statistics would collect the sample in the same manner, using only your instructions (and perhaps a brief example). *Note:* This does not mean that exactly the same sample would be obtained, just that the method implemented would be the same.

STEP 1: Describe the sampling frame

1. Assign each word in the Gettysburg Address a **unique** number or ID from 1 to _____. (*Hint:* What should this number be? What's the population size? Note that we already provided the sampling frame for you in Exploration 2.1A.)

STEP 2: Use a random mechanism (calculator/computer, random number table, "paper bag" method) to randomly select the sample of size *n* from the sampling frame

> **AP TIP**
>
> You may choose any of the three methods here. On the exam, you only need to explain one method, not multiple methods.

There are a few different ways to describe how to use a random mechanism to choose the random sample. We will illustrate each of those options now.

- *Technology*:

2. Use the random number generator on your calculator or computer to randomly select 5 *unique* values from 1 and 268. If any value is selected more than once, delete the repeat occurrence and select again. *Note:* You do not need to explain the keystrokes you would use on your calculator or computer.

Write those values here:

- *Random number table:* Typically, on the AP Exam you will be given a few lines from a random number table to illustrate your process. For example:

```
6 5 2 8 5   9 7 1 9 8   8 2 1 3 8   5 3 0 1 0   9 4 6 0 1   1 5 1 3 8
3 8 1 0 9   3 4 9 7 6   6 5 6 9 2   1 8 5 6 2   9 5 5 0 9   5 6 3 9 2
```

3. In this case, you can count off 3-digit numbers until you have 5 unique values between 001 and 268. Any values larger than 268 (269–999) and the value 000 will be ignored. Use the above two lines excerpted from the random number table to figure out what the ID values of the 5 selected words would be.

4. How would you select a simple random sample of 5 words from the Gettysburg Address using the "*paper bag*" method?

5. Why would it be incorrect to choose a slip of paper from the hat, write the word down, and put it back in the bag before choosing another one?

Definition

A random number table (RNT) is a list of numbers, composed of the digits 0, 1, 2, 3, 4, 5, 6, 7, 8, 9, and arranged so that each digit has no predictable relationship to the digits that preceded it or to the digits that follow it. Each set of digits chosen from the RNT must have the same length in order to have equal probability of being selected (e.g., if we want to select 1,000 people to survey we would assign them numbers 000 through 999 so that each person has an equal probability of being selected). To use a RNT, begin at a random spot in the table and count off by the specified number of digits moving from right to left. The gaps between every five numbers in the RNT are there to help you keep track of your place in the table. Ignore the gaps and generate the random numbers as if they are not present.

Notice in each case we clarified how we would handle repeats and values not in the range of the assigned labels, as well as how the 3-digit values would have equal probability of being selected. In particular, with the random number table, each set of digits must all have the same length.

STEP 3: Select the observational units from the population. For the first two methods, you would still need to match the 5 randomly generated numbers (IDs) with the words on the list corresponding to those numbers. Those 5 words are the sample.

6. Write out what the sample of 5 words would be if you were to use the IDs generated using technology (computer or calculator) that you found in an earlier question.

7. Write out what the sample of 5 words would be if you were to use the IDs generated using the random number table that you identified in an earlier question.

When asked to demonstrate how to choose a simple random sample, make sure each of the steps below is addressed in the context of the research question.

1. Assign each member of the population a unique label.
2. Choose a random mechanism (computer/calculator, random number table, "paper bag" method) to randomly select a sample of size n from your population of size N. Explain how you will select your sample using the chosen method. Be sure to address how repeats and values that are not in the range of the assigned labels will be handled.
3. Explain what to do with the labels selected by the random mechanism (e.g., match each number selected with the corresponding person in the population and include those people in your sample).

SECTION 2.1: Part 2 Summary

In Section 2.1 you learned that in order to generalize the results from a sample to a larger population, the sample must be representative of the population on all characteristics of interest. You learned that simple random sampling generally achieves this goal by giving every possible sample of the desired size from a population the same chance of being selected. In this Part 2 section you examined three different methods for choosing a simple random sample (technology-computer/calculator, random number table, paper bag method) and how to explain your method so that it could be replicated by another knowledgeable user of statistics. Using simple random sampling is one way to guard against nonrandom sampling errors that occur with biased sampling methods (e.g., convenience samples). In this section, you also learned about other potential sources of error in sampling and surveys, and that these can be grouped into two types of errors: random sampling errors and non-sampling errors.

- **Random sampling errors** are a way to describe sample-to-sample (chance) variability from sample to sample that is accounted for by the margin of error.
- **Non-sampling (systematic) errors** are nonrandom errors because they arise due to some systematic source such as a biased questionnaire design or nonresponse, and not from randomness.

**SECTION 2.1:
Part 3**

STRATIFIED AND CLUSTER RANDOM SAMPLING

INTRODUCTION

Earlier in this section, you learned that an important question to ask about any statistical study is how broadly the results can be generalized, and that the key to being able to generalize the results from the sample to a larger population is whether the sample is representative of the population. This representativeness depends on how the sample is selected from the population. You also learned that using some type of random mechanism to select the observational units from the population, rather than relying on a convenience sample or any type of human judgment, is essential to obtaining a representative sample. You learned that a *simple random sample (SRS)* ensures that every sample of size *n* is equally likely to be the sample selected from the population. In this section you will learn to collect data using two additional probability sampling methods, *stratified sampling* and *cluster sampling*, along with learning about their advantages and disadvantages.

2.1.3A — Medicare Fraud

Example 2.1.3A

EXAMPLE

Auditing claims from health care providers for payment by Medicare is expensive. It takes the time of a highly trained professional to evaluate the paperwork and decide whether a claim is justified. Because of the high cost, auditors do not review all existing claims. Instead, they evaluate claims in a random sample, and then generalize their findings to all claims from the provider (the population of interest). Let's look at an actual case. TrueMed, an auditing firm, requested basic summary information for all claims submitted by Family Home Health during 2009. In all, there were 11,059 claims.

Suppose the auditors decided to take a simple random sample (SRS) of 90 claims from the 11,059 submitted to Family Home Health during 2009 to review.

> **THINK ABOUT IT**
>
> What are the pros and cons of choosing an SRS of 90 claims?

An advantage is that simple random sampling is an unbiased sampling method, so there is no tendency to over- or underestimate the parameter. But what if there are far fewer claims for higher dollar amounts than for lower dollar amounts? With a simple random sample, we run the risk of obtaining too few, or possibly no claims that are of a higher dollar amount.

> **THINK ABOUT IT**
>
> Some insurance claims are for relatively small dollar amounts, while others that may involve extended hospital stays could be much higher. Would our sample be representative of all the claims submitted by Family Home Health during 2009 if none of the claims involving larger dollar amounts were included in our sample? Would a case of fraud for a large claim be more of a concern for Medicare?

We can address this disadvantage by using a modified sampling method known as stratified random sampling.

STRATIFIED RANDOM SAMPLING

When the observational units within each stratum are similar and there are substantial differences between observational units in different strata, an advantage to stratified random sampling over simple random sampling that may result is that the representativeness of the sample is improved in terms of reduced sampling error.

TrueMed classified all the 11,059 claims submitted by Family Home Health during 2009 into three strata according to the amount paid:

Stratum	Dollar range of claim	Number of claims
1	<$89	9,646
2	$89–$400	1,116
3	>400	297

Some things to note about how the strata were created for the population of 11,059 claims:

1. Every claim belongs to a stratum and no claim belongs to more than one. (This is a requirement for every stratified sampling plan.)

2. For this particular stratification plan, the strata have very different sizes. Stratum 1 is almost 9 times as large as Stratum 2 and more than 30 times as large as Stratum 3.

3. The strata were chosen so that:
   - Within each stratum, claim amounts are similar.
   - Between strata, claim amounts are different.

4. In the actual case, TrueMed took a simple random sample of size 30 from each stratum, for a total of 90 claims.

What advantage would a stratified sample provide over a simple random sample for this population?

> **THINK ABOUT IT**
>
> Suppose that, instead of stratifying, TrueMed had taken one simple random sample of size 90 from the population as a whole. Based on the number of claims in the strata, roughly how many claims from Stratum 1 would you expect in a SRS of size 90? How many from Stratum 3?

It's likely that a simple random sample of claims would contain only about 2 or 3 claims from Stratum 3, because there are fewer claims in Stratum 3 from which to choose. The advantage to a stratified sample is that you are ensuring that the sample has representation from each stratum of the population. In this case, the sample is guaranteed to have 30 claims from each stratum.

> **THINK ABOUT IT**
>
> Why does it make sense to "overrepresent" Stratum 3?

Recall that the auditor's goal is to uncover possible occurrences of Medicare fraud. Stratum 3 contains the largest claim amounts, with an average that is more than 10 times as large

---

Definition

In **stratified random sampling** you classify or break down the population into subgroups or strata in such a way that the observational units within each stratum are similar in ways that may affect the variable that you are interested in measuring (response variable), and observational units in different strata are different in ways that may affect the response variable. Once the strata are chosen, take a separate simple random sample from each stratum and combine these to form the sample.

2.1P3A.1

2.1P3A.2

as the average for Stratum 1. These large claims are more important to the audit because they contribute more to the overall total, so it makes sense to ensure that we have many claims from that stratum, rather than just 2 or 3 claims.

Although TrueMed used equal sample sizes of 30, 30, and 30, there may be other ways to choose 90 claims from among the three strata depending on the goal of the analysis. For example, *proportional sampling* would force a sample of 90 claims to consist of 79 small claims, 9 medium claims, and 2 large claims. This would mean that the proportions of the different types of claims in our sample match (roughly) the distribution in the population, and, at least on this variable, we know our sample will be representative of the population. This means the sample will probably better represent the population on other variables as well.

THINK ABOUT IT

What are some advantages of stratified sampling? When certain strata of the population are thought to be too important to the research question under consideration so that the sampling method needs to ensure observational units from the strata make it into the sample, stratified random sampling is used instead of simple random sampling. Another instance of preferring stratified random sampling to a simple random sample would be when the researcher wishes to oversample a particularly small group of interest.

There are a few advantages of stratified random sampling over simple random sampling, namely:

1. You can make sure you get enough observational units to learn about smaller strata.
2. You can get better (less sample-to-sample variability) estimates using fewer observational units.
3. You can force the sample to match particular characteristics of the population if you know them in advance.

For these reasons, stratified random sampling is used instead of simple random sampling when the categories of the strata are thought to be too distinct or too important to the research question under consideration, and/or when the researcher wishes to oversample a particularly small group of interest.

KEY IDEA

How do you choose a variable on which to stratify? Look for a variable that may be related to the variable being measured. Then see if you can divide the population into non-overlapping groups using that variable. Ideally, the variability of the response variable within the subgroups will be less than the variability when dealing with the entire population.

THINK ABOUT IT

What are some disadvantages of stratified sampling?

Notice that stratified random sampling is not possible unless you have a complete list of all the observational units in the population and enough information on each observational unit to break the population into non-overlapping strata, where the strata are related to the variable of interest. If such a list is not possible or is too expensive to get, you can't stratify. What should you do in this case? We'll discuss one option in Example 2.1.2B.

If the population does not have obvious strata (subgroups that behave differently from each other on the variable(s) of interest), then a simple random sample ensures a high degree of representativeness and is simpler and less time consuming to obtain than a stratified random sample.

 2.1P3A.3

Sizes of Trees

EXAMPLE

Suppose you want to know the distribution of tree diameters in a one-square-mile area of forest. You have a map of the area but you don't have a list of all the trees, and because you estimate that there are over a million trees in the square mile, you don't really want to try to list them all. Without such a list, you can't take a simple random sample or stratified random sample. You can, however, take a cluster sample.

 Example 2.1.3B

Cluster sampling is often used for convenience and cost-effectiveness, particularly if it is impossible or impractical to obtain a sampling frame of all the individuals in the entire population.

To collect a cluster sample, do the following:

1. Divide your entire population into non-overlapping groups called clusters, list and number the clusters, and choose a simple random sample of clusters.

   Divide your one-square-mile area into a 100 × 100 grid of squares of equal size, 52.8 feet on a side. Each square is a cluster and you have 10,000 of them in all. Number your clusters and choose a simple random sample of 40 clusters. (The choice of 40 is arbitrary. More clusters would cost more and take more time but would give more information.)

2. For each cluster in your sample, list all the units in the cluster; then either

   a. Record the value of your variable(s) for every unit in the cluster, or

   b. Take a simple random sample of units from each cluster (this is known as "multistage" sampling).

   List all the trees in each of your 40 clusters. Then either (a) measure the diameter of every tree in each square or (b) take a random sample of 15 trees in each square and measure the diameters of those trees.

THINK ABOUT IT

What is the main advantage of cluster sampling?

Definition

In ***cluster sampling*** you break down the population into subgroups or clusters based on some natural subgrouping variable (zip code, city block, etc.) such that the subgroups or clusters are heterogeneous; that is, each cluster should be a small-scale representation of the entire population. Once the clusters have been created, you take a simple random sample of clusters, and combine all or some of the observational units in the chosen clusters to form the sample.

The main advantage of cluster sampling is that instead of listing all the units in your population, you only need to list a small fraction of units—the ones in the randomly selected clusters. In the tree example, you only needed to measure or list the trees in 40 of the 10,000 little squares.

The creation of clusters in this example, as squares of a certain size, may seem a bit arbitrary. You had to choose the number/size of the square areas of land designated as clusters since there was no natural or existing clustering in the population. Another statistician might choose fewer/larger squares as clusters, and yet another more/smaller squares. This next example features a population whose structure already contains clusters.

THINK ABOUT IT

What are some disadvantages of cluster sampling?

 2.1P3B.4

 2.1P3B.5

A big disadvantage of cluster sampling is that, if you've collected a cluster sample and want to do any sort of statistical inference (e.g., test hypotheses), the methods we've shown you so far (Chapter 1) and the ones you'll learn throughout the rest of this book won't really work

2.1P3B.6

anymore. In fact, you'll probably have to consult an expert statistician! Another disadvantage can be related to the difficulty in choosing a good clustering scheme to ensure representativeness.

Example 2.1.3C

EXAMPLE

2.1.3C — First Graders in a City

For a nutrition study, you want to measure several attributes for a random sample of first-grade pupils in a major city. Although it would be possible to compile a list of all first graders in order to gather a simple random sample, it would be much quicker to use a cluster sample.

First, list all the elementary schools in the city and choose a simple random sample of schools. Then, for each school in the sample, list all the first graders and then choose a simple random sample of first graders within each selected school and record your measurements on those individual students.

> ### KEY IDEA
>
> As these two examples of cluster sampling illustrate, there is one main advantage of using clusters for choosing a random sample. Cluster sampling lets you take random samples even when you don't have and can't easily get a list of all the units in your population.

You may have noticed that strata and clusters are defined in the same way: You divide or classify your entire population into non-overlapping groups. What's the difference between a stratum and a cluster? Although the definitions of the two kinds of groups are abstractly the same, their uses are quite different. With strata, you typically have only a small number of large groups, you have a list of all the units in the whole population, and you take a SRS from every stratum. With clusters, you may have a very large number of clusters, you don't have a list of all the units in the whole population, and you don't sample from all clusters, just from a SRS of clusters. Stratifying is useful as a way to reduce the standard deviation of the overall (population) estimate. Cluster sampling is not. Cluster sampling is useful when you don't have a list of all the units in your population. Stratifying is not. Both methods should produce a representative sample, but our estimates tend to be more precise with stratified sampling.

Here's a chart that summarizes comparisons.

	Strata	Clusters
Is a listing of the whole population required	Yes	No
Number of groups	Comparatively few strata	Typically, a large number of clusters
Sizes of groups	Often large	Smaller
Measure units from	Every stratum	Only a simple random sample of clusters
Reason(s) for using	To ensure small strata are represented and to reduce the standard deviation of estimates	To get a random sample without having to list all units in the population

In cluster sampling, we expect each cluster to be representative of the population. Conversely, in stratified sampling, we expect observations within each strata to be similar to one another but different from observations in other strata.

Sampling Stars in the Sky

(Adapted from Petocz (1990), Sampling Space: Practical Experiments for Teaching Sampling)

Have you ever looked up into the night sky on a clear night and wondered how many stars there are in the sky? Figure 2.1.1 has been prepared from a photograph of part of the night sky and is assumed to represent a grid of stars observed in the sky at a given time. The negative for the photograph was used, so the stars appear as black dots and the background sky is white. In this figure, if you wanted to, you could actually count how many stars there are to find out how many stars were visible in this portion of the sky. But what if we didn't want to go through all that work?

You already know that a simple random sample is one way to use a sample to generalize to a population. In this exploration we'll see how we can use a simple random sample to help estimate the number of stars in the sky. We'll also look at two other methods that can be used to generate random samples.

Our sampling frame will be the 100 squares shown. We will randomly select 10 squares, count the stars in those 10 squares, and see how close those estimates are to the actual population. (Again, in reality we wouldn't know the population total; this exploration is to help you understand the different sampling methods.) We focus on the average number of stars per square as our parameter/statistic (we can then multiply our estimate of the average number of stars in each square by 100 to obtain an estimate of the number of stars in the entire grid).

The rows and columns in the star map are numbered 0 to 9. We identify each square by a two-digit number consisting of the number on the horizontal axis followed by the number on the vertical axis. So, for instance, the bottom right-hand square will be "90." Remember to give the horizontal number first and then the vertical.

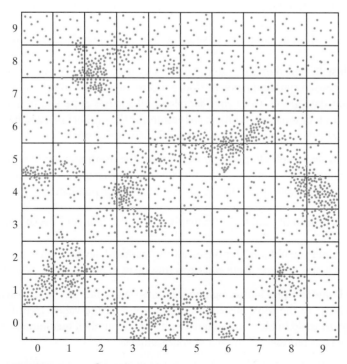

FIGURE 2.1.1 Sample space star map.

METHOD #1: Simple Random Sample

1. Describe a method you could use to select a simple random sample of 10 squares from the star map to estimate the mean number of stars in each square.

AP TIP

Recall from the previous section that your instructions for selecting a sample should be such that another knowledgeable user of statistics would collect the sample in the same manner. This does not mean that he or she would obtain exactly the same sample, but that the method implemented would be the same.

When asked to demonstrate how to choose a simple random sample, make sure each of the steps below is addressed in the context of the research question.

1. Assign each member of the population a unique label.
2. Choose a random mechanism (computer/calculator, random number table, "paper bag" method) to randomly select a sample of size n from your population of size N. Explain how you will select your sample using the chosen method. Be sure to address how repeats and values that are not in the range of the assigned labels will be handled.
3. Explain what to do with the labels selected by the random mechanism (e.g., match each number selected with the corresponding person in the population and include those people in your sample).

We have set up the **One Mean** applet on the textbook webpage to take simple random samples from this population.

2. Open the **One Mean** applet from the textbook webpage. Choose the **Stars** population and then check the **Show Sampling Options**. Type 1 for the **Number of samples** and 10 for the **Sample Size** and press the **Draw Samples** button. Report the mean number of stars and standard deviation of the number of stars for your simple random sample of 10 squares from the star map.

   Mean of Sample of 10 squares: _____   Standard deviation: _____

3. In the **Most Recent Sample** graph, a dotplot of the number of stars in each of the 10 randomly chosen squares is shown. Notice where each of the 10 values came from in the **Population data** graph. Does your sample of 10 squares appear to be representative of the population of squares? Are there any results for the number of stars that are under- or overrepresented compared to the population? If so, which ones?

4. Press the **Draw Samples** button again and report the mean number of stars and the standard deviation of the number of stars for your random sample of 10 squares from the star map. Does this sample appear to be representative of the population?

   Mean of sample of 10 squares: _____   Standard deviation: _____

5. Were the values you obtained for the mean and standard deviation the same for both samples of 10 squares of stars? Were you expecting them to be the same? Why or why not?

6. Press the **Draw Samples** button eight more times (take your time here!), each time paying close attention to the **Most Recent Sample** graph and the values from the **Population data** graph overlaid in blue. Are squares with a small number, medium number, and high number of stars represented in each of your samples?

7. Now change the **Number of samples** from 1 to 990 and press **Draw Samples**. The applet will now show the results for the mean number of stars in a square for 1,000 different random samples of 10 squares from the star map. Comment on the center, shape, and variability of the distribution of sample means for the 1,000 different simple random samples of 10 squares from the star map.

   Mean of sample means: _____   Shape: _____   Standard deviation: _____

8. Back to our original research question of estimating the number of stars in the sky based on a sample of 10 squares of stars. How will you use the mean you obtained from your sample of 10 squares of stars in #2 to estimate the total number of stars? What is your estimate?

9. Of course, we don't expect the population mean to be exactly this value, but we can use the standard deviation of the sample means to estimate how far the sample mean in #2 could plausibly be from the population mean. Does the standard deviation of the sample means you obtained in #7 seem a bit large? What does that mean practically? What is one way you can reduce the standard deviation of your estimate of the mean number of stars in the population?

Although you could increase the sample size (e.g., choose 20 squares from the star map), that may take too much time to count. There are other options for reducing the variability in the sample means that involve changing the way you obtain the 10 squares from the star map.

METHOD #2: Stratified Random Sample

If you do a quick visual inspection of the sample space star map in Figure 2.5, you will notice that some of the squares have more stars (high density) and some have fewer stars (low density). If you were going to divide the star map into two strata, high density and low density, approximately how many squares would you classify as high density and how many as low density? (Just do a quick visual inspection, no need to actually count the number of stars in each square.)

10. Estimate of number of squares classified as

   High density _____   Low density _____

11. Describe a method you could use to select a stratified random sample of 10 squares from the star map, using density as the variable to stratify on, in order to estimate the mean number of stars per square in the population.

   Note: Recall from the AP Tip in #1 what you need to demonstrate when asked to describe the method you chose for obtaining your sample.

12. We will use the **One Mean** applet to select a stratified random sample of squares from the star map in order to estimate the mean number of stars in each square, using **density** as our variable to stratify on. Check the **Stratify Samples by** box under the **Show Sampling Options** and then use the drop-down menu under **Variable** to choose **density** as the variable to stratify on. Type **1** for the **Number of samples** and **10** for the **Sample Size** and then press the **Draw Samples** button. Notice that in the **Most Recent Sample** dotplot, each square selected is color coded red if it was selected from the low-density stratum, and green if it was selected from the high-density stratum.

   How many of the 10 squares in your sample did the applet select from the low-density stratum _____

   How many from the high-density stratum? _____

   Does the proportion selected from each stratum seem reasonable based on your visual estimate of the number of squares from the star map that you classified into each stratum?

13. Report the mean and standard deviation for your stratified random sample of 10 squares from the star map (variable to stratify on = density), in addition to the number of observations from each stratum (low density or high density).

> **Definition**
>
> In **stratified random sampling** you classify or break down the population into subgroups or strata in such a manner that the observational units within each stratum are similar in ways that may affect the variable that you are interested in measuring (response variable), and observational units in different strata are different in ways that may affect the response variable. Once the strata are chosen, take a separate simple random sample from each stratum and combine these to form the sample.

Number in Sample from Low-Density Stratum	Number in Sample from High-Density Stratum	Mean $(\bar{x})$ Number of Stars Sample of 10 Squares Stratified by Density	Standard Deviation Number of Stars Sample of 10 Squares Stratified by Density

14. Press the **Draw Samples** button nine more times (take your time here!), each time paying close attention to the **Most Recent Sample** graph and the values from the **Population data** graph overlaid in blue. Are squares with a small number, medium number, and high number of stars represented in each of your samples? Does your answer differ from that in #6 for the simple random sample?

15. Now change the **Number of samples** from 1 to 990 and press **Draw Samples**. The applet will now show the results for the mean number of stars in a square for 1,000 different stratified random samples of 10 squares from the star map, using density as the variable stratified on. Comment on the center, shape, and variability of the distribution of sample means for 1,000 different stratified random samples of 10 squares from the star map.

    Mean of sample means: Shape: Standard deviation:

16. Compare your results when stratifying by density and when taking simple random samples. Is one sampling method preferable to the other? Explain how so/not. [*Hint:* Which changed the most: the center, shape, or variability? What are the implications of this change?]

METHOD #3: More Stratified Random Sampling

Why did we choose to stratify on density? Are there other options? Sure there are! Let's look at one now to help understand how to choose a "good" variable to stratify on.

17. Suppose instead of choosing density as our variable on which to stratify, we instead decided to split the star map vertically into two equal halves, where stars in the left 50 squares of the map (columns 0–4) would be in the left stratum and stars in the right 50 squares of the map (columns 5–9) would be in the right stratum. Why might using which side the stars are in (left/right) as the variable to stratify on be more feasible than knowing the density of the squares in advance?

18. Let's explore whether this sampling method is an improvement over the previous two methods (simple random sample and stratified random sample using density as the variable to stratify on). Use the drop-down menu under **Variable** to choose **side** as the variable to stratify on. Type 1 for the **Number of samples** and 10 for the **Sample Size** and then press the **Draw Samples** button.

    a. How many of the 10 squares in your sample did the applet select from the left stratum _____ and how many from the right stratum _____?

    b. You should have noticed that the applet selected an equal number of squares from each stratum, instead of the 80/20 split (low density/high density) used when stratifying on the variable density. Does it seem reasonable to select an equal number of observations from each stratum when using the side (left/right) of the star map that the square came from as our variable to stratify on?

    c. Report the mean and standard deviation for your stratified random sample of 10 squares from the star map (variable to stratify on = side).

Mean ($\bar{x}$) Number of Stars Sample of 10 Squares Stratified by Side	Standard Deviation Number of Stars Sample of 10 Squares Stratified by Side

19. Press the **Draw Samples** button nine more times (take your time here!), each time paying close attention to the **Most Recent Sample** graph and the values from the **Population data** graph overlaid in blue. Are squares with a small number, medium number, and large number of stars represented in each of your samples?

20. Now change the **Number of samples** from 1 to 990 and press **Draw Samples**. The applet will now show the results for the mean number of stars in a square for 1,000 different stratified random samples of 10 squares from the star map, using side (left/right) as the

stratifying variable. Comment on the center, shape, and variability of the distribution of sample means for 1,000 different stratified random samples of 10 squares from the star map.

Mean of sample means: Shape: Standard deviation:

21. Compare your results for the two different variables that you stratified on (density and side). Does the choice of one variable provide a statistical advantage over the other as your choice of variable to stratify on? Explain.

KEY IDEA

How do you choose a variable on which to stratify? Look for a variable that may be related to the variable being measured. Then see if you can divide the population into non-overlapping groups using that variable. Ideally, the variability of the response variable within the subgroups will be less than the variability when dealing with the entire population.

If the population does not have obvious strata (subgroups that behave differently from each other on the variable(s) of interest), then a simple random sample ensures a high degree of representativeness and is simpler and less time consuming to obtain than a stratified random sample.

METHOD #4: Cluster Random Sample

Suppose you decide to select a cluster random sample of squares from the star map, where each column is a cluster of 10 squares.

22. Describe a method you could use to select a cluster random sample of 10 squares from the star map to estimate the mean number of stars in each square, using column as the cluster variable.

    Note: Recall from the AP Tip in #1 what you need to demonstrate when asked to describe the method you chose for obtaining your sample.

23. Check the **Cluster Samples by** box under the **Show Sampling Options** and then use the drop-down menu under **Variable** to choose **column** as the cluster variable.

    a. If we want 10 squares in our sample, how many clusters should we choose? _____

    b. Type 1 for the **Number of samples** and 1 for the **Number of clusters** and then press the **Draw Samples** button. Report the mean and standard deviation for your cluster random sample of 10 squares from the star map (cluster variable = column)

Mean $(\overline{x})$ Number of Stars Sample of 10 Squares Cluster by Column	Standard Deviation Number of Stars Sample of 10 Squares Cluster by Column

24. Press the **Draw Samples** button nine more times (take your time here!), each time paying close attention to the **Most Recent Sample** graph and the values from the **Population data** graph overlaid in blue. Are squares with a small number, medium number, and large number of stars represented in each of your samples?

25. Now change the **Number of samples** from 1 to 990 and press **Draw Samples**. The applet will now show the results for the mean number of stars in a square for 1,000 different cluster random samples of 10 squares from the star map, using column as the cluster variable. Comment on the center, shape, and variability of the distribution of sample means for 1,000 different cluster random samples of 10 squares from the star map.

    Mean of sample means: Shape: Standard deviation:

26. Compare your results when selecting a cluster sample using the column as the cluster variable with stratifying by density and when taking simple random samples. Is one sampling method preferable to the other? Explain.

Definition

In *cluster sampling* you break down the population into subgroups or clusters based on some natural subgrouping variable (zip code, city block, etc.) so that the subgroups or clusters are heterogeneous; that is, each cluster should be a small-scale representation of the entire population. Once the clusters have been created, you take a simple random sample of clusters, and combine all or some of the observational units in the chosen clusters to form the sample.

27. Suppose that instead of using the column as our cluster variable, we decide to use the row as our cluster variable. Use the drop-down menu under **Variable** to choose **row** as the cluster variable.

Type 1 for the **Number of samples** and 1 for the **Number of clusters** and then press the **Draw Samples** button. Report the mean and standard deviation for your cluster random sample of 10 squares from the star map (cluster variable = row).

Mean $(\bar{x})$ Number of Stars Sample of 10 Squares Cluster by Row	Standard Deviation Number of Stars Sample of 10 Squares Cluster by Row

28. Press the **Draw Samples** button nine more times (take your time here!), each time paying close attention to the **Most Recent Sample** graph and the corresponding **Population data** graph. Are squares with a small number, medium number, and large number of stars represented in each of your samples? How does your answer compare to when your cluster variable was column?

29. Now change the **Number of samples** from 1 to 990 and press **Draw Samples**. The applet will now show the results for the mean number of stars in a square for 1,000 different cluster random samples of 10 squares from the star map, using row as the cluster variable. Comment on the center, shape, and variability of the distribution of sample means for 1,000 different cluster random samples of 10 squares from the star map.

Mean of sample means: Shape: Standard deviation:

30. Compare your results for the two different variables that you used to obtain a cluster random sample (column and row). Does the choice of one variable provide a statistical advantage over the other as your choice of cluster variable? Explain why this makes sense by looking at the rows and columns in the map.

You may have noticed that strata and clusters are defined in the same way: you divide or classify your entire population into non-overlapping groups. What's the difference between a stratum and a cluster? Although the definitions of the two kinds of groups are abstractly the same, the uses of the groups are quite different. With strata, you typically have only a small number of large groups, you have a list of all the units in the whole population, and you take a SRS from every stratum. With clusters, you may have a very large number of clusters, you don't have a listing of all the units in the whole population, and you don't sample from all clusters, just from a SRS of clusters. Stratifying is useful as a way to reduce the standard deviation of the overall (population) estimate. Cluster sampling is not. Cluster sampling is useful when you don't have a list of all the units in your population. Stratifying is not. Both methods should produce a representative sample, but our estimates tend to be more precise with stratified sampling.

Here's a chart that summarizes comparisons.

	Strata	Clusters
Is a listing of the whole population required?	Yes	No
Number of groups	Comparatively few strata	Typically, a large number of clusters
Sizes of groups	Often large	Smaller
Measure units from	Every stratum	Only a simple random sample of clusters
Reason(s) for using	To ensure small strata are represented and to reduce the standard deviation of estimates	To get a random sample without having to list all units in the population

In cluster sampling, we expect each cluster to be representative of the population. Conversely, in stratified sampling, we expect observations within each stratum to be similar to each other, but different from observations in other strata.

- -

SECTION 2.1: Part 3 Summary

Simple random sampling, ***stratified sampling***, and ***cluster sampling*** are all types of random sampling in which each sample has a known probability of being selected. This is different from judgment samples such as convenience samples picked (as the name implies) for convenience. Selecting a random sample to answer a research question is an essential step that can have a great effect on the analysis of our data.

When the observational units within each stratum are similar and there are substantial differences between observational units in different strata, an advantage to stratified sampling over simple random sampling that may result is that the representativeness of the sample is improved, as measured by reduced sampling error (which we see by having a smaller standard deviation in the statistic across repeated random samples of the same size). For populations with important distinguishing characteristics, an additional advantage is that a stratified sample can ensure representation from each stratum, whereas a simple random sample may not include any data points from smaller strata. If the population does not have obvious strata (subgroups that behave differently from each other on the variable(s) of interest), then a simple random sample ensures a high degree of representativeness and is simpler and less time consuming to obtain than a stratified random sample.

The main advantage of cluster samples is that, instead of listing all the units in your population, you only need to list a small fraction of units—the ones in the randomly selected clusters; thus, it is not necessary, as in a stratified sample, to have a complete sampling frame (list of all subjects or units from the population). A disadvantage of cluster sampling is in the difficulty of choosing heterogeneous clusters. If individuals within a cluster have similar characteristics, this may produce large sampling error and reduce the representativeness of the sample.

Whereas stratifying is useful as a way to reduce the standard deviation of the overall (population) estimate when the population is heterogeneous and it is possible to establish strata that are relatively homogeneous within each one, cluster sampling is not. Cluster sampling is useful when you don't have a list of all the units in your population. Both methods should produce a representative sample, but our estimates tend to be more precise with stratified sampling, assuming we choose a good variable on which to stratify.

- -

INFERENCE FOR A SINGLE QUANTITATIVE VARIABLE SECTION 2.2

INTRODUCTION

In the previous section we saw that:

- Selecting a random sample from a population allows us to *generalize* from our sample to the population we've sampled from, whether we have categorical or quantitative data. In particular, with categorical variables, we can make inferences about the population *proportion*; with quantitative variables, we can make inferences about the population *mean*.

- The simulation- and theory-based inference methods that we learned in Chapter 1 for analyzing sample proportions from random processes also work for random samples from large finite populations.

In this section we'll learn more about how we can draw inferences about populations when we have quantitative variables measured on random samples. We'll learn both simulation- and theory-based approaches for estimating p-values for a single population mean. We will also mention some of the differences between the mean and the median with regard to their ability to summarize the center of a distribution of a quantitative variable.

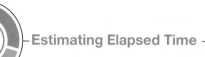

EXAMPLE

2.2 — Estimating Elapsed Time

Example 2.2

Does it ever seem like time drags on (perhaps during one of your least favorite classes) or time flies by (like a summer vacation)? Perception, including that of time, is one of the things that psychologists study. Students in a statistics class collected data on other students' perception of time. They told their subjects that they would be listening to some music and then after it was over they would be asked some questions. They played 10 seconds of the Jackson 5's song "ABC." Afterward, they simply asked the subjects how long they thought the song snippet lasted. They wanted to see whether students could accurately estimate the length of this short song segment. Let's explore this study by working through our six-step statistical investigation method.

STEP 1: Ask a research question.   Can people accurately estimate the length of a short song snippet?

STEP 2: Design a study and collect data.   The researchers asked 48 students on campus to be subjects in the experiment. The participants were asked to listen to a 10-second snippet of a song, and after it was over, they were asked to estimate how long the song snippet lasted. (The subjects did not know in advance that they would be asked this question.) Their estimates of the song length are the data that will be analyzed. Because the true length of the song is 10 seconds, we are interested in learning whether people, on average, correctly estimate the song length as 10 seconds or if they, on average, over- or underestimate the song length. Thus, we have the following hypotheses.

> Null hypothesis: People in the population accurately estimate the length of a 10-second song snippet, on average.
>
> Alternative hypothesis: People in the population do not accurately estimate the length of a 10-second song snippet, on average.

If we let μ represent the mean time estimate for the 10-second song snippet for everyone in the population, then we can write our hypotheses as follows.

> H_0: μ = 10 seconds (on average, students estimate the song length correctly)
>
> H_a: $\mu \neq$ 10 seconds (on average, students in the population over- or underestimate the song length)

STEP 3: Explore the data.   Because the estimated length of time is a quantitative variable, we use different techniques to summarize the variable than in Chapter 1. Because quantitative variables can take many, many different values, there is typically more work to do to summarize the variable's distribution.

Recall from the Preliminaries that we can use a dotplot of the variable's distribution and then describe the distribution's shape, center, and variability and identify unusual observations. The graph in Figure 2.5 displays the distribution of estimated times for the 48 subjects who participated in the study.

2.2.1

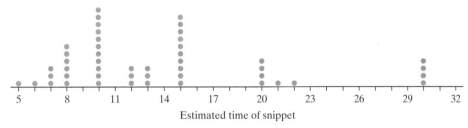

FIGURE 2.5 The results (in seconds) for 48 students trying to estimate the length of a 10-second song snippet.

> ## THINK ABOUT IT
>
> What does each dot on this dotplot represent?

In this graph the observational units are the 48 students and the variable is the estimated time of the snippet.

Shape: An important characteristic of the graph is that the distribution of time estimates is not symmetric, but instead is *right skewed*.

You can also see that responses in increments of 5 seconds were common (10, 15, 20, 30 seconds).

Center: The average estimate of the 10-second song snippet, $\bar{x}$, was 13.71 seconds. (We will refer to "seconds" here as the *measurement units* of the variable, an important description to include with numerical summaries of quantitative variables.)

> ## KEY IDEA
>
> When describing a quantitative variable, you should always be aware of the *measurement units* of the variable. Measurement units indicate information about the context and scaling of the variable (e.g., seconds vs. minutes). Always include measurement units when describing your variable.

However, when data are skewed, the mean may no longer be as appropriate a measure of center as with symmetric distributions. For example, more than half ($28/48 = 58\%$) of the estimates in this sample are less than the mean estimate (13.7 seconds). With symmetric distributions approximately half of the data values will be less than the mean (and approximately half will be more).

> ## KEY IDEA
>
> The more **right skewed** the distribution is, the larger the percentage of data values that are below the mean. Similarly, the more *left skewed* the distribution is, the larger the percentage of data values that are above the mean. (The mean is pulled in the direction of the longer tail.)

For this reason, the ***median*** is sometimes a preferred way to measure the center of a skewed distribution. The median is the middle number when the data values are sorted from smallest to largest. This implies that the median is always the number which splits the data in half so that half the data values are larger and half are smaller.

> **Definition**
>
> A distribution of data is **skewed** if it is not symmetric and, instead, the bulk of values tend to fall on one side of the distribution with a "longer tail" on the other. Right-skewed distributions have their tail on the right, and left-skewed distributions have their tail on the left.

> **Definition**
>
> The **median** is the middle data value when the data are sorted in order from smallest to largest. The location of the median can be found by determining $(n + 1)/2$, where n represents the sample size. When there are an odd number of data values, the median is the $[(n + 1)/2]$th observation. When there is an even number of data values, the median is reported as the average of the middle two numbers.

To determine the median of the students' estimates of song length, first sort the 48 estimates in order from smallest to largest. We did this in Table 2.5.

TABLE 2.5   Student estimates of song length ordered from smallest to largest

Rank	1	2	3	4	5	6	7	8	9	10	11	12	13	14	15	16	17	18	19	20	21	22	23	24
Estimate	5	6	7	7	7	8	8	8	8	8	8	10	10	10	10	10	10	10	10	10	10	10	12	12

Rank	25	26	27	28	29	30	31	32	33	34	35	36	37	38	39	40	41	42	43	44	45	46	47	48
Estimate	12	13	13	13	15	15	15	15	15	15	15	15	15	15	20	20	20	20	21	22	30	30	30	30

In this case, because there are 48 data values (an even number), the median is reported as the average of the 24th and 25th data values (12 and 12). So, the median is 12 seconds.

> **THINK ABOUT IT**
>
> Why is the median (12) lower than the mean (13.71) for this dataset?

2.2.2

Because the distribution is right skewed, the mean is "pulled" in the direction of the skewness; the median is not. It's common for the mean to be larger than the median with a right-skewed distribution and for the mean to be smaller than the median with a left-skewed distribution. With a stronger skew, the difference between the mean and median is typically larger than with a more modest skew.

> **THINK ABOUT IT**
>
> Which would change more—the mean or the median—if one of the 30-second values had instead been 120 seconds?

2.2.3

Because the median only considers the middle value, it is not affected by extreme values that do not fit the overall pattern of the distribution (sometimes called **outliers**). But because the mean considers every individual value, it can be greatly affected by outliers. In this case the mean would change considerably (from 13.7 to 15.6 seconds) if one of the 30-second values had instead been 120 seconds, but the median (12 seconds) would not change at all.

Variability: The third important way to describe a distribution is to discuss its variability. In this case, the standard deviation (s) of students' song length estimates was 6.50 seconds. This means roughly that, on average, students' song length estimates were about 6.50 seconds away from the average song length (13.71 seconds).

> **THINK ABOUT IT**
>
> Is the standard deviation resistant to outliers?

No, the standard deviation is not resistant to outliers. Calculating a standard deviation involves comparing each data value to the mean (and then squaring that distance!), so extreme outlier values can have a very large impact on the standard deviation.

Variability can also be described by commenting on where the bulk of the data values are located. In this case we could say that all students in our sample estimated the song length to be between 5 and 30 seconds, with the majority of students estimating the song length to be between 5 and 20 seconds.

Definition

- - - - - - - - - - - - - - - - - -

A statistic is ***resistant*** if its value does not change considerably when outliers are included in a data set. The median is a resistant statistic, but the mean is not.

- - - - - - - - - - - - - - - - - -

Unusual observations: Typically, the fourth part of summarizing a variable's distribution is to identify any unusual observations (outliers). Although there are some mathematical rules to define values that are outliers (e.g., a certain distance away from the bulk of the data), often a subjective description of unusual observations is sufficient. In this case, we can say that although the bulk of student estimates of song length are between 5 and 20 seconds, there were a few students who estimated the song length to be 30 seconds—substantially longer than most other students in the sample.

STEP 4: Draw inferences beyond the data.   Judging both from the graph and the mean and median, we can see that this group of subjects tended to overestimate the length of the snippet. Could this overestimate just come from random chance if, on average, the population is accurate when estimating the length of a short song snippet? Maybe the researchers were just "unlucky" in their sample, and the mean really would equal 10 seconds if the researchers had been able to ask this question of the entire population at their school.

We will now look at two approaches to evaluating hypotheses about a population mean: a simulation-based approach and a theory-based approach.

Simulation-based approach: Applying the 3S strategy to hypotheses about a population mean

First, we note that the **statistic** is the sample mean of $\bar{x}_{observed} = 13.71$ seconds. But how will we simulate values of the statistic assuming the null hypothesis to be true? Clearly, we can no longer flip coins or spin spinners. (Why not?) Instead, we need an alternative approach to simulate selecting a random sample of data assuming that the null hypothesis is true (namely, that the population mean, μ, is 10 seconds).

One option is to invent a "population" of values with a mean of 10 and then repeatedly take random samples (of this same size) from that population to simulate what samples could look like when the null hypothesis is true.

The histogram in Figure 2.6 shows a made-up population of 6,215 estimates of the length of the song, where the mean estimated song length is 10 seconds and the standard deviation is about 6.5 seconds.

 2.2.4

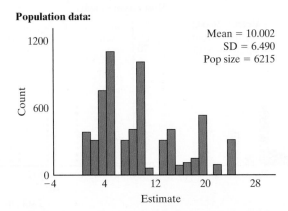

Population data:

Mean = 10.002
SD = 6.490
Pop size = 6215

FIGURE 2.6 Histogram of the distribution of song length estimates in a hypothetical population of 6,215 individuals with mean 10 seconds.

> **THINK ABOUT IT**
>
> What symbols would you use to represent the mean of 10 and standard deviation of 6.5 in the population? Why?

The mean of the population distribution is represented by the Greek letter μ. Similarly, the standard deviation of 6.5 seconds is represented by the Greek letter σ as it is also based on the population.

Notice that the distributions in Figures 2.5 (sample) and 2.6 (hypothetical population) are similar in many ways:

- Most individuals guessed whole numbers (1, 2, 3, ...) and not fractions for the length of the song.
- People were more likely to guess multiples of 5 seconds (like 5, 10, 15, 20, ...) than other whole numbers.
- The sample standard deviation in Figure 2.5 is similar to the population standard deviation in Figure 2.6.
- Both distributions are right-skewed, meaning that more people tended to guess shorter times, but a few people guessed very long times.

The main difference is that this population has a mean song length of 10 seconds, whereas our actual observed sample mean was larger (13.7 seconds). Thus, this distribution is a possible population if the null hypothesis is true. We can now apply the 3S strategy to evaluate the strength of evidence provided by the sample that the actual population did not have a mean of 10 seconds.

1. **Statistic:** The observed statistic is the average estimated song length among the 48 students in the sample, 13.7 seconds.

2. **Simulate:** We need to conduct a simulation which generates random samples of 48 students from a population where we know that the null hypothesis (the population mean, μ, is 10 seconds) is true.

One such approach is to take many random samples of size 48 from the population of 6,215 estimates shown earlier in Figure 2.6. We use the **One Mean** applet to take a random sample of 48 students from this population. Figure 2.7 shows the results. Table 2.6 summarizes the key aspects of the simulation.

FIGURE 2.7 A random sample of 48 "students" from the hypothetical population of 6,215 students. The dots represent the observed results (estimated song lengths) in the sample.

TABLE 2.6		Parallels between real study and simulation
One repetition	=	A random sample of 48 students
Null model	=	Population mean (μ) = 10 seconds
Statistic	=	Average time estimate of song by sample

Figure 2.7 shows that this simulated random sample of 48 students had an average estimated song length of 10.479 seconds, a "could-have-been" sample mean.

By now you know that when we simulate we need to repeat the simulation many, many times and keep track of the value of the statistic each time in order to build a null ("what-if") distribution ("what if the population mean was 10 seconds") of the sample statistics. So next we simulated taking 1,000 different random samples of 48 students from the same hypothetical population. Figure 2.8 illustrates the distribution of sample means in each of the 1,000 samples.

FIGURE 2.8   Distribution of sample means across 1,000 simulated random samples of 48 students from a population with $\mu = 10$ seconds.

Notice that this null distribution of sample means is centered around 10 seconds (as was the population), has a symmetric shape (unlike the population), and has much less variability than the population (standard deviation of sample means = 0.926 seconds rather than the standard deviation of time estimates in the population of 6.490 seconds). Now we can use this null distribution to assess how surprising it would be to get a sample mean of 13.71 seconds from such a population by chance (random sampling) alone.

3. **Strength of evidence:** As shown in the histogram in Figure 2.8, sample means as extreme as 13.71 (the observed sample mean) rarely occur in either direction. In fact, out of 1,000 random samples from this population, a sample mean as large as 13.71 or as small as 6.29 never occurred (see Figure 2.8). Thus, our estimated p-value from this simulation is 0, providing very strong evidence that our observed sample mean did not come from a population with a mean estimated song length of 10 seconds.

Alternatively, we could compute a standardized statistic to assess the strength of evidence by computing $(13.71 - 10)/0.926 = 4.01$. This reveals that the observed value of the sample mean is almost 4 standard deviations above the hypothesized value of 10 seconds. This large standardized statistic confirms our very strong evidence against the null hypothesis that the average estimated song length in the population is 10 seconds.

Thus, we see that the observed sample data provide very strong evidence that people in the population have a systematic tendency to, on average, overestimate how much time elapses in a song snippet.

Theory-based approach: One-sample t-test

You may have noticed a familiar pattern in the null distribution simulated in Figure 2.8. As you saw in Chapter 1, when certain validity conditions are met, it is possible to predict the distribution of the statistic when the null hypothesis is true, instead of using simulation. This same option of using a theory-based test is available when testing hypotheses about a population mean, as we will now see.

2.2.5

In Chapter 1 we used a theoretical probability distribution called a normal distribution to predict the distribution of sample proportions. In fact, a normal distribution is often a good approximation for the distribution of sample means as well.

KEY IDEA

The **central limit theorem** implies that the distribution of sample means is normal when the population distribution is normal, or is approximately normal when the sample size is large.

Furthermore, it can be shown mathematically that the mean of the distribution of sample means equals the population mean, μ, and that the standard deviation of the sample means, $SD(\bar{x})$, equals $\sigma/\sqrt{n}$. This information allows us to create a standardized statistic as we've done before:

$$\text{standardized statistic} = \frac{\text{sample mean} - \text{hypothesized population mean}}{\text{standard deviation of sample mean}} = \frac{\bar{x} - \mu}{\sigma/\sqrt{n}}$$

However, we don't usually know the value of σ, the population standard deviation. So we substitute in s, the sample standard deviation, and compute the **standard error** of the sample means: $s/\sqrt{n}$. For the original sample, $s = 6.50$ seconds, so we approximate the standard deviation of sample means ($\bar{x}$) (standard error) as $6.50/\sqrt{48} \approx 0.938$ seconds. This is similar to what we saw in the simulation, which reported the standard deviation of the 1,000 hypothetical sample means to be 0.926 seconds. Thus for this data set we have

$$\text{standardized statistic} = \frac{\bar{x} - \mu_0}{s/\sqrt{n}} = \frac{13.71 - 10}{6.50/\sqrt{48}} = \frac{3.71}{0.94} = 3.95$$

2.2.6

(where μ_0 is a symbol used to represent the hypothesized value of the population mean). As above, this feels like a large value for a standardized statistic. However, our reference distribution for this standardized statistic is no longer the normal distribution but rather the **t-distribution** (and the standardized statistic is often called a **t-statistic**). The shape of a t-distribution is still a mound-shaped curve, and it is centered at zero. It looks a lot like a normal distribution but it is a bit more spread out than a normal distribution (more observations in the "tails," less in the middle). Figure 2.9 shows the distribution of the standardized statistics for the 1,000 random samples from Figure 2.8 with the t-distribution overlaid. Even though the t-distribution extends further in each direction than a normal distribution, the good news is that t-statistics can be interpreted very similarly to z-statistics. Namely, values roughly greater than 2 (or less than −2) can be considered strong evidence against the null hypothesis.

FIGURE 2.9   The 1,000 simulated t-statistics with a t-distribution overlaid.

Obtaining the p-value from the t-distribution (0.0003) gives us a similar result to the simulation. We find a t-statistic as large as 3.95 (in either direction) occurs in only about 3 in 10,000 random samples from a population with $\mu = 10$ seconds. Figure 2.10 shows the output from the **Theory-Based Inference** applet for this data set.

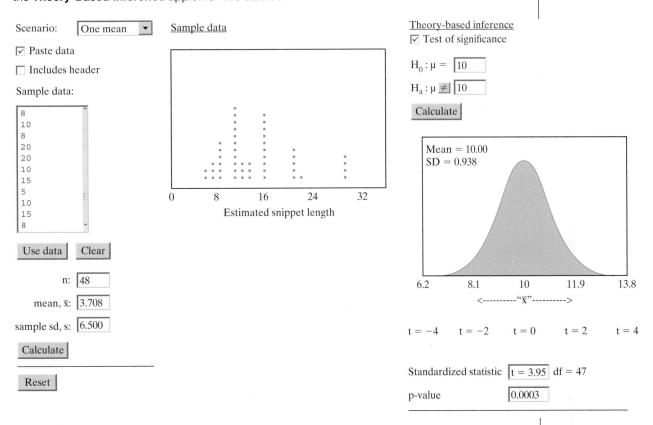

FIGURE 2.10   Theory-Based Inference for time estimate study.

VALIDITY CONDITIONS

As we discussed in Chapter 1, theory-based tests are only valid when certain conditions are met. In the case of a test on a single mean (also called a ***one-sample t-test***) the validity conditions are a little more complicated than they were for a single proportion.

VALIDITY CONDITIONS FOR A ONE-SAMPLE t-TEST

The quantitative variable should have a symmetric distribution, or you should have at least 20 observations and the sample distribution should not be strongly skewed.

It's important to keep in mind that these conditions are rough guidelines and not a guarantee. All theory-based methods are approximations. They will work best when the distributions are symmetric, the sample sizes are large, and there are no large outliers. When in doubt, use a simulation-based method as a cross-check. If the two methods give very different results, you should probably consult a statistician. For more information see FAQ 2.2.1.

FAQ 2.2.1   www.wiley.com/college/tintle

How large of a sample do I need if my data are skewed?

The sample size for the time estimates data is 48, and although the distribution is modestly skewed, it is not strongly skewed, so a theory-based approach should produce similar results to the simulation approach. As shown in Figure 2.9, the theory-based t-distribution matches the distribution of *t*-statistics from the simulation, and consequently the p-values are similar, and both are quite small.

So, in general, the *t*-statistic, a standardized statistic, for a test on a population mean can be found by using this formula:

$$t = \frac{\bar{x} - \mu_0}{s/\sqrt{n}}$$

where μ_0 is a symbol used to represent the hypothesized value of the population mean. Recall that *s* is the sample standard deviation and that *n* is the sample size. In particular, to find the *t*-statistic, subtract the hypothesized value (μ_0) from the sample statistic ($\bar{x}$) and then divide by an estimate of the standard deviation of the statistics (also known as the standard error). When simulating we divide by the standard deviation of the simulated statistics; in the theory-based approach shown here we divided by $s/\sqrt{n}$. (See FAQ 2.2.2 for more details on this and the related idea of degrees of freedom (*df*).)

> **FAQ 2.2.2**   www.wiley.com/college/tintle
>
> Why do we use *z* for π but *t* for μ?

ALTERNATIVE ANALYSIS: WHAT ABOUT THE MEDIAN?

> **THINK ABOUT IT**
>
> Because we said that the mean may not be the best way to summarize the center of the distribution, explain how you could modify the 3S strategy to use the median.

If we wanted to assess whether the sample data provided convincing evidence that the population median was equal to 10 seconds, we could simply find the value of the sample median (in this case 12 seconds) and compare it to many, many simulated sample medians from a population where the median is actually 10 seconds and see how likely the sample median (12 seconds) or more extreme would be to occur by chance (random sampling). As this straightforward analysis suggests, our simulation is quite easy to modify by using a different statistic. Figure 2.11 shows a population distribution that we created with a population median of 10 seconds and the simulated null distribution of sample medians and Table 2.7 summarizes the key elements of the simulation.

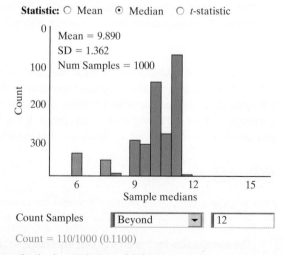

FIGURE 2.11   The distribution of song lengths in a hypothetical population of 6,215 students alongside the simulated null distribution for the sample median.

TABLE 2.7   Parallels between real study and simulation

One repetition	=	A random sample of 48 students
Null model	=	Population median = 10 seconds
Statistic	=	Sample median estimate of song

We could use the simulated results shown in Figure 2.11 to count how many simulated sample medians are larger than 12 seconds or smaller than 8 seconds to estimate the two-sided p-value. As shown, our simulation indicates that we do not have very strong evidence against this null hypothesis (p-value = 0.1100); that is, we do not have strong evidence that the median is different than 10 in the population.

Another important point is that the simulated null distribution shown in Figure 2.11 has far from a "nice" distribution, suggesting that theory-based approaches using mound-shaped, symmetric distributions may not be appropriate when using the median as the statistic. This is, in fact, the case. Although there are some theory-based tests for a median, there is no question that the simulation approach is more straightforward and easy to implement!

Now that we've completed Step 4: Draw inferences beyond the data, and learned more about t-statistics, let's now finish the last two steps of the six step statistical investigation method.

STEP 5: Formulate conclusions.   The analysis of the sample mean gave strong evidence that the population mean differs from 10 seconds. But what is an appropriate population to generalize to from this study? This study was conducted on a convenience sample of 48 college students at a Midwestern college. First, we need to recognize that this was not a random sample; thus we cannot, with certainty, generalize to any particular population. However, even though this was not a random sample, it is doubtful that there was something systematically different about this group of 48 students in their time estimation ability than those of the entire student body at the college. In fact, with regards to estimating elapsed time, it might be reasonable to consider this sample as representative of all college students in the U.S., even though the students were selected from just one Midwestern college. Of course, we have no guarantee of this because we did not take a random sample.

As noted earlier, because the data are skewed, the mean may not be the best measure of center. In our simulation-based analysis, we did not find strong evidence that the population median differs from 10 seconds. Despite a different finding in terms of strength of evidence, the ability to generalize this conclusion to all U.S. college students is the same as for the mean, with the appropriate caveats described in the previous paragraph.

STEP 6: Look back and ahead.   Researchers are interested in learning more about why certain activities seem to pass faster than others. Interestingly, we showed that among this sample of 48 college students, the average perceived time of a song snippet was significantly longer than the actual song length (mean 13.71 seconds for a 10-second snippet). Although this finding is interesting, it suggests a number of additional questions and follow-ups. In particular:

a. The sample is a convenience sample, and so the conclusion we drew is about a population mean of college students well represented by our sample. Taking a random sample would be an improvement, potentially broadening the diversity in the population (beyond just college students).

b. It is interesting that the perception of elapsed time was longer than the actual time, but it would be interesting to compare the perception of time passed while listening to different songs or completing different tasks to start suggesting why the perceived time was longer, on average, than reality. Relatedly, participants could be asked about how much they enjoyed the song/task if enjoyment is thought to be a factor impacting time perception.

c. Because the mean was statistically significant but not the median, we could further explore the skewness in the distribution. We also need to be cautious that we don't say "most students overestimate the length of the snippet." It's possible that a few long estimates are pulling up the value of the mean, whereas 10 seconds is still plausible for a "typical" student.

STEP 1: Ask a research question.   How much do students at your school sleep on a typical night? Let's make the question more specific and ask about *last* night. Is the average less than the recommended eight hours? How can we estimate this average?

1. Based on these questions, what is the population of interest? What is the parameter? What symbol do we use for this parameter?

   Population:

   Parameter:

   Symbol:

STEP 2: Design a study and collect data.   Let's investigate whether the mean amount of sleep last night for the population of all students at your school was less than 8 hours.

2. Express the null and alternative hypotheses for investigating this question.

   Null hypothesis:

   Alternative hypothesis:

To test these hypotheses we need to collect data.

3. Ideally, how should you obtain a sample from the population of all students at your school?

4. What variable would you measure on each student?

   Whereas obtaining a simple random sample of students from your school is an ideal way to attempt to get a representative sample, there is no question that it would take a fair bit of work to make that happen. So much so, that we might not want to do the study anymore! This happens frequently in statistics, and so researchers often opt to use a convenience sample instead. One choice of a convenience sample of students at your school is to use your class.

5. Identify at least one way (variable) that your class is likely a good representation of all students at your school in terms of hours slept last night.

6. Identify at least one way (variable) that your class is likely not a good representation of all students at your school in terms of hours slept last night.

7. Recall from the previous section that convenience sampling may be _____ (biased/unbiased) whereas simple random sampling is _____ (biased/unbiased).

   We will revisit the implications of using your class as a sample of students from your college later when we evaluate the study. For now, let's gather the data.

8. How much sleep (to the nearest quarter hour) did you get last night? Combine your answer with those of your classmates.

9. Did you report a number of hours or a number of minutes slept?

> ### KEY IDEA
>
> When describing a quantitative variable, you should always be aware of the **measurement units** of the variable. Measurement units indicate information about the context and scaling of the variable (e.g., hours vs. days). Always include measurement units when describing your variable.

STEP 3: Explore the data.   After you collect data, the next step is to explore the data. In the case of a quantitative variable (like we have here), exploring the data is a bit more involved than in Chapter 1. Recall from the Preliminaries that we can summarize a quantitative variable using a dotplot and then describe the shape, center, variability, and unusual observations.

Use the **Descriptive Statistics** applet to examine a dotplot of the sample data. To do this, press **Clear** to delete the existing data in the applet and then copy and paste your class data (with a one-word variable name) into the **Sample data** box and press **Use Data**.

Descriptive Statistics

☐ Stacked (Group value)

☑ Includes header

Sample data:

```
sleepHrs
6
6.5
7
7.5
8
5
10
2.5
6
```

Use data | Clear | Top/Bottom

Shape

Earlier in the book we described the shapes of distributions as either symmetric or not symmetric. When distributions are not symmetric, they can sometimes be described as skewed.

> **Definition**
>
> A distribution is called **skewed** if it is not symmetric, and, instead, the bulk of observation values tend to fall on one side of the distribution, with a longer "tail" on the other. Right-skewed distributions have their tail on the right, and left-skewed distributions have their tail on the left.

10. Describe the shape of the distribution of sleep times in the sample as symmetric, right skewed, left skewed, or something else.

Center

11. One way to summarize the center of a distribution is with the mean. Check the box next to **Actual** in the **Mean** row and record the value of the average sleep time for your class. What symbol can we use to represent this value? Also report the measurement units for the value.

   When describing the center of a distribution, the mean is not always the best option. In particular, when the distribution is skewed, the tail of the distribution pulls the mean in that direction, meaning that, in some cases, a large proportion of the data values can be above or below the mean.

> **KEY IDEA**
>
> The more **right skewed** the distribution is, the larger the percentage of data values that are below the mean. Similarly, the more **left skewed** the distribution is, the larger the percentage of data values that are above the mean. (The mean is pulled toward the longer tail.)

> **Definition**
>
> The **median** is the middle data value when the data are sorted in order from smallest to largest. The location of the median can be found by determining $(n + 1)/2$, where n represents the sample size. When there are an odd number of data values, the median is the $[(n + 1)/2]$th observation. When there is an even number of data values, the median is reported as the average of the middle two numbers.

12. For your class, how many students' sleep hours are above the mean? To find this, count the dots on the dotplot above the red arrow or simply look at the data you pasted into the applet.

13. What percentage of your class had sleep hours above the mean?

14. What does this suggest about the skewness of your class's sleep time distribution?

   Because in skewed distributions a large percentage of data values may be above or below the mean, the **median** is sometimes a preferred way to measure the center of a distribution. The median is the middle number when the data values are sorted from smallest to largest. This implies that the median is always the number which splits the data in half so that half the data values are larger and half are smaller.

15. Before you use the applet to find the median sleep hours for your class, make sure you understand how to find the median by finding the median of another (small!) class of statistics students. Here are the sleep times of a small class of six statistics students: 6, 7.5, 5.5, 8, 6.5, 7.5. What is the median for this small class? Find this by hand; don't use the applet!

16. Now, let's return to your class's data. Use the applet to find the median sleep time for your class by checking the **Actual** box in the **Median** row.

17. Do the mean and median for your class differ by much? Are the observed values of the sample mean and median preliminary evidence in favor of our alternative hypothesis?

Variability

The third way to describe a distribution is to discuss its variability. One way to summarize a distribution's variability is to report the standard deviation.

18. What is the standard deviation of sleep times for students in your class? Use the applet to find this by checking the **Actual** box next to **Std dev**.

19. Fill in the blanks to correctly interpret the standard deviation. "The standard deviation of _____ (sleep times/average sleep times) for _____ (students in my class/all students at my school) is _____ (fill in the value) _____(give the measurement units), which means that, _____ (on average/typically/ rarely), the sleep times of _____ (students in my class/all students at my school) were within _____ (fill in the value) _____ (give the measurement units) of the average (mean) sleep time of _____ (fill in the value)."

Unusual observations

Typically the fourth part of summarizing a variable's distribution is to identify any unusual observations (outliers). Although there are some mathematical rules to define values that are outliers (e.g., a certain distance away from the bulk of the data), often a subjective description of unusual observations is sufficient.

20. Are there any sleep hours in your class that you would characterize as unusual? In particular, are there sleep times that are far away from the bulk of the data (outliers)?

Resistance

Let's look at the mean-vs.-median choice in one more way.

21. In the **Sample data** box in the applet find the longest sleep hours value and change it to 20.

Find the new value of the mean:_____

How has this changed from what the mean was before? Why?

Find the new value of the median:_____

How has this changed from what the median was before? Why?

Find the new value of the standard deviation of sleep hours: _____

How has this changed from what the standard deviation was before? Why?

22. Circle which of the following three statistics are not resistant.

| Mean | Median | Standard Deviation |

Definition

- - - - - - - - - - - - - - - - -
A summary statistic is **resistant** if its value does not change considerably when outliers are included in a dataset.
- - - - - - - - - - - - - - - - -

STEP 4: Draw inferences beyond the data. Now that we have explored the data and better understand the distribution of last night's sleep hours in your class, we will learn how to use both simulation and theory-based approaches to evaluate the strength of the evidence against the null hypothesis.

Simulation-based approach: Applying the 3S strategy to hypotheses about a population mean

To evaluate the strength of evidence that your sample data provide against the null hypothesis we need to investigate how often a sample mean as small as the one observed in your sample would occur if you were selecting a random sample from a population in which the mean sleep time really is 8 hours (null hypothesis). In essence, we will apply the 3S strategy as we have done before.

1. Statistic:

23. Remind yourself of the average sleep hours last night in your class. $\bar{x} =$ _____

2. **Simulate:** First, let's *assume* that the *population* of sleep hours follows a normal distribution with mean $\mu = 8$ hours (as indicated under the null hypothesis) and standard deviation $\sigma = 1.5$ hours (probably in the ballpark to what you found in your sample). *Note:* We use the symbol σ to represent the population standard deviation.

We can then investigate whether the observed value of your sample mean is surprising to arise for a random sample from such a population.

To do this, we have manufactured a large, hypothetical population of many thousands of college students with these population parameter values (mean $\mu = 8$ hours and standard deviation $\sigma = 1.5$ hours). You will use the **One Mean** applet to take random samples of the same number of students from this population and evaluate how likely your class's mean would occur.

24. Open the **One Mean** applet. Notice that "Pop1" has been selected and a histogram displays its distribution. Verify that the population distribution looks to be normally distributed with mean very close to 8 hours and SD about 1.5 hours.

Check the **Show Sampling Options** box. Keep **Number of Samples** set to one for now. Set the **Sample Size** to match your class survey. Press **Draw Samples**. Scroll down to see the ID numbers and sleep time values that were randomly selected from this hypothetical population. Record the values of the sample mean for this sample from the "Most Recent Sample" dotplot. Notice that this sample mean is added to the "Statistic" dotplot.

First simulated sample mean =

25. Press **Draw Samples** again. You will see the second sample mean added to the "Statistic" dotplot. The average of the two sample means is reported as the mean in that dotplot. Now change the **Number of Samples** to 998 (for 1,000 samples total) and press **Draw Samples**.
    a. What is the shape of this null distribution?
    b. Where is it centered? Why does this make sense?
    c. What is the standard deviation (SD) of the null distribution?

3. Strength of evidence:

26. Change the **Count Samples** pull-down menu to **Less Than** (to match the direction of the alternative hypothesis) and specify *the observed sample mean for your class* in the box. Press the **Count** button and report the approximate p-value. Based on this p-value, do your sample data provide strong evidence that the population mean sleep time at your school last night was less than 8 hours? Justify your answer, as if to a friend who has not studied statistics.

27. Obtain the value of a standardized statistic by using the same formula we used in Section 1.3:

$$\text{standardized statistic} = \frac{\text{statistic} - \text{mean of null distribution}}{\text{SD of null distribution}}$$

28. Based on the value of the standardized statistic, summarize the strength of evidence provided by the sample data against the null hypothesis.

Theory-based approach

In the previous two chapters you've seen that we can predict the shape of the null distribution using mathematical theory instead of using simulation as long as certain validity conditions are met. We will now explore a theory-based approach for testing a single mean.

In Chapter 1 we used a theoretical probability distribution called a normal distribution to predict the distribution of sample proportions. As it turns out people typically don't predict the distribution of sample means directly; instead they predict the distribution of the standardized statistic. The mathematical distribution they use is called a *t-distribution*. The shape of a *t*-distribution is still mound-shaped, but it is centered at zero. It looks a lot like a normal distribution but it is a bit more spread out than a normal distribution (more observations in the "tails," less in the middle). For this reason, the standardized statistic for testing hypotheses about a population mean is not a *z*-statistic (normal distribution) but a *t-statistic* (*t*-distribution).

Validity conditions

As we discussed in Chapter 1, theory-based tests are valid when certain conditions are met. In the case of a test on a single mean (also called a *one-sample t-test*) the validity conditions are a little more complicated than they were for a single proportion.

VALIDITY CONDITIONS FOR A ONE-SAMPLE *t*-TEST

The quantitative variable should have a symmetric distribution or you should have at least 20 observations and the sample distribution should not be strongly skewed.

It's important to keep in mind that these conditions are rough guidelines and not a guarantee. All theory-based methods are approximations. They will work best when the distributions are symmetric, the sample sizes are large, and there are no large outliers. When in doubt, use a simulation-based method as a cross-check. If the two methods give very different results, you should probably consult a statistician.

29. Would you consider the validity conditions met for population 1?

Formula for a *t*-statistic

The central limit theorem, first seen in Chapter 1, applies for quantitative data.

KEY IDEA

The *central limit theorem* implies that the distribution of sample means is normal when the population distribution is normal, or is approximately normal when the sample size is large.

Furthermore, it can be shown mathematically that the mean of the distribution of sample means equals the population mean, μ, and that the standard deviation of the sample means, $\text{SD}(\bar{x})$, equals $\sigma/\sqrt{n}$. In practice, however, we don't know the population standard deviation, σ, so we use s (the sample standard deviation) instead.

30. Compare the standard deviation of the null distribution you reported in #25 to the value of $s/\sqrt{n}$. Why should these values be similar?

31. Thus, we can find a general formula for a standardized statistic for a test on a population mean. In particular, the t-statistic, a standardized statistic, for a test on a population mean can be found by using this formula:

$$t = \frac{\bar{x} - \mu_0}{s/\sqrt{n}}$$

where μ_0 is a symbol used to represent the hypothesized value of the population mean. Recall that s is the sample standard deviation and that n is the sample size.

Compute the value of the t-statistic for your class data.

32. The good news is that t-statistics can be interpreted very similarly to z-statistics. Namely, values greater than 2 (or less than −2) provide strong evidence against the null hypothesis. Interpret what the t-statistic is telling you about strength of evidence against the null hypothesis.

Notice that the formula for a t-statistic is very similar to how we computed the standardized statistic in the simulation. In particular, to find the t-statistic, subtract the hypothesized value (μ_0) from the sample statistic ($\bar{x}$) and then divide by something. When simulating we divide by the standard deviation of the simulated statistics, here we divide by $s/\sqrt{n}$. As it turns out, $s/\sqrt{n}$ is a prediction of the standard deviation of the simulated statistics!

33. In the **One Mean** applet, above the "Statistic" graph, change the choice of statistic from mean to **t-statistic**. Check the box to **Overlay t Distribution**. Does this theoretical model do a reasonable job of predicting the behavior of the simulated distribution of t-statistics? How does this relate to your answer to Question 29?

34. Use the applet to count the number of simulated samples with a t-statistic less than (our alternative hypothesis) the observed value of your t-statistic to find the approximate p-value (based on t-statistics).

35. The theory-based p-value (one-sample t-test) is also provided in the output. What is the theory-based p-value?

36. Why is the theory-based p-value similar to the p-value you got in #34 (using t-statistic) and in #26 (using the sample mean)?

STEP 5: Formulate conclusions.

37. Think again about how the sample was selected from the population. Do you feel comfortable generalizing the results of your analysis to the population of all students at your school? Explain.

STEP 6: Look back and ahead.

38. Looking back: Did anything about the design and conclusions of this study concern you? Issues you may want to critique include:
   - The match between the research question and the study design
   - How the observational units were selected
   - How the measurements were recorded
   - Whether what we observed is of practical value

39. Looking ahead: What should the researchers' next steps be to fix the limitations or build on this knowledge?

Follow-up #1

To carry out the above analysis, we had to make up a hypothetical population from which to sample. How sensitive is the analysis to that choice of population?

1. Simulate:

40. Now let's assume a different shape for the population of sleep times. Use the radio button to select **Pop 2**.

    a. Describe how the shape of this population is different from the population in #24. Also report the population mean and standard deviation (SD).

    b. Next determine an approximate p-value for your class results. Describe how you have done so and report this p-value. Based on this p-value, do your sample data provide strong evidence that the population mean sleep time at your school last night was less than 8 hours?

41. Does the theory-based p-value appear to be a valid approximation of the simulated p-value for population 2 and this sample size? Explain how you are deciding.

42. Did the assumed shape of the population (Pop 1 vs. Pop 2) make a substantial difference on the *distribution of sample means*? Justify your answer. (*Hint:* Think about the shape, center, and variability of the sample means.)

2. Strength of evidence:

43. Did the assumed shape of the population (Pop 1 vs. Pop 2) make a substantial difference on *the strength of evidence* against the null hypothesis? Explain.

   So, in fact, the simulation-based method may not be all that sensitive to the shape of the population that we use. One advantage of the *t*-procedure is that we don't have to generate a population to sample from at all as long as the validity conditions are met.

Follow-up #2

Earlier in this section we talked about the potential advantages of the median compared to the mean in summarizing quantitative variables when the distribution of the variable is skewed. However, we analyzed the strength of evidence with regards to a population mean. What if we used the median instead?

44. Restate the null and alternative hypotheses in terms of a population median of 8 hours.

45. Explain how you would modify the 3S strategy to test these hypotheses

    a. **Statistic:** What is the value of the new statistic?

    b. **Simulate:** How would you modify the simulation? (*Hint:* What information will you collect from each random sample?)

    c. **Strength of evidence:** How would you modify your assessment of the strength of evidence?

46. Use the **One Mean** applet to simulate 1,000 random samples from Population 1 using the **median** as the statistic. What do you conclude about the strength of evidence provided by your sample median against the null hypothesis?

47. Reexamine Population 2. Could we use it as is to test whether there is evidence that our sample median came from such a population? Explain.

   Whereas modifying the 3S strategy to test the median is not hard, a theory-based test for a median is more difficult and less common. Although there are some options to do a theory-based test for a median, there is no question that the simulation approach is more straightforward and easy to implement!

- -

SECTION 2.2   Summary

In this section we explored simulation- and theory-based approaches for evaluating claims about a single population mean. These approaches are used to estimate the population mean or to assess whether the sample mean differs significantly from a particular hypothesized value for the population (or process) mean. We also explored the idea of skewness of a distribution, and the potential use of median as a measure of center, which always divides the data in half (half the distribution larger/half the distribution smaller), unlike the mean, which, for skewed distributions, gets pulled in the direction of the skew.

- The median is the middle value in an ordered set of data values; half of the values are larger and half are smaller.
- Skewed distributions (asymmetric distributions with a "tail") pull the mean away from the median in the direction of the skew.
- The median is resistant to outliers, but the mean is not resistant. In other words, the mean can be greatly affected by a single extreme value.
- Typically, with quantitative data, the statistic of interest is the sample mean, that is, $\bar{x}$, and the parameter of interest is the population mean, μ.
- The null hypothesis then asserts a particular conjectured value for the population mean.
- The theory-based approach for testing a single mean uses a t-statistic, which is a standardized statistic that follows a theoretical probability distribution known as a t-distribution; this theory-based approach is valid if the sample data are fairly symmetric OR if there are more than 20 observations and the sample data are not strongly skewed (see the table below).
- The formula for the standardized statistic is

$$t = \frac{\bar{x} - \mu_0}{s/\sqrt{n}}$$

Summary of validity conditions and applets for a test of a single mean			
Type of data	Name of test	Applet	Validity conditions
Single quantitative variable	Theory-based test for a single mean (one-sample t-test)	One mean; Theory-based inference	The quantitative variable should have a symmetric distribution or you should have at least 20 observations and the sample distribution should not be strongly skewed.

Process vs. population

In Section 2.1 we talked about the difference between an infinite process and a finite population. Here the sample data were selected from a finite population: students at a particular college. But, there are also times when quantitative variables can be measured on sample data from an infinite process. For example, the measurements on the eruption times of Old Faithful Geyser were from a process. Just like we saw in the previous section, although the parameter may be described slightly differently (the mean in the population vs. the long-run mean of the process), all the resulting inference tools (3S strategy; one-sample t-test, etc.) are the same! Of course, sometimes the distinction between an infinite process and a finite population is not completely clear based on the context and the researcher needs to pick one model or the other and make some assumptions about the data collection process or the characteristics of the sample units.

SAMPLING DISTRIBUTION OF A SAMPLE MEAN

SECTION 2.2: Part 2

INTRODUCTION

In Section 1.6 you explored the distribution (shape, center, and variability) of a sample proportion, $\hat{p}$, using simulations of samples drawn from a process with a long-run proportion of success (π). In Section 2.1 you saw that when you took random samples from a large population, the behavior of the sample proportions was very similar. In particular, you saw that

- The distribution of sample proportions will be centered at the parameter π (in other words, the sample proportion $\hat{p}$ is an unbiased estimator of the population proportion/process probability π).
- The variability of the distribution of sample proportions will decrease as the sample size increases, and that you can use the theory-based formula $\sqrt{\pi(1-\pi)/n}$ to estimate the variability of the sampling distribution of $\hat{p}$.
- As the sample size increases, the shape of the distribution of sample proportions will become approximately normal, provided that the expected numbers of successes, $n\pi$, and failures, $n(1-\pi)$, are both large, typically at least 10.

In this section, you will explore how the **sample mean**, $\bar{x}$, which summarizes the center of the distribution of a quantitative variable, varies from sample to sample. As you've already begun to see in Sections 2.1 and 2.2 (Part 1), the sampling distribution of the sample mean is a bit more complex than the sampling distribution of the sample proportion, because the shape of the underlying population and the population variability come into play—but a variety of similarities between the two sampling distributions emerge.

Just as you did when you explored the sampling distribution for a sample proportion, you will describe the distribution of sample means by looking at the shape, center, and variability of that distribution.

Sampling Pennies

Example 2.2.2

EXAMPLE

One of the authors was curious about the ages of coins that are still in circulation. How long do coins stay in circulation? How many new coins are added into circulation? To investigate this, she had her students bring in pennies that were still in circulation (ones that they had received as change from purchases, rather than from a jar of coins that they had been saving for a period of time). The age of each of the 1,640 pennies was calculated by subtracting the year the penny was minted from the current year so that a newly minted penny would be recorded as having an age of 0 years.

> **THINK ABOUT IT**
>
> What are the observational units here? What is the variable of interest? Is it quantitative or categorical?

Each penny is an observational unit, and the variable of interest is age (years), which is a quantitative variable. You can see from the histogram of the pennies' age (Figure 2.2.1) that the mean age of the pennies is 18.278 years with standard deviation 14.171 years.

> **THINK ABOUT IT**
>
> What is the shape of the distribution of penny ages? What does the shape tell you about the ages of the 1,640 pennies?

The shape of the distribution of penny ages is skewed to the right. The most common ages of pennies in the sample were small (0–2 years since being minted), and there were few pennies over 60 years old still in circulation.

Population data:

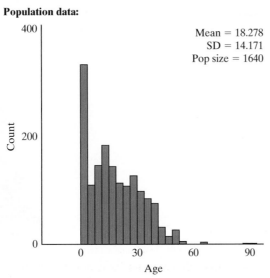

FIGURE 2.2.1 Histogram of the distribution of penny ages (current year minus year penny minted) for a population of 1,640 pennies currently in circulation.

What if you had a lot fewer pennies, say, only 5? What could you learn about the average age of pennies in circulation today with a sample of only 5 pennies? How should you obtain your 5 pennies? To investigate this question, the class decided to consider the 1,640 pennies as *a population of pennies* and to repeatedly sample 5 pennies from this population to gain an understanding of what the distribution of sample means would look like (shape, center, variability).

THINK ABOUT IT

> What will the distribution of sample mean ages of pennies from this population look like for samples of size $n = 5$? Where will this distribution be centered? Can we predict the sample-to-sample variability that we can expect in the sample means, for samples of size $n = 5$? What shape will the distribution have?

The graphs in Figure 2.2.2 were constructed using the **One Mean** applet. There is a lot going on here, so let's take a moment and make sure we understand what each of the three graphs in Figure 2.2.2 represents. The first graph, a histogram, represents the ages of the 1,640 pennies in our population of pennies, with mean $\mu = 18.278$ years and standard deviation $\sigma = 14.171$ years. (The lower-case Greek letter sigma, σ, is used to denote a population standard deviation.) The second graph, a dotplot, was generated by randomly sampling 5 pennies from the population. Each dot on the dotplot represents the age of one of the 5 randomly selected pennies from this population (where the sample mean age of these 5 pennies was $\bar{x} = 10.60$ years, with sample standard deviation of ages, $s = 10.922$ years). The third graph, a histogram, was generated by plotting the means of 1,000 different random samples, each consisting of 5 pennies selected from the population. This histogram represents the distribution of "*could have been*" sample mean ages if we took 1,000 different random samples of 5 pennies and used the resulting 1,000 sample means to construct the histogram. In this case, we find the mean of the *simulated distribution of sample means* is 18.403 years, with standard deviation of the sample means 6.342 years.

Taking 1,000 random samples of 5 pennies from our population of pennies helps us see the long-run pattern in the resulting sample mean ages. In particular, the mean of the distribution of sample mean penny ages (18.403 years) falls very near the value of the parameter—in this case, the population mean (18.278 years), the mean age of all of the pennies in our population. Recall from Section 2.1 that the sample mean is an unbiased estimator of the population mean when we use simple random sampling.

2.2P2.1

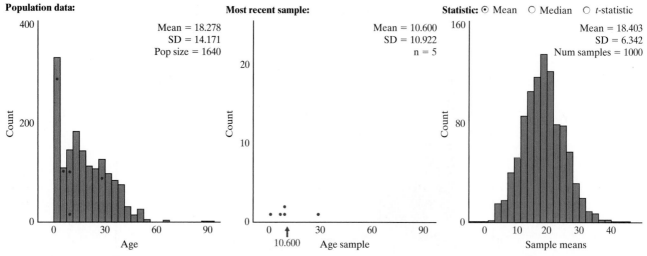

FIGURE 2.2.2   The first graph is a histogram of the ages of the 1,640 pennies in the population; the second graph is a dotplot of 5 randomly selected penny ages from the population; the third graph, a histogram, displays the "could have been" sample mean ages from each of 1,000 different random samples of 5 pennies from the population of 1,640 pennies.

Next, there is less variability in the distribution of sample mean ages than in the population of ages. The standard deviation of sample means in our simulated sampling distribution is 6.342 years, which is smaller than the standard deviation of the population of individual penny ages of 14.171 years. This should make sense as sample means vary less from sample to sample than individual ages vary from penny to penny (it's easier to get one extremely old penny than to get five extremely old pennies at once).

Furthermore, whereas the shape of the distribution of our population of penny ages for the population is skewed to the right, the shape of the distribution of sample mean penny ages taken from samples of 5 pennies is only slightly skewed to the right.

YOU MIGHT BE THINKING

Wait, why does the mean (18.403 years) of the simulated sampling distribution of sample means turn out to be so close to the population mean (18.278 years), but not exactly the same?

Recall from Section 1.6 that one key difference between a *simulated* sampling distribution and a *theoretical* sampling distribution is that the theoretical distribution is made up of every possible simple random sample of a given size n from a long-run process or specified population. Because of this, the mean of the theoretical sampling distribution is exactly equal to the population parameter, and the standard deviation will be exactly equal to the value given by the formula for the theoretical model. But in our simulations, which do not contain every possible sample of a given sample size, the mean of the distribution of sample statistics will be very close to the population parameter, and the standard deviation of the sample statistics will be close to the value given by the formula for the theoretical model.

THINK ABOUT IT

What would the distribution of sample mean ages of pennies look like if we increased the sample size? Where would the distribution of sample mean ages of pennies be centered? Can we predict the sample-to-sample variability?

Figure 2.2.3 shows the distribution of 1,000 possible sample mean penny ages for samples of 25, 50, and 100 pennies taken from the population of 1,640 pennies, and Table 2.2.1 displays the mean, standard deviation, and shape for the population distribution, the mean and standard deviation of the simulated distribution, and the theoretical standard deviation of the distribution of sample means for samples of size 5, 25, 50, and 100.

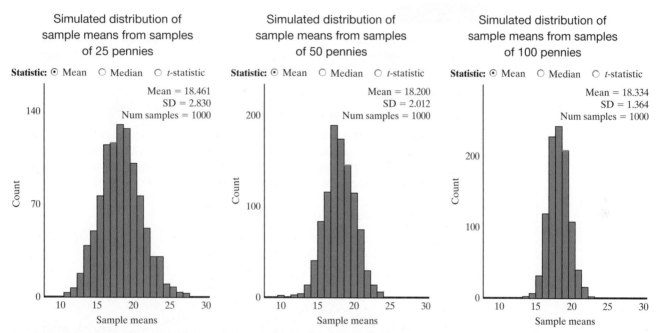

FIGURE 2.2.3   Simulated distributions of sample mean penny ages for samples of size 25, 50, and 100 taken from a population of 1,640 pennies.

TABLE 2.2.1   Comparison of sampling distributions of sample means for different sample sizes

Population Mean: μ = 18.278 years; Population SD: σ = 14.171; Population Shape: Skewed to the Right

Sample size (n)	Mean of *simulated* distribution of sample means	SD of *simulated* distribution of sample means	SD of distribution of sample means (theoretical = $\sigma/\sqrt{n}$)	Shape of distribution of sample means
5	18.403	6.342	$14.171/\sqrt{5} = 6.337$	Skewed slightly to right
25	18.461	2.830	$14.171/\sqrt{25} = 2.834$	Bell-shaped
50	18.200	2.012	$14.171/\sqrt{50} = 2.004$	Bell-shaped
100	18.334	1.364	$14.171/\sqrt{100} = 1.417$	Bell-shaped

We can see from the histograms (Figure 2.2.3) of the *simulated sampling distributions* of sample mean ages of pennies for different sample sizes that, like the sample proportion, the sample mean is an unbiased estimator of the population mean. That is, the sampling distribution of sample means (for all possible samples of a given size from a population) will be centered at the population mean μ. (If the numbers in the table aren't close enough to 18.278 for you, try taking more samples.)

As was the case with the sample proportion, the sample mean varies from sample to sample not in a haphazard manner but according to a predictable long-run pattern, and the sample-to-sample variability will decrease as the sample size increases. We can see from Table 2.2.1 that the standard deviation of our *simulated sampling distributions* is very close to what would be predicted by the theoretical formula $\sigma/\sqrt{n}$, as you saw earlier in Part 1 of this section.

2.2P2.2

2.2P2.3

In the previous part of this section, we learned that the shape of the sampling distribution of sample means will be bell-shaped when the population distribution is bell-shaped. The **central limit theorem** implies that regardless of the shape of the population, the shape of the sampling distribution of sample means will be bell-shaped for large sample sizes (typically, for sample sizes of at least 30).

> ### KEY IDEA
>
> The sampling distribution of a sample mean can be described by its shape, center (mean), and variability (standard deviation). The *sampling distribution of a sample mean* has
>
> **Center:** Mean of $\bar{x}$'s = μ
>
> **Variability:** Standard deviation of $\bar{x}$'s = $\sigma/\sqrt{n}$
>
> **Shape:** If the population distribution is bell-shaped, then the sampling distribution of sample means will be bell-shaped. By the central limit theorem (CLT), for large sample sizes (typically, $n \geq 30$), regardless of the shape of the population, the sampling distribution of sample means will be bell-shaped.
>
>

2.2P2.4

The last statement in the Key Idea box (about when you can assume the shape of the distribution of sample means is approximately normal) is often called the **central limit theorem**, one of the most important results in statistics. You were first introduced to the central limit theorem in Sections 1.5 and 1.6, and you will see various versions of the central limit theorem throughout this course.

That said, the last sentence about shape in the Key Idea box is a bit of an overstatement.

2.2P2.5

The shape of the sampling distribution of sample means really depends on the combination of the shape of the population distribution and the sample size.

> ### KEY IDEA
>
> If the population distribution is approximately normal, then we can assume normality in the distribution of sample means for any sample size. If the population is close to symmetric, then the distribution of sample means will be fairly bell-shaped even with smaller sample sizes. But if the shape of the population is very unusual (e.g., multi-modal, skewed, large outliers), then we may need a much larger sample size before the distribution of sample means is fairly bell-shaped.

In reality, we don't always know whether we have a large enough sample size. The number 30 is cited as a guideline that works in many, many cases, but you should always be looking at the distribution of your sample as well for evidence of extreme behavior in the population distribution. Remember that we expect the shape of the distribution of *sample* data will be similar to the shape of the population distribution.

Investigation of the sampling distribution of the sample mean

In Example 2.2.2 you saw that the distribution of sample means taken from random samples from a population will be centered at the population mean and that there will be less variability in the distribution of sample means than in the individual observations in the population. You also saw that as the sample size increases, the shape of the distribution of sample means will become more bell-shaped, regardless of the shape of the underlying population distribution (central limit theorem). In this exploration you will use the **One Mean** applet to investigate the shape, center, and variability of the distribution of sample means for differently shaped populations and various sample sizes.

Suppose that the population of interest is all U.S. adults, and the variable of interest is how much an adult pays for a haircut (including tips) in dollars.

1. Open the **One Mean** applet. Follow the link for **Population model**. This applet will sample from a theoretical population distribution that you specify.

2. Set the population mean to 30 dollars, the population standard deviation to 10 dollars, and the population shape to Normal. Produce a sketch of the population. In particular, record the values for the population mean and the population standard deviation with appropriate symbols.

Population mean adult haircut (including tips) in dollars:

Population standard deviation in dollars:

3. Now check the **Show Sampling Options** box and set the sample size to 5 haircuts and indicate that you want to select 1,000 samples. Press **Draw Samples**.

Show Sampling Options: ☑

Number of samples: 1000

Sample size: 5

KEY REMINDER

Remember not to confuse the *sample size* (number of observations within each sample) with the *number of samples*. We often choose a large number for the number of samples, like 1,000, so we think we are observing the long-run behavior of the sampling distribution of our sample mean.

4. Explain, in context, what the **Most Recent Sample** graph represents here.

5. Explain what the **Statistic** graph represents here.

6. Where is the sampling distribution of sample means of adult haircuts (including tips) in dollars centered? How does that compare to the population mean?

7. What is the standard deviation of the distribution of sample means of adult haircuts (including tips) in dollars? How does that compare to the population standard deviation? How does it compare to the predicted standard deviation, $\sigma/\sqrt{n}$?

8. What is the shape of the distribution of sample means of adult haircuts (including tips) in dollars? Is it approximately normal? Would this be predicted? Explain why or why not.

9. How surprised would you be to get a sample mean of 40 dollars from this population of adult haircuts (including tips) in dollars with a mean of 30 dollars? Justify your answer.

> ### KEY IDEA
>
> The sampling distribution of a sample mean can be described by its shape, center (mean), and variability (standard deviation). The *sampling distribution of a sample mean* has
>
> **Shape:** If the population distribution is bell-shaped, then the sampling distribution of sample means will be bell-shaped.
>
> By the central limit theorem (CLT), for large sample sizes (typically, $n \geq 30$), regardless of the shape of the population, the sampling distribution of sample means will be bell-shaped.
>
> **Center:** Mean of $\bar{x}$'s = μ
>
> **Variability:** Standard deviation of $\bar{x}$'s = $\sigma/\sqrt{n}$
>
>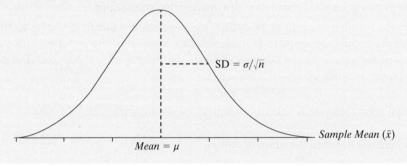

The statement in the Key Idea box about when you can assume the shape of the distribution of sample means is approximately normal is often referred to as the *central limit theorem*, one of the most important results in statistics. You were first introduced to the central limit theorem in Sections 1.5 and 1.6, and you will see various versions of the central limit theorem throughout this text.

That said, the sentence about shape in the Key Idea box is a bit of an overstatement. The shape of the sampling distribution of sample means really depends on the combination of the shape of the population distribution and the sample size. We will explore both the shape of the population and the sample size in the next few questions.

10. Now change the shape of the population distribution to **Skewed right** (suppose that there are a few adults who spend much, much more on haircuts than the typical amount spent by adults). Sketch the population below and record the population mean and standard deviation values.

11. Now create a sampling distribution of 1,000 samples of size $n = 5$ haircuts from this population. You should find the sampling distribution of sample means of adult haircuts (including tips) in dollars to be slightly skewed to the right. Why?

12. Check the box to **Overlay Normal Distribution**. Try some different sample sizes. What sample size do you need before the distribution of sample means looks approximately normal?

> ### THINK ABOUT IT
>
> What would the distribution of sample means of adult haircuts (including tips) in dollars look like if we increased the sample size? Where would the distribution of sample means be centered? Could we predict the sample-to-sample variability?

13. Now change the shape of the population distribution to **Uniform** (suppose there was a range of haircut prices that were equally likely). Change the sample size back to 5 and

generate the sampling distribution. Would you consider this sampling distribution approximately normal? What is the smallest sample size for which you would consider this
approximately normal? Is this larger or smaller than for the skewed right population?

KEY IDEA

If the population is approximately normal, then we can assume normality in the distribution of sample means for any sample size. If the population is close to symmetric,
then the distribution of sample means will be bell-shaped even with smaller sample
sizes. But if the shape of the population is very unusual (e.g., multimodal, skewed,
large outliers), then we may need a much larger sample size before the distribution of
sample means is bell-shaped.

14. Figure 2.2.4 shows a left-skewed population distribution (can you imagine a scenario for which
the population of adult haircuts (including tips) in dollars would be left-skewed?). Below the
population distribution are graphs of "could have been" sample means taken from 1,000 samples from the population for each of three sample sizes 5, 15, and 30. Write the appropriate
sample size (5, 15, or 30) for each of the distributions of sample means. Justify your choices.

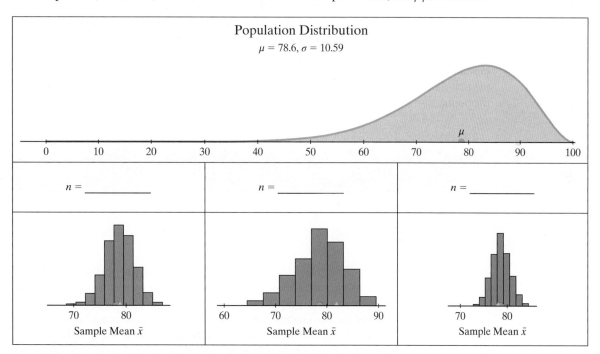

FIGURE 2.2.4   Skewed-left population with different sampling distributions of the sample mean.

15. Figure 2.2.5 shows a graph of a bimodal population. (Maybe women tend to pay more
than men and we have a few more women in the population?)

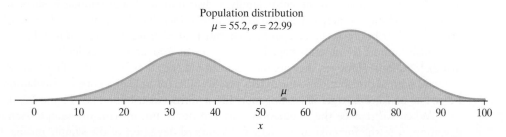

FIGURE 2.2.5   Bimodal population.

Suppose we take samples of size 5 from this population. Do you predict the sampling distribution of sample means of adult haircuts (including tips) in dollars to be approximately normal? What do you predict for the mean and for the standard deviation of the sampling distribution of the sample mean? Explain.

- -

SECTION 2.2: Part 2   Summary

You looked at three distinct distributions in this section—a population distribution, the distribution of sample data from a population, and the sampling distribution of sample means, which is the distribution of sample means obtained from repeatedly selecting samples of a given size from the same population. It is very important to be able to distinguish among these three distributions and to use proper terminology in referring to them. You should also be able to predict how the last two should behave if you are given information about the population or underlying process from which the sample is selected. The shape of the distribution of sample data will typically be similar to the shape of the population distribution. The shape of the distribution of sample means will be bell-shaped if the population is bell-shaped or, regardless of population shape, will become more bell-shaped as the sample size increases (typically, $n \geq 30$), as a result of the central limit theorem. You also observed that when the shape of the population distribution is fairly symmetric, the shape of the sampling distribution of sample means will become fairly bell-shaped faster (for smaller sample sizes). We can describe the sampling distribution of a sample statistic by noting its shape, center (mean), and variability (standard deviation). In particular, the sampling distribution of sample means (for every possible sample of size n from a population) will be centered at the population mean, μ, with standard deviation $\sigma \sqrt{n}$, where σ is the standard deviation of the population distribution.

SECTION 2.2: Part 3   ONE-SAMPLE t-TEST FOR A POPULATION MEAN

INTRODUCTION

In Section 2.2 you explored ways to assess the strength of evidence for hypotheses about a single population mean using both simulation and theory-based approaches. You saw that because you do not usually know the population standard deviation, we substitute s, the sample standard deviation, for the population standard deviation when estimating the variability of the distribution of sample means, and compute the ***standard error*** of the sample means to be $s/\sqrt{n}$. We also saw that you use a ***t-distribution*** as the theory-based model for the sample mean instead of a normal distribution, as was the case for sample proportions.

More about the t-distribution

The t-distribution is actually an entire family of distributions that are similar in shape to the normal distribution. Whereas a normal distribution is identified by its mean and standard deviation, a t-distribution is characterized by a number called its ***degrees of freedom*** (abbreviated df). t-distributions are mound-shaped and centered at zero, and so they look a lot like normal distributions. However, they are more spread out (i.e., they have wider, fatter tails) than standard normal distributions—the df tells you how like (or unlike) a normal distribution the t-distribution is, with larger df looking more like a normal distribution (see Figure 2.2.6).

When we replace the population standard deviation, σ, with the sample standard deviation, s, in the formula to estimate the standard deviation of the sample means, it is possible that two unfortunate things may occur: the sample mean may be a little farther than expected from the population mean, and the sample standard deviation may be a little less than the population standard deviation. The *t*-distribution, with appropriate degrees of freedom, accounts for this additional potential difference. As the number of degrees of freedom increases (i.e., larger sample size), the tails get lighter and the *t*-distribution gets closer and closer to a normal or *z*-distribution (which corresponds to *s* being a better approximation to σ).

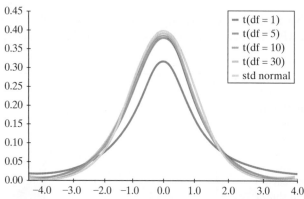

FIGURE 2.2.6   Graphs of *t*-distributions for different degrees of freedom.

In Section 1.7 you learned that when a hypothesis test is called for, you must show the following work to receive full credit on the AP Statistics exam.

2.2P3.1

1. **State the hypotheses either in words or using appropriate symbols.**

   For a claim about a single population mean, our hypotheses will take one of the following forms, where μ_0 represents the hypothesized value of the population mean.

   $H_0\colon \mu = \mu_0$

   $H_a\colon \mu < \mu_0$ or

   $\quad \mu > \mu_0$ or

   $\quad \mu \neq \mu_0$

   You can state the hypotheses in words; just make sure you clarify the direction of the alternative hypothesis.

2. **Name the test that will be used and state and verify the validity conditions for the test chosen.**

   The theory-based approach for inference for a single mean is a ***one-sample t-test***.

   Validity Conditions:

   - Data are from a random sample from the population of interest.
   - Population distribution is approximately normally distributed or sample size is large enough for the central limit theorem to apply (e.g., $n \geq 30$).
     - For smaller samples where the population shape is unknown, graph the sample data and comment on whether it is reasonable to assume that the sample data came from a population that is fairly symmetric (recall from Section 2.2, Part 2, that when the shape of the population distribution is fairly symmetric, the distribution of sample means will tend to become bell-shaped fairly quickly, even for small sample sizes). Occasionally, you may also have other reasons to suspect the population distribution is normal (e.g., historical evidence).

3. **Calculate the test statistic (standardized statistic) and corresponding p-value.**

   Test statistic: $t_{df=n-1} = \dfrac{\bar{x} - \mu_0}{s/\sqrt{n}}$

CALCULATOR TIPS

You can determine the test statistic and p-value using graphing calculators. For example:

- **TI-84:** STAT → TESTS → T-Test
- **TI-Nspire:** Statistics → Stat Tests → tTest

If you don't have access to a calculator, once you have calculated the test statistic, you can use Table B on the AP^{TM} formula sheet to find the corresponding p-value (part of the table is shown below).

Table entry for p and C is the point t^* with probability p lying above it and probability C lying between $-t^*$ and t^*. (Note: The probability C values aren't shown here.)

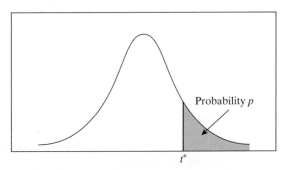

TABLE B   t-distribution critical values

df	Tail probability p									
	.25	.20	.15	.10	.05	.025	.02	.01	.005	.0025
1	1.000	1.376	1.963	3.078	6.314	12.71	15.89	31.82	63.66	127.3
2	.816	1.061	1.386	1.886	2.920	4.303	4.849	6.965	9.925	14.09
3	.765	.978	1.250	1.638	2.353	3.182	3.482	4.541	5.841	7.453
4	.741	.941	1.190	1.533	2.132	2.776	2.999	3.747	4.604	5.598
5	.727	.920	1.156	1.476	2.015	2.571	2.757	3.365	4.032	4.773
6	.718	.906	1.134	1.440	1.943	2.447	2.612	3.143	3.707	4.317
7	.711	.896	1.119	1.415	1.895	2.365	2.517	2.998	3.499	4.029
8	.706	.889	1.108	1.397	1.860	2.306	2.449	2.896	3.355	3.833
9	.703	.883	1.100	1.383	1.833	2.262	2.398	2.821	3.250	3.690
10	.700	.879	1.093	1.372	1.812	2.228	2.359	2.764	3.169	3.581
11	.697	.876	1.088	1.363	1.796	2.201	2.328	2.718	3.106	3.497
12	.695	.873	1.083	1.356	1.782	2.179	2.303	2.681	3.055	3.428
13	.694	.870	1.079	1.350	1.771	2.160	2.282	2.650	3.012	3.372
14	.692	.868	1.076	1.345	1.761	2.145	2.264	2.624	2.977	3.326
15	.691	.866	1.074	1.341	1.753	2.131	2.249	2.602	2.947	3.286
16	.690	.865	1.071	1.337	1.746	2.120	2.235	2.583	2.921	3.252
17	.689	.863	1.069	1.333	1.740	2.110	2.224	2.567	2.898	3.222

How to use Table B

One-sided test (upper tail)

Suppose that the alternative hypothesis of interest is $H_a: \mu > \mu_0$, $n = 16$, and $t = 1.83$. For this sample size, the degrees of freedom (df) $= 16 - 1 = 15$.

- In Table B, go to df $= 15$ row.
- The t-statistic 1.83 falls between 1.753 and 2.131 in that row.

- The upper-tail probability (given at the top of the corresponding columns) is between 0.05 and 0.025.

- Because our alternative hypothesis is $H_a: \mu > \mu_0$, we are looking for the probability that $t \geq 1.83$, so our p-value is between 0.025 and 0.05. (See Figure 2.2.7.)

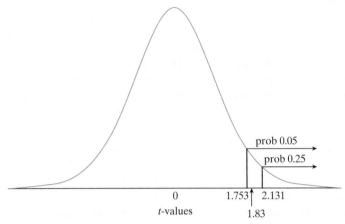

FIGURE 2.2.7 Bounding the upper tail probability.

One-sided test (lower tail)

Now suppose your alternative hypothesis had been $H_a: \mu < \mu_0$, with $n = 16$ and $t = -1.83$. Because the *t*-distributions are symmetric, the probability to the left of -1.83 $P(t \leq -1.83) = P(t \geq 1.83)$ is the same as the probability to the right of 1.83, so our p-value is between 0.025 and 0.05. (See Figure 2.2.8.)

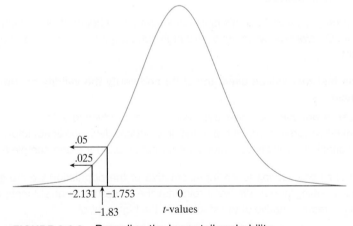

FIGURE 2.2.8 Bounding the lower tail probability.

Two-sided test

What if your alternative hypothesis had been $H_a: \mu \neq \mu_0$, with $n = 16$ and $t = -1.83$ (or $t = 1.83$)? Now you are interested in the probability of obtaining a value of t less than or equal to -1.83 or greater than or equal to 1.83. For this two-sided test, the corresponding p-value would be between $2(0.025) = 0.05$ and $2(0.05) = 0.10$, so our two-sided p-value is between 0.05 and 0.10.

4. **State your conclusion** (with appropriate justification based on your p-value and significance level) in the context of the research question.

2.2.3 — How Much Sleep Do Teens Need?

Example 2.2.3

EXAMPLE

How much sleep do teens really need? Guidelines from the 2015 National Sleep Foundation recommend eight to ten hours of sleep a night for teenagers 14 to 17 years of age. In another study conducted by Brigham Young University, economists Eric Eide and Mark Showalter (2012) found that, based on standardized test results, teens scored best with about seven hours of sleep each night. A high school teacher suspects that students at her school, on average, are getting significantly less than even the seven hours of sleep each night recommended by the BYU researchers. To test her suspicions, she asks the 17 students in her class to record the number of hours they sleep that night, to the nearest half-hour. Below are the data (in hours).

7.5	6.5	6.5	6	7	5.5	6.5	7.5	6	7	7	6	8	5	8	6.5	6.5

Suppose that we can consider the sleep habits of the students in this class to be representative of the students at this high school. Do the data provide convincing evidence at a significance level of $\alpha = 0.05$ to support the teacher's suspicion that students at this high school get less than seven hours of sleep each night, on average?

Now let's look at how to answer this research with the work required on the AP Statistics exam.

1. **State the hypotheses either in words or using appropriate symbols.**

   Let μ represent the mean number of hours of sleep each night for students at this high school.

   We want to decide whether we are convinced that students at this school get less than the claimed optimal seven hours of nightly sleep, on average. Thus, the hypotheses can be stated in symbols as

   H_0: $\mu = 7$

   H_a: $\mu < 7$ or in words as

   Null: On average, students at this high school get seven hours of sleep each night.
   Alternative: On average, students at this high school get less than seven hours of sleep each night.

2. **Name the test that will be used and state and verify the validity conditions for the test chosen.**

   We will use a one-sample t-test because we are conducting a test on a single mean (sleep = quantitative variable) and the population standard deviation is not known.
   Now let's check the validity conditions (from Section 2.2) for a one-sample t-test:

   1. We need our observations to be representative of the population we are interested in learning something about. We were told that the sleep habits of students in the class sampled are representative of the students in the high school.

   2. We do not know the shape of the population of sleep times for students at this school, and because our sample of 17 students is not large enough to appeal to the central limit theorem, we need to graph the sample data.

      A dot plot of our sample data of the number of hours slept the previous night for students in this class appears to be bell-shaped, so it is reasonable to assume that the population distribution of sleep times for students at this high school is approximately normal. The distribution of sample means for samples of this size should therefore be bell-shaped, so it is reasonable to conduct a one-sample t-test.

Hours slept

3. **Calculate the test statistic (standardized statistic) and corresponding p-value.**

   By plugging into the appropriate formulas, we find the following:

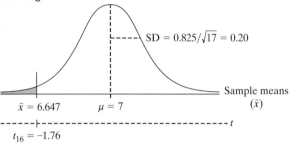

$\bar{x} = 6.647\ hrs$
$s = 0.825\ hrs$
$n = 17$
$df = 17 - 1 = 16$

$$t_{df=16} = \frac{6.647 - 7}{0.825/\sqrt{17}} \approx -1.76$$

$p-value \approx 0.048$

From Table B, we find the p-value is between 0.025 and 0.050.

TABLE B	*t*-distribution critical values										

	Tail probability *p*										
df	.25	.20	.15	.10	.05	.025	.02	.01	.005	.0025	.001	.0005
1	1.000	1.376	1.963	3.078	6.314	12.71	15.89	31.82	63.66	127.3	318.3	636.6
2	.816	1.061	1.386	1.886	2.920	4.303	4.849	6.965	9.925	14.09	22.33	31.60
3	.765	.978	1.250	1.638	2.353	3.182	3.482	4.541	5.841	7.453	10.21	12.92
4	.741	.941	1.190	1.533	2.132	2.776	2.999	3.747	4.604	5.598	7.173	8.610
5	.727	.920	1.156	1.476	2.015	2.571	2.757	3.365	4.032	4.773	5.893	6.869
6	.718	.906	1.134	1.440	1.943	2.447	2.612	3.143	3.707	4.317	5.208	5.959
7	.711	.896	1.119	1.415	1.895	2.365	2.517	2.998	3.499	4.029	4.785	5.408
8	.706	.889	1.108	1.397	1.860	2.306	2.449	2.896	3.355	3.833	4.501	5.041
9	.703	.883	1.100	1.383	1.833	2.262	2.398	2.821	3.250	3.690	4.297	4.781
10	.700	.879	1.093	1.372	1.812	2.228	2.359	2.764	3.169	3.581	4.144	4.587
11	.697	.876	1.088	1.363	1.796	2.201	2.328	2.718	3.106	3.497	4.025	4.437
12	.695	.873	1.083	1.356	1.782	2.179	2.303	2.681	3.055	3.428	3.930	4.318
13	.694	.870	1.079	1.350	1.771	2.160	2.282	2.650	3.012	3.372	3.852	4.221
14	.692	.868	1.076	1.345	1.761	2.145	2.264	2.624	2.977	3.326	3.787	4.140
15	.691	.866	1.074	1.341	1.753	2.131	2.249	2.602	2.947	3.286	3.733	4.073
16	.690	.865	1.071	1.337	1.746	2.120	2.235	2.583	2.921	3.252	3.686	4.015
17	.689	.863	1.069	1.333	1.740	2.110	2.224	2.567	2.898	3.222	3.646	3.965
18	.688	.862	1.067	1.330	1.734	2.101	2.214	2.552	2.878	3.197	3.611	3.922
19	.688	.861	1.066	1.328	1.729	2.093	2.205	2.539	2.861	3.174	3.579	3.883
20	.687	.860	1.064	1.325	1.725	2.086	2.197	2.528	2.845	3.153	3.552	3.850

4. **State your conclusion (with appropriate justification based on your p-value and stated significance level) in the context of the research question.**

   We obtained a p-value of 0.048, which is smaller than our significance level of 0.05. Therefore, we have sufficient evidence to claim that students at this high school get less than seven hours of sleep a night, on average.

   This conclusion is only valid if the sleep times for this class are representative of sleep times for students at the entire school.

2.2P3.2

Texting

EXPLORATION

2.2.3

After reading a Pew Research Center report saying that adult cellphone users in the U.S. text, send, and receive an average of 40 text messages daily, one of the authors who suspected that students at her school send/receive more than 40 texts daily surveyed a sample of 64 students. Based on the survey data, she found the sample mean and standard deviation to be 69.75 texts daily and 99.27 texts daily, respectively.

Suppose that you can consider the texting habits of the students in this sample to be representative of the students at this school. Do the data provide convincing evidence at a significance level of $\alpha = 0.05$ to support the teacher's suspicion that students at this school send/receive more than 40 text messages daily, on average?

Recall that the AP Statistics exam requires four parts when a hypothesis test is called for (the order of the parts is arbitrary). To practice including all four parts, you will answer the research question in the following four steps.

1. **State the hypotheses either in words or using appropriate symbols.**

Hints: What is the parameter of interest here? What is the symbol used to represent this parameter? If you decide to state your hypotheses in symbols, remember to use the appropriate symbol for the population parameter (never the symbol for the statistic!). And, of course, if you decide to state your hypotheses in words, be sure to do so in context and to refrain from using past tense (e.g., "on average, the students sent more than 40 texts" makes it sound as if your hypotheses are about the sample of students, rather than the population of students at the school.)

2. **Name the test that will be used and state and verify the validity conditions for the test chosen.**

Hints: Validity conditions deal with how the data were collected (e.g., when sampling, you should check the reasonableness that the obtained sample is representative of the population of interest), and with the appropriateness of the theoretical model chosen (for a single mean, population approximately normally distributed or sample size large enough for the central limit theorem (CLT) to apply).

3. **Calculate the test statistic (standardized statistic) and corresponding p-value.**

Hints: You can complete this step using either a graphing calculator or the appropriate formula and Table B from the AP formula sheet. If you don't have access to a graphing calculator, then you have to first find the appropriate test statistic. Next, you use Table B to find the p-value. In either case, show your work by plugging in the relevant numbers in the appropriate formula and record both the test statistic and the p-value.

4. **State your conclusion (with appropriate justification based on your p-value and stated significance level) in the context of the research question.**

Hints: Is the p-value small enough to convince us that the students at this school send/receive more than 40 texts daily, on average? State the criteria you used to determine if the p-value is small enough (compare to α-level). Be sure to state your conclusion in the context of the study and in terms of the alternative (research) hypothesis.

SECTION 2.2: Part 3   Summary

In this section we reviewed the work necessary to receive full credit on the AP Statistics examination when a hypothesis test (test of significance) for a single mean is called for. Specifically, we looked at the validity conditions for a one-sample t-test and how to compute a t-statistic (test statistic) and corresponding p-value to measure our strength of evidence against the null hypothesis using a theory-based approach for inference for a single mean. We saw that all hypothesis tests follow the same basic format:

1. State the hypotheses either in words or using appropriate symbols.
2. Name the test that will be used and state and verify the validity conditions for the test chosen.
3. Calculate the test statistic (standardized statistic) and corresponding p-value.
4. State your conclusion (with appropriate justification based on your p-value and stated significance level) in the context of the research question.

In this chapter we focused on Step 4 of the statistical investigation method for a quantitative variable: assessing the statistical significance of an observed result against some claim about the mean of a population.

In the next chapter we switch our focus to estimating the parameter value, rather than testing a claim about a single value. We will see how we can use *confidence intervals* to estimate a long-run proportion (probability) or a population proportion or mean. We will also examine the relationship between a confidence interval and the corresponding test of significance.

ERRORS AND SIGNIFICANCE

INTRODUCTION

We have seen that a test of significance assesses the *strength of evidence* that sample data provide against a null hypothesis, in favor of an alternative hypothesis. A slightly different approach is to use a test of significance to make a *decision* about whether the data provide sufficiently strong evidence to *reject* the null hypothesis. When we make such a decision, we naturally hope that we are making the correct one. But of course mistakes happen. There are two different types of errors that can be made in these situations. In this section, we will explore these two types of errors and see how the probability of making one of them can be determined.

Heart Transplant Operations *(continued)*

Example 2.3

In Example 1.3, we looked at a study published in the *British Medical Journal* (2004) in which it was reported that heart transplantations at St. George's Hospital in London had been suspended in September 2000, after a sudden spike in mortality rate. Of the last 10 heart transplants, 80% had resulted in deaths within 30 days of the transplant. Newspapers reported that this mortality rate was over five times the national average. Based on historical national data, the researchers used 15% as a reasonable value for comparison.

We tested whether the data observed at St. George's (8 deaths in 10 operations) provided strong evidence that the probability of death at St. George's exceeded the national value of 0.15. In other words, we tested the following hypotheses:

Null hypothesis: Probability of dying within 30 days of a heart transplant at St. George's is the same as the national rate ($\pi = 0.15$).

Alternative hypothesis: Probability of dying within 30 days of a heart transplant at St. George's is higher than the national rate ($\pi > 0.15$).

Using the **One Proportion** applet, we simulated 1,000 repetitions of 10 heart transplant cases, assuming 0.15 for the death probability. In none of those 1,000 repetitions did we find 8 or more deaths. Our approximate p-value was therefore essentially zero, and we concluded that 8 deaths in 10 operations provided extremely strong evidence that the death rate at St. George's was higher than the national rate.

Notice that this conclusion is phrased in terms of strength of evidence. Another way to approach this situation is by considering whether the data provide sufficiently strong evidence to *reject* the null hypothesis (that the death rate at St. George's is 0.15) in favor of the alternative hypothesis (that the death rate at St. George's is greater than 0.15). In other words, this second approach is about making a *decision* rather than simply assessing strength of evidence. For example, suppose that some government agency is investigating another hospital and must decide whether or not to suspend the hospital from performing heart transplants or not. They need to make a yes or no decision, not simply characterize the results as moderately, strongly, or very strongly significant.

Table 2.8 gives the p-value for various possible outcomes for the observed numbers of deaths in 10 operations, investigating whether the probability of dying within 30 days of a heart transplant at St. George's is higher than the national rate of 15%.

TABLE 2.8 p-values for different numbers of deaths							
Number of deaths	2	3	4	5	6	7	8
p-value	0.456	0.180	0.050	0.010	0.001	0.0001	0.00001

It seems clear that with only 2 or 3 deaths in 10 operations, there's not strong evidence to reject the hypothesis that the underlying death probability is 0.15. It also seems safe to conclude that the underlying death probability is indeed greater than 0.15 if the 10 operations were to result in 7 or 8 deaths. But for other values, the strength of evidence is less definitive. If we (or the government agency) need to make a yes or no decision, then we need to have a clear criterion in mind for deciding how small the p-value must be to provide convincing evidence against the null hypothesis, and we need to specify this criterion *before* collecting the data.

> ### THINK ABOUT IT
>
> Where would you draw the line? How small would the p-value have to be before you would be sufficiently convinced to reject the null hypothesis and conclude that the death rate is actually larger than 0.15?

2.3.1

Definition

The ***significance level*** is a value used as a criterion for deciding how small a p-value needs to be to provide convincing evidence to reject the null hypothesis.

Remember that the meaning of a p-value in this context is the probability of observing at least as many deaths in the sample if in fact the probability of death at the hospital were 0.15. Let's say that you choose 0.05 as your cutoff value. Using 0.05 as the criterion for the p-value being small enough to reject the null hypothesis means that if the null hypothesis really were true, 5% of random samples would produce a sample proportion extreme enough to reject the null hypothesis (even though it actually is true). (From the above table, we see that getting 4 or more deaths in 10 operations happens about 5% of the time when $\pi = 0.15$.) So, by specifying 0.05 as the cutoff, we are saying that we are willing to allow this type of error, where we reject the null hypothesis when it is true, to happen 5% of the time. This 0.05 or 5% criterion that we are using to determine whether or not to reject the null hypothesis is known as the ***significance level***, often denoted by the Greek letter α ("*alpha*").

> ### KEY IDEA
>
> When the p-value is larger than the prespecified significance level, we *do not have enough evidence to reject* the null hypothesis. When the p-value is less than or equal to the significance level, we *do have enough evidence to reject* the null hypothesis in favor of the alternative hypothesis.

> ### THINK ABOUT IT
>
> Suppose that you believe that a stricter standard is necessary before you would be convinced to reject the null hypothesis and conclude that St. George's death probability is actually larger than the national rate of 0.15. Would you choose a larger or smaller value for the significance level α? Why?

2.3.2

Achieving a stricter standard of evidence requires a *smaller* significance level. For example, if you want to insist on stronger evidence than at the 0.05 level before you'll be convinced to conclude that St. George's has a higher death rate than 0.15, then you could select 0.01 (or any other value less than 0.05) for the significance level.

> ### KEY IDEA
>
> The significance level controls the probability that you mistakenly reject a null hypothesis that is true. To achieve a stricter standard for rejecting the null hypothesis, use a smaller significance level.

Type I and Type II errors

Two kinds of errors can occur with any test of significance. If the null hypothesis is actually *true* but the data lead a researcher to *reject* the null hypothesis, then the researcher has made an error. This error is sometimes called a *false alarm*, because the researcher believes that he or she has discovered an effect/difference when there is actually no effect/difference. On the other hand, if the null hypothesis is actually *false* but the data do *not* lead the researcher to reject the null hypothesis, then the researcher has made a different kind of error. This error is sometimes called a *missed opportunity*, because the researcher fails to detect an effect or difference that really is present. These errors are summarized in Table 2.9.

 2.3.3

 2.3.4

Definitions

A **Type I error** (false alarm) occurs when a true null hypothesis is rejected. A **Type II error** (missed opportunity) occurs when a false null hypothesis is not rejected.

TABLE 2.9   A summary of Type I and Type II errors

		What is true (unknown to us)	
		Null hypothesis is true	Null hypothesis is false
What we decide (based on data)	Reject null hypothesis	Type I error (false alarm)	Correct decision
	Do not reject null hypothesis	Correct decision	Type II error (missed opportunity)

 2.3.5

To make a Type I error in the heart transplant example, we would conclude that the death rate within 30 days of a heart transplant at the hospital is higher than the national benchmark when in fact it is not. This is a false alarm, which would lead to an untrue allegation being propagated against the hospital. A consequence is that the hospital might not be allowed to continue performing heart transplant operations, even though its underlying death rate is no higher than the national rate. To make a Type II error, we would not conclude the death rate at the hospital is higher than the national benchmark when in reality this probability really is higher than the benchmark. This is a missed opportunity in the sense that researchers should have concluded that something unusual was happening at the hospital but they failed to do so. In real-world situations, we never know for sure whether we make an error or make a correct decision, because we never know for sure whether the null hypothesis is true or not. So it is important to consider the possible consequences of each type of error in advance.

Hopefully you can see that these are two very different errors. To get a better feeling for this, it may be helpful to relate them to a jury trial example. Perhaps you can even try to put yourself in the place of a juror or the defendant.

We mentioned briefly in Chapter 1 that significance testing can be thought of like a criminal trial. Suppose a person is charged with a crime and is given a trial. This person, the defendant, is either innocent or guilty. You can think of the null hypothesis being that the defendant is innocent and the alternative being that the defendant is guilty. In the trial, we initially assume the defendant is innocent and the prosecution brings evidence to try to show that the defendant is guilty. In tests of significance, we initially assume the null hypothesis to be true and we try to bring evidence (in the form of data from a sample) against the null hypothesis and in favor of the alternative hypothesis. The jury then makes a conclusion. Hopefully the conclusion they make is correct. If it is not, then they have made one of two kinds of errors. Finding an innocent person guilty is equivalent to making a Type I error. Finding a guilty person not guilty is equivalent to making a Type II error. (See Table 2.10.)

TABLE 2.10   Type I and Type II errors summarized in context of jury trial

		What is true (unknown to the jury)	
		Null hypothesis is true (defendant is innocent)	Null hypothesis is false (defendant is guilty)
What jury decides (based on evidence)	Reject null hypothesis (Jury finds defendant guilty)	Type I error (false alarm)	Correct decision
	Do not reject null hypothesis (Jury finds defendant not guilty)	Correct decision	Type II error (missed opportunity)

Our judicial system is set up to make the likelihood of making a Type I error (finding an innocent person guilty) as small as possible. We don't want to send innocent people to prison. However, by focusing on making the probability of a Type I error small, the likelihood of making a Type II error (finding a guilty person not guilty) can be large. The same holds true when doing a test of significance. When we make the probability of a Type I error smaller by selecting a smaller significance level, then we unfortunately make the probability of a Type II error larger.

2.3.6 ▶

Why does reducing the probability of a Type I error change the probability of a Type II error? Return to our criminal justice system analogy: If we make it harder to convict someone, this will result in fewer innocent people in jail (lower significance level); however this will also result in more guilty people not being convicted because it is harder to be convicted. A guilty person going free is a Type II error. Hence, lowering the Type I error rate increases the Type II error rate.

> **KEY IDEA**
>
> One trade-off for selecting a lower significance level (probability of Type I error if null hypothesis is true) is that the probability of a Type II error will increase.

Definition

The probability of rejecting a false null hypothesis is called the ***power*** of the test. Tests with higher values of power are preferred over tests with lower values of power. Power can also be thought of as one minus the probability of a Type II error.

Power and the probability of a Type II error

Just like the significance level is the probability of making a Type I error, researchers can also find the probability of making a Type II error. However, typically, researchers don't talk about the probability of a Type II error directly; instead they choose to talk about the ***power*** of the test—the probability of rejecting the null hypothesis when the alternative hypothesis is true (a correct decision), which is simply one minus the probability of a Type II error.

For this reason, researchers would like their tests to be powerful, meaning the power of the test (probability of correctly rejecting the null hypothesis if the alternative hypothesis is true) is high. Later we'll talk more about how researchers can control the power of their test.

EXPLORATION | Parapsychology Studies
2.3

Statistician Jessica Utts has conducted an extensive analysis of Ganzfeld studies that have investigated psychic functioning. Ganzfeld studies involve a "sender" and a "receiver." Two people are placed in separate acoustically shielded rooms. The sender looks at a "target" image on a television screen (which may be a static photograph or a short movie segment playing repeatedly) and attempts to transmit information about the target to the receiver. The receiver is then shown four possible choices of targets, one of which is the correct target and the other three are "decoys." The receiver must choose the one he or she thinks best matches the description transmitted by the sender. If the correct target is chosen by the receiver, the session is a "hit." Otherwise, it is a miss. Utts reported that her analysis considered a total of 2,124 sessions and found a total of 709 "hits" (Utts, 2010).

1. If the subjects in these studies have no psychic ability, what would be the long-run probability that the receiver would identify the correct target?

2. State the appropriate null and alternative hypotheses for testing whether the data provide strong evidence of psychic ability. Be sure to define the parameter clearly in your hypotheses.

3. Calculate the proportion of "hits" (successful transmissions of the target image) among the 2,124 sessions that the researcher analyzed. Is this proportion larger than the null-hypothesized value for the probability of a successful transmission?

4. Use a simulation-based method to determine an approximate p-value for testing the hypotheses stated in #2.

5. Confirm that the validity conditions for a theory-based method are satisfied. Then use the theory-based method to calculate a standardized statistic and p-value for testing the hypotheses stated in #2.

6. Based on the p-values and standardized statistic, would you characterize the evidence against the null hypothesis as weak, moderate, strong, or very strong? Explain.

7. What if you had to make a yes or no decision about psychic ability based on these data—would you decide to "reject" the null hypothesis of no psychic ability in favor of the alternative hypothesis that the subjects have some psychic ability? Why would you make this decision?

8. How small of a p-value would you need to see to convince you to reject the null hypothesis of no psychic ability in favor of the alternative hypothesis that the subjects have some psychic ability? In other words, what value would you use for a cutoff value for determining whether a p-value is small enough to provide convincing evidence to reject the null hypothesis?

Definition

The ***significance level***, often denoted by the Greek letter α ("*alpha*"), is a value used as a criterion for deciding how small a p-value needs to be to provide convincing evidence to reject the null hypothesis.

> ### KEY IDEA
>
> When the p-value is larger than the prespecified significance level, we *do not have enough evidence to reject* the null hypothesis. When the p-value is less than or equal to the significance level, we *do have enough evidence to reject* the null hypothesis in favor of the alternative hypothesis.

9. Using a 0.05 significance level, would you reject the null hypothesis of no psychic ability?

10. If your friend has a stricter criterion than you, requiring stronger evidence before deciding to reject the null hypothesis, would your friend use a smaller or a larger significance level than you? Explain.

> ### KEY IDEA
>
> The significance level controls the probability that you mistakenly reject a null hypothesis that is true. To achieve a stricter standard for rejecting the null hypothesis, use a smaller significance level.

Two kinds of errors can occur with any test of significance. If the null hypothesis is actually *true* but the data lead a researcher to *reject* the null hypothesis, then the researcher has made an error. This error is sometimes called a *false alarm*, because the researcher believes that he or she has discovered an effect/difference when there is actually no effect/difference. On the other hand, if the null hypothesis is actually *false* but the data do *not* lead the researcher to reject the null hypothesis, then the researcher has made a different kind of error. This error is sometimes called a *missed opportunity*, because the researcher fails to detect an effect/difference that really is present.

Definitions

A ***Type I error*** (false alarm) occurs when a true null hypothesis is rejected. A ***Type II error*** (missed opportunity) occurs when a false null hypothesis is not rejected.

These types of errors can be represented as in Table 2.11.

TABLE 2.11   A summary of Type I and Type II errors

		What is true (unknown to us)	
		Null hypothesis is true	Null hypothesis is false
What we decide (based on data)	Reject null hypothesis	Type I error (false alarm)	Correct decision
	Do not reject null hypothesis	Correct decision	Type II error (missed opportunity)

11. Using a 0.05 significance level, which type of error (false alarm or missed opportunity) could Utts and her colleagues conceivably have made in this ESP study? Explain your answer. (*Hint:* First ask whether the data led to rejecting the null hypothesis or not. Then ask what kind of error is possible with that decision.)

The article by Utts (2010) also refers to 56 individual studies that led to the combined total of 2,124 sessions that you have analyzed here. Most of these studies involved a sample size of about 50 sessions. One particular study involved 50 sessions and resulted in 15 "hits."

12. Use a simulation- or theory-based analysis to approximate the p-value for a study that produces 15 hits in 50 sessions. Is this p-value small enough to reject the null hypothesis of no psychic ability at the 0.05 significance level? What about the 0.10 level?

13. What type of error could you be making with your decision in #12? Explain what this error means in the context of this study.

14. What if the researchers used a very small significance level? Say, 0.0001. How does this decision affect the probability of making a Type I error? Explain this in context.

15. There is another consequence of the choice of a very small significance level as chosen in the previous question. Explain what you think will happen to the probability that the researchers find significant evidence of psychic ability if the true probability of a hit is greater than 25% for this lower level of significance? Why?

> ### KEY IDEA
>
> One trade-off for selecting a lower significance level (probability of Type I error if null hypothesis is true) is that the probability of a Type II error will increase.

Power and the probability of a Type II error

Definition

The probability of rejecting a false null hypothesis is called the **power** of the test. Tests with higher values of power are preferred over tests with lower values of power. Power can also be thought of as one minus the probability of a Type II error.

Just like the significance level is the probability of making a Type I error, researchers can also find the probability of making a Type II error. However, typically, researchers don't talk about the probability of a Type II error directly; instead they choose to talk about the power of the test—the probability of rejecting the null hypothesis when the alternative hypothesis is true (a correct decision), which is simply one minus the probability of a Type II error.

For this reason, researchers would like their tests to be powerful. In other words, researchers want the power of the test (probability of correctly rejecting the null hypothesis if the alternative hypothesis is true) to be high. Later we'll talk more about how researchers can control the power of their test.

16. If the probability of a hit is actually 33%, then which hypothesis is true? Which error is possible?

17. If the probability of a hit is actually 33%, the sample size is 50, and the researchers use a significance level of 5%, the Type II error rate is 77.5%. What is the power of this test? Name at least one thing the researchers could do to improve the power of this test.

SECTION 2.3 Summary

As opposed to assessing strength of evidence against a null hypothesis, another approach to tests of significance is to make a decision about whether or not the sample data provide sufficiently strong evidence to reject the null hypothesis. The key idea with this approach is to specify, before collecting the data, a **significance level** that will be regarded as a cutoff value for how small the p-value needs to be in order to provide convincing evidence to reject the null hypothesis. The smaller the significance level, the stronger the evidence that is required to reject the null hypothesis. See FAQ 2.3.1 for more details.

FAQ 2.3.1   www.wiley.com/college/tintle

If I get a p-value ≤ 0.05 then my results are always significant, right?

Two kinds of errors can occur with any test of significance. If the null hypothesis is actually *true* but the data lead a researcher to *reject* the null hypothesis, then the researcher has made a **Type I error**. We can call this a *false alarm*, because the researcher believes that he or she has discovered an effect or difference when there actually is none. On the other hand, if the null hypothesis is actually *false* but the data do *not* lead the researcher to reject the null hypothesis, then the researcher has made a **Type II error**. This error is sometimes called a *missed opportunity*, because the researcher fails to detect an effect/difference that really is present.

- A **Type I error** (false alarm) occurs when a true null hypothesis is rejected.
- A **Type II error** (missed opportunity) occurs when a false null hypothesis is not rejected.

The significance level of the test determines the probability of committing a Type I error. Selecting a smaller significance level makes it harder to reject the null hypothesis and produces a smaller probability of Type I error. Unfortunately, selecting a smaller significance level also increases the probability of making a Type II error.

CHAPTER 2   Summary

In this chapter, you first learned how random sampling works and when you can draw valid inferences from a sample to a population. You learned that **simple random sampling** is an **unbiased** sampling method, meaning that sample statistics do not have a tendency to systematically under- or overestimate the population parameter. You explored different types of random sampling methods, namely **stratified sampling** and **cluster sampling**, and considered the advantages and disadvantages of these methods compared to simple random sampling.

You also took a closer look at **quantitative data**, learning how random sampling suggests how to make inferences about a population mean and that the reasoning process from Chapter 1 works for inference about a population mean also. You learned some properties of a **sampling distribution of a sample mean**, as well as the steps required to complete a **one-sample t-test**. Finally, you were reminded that when we make inferences, there is always the chance that we will make the wrong decision (**type 1** and **type 2 errors**), and you examined the different consequences of these errors.

CHAPTER 2
GLOSSARY

biased   A sampling method is biased if statistics from different samples consistently overestimate or consistently underestimate the population parameter of interest.

census   When data are gathered on all individuals in the population.

central limit theorem   The distribution of sample means is normal or approximately normal with mean equal to the population mean, μ, and standard deviation equal to $\sigma/\sqrt{n}$, which can be estimated by $s/\sqrt{n}$.

cluster sampling   A sampling method in which you break down the population into subgroups or clusters based on some natural subgrouping variable (zip code, city block, etc.) such that the subgroups or clusters are heterogeneous; that is, each cluster should be a small-scale representation of the entire population. Once the clusters have been created, you take a simple random sample of clusters, and combine all or some of the observational units in the chosen clusters to form the sample.

convenience sample   A nonrandom sample of a population.

data table   Format for storing data values.

generalization   Extension of conclusions from a sample to a population; this is only valid when the sample is representative of the population.

generalize   To extend conclusions from a sample to a population; this is only valid when the sample is representative of the population.

histogram   A graph used with quantitative variables.

left skewed   The bulk of the observations tend to fall on the right side of the distribution with a tail on the left.

measurement units   The units of measurement (e.g., seconds vs. hours) of your quantitative variable.

median   The middle data value when the data are sorted in order from smallest to largest.

non-sampling (systematic) errors   Non-random errors because they arise due to some systematic source such as a biased questionnaire design or non-response, and not from randomness.

one-sample t-test A theory-based approach to test inferences about a population mean.

outlier An observation that does not fit the overall pattern of the distribution.

parameter A number calculated from the underlying process or population which summarizes information about the variable of interest.

population The entire collection of observational units we are interested in.

power The probability of rejecting a false null hypothesis.

quantitative variable Measures on an observational unit for which arithmetic operations (e.g., adding, subtracting) make sense.

random number table A list of numbers, composed of the digits 0-9 and arranged so that each digit has no predictable relationship to the digits that preceded it or to the digits that follow it.

random sampling Using a probability device to select observational units from a population or process.

random sampling errors A way to describe sample-to-sample (chance) variability from sample to sample that is accounted for by the margin of error.

representative A sample is representative if it has the same characteristics as the population.

resistant A statistic is resistant if its value does not change considerably when extreme observations are removed from a data set.

right skewed The bulk of the observations tend to fall on the left side of the distribution with a tail on the right.

sample A subset of the population on which we record data.

sampling frame A list of all of the members of the population of interest from which random samples are taken; if the sampling frame does not contain all the members of the population of interest, the resulting sampling method could be biased.

sampling variability The amount that a statistic changes as it is observed repeatedly.

significance level A value used as a criterion for deciding how small a p-value needs to be to provide convincing evidence against the null hypothesis.

simple random sample A sampling method that ensures that every sample of size n is equally likely to be the sample selected from the population. In particular, each observational unit has the same chance of being selected as every other observational unit.

skewed distrbution The bulk of observations tend to fall on one side of the distribution.

standard error An estimate of the standard deviation of sample statistics across many samples.

statistic A number calculated from the observed data which summarizes information about the variable of interest.

stratified random sampling A sampling method in which you classify or break down the population into subgroups or strata in such a way that the observational units within each stratum are similar in ways that may be related to the variable that you are interested in measuring (response variable), and observational units in different strata are different in ways that may be related to the response variable. Once the strata are chosen, take a separate simple random sample from each stratum and combine these to form the sample.

t-distribution A mathematical model for t-statistics.

t-statistic The standardized statistic for the sample mean using the standard deviation of $\bar{x}$ (the standard error) $s/\sqrt{n}$.

Type I error Rejecting the null hypothesis when it is actually true (false alarm).

Type II error Failing to reject a null hypothesis that is actually false (missed opportunity).

unbiased A sampling method is unbiased if, on average across many random samples, it produces statistics whose average is the value of the population parameter.

validity conditions for one-sample t-test The quantitative variable should have a symmetric distribution, or you should have at least 20 observations and the sample distribution should not be strongly skewed.

$\bar{x}$ The sample average of a quantitative variable.

CHAPTER 2
EXERCISES

SECTION 2.1

2.1.1* The population will always be _____ the sample.

A. At least as large as

B. Smaller than

2.1.2 In most statistical studies the _____ is unknown and the _____ is known.

A. Parameter/statistic

B. Statistic/parameter

2.1.3* The reason for taking a random sample instead of a convenience sample is:

A. Random samples tend to be smaller and so take less time to collect.

B. Random samples tend to represent the population of interest.

C. Random samples always have 100% participation rates.

D. Random samples tend to be easier to implement and be successful.

2.1.4 True or false?

A. Larger samples are always better than smaller samples, regardless of how the sample was collected.

B. Larger random samples are always better than smaller random samples.

C. You shouldn't take a random sample of more than 5% of the population size.

2.1.5* True or false?

A. Random samples only generate unbiased estimates of long-run proportions, not long-run means.

B. Nonrandom samples are always biased.

C. There is no way that a sample of 100 people can be representative of all adults living in the United States.

2.1.6 When stating null and alternative hypotheses, the hypotheses are:

A. Always about the parameter only

B. Always about the statistic only

C. Always about both the statistic and the parameter

D. Sometimes about the statistic and sometimes about the parameter

2.1.7* When using simulation- or theory-based methods to test hypotheses about a proportion, the process of computing a p-value is:

A. Different if the sample is from a process instead of from a finite population

B. The same if the sample is from a process instead of from a finite population

C. Sometimes different and sometimes the same if the sample is from a process instead of a finite population

School cafeteria

2.1.8 Argue whether or not you believe using a sample of students from your school's cafeteria (you recruit the next 100 people to visit the cafeteria to participate) may or may not yield biased estimates based on the variable being measured/research question being investigated in each of the following situations.

a. Using the proportion of students with Type O blood to learn about the proportion of U.S. adults with Type O blood

b. Using the proportion of students who eat fast food regularly to learn about the proportion of U.S. college students who eat fast food regularly

c. Using the proportion of students who have brown hair to learn about the proportion of all students at your school who have brown hair

d. Using the proportion of students who have brown hair to learn about the proportion of all U.S. adults who have brown hair

Sample of birds

2.1.9* Argue whether or not you believe using a sample of birds which visit a bird feeder in your yard (the next 50 birds that visit) may or may not yield biased estimates based on the variable being measured/research question being investigated in each of the following situations.

a. Using the proportion of finches (out of 50) that visit the bird feeder to estimate the proportion of finches among all birds that live near your backyard

b. Using the proportion of finches (out of 50) that are at the bird feeder when another finch is also at the bird feeder to estimate the proportion of the time that finches prefer to eat with other finches

c. Using the proportion of male birds (out of 50) that visit the bird feeder to estimate the proportion of male birds among all birds that live near your backyard

d. Using the proportion of male birds that visit the bird feeder to estimate the proportion of male birds that typically visit bird feeders

Class survey

Exercises 2.1.10 to 2.1.17 refer to the following study. In order to estimate the typical amount of TV watched per day by students at her school of 1,000 students, a student has all of the students in her statistics class (30 students) take a short survey, finding that, on average, students in her statistics class report watching 1.2 hours of television per day.

2.1.10 Use the previous information to answer the following questions.

a What is the population of interest?

b. Do you believe that the average hours of television per day in the sample is likely less than, similar to, or greater than the average hours of television watched per day in the population? Why?

2.1.11 Use the previous information to answer the following questions about the class survey.

a. Describe in words the parameter of interest.

b. Identify the numeric value of the statistic corresponding to the above parameter.

2.1.12 Use the previous information to answer the following questions about the class survey.

a. Identify the variable measured on each student.

b. Is the variable categorical or quantitative?

c. Identify at least two statistics that the student could use to summarize the variable.

d. Identify at least one graph that the student could use to summarize the variable.

2.1.13 In the survey the student also asked students whether or not they watched at least 10 minutes of TV yesterday. The student found that 21 of 30 students reported watching at least 10 minutes of TV yesterday.

a. Identify the variable measured on each student.

b. Is the variable categorical or quantitative?

c. Identify at least one statistic that the student could use to summarize the variable.

d. Identify at least one graph that the student could use to summarize the variable.

2.1.14 Using the information from the previous question, the student wishes to test whether there is evidence that more than 50% of students at the school watched at least 10 minutes of TV yesterday.

a. State the null and alternative hypotheses for this test.

b. Describe the parameter of interest for this research question.

c. What is the numeric value of the statistic?

2.1.15 Evaluate the strength of evidence for the hypotheses in the previous question.

a. Find the p-value for the hypotheses in the previous question using a simulation-based approach.

b. Based on the p-value evaluate the strength of evidence and state a conclusion about the TV watching among students yesterday.

c. To which population, if any, are you comfortable drawing your conclusion? Why?

d. If a theory-based approach would be reasonable for these data, find the p-value and comment on the similarity of the p-value from the theory-based approach to the p-value you found in (a). If a theory-based approach would not be reasonable for these data, explain why not.

2.1.16 Among the students in her class, the information for three particular students is given here:

(i) Alejandra reported watching 2 hours of TV a day, but not watching TV yesterday.

(ii) Ben reported watching 4 hours of TV a day and watching TV yesterday.

(iii) Cassie reported watching 30 minutes of TV a day and not watching TV yesterday.

Use this information to fill in the blank data table below, where the last row (...) indicates that additional information is present in the real data table since there were actually 30 students in the survey. Be sure to provide appropriate labels/headings for each of the three columns.

...	...	...

2.1.17 Consider how the student obtained her sample for her study. If her study was conducted by taking a random sample, explain (in enough detail that someone could follow your directions to obtain the sample) how it could have been done. If her study was not conducted by taking a random sample, explain how you could modify the study design to make it be a random sample, and explain (in enough detail that someone could follow your directions to obtain the sample) how it could have been done.

Political survey*

Exercises 2.1.18 to 2.1.25 refer to the following study. In order to estimate the proportion of all likely voters who will likely vote for the incumbent in the upcoming city's mayoral race, a random sample of 267 likely voters is taken, finding that 65% state they will likely vote for the incumbent.

2.1.18 Use the previous information to answer the following questions.

a. What is the population of interest?

b. Do you believe that the proportion of likely voters for the incumbent in the sample is likely less than, similar to, or greater than the proportion of likely voters who would say they will vote for the incumbent in the population? Why?

2.1.19 Use the previous information to answer the following questions about the political survey.

a. Describe in words the parameter of interest.

b. Identify the numeric value of the statistic corresponding to the above parameter.

2.1.20 Use the previous information to answer the following questions about the political survey.

a. Identify the variable measured on each likely voter.

b. Is the variable categorical or quantitative?

c. Identify at least one statistic that the polling agency could use to summarize the variable.

d. Identify at least one graph that the polling agency could use to summarize the variable.

2.1.21 The polling agency wishes to test whether there is evidence that more than 50% of likely voters will likely vote for the incumbent.

a. State the null and alternative hypotheses for this test.

b. What is the value of the statistic?

2.1.22 Evaluate the strength of evidence for the hypotheses in the previous question.

a. Find the p-value for the hypotheses in the previous question using a simulation-based approach.

b. Based on the p-value evaluate the strength of evidence and state a conclusion about the likely voting outcome in the mayoral race if the election were to take place today.

c. To which population, if any, are you comfortable drawing your conclusion? Why?

d. If a theory-based approach would be reasonable for these data, find the p-value and comment on the similarity of the p-value from the theory-based approach to the p-value you found in (a). If a theory-based approach would not be reasonable for these data, explain why not.

2.1.23 The poll also asked voters to report the amount of time that the respondent spent reading or learning about local politics over the last week. The poll finds that, on average, respondents have spent 42 minutes learning or reading about local politics over the last week.

a. Identify the variable measured on each likely voter.

b. Is the variable categorical or quantitative?

c. Identify at least two statistics that the polling agency could use to summarize the variable.

d. Identify at least one graph that the polling agency could use to summarize the variable.

2.1.24 Among the sample, the information for three particular likely voters is given here:

(i) Likely voter 1 reported spending 0 minutes in the last week learning/reading about local politics and likely voting for the incumbent.

(ii) Likely voter 2 reported spending 0 minutes in the last week learning/reading about local politics and likely voting for the incumbent.

(iii) Likely voter 3 reported spending 60 minutes in the last week learning/reading about local politics and likely voting for the challenger (not the incumbent).

Use this information to fill in the blank data table below, where the last row (...) indicates that additional information is present in the real data table since there were actually 267 likely voters in the survey. Be sure to provide appropriate labels/headings for the columns.

...	...	...

2.1.25 Consider how the sample was selected for the study. If the study was conducted by taking a random sample, explain (in enough detail that someone could follow your directions to obtain the sample) how it could have been done. If the study was not conducted by taking a random sample, explain how you could modify the study design to make it be a random sample, and explain (in enough detail that someone could follow your directions to obtain the sample) how it could have been done.

Television news survey

Exercises 2.1.26 to 2.1.33 refer to the following study. In order to understand more about how people in the U.S. feel about the outcome of a recent criminal trial in which the defendant was found not guilty, a television news program invites viewers to go the news programs website and indicate their opinion about the event. At the end of the show 82% of the people who voted in the poll indicated they were unhappy with the verdict.

2.1.26 Use the previous information to answer the following questions.

a. What is the population of interest?

b. Do you believe that the proportion of people unhappy with the verdict in the sample is likely less than, similar to, or greater than the proportion of individuals unhappy with the verdict in the population? Why?

2.1.27 Use the previous information to answer the following questions about the news program survey.

a. Describe in words the parameter of interest.

b. Identify the numeric value of the statistic corresponding to the above parameter, as found in the television news survey.

2.1.28 Use the previous information to answer the following questions about the news program.

a. Identify the variable measured on each participant in the survey.

b. Is the variable categorical or quantitative?

c. Identify at least one statistic that the news program could use to summarize the variable.

d. Identify at least one graph that the news program could use to summarize the variable.

2.1.29 The news program wishes to test whether there is evidence that more than three-quarters of U.S. adults are opposed to the verdict. Five hundred and sixty-two participants participated in the survey, of which 82% said that they were unhappy with the verdict.

a. State the null and alternative hypotheses for this test.

b. What is the value of the statistic?

2.1.30 Evaluate the strength of evidence for the hypotheses in the previous question.

a. Find the p-value for the hypotheses in the previous question using a simulation-based approach.

b. Based on the p-value evaluate the strength of evidence and state a conclusion about the opinions of U.S. adults about the verdict.

c. To which population, if any, are you comfortable drawing your conclusion? Why?

d. If a theory-based approach would be reasonable for these data, find the p-value and comment on the similarity of the p-value from the theory-based approach to the p-value you found in (a). If a theory-based approach would not be reasonable for these data, explain why not.

2.1.31 The survey also asked participants to report the time the respondent spent reading or watching news coverage about the trial during the last three days. The poll found that, on average, respondents had spent 92 minutes reading or watching news coverage about the trial during the last three days.

a. Identify the variable measured on each respondent.

b. Is the variable categorical or quantitative?

c. Identify at least two statistics that the news program could use to summarize the variable.

d. Identify at least one graph that the news program could use to summarize the variable.

2.1.32 Among the sample, the information for three particular respondents is given here:

(i) Respondent 1 reported spending 240 minutes in the last three days reading/watching news coverage about the trial and not being happy with the verdict.

(ii) Respondent 2 reported spending 90 minutes in the last three days reading/watching news coverage about the trial and not being happy with the verdict.

(iii) Respondent 3 reported spending 30 minutes in the last three days reading/watching news coverage about the trial and being happy with the verdict.

Use this information to fill in the blank data table below, where the last row (…) indicates that additional information is present in the real data table since there were actually 562 likely voters in the survey. Be sure to provide appropriate labels/headings for the table columns.

…	…	…

2.1.33 Consider how the sample for the study was selected. If the study was conducted by taking a random sample, explain (in enough detail that someone could follow your directions to obtain the sample) how it could have been done. If the study was not conducted by taking a random sample, explain how you could modify the study design to make it be a random sample, and explain (in enough detail that someone could follow your directions to obtain the sample) how it could have been done.

Shark survey*

Exercises 2.1.34 to 2.1.41 refer to the following study. A zoologist at a large metropolitan zoo is concerned about a potential new disease present among the 243 sharks living in the large aquarium at the zoo. The zoologist takes a random sample of 15 sharks from the aquarium, temporarily removes the sharks from the tank, and tests them for the disease. He finds that 3 of the sharks have the disease.

2.1.34 Use the previous information to answer the following questions.

a. What is the population of interest?

b. Do you believe that the proportion of diseased sharks in the sample is likely less than, similar to, or greater than the proportion of diseased sharks in the population? Why?

2.1.35 Use the previous information to answer the following questions about the shark survey.

a. Describe in words the parameter of interest.

b. Identify the numeric value of the statistic corresponding to the above parameter.

2.1.36 Use the previous information to answer the following questions about the study.

a. Identify the variable measured on each shark.

b. Is the variable categorical or quantitative?

c. Identify at least one statistic that the zoologist could use to summarize the variable.

d. Identify at least one graph that the zoologist could use to summarize the variable.

2.1.37 The zoologist wishes to test whether there is evidence that less than one-fourth of the sharks in the aquarium are diseased.

a. State the null and alternative hypotheses for this test.

b. What is the value of the statistic?

2.1.38 Evaluate the strength of evidence for the hypotheses in the previous question.

a. Find the p-value for the hypotheses in the previous question using a simulation-based approach.

b. Based on the p-value evaluate the strength of evidence and state a conclusion about diseased sharks.

c. To which population, if any, are you comfortable drawing your conclusion? Why?

d. If a theory-based approach would be reasonable for these data, find the p-value and comment on the similarity of the p-value from the theory-based approach to the p-value you found in (a). If a theory-based based approach would not be reasonable for these data, explain why not.

2.1.39 Because the disease affects a shark's ability to extract oxygen from the water, the zoologist also measures the shark's blood oxygen content. The zoologist finds that, on average, shark's blood oxygen content is 4.2%.

a. Identify the variable measured on each shark.

b. Is the variable categorical or quantitative?

c. Identify at least two statistics that the zoologist could use to summarize the variable.

d. Identify at least one graph that the zoologist could use to summarize the variable.

2.1.40 Among the sample, the information for three particular sharks is given here:

(i) Shark 1 had the disease and had a blood oxygen level of 1.2%.

(ii) Shark 2 did not have the disease and had a blood oxygen level of 5.6%.

(iii) Shark 3 did not have the disease and had a blood oxygen level of 6.2%.

Use this information to fill in the blank data table below, where the last row (…) indicates that additional information is present in the real data table since there were actually 15 sharks in the sample. Be sure to provide appropriate labels/headings for the columns of the table.

…	…	…

2.1.41 Consider how the sample for the study was selected. If the study was conducted by taking a random sample, explain (in enough detail that someone could follow your directions to obtain the sample) how it could have been done. If the study was not conducted by taking a random sample, explain how you could modify the study design to make it be a random sample, and explain (in enough detail that someone could follow your directions to obtain the sample) how it could have been done.

School survey

Exercises 2.1.42 and 2.1.43 use the following information. In order to investigate how many hours a day students at their school tend to spend on course work outside of regularly scheduled class time, a statistics student takes a random sample of 150 students from their school by randomly choosing names from a list of all full-time students at their school that semester. The student finds that the average reported daily study hours among the 150 students is 2.23 hours.

2.1.42 Identify each of the following by describing it or stating its value (where possible).

a. Population of interest

b. Sample

c. Parameter of interest

d. Statistic

2.1.43 In the previous exercise, explain whether or not you believe the sample is representative of the population of interest and why.

Business survey*

Exercises 2.1.44 and 2.1.45 use the following information. In order to understand reasons why consumers visit their store, a local business conducts a survey by asking the next 100 people who visit their store to fill out a short survey. The business finds that 40 of the 100 people state that the main reason they visited the store was because the store is running a sale on coats that week.

2.1.44 Identify each of the following by describing it or stating its value (where possible).

a. Population of interest

b. Sample

c. Parameter of interest

d. Statistic

2.1.45 In the previous exercise, explain whether or not you believe the sample is representative of the population of interest and why.

FAQ

2.1.46 Read FAQ 2.1.1 and answer the following question.

Explain, as if to someone who doesn't know statistics, why taking a random sample of only 1500 people from a very large population is representative, even of rare subpopulations.

2.1.47 Read FAQ 2.1.1 and answer the following question.

True or false? Increasing the sample size n, always helps improve the bias in the sample. Explain.

2.1.48 Read FAQ 2.1.2 and answer the following question. Referring to Example 1.1. about Doris and Buzz, explain where randomization could come into play in the study design.

2.1.49 Read FAQ 2.1.2 and answer the following question.

Referring to Example 1.1 about Doris and Buzz, explain where randomization occurs in your chance model but may not be truly random chance in the study.

SECTION 2.1: Part 2

2.1.50* Which of the following is NOT a non-sampling (systematic) error?

A. Difficult wording of a question

B. People lying on a survey

C. People randomly picked to complete a survey decide not to do it

D. A certain order of questions that can influence the responses

E. The chance variation you get through using random chance to select a sample

2.1.51 Suppose we have a list of all 300 people in your high school and we randomly choose 30 from that list. Each of these 30 people is sent a survey and 25 are returned. In this scenario, what is the sampling frame?

A. The 30 people sent the survey

B. The 25 people that returned the survey

C. The list of all 300 people in the high school

D. The survey

E. The mechanism used to randomly choose the 30 students

2.1.52* When it is stated that 20 *unique* values were chosen between 1 and 500, what is meant by unique?

A. The 20 numbers don't have any special properties in common, such as all being even

B. No two of the numbers are the same value in the set of 20

C. The 20 numbers are randomly chosen

D. All of the numbers represent something in the population

E. The 20 numbers are all values between 1 and 500

2.1.53 You need to select 5 random numbers from 1 to 700. Starting at the beginning of the random number table shown below and reading left to right, what are your 5 numbers?

| 73416 15428 44640 50670 87660 26047 87010 15513 18703 38041 |
| 64674 55948 86853 49298 51088 90901 88174 75497 80880 12293 |

2.1.54* You need to select 5 random numbers from 1 to 50. Starting at the beginning of the random number table shown in the previous question, what are your 5 numbers?

2.1.55 Suppose you have the list of names of all 530 students in your high school and you want to randomly choose 40 of them to interview. Explain how you would randomly choose these students with the aid of technology (a random number generator).

2.1.56* Suppose you have the list of names of all 2,237 people who voted in your town's last election and you want to randomly choose 100 of them so you can send them a survey. Explain how you would randomly choose these voters with the aid of technology (a random number generator).

SECTION 2.1: Part 3

2.1.57* Suppose a high school consists of 1,000 students such that 30% are freshmen, 25% are sophomores, 25% are juniors, and 20% are seniors. You want to collect a representative sample of the student body so you randomly select 30 freshmen, 25 sophomores, 25 juniors, and 20 seniors. This type of sampling method is known as:

A. Simple random sampling

B. Stratified sampling

C. Cluster sampling

D. Biased sampling

2.1.58 Suppose a group of researchers want to conduct face-to-face interviews of a sample of Michigan residents. They first randomly choose 20 counties in the state. They then randomly choose five townships in each of their chosen counties. Finally, they randomly choose 10 households in each of these townships. This type of sampling method is known as:

A. Simple random sampling

B. Stratified sampling

C. Cluster sampling

D. None of the above

2.1.59* Suppose you want to sample 300 registered voters in your city. You get a list of all registered voters in the city and randomly choose 300 of them. This type of sampling method is known as:

A. Simple random sampling

B. Stratified sampling

C. Cluster sampling

D. Biased sampling

2.1.60 Stratified random sampling may be advantageous over simple random sampling because:

A. Every observational unit has an equal chance of being chosen.

B. Random sampling error might be reduced.

C. The sample will always be more representative.

D. The sample will be less biased.

2.1.61* Cluster sampling may be advantageous over other sampling methods when:

A. The sampling frame is not available.

B. All the observational units in population are listed.

C. Every observational unit must have an equal chance of being chosen.

D. You must have a non-biased sample.

2.1.62 In both stratified sampling and cluster sampling the population is broken down into groups (either strata or clusters). In which type of sampling are measurements typically taken from all the groups?

A. Stratified sampling

B. Cluster sampling

C. Both stratified and cluster sampling

D. Neither stratified nor cluster sampling

School District*

2.1.63 Suppose a school district consists of six elementary schools, two middle schools, and one high school with about 500 students at each grade level. Also suppose administrators at the school want to obtain a sample of the students' parents to ask questions about the school district's website.

a. If a stratified sample is used, what is a useful variable on which to stratify the sample?

b. Explain why a stratified sample has advantages over a simple random sample in this case.

Hope College

2.1.64 The following table shows enrollment at Hope College in the fall of 2016.

	Men	Women	Total
Freshmen	296	439	735
Sophomore	332	453	785
Junior	260	443	703
Senior	302	515	817
Total	1,190	1,850	3,040

a. Suppose you want to sample 200 students stratified by year in school so each student has approximately the same chance of being chosen. How many of each grade level would you include in your sample?

b. Suppose you want to sample 200 students stratified by sex so each student has approximately the same chance of being chosen. How many males and how many females would you include in your sample?

2.1.65 Recall the previous question about Hope College enrollment. Suppose you want to sample 200 students stratified by both year in school and sex so each student has approximately the same chance of being chosen. How many in each of the eight categories would you include in your sample?

Cal Poly*

2.1.66 The following table shows the enrollment in the various colleges at Cal Poly University in the fall of 2016. Suppose you wanted to sample 500 students stratified by which college they are enrolled in. How many students from each college would you include in your sample?

Ag, Food & Environmental Sciences	3,900
Architecture & Environmental Design	1,779
Engineering	5,847
Liberal Arts	3,235
Business	2,870
Science & Math	2,736
Total	**20,367**

Mt. Holyoke

2.1.67 The following table shows enrollment at Mt. Holyoke College for the spring of 2017.

	U.S. Residents	Non-U.S. Residents	Total
Freshmen	325	124	**449**
Sophomore	414	167	**581**
Junior	404	167	**571**
Senior	463	155	**618**
Total	**1,606**	**613**	**2,219**

a. Suppose you want to sample 400 students stratified by year in school so each student has approximately the same chance of being chosen. How many of each grade level would you include in your sample?

b. Suppose you want to sample 400 students stratified by whether or not they were a U.S. resident so each student has approximately the same chance of being chosen. How many U.S. residents and non-U.S. residents would you include in your sample?

Manistee National Forest*

2.1.68 The Manistee National Forest consists of about 540,000 acres mostly covered in trees. Suppose you are asked to estimate the proportion of trees that are sugar maples in the forest. Describe a cluster sampling method that you would use to accomplish this. (*Hint*: In Michigan, land is divided into sections consisting of 640 acres, which is one square mile.)

Chicago Intersections

2.1.69 The city of Chicago maintains 3,035 intersections that contain traffic signals. Suppose you want to estimate the proportion of cars making left turns at these types of intersections (with traffic signals) that fail to use their turn signals during the evening rush hour (5-6 pm on a weekday). Indicate what type of sampling method would you use and describe how you might accomplish this.

American Statistical Association*

2.1.70 In 2014, 605 members of the American Statistical Association were listed as donating to the annual fund. There were 37 listed as giving $500 or more, 148 as giving $100-$499, and 420 giving less than $100. Suppose we want to sample 30 of these donors to interview them about donating. What is an advantage of doing a stratified sample by randomly choosing 10 from each of the three donation groups as opposed to a simple random sample?

Student Council

2.1.71 Suppose the student council at a very large high school, consisting of about 50% female and 50% male students, is assigned to get a random sample of 10 students to be interviewed. The person in charge of this comes back with a sample consisting of all males. Two explanations as to why the

sample consists of all males are that (A) it was not random and (B) it was random, but just a fairly unlikely event happened. Which explanation would you support and why? (*Hint*: You may want to use the One Proportion applet to help you out.)

Statistics Project*

2.1.72 College students presenting a statistics project claimed they took a random sample of students by sitting outside one of the school cafeterias during lunch time (where a majority of students living on campus eat) and asked students coming by to take their survey. Is that sampling method really random? Explain.

Underwater weights

2.1.73 At the beginning of the semester, students in a health class at Hope College are measured to determine their body fat composition. To accomplish this, one of the measurements taken is underwater weight (in kilograms). The histogram below shows underwater weights for a population of females (on top) and males (on bottom).

As you can see, the weights of these two population groups are quite different. We took many samples of 30 weights from this population, calculated the sample mean weight, and repeated this many, many times. One time we did it using simple random samples and one time using stratified random samples, stratified proportionally on sex. Below are histograms of the two results. Which histogram belongs to which type of sampling method and why?

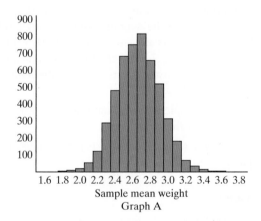

Sample mean weight
Graph A

EXERCISE 2.1.73

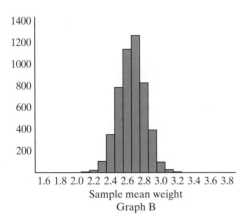

Sample mean weight
Graph B

Build a gym?

2.1.74 The management at the local high school is considering building a new gym on campus. To find out how students feel about this, the school newspaper decides to conduct a survey of the students. For each of the following sampling plans described below, identify the sampling method (simple random sampling, stratified sampling, cluster sampling, or convenience sampling) and whether the results may potentially be biased:

a. Survey students who are leaving after school sports practices.

b. Randomly sample students within each grade level and survey the selected students.

c. Randomly select two classes from the 50 classes at the school and survey all students from those two classes.

d. Obtain a list of all students attending the high school, randomly select students from the list, and survey the students selected.

SECTION 2.2

2.2.1* On January 28, 1986, the Space Shuttle *Challenger* broke apart 73 seconds into its flight, killing all seven astronauts on board. All investigations into reasons for the disaster pointed towards the failure of an O-ring in the rocket's engine. Given below is a dotplot and some descriptive statistics on O-ring temperature (°F) for each test firing or actual launch of the shuttle rocket engine.

a. The numeric values of two possible measures of center are calculated to be 65.86°F and 67.50°F. Which one of these is the mean and which the median? How are you deciding?

b. If we removed the observation 31°F from the data set, how would the following numerical statistics change, if at all?

	Smaller	Same	Larger
Mean:	Smaller	Same	Larger
Median:	Smaller	Same	Larger
Standard deviation:	Smaller	Same	Larger

Salaries

Exercises 2.2.2 to 2.2.5 use the same data.

2.2.2. The monthly salaries of the three people working in a small firm are $3,500, $4,000, and $4,500. Suppose the firm makes a profit and everyone gets a $100 raise. How, if at all, would the **average** of the three salaries change?

A. The average would stay the same.

B. The average would increase.

C. The average would decrease.

D. Cannot be answered without doing calculations.

2.2.3 Reconsider the previous exercise. The monthly salaries of the three people working in a small firm are $3,500, $4,000, and $4,500. Suppose the firm makes a profit and everyone gets a $100 raise. How, if at all, would the **standard deviation** of the three salaries change?

A. The standard deviation would stay the same.

B. The standard deviation would increase.

C. The standard deviation would decrease.

D. Cannot be answered without doing calculations.

2.2.4 Reconsider the previous exercise where the monthly salaries of the three people working in a small firm are $3,500, $4,000, and $4,500. If instead of a $100 raise, everyone gets a 10% raise, how, if at all, would the **average** of the three salaries change?

A. The average would stay the same.

B. The average would increase.

C. The average would decrease.

D. Cannot be answered without doing calculations.

2.2.5 Reconsider the previous exercise where the monthly salaries of the three people working in a small firm are

O-ring temperature (°F)

EXERCISE 2.2.1

$3,500, $4,000, and $4,500. If instead of a $100 raise, everyone gets a 10% raise, how, if at all, would the **standard deviation** of the three salaries change?

A. The standard deviation would stay the same.

B. The standard deviation would increase.

C. The standard deviation would decrease.

D. Cannot be answered without doing calculations.

Exam scores*

2.2.6

a. Suppose that an instructor decides to add five points to every student's exam score in a class. What effect would this have on the mean exam score for the class? On the median exam score? What effect would this have on the standard deviation of exam scores? Explain.

b. Suppose that an instructor decides to add five points only to the exam score for the highest scoring student in the class. What effect would this have on the mean exam score for the class? On the median exam score? What effect would this have on the standard deviation of exam scores? Explain.

c. Suppose that an instructor decides to add five points only to the exam score for the lowest scoring student in the class. What effect would this have on the mean exam score for the class? On the median exam score? What effect would this have on the standard deviation of exam scores? Explain.

States visited

2.2.7 An instructor collected data on the number of states students in her class have visited in the U.S. A dotplot for the collected data is shown below.

a. Identify the observational units.

b. Identify the variable recorded and whether it is categorical or quantitative.

c. Describe what the graph tells us about distribution of the variable recorded. Be sure to comment on shape, center, and variability.

d. Use the dotplot to find and report the median value for the number of states visited by the students in this study.

e. Would the mean value for these data be smaller than, larger than, or the same as the median, as reported in (d)? Explain your reasoning.

f. Suppose that the observation recorded as 43 states is a typo and was meant to be 34. If we corrected this entry in the data set, how would the following numerical statistics change, if at all?

Mean:	Smaller	Same	Larger
Median:	Smaller	Same	Larger
Standard deviation:	Smaller	Same	Larger

Birth weights*

2.2.8 Suppose that birth weights of babies in the U.S. have a mean of 3250 grams and standard deviation of 550 grams. Based on this information, which of the following is *more unlikely*? Circle one.

A. A randomly selected baby has a birth weight greater than 4000 grams.

B. A random sample of 10 babies has an average birth weight greater than 4000 grams.

C. Both are equally likely.

D. Cannot be answered without doing calculations.

Heights

2.2.9 In which scenario would you expect to see more variability in the data: heights of a random sample of 100 college students or heights of a random sample of 500 college students?

A. Random sample of 100 college students

B. Random sample of 500 college students

C. Both samples will have similar variability

D. Cannot be answered without doing calculations

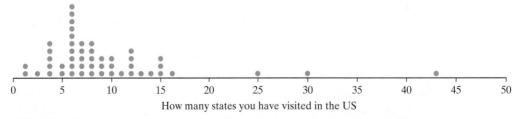

How many states you have visited in the US

EXERCISE 2.2.7

Haircuts*

2.2.10 Students in a statistics class were asked the cost of their last haircut. The data set can be found on the textbook website as **HaircutCosts**. Put this data set into the **Descriptive Statistics** applet and answer the following questions.

a. Is the distribution of haircut costs symmetric, skewed to the left, skewed to the right, or something else?

b. Would you think the mean haircut cost is about the same as the median, higher than the median, or lower than the median? Why?

c. Find and report both the mean and median haircut costs. Were you correct in your answer to the previous question?

d. The highest haircut cost is $150 and there were three of these. Suppose one of the students who reported $150 actually had a haircut cost of $300 but reported it to be $150. If this student's haircut value were changed, how, if at all, would it change the mean haircut cost for the class? How, if at all, would it change the median? (Change one of the $150 to $300 and verify your answer.)

How much TV do you watch?

Exercises 2.2.11 to 2.2.15 refer to the same study.

2.2.11 According to a 2011 report by the U.S. Department of Labor, civilian Americans spend 2.75 hours per day watching television. A faculty researcher, Dr. Sameer, at California Polytechnic State University (Cal Poly) conducts a study to see whether a different average applies to Cal Poly students.

a. Identify the variable of interest and whether the variable is categorical or quantitative.

b. Describe Dr. Sameer's parameter of interest and assign an appropriate symbol to denote it.

c. Write the appropriate hypotheses using symbols.

2.2.12 Reconsider Dr. Sameer's research question about how much time Cal Poly students spend on watching television. Suppose that Dr. Sameer surveys a random sample of 100 Cal Poly students, and for this sample the mean number of hours per day spent watching TV turns out to be 3.01 hours.

a. Is the number 3.01 a parameter or a statistic?

b. Assign an appropriate symbol to the number 3.01.

c. Describe how you can conduct a simulation-based test of significance to investigate whether the data provide evidence that the average number of hours per day Cal Poly students spend watching TV is different from 2.75 hours. Be sure to provide details on how one would find a p-value.

d. For the following table, complete the column on the right to draw parallels between the simulation and the real study:

Simulation		Real study
One repetition	=	
Null model	=	
Statistic	=	

2.2.13 Reconsider Dr. Sameer's research question about how much time Cal Poly students spend on watching television.

a. Suppose that on analyzing the data from the survey of a random sample of 100 Cal Poly students, the p-value for Dr. Sameer's study was computed to be 0.16. Interpret what this p-value means in the context of the study. (*Hint:* This question is *not* asking for a *conclusion* from the p-value.)

b. Another faculty researcher, Dr. Elliot, had hypothesized that Cal Poly students spend more than 2.75 hours/day watching TV, on average. If Dr. Elliot were to use the same data as Dr. Sameer to conduct an investigation, how, if at all, would this researcher's p-value compare to the p-value reported in (a)? Explain how you are deciding. (*Hint:* Bigger, smaller, or about the same? If bigger or smaller, by how much?)

2.2.14 Reconsider Dr. Sameer's research question about how much time Cal Poly students spend on watching television. Suppose that for the random sample of 100 Cal Poly students the mean number of hours per day spent watching TV turns out to be 3.01 hours, and the standard deviation of the number of hours per day spent watching TV turns out to be 1.97 hours.

a. Is the number 1.97 a parameter or a statistic? Assign an appropriate symbol to this number.

b. Find the standardized statistic to investigate whether the data provide evidence that the average number of hours per day Cal Poly students spend watching TV is different from 2.75 hours.

c. What is your conclusion about the hypotheses, based on the calculated value of the standardized statistic? How are you deciding?

2.2.15 Reconsider Dr. Sameer's research question about how much time Cal Poly students spend on watching television, and recall that for the random sample of 100 Cal Poly students' number of hours per day spent watching TV the mean and standard deviation turned out to be 3.01 hours and 1.97 hours, respectively.

a. In the context of this study, is the theory-based approach (one-sample t-test) valid to find a p-value to investigate whether the data provide evidence that the average number of hours per day Cal Poly students spend watching TV is different from 2.75 hours? Explain.

b. Regardless of your answer in (a), use the **Theory-Based Inference** applet to conduct a one-sample t-test to find and report a standardized statistic (t-statistic) and a p-value for Dr. Sameer's hypotheses.

c. State your conclusion from this study based on the p-value reported in (b), being sure to provide justification for your conclusion.

What's the SPF of your sunscreen?*

Exercises 2.2.16 to 2.2.18 refer to the following sunscreen data.

2.2.16 Most dermatologists recommend using sunscreens that have a sun protection factor (SPF) of at least 30. One of the authors wanted to find out whether the SPF of sunscreens used by students at her school (which is in a very sunny part of the U.S.) exceeds this value, on average?

a. Identify the variable of interest and whether the variable is categorical or quantitative.

b. Describe the author's parameter of interest and assign an appropriate symbol to denote it.

c. Write the appropriate hypotheses using symbols.

To collect data, the author surveyed students in her Introductory Statistics course and found that in a sample of 48 students the average SPF was 35.29 and the standard deviation of SPF was 17.19.

d. Assign appropriate symbols to the numbers 48, 35.29, and 17.19.

e. Do the data come from a *random* sample? Explain.

f. Do you think the students in the Introductory Statistics course are representative of all students at this school, with regard to SPF of their sunscreens? Why or why not?

g. Describe a population for which this sample is surely *not* representative, with regard to SPF of sunscreens used.

2.2.17 Reconsider the study about one of the authors wanting to find out whether the SPF of sunscreens used by students at her school (which is in a very sunny part of the U.S.) exceeds 30, on average.

a. Describe how you can conduct a simulation-based test of significance to investigate whether the data provide evidence that the average SPF of sunscreens used by students

at this school exceeds 30. Be sure to provide details on how one would find a p-value.

b. For the following table, complete the column on the right to draw parallels between the simulation and the real study:

Simulation		Real study
One repetition	=	
Null model	=	
Statistic	=	

2.2.18 Reconsider the study about one of the authors wanting to find out whether the SPF of sunscreens used by students at her school (which is in a very sunny part of the U.S.) exceeds 30, on average.

a. In the context of this study, is the theory-based approach (one-sample t-test) valid to find a p-value to investigate whether the data provide evidence that the average SPF of sunscreens used by students at this school exceeds 30? Explain.

b. Regardless of your answer in (a), use the **Theory-Based Inference** applet to conduct a one-sample t-test to find and report a standardized statistic (t-statistic) and a p-value.

c. Interpret the p-value reported in (b).

d. State your conclusion from this study based on the p-value reported in (b), being sure to provide justification for your conclusion.

Needles!

Exercises 2.2.19 to 2.2.21 refer to the following data on needles.

2.2.19 Consider a manufacturing process that is producing hypodermic needles that will be used for blood donations. These needles need to have a diameter of 1.65 mm—too big and they would hurt the donor (even more than usual), too small and they would rupture the red blood cells, rendering the donated blood useless. Thus, the manufacturing process would have to be closely monitored to detect any significant departures from the desired diameter. During every shift, quality control personnel take a random sample of several needles and measure their diameters. If they discover a problem, they will stop the manufacturing process until it is corrected. For now, suppose that a "problem" is when the sample average diameter turns out to be statistically significantly different from the target of 1.65 mm.

a. Identify the variable of interest and whether the variable is categorical or quantitative.

b. Write the appropriate hypotheses using appropriate symbols to test whether the average diameter of needles from the manufacturing process is different from the desired value.

c. Suppose that the most recent random sample of 35 needles have an average diameter of 1.64 mm and a standard deviation of 0.07 mm. Assign appropriate symbols to these numbers.

d. Suppose that the diameters of needles produced by this manufacturing process have a bell-shaped distribution. Sketch the distribution of the average diameter of samples of 35 needles, assuming that the process is not malfunctioning. Be sure to clearly label the axis of the graph and provide values for what you think the mean and standard deviation for this distribution should be.

2.2.20 Consider the investigation of the manufacturing process that is producing hypodermic needles.

a. Describe how you can conduct a simulation-based test of significance to investigate whether the data provide evidence that the average diameter of needles produced by this manufacturing process is different from 1.65 mm. Be sure to provide details on how one would find a p-value.

b. For the following table, complete the column on the right to draw parallels between the simulation and the real study:

Simulation		Real study
One repetition	=	
Null model	=	
Statistic	=	

2.2.21 Consider the investigation of the manufacturing process that is producing hypodermic needles. Recall that the most recent random sample of 35 needles have an average diameter of 1.64 mm and a standard deviation of 0.07 mm.

a. Use the **Theory-Based Inference** applet to find and report a standardized statistic (*t*-statistic) and a p-value to investigate whether the average diameter of needles produced by this manufacturing process is different from 1.65 mm.

b. Based on your p-value, write out a conclusion, being sure to include justification.

How cool are you?*

2.2.22 The data set **MaleTemps** (found on the textbook website) consists of 65 body temperatures from healthy male

volunteers aged 18 to 40 that were participating in vaccine trials. Put this data set into the **Descriptive Statistics** applet and answer the following questions.

a. Is the distribution of temperatures symmetric, skewed to the left, skewed to the right, or something else?

b. Would you think the mean temperature for the 65 males in the study is about the same as the median, higher than the median, or lower than the median? Why?

c. Find and report both the mean and median temperatures. Were you correct in your answer to the previous question?

d. Remember that the standard deviation can be described as roughly the average distance between a data value in the distribution and the mean of the distribution. Check the **Guess** box next to the **Std dev** box in the applet. You should see a box centered on the mean. Adjust the "length" of this box with your mouse so it extends as wide as what you think is one standard deviation in each direction based on the description of standard deviation given above. Now check the **Show actual** box for the standard deviation. What is the actual standard deviation? Where you accurate in your guess?

2.2.23 Normal (or average) body temperature of humans is often thought to be 98.6°F. Is that number really the average body temperature for human males? To test this, we will use the **MaleTemps** data set (available from the textbook website) from the previous exercise.

a. Write out the null and alternative hypotheses for our test in words or in symbols.

b. You should have found (in the previous exercise) the sample mean body temperature for the 65 males in our sample to be 98.105°F and the standard deviation to be 0.699°F. Use the **Theory-Based Inference** applet to find and report a standardized statistic (*t*-statistic) and a p-value for the test.

c. Based on your p-value, write out a conclusion, being sure to include justification.

d. The data did not come from a random sample; rather it came from a convenience sample of healthy adults that were involved in a vaccine study. Given that information, to what population do you think we can generalize our results?

2.2.24 In the same study as was mentioned in the previous two exercises, data were also collected on 65 healthy female volunteers aged 18 to 40 that were participating in the vaccine trials. The data set **FemaleTemps** consisting of body temperatures from the 65 females is available from the textbook website. You will use the data to investigate whether the average body temperature of healthy adult females is different from 98.6°F.

a. Write out the null and alternative hypotheses in words or in symbols.

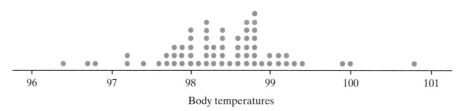

Body temperatures

EXERCISE 2.2.24

b. The 2.2.24 dotplot shows the 65 body temperatures above. Based on this dotplot, does it appear the average body temperature is different than 98.6°F? How are you deciding?

c. The sample mean body temperature for the 65 females in our sample is 98.39°F and the standard deviation is 0.743°F. Use the **Theory-Based Inference** applet to find and report a standardized statistic (*t*-statistic) and a p-value for the test.

d. Based on your p-value, write out a conclusion, being sure to include justification.

Commute time

2.2.25 According to a Pew Research Center report from 2012, the average commute time to work in California is 27.5 minutes. To investigate whether a different average is true for the small city that she lives in, a California high school student surveys 45 people she knows—her teachers, her parents and their friends and co-workers—and finds the average commute time for this sample to be 24.33 minutes, with a standard deviation of 9.53 minutes.

a. Write out the null and alternative hypotheses for our test in words or in symbols.

b. Use the **Theory-Based Inference** applet to find and report a standardized statistic (*t*-statistic) and a p-value for the test.

c. Based on your p-value, write out a conclusion, being sure to include justification.

d. The data did not come from a random sample; rather it came from a convenience sample of people to whom the student had access. Given that information, to what population do you think we can generalize our results?

FAQ

2.2.26 Read FAQ 2.2.1 and answer the following question. In your own words, explain why (mean − median)/SD is a good measure of skewness.

2.2.27 Read FAQ 2.2.2 and answer the following question. In your own words, explain the concept of degrees of freedom as it relates to *t*-distributions, including discussion of how a *t*-distribution begins to look like a normal distribution as the degrees of freedom change.

SECTION 2.2: Part 2

2.2.28* Which of the following best describes a sampling distribution of a sample mean?

A. A distribution of sample means.

B. A distribution of all possible samples of a certain size from the same population.

C. A distribution of the sample means from all possible samples of a certain size from the same population.

D. A distribution of many sample means of a certain size from the same population.

2.2.29 The sampling distribution of a sample mean will be approximately normal:

A. Always.

B. For most population distributions as long as the sample size is fairly small (at most 10).

C. For most population distributions as long as the sample size is fairly large (at least 30).

D. For skewed distributions of any size.

2.2.30* The sampling distribution of a sample mean will become more normally shaped when:

A. The sample size decreases and the population distribution gets more skewed.

B. The sample size decreases and the population distribution gets more symmetric.

C. The sample size increases and the population distribution gets more skewed.

D. The sample size increases and the population distribution gets more symmetric.

2.2.31 What are the means and standard deviations of sampling distributions of sample means with the following parameters and sample sizes?

a. $\mu = 2.44, \sigma = 1.18, n = 10$

b. $\mu = 5.48, \sigma = 2.33, n = 50$

2.2.32* What are the means and standard deviations of sampling distributions of sample means with the following parameters and sample sizes?

a. $\mu = 10, \sigma = 4, n = 25$

b. $\mu = 10, \sigma = 4, n = 100$

2.2.33 From the formula for the standard deviation of a sampling distribution for a sample mean, SD of $\bar{x} = \sigma/\sqrt{n}$, you can see that the standard deviation of the sample mean is affected only by the population standard deviation and the sample size.

a. As the sample size increases, how does the value of SD of $\bar{x}$ change? Does it increase or decrease?

b. As the population standard deviation increases, how does the value of SD of $\bar{x}$ change? Does it increase or decrease?

c. For what sample size is the SD of $\bar{x}$ one-tenth the size of the population standard deviation?

2.2.34* For a given population of a single quantitative variable, by what factor must the sample size increase in order for the standard deviation of the sampling distribution of the mean to be half as large?

2.2.35 Intelligence Quotient or IQ is a score obtained from a standardized test that is supposed to measure human intelligence. The scores on these tests are designed so the median is 100 points and a standard deviation is 15 points. (We will assume the mean is also 100 points.)

a. What are the mean and standard deviation of the sampling distribution of mean IQ scores when the sample size is 20?

b. What sample size is needed so the standard deviation of the sampling distribution is half that of a sample size of 20?

c. What sample size is needed so the standard deviation of the sampling distribution is one-quarter that of a sample size of 20?

2.2.36* According to data from the Centers for Disease Control and Prevention (CDC), the average weight of newborn boys is about 3.53 kg and the standard deviation is about 0.55 kg. The population data distribution is a bit skewed toward the low numbers (smaller weights).

a. What are the mean and standard deviation of a sampling distribution of mean male birthweights when the sample size is 20, or can't this be predicted?

b. What are the mean and standard deviation of a sampling distribution of mean male birthweights when the sample size is 40, or can't this be predicted?

c. Produce a well-labeled sketch of the sampling distribution from (b). Can you predict the shape? Explain.

d. According to your sketch in (c), how surprising would it be for a random sample of 40 newborn boys to average more than 3.70 kg?

2.2.37 According to data from the Centers for Disease Control and Prevention (CDC), the average weight of newborn girls is about 3.40 kg and the standard deviation is about 0.49 kg. The population data distribution is a bit skewed toward the low numbers (smaller weights).

a. What are the mean and standard deviation of a sampling distribution of mean female birthweights when the sample size is 10, or can't this be predicted?

b. What are the mean and standard deviation of a sampling distribution of mean female birthweights when the sample size is 40, or can't this be predicted?

c. Produce a well-labeled sketch of the sampling distribution from (b). Can you predict the shape? Explain.

d. According to your sketch in (c), how surprising would it be for a random sample of 40 newborn girls to average more than 3.70 kg?

2.2.38* The two distributions below are the mean length of words from samples of 10 words and 30 words from the Gettysburg Address. Which distribution comes from samples of size 10 and which from 30? Explain.

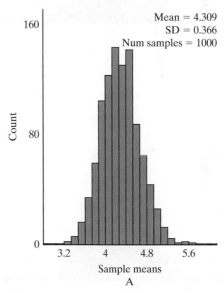

Mean = 4.309
SD = 0.366
Num samples = 1000

A

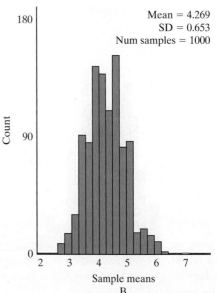

Mean = 4.269
SD = 0.653
Num samples = 1000

B

2.2.39 The graphs below show a population distribution of heights (in cm) of high school juniors in the United States, a distribution of many, many sample means from samples of size 10 from the population of heights, and a distribution of many, many means from samples of size 50 from the population of heights. Which graph is which?

Graph A

Graph B

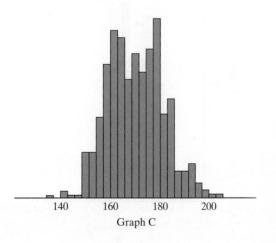

Graph C

2.2.40 Go to the **One Mean** applet and load some penny data by clicking the Pennies radio button located just to the right of the data window. This contains the last two digits of the year on 1,000 pennies collected in 1999. Click on the Show Sampling Options box and draw 1,000 samples of size 20 and the applet will develop a distribution of the means of your 1,000 samples.

a. What is the mean of your distribution of 1,000 sample means? What did you expect it would be?

b. What is the standard deviation of your distribution of 1,000 sample means? What did you expect it would be?

c. Is your distribution of sample means skewed one way or the other? If so, in which direction is it skewed?

d. Now have the applet draw 1,000 samples of size 50 (you can fix the axis scaling first if you prefer) from the population of pennies and answer parts (a), (b), and (c) again using the new distribution of sample means.

2.2.41* In Example 2.1 we looked at data from the College of the Midwest that included whether or not a student lived on campus and the GPA for all 2,919 students enrolled. Clear out the data in the **One Mean** applet, copy the CollegeMidwest data set from the textbook website, paste it in the applet's data window, and click on Use Data. The variable should be set at CumGpa and you should see a distribution of the GPAs of all 2,919 students displayed.

a. What *shape* does this population distribution have? Explain why this shape makes sense in this context.

b. Draw 1,000 samples of size 10 and the applet will develop a distribution of the means of your 1,000 samples.

   (i) What is the mean of your distribution of 1,000 sample means? What did you expect it would be?

   (ii) What is the standard deviation of your distribution of 1,000 sample means? What did you expect it would be?

   (iii) Is your distribution of sample means skewed one way or the other? If so, in which direction is it skewed?

c. Now have the applet draw 1,000 samples of size 40 from the population (you can fixed the axis scaling first if you prefer) and answer (i), (ii), (iii) under part (b) again using the new distribution of sample means.

2.2.42* In the previous exercise we looked at data from the College of the Midwest (also in Example 2.1) that included whether or not a student lived on campus and the GPA for all 2,919 students enrolled. In that exercise we looked at sampling from the GPAs of the students (a quantitative variable). We will now sample from the data of whether or not the student lived on campus (a categorical variable). We looked at these types of variables in Section 1.6. Clear out the data in the Sampling Words applet, copy the College Midwest data set from the textbook website, paste it in the applet's data window, and click on Use Data. Make sure the variable is set at OnCampus and you should see a distribution of the proportion of students that lived on campus (Y) and those that did not (N). Draw 1,000 samples of size 20 and the applet will develop a distribution of the proportions of yesses in your 1,000 samples. (If we let yes = 1 and no = 0, this is the same as the sample means of the 1s and 0s.)

a. What is the mean of your distribution of 1,000 sample means? What did you expect it would be?

b. Use $\pi = 0.776$ and compute $\sqrt{\pi(1 - \pi)/n}$.

c. If my population has 2,265 ones and 654 zeros, then you can show that the standard deviation of those values is equal to $\sqrt{(2,265(1 - 0.776)^2 + 654(1 - 0.776)^2)/2,919} \approx 0.417$. Use this for the value of σ and compute $\sigma/\sqrt{n}$. How does this compare to your answer to (b)?

d. Is your distribution of sample means skewed one way or the other? If so, in which direction is it skewed?

e. Now have the applet draw 1,000 samples of size 100 from the population and answer parts (a), (b), and (d) again using the new distribution of sample means.

f. What is the minimum sample size needed so that a normal distribution would be appropriate to model a sampling distribution of the sample proportion of students that live on campus? (Consider both guidelines you have learned so far; do the answers differ much?)

2.2.43 In 2005 the boat *Ethan Allen* sunk in Lake George, New York, and 20 of its 47 passengers died. The boat was certified to carry up to 50 passengers. However, the Coast Guard typically estimates the average weight of an adult to be about 150 pounds when determining the maximum capacity, and there were concerns that this was an underestimate and therefore the boat may have been carrying too much weight. Let's consider the worst-case weight scenario and assume the boat had a passenger list of all males. Around this time, the average weight of males in the U.S. was about 196 pounds with a standard deviation of about 74 pounds.

a. Suppose we are drawing samples of size 47 from the population of U.S. adult males in 2010. What are the mean and standard deviation of this sampling distribution?

b. Produce a well-labeled sketch of the sampling distribution from (a).

c. Where does the 150-lb average that the Coast Guard uses for average weight lie in your distribution from part (b)? Based on this, does it seem unlikely that a random sample of 47 would have an average weight of 150 pounds or less?

2.2.44 Recall the previous exercise about the boat *Ethan Allen*. We assumed the passenger list consisted of 47 males. Let's now look at the best-case weight scenario and assume that the passenger list consisted of 47 females. The average weight of females in the U.S. was approximately 166 pounds with a standard deviation of about 60 pounds.

a. Suppose we are drawing samples of size 47 from the population of U.S. adult females. What are the mean and standard deviation of this sampling distribution?

b. Produce a well-labeled sketch of the sampling distribution from (a).

c. Where does the 150-lb average that the Coast Guard uses for average weight lie in your distribution from part (b)? Based on this, does it seem unlikely that a random sample of 47 would have an average weight of 150 pounds or less?

2.2.45* Open up the **One Mean** applet and you should see that Pop 1 is chosen. This represents a fairly normally distributed population of sleep times that has a mean of about 8 hours.

a. Suppose you take 10,000 samples from this population where the sample size is 10. What do you expect the mean, standard deviation, and shape of distribution of sample means to be?

b. Click on the Show Sampling Options and collect 10,000 samples of size 10. Do the mean, standard deviation, and shape match your prediction?

2.2.46 Open up the **One Mean** applet and click on Pop 2. This represents a right-skewed distributed population of sleep times that has a mean of about 8 hours.

a. Suppose you take 10,000 samples from this population where the sample size is 10. What do you expect the mean, standard deviation, and shape of distribution of sample means to be?

b. Click on the Show Sampling Options and collect 10,000 samples of size 10. Do the mean, standard deviation, and shape match your prediction?

2.2.47* Open up the **One Mean** applet and click on Pop 3. This represents a fairly uniformly distributed population of sleep times that has a mean of about 8 hours.

a. Suppose you take 10,000 samples from this population where the sample size is 10. What do you expect the mean, standard deviation, and shape of distribution of sample means to be?

b. Click on the Show Sampling Options and collect 10,000 samples of size 10. Do the mean, standard deviation, and shape match your prediction?

c. How did your answers to Questions 18, 19, and 20 change with the change in the population?

SECTION 2.2: Part 3

2.2.48.* The following figure shows two *t*-distributions, one superimposed on top of the other. One is labeled A and one is labeled B. One has 5 degrees of freedom and one has 100 degrees of freedom. Which is which? How did you decide?

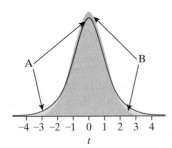

2.2.49 If you are doing a one-sample *t*-test with a sample size of 28, how many degrees of freedom will the *t*-distribution have that you will need to use?

2.2.50* Suppose you are using a sample size of 20 to test a single mean and get a p-value of 0.02. You then realize you used a normal distribution instead of a *t*-distribution to find your p-value. When you recompute your p-value with a *t*-distribution, will you get a larger, smaller, or the same p-value? Explain.

2.2.51 Suppose you are conducting a one-sample *t*-test with the hypotheses $H_0: \mu = 10$, $H_a: \mu < 10$. In doing so, you get a p-value of 0.06. If you conduct another test with the same data except you switch the alternative hypothesis to $H_a: \mu \neq 10$, what is your new p-value?

2.2.52* The average human body temperature (taken orally) is supposed to be 37°C. Some people think this is too high for the general population and should really be lower. Which of the following is an appropriate way to write out the hypotheses to test this?

A. $H_0: \bar{x} = 37°C$, $H_a: \bar{x} < 37°C$
B. $H_0: \bar{x} = 37°C$, $H_a: \bar{x} \neq 37°C$
C. $H_0: \mu = 37°C$, $H_a: \mu < 37°C$
D. $H_0: \mu = 37°C$, $H_a: \mu > 37°C$
E. $H_0: \pi = 37°C$, $H_a: \pi < 37°C$
F. $H_0: \pi = 37°C$, $H_a: \pi \neq 37°C$

2.2.53 Suppose you have a friend Cliff who is always telling you interesting "facts" and one day he says, "Did you know the average heart rate of the ruby-throated hummingbird in flight is 1,263 beats per minute?" You decide to call him on this one and collect data to try to show that the heart rate of these hummingbirds is not what Cliff says. You collect data on 30 hummingbirds and find the average heart rate for your 30 birds is 997 bpm. Which of the following is an appropriate way to write out the hypotheses for your study?

A. $H_0: \bar{x} = 1{,}263$ bpm, $H_a: \bar{x} < 1{,}263$ bpm
B. $H_0: \bar{x} = 997$ bpm, $H_a: \bar{x} \neq 997$ bpm
C. $H_0: \mu = 1{,}263$ bpm, $H_a: \mu < 1{,}263$ bpm
D. $H_0: \mu = 1{,}263$ bpm, $H_a: \mu \neq 1{,}263$ bpm
E. $H_0: \pi = 1{,}162$ bpm, $H_a: \pi < 997$ bpm
F. $H_0: \pi = 997$ bpm, $H_a: \pi \neq 997$ bpm

2.2.54* Suppose you are conducting a two-sided, one-sample *t*-test and calculate a *t*-statistic of 2.13. Which of the following is a plausible p-value you would get for this test?

A. 0.002
B. 0.014
C. 0.048
D. 0.273
E. 0.729

2.2.55 Suppose you are conducting a two-sided, one-sample *t*-test and calculate a *t*-statistic of −0.35. Which of the following is a plausible p-value you would get for this test?

A. 0.002
B. 0.014
C. 0.048
D. 0.273
E. 0.729

2.2.56* Suppose you are testing to see whether bags of potato chips have an average weight that is larger than their label weight with the following hypotheses: $H_0: \mu = 10$ oz, $H_a: \mu > 10$ oz. You collect a sample of 15 bags and find a mean weight of 10.15 oz and a SD of 0.23 oz. From this, you calculate a p-value of 0.01. Which of the following individual changes in your summary statistics (without changing anything else) would get you a smaller p-value? (Choose all that apply.)

A. A larger sample size
B. A smaller sample size
C. A larger sample mean
D. A smaller sample mean
E. A larger sample standard deviation
F. A smaller sample standard deviation

2.2.57 Suppose you are testing to see whether body temperatures tend to be lower than what is thought to be the average body temperature with the following hypotheses: $H_0: \mu = 98.6°F$, $H_a: \mu < 98.6°F$. You recruit 30 subjects and find their mean body temperature is 98.4°F with a SD of 0.75°F. From this, you calculate a p-value of 0.08. Which of the following individual changes in your summary statistics (without changing anything else) would get you a larger p-value? (Choose all that apply.)

A. A larger sample size

B. A smaller sample size

C. A larger sample mean

D. A smaller sample mean

E. A larger sample standard deviation

F. A smaller sample standard deviation

2.2.58* The 2010 Honda Civic has a fuel usage estimate of 36 miles per gallon (mpg) when driven on a highway. One of the authors has such a car and believes it gets better mileage than what is reported. Suppose he tests this on 15 trip segments (where he fills up the tank after each segment) on highways. He calculates his mean mileage to be 38.8 mpg with a standard deviation of 0.9 mpg. Calculate and interpret the value of the t-statistic for this test.

2.2.59 Suppose you need to determine the airspeed velocity of an unladen (European) swallow. You test a random sample of 42 swallows and find their mean airspeed is 10.6 meters per second with a standard deviation of 2.2 meters per second and you want to test this against the commonly known "fact" that its airspeed is 11 meters per second. Calculate and interpret the value of the t-statistic for this test.

2.2.60* Ten "5 lb" bags of Michigan apples were weighed and the sample mean, $\bar{x}$, was found to be 90.3 ounces and the sample standard deviation, s, was 5.0 ounces. The sample distribution of the 10 weights was fairly symmetric, and we will assume (perhaps wrongly) that this sample is representative of the type of apple and size of bag from this certain packer. Complete a test of significance to determine whether there is strong evidence that the population mean weight is greater than the label weight of 80 ounces by stating the hypotheses, naming the test used, verifying the validity conditions for the test, calculating the test statistic and p-value, and stating an appropriate conclusion.

2.2.61 The package weight for a certain size of Snickers bars is 2.75 ounces. A student weighed 30 bars and found a mean of 2.842 ounces and a standard deviation of 0.156 ounces. The sample distribution of weights was fairly symmetric. We will assume this sample is representative of the population of this size of Snickers bar. Complete a test of significance to determine whether there is strong evidence that the population mean weight is larger than the label weight of 2.75 ounces by stating the hypotheses, naming the test used, verifying the validity conditions for the test, calculating the test statistic and p-value, and stating an appropriate conclusion.

2.2.62* In a study conducted by *QSR* (a journal for Quick Service Restaurants), they determined that Wendy's restaurant had the fastest drive-through of all national chains. Their mean time from the time an order was placed to its delivery was 134 seconds. Students in Holland, Michigan, wanted to see if the drive-through times of the Wendy's in Holland might be different from the national average. They collected the following sample of 27 drive-through times (in seconds) from this restaurant:

47, 50, 31, 175, 65, 68, 87, 114, 135, 116, 125, 130, 127, 150, 50, 52, 226, 34, 45, 85, 130, 102, 108, 58, 63, 84, 80

We will assume this sample is representative of all the drive-through times at this restaurant. Complete a test of significance to determine whether there is strong evidence that the population mean drive-through time is different from the reported national average by stating the hypotheses, naming the test used, verifying the validity conditions for the test, calculating the test statistic and p-value, and stating an appropriate conclusion.

2.2.63 Right after 27 students in a college mathematics class were finished taking a test, they were asked to write down the score they thought they got on the test. After it was graded, their predicted score was subtracted from their actual score and those results are shown below. A positive difference means their actual score was higher than predicted and a negative difference means their actual score was lower than predicted.

−8, −7, 3, −13, 9, 9, −1, −1, −18, 2, 2, −6, 2, −24, 13, 0, −9, −1, 2, −14, 8, 1, −4, −2, 6, −7, −9

We will assume this sample is representative of all students that take this mathematics class. Complete a test of significance to determine whether there is strong evidence that, in the population, students' actual scores on tests in this class are different from their predicted scores, on average, by stating the hypotheses, naming the test used, verifying the validity conditions for the test, calculating the test statistic and p-value, and stating an appropriate conclusion.

2.2.64* Do people think they look different than they actually do? In particular, do they think they look better? Researchers Epley and Whitchurch (2008) tried to answer this question by taking pictures of 27 subjects (both male and female). They then had the picture of each subject's face morphed with that of someone that was thought to be better looking. The images were morphed in 10% increments so that the first morph was 90% the subject and 10% the better-looking person, the second was 80% subject and 20% better-looking person. This continued until the face was 50% of each person. They did the same thing with a picture of a person that was thought to be not good looking. The researchers then had 11 pictures for each subject, one of the actual subject and 10 with various morphings. Each subject was presented with the 11 pictures, in random order, and asked which was the actual picture of their face. If they picked one that was composed of 20% of the better-looking face, their score was 20. If they picked one that was composed of 10% of the worse-looking face, their score was −10. Of course, if they picked the picture of their own face, their score was 0. The average score of the 27 subjects was 6.3 with a standard deviation of 12.45. A distribution of the results was fairly symmetric. Complete a test of significance to determine whether there is strong evidence that, on average, people tend to pick a face that is different from their own. Do this by stating the hypotheses, naming the test used, verifying the validity conditions for the test, calculating the test statistic and p-value, and stating an appropriate conclusion.

2.2.65 Recall the previous exercise about whether or not people recognize their face as being more attractive than it actually is. Because people often see their face in a mirror, the researchers wanted to make sure that this wasn't biasing the results. So they repeated the test, but used mirror images of the subject's face and all its morphings. They again used the same scale so a positive number indicated the subject identified their own face as being more attractive than it was, a negative score meant less attractive, and a score of 0 meant they correctly identified their own face. The average score of the 15 subjects was 12.0 with a standard deviation of 19.71. A distribution of the results was fairly symmetric. Complete a test of significance to determine whether there is strong evidence that, on average, people tend to pick a face that is different from theirs. Do this by stating the hypotheses, naming the test used, verifying the validity conditions for the test, calculating the test statistic and p-value, and stating an appropriate conclusion.

2.2.66* Recall the previous two exercises about whether or not people recognize their face as being more attractive than it actually is. The researchers were also interested in whether people rate a friend's face as being more attractive than it really is. So they asked 24 subjects to bring a close friend along with them to the experiment. They again morphed the friends' faces with those of more attractive and less attractive faces. They used the same scale so a positive number indicated the subject identified their friend's face as being more attractive than it was, a negative score meant less attractive, and a score of 0 meant they correctly identified their friend's face. The average score of the 24 subjects was 10.09 with a standard deviation of 19.00. A distribution of the results was fairly symmetric. Complete a test of significance to determine whether there is strong evidence that, on average, people tend to pick a face that is different than the actual face of a close friend. Do this by stating the hypotheses, naming the test used, verifying the validity conditions for the test, calculating the test statistic and p-value, and stating an appropriate conclusion.

2.2.67 Recall the previous three exercises about whether or not people recognize their face as being more attractive than it actually is. The researchers were also interested in whether people rate a relative stranger's face as being more attractive than it really is. The subjects had an initial encounter with a researcher. They morphed the researcher's face with those of more attractive and less attractive faces. The subjects were brought back a couple weeks later and given the matching test by a different researcher. They used the same scale so a positive number indicated the subject identified their researcher's face as being more attractive than it was, a negative score meant less attractive, and a score of 0 meant they correctly identified the researcher's face. The average score of the 24 subjects was 1.3 with a standard deviation of 18.72. A distribution of the results was fairly symmetric. Complete a test of significance to determine whether there is strong evidence that, on average, people tend to pick a face that is different than that of a relative stranger. Do this by stating the hypotheses, naming the test used, verifying the validity conditions for the test, calculating the test statistic and p-value, and stating an appropriate conclusion.

SECTION 2.3

2.3.1* Suppose that we conduct a test of significance using 5% as our level of significance.

a. What is the probability of making a Type I error (if the null hypothesis is true)?

b. Suppose we conduct 10 different tests of significance each using a 5% significance level (and again where all the null hypotheses are true). How do you think the probability of making at least one Type I error in those 10 tests will compare with your answer to the previous question: will it be the same, be smaller, or be larger? Explain.

2.3.2 Indicate whether or not you would reject the null hypothesis, at the $\alpha = 0.05$ significance level, for the following p-values.

a. p-value $= 0.078$ b. p-value $= 0.045$

c. p-value $= 0.001$ d. p-value $= 0.051$

2.3.3* Indicate whether or not you would reject the null hypothesis, with a p-value of 0.064, for the following significance levels.

a. $\alpha = 0.05$ b. $\alpha = 0.10$

c. $\alpha = 0.01$ d. $\alpha = 0.065$

2.3.4 Suppose that you perform a significance test and, based on the p-value, decide to reject the null hypothesis at the $\alpha = 0.05$ significance level. Then suppose that your colleague decides to conduct the same test on the same data but using a different significance level. For each of the following significance levels, indicate whether you would reject the null hypothesis, fail to reject the null hypothesis, or do not have enough information to say. (*Hint*: First ask yourself what must be true about the p-value based on your decision to reject the null hypothesis at the $\alpha = 0.05$ significance level.)

a. $\alpha = 0.10$ **b.** $\alpha = 0.01$

c. $\alpha = 0.0001$ **d.** $\alpha = 0.065$

2.3.5* Suppose that you perform a significance test and, based on the p-value, decide to reject the null hypothesis at the $\alpha = 0.01$ significance level. Then suppose that your colleague decides to conduct the same test on the same data but using a different significance level. For each of the following significance levels, indicate whether you would reject the null hypothesis, fail to reject the null hypothesis, or do not have enough information to say. (*Hint*: First ask yourself what must be true about the p-value.)

a. $\alpha = 0.10$ **b.** $\alpha = 0.05$

c. $\alpha = 0.0001$ **d.** $\alpha = 0.065$

2.3.6* Suppose that you perform a significance test using the $\alpha = 0.05$ significance level.

a. For what p-values would you reject the null hypothesis?

b. For what p-values would you fail to reject the null hypothesis?

2.3.7 Suppose that you perform a significance test and obtain a p-value of 0.036.

a. For what significance levels α would you reject the null hypothesis?

b. For what significance levels α would you fail to reject the null hypothesis?

2.3.8* A researcher decides to set the significance level to 0.001.

a. If the null hypothesis is true, what is the probability of a Type I error?

b. If the researcher chooses a larger significance level, what will be the impact on the probability of a Type II error, assuming the alternative hypothesis is true?

2.3.9 A researcher decides to set the significance level to 0.10.

a. If the null hypothesis is true, what is the probability of a Type I error?

b. If the researcher chooses a smaller significance level, what will be the impact on the probability of a Type II error, assuming the alternative hypothesis is true?

Doris and Buzz*

Exercises 2.3.10 and 2.3.11 refer to the Doris and Buzz study.

2.3.10 In Example 1.1, we looked at a study to investigate whether dolphins could communicate. In doing so, we tested whether Buzz, one of the dolphins, could push the correct button more than 50% of the time in the long run.

a. Describe what a Type I error would be in this study.

b. Describe what a Type II error would be in this study.

2.3.11 Reconsider dolphins Buzz and Doris from Example 1.1 and the previous exercise. We found that the observed data provided very strong evidence that Doris and Buzz were actually communicating better than random chance. Which type of error (I or II) could we possibly be making with this conclusion? What does this type of error mean in this context?

Harley the dog

Exercises 2.3.15 and 2.3.16 refer to Harley the dog data.

2.3.12 In Exploration 1.1, we looked at a study to investigate whether Harley the dog could select the correct cup more than 50% of the time in the long run.

a. Describe what a Type I error would be in this study.

b. Describe what a Type II error would be in this study.

2.3.13 Reconsider Harley the dog from Exploration 1.1 and the previous exercise. We found that the observed data provided very strong evidence that Harley the dog was doing better than random chance. Which type of error (I or II) could we possibly be making with this conclusion? What does this type of error mean in this context?

Error trade-off*

2.3.14 The significance level α determines the probability of making a Type I error. Errors are bad. So, why don't we always set α to be extremely small, such as 0.0001?

Needles

Exercises 2.3.15 and 2.3.16 refer to the needle data.

2.3.15 Consider a manufacturing process that is producing hypodermic needles that will be used for blood donations. These needles need to have a diameter of 1.65 mm—too big and they would hurt the donor (even more than usual), too small and they would rupture the red blood cells, rendering the donated blood useless. Thus, the manufacturing process would have to be closely monitored to detect any significant departures from the desired diameter. During every shift, quality control personnel take a sample of several needles and measure their diameters. If they discover a problem, they will stop the manufacturing process until it is corrected.

a. Define the parameter of interest in the context of this study and assign an appropriate symbol to it.

b. State the appropriate null and alternative hypotheses using the symbol defined in (a).

c. Describe what a Type I error would be in this study. Also, describe the consequence of such an error in the context of this study.

d. Describe what a Type II error would be in this study. Also, describe the consequence of such an error in the context of this study.

2.3.16 Recall that the two errors discussed in this chapter were regarded as "false alarm" and "missed opportunity." In some fields, these errors are also regarded as "consumer's risk" and "producer's risk." With regard to the previous exercise about the hypodermic needle manufacturing process, do you think the Type I error is the consumer's risk or the producer's risk? What about the Type II error?

Campus newspaper*

2.3.17 Suppose that you are considering whether to publish a weekly alternative newspaper on campus. You decide to survey a random sample of students on your campus to ask if they would be likely to read such a newspaper. Your plan is to proceed with publication only if the sample data provide strong evidence that more than 10% of all students on your campus would be likely to read such a newspaper.

a. Identify the parameter of interest, in words.

b. Express the appropriate null and alternative hypotheses for conducting this test.

c. Specify what Type I error represents in this situation. Also indicate a potential consequence of Type I error.

d. Specify what Type II error represents in this situation. Also indicate a potential consequence of Type II error.

Diagnostic tests

2.3.18 As with a jury trial, another analogy to hypothesis testing involves medical diagnostic tests. These tests aim to indicate whether or not the patient has a particular disease. But the tests are not infallible, so errors can be made. The null hypothesis can be regarded as the patient being healthy. The alternative hypothesis can be regarded as the patient having the disease.

a. Describe what Type I error represents in this situation. Also indicate a potential consequence of Type I error.

b. Describe what Type II error represents in this situation. Also indicate a potential consequence of Type II error.

c. Which type of error would you consider to be more serious in this situation? Explain your thinking.

Lie detectors*

2.3.19 Lie detector tests are similar to hypothesis tests in that there are two possible decisions and two possible realities and therefore two kinds of errors that can be made. The hypotheses can be considered as:

H_0: Subject is actually telling the truth.

H_a: Subject is actually lying.

a. Describe what rejecting H_0 means in this context.

b. Describe what failing to reject H_0 means in this context.

c. Describe what Type I error means in this context.

d. Describe what Type II error means in this context.

Spam filters

2.3.20 Spam filters in an email program are similar to hypothesis tests in that there are two possible decisions and two possible realities and therefore two kinds of errors that can be made. The hypotheses can be considered as:

H_0: Incoming email message is legitimate.

H_a: Incoming email message is spam.

a. Describe what rejecting H_0 means in this context.

b. Describe what failing to reject H_0 means in this context.

c. Describe what Type I error means in this context.

d. Describe what Type II error means in this context.

Treatments*

2.3.21 Later in the book you will encounter many hypotheses of the following type:

H_0: New treatment is *no* better than current treatment.

H_a: New treatment *is* better than current treatment.

a. Describe what Type I error means in this context.

b. Describe what Type II error means in this context.

Sex differences

2.3.22 Later in the book you will encounter hypotheses of the following type:

H_0: Men and women do *not* differ on average with regard to the variable of interest.

H_a: Men and women *do* differ on average with regard to the variable of interest.

a. Describe what Type I error means in this context.

b. Describe what Type II error means in this context.

Organ donation*

2.3.23 Example P.1 describes a study that compared proportions of people who agreed to become organ donors, depending on the type of default option used. The null hypothesis is that all three default options have the same probability of a person agreeing to become an organ donor. The alternative hypothesis is that at least two of the default options have different probability of a person agreeing to become an organ donor.

a. Describe what Type I error means in this context.

b. Describe what Type II error means in this context.

Election winners

2.3.24 Reconsider Example 1.4 about whether winners of elections can be predicted better than random chance simply by considering the faces of the candidates.

a. Describe what Type I error means in this context.

b. Describe what Type II error means in this context.

c. Based on the p-value in that study (which produced 23 successful predictions in 32 elections), would you reject the null hypothesis at the 0.01 significance level?

d. Based on your answer to part (c), which type of error could you possibly be making?

Trick or treat*

2.3.25 Reconsider Example 1.5 about whether trick-or-treaters have an overall preference between Halloween toys or candy.

a. Describe what Type I error means in this context.

b. Describe what Type II error means in this context.

c. Based on the p-value in that study (in which 148 trick-or-treaters in the sample selected candy and 135 selected toys), would you reject the null hypothesis at the 0.10 significance level?

d. Based on your answer to part (c), which type of error could you possibly be making?

FAQ

2.3.26 Read FAQ 2.3.1 and answer the following question. Explain, as if to someone who doesn't know much about statistics, why it's dangerous to reach dramatically different conclusions for p-values of 0.04999 and 0.50001 obtained on the same dataset.

END OF CHAPTER

Major league baseball games*

2.CE.1 Suppose that you select Major League Baseball (MLB) games played during the second week in April as a sample of all MLB games played in the upcoming season.

a. Would this be a simple random sample? Explain briefly.

b. Following up on part (a), consider two variables that you could record about each game: attendance and number of runs scored. With which of these two variables is the sample (of games played during the second week in April) more likely to be representative of the population? Explain briefly.

Sampling students

2.CE.2 Suppose that you select a sample of students at your university by standing in front of the library and asking students who pass by to take a survey.

a. Would this be a simple random sample from the population of all students at your university? Explain briefly.

b. Name a variable for which you believe that this sample would be representative of the population of all students at your university. Explain briefly.

c. Name a variable for which you believe that this sample would *not* be representative of the population of all students at your university. Explain briefly.

Big bang theory*

2.CE.3 A reader wrote in to the "Ask Marilyn" column in *Parade* magazine to say that his grandfather told him that in three-fourths of all baseball games, the winning team scores more runs in one inning than the losing team scores in the entire game. (This phenomenon is known as a "big bang.") Marilyn responded that this proportion seemed to be too high to be believable. To investigate this claim, an instructor examined the 45 MLB games played on September 17–19, 2010.

a. Was this a random sample of all MLB games played in the 2010 season? Explain briefly.

b. Restate the grandfather's assertion as a null hypothesis and Marilyn's response as an alternative hypothesis, in both symbols and in words.

The instructor found that 21 of the 45 games played on those dates contained a big bang.

c. Calculate the sample proportion of games that had a big bang and denote it with the appropriate symbol.

d. Assume (for now) that the grandfather's claim is true and use the **One Proportion** applet to simulate 1,000 samples of 45 games per sample. Describe how to calculate the approximate p-value from this simulation and report its value.

e. Would you conclude that the sample data provide strong evidence to support Marilyn's contention that the proportion cited by the grandfather is too high to be the actual value? Explain your reasoning, as if writing to the grandfather, who has never taken a statistics course.

Reading on the bowl

2.CE.4 A study published in 2009 (Goldstein et al., 2009) involved a sample of 499 adults selected from various regions across the country of Israel. These adults were approached by interviewers in public gathering areas and asked to complete a survey about whether or not they read while using the toilet. The researchers found that 263 of the 499 adults responded that they do read while using the toilet.

a. Calculate the sample proportion who responded that they read while using the toilet.

b. Is this proportion a parameter or a statistic? Explain, and indicate the appropriate symbol to represent this proportion.

c. Sketch a graph to display the data gathered from the study. What kind of graph did you sketch?

d. Assuming half of all persons in Israel read while using the toilet, describe how to calculate a p-value from these data. Use the simulation-based **One Proportion** applet to calculate an approximate p-value. Based on this p-value, would you conclude that the population proportion who read while using the toilet differs from 1/2? Explain.

e. To what population do you feel comfortable generalizing the results of this study? For example, would you generalize the results to all adults in Israel? How about all adults in the world, or in another country such as the U.S.? Explain.

Keeping their names*

Exercises 2.CE.5 and 2.CE.6 refer to the following data.

2.CE.5 What percentage of U.S. brides keep their own names after marriage, as opposed to taking their husband's name or using some modification (such as hyphenation) of her name and her husband's? Researchers investigated this question by selecting a sample of wedding announcements in the *New York Times* newspaper (Kopelman et al., 2009). They found that 18% of a sample of 600 brides sampled between 2001 and 2005 kept their own names.

a. Identify the observational units and variable in this study.

b. Identify the population and sample in this study.

c. Identify (in words) the parameter of interest.

d. Based on how the sample was selected, do you have any concerns about generalizing the sample result to the population of all brides in the U.S. between 2001 and 2005? To what population would you feel comfortable generalizing the result? Explain.

2.CE.6 Refer to Exercise 2.CE.5. Suppose you are testing to see if the population proportion of all brides who keep their own name is different from 15%.

a. If testing at a significance level of 5%, would you find evidence for the population proportion of brides between 2001 and 2005 who kept their own names to differ from 15%? Explain using the p-value you found.

b. If testing at a significance level of 10%, would you find evidence for the population proportion of brides between 2001 and 2005 who kept their own names to differ from 15%? Explain using the p-value you found.

c. If testing at a significance level of 1%, would you find evidence for the population proportion of brides between 2001 and 2005 who kept their own names to differ from 15%? Explain using the p-value you found.

Biased samples

Exercises 2.CE.7 and 2.CE.8 refer to biased samples.

2.CE.7 Which samples do you think are nonbiased samples of the population of all students at a college/four-year university? If it is a biased sample, is there a different population for which you believe the sample could be considered a nonbiased sample?

a. A random sample of 100 students from the registrar's student list

b. A random sample of 100 students in the library on a Thursday night

c. A random sample of 100 students in the student center on a Friday night

d. A random sample of 100 students at a basketball game on a Tuesday night

e. A random sample of 10 students from 10 randomly chosen dorms on campus

f. A random sample of 100 students from cars registered on campus

2.CE.8 Biased samples either overestimate or underestimate the parameter of interest. List the samples from Exercise 2.CE.7 you think might overestimate the following parameters.

a. Average student GPA

b. Proportion of male students

c. Proportion of female students

d. Proportion of out-of-state students

Body temperatures*

Exercises 2.CE.9 and 2.CE.10 refer to the body temperature data.

2.CE.9 Body temperatures were measured on a random sample of 20 females and 20 males applying for health insurance.

Together, their average temperature was 98.8°F with a standard deviation of 0.2°F.

a. Are validity conditions met to carry out a theory-based test of significance to see if average adult body temperature is different from 98.6? Explain why or why not. Is there any other information you would like to know?

b. Carry out a theory-based test of significance for a single mean. Report the p-value and include a conclusion based on this p-value.

c. What is the value of the standardized test statistic and what does this tell you about your sample mean?

d. Does your answer to (c) coincide with your answer to (b)? Explain.

2.CE.10 Refer to Exercise 2.CE.9.

a. Based on the test results found in Exercise 2.CE.9, part (b), if you are testing at a significance level of 5% and you have made an error, what type of error have you made? (Type I or Type II?)

b. If you are testing at the 5% level of significance and you have made a Type II error, what can you say about the p-value of the test?

c. Name two ways in which you could decrease the probability of a Type I error.

INVESTIGATION: FAKING CELL PHONE CALLS

Have you ever pretended to be talking on your cell phone in order to avoid interacting with people around you? Is faking cell phone calls a common practice among cell phone users? A recent survey conducted by the Pew Research Center during April 26–May 22, 2011, asked cell phone users about this issue and many others regarding the respondents' cell phone usage in the past 30 days. The survey involved selecting a random sample of 1,858 American cell phone users.

1. Was the sample random?
2. Was the sampling method unbiased?
3. Do you feel comfortable generalizing your conclusions to all cell phone users? If not, is there a population (broader than the sample) you feel you can generalize your conclusions to?

Suppose instead your data came from a random sample of 1,858 college students.

4. Was the sample random?
5. Was the sampling method unbiased?
6. Do you feel comfortable generalizing your conclusions to all cell phone users? If not, is there a population you feel you can generalize your conclusions to?

Now suppose you asked 1,858 people walking on Wall Street (in New York City) throughout the day on a Monday.

7. Was the sample random?
8. Was the sampling method unbiased?
9. Do you feel comfortable generalizing your conclusions to all cell phone users? If not, is there a population you feel you can generalize your conclusions to?

A reporter for *International Business Times* took the Pew survey results and wrote that more than 1 in 10 cell phone users in the U.S. has engaged in such fake cell phone use in the past 30 days. Notice that the reporter's claim is about the population of all cell phone users in the U.S. In the following questions, we will investigate whether the survey results provide evidence that more than 1 in 10 cell phone users have faked cell phone calls in the last 30 days.

STEP 1: Ask a research question.

10. What is our research question?

STEP 2: Design a study and collect data.

11. What are the observational units?

12. What is the variable that is measured/recorded on each observational unit?

13. Describe the parameter of interest in words. (You can use the symbol π to represent this parameter.)

14. State the appropriate null and alternative hypotheses to be tested.

Of the 1,858 cell phone users, 13% admitted to faking cell phone calls in the past 30 days.

15. If another sample of 1,858 American cell phone users were surveyed, could the percentage admitting to faking cell phone calls in the past 30 days change? Explain your reasoning.

STEP 3: Explore the data.

16. Is the 13% a statistic or a parameter? How are you deciding?

STEP 4: Draw inferences.

Let's use the 3S strategy to help us investigate how much evidence the sample data provide to support the conjecture that more than 1 in 10 cell phone users fake cell phone calls.

Statistic

17. What is the statistic that you can use to summarize the data collected in the study?

Simulate

18. If we assume that the population proportion of cell phone users who fake cell phone calls is actually 0.10, is it possible that we could observe the statistic we did from this sample of 1,858 cell phone users? Why?

19. Use the **One Proportion** applet to simulate 1,000 repetitions of a random process, assuming that the proportion of cell phone users who fake calls is 0.10. Report what values you input into the applet.

20. What is the center of your simulated null distribution? Does it make sense that this is the center? Explain.

21. Are there any values of *simulated* sample proportions that are less than 0.10? Are there any values of *simulated* sample proportions that are greater than 0.10? What does that tell you?

Strength of evidence

22. Based on the null distribution generated using the 1,000 simulated values of the statistic, what values would you consider typical values and what would you consider atypical values of the statistic?

23. How do the actual study results compare to the null distribution obtained when simulating assuming 0.10 of the population faked cell phone calls? Do you believe the study results provide convincing evidence against the "1 in 10 cell phone users fake cell phone calls" null hypothesis and in favor of the "more than 1 in 10 cell phone users fake cell phone calls" alternative hypothesis? Why or why not?

24. Determine the approximate p-value from your simulation analysis. Also interpret what this p-value represents (i.e., the probability of what, assuming what?).

STEP 5: Formulate conclusions.

25. Now, let's step back a bit and think about the scope of our inference. What are the wider implications? Do you think that your conclusion holds true for people in general? What is

the broader population we are able to generalize to? It is important to remember how we gathered our data to answer these questions.

STEP 6: Look back and ahead.

26. Summarize your findings. If you were to repeat this study, would you gather your sample in a different way? Are there things about the study you would change? What further research might you follow up with from what you have learned in this study?

Research Article   www.wiley.com/college/tintle

Social evaluation   Read the article "Social evaluation by preverbal infants," including the full (online) methods found in the journal *Nature*, Vol. 450, pp. 557–559, November 22, 2007, by J. K. Hamlin, K. Wynn, and P. Bloom and accessible at http://www.nature.com/nature/journal/v450/n7169/full/nature06288.html via your school's library or from your instructor.

Embedded in the article are links to short video clips which may be useful in understanding the research design.

CHAPTER

① ② ③ ④ ⑤ ⑥ ⑦ ⑧ ⑨ ⑩ ⑪ ⑫

Estimation: How Large Is the Effect?

This chapter is about **estimation**, one of the four pillars of inference: strength, *size*, breadth, and cause. Often, estimation tells *how large* the effect is, not by giving us a single number, but by giving us an interval of values. For example, we might find in the organ donations study (Example P.1) that we are "95% confident that the 'true' effect of forcing people to make a choice between becoming an organ donor or not, rather than the opt-in setting where the default is that a person is not a donor, is to increase the probability of people agreeing to be organ donors by somewhere between 20 percentage points and 55 percentage points."

The goal of this chapter is to help you understand the logic that statisticians use to compute an interval of plausible (i.e., believable) values for the size of the effect we want to know about. This set of values, called a **confidence interval**, comes with a measure of reliability, typically 95%, called the **confidence level**. For the organ donations study, the 95% confidence interval for the increase in the probability of organ donors when forcing people to make a choice between being a donor or not rather than giving them the choice to opt in extends from 20 to 55 percentage points.

In this chapter, you will see three different ways to find confidence intervals, all based on methods from Chapters 1 and 2. The first method (Section 3.1) specifies an interval of **plausible values** to be those values of the parameter that are not rejected in a (two-sided) test of significance.

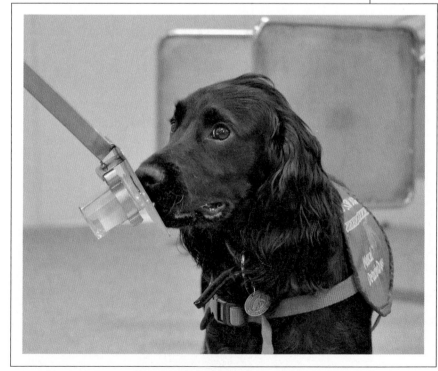

Universal History Archive/UIG via / Getty Images, Inc.

The second method (Section 3.2) approximates an interval of plausible values for the parameter to be those values that fall within 2 standard deviations of the statistic. The third method, a theory-based approach (also in Section 3.2), uses similar logic but allows a more precise and flexible interval calculation. We show you all three methods to illustrate the logic of confidence intervals and how they are related to tests of significance, but the third method is the most commonly used in practice. Although most of this chapter will focus on confidence intervals for a population proportion, we will take a look at confidence intervals for a population mean in Section 3.3. Theory-based approaches also allow us to easily explore factors that impact the width of the confidence interval (e.g., our level of *precision*) in Section 3.4. The chapter ends with some final warnings and cautions about statistical inference in general in Section 3.5.

STATISTICAL INFERENCE: CONFIDENCE INTERVALS

SECTION 3.1

INTRODUCTION

Up to this point, you have been able to make conclusions such as "we have strong evidence that the long-run proportion is larger than 0.50." A natural next question is "How much larger than 0.50?" Or our research question may have been initially phrased as "what is the probability that...." Our main goal may be to estimate the parameter value rather than having a single natural value to test. Up until now, we've not been able to answer these kinds of questions, which relate to the size of the parameter. Although the observed statistic gives us an estimate of the actual parameter value (e.g., 71.9% of elections are correctly predicted with the competent-face method from Example 1.4), this does not take into account the random variation associated with that statistic. What we would like is a method for saying something like "I believe 69% to 75% of all elections can be correctly predicted by the competent-face method." This would give us very different information than if we were to say "I believe 55% to 89% of all elections can be correctly predicted by the competent-face method." In both cases our estimate exceeds 0.50, but the interval is much wider in the second case and our estimate much less precise.

In this section, we will see how we can use a ***confidence interval*** to estimate a long-run proportion (probability) or population proportion. In particular, we will see how one way to create a confidence interval is to consider many different significance tests about the parameter.

Can Dogs Sniff Out Cancer?

Example 3.1

STEP 1: Ask a research question.   We all know that dogs have an amazing sense of smell. They are used to help hunters find their prey, determine the location of missing people, and screen luggage for drugs. But can a dog's keen sense of smell also be used to determine whether a patient has cancer? This is a question that has been asked recently and studies have been conducted to try to answer it.

STEP 2: Design a study and collect data.   In 2011, an article published by the medical journal *Gut—An International Journal of Gastroenterology and Hepatology* (Sonoda et al.) reported the results of a study conducted in Japan in which a dog was tested to see whether she could detect colorectal cancer. The dog used was an eight-year-old black Labrador named Marine. (As her name might suggest, she was originally trained for water rescues.)

The study was designed so that the dog first smelled a bag that had been breathed into by a patient with colorectal cancer. This was the standard that the dog would use to judge the other bags. Marine then smelled the breath in five different bags from five different patients, only one of which contained breath from a colorectal cancer patient (not the same as the original patient); the others contained breath from noncancer patients. The dog was then trained to sit next to the bag which she thought contained breath from a cancer patient (i.e., had the cancer scent). If she sat down next to the correct bag, she was rewarded with a tennis ball.

Marine completed 33 attempts of this experimental procedure, with a different set of five patients each time: four noncancer patients and one cancer patient. And, each time, whether or not she correctly identified the bag with the breath of the cancer patient was recorded.

THINK ABOUT IT

What are the observational units in this scenario? What is the variable? Is the variable categorical or quantitative? If categorical, is it binary?

The observational units are Marine's 33 attempts. (Notice, $n = 33$, indicating that 33 measurements were taken. If you incorrectly consider "Marine" as the observational unit, this would imply $n = 1$.) The variable is whether or not she identifies the correct bag, and this is a categorical and binary variable. Also note that order in which she sniffed the bags was randomly determined each time. We will use Marine's results to investigate how often dogs can successfully detect a patient with cancer by smelling their breath, in the long run.

Let's first consider whether Marine performed significantly better than random chance if she was simply guessing among the five bags. We can state our hypotheses as follows (where π represents her long-run proportion of times the cancer patient is correctly identified):

Null hypothesis (H_0): Marine is randomly guessing among the five bags ($\pi = 0.20$).

Alternative hypothesis (H_a): Marine's ability to detect cancer is better than random guessing ($\pi > 0.20$).

THINK ABOUT IT

Why do we set π to be 0.20 under the null? Why don't we set the long-run proportion of times the cancer patient is correctly identified to 0.50 to represent simply guessing?

Because Marine is choosing between five bags, she has a 1 in 5 chance, or 0.20, probability of correctly identifying the cancer patient if she is simply guessing.

STEP 3: Explore the data. In her 33 attempts, Marine correctly identified the bag containing the breath of the cancer patient 30 times ($\hat{p} = 30/33 \approx 0.909$). This result is definitely in the direction of the research conjecture that dogs can sniff out cancer!

STEP 4: Draw inferences beyond the data. But what does this tell us about Marine's underlying probability of identifying the breath of the cancer patient? We could first consider that she was randomly guessing among the five bags. Figure 3.1 displays the results from the **One Proportion** applet.

We see that 0.909 is not only in the tail of this null distribution, it is way beyond these 1,000 simulated proportions! In fact, a sample proportion of 0.909 is more than 10 [$z = (0.909 - 0.20)/0.07 \approx 10.13$] standard deviations away from the hypothesized probability of 0.20! Therefore the sample provides extremely strong evidence that π, the probability that Marine correctly identifies the cancer patient, is greater than 0.20.

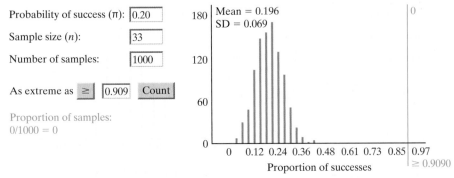

FIGURE 3.1 Estimating a p-value from simulating samples of 33 attempts with $\pi = 0.20$ and counting the number of repetitions where the simulated sample proportion was 0.909 or higher.

So what is her long-run proportion of correct identifications? We suspect it's much closer to 0.90 than to 0.20, but what about other values? Is it plausible that Marine's probability is actually 0.70, but she had a lucky day? In other words, would it be surprising to find $\hat{p} \approx 0.909$ if $\pi = 0.70$? Well, let's test whether these sample data provide convincing evidence that π differs from 0.70. For this test, we have turned the question around and simply want to know if $\pi = 0.70$ or not, a two-sided test. See Figure 3.2.

 3.1.1

THINK ABOUT IT

Based on the two-sided p-value estimated in Figure 3.2, what would you conclude about whether or not Marine's long-run proportion of correct identifications equals 0.70? How are you deciding whether the p-value is small enough?

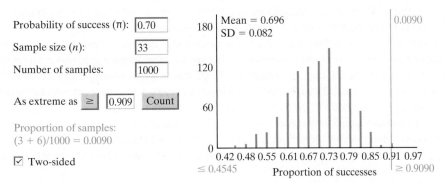

FIGURE 3.2 Estimating a p-value from simulating samples of 33 attempts from a process with a long-run proportion of success equal to 0.70.

Most statisticians would consider a p-value of 0.009 to be convincing evidence against the null hypothesis. Therefore we have strong evidence that Marine's probability of correctly identifying the cancer patient is not equal to 0.70.

So what about 0.80? Do you think a sample proportion of 0.909 is unlikely to arise from a process with $\pi = 0.80$?

THINK ABOUT IT

What will be different about the null distribution now? Will we have stronger or weaker evidence against this null hypothesis ($\pi = 0.80$) than Figure 3.2?

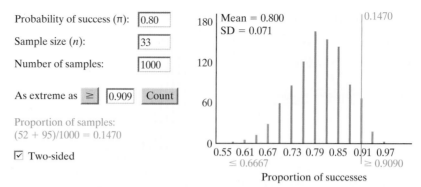

FIGURE 3.3 Estimating a p-value from simulating samples of 33 attempts from a process with a long-run proportion of success equal to 0.80.

As you can see in Figure 3.3, when we increased the probability of success in the null hypothesis and moved it closer to our sample proportion, we got a larger p-value. (This is consistent with the effect of the difference between the observed proportion value and the conjectured probability value that we saw in Section 1.4.) This p-value of 0.147 would not be considered strong evidence against the null hypothesis. From this we would conclude that 0.80 is a **plausible value** for Marine's long-run proportion of success. We haven't *proven* that π equals 0.80 but we can say that we don't have convincing evidence against that value.

THINK ABOUT IT

Now that we have decided that 0.80 is a plausible value for Marine's probability of successfully detecting the cancer patient, are there other values that are plausible as well?

Note that 0.80 was smaller than our sample proportion of 0.909 and was found to be plausible. But 0.70 was not a plausible value for Marine's probability. Now we are interested in finding other plausible values for π. We would like some way of deciding which values are plausible and which are not. In this case, we are less interested in assessing the strength of evidence against one particular hypothesized probability, but we are more interested in making a decision as to which values we will consider plausible. To do this, we can specify a significance level. Remember from Section 2.3 that a significance level is the value used as a criterion for deciding how small a p-value needs to be to provide convincing evidence against the null hypothesis. The most common significance level used is 0.05. So any hypothesized probability that produces a two-sided p-value larger than 0.05 will be considered plausible, and any hypothesized probability with a two-sided p-value less than or equal to 0.05 will not be considered plausible.

KEY IDEA

We will consider a value of the parameter to be plausible if the two-sided p-value for testing that parameter value is larger than the level of significance.

So if we use 0.05 as our significance level, where is the boundary between plausible and not plausible for Marine's probability? In other words, for what hypothesized value of π does our two-sided p-value change from being larger than 0.05 to smaller than 0.05? From our work above, we know one of these boundaries is somewhere between 0.70 and 0.80.

Testing a null probability value of 0.79, we find a two-sided p-value of 0.131, so we include 0.79 in our list of plausible values. Testing the value 0.78, we find a two-sided p-value of 0.097 and include 0.78 in our list of plausible values. Testing the value of 0.77 we again get a p-value larger than 0.05 (0.066) and thus include 0.77 in our list of plausible values. Finally, testing the value of 0.76 we get a p-value of 0.044. Because this p-value is less than our significance value of 0.05 we conclude that the data provide convincing evidence that Marine's probability of success is *not* 0.76. Thus we have found 0.77 to be a lower bound for Marine's interval of plausible values. It should be noted that as these p-values were found using simulations, they will most likely vary slightly each time the simulation is run. This may lead to a slight change in the final interval of plausible values.

What about values larger than 0.80? We know any probability close to 0.909 will also be plausible. What about values on the other side of 0.909? It's possible that Marine actually performed below her true long-run proportion on this day. You can see the results for testing some probability values larger than 0.909 in Table 3.1.

TABLE 3.1 Results of testing different values of probabilities under the null hypothesis

Probability under the null	0.93	0.94	0.95	0.96	0.97	0.98	0.99
(Two-sided) p-value	0.501	0.447	0.227	0.144	0.076	0.028	0.004
Decision at a 0.05 significance level	Do not reject null	Do not reject null	Do not reject null	Do not reject null	Do not reject null	Reject null	Reject null
Plausible value of π?	Yes	Yes	Yes	Yes	Yes	No	No

Putting these results together, we would say any value between 0.77 and 0.97 is a plausible value for Marine's probability, π. In other words, we think our sample proportion of 0.909 arose randomly from a process with a long-run proportion of success between 0.77 and 0.97.

If we zoomed in even more closely on the two boundaries corresponding to our level of significance, we would find results as in Table 3.2.

TABLE 3.2 Results of testing different values of probabilities under the null

Probability under null	0.759	0.760	0.761	0.762		0.973	0.974	0.975	0.976
p-value	0.042	0.043	0.063	0.063	....	0.059	0.054	0.049	0.044
Plausible?	No	No	Yes	Yes	.... Yes	Yes	Yes	No	No

So, a more precise statement of the interval for estimating Marine's probability of success is 0.761 to 0.974, also written as (0.761, 0.974). This interval estimates the long-run proportion of times that Marine correctly identifies the cancer patient. This interval is called a *confidence interval for* π. Because we used 5% as our significance level to decide whether or not to consider the value under the null hypothesis to be plausible, our interval of 0.761 to 0.974 is called a 95% confidence interval, where the 95% comes from 100% minus the significance level of 5%. This 95% is called the **confidence level**.

 3.1.2

> **KEY IDEA**
>
> The interval of *plausible* values is also called a **95% confidence interval for** π. Why is this called *95% confidence*? This corresponds to the 5% (0.05) significance level that was used to decide whether there was enough evidence against a hypothesized value. Notice that 95% and 5% add up to give 100%. The 95% is called the **confidence level**, and is a measure of how confident we are about our interval estimate of the parameter. In this case, we are 95% confident that the long-run proportion of times Marine correctly identifies the cancer patient is in the interval that we found.

STEP 5: Formulate conclusions. To interpret these results, we state that we are 95% confident that Marine's probability of correctly picking the bag with breath from the cancer patient from among five bags is between 0.761 and 0.974. Notice that this is a much stronger statement than our initial significance test, which concluded simply that Marine's probability was larger than 0.20.

EFFECT OF CONFIDENCE LEVEL

THINK ABOUT IT

If we increase the confidence level from 95% to 99%, what do you think would happen to the interval of plausible values for the parameter?

The confidence level of 95% gives some indication of how sure we are that we have captured the actual value of the parameter in our interval. If we want to be more sure (i.e., more confident) that our interval contains the parameter value, our interval of plausible values for the parameter should be wider. To obtain a wider interval of plausible values, we need to make it harder to reject the values of the parameter specified by the null hypothesis—so use a smaller significance level. More specifically, if we want the confidence level to be 99%, we should use a 1% significance level. Examining the results in Table 3.3 for plausible values of Marine's long-run proportion of success, we now look for values that correspond to two-sided p-values larger than 0.01.

TABLE 3.3 Results of testing different values of probabilities under the null

Probability under null	0.70	0.71	0.72	...	0.97	0.98	0.99
p-value	0.007	0.011	0.018	...	0.076	0.028	0.004

Thus a 99% confidence interval for Marine's long-run proportion of success extends from 0.71 to 0.98. Notice that, as expected, when the confidence level is higher, the interval of plausible values for the parameter is wider.

KEY IDEA

As the confidence level increases, the *width* of the confidence interval also increases.

The correspondence between tests and intervals

3.1.3

Confidence intervals and tests of significance generally give complementary information. Values that are not considered plausible by the (two-sided) test of significance should not be contained in the corresponding confidence interval (confidence level = 100% − level of significance). Because 0.50 is not inside the confidence interval, this matches the test. It is not "further evidence against the null" but confirms that the calculations agree. The confidence interval then gives us additional information in telling us how large the proportion is. (See FAQ 3.1.1.)

FAQ 3.1.1   www.wiley.com/college/tintle

Interval or test or both?

STEP 6: Look back and ahead.   From our study we have strong evidence that Marine can correctly identify the cancer patient more than 20% of the time, leading us to believe Marine can reliably detect cancer in a patient by smelling a bag of their breath. We are 95% confident the long-run proportion of times that Marine can correctly identify the cancer patient by smelling their breath is between 0.761 and 0.974. It is important to keep in mind the limitations in this study. For one, the results really only apply to Marine. We should be cautious in generalizing this behavior to dogs in general, at least until we know more about Marine. Although if we did see similar success probabilities in other dogs, especially across breeds, this would be very compelling. Further studies should include not only different breeds of dogs but also different kinds of cancer. It is also not clear how practical this method of smelling breaths for identifying cancer is in general and whether five bags is a reasonable comparison group.

Kissing Right?

Most people are right handed, and even the right eye is dominant for most people. Developmental biologists have suggested that late-stage human embryos tend to turn their heads to the right. In a study reported in *Nature* (2003), German bio-psychologist Onur Güntürkün conjectured that this tendency to turn to the right manifests itself in other ways as well, so he studied kissing couples to see which side they leaned their heads to while kissing. He and his researchers observed kissing couples in public places such as airports, train stations, beaches, and parks. They were careful not to include couples who were holding objects such as luggage that might have affected which direction they turned. For each kissing couple observed, the researchers noted whether the couple leaned their heads to the right or to the left. They observed 124 couples, ages 13 to 70 years.

1. Identify the observational units in this study.
2. Identify the variable recorded in this study. Classify it as categorical or quantitative.

You will first use Güntürkün's data to test his conjecture that kissing couples tend to lean their heads to the right. Use the symbol π to denote the proportion of all kissing couples in these countries that lean their heads to the right.

3. Is π a parameter or a statistic? Explain how you are deciding.
4. Do we know the exact value of π based on the observed data? Explain.
5. State the appropriate null and alternative hypotheses, both in words and in terms of the parameter π, for testing the conjecture that kissing couples tend to lean their heads to the right more often than by random chance.

Of the 124 couples observed, 80 leaned their heads to the right while kissing.

6. Calculate the sample proportion of the observed couples who leaned their heads to the right while kissing. Also indicate the symbol used to denote this value.
7. Conduct a simulation analysis (using the **One Proportion** applet) to assess the strength of evidence that the sample data provide for Güntürkün's conjecture that kissing couples tend to lean their heads to the right more often than they would by random chance. Report the approximate p-value and summarize your conclusion about this strength of evidence.

Your simulation analysis should convince you that the sample data provide very strong evidence to believe that kissing couples lean their heads to the right more than half the time in the long run. That leads to a natural follow-up question: How much more than half the time? In other words, we have strong evidence that the long-run proportion of kissing couples who lean to the right is greater than 1/2, but can we now estimate the value for that probability? We will do this by testing many different (null) values for the probability that a couple leans to the right when kissing.

8. Now test whether the data provide evidence that the probability that a couple leans their heads to the right while kissing (π) is different from 0.60. Use the **One Proportion** applet to determine the p-value for testing the null value of 0.60. Report what you changed in the applet and report your p-value.

THINK ABOUT IT

What kind of test are we conducting if we want to determine whether the population parameter is different from a hypothesized value—a one-sided test or a two-sided test?

Remember from Section 1.4 that if we don't have a specific direction we are testing, greater than or less than, we need to use a two-sided test of significance. If you used a one-sided alternative in #8, determine the two-sided p-value now by checking the **Two-sided** box.

Recall from Section 2.3 that we can specify a *level of significance* in order to decide whether the p-value is small. For example, we can say a p-value of 0.05 or less is strong evidence against the null hypothesis and in favor of the alternative hypothesis. Thus, we can *reject* the null hypothesis when the p-value is less than or equal to 0.05. Otherwise, when the p-value is greater than 0.05, we do not have strong enough evidence against the null hypothesis and so we consider the null value to be *plausible* for the parameter.

KEY IDEA

We will consider a value of the parameter to be plausible if the two-sided p-value for testing that parameter value is larger than the level of significance.

9. Is the p-value for testing the null value of 0.60 less than 0.05? Can the value 0.60 be rejected, or is the value 0.60 plausible for the probability that a couple leans their heads to the right while kissing?

The p-value you found in the previous question should not have been smaller than 0.05. Hence, you do not reject the null hypothesis at the 0.05 level of significance and therefore you do not reject 0.60 as a plausible value for π. Thus, it is plausible (i.e., believable) that the probability a kissing couple leans their heads to the right is 0.60.

10. Does this mean that you've *proven* that exactly 60% of kissing couples lean right? Why or why not?

Because there are still other plausible values, now we want to "zoom in" on which values for the probability are plausible and which can be rejected at the 0.05 significance level.

11. Use the applet to test the probability values given in the following table.
   - Each time, change the **Probability of success** to match the value that you are testing (keeping the observed sample proportion that you count beyond the same).
   - Everything else should stay the same; press **Draw Samples** and then **Count** to see the new two-sided p-value (with the **Two-sided** box checked). You can also check the **Show sliders** box and double click on the orange value to change the value of π and press Enter.

Probability under H_0	0.54	0.55	0.56	0.57	0.58	0.59	0.60
(Two-sided) p-value							
Reject or plausible?							

Probability under H_0	0.70	0.71	0.72	0.73	0.74	0.75	0.76
(Two-sided) p-value							
Reject or plausible?							

12. Using a 0.05 significance level and your results from #11, provide a list of plausible values for π, the long-run proportion of kissing couples who lean their heads to the right.

This list of values represents an interval containing all values between two *endpoints*.

> **KEY IDEA**
>
> The interval of *plausible* values that you wrote down in #12 is also called a **95% confidence interval for π**. Why is this called *95% confidence*? This corresponds to the 5% (0.05) significance level that was used to decide whether there was enough evidence against a hypothesized value. Notice that 95% and 5% add up to give 100%. The 95% is called the **confidence level**, and is a measure of how confident we are about our interval estimate of the parameter. In this case, we are 95% confident that the population proportion of all couples who lean their heads to the right while kissing is in the interval that you found.

13. Does your 95% confidence interval from #12 include the value of 0.50? Does it include the value 0.60? Explain how your answers relate to the significance test and p-value that you calculated in #7 and #8.

14. Now suppose we were to use a significance level of 0.01 instead of 0.05 to decide whether or not to reject the corresponding null hypothesis for each listed value of π. How would you expect the interval of plausible values to change: wider, narrower, or no change? Explain your reasoning.

15. Implement the 0.01 significance level to determine plausible values for the population proportion of all kissing couples that lean their heads to the right. (*Hint:* Start with the null values listed in the table in #11, although you might have to test more null values as well. You can also change the success probability on the slider box by clicking on the bar and then using the arrow keys to move the slider value left and right.) Report the interval of plausible values.

16. How confident are you about the interval of plausible values that you listed in #15?

17. What is the primary difference between the 95% confidence interval reported in #12 and the 99% confidence interval reported in #15? Which interval is wider? Is this consistent with what you predicted in #14?

18. How would you expect a 90% confidence interval to compare to the 95% and 99% confidence intervals? Explain.

> **KEY IDEA**
>
> As the confidence level increases, the *width* of the confidence interval also increases.

You should have found very strong evidence, based on a small p-value, that a majority of kissing couples in the population lean their heads to the right. Moreover, your confidence intervals, which provide plausible values of the population proportion that lean to the right, contain only values above 0.50, confirming the conclusion made from the p-value.

In fact, confidence intervals and tests of significance generally give complementary information. Values that are not considered plausible by the (two-sided) test of significance should not be contained in the corresponding confidence interval (confidence level = 100% − level of significance). Because 0.50 is not inside the confidence interval, this matches the test. It is not "further evidence against the null" but confirms that your calculations agree. The confidence interval then gives us additional information in how large this majority is.

SECTION 3.1 Summary

Once a sample proportion has been determined to differ significantly from a hypothesized value for the long-run process probability, a typical next step is to estimate the value of the long-run process probability with an interval of values, the **confidence interval** for the parameter. Or our research question may be phrased such that a confidence interval is the more appropriate tool (e.g., "what is the probability that...") in the first place.

- This interval can be thought of as containing plausible values of the parameter.
- A parameter value is considered to be plausible if it does not produce a small (two-sided) p-value when tested in a null hypothesis.
- With this approach, the **confidence level** of an interval is equal to 1 minus the significance level used for determining rejection/plausibility.
  - Using a larger confidence level produces a wider interval of plausible values.
- Confidence intervals and tests of significance generally give complementary information. That is, null hypothesis values that can be rejected will not be in the confidence interval and vice versa.

SECTION 3.2

2SD AND THEORY-BASED CONFIDENCE INTERVALS FOR A SINGLE PROPORTION

INTRODUCTION

In the last section we explored a method for estimating a confidence interval for a long-run proportion or population proportion. We found the confidence interval by conducting repeated tests of significance and changing the probability specified by the null hypothesis to see whether or not the hypothesized value was plausible. As suggested in the overview of this chapter, there are other ways to approximate a confidence interval. In this section, we will explore how we can use the idea of standardization to construct confidence intervals. In particular, we will see that a method we call the "two standard deviation method" (or 2SD method) gives us an approximate 95% confidence interval.

Whereas the 2SD method is typically based on simulation, in this section we will also see a theory-based approach to generating confidence intervals, which avoids the need to use simulation altogether. The theory-based approach also allows us to easily use any confidence level we would like, not just 95%.

The Affordable Care Act

Example 3.2

A November 23–24, 2013, Gallup poll based on a random sample of 1,034 adults asked whether the new healthcare law (the Affordable Care Act) had affected the respondents or their family. Sixty-nine percent responded that the law had no effect. Gallup (www.gallup.com) reports that interviews are "conducted with respondents on landline telephones and cellular phones, with interviews conducted in Spanish for respondents who are primarily Spanish-speaking … Landline and cell telephone numbers are selected using random-digit-dial methods. Landline respondents are chosen at random within each household on the basis of which member had the most recent birthday."

You will see numerous differences between this sampling method and that of the *Literary Digest* that will be discussed in Section 3.5. Organizations like Gallup are constantly revising methods to ensure representation of women, minority groups, and younger individuals. So we have some faith that this sample will indeed be representative of all American adults.

> **THINK ABOUT IT**
>
> So is it sufficient to announce that 69% of adult Americans have not felt any impact from the Affordable Care Act?

Although we expect the population proportion (call this π) to be close to 0.69, we know that a different random sample would likely lead to a different sample proportion and that our sample proportion can't be expected to exactly match the population proportion, just from the random chance in the sampling process. Our goal with a confidence interval is to account for the likely size of this random sampling error. In this context, we aren't necessarily interested in deciding whether π is larger than say 0.5, but our goal is to give an interval of plausible values for π.

We could repeat the procedure we used in Section 3.1 to create an interval of plausible values for the proportion of the population of adult Americans who would choose "no effect." Table 3.4 shows the results using a level of significance of 0.05.

TABLE 3.4   Finding an interval of plausible values using 0.05 as the significance level

Probability under null	0.659	0.660	**0.661**	...	**0.717**	0.718	0.719
(Two-sided) p-value	0.0388	0.0453	**0.0514**	...	**0.0517**	0.0458	0.0365
Plausible value (0.05)?	No	No	**Yes**	...	**Yes**	No	No

This method gives us an interval of (0.661, 0.717), indicating that we are 95% confident that the proportion of all American adults who had not felt any impact from the Affordable Care Act was between 0.661 and 0.717. In other words, we are about 95% confident that between 66.1% and 71.7% of all adult Americans had not felt any impact from the Affordable Care Act in November 2013. Notice that the *midpoint* of this interval, $(0.661 + 0.717)/2 = 0.689$, is essentially the observed value of the sample proportion who said no impact. The width of our interval is $0.717 - 0.661 = 0.056$. Half of the width of our confidence interval, $0.056/2 = 0.028$, is called the **_margin of error_**. We can use our sample proportion and the margin of error to write our confidence interval as 0.690 ± 0.028. Also notice that we are distinguishing between saying "95% confidence" and "95% chance." (See FAQ 3.2.1.)

 3.2.1

FAQ 3.2.1	www.wiley.com/college/tintle

What does 95% confidence mean?

You will see this general form of writing a confidence interval as the observed statistic plus/minus a measure of the accuracy of the statistic with different data types in future chapters.

The plausible values method (Section 3.1) for determining a confidence interval requires conducting quite a few null distribution simulations to zoom in on the endpoints of the confidence interval. What we would like is a simpler method for estimating the margin of error.

 3.2.2

A shortcut is provided by noticing that null distributions often have the familiar symmetric, bell-shaped distribution that we have seen before, regardless of the null probability used in the simulation. We saw in Chapter 1 that with such null distributions most random samples (about 95%) generate a value of the statistic that falls within 2 standard deviations (2SDs) of the mean of the null distribution. Recall that we considered a statistic to be in the tail of the distribution if it was more than 2 standard deviations from the mean. (See Figure 3.4.)

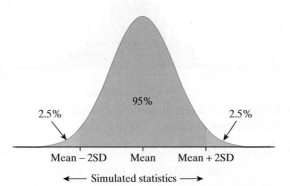

FIGURE 3.4   When a null distribution is bell-shaped, about 95% of the statistics will fall within 2 standard deviations of the mean with the other 5% outside this region.

> **KEY IDEA**
>
> When a distribution is bell-shaped, as the null distribution is for this study, approximately 95% of the statistics in the null distribution will fall within 2 standard deviations of the mean. This implies that 95% of sample proportions will fall within 2 standard deviations of the parameter (π), which means that π is within 2 standard deviations of the observed sample proportion for 95% of all samples.

We can extend this reasoning to generate a confidence interval for a long-run proportion or population proportion. In particular, a parameter value is considered plausible if it is *not* more than 2 standard deviations from the observed value of the statistic. (This should roughly correspond to having a two-sided p-value less than 0.05.) Thus, another way to construct a 95% confidence interval is to include all values of π that are within 2 standard deviations of the observed sample proportion $\hat{p}$.

> **KEY IDEA**
>
> We can construct a 95% confidence interval of plausible values for a parameter by including all values that fall within 2 standard deviations of the sample statistic. This method is only valid when the null distribution follows a bell-shaped, symmetric distribution. We call this the **2SD method**. Thus we can present the 95% confidence interval for the long-run proportion (or population proportion), π, in symbols as
>
> $$\hat{p} \pm 2 \times SD(\hat{p})$$
>
> where $\hat{p}$ is the sample proportion and $SD(\hat{p})$ is the standard deviation of the null distribution of sample proportions. The value of $2 \times SD$, which represents half the width of the confidence interval, is called the **margin of error** for 95% confidence intervals.

But, how do we estimate the standard deviation of the distribution of sample proportions? There are actually several reasonable approaches. One is to simulate just one null distribution, read off its standard deviation, and use that value. But we need a value of π to conduct the simulation. In Chapter 1, you may have noticed that the standard deviation of the sample proportion is largest when $\pi = 0.50$. So using 0.50 in our simulation (Figure 3.5) should give us an upper bound on the standard deviation.

FIGURE 3.5 Null distribution of sample proportions for Affordable Care Act with $\pi = 0.50$.

Using 0.016 as the standard deviation, we could construct our confidence interval to be

$$0.69 \pm 2(0.016) = 0.69 \pm 0.032$$

or approximately (0.658, 0.722). Notice this interval is similar (but wider) compared to what we found with the plausible values method. The main distinction between the methods is that the plausible values method will allow the standard deviation to change when different values of π are utilized. When the sample size is large, you won't see much difference between these methods, with the 2SD method being much more convenient.

Another method for estimating the standard deviation of sample proportions is to use the formula we saw in Chapter 1: $SD(\hat{p}) = \sqrt{\pi(1 - \pi)/n}$. But, again, what to use for the value of π? We could substitute the conservative value of 0.50, giving us $0.50/\sqrt{n}$. In fact, when we apply the 2SD method with this standard deviation, our margin of error simplifies to $1/\sqrt{n}$!

More generally, we can substitute the observed sample proportion in for π, giving us the "standard error of $\hat{p}$," $SE(\hat{p}) = \sqrt{\hat{p}(1 - \hat{p})/n}$. This allows the standard deviation we use to slightly differ depending on the size of the sample proportion.

THEORY-BASED APPROACH

Regardless of our choice for how to estimate the SD of the sample proportion, one limitation to the 2SD method it is only applies to 95% confidence. A more general method, valid for any confidence level, is to estimate the value of the parameter with

$$\text{statistic} \pm \text{multiplier} \times (\text{SD of statistic})$$

or, in this example of estimating a population proportion, with

$$\hat{p} \pm \text{multiplier} \times \sqrt{\hat{p}(1 - \hat{p})/n}.$$

When we want a 95% confidence interval, the multiplier is approximately 2, hence the use of the name "2SD method." If we want to change the confidence level, we change the multiplier. When the distribution of the sample proportion is approximately normal, this multiplier will come from the standard normal distribution (with mean 0 and standard deviation 1). In Figure 3.6 we show corresponding multipliers for different confidence levels. For example, 90% of observations in a normal distribution should fall within 1.645 standard deviations of the mean of the distribution.

 3.2.3

> **Definition**
>
> An estimate of the standard deviation of a statistic, based on sample data, is called the **standard error (SE)** of the statistic. In this case $\sqrt{\hat{p}(1 - \hat{p})/n}$ is the standard error of a sample proportion $\hat{p}$.

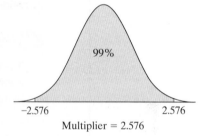

−1.645 1.645	−1.960 1.960	−2.576 2.576
Multiplier = 1.645	Multiplier = 1.960	Multiplier = 2.576

FIGURE 3.6 Change in confidence interval multiplier with change in confidence level.

We learn several things from these graphs:

- You may notice that we can be a bit more precise than "2" with 95% confidence; that actually corresponds to a multiplier of 1.96.
- The multiplier increases as the confidence level increases. This agrees with what we learned in Section 3.1 about the effect of confidence level on the width of the interval.

So for 95% confidence, this formula gives us the interval $0.69 \pm 1.96\sqrt{0.69(1 - 0.69)/1{,}034}$ or 0.69 ± 0.028 or $(0.662, 0.718)$. This is the formula used by the **Theory-Based Inference** applet by checking the **Confidence interval** box and pressing **Calculate CI** (Figure 3.7).

FIGURE 3.7 Using the **Theory-Based Inference** applet we can find a 95% confidence interval when the sample size is 1,034 and the sample proportion is 0.690.

3.2.4

As with all theory-based approaches, this method predicts the confidence interval you would have obtained from simulation. This approach uses the standard error formula to estimate the standard deviation of the sample proportions rather than carrying out a simulation to estimate that standard deviation. In fact, this approach makes no initial ballpark guesses for π. The advantage to using the theory-based approach over the 2SD method is that we can change the confidence level to anything we would like, not just 95%. The output shown in Figure 3.8 shows the 90% and 99% confidence intervals.

confidence level [90] %   confidence level [99] %

(0.6663, 0.7137)   (0.6530, 0.7270)

FIGURE 3.8   Using a theory-based confidence interval allows us to easily change the confidence level.

Two things to observe about these intervals:

- The midpoint of each interval equals 0.690, the value of the observed sample proportion.
- The larger the confidence level, the wider the interval (smaller lower endpoint, larger upper endpoint).

In the next section, you will explore other factors that affect these interval calculations in general.

As we learned in Chapter 1, theory-based methods are only accurate when certain validity conditions are met.

VALIDITY CONDITION

The theory-based approach for finding a confidence interval for π (called a **one-sample z-interval**) is considered valid if there are at least 10 observational units in each category of the categorical variable (i.e., at least 10 successes and at least 10 failures).

In this study, the validity condition is met because the sample included 713 who said "no effect" and 321 who cited an effect, which are both considerably greater than 10.

EXPLORATION | American Exceptionalism

3.2

The Gallup organization conducted a survey with a random sample of 1,019 adult Americans on December 10–12, 2010. They found that 80% of the respondents agreed with the statement that the United States has a unique character that makes it the greatest country in the world.

1. Identify the population and sample in this survey.

   Population:

   Sample:

2. Is it reasonable to believe that the sample of 1,019 adult Americans is representative of the larger population? Explain why or why not.

3. Explain why 80% is a statistic and not a parameter. What symbol would you use to represent it?

4. Identify (in words) the parameter that the Gallup organization was interested in estimating.

5. Is it reasonable to conclude that exactly 80% of all adult Americans agree with the statement about American exceptionalism? Explain why or why not.

6. Although we expect π to be close to 0.80, we realize there may be other plausible values for the population proportion as well. First consider the value of 0.775. Is this a plausible

value for π? Use the **One Proportion** applet to simulate random samples of 1,019 people from such a population. (*Hint*: Keep in mind that 0.775 is what we are assuming for the population proportion and 0.80 is the observed sample proportion.) What do you estimate for the two-sided p-value? Would you reject or fail to reject the null hypothesis at the 5% level of significance?

7. Also check the **Summary Stats** box and report the mean and standard deviation of this null distribution.

8. Now consider 0.50. Is this a plausible value for π? Repeat #6 and record the mean and standard deviation for this null distribution as well.

Clearly 0.50 is going to be "too far" from $\hat{p} = 0.80$ to be plausible. But how far is too far? We could use the plausible values method from Section 3.1 to produce a confidence interval for the proportion of all adult Americans who agree with the statement. But that approach is somewhat cumbersome and time-intensive, so we'll now learn some shortcut approaches.

9. Reconsider our first guess of $\pi = 0.775$. How many standard deviations is 0.80 from 0.775? (*Hint*: Standardize the value by looking at the difference between 0.775 and 0.80 and divide by the standard deviation you found in #7.)

You should notice that 0.775 and 0.80 are about 2 standard deviations apart AND that the two-sided p-value is around 0.05, so this value (0.775) is close to the edge of values that can be considered plausible for π. Values between 0.80 and 0.775 are considered plausible and values smaller than 0.775, or more than 2 standard deviations below 0.80, will not be plausible values for the population proportion.

KEY IDEA

When a distribution is bell-shaped, as your null distribution should be for this study, approximately 95% of the statistics in the null distribution will fall within 2 standard deviations of the mean. This implies that 95% of sample proportions will fall within 2 standard deviations of the parameter (π), which means that π is within 2 standard deviations of the observed sample proportion for 95% of all samples.

We can then extend this idea to construct a 95% confidence interval.

KEY IDEA

We can construct a 95% confidence interval of plausible values for a parameter by including all values that fall within 2 standard deviations of the sample statistic. This method is only valid when the null distribution follows a bell-shaped, symmetric distribution. We call this the *2SD method*. Thus we can present the 95% confidence interval for the long-run proportion (or population proportion), π, in symbols as

$$\hat{p} \pm 2 \times SD(\hat{p})$$

where $\hat{p}$ is the sample proportion and $SD(\hat{p})$ is the standard deviation of the null distribution of sample proportions. The value of $2 \times SD$, which represents half the width of the confidence interval, is called the *margin of error* for 95% confidence intervals.

THINK ABOUT IT

So how do we find the standard deviation to use for the 2SD method?

10. How did the standard deviations you found in #7 (with $\pi = 0.775$) and in #8 (with $\pi = 0.50$) compare?

You should see that the standard deviation changes slightly when we change π, but not by much. We saw in Chapter 1 that the variability in the sample proportions is in fact largest when $\pi = 0.50$. So one approach would be to carry out one simulation (with lots of trials) using $\pi = 0.50$ and use that value of the standard deviation to calculate the margin of error.

11. Determine a 95% confidence interval using the 2SD method:

    a. First calculate 2 × (standard deviation for your null distribution of sample proportions) using 0.5 in the simulation to estimate the SD. (This is the margin of error.)

    b. Use this SD to produce a 95% confidence interval for π. (*Hint:* Subtract the margin of error from $\hat{p}$ to determine the lower endpoint of the interval and then add the margin of error to $\hat{p}$ to determine the upper endpoint of the interval.)

    c. Interpret the confidence interval: You are 95% confident that *what* is between what two values?

One limitation to this method is that it only applies for 95% confidence. What if we wanted to be 90% or 99% confident instead? We can extend this 2SD method to a more general theory-based approach. As we saw in Chapter 1, we don't always need to simulate a null distribution—not if we can accurately predict what would happen if we were to simulate. Instead, we can predict the standard deviation by the formula $\sqrt{\pi(1 - \pi)/n}$. But when constructing a confidence interval, we don't have a hypothesized value of π, so to estimate this standard deviation, we will substitute the observed sample proportion.

12. Calculate the standard error for this study. How does it compare to the standard deviations you found in #7 and #8?

So a more general formula for using the 2SD method to estimate a population proportion would be

$$\hat{p} \pm 2\sqrt{\hat{p}(1 - \hat{p})/n}.$$

But then how do we change the confidence level?

The 2SD method was justified by saying 95% of samples yield a sample proportion within 2 standard deviations of the population proportion. If we want to be more confident that the parameter is within our margin of error, we can create a larger margin of error by increasing the multiplier. In fact a multiplier of 2.576 gives us a 99% confidence level, whereas a multiplier of 1.645 gives us only 90% confidence.

13. We will rely on technology to find the multiplier appropriate for our confidence level.

    a. In the **Theory-Based Inference** applet, specify the sample size (n) of 1019 and the sample proportion of 0.80 (or the sample count of 815) and press **Calculate**. (The applet will fill in the count.)

    b. Check the box for **Confidence Interval**, confirm the confidence level is 95% and press **Calculate CI** to generate a theory-based confidence interval. Report the 95% theory-based confidence interval.

14. Is this theory-based confidence interval similar to the one you obtained using the 2SD method?

VALIDITY CONDITION

The theory-based approach for finding a confidence interval for π (called a **one-sample z-interval**) is considered valid if there are at least 10 observational units in each category of the categorical variable (i.e., at least 10 successes and at least 10 failures).

Because we have a large sample size here, the theory-based approach should produce very similar results to the plausible values method and the 2SD method. In such a case, the theory-based approach is often the most convenient, especially if our confidence level is not 95%.

15. Change the confidence level in the applet from 95% to 99% and press the **Calculate CI** button again. Report the 99% confidence interval given by the applet. How does it compare to the 95% interval? (Compare both the midpoint of the interval = (lower endpoint + upper endpoint)/2 and the margin of error = (upper endpoint − lower endpoint)/2.)

SECTION 3.2   Summary

The plausible values method for determining a confidence interval for a parameter reminds us that the confidence interval represents all possible values of the parameter that are considered "plausible" based on not putting the observed statistic too far in the tail of the distribution (two-sided p-value is not small, not below the significance level). However, this method is fairly tedious, because it requires performing many significance tests to determine which parameter values are rejected and which are plausible.

An alternative is to produce a confidence interval using **statistic ± margin of error**.

- This approach is valid when the null distribution is bell-shaped and symmetric.
- The **midpoint** of this confidence interval is the observed value of the sample statistic.
- The **margin of error** for 95% confidence can be approximated as 2 × (SD of the statistic).
  - This corresponds to the prediction that 95% of samples produce a statistic that lies within 2 standard deviations of the underlying parameter.

In this section, our statistic was the sample proportion $\hat{p}$. One way to estimate the SD of the sample proportion is to simulate a null distribution (e.g., for $\pi = 0.50$).

A third approach for determining a confidence interval for a process probability or population proportion uses a **theory-based approach** based on the normal distribution.

- The theory-based approach also uses the form **statistic ± margin of error**.
  - The margin of error can be calculated as multiplier × standard error, which in the case of estimating a population proportion is multiplier × $\sqrt{\hat{p}(1 - \hat{p})/n}$.
- This interval can be calculated with technology, without the need to perform a simulation analysis first.
- This method can be performed for any **confidence level**.
  - The most common confidence level is 95%, followed by 90% and 99%.
  - Increasing the confidence level increases the multiplier and widens the interval.
- The **validity condition** for applying this theory-based approach is that each category (successes, failures) includes at least 10 observations.

Summary of validity conditions for a theory-based interval on a single proportion			
Type of data	**Name of test**	**Applet**	**Validity conditions**
Single binary variable	Theory-based interval for a single proportion (one-proportion z-interval)	One proportion; theory-based inference	At least 10 successes and at least 10 failures in sample

ONE-PROPORTION z-INTERVAL FOR A SINGLE PROPORTION

INTRODUCTION

In Section 3.1 we used the "plausible values" approach to construct an interval of plausible (believable) values for the population parameter. This approach helped you understand which values are plausible values of the unknown parameter and which are not! In the first part of Section 3.2, we looked at a theory-based approach that uses a theoretical probability distribution called the normal distribution to predict the behavior of the standardized statistic for a sample proportion. This method is less tedious and can be used if you have at least ten responses of each kind (10 successes and 10 failures). The theory-based approach for constructing an interval of plausible values for a population proportion or long-run process proportion is referred to as a ***one-sample z-interval*** or ***one-proportion z-interval***. We saw that a general method, valid for any confidence level (not just the 95% level that we approximated with the 2SD method), is to estimate the parameter with

$$\text{statistic} \pm \text{multiplier} \times (\text{SD of statistic})$$

or, more specifically, when estimating a population proportion, by using

$$\hat{p} \pm \text{multiplier} \sqrt{\hat{p}(1 - \hat{p})/n}.$$

Definition

Confidence interval for a population proportion, π:

$$\hat{p} \pm z^* \sqrt{\hat{p}(1 - \hat{p})/n}$$

where $\hat{p}$ denotes the sample proportion, n is the sample size, and z^* represents the critical value from the standard normal distribution for the confidence level desired.

In the previous section, we used a value of 2 as the approximate multiplier for a 95% confidence interval, and let the applet obtain the confidence interval for other desired confidence levels. For the AP exam, you will need to use your calculator or the table on the formula sheet provided to obtain the multiplier yourself and then plug into the formula. You find this multiplier, called the ***critical value***, using the normal distribution. It is often denoted by z^*.

Let us take a look at the steps involved in finding the critical value (z^*) for a 98% confidence interval for π:

STEP 1. Draw a sketch of the standard normal curve and shade the area corresponding to the middle 98% of the distribution. Also, indicate roughly where $-z^*$ and z^* are in your sketch. Note that, for the middle to correspond to 0.98, this implies we want $(1 - 0.98)/2 = 0.01$ of the distribution in each tail.

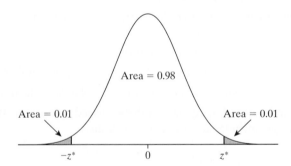

STEP 2.
A. You may use your calculator to find the z^* critical value: When you want to find a z-statistic for a given area under the Standard Normal Distribution ($\mu = 0, \sigma = 1$), you use the *invNorm* command and input the area to the left of the z^* critical value that you are interested in finding.

> ## CALCULATOR HINTS
>
> In confidence interval calculations, sometimes you are looking for only the critical value rather than the entire interval calculation. In this case, you can use the calculator to input a probability and determine the corresponding critical value. For example,
>
> - **TI-84:** invNorm(area: 0.01, μ:0, σ:1), where area refers to the lower tail area (in this case 0.01). invNorm(0.01, 0, 1) $\approx$ −2.326. We use 2.326 as our z^* critical value.
> - **TI-Nspire:** Menu → Statistics → Distribution → Inverse Normal(area: 0.01, μ:0, σ:1) invNorm(0.01, 0, 1) $\approx$ −2.326. We use 2.326 as our z^* critical value.

Or,

B. You may use Table A on the AP formula sheet to find the z^* critical value:
For a 98% confidence interval, the lower tail area is 0.01. Look in the body of Table A (standard normal probabilities) to find the lower tail value closest to 0.01 (.0099), which corresponds to a standardized statistic of −2.33. We use 2.33 as our z^* critical value.

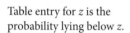

Table entry for z is the probability lying below z.

TABLE A	Standard normal probabilities									
z	.00	.01	.02	.03	.04	.05	.06	.07	.08	.09
−3.4	.0003	.0003	.0003	.0003	.0003	.0003	.0003	.0003	.0003	.0002
−3.3	.0005	.0005	.0005	.0004	.0004	.0004	.0004	.0004	.0004	.0003
−3.2	.0007	.0007	.0006	.0006	.0006	.0006	.0006	.0005	.0005	.0005
−3.1	.0010	.0009	.0009	.0009	.0008	.0008	.0008	.0008	.0007	.0007
−3.0	.0013	.0013	.0013	.0012	.0012	.0011	.0011	.0011	.0010	.0010
−2.9	.0019	.0018	.0018	.0017	.0016	.0016	.0015	.0015	.0014	.0014
−2.8	.0026	.0025	.0024	.0023	.0023	.0022	.0021	.0021	.0020	.0019
−2.7	.0035	.0034	.0033	.0032	.0031	.0030	.0029	.0028	.0027	.0026
−2.6	.0047	.0045	.0044	.0043	.0041	.0040	.0039	.0038	.0037	.0036
−2.5	.0062	.0060	.0059	.0057	.0055	.0054	.0052	.0051	.0049	.0048
−2.4	.0082	.0080	.0078	.0075	.0073	.0071	.0069	.0068	.0066	.0064
−2.3	.0107	.0104	.0102	(.0099)	.0096	.0094	.0091	.0089	.0087	.0084
0.0	0130	0126	0128	0120	0125	0122	0110	0116	0112	0110

Or,

C. You may use Table B on the AP formula sheet to find the z^* critical value:
Recall from Section 2.2, Part 3, that we saw that as the sample size increases (and correspondingly the degrees of freedom increase), the t-distribution becomes almost indistinguishable from the standard normal distribution. This implies that we can use the t-distribution with ∞ degrees of freedom to find our z^* critical value for common confidence levels. Find the

confidence level you want across the bottom of the table. The value above it is the critical value for a *t*-distribution with infinite degrees of freedom, which corresponds to the z^* critical value. Notice that the top row in the table gives the upper tail probability *p*, which would be 0.01 for a 98% confidence interval.

TABLE B *t*-distribution critical values												
	Tail probability *p*											
df	.25	.20	.15	.10	.05	.025	.02	.01	.005	.0025	.001	.0005
1	1.000	1.376	1.963	3.078	6.314	12.71	15.89	31.82	63.66	127.3	318.3	636.3
2	.816	1.061	1.386	1.886	2.920	4.303	4.849	6.965	9.925	14.09	22.33	31.60
.												
.												
.												
100	.677	.845	1.042	1.290	1.660	1.984	2.081	2.364	2.626	2.871	3.174	3.390
1000	.675	.842	1.037	1.282	1.646	1.962	2.056	2.330	2.581	2.813	3.098	3.300
∞	.674	.841	1.036	1.282	1.645	1.960	2.054	**2.326**	2.576	2.807	3.091	3.291
	50%	60%	70%	80%	90%	95%	96%	**98%**	99%	99.5%	99.8%	99.9%
	Confidence level *C*											

Now that you know how to use your calculator, Table A, or Table B to find a critical value, we will look at the work you need to show on the AP Statistics exam when the question asks you to construct a confidence interval for a population proportion or long-run process proportion.

Generation M

Example 3.2.2A

EXAMPLE

The generation of children raised in the 1990s and 2000s has been dubbed Generation M because of the impact of media on their lives. The Kaiser Family Foundation conducted an extensive survey in 2004 that investigated the degree to which American youth aged 8–18 have access to various forms of media. They distributed written questionnaires to a random sample of 2,032 youths in this age range. One of the many questions on the survey asked respondents whether or not they have a television in their bedroom; 68% answered yes. Use the data from this sample to construct a 95% confidence interval for π, the proportion of all American 8- to 18-year-olds (in 2004) who had a television in their bedroom. On the AP exam, you can construct this interval in four logical steps.

> ### THINK ABOUT IT
>
> What is the parameter of interest? In other words, what is the number that we are trying to estimate? What symbol is used to represent this parameter?

1. **Identify the parameter you want to estimate and the theory-based model you will use.** Let π represent the proportion of all American 8- to 18-year-olds who (in 2004) had a television in their bedroom.

    We will use a one-proportion *z*-interval to construct a 95% confidence interval for π.

What are the conditions under which it is valid to use the one-sample *z*-interval? How do you check whether or not they are met?

2. **Verify the validity conditions for the theory-based method you have chosen.**
   Validity conditions for a one-proportion *z*-interval:

   - We need our observations to be representative of all American youth aged 8–18 in 2004 with respect to our variable of interest, whether or not they had a television in their bedroom. Is the population of interest well represented by our sample? We are told that the Kaiser Family Foundation took a random sample of American youth aged 8–18 in 2004, so the sample should be representative of this population.

   - A normal distribution is an appropriate model if there are at least 10 successes and 10 failures in the sample.
     - $n\hat{p} = 0.68(2,032) \approx 1,382$ *and* $n(1 - \hat{p}) = 0.32(2,032) \approx 650$
       Both the number of successes and the number of failures are much greater than 10, so it is reasonable to use a one-proportion *z*-interval.

What is the formula for the confidence interval for the population proportion, π?

3. **Construct the confidence interval, showing the values that you substitute into the formula.** 95% C.I. for π:
   Recall that the confidence interval for a population proportion, π, is given by

   $$\hat{p} \pm z^{*}\sqrt{\hat{p}(1 - \hat{p})/n}$$

   We can substitute the relevant numbers into the formula and calculate the confidence interval as follows:

   $$0.68 \pm 1.960\sqrt{0.68(1 - 0.68)/2,032}$$
   $$(0.66, 0.70)$$

 3.2P2.1

You can find the confidence interval on your calculator but you still need to show the values that you would substitute into the confidence interval formula (as shown above):

- **TI-84:** Stat → Tests → 1-PropInt
- **TI-Nspire:** Menu → Stat → Confidence Intervals → 1-Prop z Interval

How would you interpret this confidence interval (0.66, 0.70)?

4. **Interpret the confidence interval you obtained in the context of the problem.**
   We can be 95% confident that (in 2004) the proportion of all American 8- to 18-year-olds who had a television in their bedroom is captured in the interval (0.66, 0.70), assuming that the sample taken is representative of all American 8- to 18-year-olds in 2004. Said another way, we can be 95% confident that between 66% and 70% of all American 8- to 18-year-olds in 2004 had a television in their bedroom.

 3.2P2.2

3.2P2.3

Possible follow-up questions to a question asking you to construct a confidence interval:

- Explain what is meant in this context by a 95% confidence level.

  If we repeatedly sampled from this population, and for each sample proportion obtained constructed a 95% confidence interval, in the long run 95% of the intervals constructed would succeed in capturing the population parameter, the proportion of all American 8- to 18-year-olds who had a television in their bedroom in 2004.

- A test of significance was conducted to determine whether the proportion of 8- to 18-year-old American youth in 2004 with a television in their bedroom differed from 0.60 at a 0.05 significance level. The p-value for the test was calculated to be approximately zero. Explain how the p-value obtained from the significance test agrees with the 95% confidence interval of (0.66, 0.70) that you obtained.

  With a p-value of approximately zero, we would reject the null hypothesis at a 0.05 level of significance that the proportion of all American 8- to 18-year-olds (in 2004) with a television in their bedroom was 0.60. The confidence interval obtained gives a range of plausible values, with 95% confidence, for the proportion of all American youth aged 8 to 18 years old in 2004 that had a television in their bedroom. Because the interval falls entirely above 0.60, it agrees with the conclusion that 0.60 is not a plausible value for the population proportion of American 8-to 18-year-olds (in 2004) with a television in their bedroom. Confidence intervals and tests of significance generally give complementary information. Values that are not considered plausible by the (two-sided) test of signif icance should not be contained in the corresponding confidence interval (confidence level = 100% − level of significance).

3.2P2.4

 Generation M Revisited

 EXAMPLE

We will now look at how to calculate the sample size necessary so that the margin of er- ror (variability in estimating the population parameter) of the confidence interval we wish to construct is less than or equal to a specified value for a given confidence level. Reconsider the Kaiser Foundation survey that found 68% of a sample of 2,032 American youth had a television in their bedroom. We were able to estimate the population proportion with 95% confidence to be 0.68 ± 0.0203 (the margin of error), for a confidence interval (0.66, 0.70).

Suppose you intend to do a follow-up study to see whether the population proportion today has changed from what the Kaiser Foundation reported in 2004, and you want the mar- gin of error to be no larger than 0.03 or 3 percentage points. That is, you want to estimate the population proportion with a TV in their room to within ±0.03.

THINK ABOUT IT

If you keep the confidence level at 95% and want the margin of error to be no larger than 0.03, will you need a sample size larger or smaller than 2,032, the original study's sample size? How are you deciding?

If the value of the sample proportion from the original study is a reasonable estimate of the population proportion, you won't need as many youth as in the original study (2,032), be- cause the margin of error from the original study's data was 0.0203 and you are now allowing the margin of error to be bigger (at 0.03)—so a smaller sample size will do.

THINK ABOUT IT

If you keep the confidence level at 95%, what size sample will be required to achieve this margin of error? How would you calculate the required sample size?

The calculation for the margin of error for a one-proportion z-interval is

$$z^*\sqrt{\hat{p}(1-\hat{p})/n}$$

We want this value to be no more than 0.03:

$$z^*\sqrt{\hat{p}(1-\hat{p})/n} \leq 0.03$$

We don't know the value of $\hat{p}$, so we can estimate it by either using a value from a previous study (in this case 0.68 would be a reasonable estimate) or by using 0.50 as a conservative estimate, as it will yield the largest sample size for the given confidence level and margin of error, guaranteeing that the margin of error we actually obtain in our sample will be less than or equal to the desired ± 0.03.

Using the 0.68 that the Kaiser Foundation obtained in 2004 and solving for n, we obtain

$$\text{Margin of Error} \leq 0.03$$
$$1.96\sqrt{(0.68)(1-0.68)/n} \leq 0.03$$
$$\sqrt{(0.68)(1-0.68)/n} \leq 0.03/1.96$$
$$(0.68)(1-0.68)/n \leq (0.03/1.96)^2$$
$$(0.68)(1-0.68) \leq n(0.03/1.96)^2$$
$$(0.68)(1-0.68)(1.96/0.03)^2 \leq n$$
$$n \geq 928.8$$
$$n \geq 929$$

Because we can't have part of a person in our sample, we round up (to be conservative) for a minimum sample size of 929 in order to guarantee a margin of error of no more than 0.03 with a confidence level of 95%.

Using the conservative estimate of 0.50 in place of $\hat{p}$, we obtain

$$1.96\sqrt{(0.50)(1-0.50)/n} \leq 0.03$$
$$\sqrt{(0.50)(1-0.50)/n} \leq 0.03/1.96$$
$$(0.50)(1-0.50)/n \leq (0.03/1.96)^2$$
$$(0.50)(1-0.50) \leq n(0.03/1.96)^2$$
$$(0.50)(1-0.50)(1.96/0.03)^2 \leq n$$
$$n \geq 1067.1$$
$$n \geq 1,068$$

With this approach, we would report that the minimum sample size needed for a 95% confidence interval with a margin of error no more than 0.03 for the population proportion with a TV in their room, using 0.50 as our estimate of $\hat{p}$, is 1,068 American youth aged 8–18 years old. This sample size is larger and more conservative than the sample size computed when 0.68 was used as the estimated proportion, but if π differs from 0.50, then if anything, we will have a smaller margin of error.

 3.2P2.5

THINK ABOUT IT

What if you had wanted a 99% confidence interval to have a margin of error of at most 0.03. Would you need a larger or a smaller sample size than when the confidence level is 95%?

KEY IDEA

The general formula for finding the minimum sample size needed for a given confidence level (critical value z^*) and margin of error is

$$n \geq (\hat{p})(1-\hat{p})(z^*/margin\ of\ error)^2$$

As the confidence level increases (for example, from 95% to 99%), the z^* critical value increases (in this case from 1.96 to 2.576), increasing the minimum sample size needed for the specified margin of error. Thus, if you wanted a 99% confidence interval to have a margin of error of at most 0.03, you would need a sample size larger than what was needed for a 95% confidence level.

EXPLORATION | Reading Harry Potter
3.2.2A

The 2008 *Kids and Family Reading Report* describes a survey of 501 children aged 5–17 from 25 major cities around the United States. Suppose that we can regard this sample as representative of the population of all American children aged 5–17. The survey found that 58% of these kids had read at least one Harry Potter book. You will now use the result from this sample to construct and interpret a 95% confidence interval for the proportion of all American children aged 5–17 who had read at least one Harry Potter book in 2008.

To construct this interval in a manner that follows the AP style, you will carry out four logical steps.

STEP 1: Identify the parameter you want to estimate and the theory-based method you will use.

1. What is the parameter of interest? Describe it in words and also provide the symbol used to represent it.

2. What is the theory-based method that you will use to create the 95% confidence interval to estimate the parameter of interest?

STEP 2: Verify the validity conditions for the theory-based method you have chosen.

3. What are the conditions under which it is valid to use the one-sample z-interval? How do you check whether or not they are met? (Remember to discuss representativeness and sample size.)

STEP 3: Construct the confidence interval, showing the values that you substitute into the formula. Recall that the theory-based *confidence interval for a population proportion* π is given by

$$\hat{p} \pm z^* \sqrt{\hat{p}(1 - \hat{p})/n}$$

4. Use the appropriate values in this formula to calculate the confidence interval, being sure to show the values that you substitute into the formula.

STEP 4: Interpret the confidence interval you obtained in the context of the problem.

5. In the context of the study, interpret the confidence interval obtained in #4.

6. Explain what is meant in this context by a 95% confidence level.

EXPLORATION | Reading Harry Potter (revisited)
3.2.2B

The 2008 *Kids and Family Reading Report* describes a survey of 501 children aged 5–17 from 25 major cities around the United States. Suppose that we can regard this sample as representative of the population of all American children aged 5–17. The survey found that 58% of these kids had read at least one Harry Potter book. Use your results from Exploration 3.2.2A to answer the following questions regarding the proportion of American children aged 5–17 who had read at least one Harry Potter book in 2008.

1. If a test of significance was run on the data at a 0.05 level of significance to determine whether the proportion of all American children aged 5–17 who had read at least one Harry Potter book differed from 0.50, would the test reject the null hypothesis? Explain how you are deciding based on the 95% confidence interval you found in the previous exploration.

2. Suppose you wanted the margin of error of your 95% confidence interval to be no more than 0.03. Would you need a sample size that was smaller or larger than 501? How are you deciding? Explain.

KEY IDEA

The general formula for finding the minimum sample size needed for a given confidence level (critical value z^*) and margin of error is

$$n \geq (\hat{p})(1 - \hat{p})(z^*/margin\ of\ error)^2$$

---

3. How many American children aged 5–17 would you need to sample? Show all work and explain why the answer makes sense. (*Hint:* You'll need to use the formula in the Key Idea box, but, what will you use in place of $\hat{p}$? You could use an estimate from a previous study or you could use 0.50, the worst-case scenario.)

4. Does your answer in the previous part change depending on whether you use an estimate from a previous study (0.58) or you use 0.50 as a reasonable value of $\hat{p}$ in the formula?

5. Explain why the way the answer changes makes sense.

6. What if you had wanted a 99% confidence interval to have a margin of error of at most 0.03? Would you need a larger or a smaller sample size compared to when the confidence level is 95%? How are you deciding?

SECTION 3.2: Part 2   Summary

In this section we used theory-based techniques to find a confidence interval for a single proportion. More specifically, you looked at how this should be done following the four steps that should be used on the AP exam. Namely:

1. Identify the parameter you want to estimate and the theory-based model used. (In this section, the parameter is a population proportion and the theory-based model is called a one-proportion z-interval.)

2. Verify the validity conditions for the theory-based method you have chosen. (Both the number of success and the number of failures in the sample need to be at least 10 and the data are from a random sample of the population of interest.)

3. Construct the confidence interval, showing the values that you substitute into the formula. (The confidence interval formula is $\hat{p} \pm z^* \sqrt{\hat{p}(1 - \hat{p})}/n$. The sample proportion and sample size will be given to you. You can find the critical value, z^*, from the Table A, Table B, or your calculator.

4. Interpret the confidence interval you obtained in the context of the problem. (When you do this, make sure you describe your results in terms of the population and not the sample.)

We also looked at how to determine the sample size needed for a confidence interval to have a specific margin of error and confidence level. The formula, found by rearranging the terms of the confidence interval formula, is $n \geq \hat{p}(1 - \hat{p})\left(\frac{z^*}{margin\ of\ error}\right)^2$. The confidence level determines the value of z^*. You may be given an estimate for $\hat{p}$ or, if not, you can use the conservative estimate of 0.50.

2SD AND THEORY-BASED CONFIDENCE INTERVALS FOR A SINGLE MEAN

INTRODUCTION

In the previous sections we saw that we can calculate confidence intervals for a population proportion by:

- Testing different values for the parameter to see whether they are plausible based on the observed proportion.
- Using the 2SD method to extend 2 standard deviations from each side of the statistic.
- Using a theory-based approach when certain validity conditions are met.

(You may want to review FAQ 3.3.1: Which interval do I use?)

FAQ 3.3.1   www.wiley.com/college/tintle

Which interval do I use?

In Sections 3.1 and 3.2 we were focusing on inferences about a population *proportion* because our data consisted of a single categorical variable. In this section we will focus on data consisting of a single quantitative variable. Hence, we will make inferences about a population *mean* by creating confidence intervals. We will again consider a shortcut 2SD approach as well as a theory-based approach.

3.3 — Used Cars

Example 3.3

EXAMPLE

Suppose you are in the market for a used car. You know you want a Honda Civic, but you have no idea how much you should expect to pay. The histogram in Figure 3.9 displays data collected on 102 used Honda Civics for sale on the Internet in July 2006.

FIGURE 3.9   Histogram of asking prices of 102 Honda Civics for sale on the Internet.

THINK ABOUT IT

The average price in this sample is $\bar{x} = \$13{,}292$ with standard deviation $s = \$4{,}535$. Based on this information, what can you say about μ, the average price of all used Honda Civics?

First note that we should be cautious of whether the population of interest is well-represented by this sample. Was this a random sample of cars on sale on the Internet? Do prices on the Internet differ from prices of cars sold but not advertised on the Internet? Also keep in mind that these data were for the *asking price* and we do not have information on the actual selling prices.

Although we should be very cautious in doing so, let's treat this sample as representative of all such used Honda Civics for sale for this example. We don't presume that $\mu = \$13{,}292$ exactly, yet it should be close. But how close? How much do we think the sample mean might wander away from the population mean? The answer to this question will help us find a confidence interval for μ.

To find a confidence interval for μ, we can use either a 2SD method or a theory-based method. Both methods we'll look at in this section will have similarities to the approaches we used in the previous section.

Let us revisit the idea behind how a confidence interval gets computed. The general form of a confidence interval for a parameter is

 3.3.1

$$\text{statistic} \pm \text{multiplier} \times (\text{SD of statistic}),$$

where the choice of "*statistic*" should match the parameter being estimated. Meaning, if the parameter is the population proportion, the statistic should be a sample proportion. Similarly, if the parameter is a population average, the statistic should be a sample average, and so on. Recall that when we want a 95% confidence interval, the multiplier is approximately 2, hence the use of the name "2SD method."

So with quantitative data we could use

$$\bar{x} \pm 2 \times (\text{SD of } \bar{x})$$

It is critical to keep in mind the distinction between "SD of statistic" and "SD of sample." In this example, $s = \$4{,}535$ tells us the amount of variability in asking price *from car to car*. What we need to know for our confidence interval is the variability in *average asking price* from *sample to sample*.

KEY IDEA

There will be less sample-to-sample variability in the sample mean than car-to-car variability in prices.

In Section 2.2, we created a fake population and took repeated samples from that population to estimate this sample-to-sample variability. But that was more to convince us the variability in the sample means from different samples follows the formula $\sigma/\sqrt{n}$. And when we didn't know σ (the population standard deviation), we could approximate $\sigma/\sqrt{n}$ with the standard error $s/\sqrt{n}$.

KEY IDEA

An approximate 2SD method for a 95% confidence interval for a population mean μ is $\bar{x} \pm 2 \times s/\sqrt{n}$. This method is valid when the null distribution follows a bell-shaped, symmetric distribution.

For this example, with $\bar{x} = 13{,}292$ and $s = 4{,}535$, our 2SD interval would be

$$13{,}292 \pm 2 \times (4{,}535/\sqrt{102}) \approx 13{,}292 \pm 898.1$$

or approximately (12,393.9, 14,190.1). From this we would say we are about 95% confident that the average price of all Honda Civics for sale on the Internet around this time was between \$12,394 and \$14,190 (assuming the sample had been representative).

This approach should be reasonable as long as the null distribution of the sample means is reasonably symmetric. But what about a more general theory-based approach that allows us to change the multiplier and achieve different confidence levels?

THEORY-BASED APPROACH

3.3.2

In Section 2.2, we saw a theory-based method to find the p-value when testing hypotheses about a single population mean. Recall that the theory-based approach used a theoretical probability distribution called the *t*-distribution to predict the behavior of the standardized statistic and that this approach required certain validity conditions to be met. The implication here is that for a confidence interval for a population mean the multiplier will come from a *t*-distribution rather than the normal distribution. And in fact this multiplier will change depending on the sample size involved. We will let the technology figure that out, but do keep in mind that for 95% confidence, the multiplier is roughly 2, which is what we used as a shortcut earlier.

Using the **Theory-Based Inference** applet (see Figure 3.10), we can choose the one-mean scenario and specify the summary statistics (or you can paste in the individual data values).

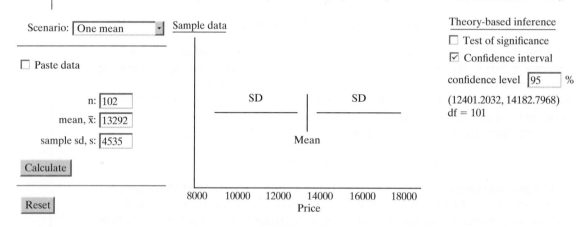

FIGURE 3.10 Theory-based inference confidence interval for mean used Honda asking price.

This interval (12,401, 14,183) is similar to what we found with the 2SD method but is using a slightly different multiplier. The important thing to keep in mind is that this is an interval for the *population mean asking price*, not the price of one car. The rough sketch in Figure 3.10 shows that most cars are typically between $9,000 and $18,000, a much wider range than our confidence interval for the population mean asking price. As before, the multiplier will increase as we increase our confidence level. (See Figure 3.11.)

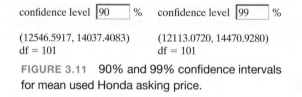

FIGURE 3.11 90% and 99% confidence intervals for mean used Honda asking price.

Also keep in mind that this method should only be used when the validity conditions are met.

VALIDITY CONDITIONS

The theory-based interval for a population mean (called a ***one-sample t-interval***) requires that the quantitative variable should have a symmetric distribution, or you should have at least 20 observations and the sample distribution should not be strongly skewed.

Keep in mind that the larger the sample size the more skewness in the sample you can tolerate. In the context of the used Honda Civic asking prices, the sample shows slight skewness to the left in Figure 3.9. Is this enough skewness to doubt the validity of our procedure? Perhaps, though a sample size of 102 should be enough to compensate for such slight skewness. If you are concerned, then you should use an alternative method like transforming the data first.

In summary, the formula for a theory-based confidence interval for a population mean (μ) is given by

$$\bar{x} \pm \text{multiplier} \times s/\sqrt{n},$$

where $\bar{x}$ denotes the sample mean, s denotes the sample standard deviation, and n is the sample size. This approach uses $s/\sqrt{n}$ to approximate the sample-to-sample variability in the sample means. When this is the case, we use a multiplier from the t-distribution rather than the normal distribution as we did for proportions. Or, for 95% confidence we can continue to approximate this multiplier by 2, giving a quick approximation to the interval found by the **Theory-Based Inference** applet. The multiplier, and therefore the width of the confidence interval, will increase if the confidence level increases.

Sleepless Nights? (*continued*)

EXPLORATION

3.3

Recall Exploration 2.2 where you investigated whether, on average, students at your school get less than 8 hours of sleep on a typical night. Even though 8 hours is often cited as the recommended amount, many people believe that college students will average less than 8 hours. But how much less? In this exploration, you will use the same data to estimate the average number of hours of sleep students at your school get.

1. Let μ represent the average number of hours of sleep all the students at your school got the previous night. The question we asked in Exploration 2.2 was, "How much sleep (to the nearest quarter hour) did you get last night?" If you still have the data from that exploration, give the summary statistics here. If not, collect a new set of data from your class and give those summary statistics here.

   Sample size, $n =$

   Sample mean, $\bar{x} =$

   Sample SD, $s =$

   Similar to what you did in Exploration 3.1, we could conduct a simulation to generate a null distribution of the sample mean number of hours of sleep, assuming different values for μ to determine which are plausible. (In the **One Mean** applet, you can use a slider below the population to quickly change the value of the population mean.) Recall that such an interval is called a confidence interval. But this would be rather tedious, so in this exploration we will consider some shortcuts to estimating a confidence interval for μ.

2. Based on your sample data, what is your best guess or estimate for the value of μ, that is, the average number of hours of sleep students at your school got the previous night?

3. Suppose you repeated the survey by asking a different group of students at your school. Will the average for this new sample be exactly the same as the original sample average reported in #2? Why or why not?

   A natural guess or estimate for the population average number of hours of sleep students at your school got the previous night (μ) is the observed value of the sample average sleep time. But, we know that if we were to conduct this study again we would most likely observe a different value for the sample average due to *sampling variability*—we need to account for this in our estimate for μ. To do so, we create a confidence interval for μ by using the formula

$$\text{sample mean} \pm \text{multiplier} \times (\text{SD of sample mean})$$

where the "*SD of sample mean*" accounts for the sample-to-sample variability that we expect in the sample average, the "*multiplier*" accounts for the confidence level, and the "±" allows us to create an interval around the sample mean (these are the plausible parameter values that are not too far from the observed sample mean). Recall that when the confidence level is 95%, the multiplier is approximately 2.

To find a 95% confidence interval for μ we can use the 2SD method that you saw in Section 3.2, but we need to know what to use for the *SD of the sample mean*.

4. In #25 of Exploration 2.2, when you simulated the distribution of sample means from the hypothetical population of sleep times (population 1), what did you find for the standard deviation of the null distribution? How did this value compare to the standard deviation of your sample?

KEY IDEA

There will be less sample-to-sample variability in the sample mean than person-to-person variability in sleep times.

5. In Exploration 2.2, we saw that $s/\sqrt{n}$ could be used to approximate the standard deviation of the sample means. Report this value.

KEY IDEA

An approximate 2SD method for a 95% confidence interval for a population mean μ is $\bar{x} \pm 2 \times s/\sqrt{n}$. This method is valid when the null distribution follows a bell-shaped, symmetric distribution.

6. Use the value of $s/\sqrt{n}$ you found in the previous question and the 2SD method to approximate a 95% confidence interval for μ in the context of the sleep study, and then interpret this interval. (*Hint*: When interpreting the interval, be clear about what the interval estimates. You are estimating not the individual sleep times of students but how much sleep students at your school get on…)

7. Does the 95% confidence interval reported in #6 contain 8 (the population mean under the original null hypothesis)? Explain how you could have known this in advance based on your p-value from Exploration 2.2.

Theory-based approach

In Section 2.2, you saw a theory-based approach to find the p-value when testing hypotheses about a single population mean. This approach uses a more precise value of the multiplier in the confidence interval formula based on the *t*-distribution.

8. Go to the **Theory-Based Inference** applet, and select the **One Mean** option from the **Scenario** pull-down menu. Then, you can either copy and paste your class data or just enter the sample statistics (as recorded in #2). Press **Calculate**, check the **Confidence Interval** box, and press **Calculate CI**. Report the 95% confidence interval and compare it to the interval you found in #6. Are they about the same? Same midpoint? Same width? Could you have anticipated this? Explain your reasoning.

Recall that the theory-based approach uses a theoretical probability distribution called the *t*-distribution to predict the behavior of the standardized statistic (denoted by *t*) and that this approach required certain validity conditions to be met.

VALIDITY CONDITIONS

The theory-based interval for a population mean (called a ***one-sample t-interval***) requires that the quantitative variable should have a symmetric distribution or you should have at least 20 observations and the sample distribution should not be strongly skewed.

9. Are the validity conditions for using the 2SD or *t*-distribution based method to find a confidence interval met for your class data? Explain why or why not.

In summary, the formula for a theory-based confidence interval for a population mean (μ) is given by

$$\bar{x} \pm \text{multiplier} \times s/\sqrt{n},$$

where $\bar{x}$ denotes the sample mean, s denotes the sample standard deviation, and n is the sample size. We will rely on technology to find the appropriate multiplier for our sample size and our confidence level. Keep in mind that the multiplier is approximately 2 for 95% confidence and increases if we increase the confidence level.

SECTION 3.3   Summary

In this section we explored simulation- and theory-based approaches for finding confidence intervals for a single population mean.

- The general form of a confidence interval is statistic $\pm$ multiplier $\times$ (SD of statistic).
- When the parameter of interest is the population mean, μ, the statistic is the sample mean, that is, $\bar{x}$.
- The general form of a confidence interval for a population mean (μ) is given by *sample mean $\pm$ multiplier $\times$ (SD of sample mean)*.
  - For 95% confidence, the multiplier will be roughly in the ballpark of 2.
  - The standard deviation of the sample mean can be approximated by $s/\sqrt{n}$.
  - The theory-based confidence interval is $\bar{x} \pm$ multiplier $\times s/\sqrt{n}$ where the multiplier comes from the *t*-distribution.
  - These methods are valid if the population distribution is normally distributed (make sure the sample is roughly symmetric) or the sample size is large (at least 20 or quite large if the sample is more heavily skewed).
- A confidence interval for a population mean estimates the value of the population mean, not the value of individual observations in the population.
- Notice we are not presenting a method for finding the confidence interval for a population median. Because the null distribution for medians did not follow the familiar symmetric, bell-shaped pattern, the approach outlined here would not be valid in most cases. If the parameter of interest is a median, you will need to consider more sophisticated approaches.

Summary of validity conditions and applets for a confidence interval of a single mean			
Type of data	**Name of test**	**Applet**	**Validity conditions**
Single quantitative variable	Theory-based interval for a single mean (one-sample *t*-interval)	One mean; theory-based inference	The quantitative variable should have a symmetric distribution or you should have at least 20 observations and the sample distribution should not be strongly skewed.

ONE-SAMPLE *t*-INTERVAL FOR A SINGLE MEAN

SECTION 3.3:
Part 2

INTRODUCTION

Earlier in this section, we saw that when we have a single quantitative variable, we can calculate confidence intervals for a population mean by using a theory-based approach that uses a theoretical probability distribution called the *t*-distribution. We saw that a general method, valid for any confidence level (not just the 95% we approximated with the 2 SD method), is to estimate the parameter with

$$\text{statistic} \pm \text{multiplier} \times (\text{SD of statistic})$$

or, when estimating a population mean, with

$$\bar{x} \pm \text{multiplier} \times s/\sqrt{n},$$

where $\bar{x}$ denotes the sample mean, s denotes the sample standard deviation, and n is the sample size.

In Section 2.2 we saw that because we do not usually know the population standard deviation, we substitute s, the sample standard deviation, and compute the **standard error** of the sample mean, which is $s/\sqrt{n}$. Because we are using our sample standard deviation to estimate the population standard deviation to predict the sample-to-sample variability in the distribution of standardized statistics, we will use a **t-distribution** with $n - 1$ degrees of freedom (where n is the sample size) as our theory-based model, rather than the z-distribution we used for sample proportions. Earlier in this section we used the applet to obtain the value of the multiplier for our desired confidence level. For the AP exam, you will need to use your calculator or the t-table on the provided formula sheet to obtain the multiplier.

Recall from Section 2.2, Part 3, that the t-distribution is actually an entire family of distribution curves characterized by a number called its degrees of freedom (abbreviated df). For a one-sample t-interval, the degrees of freedom are equal to the sample size minus 1 (df = $n - 1$). To find the multiplier, called the t-critical value, that is used in the construction of the margin of error, you will use the t-distribution with appropriate degrees of freedom. The multiplier is often denoted by t^*.

Let's see how you could go about finding a t-critical value (t^*) for a 95% confidence interval for the unknown value of μ with sample size $n = 12$.

STEP 1.   Draw a sketch of a bell-shaped distribution and shade the area corresponding to the middle 95% of the distribution. Also indicate roughly where $-t^*$ and t^* are in your sketch. Note that the middle 95% corresponds to 2.5% in each tail.

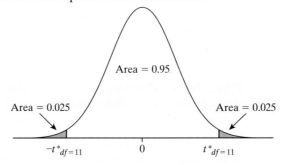

STEP 2.
A. You may use your calculator to find the t^*-critical value: When you want to find a t-statistic for a given area under the t-distribution ($\mu = 0, \sigma = 1$), you use the *invT* command and input the area to the left of the t^*-critical value you are interested in finding.

CALCULATOR TIPS

You can use the "inverse" commands to provide the calculator with a tail probability and have it find the corresponding critical value. For example,

- **TI-84:** invT(area: 0.025, df: 11), where area refers to the lower tail area (in this case 0.025) and df refers to the degrees of freedom (in this case $n - 1 = 12 - 1 = 11$). invT(0.025, 11) ≈ -2.201. We use 2.201 as our $t^*_{df=11}$, the t-critical value.
- **TI-Nspire:** Menu → Statistics → Distribution → Inverse t(area: 0.025, df: 11) invT(0.025, 11) ≈ -2.201), where area refers to the lower tail area (in this case 0.025) and df refers to the degrees of freedom (in this case $n - 1 = 12 - 1 = 11$). We use 2.201 as our $t^*_{df=11}$, the t-critical value.

Or,

B. You may use Table B on the AP formula sheet to find the *t**-critical value:

- Go to the bottom of the table, *Confidence Level C*, to the column for 95%.
- Go to df = 11 row (because df = $n - 1 = 12 - 1 = 11$).
- Find the value at the intersection of df = 11 and 95% confidence level. This is your *t**-critical value for a 95% confidence interval for μ with 11 degrees of freedom ($t^*_{11} = 2.201$). Note that the 95% confidence level corresponds to an upper tail probability of 0.025.
- Note that after 30, the increment for the degrees of freedom is no longer 1. If the value for your degrees of freedom is not given in the table, use the next lowest value as a conservative estimate (the t^* will be larger than you need).

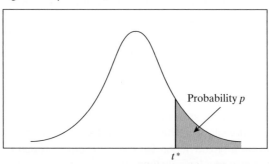

Table entry for *p* and *C* is the point t^* with probability *p* lying above it and probability *C* lying between $-t^*$ and t^*.

Probability *p*

t^*

TABLE B   *t*-distribution critical values

df						Tail probability *p*						
	.25	.20	.15	.10	.05	.025	.02	.01	.005	.0025	.001	.0005
1	1.000	1.376	1.963	3.078	6.314	12.71	15.89	31.82	63.66	127.3	318.3	636.3
2	.816	1.061	1.386	1.886	2.920	4.303	4.849	6.965	9.925	14.09	22.33	31.60
3	.765	.978	1.250	1.638	2.353	3.182	3.482	4.541	5.841	7.453	10.21	12.92
4	.741	.941	1.190	1.533	2.132	2.776	2.999	3.747	4.604	5.598	7.173	8.610
5	.727	.920	1.156	1.476	2.015	2.571	2.757	3.365	4.032	4.773	5.893	6.869
6	.718	.906	1.134	1.440	1.943	2.447	2.612	3.143	3.707	4.317	5.208	5.959
7	.711	.896	1.119	1.415	1.895	2.365	2.517	2.998	3.499	4.029	4.785	5.408
8	.706	.889	1.108	1.397	1.860	2.306	2.449	2.896	3.355	3.833	4.501	5.041
9	.703	.883	1.100	1.383	1.833	2.262	2.398	2.821	3.250	3.690	4.297	4.781
10	.700	.879	1.093	1.372	1.812	2.228	2.359	2.764	3.169	3.581	4.144	4.587
11	.697	.876	1.088	1.363	1.796	**2.201**	2.328	2.718	3.106	3.497	4.025	4.437
...												
29	.683	.854	1.055	1.311	1.699	2.045	2.150	2.462	2.756	3.038	3.396	3.659
30	.683	.854	1.055	1.310	1.697	2.042	2.147	2.457	2.750	3.030	3.385	3.646
40	.681	.851	1.050	1.303	1.684	2.021	2.123	2.423	2.704	2.971	3.307	3.551
50	.679	.849	1.047	1.299	1.676	2.009	2.109	2.403	2.678	2.937	3.261	3.496
60	.679	.848	1.045	1.296	1.671	2.000	2.099	2.390	2.660	2.915	3.232	3.460
80	.678	.846	1.043	1.292	1.664	1.990	2.088	2.374	2.639	2.887	3.195	3.416
100	.677	.845	1.042	1.290	1.660	1.984	2.081	2.364	2.626	2.871	3.174	3.390
1000	.675	.842	1.037	1.282	1.646	1.962	2.056	2.330	2.581	2.813	3.098	3.300
∞	.674	.841	1.036	1.282	1.645	1.960	2.054	2.326	2.576	2.807	3.091	3.291
	50%	60%	70%	80%	90%	**95%**	96%	98%	99%	99.5%	99.8%	99.9%
						Confidence level *C*						

Now that you know how to use your calculator or Table B to find a t^*, that is, the t-critical value with the appropriate degrees of freedom, we will look at the work you need to show on the AP Statistics exam when the question asks you to construct a confidence interval for a population mean.

3.3.2 — How Much Sleep Do Teens Need? Revisited —————

Example 3.3.2

Recall from Example 2.2.3 *How Much Sleep Do Teens Need?* that a study conducted by Brigham Young University economists Eric Eide and Mark Showalter (2012) found that, based on standardized test results, teens scored best with about seven hours of sleep each night. A high school teacher wanted to know, on average, how much sleep students at her school get on a typical night. To answer this question, she asked the 17 students in her class to record the number of hours they sleep that night, to the nearest half-hour. The data are below (in hours).

7.5	6.5	6.5	6	7	5.5	6.5	7.5	6	7	7	6	8	5
8	6.5	6.5											

Suppose that we can consider the sleep habits of the students in this class to be representative of the students at this high school. Use the data from this sample to construct a 95% confidence interval for μ, the mean number of hours of sleep that all students at this high school get on a typical night. On the AP exam, you can compute the corresponding confidence interval in four logical steps.

> **THINK ABOUT IT**
>
> What is the parameter of interest? In other words, what is the number that we are trying to estimate? What symbol is used to represent this parameter?

STEP 1: Identify the parameter to be estimated and the theory-based method to be used. Let μ represent the mean number of hours of sleep all students at this school get on a typical night.

We will use a one-sample t-interval to construct a 95% confidence interval for μ because we have a single mean (sleep = quantitative variable) and the population standard deviation is not known.

> **THINK ABOUT IT**
>
> What are the conditions under which it is valid to use the one-sample t-interval? How do you check whether or not they are met?

STEP 2: Verify the validity conditions for the chosen theory-based method. Validity conditions for a one-sample t-interval

- We need our observations to be representative of the population we are interested in learning something about. We were told to assume that the sleep habits of students in the class sampled are representative of the students in the high school.

- We do not know the shape of the population distribution of sleep times for students at this school, and because our sample of 17 students is not large enough to meet the theory-based condition based on the central limit theorem (how many would you need for that?), we need to graph the sample data.

   A dotplot of our sample data for the number of hours slept the previous night for students in this class appears to be bell-shaped, so it is reasonable to assume that the population distribution of sleep times for students at this high

Hours slept

school is approximately normal. The distribution of sample means for samples of this size should therefore be bell-shaped, so it is reasonable to calculate a one-sample *t*-interval.

> **THINK ABOUT IT**
>
> What is the formula for the confidence interval for the population mean, μ?

STEP 3: Construct the confidence interval, showing the values to be substituted into the formula. Recall that the **confidence interval for a population mean μ** is given by $\bar{x} \pm t^*_{df = n - 1}(s/\sqrt{n})$.

Thus, the 95% C.I. for μ in this context can be calculated as follows:

$\bar{x} = 6.647$ hrs $\qquad 6.647 \pm 2.120\,(0.825/\sqrt{17})$

$s = 0.825$ hrs $\qquad = (6.22, 7.07)$ hours

$n = 17 \qquad\qquad\quad$ t^* with df $= 16$ and 95% confidence from Table B $= 2.120$

$df = 17 - 1 = 16$

3.3P2.1

Note: You can use your calculator to find the confidence interval.

TI-84: Stat → Tests → Tinterval

TI-Nspire: Menu → Statistics → Confidence Intervals → *t* Interval

> **THINK ABOUT IT**
>
> How would you interpret this confidence interval: (6.22, 7.07) hours?

STEP 4: Interpret the confidence interval obtained in the context of the problem. We can be 95% confident that the mean number of hours of sleep on a typical night for all students at this school is between 6.22 hours and 7.07 hours (assuming the sample is indeed representative of this entire population). Because the 95% confidence interval contains 7, it is plausible that students at this school average 7 hours of sleep on a typical night.

Keep in mind that this is an interval for the *population mean*. We *cannot* claim that 95% of students in this school sleep between 6.22 and 7.07 hours!

3.3P2.2

FOLLOW-UP QUESTION

A possible follow-up question would be to ask you to interpret what is meant by the phrase "95% confident" in this context. In this case, you would want to describe the reliability of this confidence interval method. For example, if we were to repeatedly sample students from this school (using the same sample size), then in the long run, we expect 95% of the intervals we have constructed to capture the actual population mean, whatever value it may be. Note that we haven't referred to any particular interval; we are focusing on the method instead.

Estimating Time Length

EXPLORATION

3.3.2

Time can seem to fly or crawl depending on the activity you are engaging in. Can you tell (without looking at a clock) how long it has been since you started reading this section? Can students estimate how long a snippet of a song has been playing? Recall Example 2.2, where student researchers played a 10-second snippet of the song *ABC* by the Jackson 5 to 48 subjects. The summary statistics for the estimated time that the song played are given below.

$$\bar{x} = 13.71 \text{ seconds}, \ s = 6.50 \text{ seconds}, \ n = 48$$

Suppose that you can consider the estimating ability of these students about how long a song has been playing to be representative of all students at this school. You will now use the above summary statistics to construct a 98% confidence interval for the mean time that would be estimated by all students at this school for the length of time (in seconds) that the song snippet played.

To construct this interval in a manner that follows the AP style, you will carry out four logical steps.

STEP 1: Identify the parameter you want to estimate and the theory-based method you will use.

1. What is the parameter of interest? Describe it in words and also provide the symbol used to represent it.

2. What is the theory-based method that you will use to create the 98% confidence interval to estimate the parameter of interest?

STEP 2: Verify the validity conditions for the theory-based method you have chosen.

3. What are the conditions under which it is valid to use the one-sample t-interval? How do you check whether or not they are met? (Remember to discuss representativeness and sample size.)

STEP 3: Construct the confidence interval, showing the values that you substitute into the formula.

4. Recall that the theory-based *confidence interval for a population mean* μ is given by

$$\bar{x} \pm t^*_{df=n-1}(s/\sqrt{n})$$

Substitute the appropriate values into this formula and calculate the confidence interval, being sure to show the values you substituted into the confidence interval formula.

STEP 4: Interpret the confidence interval you obtained in the context of the problem.

5. In the context of the study, interpret the confidence interval obtained above.

6. Suppose that, instead of constructing a 98% confidence interval for the mean time that would be estimated by all students at this school for the length of time (in seconds) that the song snippet played, you instead constructed a 95% confidence interval. How would this change affect the width of your interval? Why?

7. Suppose you conduct a test of significance to determine whether the mean time that would be estimated by all students at this school for the length of time (in seconds) that the song snippet played is different from 10 seconds. Use the confidence interval obtained to determine whether the mean time that would be estimated by all students at this school for the length of time (in seconds) that the song snippet played is significantly different from 10 seconds.

SECTION 3.3: Part 2   Summary

In this section you used theory-based techniques to find a confidence interval for a single mean. More specifically, you looked at how this should be done following the four steps that should be used on the AP exam. Namely:

1. Identify the parameter you want to estimate and the theory-based model used. (In this section, the parameter is a population mean and the theory-based model is called a one-sample t-interval.)

2. Verify the validity conditions for the theory-based method you have chosen. (You should have a sample size of at least 30 or your sample data should be quite symmetric. If your sample data are highly skewed, then the sample size should be even larger and data are from a random sample from the population of interest.)

3. Construct the confidence interval, showing the values that you substitute into the formula. (The confidence interval formula is $\bar{x} \pm t^*_{df=n-1} s/\sqrt{n}$. The sample mean, standard deviation, and sample size will be given to you if you are not given the sample data. You can find the critical value, t^*, from the t-table, Table B, or your calculator.)

4. Interpret the confidence interval you obtained in the context of the problem. (When you do this, make sure you describe your results in terms of the population and not the sample and that you are clearly talking about the population *mean*, not individual values.)

FACTORS THAT AFFECT THE WIDTH OF A CONFIDENCE INTERVAL

SECTION 3.4

INTRODUCTION

In the previous two sections we explored some different ways to construct confidence intervals for long-run proportions or population proportions and for population means. These different methods were more efficient than the plausible values method seen in Section 3.1, but the end result is interpreted the same way. In this section, we will explore how the sample size and the sample statistics can influence the width of confidence intervals. Finally, an interpretation of confidence *level* will be discussed in Exploration 3.4B.

The Affordable Care Act (*continued*)

Recall the 2013 Gallup poll based on a random sample of 1,034 adults which asked whether the new healthcare law (the Affordable Care Act) had affected the respondents or their family (Example 3.2). Sixty-nine percent of the sample responded that the laws had had no effect.

We saw that changing the confidence level impacted the width of the interval. The theory-based confidence intervals for the three most common confidence levels are reproduced in Table 3.5.

 Example 3.4

TABLE 3.5 90, 95, and 99% confidence intervals for the proportion of adult Americans not affected by the Affordable Care Act in November 2013

90%	95%	99%
(0.6663, 0.7137)	(0.6618, 0.7182)	(0.6530, 0.7270)
width = 0.0474	width = 0.0564	width = 0.0740

Thus, as we saw in the previous sections, as the confidence level increases, the confidence interval gets wider. Many students find this, initially, counterintuitive. Remember, this is an interval of plausible values for the parameter—we are hoping to "catch" the parameter in our interval. If you want to be more confident that you catch the parameter in your interval, then you need a wider interval. Read more on the idea of "catching" the parameter in Exploration 3.4B.

 3.4.1.1

SAMPLE SIZE
A key subgroup of interest in this survey is those currently without health insurance, one group the law is specifically designed to help. Interestingly, the poll found that 70% of people in this subgroup stated that the law had not affected them—very similar to the 69% found in the overall sample.

 3.4.1.2

> **THINK ABOUT IT**
>
> How will the confidence interval for the proportion of all uninsured Americans who feel the law has not impacted them differ from the original confidence interval?

To answer this question, we need to know the sample size—how many in the survey were not insured. Using the theory-based inference applet in Figure 3.12, we show 95% confidence intervals for three different sample sizes.

n: 100	n: 200	n: 400
count: 70	count: 140	count: 280
sample $\hat{p}$: 0.7000	sample $\hat{p}$: 0.70	sample $\hat{p}$: 70
confidence level 95 %	confidence level 95 %	confidence level 95 %
(0.6102, 0.7898)	(0.6365, 0.7635)	(0.6551, 0.7449)
0.70 ± 0.0898	0.70 ± 0.0635	0.70 ± 0.0449

FIGURE 3.12   95% confidence intervals for different subgroup sizes.

THINK ABOUT IT

So what are the commonalities and differences among these intervals?

Because the sample proportion, $\hat{p} = 0.70$, is the same in all three cases, the midpoints of the intervals are all the same. However, the widths of the intervals change. The width for $n = 400$ is half the width with $n = 100$. (So we need to multiply the sample size by 4 to cut the margin of error in half.) See FAQ 3.4.1 for more discussion of the role of sample size.

FAQ 3.4.1   www.wiley.com/college/tintle

How does one cut the margin of error in half?

Thus, we see that the width of confidence intervals is smaller when based on a larger sample size. This should make intuitive sense. When we have more information (based on a larger sample size), we can be more *precise* in our estimate of the long-run proportion as evidenced by a narrower confidence interval.

KEY IDEA

The width of a confidence interval decreases as the confidence level decreases (for a fixed sample size) or as the sample size increases (for a fixed confidence level).

Do keep in mind that with the larger sample size we have made our estimate of the parameter more precise by specifying a smaller (narrower) interval of plausible values for the parameter, but we are still 95% confident in this interval.

With quantitative data, another factor that will impact the margin of error is the variability in the sample through the standard error $s/\sqrt{n}$. (See Exploration 3.4A.) If our sample data are more precise (less variable), then our confidence interval will also be more precise (narrower). Though not as dramatic, the sample proportion is also related to the standard error used in the confidence interval as discussed next.

3.4.1.3

OPTIONAL: EFFECT OF SAMPLE PROPORTION

So far in this example we have focused on the proportion who said they had not been affected by the new health law. What if we focused on those who said they felt hurt by the new law? In the November 2013 study that sample proportion was 0.19.

3.4.1.4

THINK ABOUT IT

Will the width of this confidence interval be larger or smaller than for $\hat{p} = 0.69$?

Returning to our sample size of n = 1,034, we can still use the theory-based confidence interval because we will have 196 "successes" and 838 "failures" (Figure 3.13).

FIGURE 3.13 A 95% confidence interval for proportion of American adults who feel hurt by the Affordable Care Act.

The confidence interval of (0.1661, 0.2139) has a margin of error of (0.2139 − 0.1661)/2 = 0.0239. This is actually a bit smaller than the margin of error we found with $\hat{p}$ = 0.69(0.0282). This is expected because the margin of error will be larger when $\hat{p}$ is closer to 0.50. So it is actually "easier" to (more precisely) estimate a population proportion that is not as close to 0.50.

Holiday Spending Habits

EXPLORATION

3.4A

A November 7–10, 2013, Gallup poll asked 1,039 U.S. adults how much they planned to personally spend on Christmas gifts this year. The report cited an average of $704.

1. Identify the observational units and variable in this study. Classify the variable as quantitative or categorical.

2. Define the parameter of interest in this study. (*Hint:* Do you want to estimate a mean or a proportion? For what population?)

Because our variable of interest (dollar amount intending to spend) is quantitative, the parameter of interest here is the population mean for all adult Americans; call this μ. To construct a confidence interval for μ, we need to know the sample size, the sample mean, and the sample standard deviation.

3. Which two of these three quantities do you know? What symbols can be used to represent them?

What we are not told by Gallup is s, the sample standard deviation.

4. Explain in your own words what s represents in this context.

5. Suppose s was equal to $150. Use the 2SD method (*Hint:* Reminder to consider the SD of the sample mean) to approximate and interpret a 95% confidence interval for μ. (*Hint:* You are 95% confident that *what* is between what two values?)

6. Suppose s was equal to $300. Use the 2SD method to approximate the 95% confidence interval for μ. How does this interval compare to the interval from #5 (examine both the midpoint and the width of the interval)? Explain why the changes you observe make intuitive sense.

The impact of sample size

7. The poll involved 562 men and 477 women. Suppose we looked at only one of these subgroups. How do you expect the width of the intervals to compare to the interval based on the total sample (wider, narrower, or the same width as before)? Explain briefly.

8. Suppose the women reported planning to spend an average of $704 with standard deviation $150. Compare the margin of error of this interval (*Hint:* 2SD) to that in #5. Was your prediction correct?

9. In general, how does the width of a confidence interval change as the sample size increases? Why?

You should have seen that a smaller sample size produced a wider confidence interval. This makes sense because a smaller sample size conveys less information and therefore leaves more uncertainty about the actual value of the population mean. More directly, as we discussed in Chapters 1 and 2, increasing the sample size reduces the variability in the null distribution; thus the SD of the null distribution will be smaller, and so the confidence interval will also be narrower.

You also saw in Section 3.3 that the confidence level will impact the width of the interval as well. So with quantitative data, there are three main factors that impact the width of the confidence interval, the sample standard deviation (variability within the sample), the sample size (variability between samples), and the confidence level.

KEY IDEA

The width of a confidence interval for a population mean, μ, decreases

a. as the confidence level decreases (for a fixed sample size and fixed sample standard deviation), or

b. as the sample size increases (for a fixed confidence level and fixed sample standard deviation), or

c. as the sample standard deviation decreases (for a fixed confidence level and fixed sample size).

The Gallup poll did give us a bit more information; see Table 3.6.

TABLE 3.6   Categorized responses to how much money respondents expected to spend on Christmas gifts 2013 (Gallup.com)

	$1,000 or more	$500–999	$250–499	$100–249	Under $100	No opinion	Median	Mean (w/zero)	Mean (w/o zero)
2013 Nov 7–10	26	21	16	19	4	14	$500	$704	$773

10. Based on this information, which appears to be a more reasonable guess ($150 or $300) for the sample standard deviation? Explain your reasoning.

11. Based on this information, do you think the theory-based inference method is valid for these data? (*Hint:* Do you think the sample data are roughly symmetric? What is the sample size?)

The information provided in Table 3.6 is enough to tell us that the sample distribution is skewed. We can consider the 2SD and theory-based approaches valid as long as the sample size is large. Our original sample size of 1,039 respondents should be sufficient to consider these methods valid. But with such a strong skewness in spending amounts, you may want to be cautious or consider first transforming your data.

We have calculated 90%, 95%, and 99% confidence intervals, and we have seen that using a higher confidence level produces a larger margin of error and therefore a wider confidence interval. But what does it mean to say that we have "95% confidence" that an interval contains the parameter of interest? This next exploration leads you to investigate this question.

3.4.2

EXPLORATION | Reese's Pieces

3.4B

Reese's Pieces® candies come in three colors: orange, yellow, and brown. Suppose that you take a random sample of candies and want to estimate the long-run proportion of candies that is orange. Let's assume for now (although we would not know this when conducting the study) that this long-run proportion, symbolized by π, is equal to 0.50.

1. Suppose that you take a random sample of 100 Reese's Pieces candies and find the sample proportion of orange. Is there any guarantee that the sample proportion will equal 0.50?

2. Suppose we calculate a confidence interval from this sample proportion. Is there any guarantee that the interval will contain the value 0.50?

3. Suppose that you select another random sample of 100 Reese's Pieces candies. Is there any guarantee that the sample proportion will be the same as for the first sample? Will the confidence interval based on the new sample necessarily be the same as the confidence interval based on the first sample? How do you think they will differ?

4. To explore the behavior of confidence intervals arising from different random samples with a sample size of 100 from the same population with 50% orange, open the **Simulating Confidence Intervals** applet.

   - Make sure that **Proportions** and **Wald** are selected from the pull-down menus.
   - Set π to be 0.50 and n to be 100.
   - Let **Intervals** be set to 1.
   - Make sure that **Conf level** is set to 95%.
   - Press **Sample**.
   - Notice that this adds an interval (depicted by a horizontal line) to the graph in the middle with a dot corresponding to the observed sample proportion value to the graph labeled "*Sample Statistics*." Click on this interval. Doing this reveals the value of the midpoint ($\hat{p}$) (at the bottom) and the endpoints of the 95% confidence interval based on the sample proportion.

   Record the following:

   a. Sample proportion:

   b. Endpoints of the 95% confidence interval

   Lower endpoint: Upper endpoint:

   c. Is the sample proportion within the confidence interval? Explain why this does not surprise you.

   d. Is the specified long-run proportion ($\pi = 0.50$) within the confidence interval?

   Notice that 0.50 is either in the interval reported in #4b or not. Suppose the interval turned out to be (0.473, 0.537). It's not like 0.50 is sometimes between 0.473 and 0.537 and sometimes not between those two values. Similarly, even if we didn't know the value of π, the long-run proprotion is still some value, it doesn't change if you take a different sample. Therefore, it's technically incorrect to make a statement like "there is a 95% probability that π is between 0.473 and 0.537." This doesn't fit our "long-run proportion" interpretation of *probability*. So what is happening 95% of the time?

5. Return to the **Simulating Confidence Intervals** applet.

   - Change **Intervals** from 1 to 99 for a total of 100 random samples from a process where $\pi = 0.50$.
   - Press **Sample**.
   - Notice that this produces a total of 100 possible values of a sample proportion which are graphed in the graph labeled "*Sample Statistics*" and the 100 confidence intervals (with 95% confidence) that are based on these sample proportions.

     a. Study the graph labeled "*Sample Statistics*" closely. At about what number is this graph of sample proportions centered? Were you expecting this? Why or why not?

     b. Notice that some of the dots on the "*Sample Statistics*" graph are colored red and some are colored green.

- Click on any one of the *red* dots. Doing this will reveal the value of the sample proportion and the corresponding 95% confidence interval. Record the following:

  i. Sample proportion

  ii. Endpoints of the 95% confidence interval

  iii. Is the sample proportion within the confidence interval?

  iv. Is the probability you set for the overall process ($\pi = 0.50$) within the confidence interval?

- Now click on any one of the *green* dots. Doing this will reveal the value of the sample proportion and the corresponding 95% confidence interval. Write down the following:

  i. Sample proportion

  ii. Endpoints of the 95% confidence interval

  iii. Is the sample proportion within the confidence interval?

  iv. Is the long-run proportion of orange ($\pi = 0.50$) within the confidence interval?

- The graph in the middle displays the 100 different 95% confidence intervals, depicting in green the ones that succeed in capturing the actual value of the long-run proportion (which, you'll recall, we assumed to be $\pi = 0.50$) and in red the intervals that fail to capture the actual value of π.

  c. In the bottom left corner, the applet maintains a "*Running total*" for the percentage of the intervals produced so far that contain $\pi = 0.50$. Report this percentage here. That is, what percentage of the 100 random intervals you have generated succeeded in capturing the value of 0.50 inside the interval?

  d. Now press the **Sample** button a few times and watch how, if at all, the percentage reported under "*Running total*" changes. Now record what you think the percentage would be if you were to repeat this process forever.

  e. Based on your observations from #5a–d, fill in the blanks:

     Thus, 95% confidence means that if we repeatedly sampled from a process and used the sample statistic to construct a 95% confidence interval, in the long run, roughly _____% of all those intervals would manage to capture the actual value of the long-run proportion , and the remaining _____% would not.

6. Now consider changing the confidence level to 90%.

   a. Before you make this change, first predict what will happen to the resulting confidence intervals:

      i. How will the widths of the confidence intervals change (if at all)?

      ii. How will the breakdown of successful/unsuccessful (green/red) intervals change? (What percentage of intervals do you suspect will be green in the long run?)

   b. Now change **Conf level** to 90% and (watch what happens as you) press **Recalculate** and then **Sample**.

      i. How do the widths of the intervals change? Why does this make sense?

      ii. How does the running total change? Why does this make sense?

KEY IDEA

The *confidence level* indicates the long-run percentage of confidence intervals that would succeed in capturing the (unknown) value of the parameter if random samples were to be taken repeatedly from the population/process and a confidence interval produced from each sample. So, a 95% confidence level means that 95% of all samples would produce an interval that succeeded in capturing the unknown value of the parameter.

c. Now consider making the sample size four times as large, that is, 400 candies, while keeping the confidence level at 90%. Before you make this change, first predict what will happen to the resulting confidence intervals:

 i. How will the widths of the confidence intervals change (if at all)?

 ii. How will the percentage of successful (green) intervals change?

d. Now change n to 400 and (watch what happens as you) press **Sample**.

 i. How do the widths of the intervals change? Why does this make sense?

 ii. How does the running total change? Why does this make sense?

e. To check your understanding about what 99% confidence means, suppose that you calculate a 99% confidence interval for the long-run proportion of orange to be (0.461, 0.589). For each of the following statements, indicate whether or not it is valid. If you think it is invalid, explain why.

 i. There is a 99% chance that the long-run proportion of Reese's Pieces candy that is orange is between 0.461 and 0.589.

 ii. We are 99% confident that the long-run proportion of Reese's Pieces candy that is orange is between 0.514 and 0.566.

 iii. If we were to repeat the process of taking random samples of 100 Reese's Pieces and then calculate a 99% confidence interval from the sample data for each of those samples, then in the long run, 99% of all those confidence intervals would contain the long-run proprotion of Reese's Pieces candy that is orange.

- -

SECTION 3.4   Summary

Confidence intervals generally have the form **statistic ± margin of error** where the margin of error is roughly approximated by two times the standard deviation of the statistic (for 95% confidence). For other confidence levels, we use a different multiplier. So the "accuracy" of our confidence interval depends on that multiplier and on the standard deviation of the statistic.

In estimating a population proportion (or process probability), the **midpoint** of the confidence interval is the observed value of the sample proportion, $\hat{p}$, and the **margin of error** depends on two main factors:

- Using a larger confidence level produces a larger margin of error and a wider confidence interval.

- A larger sample size produces a smaller margin of error and a narrower confidence interval.

A factor we have less control over is the value of the sample proportion. Values closer to 0.50 generally correspond to wider intervals.

In estimating a population mean, the **midpoint** of this confidence interval is the observed value of the sample mean, $\bar{x}$, and the **margin of error** depends on three main factors:

- Using a larger confidence level produces a larger margin of error and a wider confidence interval.

- A larger sample size produces a smaller margin of error and a narrower confidence interval.

- A smaller sample standard deviation produces a smaller margin of error and a narrower confidence interval.

Notice that the confidence level and sample size are chosen separately; neither one determines the other. Exploration 3.4B also illustrated how the confidence level provides a measure of how reliable our confidence interval method is. That is, how often, in the long run, we expect the confidence interval to successfully capture the actual parameter value of interest.

- -

INTRODUCTION

You have now studied many of the concepts related to drawing inferences about populations and processes based on samples. In this section we will examine several cautions related to making such inferences. Some of these cautions are related to difficulties with selecting a random sample, but some difficulties arise even with a random sample (the first part of this section). More issues are related to the difference between statistical significance and practical importance and to the kinds of errors that can occur with tests of significance (second part of this section).

3.5A ─ The Controversial "Bradley Effect"

Example 3.5A ▶

EXAMPLE

Tom Bradley, long-time mayor of Los Angeles, ran as the Democratic Party's candidate for governor of California against Republican candidate George Deukmejian in 1982. Political polls of samples of likely voters showed Bradley with a substantial lead in the days before the election. Even exit polls favored Bradley significantly, with many media outlets projecting Bradley as the winner. However, Bradley ended up narrowly losing the overall race. After the election, research suggested that a smaller percentage of white voters had voted for Bradley than polls had predicted and a very large proportion of voters who, in the polls, claimed to be undecided, had voted for Deukmejian.

> **THINK ABOUT IT**
>
> What are some explanations for this discrepancy?

Some have argued that the reason for the discrepancies in the polling numbers and the outcome of the election was what has since come to be known as the "Bradley effect." Namely, that the way likely voters answered the questions was subject to "social desirability bias"—meaning that some people answered the polling questions in the way that they thought the interviewer wanted them to answer—the politically correct way. Tom Bradley is black and George Deukmejian is white, so many respondents may have indicated they would vote for the black candidate, but then, given the anonymity of the voting booth, they voted for the white candidate.

Since the 1982 election, the Bradley effect has been cited in numerous races and extended beyond race to include sex and other stances on political issues. More recently, in the 2008 presidential primaries for the Democratic candidate, the Bradley effect was cited as a possible explanation for unexpected polling versus voting results in the New Hampshire and other primaries. In the 2008 New Hampshire Democratic primary, Hillary Clinton received 112,404 votes compared to Barack Obama's 104,815 votes. As 287,527 voters participated in the primary, this meant that Obama received only 36.45% of the primary votes compared to 39.09% of the voters selecting Clinton. This result shocked many, because in the days leading up to the primary, Obama seemed to hold a commanding lead over Clinton. Specifically, in a *USA Today/Gallup* poll of 778 likely voters, only days before the primary, 319/778, or 41% of likely voters, said they would vote for Obama, compared to only 218/778, or 28% of likely voters, saying they would vote for Clinton. How unlikely are the Clinton and Obama poll numbers given that 39.09% and 36.45% of actual primary voters voted for Clinton and Obama, respectively?

We will use a test of significance to evaluate this question, but let's talk about the assumptions our chance model will be making before we apply it.

We're assuming that the 778 people in the survey are a good representation of the people who will vote on primary day. But, there is no way that the 778 people in the survey are a simple random sample of primary voters. In order to take a simple random sample, pollsters would need to have a list of all voters in the election and randomly choose some, but that list (sampling frame) is impossible to obtain.

 3.5.1

Instead pollsters used **random digit dialing** and asked whether respondents were planning to vote in the upcoming Democratic primary. Only 9% of people (a total of 8,644 people were contacted) agreed to participate in the survey. Of these, 319 and 218, respectively, said that they planned to vote for Obama and Clinton in the upcoming election.

So, our model makes the following assumptions:

 3.5.2

1. Random digit dialing is a reasonable way to get a representative sample of likely voters.
2. The 9% of individuals reached by phone who agree to participate are like the 91% who didn't.
3. Voters who said they plan to vote in the upcoming Democratic primary will actually vote in the upcoming primary.
4. Respondents' answers to whom they say they will vote for matches who they actually vote for in the primary.

The parameter of interest in this study, denoted by π, is the probability a poll respondent will claim he or she will vote for Obama. The question is whether this parameter value is the same as the proportion of all likely voters who actually vote for Obama (observed on primary day to be 0.3645). If the Bradley effect is at play, the value of our parameter will be larger than 0.3645. In other words, people are more likely to say they will vote for Obama than they are to actually vote for Obama.

So the null and alternative hypotheses for our test of significance are:

H_0: The proportion of voters who will claim he or she plans to vote for Obama is 0.3645 ($\pi = 0.3645$).

H_a: The proportion of voters who will claim to vote for Obama is higher than 0.3645 ($\pi > 0.3645$).

Here are the results from a simulation where we simulated selecting 1,000 samples of 778 individuals randomly chosen from a large population where 36.45% of the individuals in the population vote for Obama (with the population proportion equal to 0.3645). We see in the output in Figure 3.14 that the probability of getting a sample proportion of at least $319/778 \approx 0.41$ successes is very small if the population proportion were 0.3645 (p-value is 0.004). In other words, it's very surprising for 41% to say they plan to vote for Obama in our poll if in reality only 36.45% plan to vote for Obama.

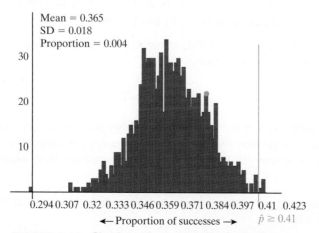

FIGURE 3.14 Simulated-based p-value for testing whether significantly more respondents indicated they planned to vote for Obama vs. Clinton.

So, the Obama poll result of 41% is significantly different from what happened on primary day. We have convincing evidence that the discrepancy between what people said they would do and how they actually voted is not explained by random chance alone (from the random sampling of the poll), suggesting that at least one of the four model assumptions is not true. Let's look at these explanations now.

Assumption #1. Random digit dialing is a reasonable way to get a sample of likely voters

Random digit dialing involves having a computer dial random phone numbers (in this case random digits after a New Hampshire area code) in order to select participants. Random digit dialing is roughly equivalent to a simple random sample of all New Hampshire residents who have a landline or cell phone, except for slightly overrepresenting individuals who have more than one phone. Random digit dialing is a common survey technique in cases where a sampling frame (list of all members of the population) is unavailable.

Assumption #2. The 9% of individuals reached by phone who agree to participate are like the 91% who didn't

Only 9% of individuals reached by phone agreed to participate. The 91% of people who didn't participate includes people who didn't answer their phone and individuals who said they did not wish to participate. The assumption is that the respondents are like the nonrespondents. Although the **response rate** was very low, it is in line with many polls and other surveys conducted by phone. So, though it is possible for nonrespondents to be the cause of the bias observed, many other political surveys (of different candidates and other voting issues) conducted around the same time had similar response rates but no bias. Of course, there is no guarantee that the 9% are representative.

Assumption #3. Voters who said they plan to vote in the upcoming Democratic primary will vote in the upcoming primary

It is typical to ask voters whether they plan to vote in the upcoming election/primary. But, there is no guarantee that they actually will. Sometimes the pollster will ask if the person voted in the previous election to gauge their commitment to voting in the upcoming election, but there is no guarantee they answer that question accurately either.

Assumption #4. Respondents' answers to whom they say they will vote for match who they actually vote for in the primary

There is no guarantee that people won't do something different in the voting booth from what they say they will do when on the phone.

EXPLANATION

Because of the wide disparity in the *USA Today/Gallup* poll, as well as nearly every other poll conducted prior to the New Hampshire primary, the AAPOR conducted an independent investigation and concluded the following were among the most likely explanations for the discrepancies:

1. People changed their opinion about who they were voting for at the last minute (Assumption #4).
2. People in favor of Hillary Clinton were more likely to be nonrespondents. Nonrespondents were more likely union households and those with less than a college education—groups that were more likely in favor of Clinton (Assumption #2).

3. Social desirability based on the race of the interviewer: black telephone interviewers were more likely to generate respondents who were in favor of Obama than were white interviewers, even though the race of the interviewer was randomly assigned to survey participants (Assumption #4). This is an example of the Bradley effect.

4. Clinton was listed before Obama on every ballot (Assumption #4).

If Assumption #4 is not valid, then even a pure random sample would have still exhibited this discrepancy in the results. Simple random samples should produce a representative sample, but they do nothing to control for the actions of the individuals in the sample. Having respondents change their minds or misrepresent their answers are examples of **nonrandom errors**, reasons why the statistic may not be close to the parameter that are separate from random errors (sample-to-sample variability by chance alone).

Furthermore, in this case, with only 9% of those called choosing to participate, there is the potential for large differences between the sample and population on any number of characteristics. In particular, because the resulting sample willing to participate is not a random sample, there is no guarantee that it is representative of likely primary voters.

KEY IDEA

Nonrandom (systematic) errors would still be a concern even if you could interview every single member of the population. In addition to the suspect memories and truthfulness of individuals when answering survey questions, other examples of nonrandom errors include the effects that the wording of a question can have on people's responses (e.g., how extreme the phrasing is) and the effects that the interviewer can have by virtue of his or her demeanor, sex, race, and other characteristics.

Voting for President

EXPLORATION

3.5A

In the 1998 General Social Survey, a random sample of 2,613 adult Americans revealed that 1,783 claimed to have voted in the 1996 presidential election.

1. Calculate the sample proportion who claimed to have voted. What symbol do we use for this value?

2. Describe (in words) the parameter that this sample proportion estimates.

3. Use the **Theory-Based Inference** applet to produce a 99% confidence interval for the population parameter.

4. Do you have 99% confidence that this interval captures the actual proportion of adult Americans who voted in the 1996 presidential election? Explain. (*Hint:* Think about a subtle distinction between the parameter and what this question asks.)

5. The Federal Election Commission reported that 49.0% of those eligible to vote in the 1996 presidential election actually voted. Is this value included within your 99% confidence interval?

6. Do not bother to conduct a significance test. But if you were to conduct a significance test of whether the sample data provide strong evidence to reject that the population proportion differs from 0.490, what can you say about how the p-value would turn out? Explain. (*Hint:* Base your answer on the 99% confidence interval.)

This example illustrates that a very difficult issue when conducting surveys is trying to elicit truthful responses from respondents. People may forget, or be unsure of how to answer an opinion question, or may outright lie in response to survey questions, especially if there is any "social expectation" to their answers. Statistical inference techniques such as confidence intervals and significance tests do not take these possible sources of **nonrandom error** into account.

> ### KEY IDEA
>
> Nonrandom (systematic) errors would still be a concern even if you could interview every single member of the population. In addition to the suspect memories and truthfulness of individuals when answering survey questions, other examples of nonrandom errors include the effects that the wording of a question can have on people's responses and the effects that the interviewer can have by virtue of his or her demeanor, sex, race, and other characteristics.

Another famous case of problems in presidential election polling

Founded in 1890, The *Literary Digest* was a popular magazine in the early 1900s. The magazine had correctly predicted the outcomes of the 1916, 1920, 1924, 1928, and 1932 presidential elections by conducting polls. With the Great Depression in full swing, the magazine ventured forth in 1936 to predict another presidential election outcome. Questionnaires were mailed out to more than 10 million adult Americans whose names and addresses were obtained from subscribers to the magazine and also from phone books and vehicle registration lists. More than 2.4 million responses were received, the largest survey that had ever been undertaken at that time, with 57% indicating that they planned to vote for Republican challenger Alf Landon over Democrat incumbent Franklin Roosevelt.

7. Identify the population and sample in this study. Also indicate (in words) what the relevant parameter and statistic are. If either of these values can be determined, perform the calculation(s).

   Population: _____

   Sample: _____

   Parameter: _____ (Known?) _____

   Statistic: _____ (Known?) _____

8. Do you expect a 99.9% confidence interval based on this sample result to be narrow or wide? Explain why.

   With such a huge sample size, we should have no hesitation in using the theory-based inference procedures for one proportion.

9. Use the **Theory-Based Inference** applet to produce a 99.9% confidence interval for the proportion of all adult Americans who intended to vote for Alf Landon in 1936. Report the value of the statistic and margin of error as well as the endpoints of the interval.

Estimate:	Endpoints:	Margin of error:

10. Did your answer to #8 turn out to be correct?

11. Alf Landon actually received 36.5% of the votes cast in the election. Does your 99.9% confidence interval include this value? Does it come close?

12. Do you think the *Literary Digest*'s extremely misleading result can be blamed on selecting a nonrepresentative sample or on nonrandom errors? Explain your answer.

The *Literary Digest* fiasco again illustrates the difficulty of selecting a representative sample from a population, even when a very large sample is selected. ***Voluntary response*** is an issue with many surveys, because those who choose to respond may be systematically different than those who choose not to respond.

13. An up-and-coming pollster named George Gallup made his first election prediction in 1936, the same year as the infamous *Literary Digest* poll. Gallup surveyed a sample of only 50,000 adult Americans and was able to predict the election result correctly. Do you think Gallup just got lucky or how do you suspect that he did better than *Literary Digest*?

The secret to Gallup's success was ***random sampling***. His success revealed that a random sample, even of a smaller size, is much more informative and valuable than a large sample from a biased sampling method. For any study that fails to use random sampling methods to select the sample, you should be very cautious in generalizing the results to a larger population. Also be aware that issues not associated with selecting a sample should be considered when drawing conclusions from survey results. People can often give inaccurate replies as a result of a poorly worded question, not being able to remember things correctly, or simply lying.

> ## KEY IDEA
>
> Consider two kinds of "errors":
>
> 1. *Nonrandom errors are mistakes.* They come from a bad choice of sampling methods, such as voluntary response and convenience sampling. They can also occur from biased ways of asking a question, bias from nonresponse, etc. Theory can't help fix nonrandom errors after the data have been collected.
> 2. *Random errors are not mistakes.* They are not errors in the everyday sense. These "errors" are planned; they come from the deliberate use of random chance to choose your sample. The margin of error tells the likely size of these errors. (Even though the term "error" is misleading, the word is still used because of its history in science.)
>
> Both types of errors still need to be considered even with a random sampling method.

SUMMARY

Nonrandom (systematic) errors describe reasons why sample results may not reflect the actual population for reasons other than poor sampling techniques. Examples of sources of nonrandom errors are:

- Wording of a question can make people respond differently.
- Order of questions can influence how a person responds.
- "Social desirability" can influence how a person responds to a question.
- The interviewer can affect how someone responds.
- People sometimes forget or misrepresent the truth.
- The measurement instrument used may not be accurate or valid or reliable.
- The sample is not taken randomly and may not be representative of the population.
- The participants are selected randomly, but because people choose not to participate, the sample is no longer representative.

Random errors are a way to describe sample-to-sample (chance) variability that is accounted for by the margin of error.

3.5B **Parapsychology Studies (*continued*)**

Example 3.5B

Recall the parapsychology study from Exploration 2.3. The receivers in the study tried to identify the target image that was being transmitted by the sender from a group of four possible target images. Statistician Jessica Utts reported that her analysis considered a total of 2,124 sessions and found a total of 709 "hits" (Utts, 2010).

For testing whether the sample data provide strong evidence that the long-run proportion of a successful transmission exceeds 1/4, the z-statistic turns out to be 8.9. In other words, the observed sample proportion of 0.334 is 8.94 standard deviations above the null value of 0.25. The p-value is essentially zero, and the observed result is statistically significant at every reasonable significance level. The test leaves virtually no doubt that the long-run proportion of a correct transmission is larger than 1/4.

> ### THINK ABOUT IT
>
> But is the probability of a successful transmission much greater than 1/4? How is this question different from what the test and p-value address? How could you investigate that question?

The test result and p-value only reveal that the data provide extremely strong evidence that the long-run proportion of a successful transmission is larger than 1/4. The test and p-value have nothing to say about *how much* larger than 1/4 this probability is. We can address this question (of how much larger) by producing a confidence interval to estimate the long-run proportion of a successful transmission.

Using the theory-based method, which is justified by the large number of successes (709) and failures (1,415) in the sample, a 95% confidence interval for this probability turns out to be (0.314, 0.354), and a 99% confidence interval is (0.307, 0.360).

> ### THINK ABOUT IT
>
> Determine the margin of error for the 95% confidence interval. Why are these confidence intervals quite narrow? Which interval is wider?

The margin of error for the 95% confidence interval is ± 0.020, because the interval can be written as 0.334 ± 0.020. These confidence intervals are quite narrow because the sample size (2,124 sessions) is fairly large. The 99% confidence interval is wider than the 95% confidence interval, because achieving more confidence requires a wider interval (more plausible values).

> ### THINK ABOUT IT
>
> Would you say that these confidence intervals contain values that are *much* larger than 1/4?

3.5.4

Even with a confidence level of 99%, the interval extends only to the value 0.36. Is a 36% success percentage much greater than 25%?

On the one hand, these data suggest that there may be some validity to the claims of psychics; the significance test leaves little doubt that the probability of a successful transmission in these studies is larger than 1/4. However, it is important to realize that although there is strong evidence that psychics *are* doing better than guessing, the confidence interval reveals that they are not doing *much* better than guessing. How practically important is that fact? That's a judgment call. But, this brings up an important point: just because a result is statistically significant does not mean that it is practically important. Of course, whether or not a result is of practical importance can be a subjective opinion left somewhat up to the person interpreting the research. The important thing to remember is that, especially when the sample size is large (so your confidence interval will be narrow), you may have a statistically significant result that doesn't necessarily provide a very practically important result.

> **KEY IDEA**
>
> Significant is not the same as important.
> 1. "Significant" means "statistically significant" and that means "too unlikely (when the null is true) to be plausible due to chance alone."
> 2. "Important" means "practically important" and that means the difference is large enough to matter in the real world.
>
> To be clear, always use the adjective: *statistically* significant, *practically* important.

> **KEY IDEA**
>
> Especially with large sample sizes, even a fairly small difference between an observed and hypothesized value can be statistically significant. In such cases a confidence interval for the parameter can help to decide whether the difference is **practically important**.

The article by Utts (2010) also refers to 56 individual studies that led to the combined total of 2,124 sessions that you have analyzed here. Most of these studies involved a sample size of about 50 sessions.

> **THINK ABOUT IT**
>
> Suppose that the actual value of the long-run proportion of a successful transmission is 1/3 rather than 1/4. In this situation, do you think it's very likely that a sample of 50 sessions will lead to correctly rejecting the null hypothesis that the long-run proportion is 1/4? Why or why not?

If π is equal to 1/3 and we fail to reject 1/4 as a plausible value, then we have committed a Type II error (see Section 2.3). The question now is how often we can expect to make such an error. As we discussed in Section 2.3, researchers usually talk about 1 minus the probability of a Type II error—the *power* of a study. Recall that power can be thought of as the probability of correctly rejecting a false null hypothesis.

 3.5.5

Let's investigate this question with simulation. The graph on the left in Figure 3.15 shows the could-have-been results (sample proportions) from simulating 10,000 samples of 50 sessions with a 0.25 probability of success per session. If we are using the $\alpha = 0.05$ significance level, then we will reject the null hypothesis that $\pi = 0.25$ whenever the sample proportion of successful transmissions is 0.38 or larger, because this is the smallest sample proportion that produces a p-value of 0.05 or less, as shown in the graph on the right.

FIGURE 3.15 Distributions of sample proportions when $\pi = 0.25$, with sample proportion corresponding to one-sided p-values below 0.05.

Now let's suppose that the actual long-run proportion of success is 1/3 rather than 1/4. In this case the alternative hypothesis is true, so we want to reject the null hypothesis. But is it likely that a sample of 50 sessions would produce a sample proportion of 0.38 or greater for the proportion of successful transmissions?

> **THINK ABOUT IT**
>
> How often do you think we would obtain a sample proportion of 0.38 or more (with a sample size of 50) when the actual long-run proportion of success is 1/3 rather than 1/4?

We can use another simulation to determine how likely it is to correctly reject the null hypothesis (of no psychic ability) when in fact the long-run proportion of success is 1/3 (Figure 3.16). The graph on the left below shows the results of 10,000 repetitions. The corresponding graph on the right reveals that only about 30% of the 10,000 samples produced a sample proportion of 0.38 or greater. This means that there's only about a 30% chance of rejecting the null hypothesis ($\pi = 1/3$), even though the null hypothesis is false in this situation ($\pi = 1/4$). This means that the power of the test is only about 30%; there is approximately a 70% chance of making a Type II error if the true success probability is 1/3 for this sample size.

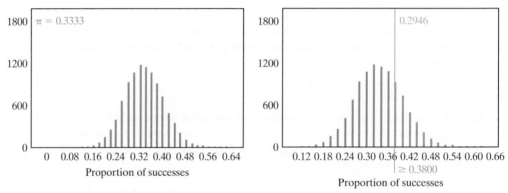

FIGURE 3.16 Distributions of sample proportions when $\pi = 0.3333$ and percentage that yield a sample proportion of at least 0.38.

> **THINK ABOUT IT**
>
> Would increasing or decreasing the significance level result in greater power? Would increasing or decreasing the sample size result in greater power? Explain your answers.

The power of a test is influenced by the significance level used and by the sample size:

- Using a larger significance level results in greater power. One way to understand this is that using a larger significance level means that you don't require as strong of evidence to reject the null hypothesis. This means that it's easier to reject the null hypothesis, whether that null hypothesis is true or not. This means that you're more likely to reject the null hypothesis when it is false, which results in greater power.
  - Greater power means a smaller probability of making a Type II error, so this is a good thing. The downside is that increasing the significance level means increasing the probability of making a Type I error.
- Increasing the sample size results in greater power. One way to understand this is that with a larger sample size, sample proportions vary less about the true parameter value (which is not the hypothesized value), so it's easier to obtain a sample proportion extreme enough to warrant rejecting the null hypothesis.
  - The downside is that using a larger sample size requires greater time, effort, and expense.

Power is also affected by a third factor:

- If the actual value of the parameter is farther away from the null value, then the test is more powerful.
  - So, for example, if the actual probability of a successful transmission is 1/2, then the power of the test is larger than if the probability is actually 1/3. We will be much more likely to obtain a sample proportion that is far from 1/3 if the actual process probability is 1/2 rather than 1/4. (See Figure 3.17.)

FIGURE 3.17   Distributions for sample proportions when $\pi = 0.50$ and proportion that yields a sample proportion of at least 0.38.

Cat Households

EXPLORATION

3.5B

A survey of 47,000 American households in 2007 found that 32.4% own a pet cat.

1. Is the value 32.4% (or, as a decimal, 0.324) a parameter or a statistic? What symbol would you use to represent this value?

2. Describe (in words) the parameter of interest here. What symbol would you use to represent this parameter?

3. Conduct a theory-based significance test of whether the sample data provide strong evidence that less than one-third of all American households own a pet cat. Specify the null and alternative hypotheses and calculate the z-statistic and p-value. Also indicate whether the sample result is statistically significant at the $\alpha = 0.001$ level. Summarize your conclusion and explain how it follows from the test.

4. Determine a 99.9% confidence interval for the proportion of all American households that have a pet cat.

5. Explain why this confidence interval is so narrow.

   Consider the following two possible conclusions:

- The sample data provide *very* strong evidence that less than one-third of all American households own a cat.

- The sample data provide strong evidence that *much* less than one-third of all American households own a cat.

6. Explain the difference between these two statements.

7. Which of these two statements can you use a p-value to assess? Which can you use a confidence interval to assess?

8. Which of the two conclusions would you draw from your analysis of these data? Explain your answer.

> ### KEY IDEA.
>
> Especially with large sample sizes, even a fairly small difference between an observed and hypothesized value can be statistically significant. In such cases a confidence interval for the parameter can help to decide whether the difference is ***practically important***.

Now suppose that you plan to take a random sample of only 100 American households and test whether the sample data provide strong evidence that less than one-third of all American households have a pet cat.

9. Use the **One Proportion** applet to simulate 1,000 random samples of 100 households each, assuming that one-third of all households have a pet cat. Use trial and error (or use your mouse to drag the red line) to determine which values of the sample proportion (below 0.3333) would produce a p-value of less than 0.05. (Note that these values would lead to rejecting the null hypothesis at the 0.05 significance level.)

Now suppose that the 30% of all American households have a pet cat, so the actual value of the population parameter is 0.3.

10. Do you suspect that a test of significance, based on a random sample of 100 households, will be likely to reject the null hypothesis that one-third of all households have a pet cat if in fact 30% of all households have a pet cat?

11. Use the **One Proportion** applet to simulate 1,000 random samples of 100 households each, assuming that 30% of all households have a pet cat. Use the applet to count how many and what proportion of the 1,000 samples produce a sample proportion of (your answer to #9) or smaller.

12. Reanswer #10 based on your answer to #11.

Recall that the probability of rejecting a false null hypothesis is called the *power* of the test. Tests with higher values of power are preferred over tests with lower values of power. Power can also be thought of as 1 minus the probability of a Type II error.

13. Based on your simulation analysis in #9 and #11, what is the approximate power of this test with a sample size of 100, a significance level of 0.05, and an alternative value of 30%?

14. Do you suspect that increasing or decreasing the significance level results in greater power? Explain your thinking.

15. Use the **One Proportion** applet to investigate the issue in #14 by changing the significance level from 0.05 to 0.10. First reanswer #9 using 0.10 as the significance level. Then reanswer #11, again assuming that 30% of all households have a pet cat but using the sample proportions determined for the new significance level. Report the approximate power and comment on whether power has increased or decreased from using a significance level of 0.05.

16. Do you suspect that increasing or decreasing the sample size results in greater power? Explain your thinking.

17. Use the **One Proportion** applet to investigate the issue in #16 by changing the sample size from 100 to 500. First reanswer #9 using 500 as the sample size. Then reanswer #11, again assuming that 30% of all households have a pet cat but for the sample proportions determined in #9 in a sample size of 100. Report the approximate power and comment on whether power has increased or decreased from using a sample size of 100.

18. Do you suspect that increasing or decreasing the actual value of the population proportion with a pet cat would result in greater power? Explain your thinking.

19. Use the **One Proportion** applet to investigate the issue in #18 by changing the population proportion from 0.30 to 0.20. Report the approximate power, explaining how you found it, and comment on whether power has increased or decreased from using a sample size of 100.

SECTION 3.5   Summary

Keep in mind that a test of significance or a confidence interval is only as good as the data you give it. If you have sampling errors or nonrandom errors in your data collection, then the results from our simulation-based and theory-based procedures could be quite misleading.

Two other cautions to keep in mind with regard to drawing inferences concern statistical significance vs. practical importance and the power of a test.

A result can be statistically significant without being practically important. A statistically significant result is simply one that is unlikely to have occurred by chance alone (a small p-value). However, even a small p-value does not tell you how much the statistic varies from the parameter and whether this is a meaningful difference. Practical importance can be assessed by producing a confidence interval. Especially with large sample sizes, a sample result can be statistically significant without being practically important. Judging the practical importance of a result depends upon the context and is best judged by the researchers who know the context well.

The power of a test is the probability of rejecting the null hypothesis when the null hypothesis is false. Especially with a small sample size, a significance test may fail to detect an effect that may really be present because the test is not powerful enough. Factors that influence power are:

- Using a larger significance level results in greater power. One way to understand this is that using a larger significance level means that you don't require as strong of evidence to reject the null hypothesis. This means that it's easier to reject the null hypothesis, whether that null hypothesis is true or not. This means that you're more likely to reject the null hypothesis when it is false, which results in greater power.

  - Greater power means a smaller probability of making a Type II error, so this is a good thing. The downside is that increasing the significance level means increasing the probability of making a Type I error.

- Increasing the sample size results in greater power. One way to understand this is that with a larger sample size, sample proportions vary less about the true parameter value so it's easier to obtain a sample proportion extreme enough to warrant rejecting the null hypothesis.

  - The downside is that using a larger sample size requires greater time, effort, and expense.

- If the actual value of the parameter is farther away from the null value, then the test is more powerful.

CHAPTER 3   Summary

In this chapter you learned about the logic that statisticians use to compute an interval of plausible (i.e., believable) values for a population parameter. This set of plausible values, called a **confidence interval**, comes with a measure of reliability, typically 95%, called the **confidence level**.

You explored how to determine confidence intervals for a population proportion in three different ways. In the first method you conducted repeated tests of significance to determine which values under the null would be rejected and which would be plausible. Doing so you learned the relationship between a p-value of a two-sided test and whether the value under the null will be contained in the corresponding interval. The second method, called the **2SD method**, approximated a 95% confidence interval of plausible values for the parameter as those values that fall within 2 standard deviations of the statistic. The third method, a theory-based approach or **one-proportion z-interval**, used similar logic to the 2SD method but allowed for a more precise interval as well as the use of various confidence levels. This third method is most commonly used in practice.

Most of this chapter focused on confidence intervals for a population *proportion*, but we also looked at confidence intervals for a population *mean*, using both a 2SD approach as well as the much more commonly used theory-based approach called the **one-sample t-interval**. You also explored factors like sample size and confidence level that impact the width of confidence intervals and then were reminded of some cautions about statistical inference in general.

CHAPTER 3
GLOSSARY

2SD method Approximating a confidence interval by taking the statistic and the standard deviation of the statistic (from simulation or formula) and extending two standard deviations in each direction from the statistic.

confidence intervals An inference tool used to estimate the value of the parameter, with an associated measure of uncertainty due to the randomness in the sampling method.

confidence level A statement of reliability in the confidence interval method.

critical value The multiplier, z^* or t^*, used in calculating the margin of error for a confidence interval.

estimation Describes how large the effect is in terms of a range of values for the parameter.

margin of error The half-width of a confidence interval.

nonrandom errors Reasons why the statistic may not be close to the parameter that are separate from random errors, which are accounted for by quantifying chance variability.

one-sample z-interval Theory-based confidence interval for a population proportion.

plausible value A parameter value tested under the null hypothesis where, based on the data gathered, we do not find strong evidence against the null.

practically important A large enough discrepancy between the statistic and the hypothesized parameter to be of interest in context.

random digit dialing A common sampling technique when a sampling frame is unavailable. It involves a computer randomly dialing phone numbers within a certain area code by randomly selecting the digits to be dialed after the area code.

response rate Of those selected to be in the sample, the percentage that respond.

standard error (SE) An estimate of the standard deviation of a statistic that is based on the data.

validity condition for one-sample z-procedures At least 10 successes and at least 10 failures.

validity conditions for one-sample t-interval The quantitative variable has a symmetric distribution or you have at least 20 observations and the sample distribution is not strongly skewed.

voluntary response Those included in the sample are self-selected by virtue of their response, they are not randomly selected to participate.

CHAPTER 3
EXERCISES

SECTION 3.1

3.1.1* Let π denote some population proportion of interest and suppose a 95% confidence interval for π is calculated to be (0.6, 0.7). Also, suppose that we want to test

$$H_0: \pi = 0.63 \quad \text{vs.} \quad H_a: \pi \neq 0.63$$

What can you say about the corresponding p-value?

A. The corresponding p-value will be smaller than 0.05.

B. The corresponding p-value will be larger than 0.05.

C. Need more information to answer this.

3.1.2 Let π denote some population proportion of interest and suppose a 99% confidence interval for π is calculated to be (0.60, 0.70). Also, suppose that we want to test

$$H_0: \pi = 0.74 \quad \text{vs.} \quad H_a: \pi \neq 0.74$$

What can you say about the corresponding p-value?

A. The corresponding p-value will be smaller than 0.05 but larger than 0.01.

B. The corresponding p-value will be larger than 0.05.

C. The corresponding p-value will be smaller than 0.01.

D. I can't say anything about the corresponding p-value until I run the test.

3.1.3* Let π denote some population proportion of interest and suppose a 95% confidence interval for π is calculated to be (0.63, 0.73) and a 99% confidence interval for π is calculated to be (0.61, 0.75). Also, suppose that we want to test

$$H_0: \pi = 0.74 \quad \text{vs.} \quad H_a: \pi \neq 0.74$$

What can you say about the corresponding p-value?

A. The corresponding p-value will be smaller than 0.05 but larger than 0.01.

B. The corresponding p-value will be larger than 0.05.

C. The corresponding p-value will be smaller than 0.01.

D. I can't say anything about the corresponding p-value until I run the test.

Cayle the cat

3.1.4 Suppose I am conducting a test of significance where the null hypothesis is my cat Cayle will pick the correct cancer specimen 25% of the time and the alternative hypothesis is that she will pick the cancer specimen at a rate different than 25%. I end up with a p-value of 0.002. I also construct 95% and 99% confidence intervals from my data. What will be true about my confidence intervals?

A. Both the 95% and the 99% intervals will contain 0.25.

B. Neither the 95% nor the 99% intervals will contain 0.25.

C. The 95% interval will contain 0.25, but the 99% interval will not contain 0.25.

D. The 95% interval will not contain 0.25, but the 99% interval will contain 0.25.

Grayce the cat*

3.1.5   Suppose I am conducting a test of significance where the null hypothesis is my cat Grayce will pick the correct cancer specimen 25% of the time and the alternative hypothesis is that she will pick the cancer specimen at a rate different than 25%. I end up with a p-value of 0.02. I also construct 95% and 99% confidence intervals from my data. What will be true about my confidence intervals?

A. Both the 95% and the 99% intervals will contain 0.25.

B. Neither the 95% nor the 99% intervals will contain 0.25.

C. The 95% interval will contain 0.25, but the 99% interval will not contain 0.25.

D. The 95% interval will not contain 0.25, but the 99% interval will contain 0.25.

Cayce the cat

3.1.6   Suppose I am conducting a test of significance where the null hypothesis is my cat Cayce will pick the correct cancer specimen 25% of the time and the alternative hypothesis is that he will pick the cancer specimen at a rate different than 25%. I end up with a p-value of 0.07. I also construct 95% and 99% confidence intervals from my data. What will be true about my confidence intervals?

A. Both the 95% and the 99% intervals will contain 0.25.

B. Neither the 95% nor the 99% intervals will contain 0.25.

C. The 95% interval will contain 0.25, but the 99% interval will not contain 0.25.

D. The 95% interval will not contain 0.25, but the 99% interval will contain 0.25.

Spinning rackets*

3.1.7   Tennis players often spin a racquet to decide who serves first. The spun racquet can land with the manufacturer's label facing up or down. A reasonable question to investigate is whether a spun tennis racquet is equally likely to land with the label facing up or down. (If the spun racquet is equally likely to land with the label facing in either direction, we say that the spinning process is fair.) Suppose that you gather data by spinning your tennis racquet 100 times, each time recording whether it lands with the label facing up or down. Further suppose that the 100 spins result in 46 with the label facing up and 54 with the label facing down. The resulting 95% confidence interval on the long-run proportion of times the racket lands face up is 0.36 to 0.56. This means that:

A. There is strong evidence the racket lands face up less than 50% of the time.

B. There is not strong evidence that the racket lands face up less than 50% of the time.

3.1.8   When conducting a two-sided test of significance, the value of the parameter under the null hypothesis is plausible and will be contained in a 95% confidence interval when:

A. The p-value is less than or equal to 0.05.

B. The p-value is greater than 0.05.

C. There is no relationship between the p-value and the confidence interval.

3.1.9*   When conducting a two-sided test of significance, the value of the parameter under the null hypothesis is not plausible and will not be contained in a 95% confidence interval when:

A. The p-value is less than or equal to 0.05.

B. The p-value is greater than 0.05.

C. There is no relationship between the p-value and the confidence interval.

3.1.10   We use confidence intervals to estimate the value of:

A. The population proportion

B. The sample proportion

C. The p-value

D. The standard deviation

3.1.11*   When we say that 0.50 is a plausible value for the population proportion, plausible means 0.50 will:

A. Be in the 95% confidence interval

B. Not be in the 95% confidence interval

3.1.12   Suppose a 95% confidence interval is constructed from a sample proportion and 0.50 is contained in the interval. Which of the following are true?

A. A 90% confidence interval constructed from the same sample proportion will definitely contain 0.50.

B. A 90% confidence interval constructed from the same sample proportion will definitely NOT contain 0.50.

C. A 99% confidence interval constructed from the same sample proportion will definitely contain 0.50.

D. A 99% confidence interval constructed from the same sample proportion will definitely NOT contain 0.50.

Dining out*

3.1.13 What proportion of San Luis Obispo (SLO) residents dine at restaurants at least once a week? To investigate, a local high school student, Deidre, decides to conduct a survey. She selects a random sample of adult residents of SLO, asks each participant whether he/she dines at restaurants at least once a week, and records their responses. Then, she uses her data to find a 95% confidence interval for the proportion of SLO adults who dine out at least once a week to be (0.38, 0.44).

a. The 99% confidence interval based on the same data would be:

   A. Narrower, because the more confident we are the narrower the interval

   B. Wider, because to be more confident we need to widen the interval

   C. We need more information to answer this.

b. According to the 95% confidence interval:

   A. There is not convincing evidence that less than half of SLO residents dine at restaurants at least once a week, because the interval does not contain 0.50.

   B. There is convincing evidence that less than half of SLO residents dine at restaurants at least once a week, because the interval does not contain 0.50.

   C. None of the above, because the confidence interval is unrelated to strength of evidence.

3.1.14 To determine a 95% confidence interval using the interval of plausible values method, what significance level should be used on the two-sided tests?

3.1.15* To determine a 99% confidence interval using the interval of plausible values method, what significance level should be used on the two-sided tests?

October 2013 Gallup poll

3.1.16 Based on an October 2013 Gallup poll, a 95% confidence interval for the proportion of American adults that think a degree from a well-respected university is more important for a young person to succeed than obtaining knowledge or skills to do a specific job is 0.43 to 0.51. Explain exactly what the confidence interval is estimating.

August 2013 Gallup poll*

3.1.17 Based on an August 2013 Gallup poll, a 95% confidence interval for the proportion of American adults that thought math was the most valuable subject they studied in school is 0.31 to 0.37. Explain exactly what the confidence interval is estimating.

3.1.18 Suppose we are constructing a confidence interval using repeated tests of significance to develop an interval of plausible values. Using two-sided tests each time with the following null hypotheses, we obtain the resulting p-values.

Null	p-value	Null	p-value
Proportion = 0.45	0.014	Proportion = 0.53	0.787
Proportion = 0.46	0.032	Proportion = 0.54	0.572
Proportion = 0.47	0.062	Proportion = 0.55	0.373
Proportion = 0.48	0.126	Proportion = 0.56	0.142
Proportion = 0.49	0.371	Proportion = 0.57	0.077
Proportion = 0.50	0.598	Proportion = 0.58	0.042
Proportion = 0.51	0.733	Proportion = 0.59	0.021
Proportion = 0.52	0.986	Proportion = 0.60	0.003

a. Using the results from the table, give a 90% confidence interval.

b. Using the results from the table, give a 95% confidence interval.

3.1.19* Suppose we are constructing a confidence interval using repeated tests of significance to develop an interval of plausible values. Using two-sided tests each time with the following null hypotheses, we obtain the resulting p-values.

Null	p-value	Null	p-value
Proportion = 0.45	0.007	Proportion = 0.53	0.602
Proportion = 0.46	0.012	Proportion = 0.54	0.124
Proportion = 0.47	0.045	Proportion = 0.55	0.084
Proportion = 0.48	0.079	Proportion = 0.56	0.052
Proportion = 0.49	0.121	Proportion = 0.57	0.034
Proportion = 0.50	0.254	Proportion = 0.58	0.019
Proportion = 0.51	0.643	Proportion = 0.59	0.012
Proportion = 0.52	0.986	Proportion = 0.60	0.004

a. Using the results from the table, give a 95% confidence interval.

b. Using the results from the table, give a 99% confidence interval.

3.1.20 Construct a 95% confidence interval for a population proportion using repeated tests of significance to develop an interval of plausible values based on a sample proportion of 0.52 from a sample of 300. Use two-sided tests with the following values under the null hypothesis to find the needed corresponding p-values to construct the interval.

Null	p-value	Null	p-value
Proportion = 0.45		Proportion = 0.53	
Proportion = 0.46		Proportion = 0.54	
Proportion = 0.47		Proportion = 0.55	
Proportion = 0.48		Proportion = 0.56	
Proportion = 0.49		Proportion = 0.57	
Proportion = 0.50		Proportion = 0.58	
Proportion = 0.51		Proportion = 0.59	
Proportion = 0.52		Proportion = 0.60	

3.1.21* Construct a 95% confidence interval for a population proportion using repeated tests of significance to develop an interval of plausible values based on a sample proportion of 0.52 from a sample of 600. Use two-sided tests with the following values under the null hypothesis to find the needed corresponding p-values to construct the interval.

Null	p-value	Null	p-value
Proportion = 0.45		Proportion = 0.53	
Proportion = 0.46		Proportion = 0.54	
Proportion = 0.47		Proportion = 0.55	
Proportion = 0.48		Proportion = 0.56	
Proportion = 0.49		Proportion = 0.57	
Proportion = 0.50		Proportion = 0.58	
Proportion = 0.51		Proportion = 0.59	
Proportion = 0.52		Proportion = 0.60	

July 2012 Gallup poll

3.1.22 In a July 2012 Gallup poll based on a representative sample of 1014 adult Americans, 48% reported drinking at least one glass of soda pop on a typical day. Now suppose that we test the null hypothesis $\pi = 0.50$ vs. the alternative hypothesis $\pi \neq 0.50$.

a. Describe (in words) what the symbol π represents here.

b. Use the **One Proportion** applet to determine the (approximate) two-sided p-value.

c. Based on the two-sided p-value you reported in part (b), does 0.50 appear to be a plausible value for π? Explain your reasoning.

d. How would this two-sided p-value compare to a one-sided p-value: larger, smaller, or the same?

e. Use the **One Proportion** applet for a single proportion, repeatedly testing other possible values for π, to determine plausible values and construct a 95% confidence interval for π.

f. Interpret the 95% confidence interval you reported in part (e).

3.1.23 The previous question gave the results of the Gallup poll where 48% of a sample of 1,014 adult Americans reported drinking at least one glass of soda pop on a typical day. Use the **One Proportion** applet, repeatedly testing possible values for π, to determine plausible values and construct a 99% confidence interval for π.

May 2013 Gallup poll*

3.1.24 In a May 2013 Gallup poll based on a representative sample of 1,535 adult Americans, 53% responded that they thought same-sex marriages should be legal and have the same rights as traditional marriages. Now suppose we test the null hypothesis $\pi = 0.50$ vs. the alternative hypothesis $\pi \neq 0.50$.

a. Describe (in words) what the symbol π represents here.

b. Use the **One Proportion** applet to determine the (approximate) two-sided p-value.

c. Based on the two-sided p-value you reported in part (b), does 0.50 appear to be a plausible value for π? Explain your reasoning.

d. Use the **One Proportion** applet, repeatedly testing other possible values for π, to determine plausible values and construct a 95% confidence interval for π.

e. Interpret the 95% confidence interval you reported in part (d).

3.1.25 The previous question gave the results of the Gallup poll where 53% of a sample of 1,535 adult Americans responded that they thought same-sex marriages should be legal and have the same rights as traditional marriages. Use the **One Proportion** applet, repeatedly testing possible values for π, to determine plausible values and construct a 99% confidence interval for π.

FAQ

3.1.26 Read FAQ 3.1.1 and then answer the following question.

Reporting a confidence interval is more informative than a test of significance.

A. Always.

B. Only if you are concerned with a reject or fail to reject test outcome, rather than measuring strength of evidence.

C. Never, the test of significance is always more informative.

3.1.27 Read FAQ 3.1.1 and then answer the following question.

True or false? You can find the strength of evidence of a test by looking at the confidence interval.

3.1.28 Read FAQ 3.1.1 and then answer the following question.

True or false? A confidence interval informs on all parameter values that are plausible, the test of significance only tells us about one parameter value.

SECTION 3.2

May 2011 Gallup poll*

3.2.1 A Gallup survey of 1001 randomly selected U.S. adults conducted May 2011 asked, "*In your opinion, which one of the following is the main reason why students get education beyond high school?*" Fifty three percent chose "to earn more money." Based on these data, I found the 95% confidence interval for the proportion of U.S. adults who choose "to earn more money" to be (0.499, 0.561). Which of the following is a valid statement?

A. A 99% confidence interval based on the same data would be narrower.

B. A 99% confidence interval based on the same data would be wider.

C. A 99% confidence interval based on the same data would have the same width as the 95% confidence interval.

Recent Gallup poll

3.2.2 A recent Gallup poll showed the president's approval rating at 60%. Some friends use this information (along with the sample size from the poll) and find theory-based confidence intervals for the proportion of all adult Americans that approve of the presidents performance. Of the following four confidence intervals, identify the ones that were definitely done *incorrectly*. (There may be more than one interval that is incorrect.)

A. (0.57, 0.63)

B. (0.60, 0.66)

C. (0.58, 0.62)

D. (0.47, 0.53)

3.2.3* Suppose a 95% confidence interval for a population proportion is found using the 2SD or theory-based method. Which of the following will *definitely* be contained in that interval?

A. The population proportion

B. The sample proportion

C. The p-value

D. All of the above

3.2.4 Which of the following is true of a 2SD confidence interval?

A. They are approximate 95% confidence intervals.

B. They can be used for any confidence level.

C. They give exactly the same results as a theory-based interval.

D. The SD represents the standard deviation of the sample data.

3.2.5* Which of the following is NOT true about theory-based confidence intervals for a population proportion?

A. They should only be used when you have at least 10 successes and 10 failures in your sample data.

B. The process used to construct the interval relies on a normal distribution.

C. They can be calculated using different confidence levels.

D. For a given sample proportion, sample size, and confidence level, different intervals can be obtained because of their random nature.

3.2.6 Suppose a 95% confidence interval for a population proportion is (0.30, 0.60). Rewrite this interval in the form of $\hat{p} \pm$ margin of error.

3.2.7* Suppose a 95% confidence interval for a population proportion is (0.27, 0.49). Rewrite this interval in the form of $\hat{p} \pm$ margin of error.

Election poll

3.2.8 To estimate the proportion of city voters who will vote for the Republican candidate in the election, two students, Manny and Nina, each decide to conduct polls in the city. Manny selects a random sample of 50 voters, while Nina selects a random sample of 100 voters. Suppose both samples result in 48% of the voters saying they will vote for the Republican candidate. Whose 95% confidence interval will have the larger margin of error: Manny's or Nina's? How are you deciding?

Board games*

3.2.9 The *2011 Statistical Abstract of the United States* includes a table reporting that a national survey in the fall of 2009 found that 18.2% of American adults played a board game in the past year. We can use this sample result to estimate the proportion of *all* adult Americans who had played a board game in the past year.

a. What additional information do you need in order to determine a 95% confidence interval for the probability that a randomly selected American adult had played a board game in the past year?

b. Consider three possible sample sizes for this study: 250, 1,000, and 4,000. Without performing any calculations, how do you expect three confidence intervals based on these sample sizes to compare to each other? Explain your reasoning.

c. Carry out the simulation at each sample size to get the SD and use the 2SD method to approximate the margin of error with each of these three sample sizes. Then produce the 95% confidence interval for each of these three sample sizes.

d. How do the midpoints of these intervals compare?

e. How do the widths of these intervals compare?

f. By how many times must the sample size increase in order to cut the margin of error in half?

g. Suppose that the sample size was really 1,000. Based on the confidence interval, do the sample data suggest that fewer than 25% of all adult Americans had played a board game in the past year?

Hearing loss in teens

3.2.10 A recent study examined hearing loss data for 1,771 U.S. teenagers. In this sample, 333 were found to have some level of hearing loss. News of this study spread quickly, with many news articles blaming the prevalence of hearing loss on the higher use of ear buds by teens. At MSNBC.com (8/17/2010), Carla Johnson summarized the study with the headline: "1 in 5 U.S. teens has hearing loss, study says." To investigate whether this is an appropriate or a misleading headline, you will conduct a test of significance with the following hypotheses:

Null: $\pi = 0.20$ Alternative: $\pi \neq 0.20$

a. Describe what the symbol π stands for in this context.

b. Use the **Theory-Based Inference** applet to determine a p-value.

c. Based on your p-value is there strong evidence that the proportion of all U.S. teens with some hearing loss is different than 1 in 5 (or 20%)?

d. Using the applet, find a 95% confidence interval for the proportion of U.S. teens that have some hearing loss.

e. What is the margin of error for you confidence interval from part (d) of this question?

f. Based on your confidence interval, is 0.20 a plausible value for the proportion of the population that has some hearing loss? Explain why or why not.

g. Based on your p-value, is 0.20 a plausible value for the proportion of the population that has some hearing loss? Explain why or why not.

Spinning dancer*

3.2.11 The spinning dancer (or silhouette illusion) is a moving image of a woman that appears to be spinning. Some people see her spinning clockwise and some see her spinning counterclockwise. A student showed other students this and found that 30 out of 50 (or 60%) of them saw her spinning clockwise. The student researcher was interested in the proportion of people that would see the dancer spinning clockwise. He created the following null distribution for this:

Probability of heads: 0.5

Number of tosses: 50

Number of repetitions: 1000

☑ Animate

Toss Coins

Total = 1000

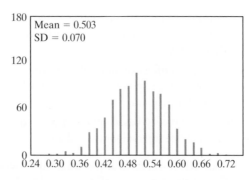

a. Using the information provided above, determine a 2SD 95% confidence interval for the population proportion of people that would see the woman spinning clockwise.

b. Based on your confidence interval, can you conclude the population proportion of people that will see the woman spinning clockwise is greater than 50%? Explain.

3.2.12 Using the sample proportion of 30 out of 50 students that saw the spinning dancer spin clockwise (see Exercise 3.2.11), answer the following:

a. Using the **Theory-Based Inference** applet, determine a 95% confidence interval for the probability a randomly chosen student would see the woman spinning *clockwise*.

b. Using the **Theory-Based Inference** applet, determine a 95% confidence interval for the probability a randomly chosen student would see the woman spinning *counterclockwise*.

Competent faces

3.2.13 In Example 1.4 we looked to see whether the competent-face method could be used to predict the results of Senate races. We found this method worked in 23 out of 32 races. When testing to see if the probability of this method working is more than 0.50, we obtained a null distribution similar to that shown.

Probability of heads: 0.5

Number of tosses: 32

Number of repetitions: 1000

☑ Animate

Toss Coins

Total = 1000

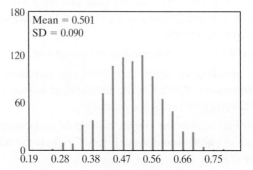

a. Using the information provided above, determine a 2SD 95% confidence interval for the probability the competent-face method will work.

b. Based on your confidence interval, can you conclude the probability the competent-face method will work is greater than 50%? Explain.

c. Why shouldn't a theory-based approach be used to compute the confidence interval for these data?

3.2.14 Recall that researchers also conducted a follow-up study predicting the outcomes of races in the House of Representatives with 189 correct predictions out of 279.

a. Use a simulation and the 2SD method to compute a 95% confidence interval.

b. Use a theory-based approach to generate the 95% confidence interval for these data.

c. Compare the intervals you computed in parts (a) and (b), why are they similar?

Water taste test*

3.2.15 Students at Hope College were tested to see if they could determine the difference between tap water and bottled water. Of the 63 students tested, 42 correctly identified which was which. We will assume the students tested are representative of all students at Hope College.

a. Find a theory-based 95% confidence interval for the population proportion that can correctly distinguish tap water from bottled water.

b. Find a theory-based 99% confidence interval for the population proportion that can correctly distinguish tap water from bottled water.

c. Suppose π is the proportion of all Hope College students that can correctly distinguish tap water and bottled water and we are testing the hypotheses Null: $\pi = 0.50$ and Alternative: $\pi \neq 0.50$. Based on just the confidence intervals you found in the previous questions, what can you say about the value of the p-value for this test?

3.2.16 Refer to the data in the previous question. Use the 2SD rule to find the 95% confidence interval. Why is it similar to the one you obtained in part (a) of the previous question?

July 2012 Gallup poll

3.2.17 In a July 2012 Gallup poll that surveyed 1014 randomly selected U.S. adults, 5% said that they considered themselves vegetarians.

a. Describe what the parameter is in this context.

b. The standard deviation (SD) from the simulated null distribution is 0.007. Use the 2SD method to find a 95% confidence interval for the parameter.

c. If we had 2020 in our sample, how would that change the width of our 95% confidence interval? (Circle the correct answer.)

Wider   Same width   Narrower

d. Using the **Theory-Based Inference** applet we find both 95% and 99% confidence intervals as shown below. Denote which is which.

(0.032, 0.068)   (0.037, 0.063)

Coke or Pepsi?*

3.2.18 Statistics students were conducting a test to see if people could taste the difference between Coke and Pepsi. They fill two cups with Coke and a third with Pepsi. They then asked their subjects which cola tasted different than the other two. Of the 64 people they tested, 22 were able to correctly identify which of the three cups of colas tasted different (i.e., which of the three cups was the Pepsi).

a. Conduct a simulation-based test of significance to determine if the proportion of people that correctly identify the different cola is greater than what would occur by just randomly guessing. Give the hypotheses, the p-value, and a conclusion.

b. Using the standard deviation from your null distribution in part (a), determine a 2SD confidence interval for the population proportion that can correctly identify the cola that is different?

c. Is the proportion under your null hypothesis from part (a) contained in your confidence interval from part (b)? Explain how this relates to the size of your p-value from part (a).

3.2.19 Statistics students conducted a test to see if people could taste the difference between Coke and Pepsi. They fill two cups with Coke and a third with Pepsi. They then asked their subjects which tasted different than the other two. Of the 64 people they tested, 22 were able to correctly identify which of the three cups of colas tasted different.

a. Determine a 95% theory-based confidence interval for the population proportion that can correctly identify the cola that is different?

b. What is the margin of error from your interval from part (a)?

Handedness

3.2.20 From a random sample of 97 male students at Hope College, 12 were left-handed. Determine a 99% confidence interval for the proportion of all male students at Hope College that are left-handed.

3.2.21 From a random sample of 92 female students at Hope College, 10 were left-handed. Determine a 99% confidence interval for the proportion of all female students at Hope College that are left-handed.

Facebook friend request*

3.2.22 In order to determine who would accept a Facebook friend request from someone they didn't know, a student researcher made up a phony Facebook profile that represented a female student at her college. She then sent out 118 friend requests and 61 of these accepted the request. Find a 95% confidence interval for the proportion of all students that would accept a Facebook request from a female at their college that they did not know.

3.2.23 In order to determine who would accept a Facebook friend request from someone they didn't know, a student researcher made up a phony Facebook profile that represented a male student at her college. She then sent out 101 friend requests and 18 of these accepted the request. Find a 95% confidence interval for the proportion of all students that would accept a Facebook request from a male at their college that they did not know.

Tasting Skittles

3.2.24 A sample of healthy students were blindly given a single Skittles candy to put in their mouth. They were told the five possible flavors and then were asked which flavor they had. Of the 154 students tested, 78 gave the correct answer. Find a 95% confidence interval for the proportion of all healthy students that could correctly identify a Skittles flavor blindly.

3.2.25 A sample of students that had stuffy or runny noses were blindly given a single Skittles candy to put in their mouth. They were told the five possible flavors and then were asked which flavor they had. Of the 118 students tested, 44 gave the correct answer. Find a 95% confidence interval for the proportion of all students with stuffy or runny noses that could correctly identify a Skittles flavor blindly.

3.2.26 Using the formula $\hat{p} \pm 1.96\sqrt{\hat{p}(1-\hat{p})/n}$, compute a 95% confidence interval for a population proportion given the sample proportion is 0.35 and the sample size is 1,000.

3.2.27 Using the formula $\hat{p} \pm 1.96\sqrt{\hat{p}(1-\hat{p})/n}$, compute a 95% confidence interval for a population proportion given the sample proportion is 0.65 and the sample size is 500.

3.2.28 Show that the margin-of-error formula $1.96\sqrt{\hat{p}(1-\hat{p})/n}$ simplifies to approximately $1/\sqrt{n}$ when $\hat{p} = 0.5$.

3.2.29 Using the simplified version for the margin of error from the previous exercise, $1/\sqrt{n}$, determine the smallest sample size needed so the margin of error is:

a. 0.06

b. 0.03

c. 0.01

FAQ

3.2.30 Read FAQ 3.2.1 and then answer the following question.

Match confidence interval terminology to the game of horseshoes.

A. Parameter	1. horseshoe
B. Confidence interval	2. proportion of times horseshoe is around stake
C. Coverage probability	3. Stake

3.2.31 Read FAQ 3.2.1 and then answer the following question.

True or False? There is a 95% chance that the parameter is contained in a 95% confidence interval.

3.2.32 Read FAQ 3.2.1 and then answer the following question.

True or False? For 95% confidence intervals constructed from repeated samples from the same population, 95% of the intervals contain the parameter.

SECTION 3.2: Part 2

3.2.33* In a 2009 Kaiser Family Foundation poll, 65% of the responding 8- to 18-year-olds said they played Super Mario at some time. The poll's margin of error at a 99% confidence level is about 3%. Based on these results, which of the following statements can we make (choose the best one)?

A. The percentage of all 8- to 18-year-olds that have played Super Mario is definitely between 62% and 68%.

B. We are 99% confident that the sample proportion that played Super Mario is between 62% and 68%.

C. The methods used in this poll will result in getting a sample proportion that is within 0.03 of the population proportion of 8- to 18-year-olds that have played Super Mario about 99% of the time (repeated samples from the same population).

D. The methods used in this poll will result in getting 99% of all sample proportions between 62% and 68%.

3.2.34 If you are testing the hypotheses H_0: $\pi = 0.60$ and H_0: $\pi \neq 0.60$, have a sample proportion of 0.75, and get a p-value of 0.021, what can you say about a 95% z-interval constructed using the same data?

A. The 95% confidence interval will definitely contain 0.021.

B. The 95% confidence interval will definitely not contain 0.75.

C. The 95% confidence interval will definitely contain 0.60.

D. The 95% confidence interval will definitely not contain 0.60.

E. None of the above

3.2.35* If you are testing the hypotheses H_0: $\pi = 0.50$ and H_0: $\pi \neq 0.50$, have a sample proportion of 0.60, and get a p-value of 0.321, what can you say about a 95% z-interval constructed using the same data?

A. The 95% confidence interval will definitely contain 0.321.

B. The 95% confidence interval will definitely not contain 0.321.

C. The 95% confidence interval will definitely not contain 0.60.

D. The 95% confidence interval will definitely contain 0.50.

E. The 95% confidence interval will definitely not contain 0.50.

3.2.36 Suppose you have a data set with the following summary statistics: $n = 500$ and $\hat{p} = 0.43$. Also suppose a 95% confidence interval is constructed from the summary statistics. If you realize that the sample proportion was supposed to be 0.33 and not 0.43, how would your confidence interval change? (Choose all that apply.)

A. Its center would increase.

B. Its center would decrease.

C. It would be wider.

D. It would be narrower.

E. It would have the same width.

3.2.37* Suppose you are calculating a 95% confidence interval for the proportion of all students at your school who have ever taken piano lessons. You survey 100 students and find that 60% of them had taken piano lessons in the past. From this, you determine your 95% confidence interval. Which of the following individual changes in your summary statistics (without changing anything else) would get you a narrower interval? (Choose all that apply.)

A. A larger sample size

B. A smaller sample size

C. A larger sample proportion

D. A larger confidence level

E. A smaller confidence level

Video games

3.2.38 Based on a 2009 Kaiser Family Foundation poll, a 95% confidence interval for the proportion of all U.S. 8- to 18-year-olds that have ever played either Guitar Hero or Rock Band is 0.69 to 0.73.

a. What proportion of the sample responded that they played Guitar Hero or Rock Band?

b. What is the margin of error for the confidence interval?

c. Explain what is measured by this margin of error.

3.2.39* Find the critical value z^* (or multiplier) that is needed for an 80% confidence interval.

3.2.40 Find the critical value z^* (or multiplier) that is needed for a 98% confidence interval.

3.2.41* You often see margins of errors in polling results listed as $\pm 3\%$. Using a conservative estimate for the population proportion, what sample size do you need to have a margin of error of at most 0.03 for a 95% confidence inter-

val? What sample size do you need to have a margin of error of at most 0.03 for a 99% confidence interval?

Espresso-based beverages

3.2.42 According to the National Coffee Drinking Study from the National Coffee Association, in 2016 36% of U.S. 18- to 24-year-olds reported that they daily consumed espresso-based beverages. Using this sample proportion as an estimate for the population proportion, what sample size would you need to get a 95% confidence interval with a margin of error of:

a. 3%.

b. 1%.

Cell phone*

3.2.43 In a survey conducted in 2009 by the Kaiser Family Foundation, a random sample of 2,002 American youth, 8–18 years of age, was asked a number of questions. One question was whether they *personally* had a cell phone and 66% answered yes.

a. Identify the parameter estimated by the poll and the theory-based method you will use to construct a confidence interval.

b. Verify the validity conditions for the theory-based method you have chosen.

c. Construct a 95% confidence interval, showing the values that you substitute into the formula.

d. Interpret the confidence interval you obtained in the context of the problem.

e. Is it plausible that 70% of American youth personally own a cell phone? Explain how you are deciding.

3.2.44 Repeat parts (c) and (d) from the previous question, but construct a 90% confidence interval. How do the width and midpoint of this confidence compare to the 95% confidence interval?

3.2.45 Use the sample proportion found in Question 3.2.43 as an estimate for the population proportion to find the minimum sample size needed to have a margin of error of at most 0.01 for a 95% confidence interval.

No more cash?

3.2.46 With the increased use of credit cards, debit cards, and other electronic methods of payment, will the United States eventually stop using cash? In a July 2016 Gallup poll of a random sample of 1,024 U.S. adults, 635 of them thought the United States would become a cashless society in their lifetimes.

a. Identify the parameter estimated by the poll and the theory-based method you will use to construct a confidence interval.

b. Verify the validity conditions for the theory-based method you have chosen. In particular, do you believe the population size is much larger than the sample size?

c. Construct a 95% confidence interval, showing the values that you substitute into the formula.

d. Interpret the confidence interval you obtained in the context of the problem.

3.2.47 Repeat parts (c) and (d) from the previous question, but construct a 99% confidence interval. How do the width and midpoint of this confidence compare to the 95% confidence interval?

3.2.48 Use the sample proportion found in Question 3.2.46 as an estimate for the population proportion to find the minimum sample size needed to have a margin of error of at most 0.01 for a 99% confidence interval.

Climate change*

3.2.49 A poll sponsored by the Nature Conservancy surveyed a random sample of 602 American high-school-age students in 2011. They found that 76% of them strongly agree with the statement, "Issues like climate change can be solved if action is taken now."

a. Identify the parameter estimated by the poll and the theory-based method you will use.

b. Verify the validity conditions for the theory-based method you have chosen.

c. Construct a 95% confidence interval, showing the values that you substitute into the formula.

d. Interpret the confidence interval you obtained in the context of the problem.

e. Are you convinced that more than half of American high-school students believe climate change can be solved if action is taken now? Explain how you are deciding.

3.2.50 Repeat parts (c) and (d) from the previous question, but construct a 90% confidence interval. How do the width and midpoint of this confidence compare to the 95% confidence interval?

3.2.51 Reconsider Question 3.2.49, where 76% of high school students agreed with the statement, "Issues like climate change can be solved if action is taken now."

a. Use the sample proportion found in Question 3.2.49 as an estimate for the population proportion to find the minimum sample size needed to have a margin of error of at most 0.03 for a 95% confidence interval.

b. Would the sample size need to be larger or smaller for 90% confidence? Explain.

c. Explain how the sample size requirement would change for part b if instead we planned to sample all American high-school and middle-school students.

Spinning coins

3.2.52 Although flipping a coin should result in 50% heads in the long run, what proportion of the time will spinning coins on a table result in landing heads up? Determine this with a coin of your choice, making sure you have enough trials to meet the validity conditions of a one-proportion z-interval. In doing so,

a. State and verify the validity conditions for the one-proportion z-interval.

b. Give the sample statistic.

c. Determine a 95% confidence interval.

d. Interpret the confidence interval you obtained in the context of the problem.

SECTION 3.3

3.3.1* True or false? When using the 2SD method to find a 95% confidence interval for the mean, multiply the standard deviation of the quantitative variable by 2 to obtain the margin of error.

3.3.2 True or false? In general, there will be more variability in the sample means across samples than in the variability in the quantitative variable across observational units.

3.3.3* True or false? If you are concerned that the validity conditions aren't met, use a theory-based approach to compute a confidence interval for the mean.

How much TV do you watch?

3.3.4 According to a 2011 report by the United States Department of Labor, civilian Americans spend 2.75 hours per day watching television. A faculty researcher, Dr. Sameer, at California Polytechnic State University (Cal Poly) conducts a study to see whether a different average applies to Cal Poly students. Suppose that for a random sample of 100 Cal Poly students, the mean and standard deviation of hours per day spent watching TV turns out to be 3.01 and 1.97 hours, respectively. The data were used to find a 95% confidence interval: (2.619, 3.401) hours/day. Which of the following are valid interpretations of the 95% confidence interval? For each of the following, statements, say whether it is VALID or INVALID.

a. About 95% of all Cal Poly students spend between 2.619 and 3.401 hours/day watching TV.

b. There is a 95% chance that, on average, Cal Poly students spend between 2.619 and 3.401 hours/day watching TV.

c. We are 95% confident that, on average, these 100 Cal Poly students spend between 2.619 and 3.401 hours/day watching TV.

d. In the long run, 95% of the sample means will be between 2.619 and 3.401 hours.

e. None of the above.

3.3.5   Reconsider the previous question about hours spent watching TV every day. Suppose that the data had actually been collected from a sample of 150 students, and *not* 100, but everything else (mean and SD) was the same as reported earlier. How, if at all, would the *new* 95% confidence interval based on these data differ from the interval mentioned earlier: (2.619, 3.401) hours?

a. The *new* interval would still be (2.619, 3.401) hours, because we are still 95% confident.

b. The *new* interval would be narrower than (2.619, 3.401) hours, because the sample size is bigger.

c. The *new* interval would be wider than (2.619, 3.401) hours, because the sample size is bigger.

d. More information is needed to answer this question.

Rattlesnakes*

3.3.6   Here is a dotplot for the ages of 21 male rattlesnakes captured at a single site. Assume that these 21 snakes can be regarded as a random sample of all male rattlesnakes at that site. The average age is 8.571 years, with a standard deviation of 2.942 years. An approximate 95% confidence interval is calculated to be (7.2318, 9.9102).

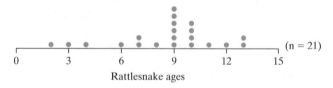

Rattlesnake ages

a. What is the observational unit for this data set? What is the population? What is the sample?

b. Which, if any, of the validity conditions for using a theory-based interval are satisfied? Explain your answer.

c. What is the parameter being estimated by the interval?

d. True or false? The chance that the interval contains the parameter value is about 95%. Explain your answer.

Sunscreen

3.3.7   Most dermatologists recommend using sunscreens that have a Sun Protection Factor (SPF) of at least 30. One of the authors wanted to find out whether the SPF of sunscreens used by students at her school exceeds this value on average? To collect data, the author surveyed students in her introductory statistics course and found that in a sample of 48 students the mean SPF was 35.29 and the standard deviation of SPF was 17.19. The data were not strongly skewed.

a. Identify the observational units for this study.

b. Identify the variable of interest and whether it is categorical or quantitative.

c. Use the **Theory-Based Inference** applet to find and report the 95% confidence interval for the parameter of interest *and* provide an interpretation of the interval, in the context of the study.

d. Assuming she has a representative sample, based on the confidence interval, is the average SPF of sunscreens of the students at the author's school higher than 30? How are you deciding?

e. Are the conditions required for the validity of the above results satisfied? State the condition(s) and explain your reasoning.

Studying statistics*

3.3.8   In a precourse, anonymous survey of students in her introductory statistics course, one of the authors asked her students how many hours per week they expected to spend studying statistics outside of class. Forty-nine students responded to that question, with an average of 8.2 hours and a SD of 3.79 hours. The data were not strongly skewed.

a. Identify the observational unit for this study.

b. Identify the variable of interest and whether it is categorical or quantitative.

c. Use the **Theory-Based Inference** applet to calculate and report the 95% confidence interval for the parameter of interest.

d. In the context of this study, was it valid to use the theory-based (*t*-distribution) approach to find a confidence interval? Explain your reasoning.

e. Interpret the 95% confidence interval reported in part (c) in the context of the study.

How cool are you?

3.3.9   Normal (or average) body temperature of humans is often thought to be 98.6° F. Is that number really the average? To test this, we will use a data set obtained from 65 healthy female volunteers aged 18 to 40 that were participating in vaccine trials. We will assume this sample is representative of a population of all healthy females.

a. The mean body temperature for the 65 females in our sample is 98.39° F and the standard deviation is 0.743° F. The data are not strongly skewed. Use the **Theory-Based Inference** applet to find a 95% confidence interval for the population mean body temperature for healthy females.

b. Based on your confidence interval, is 98.6° F a plausible value for the population average body temperature or is the average significantly more or less than 98.6° F? Explain how you are determining this.

c. In the context of this study, was it valid to use the theory-based (*t*-distribution) approach to find a confidence interval? Explain your reasoning.

3.3.10   As was explained in the previous question, the normal (or average) body temperature of humans is often thought to be 98.6° F. Is that number really the average? To test this, we will use a data set obtained from 65 healthy male volunteers aged 18 to 40 that were participating in vaccine trials. We will assume this sample is representative of a population of all healthy males.

a. The data set can be found on the textbook website as **MaleTemps**. Use the **Theory-Based Inference** applet to find a 95% confidence interval for the population mean body temperature for healthy males.

b. Based on your confidence interval, is 98.6° F a plausible value for the population average body temperature or is the average significantly more or less than 98.6° F? Explain how you are determining this.

c. In the context of this study, was it valid to use the theory-based (t-distribution) approach to find a confidence interval? Explain your reasoning.

Traveling across the USA*

3.3.11 One of the authors came across an article (*USA Today*, 2008) that said that on average Americans have visited 16 states in the United States. In a survey of 50 students in her introductory statistics class, she found the average number of states the students had visited to be 9.48 and the standard deviation to be 7.13. The data were not strongly skewed.

a. Identify the observational unit for this study.

b. Identify the variable of interest and whether it is categorical or quantitative.

c. Clearly the sample is not a randomly selected sample but a convenience sample. With this in mind, would it still be okay to treat the sample as representative of the population of students at the author's school with regard to "number of states visited"? Explain.

d. Regardless of your answer to part (c), state the null and the alternative hypotheses in symbols, to test whether the average number of states all students at the author's school have visited is different from 16.

e. Use the 2SD approach to find a 95% confidence interval for the average number of states all students at the author's school have visited.

3.3.12 Reconsider the previous question about the average number of states all students at the author's school have visited. Recall that in the author's sample of 50 students the average number of states the students had visited was 9.48 and the standard deviation was 7.13.

a. Use the **Theory-Based Inference** applet to find a 95% confidence interval for the average number of states all students at the author's school have visited.

b. Does the 95% confidence interval that you have reported in part (a) provide evidence that the average number of states all students at the author's school have visited is different from 16?

c. In the context of this study, was it valid to use the theory-based (t-distribution) approach to find a confidence interval? Explain your reasoning.

3.3.13 Reconsider the previous exercises about the average number of states all students at the author's school have visited. Recall that in the author's sample of 50 students the average number of states the students had visited was 9.48 and the standard deviation was 7.13.

a. Use the **Theory-Based Inference** applet to find and report an 88% confidence interval and interpret this interval in the context of the study.

b. Explain why you cannot use a simulation-based 2SD method to find an 88% confidence interval for the average number of states all students at the author's school have visited.

3.3.14 Reconsider the previous exercises about the average number of states all students at the author's school have visited. Using the data from the author's sample, a 99% confidence interval for the average number of states all students at the author's school have visited is found to be (6.78, 12.18). For each of the following statements, say whether VALID or INVALID.

a. We are 99% confident that the average number of states visited by the 50 students the author surveyed is between 6.78 and 12.18.

b. Based on the 99% confidence interval, there is evidence that the number of states all students at the author's school have visited is different from 16.

c. Based on the 99% confidence interval, there is evidence that the number of states all students at the author's school have visited is 16.

d. We are 99% confident that the average number of states visited by all students at the author's school is between 6.78 and 12.18.

e. About 99% of the students at the author's school have visited between 6.78 and 12.18 states.

f. If we want to be less than 99% confident, we should take a smaller sample of students.

Needles!

3.3.15 Consider a manufacturing process that is producing hypodermic needles that will be used for blood donations. These needles need to have a diameter of 1.65 mm—too big and they would hurt the donor (even more than usual), too small and they would rupture the red blood cells, rendering the donated blood useless. Thus, the manufacturing process would have to be closely monitored to detect any significant departures from the desired diameter. During every shift, quality control personnel take a random sample of several needles and measure their diameters. If they discover a problem, they will stop the manufacturing process until it is corrected. Suppose the most recent random sample of 35 needles have an average diameter of 1.64 mm and a standard deviation of 0.07 mm. Also, suppose the diameters of needles produced by this manufacturing process have a bell-shaped distribution.

a. Identify the observational unit for this study.

b. Identify the variable of interest and whether it is categorical or quantitative.

c. Use the 2SD approach to find a 95% confidence interval for the average diameter of needles produced by this manufacturing process.

3.3.16 Reconsider the investigation of the manufacturing process that is producing hypodermic needles. Recall that the most recent random sample of 35 needles have an average diameter of 1.64 mm and a standard deviation of 0.07 mm.

a. In the context of this study, explain why it is valid to use the theory-based (*t*-distribution) approach to find a confidence interval?

b. Use the **Theory-Based Inference** applet to find and report a 95% confidence interval for the average diameter of needles produced by this manufacturing process.

c. Based on the above 95% confidence interval alone, is there evidence that the average diameter of needles produced by this manufacturing process is different from 1.65 mm? How are you deciding?

3.3.17 Reconsider the investigation of the manufacturing process that is producing hypodermic needles. Recall that the most recent random sample of 35 needles have an average diameter of 1.64 mm and a standard deviation of 0.07 mm.

a. Use the **Theory-Based Inference** applet to find and report a 98% confidence interval and interpret this interval in the context of the study.

b. Explain why you cannot use a simulation-based 2SD method to find a 98% confidence interval for the average diameter of needles produced by this manufacturing process.

3.3.18 Reconsider the investigation of the manufacturing process that is producing hypodermic needles. Using the data from the most recent sample of needles, a 90% confidence interval for the average diameter of needles is found to be (1.62 mm, 1.66 mm). For each of the following statements, say whether VALID or INVALID.

a. We are 90% confident that the average diameter of the sample of 35 needles is between 1.62 and 1.66 mm.

b. Based on the 90% confidence interval, there is evidence that the average diameter of needles produced by this manufacturing process is 1.65 mm.

c. Based on the 90% confidence interval, there is evidence that the average diameter of needles produced by this manufacturing process is different from 1.65 mm.

d. We are 90% confident that the average diameter of needles produced by this manufacturing process is between 1.62 and 1.66 mm.

e. About 90% of the needles produced by this manufacturing process have a diameter between 1.62 and 1.66 mm.

f. If we want to be more than 90% confident, we should take a larger sample of needles.

Facebook friends*

3.3.19 In a survey of her introductory statistics class, an instructor found the average number of Facebook friends the 49 respondents had was 539.2 and the standard deviation was 298. The data on number of Facebook friends are not strongly skewed.

a. Identify the observational unit for this study.

b. Identify the variable of interest and whether it is categorical or quantitative.

c. In the context of this study, explain why it is valid to use the theory-based (*t*-distribution) approach to find a confidence interval?

d. Use the **Theory-Based Inference** applet to find and report a 95% confidence interval for the parameter of interest. Also, interpret the interval in the context of the study.

3.3.20 Reconsider the previous question about number of Facebook friends. Using the data from the sample of 49 students, a 99% confidence interval for the average number of Facebook friends is found to be (425.0, 653.4). For each of the following statements, say whether VALID or INVALID.

a. We are 99% confident that the average number of Facebook friends the 49 students who were surveyed have is between 425 and 653.4.

b. We are 99% confident that the average number of Facebook friends all such people have is between 425 and 653.4.

c. About 99% of all such people have between 425 and 653.4 number of friends, on average.

Textbook prices

3.3.21 Two Cal Poly freshmen gathered data on the prices for a random sample of 30 textbooks from the campus bookstore. They found the average price was $65.02, and the standard deviation of prices was $51.42. The data are not strongly skewed.

a. Identify the observational unit for this study.

b. Identify the variable of interest and whether it is categorical or quantitative.

c. Explain how you know from the sample average and sample standard deviation that the distribution of textbook prices is not bell-shaped.

d. In the context of this study, explain why it is valid to use the theory-based (*t*-distribution) approach to find a confidence interval?

e. Use the **Theory-Based Inference** applet to find and report a 95% confidence interval for the parameter of interest. Also, interpret the interval in the context of the study.

Mercury level in tuna*

3.3.22 Data were collected on random specimens of tuna from 1991 and 2010. The mercury level for each fish specimen was recorded. For the sample of 43 specimens of Albacore tuna, the average mercury level was found to be 0.358 parts per million (ppm) and the standard deviation of mercury level to be 0.138 ppm. The data are not strongly skewed.

a. Identify the observational unit for this study.

b. Identify the variable of interest and whether it is categorical or quantitative.

c. In the context of this study, explain why it is valid to use the theory-based (*t*-distribution) approach to find a confidence interval?

d. Use the **Theory-Based Inference** applet to find and report a 95% confidence interval for the parameter of interest. Also, interpret the interval in the context of the study.

3.3.23 Data were collected on random specimens of Yellowfin tuna from 1991 and 2010. For the sample of 231 specimens of Yellowfin tuna, the average mercury level was found to be 0.354 ppm and the standard deviation of mercury level to be 0.231 ppm. The data are not strongly skewed.

a. In the context of this study, explain why it is valid to use the theory-based (*t*-distribution) approach to find a confidence interval?

b. Use the **Theory-Based Inference** applet to find and report a 95% confidence interval for the parameter of interest. Also, interpret the interval in the context of the study.

Haircut prices

3.3.24 How much do you typically pay, including tips, for a haircut? In a survey of 50 students in her class, one of the authors found the average amount paid for haircuts to be $45.68 and the standard deviation to be $39.95. The data are not strongly skewed.

a. Explain how you know from the sample average and sample standard deviation that the distribution of price of haircuts is not bell-shaped.

b. In the context of this study, explain why it is valid to use the theory-based (*t*-distribution) approach to find a confidence interval?

c. Use the **Theory-Based Inference** applet to find and report a 95% confidence interval for the parameter of interest. Also, interpret the interval in the context of the study.

Close friends*

3.3.25 One of the questions asked of a random sample of adult Americans on the 2004 General Social Survey (GSS) was:

From time to time, most people discuss important matters with other people. Looking back over the last six months—who are the people with whom you discussed matters important to you? Just tell me their first names or initials.

The interviewer then recorded how many names each person gave. The GSS is a survey of a representative sample of U.S. adults who are not institutionalized.

There were 1467 responses, and the average number of close friends reported was 1.987, with a standard deviation of 1.771. The data are not strongly skewed.

a. Explain how you know from the sample average and sample standard deviation that the distribution of number of close friends people tend to report is not bell-shaped.

b. In the context of this study, explain why it is valid to use the theory-based (*t*-distribution) approach to find a confidence interval?

c. Use the **Theory-Based Inference** applet to find and report a 99% confidence interval for the parameter of interest. Also, interpret the interval in the context of the study.

d. Based on the above 99% confidence interval alone, is there evidence that the average number of close friends people tend to report is different from 2? How are you deciding?

FAQ

3.3.26 Read FAQ 3.3.1 and then answer the following question.

Describe three different methods for constructing a confidence interval for a population proportion.

3.3.27 Read FAQ 3.3.1 and then answer the following question.

Which method can only construct a 95% confidence interval?
A. Range of plausible values
B. 2 SD
C. Theory-based one-proportion *z*-interval

SECTION 3.3: Part 2

3.3.28* If you are testing the hypotheses $H_0: \mu = 3$ and $H_a: \mu \neq 3$, have a sample mean of 2, and get a p-value of 0.341, what can you say about a 95% *t*-interval constructed using the same data?

A. The 95% confidence interval will definitely contain 0.341.
B. The 95% confidence interval will definitely not contain 0.341.
C. The 95% confidence interval will definitely not contain 2.
D. The 95% confidence interval will definitely contain 3.
E. The 95% confidence interval will definitely not contain 3.

3.3.29 If you are testing the hypotheses $H_0: \mu = 4$ and $H_a: \mu \neq 4$, have a sample mean of 5, and get a p-value of 0.021, what can you say about a 95% *t*-interval constructed using the same data?

A. The 95% confidence interval will definitely contain 0.021.

B. The 95% confidence interval will definitely not contain 5.

C. The 95% confidence interval will definitely contain 4.

D. The 95% confidence interval will definitely not contain 4.

E. None of the above.

3.3.30* Suppose you have a data set with the following summary statistics: $n = 30$, $\bar{x} = 5.23$ and $s = 1.96$. Also suppose a 95% confidence interval is constructed from the summary statistics. If you realize that the standard deviation was supposed to be 2.96 and not 1.96, how would your confidence interval change?

A. Its center would move up one unit.

B. Its center would move down one unit.

C. It would be wider.

D. It would be narrower.

E. It would have the same width.

3.3.31 Suppose we have a collection of the heights of all students at your school. Also suppose 100 random samples of size 40 are taken from these heights, and from each of these samples a 95% confidence interval for the mean height of all students at your school is constructed. Which of the following statements about the 100 confidence intervals is most accurate?

A. About 95% of the heights of all students at the college will be contained in these intervals.

B. About 95% of the time, the sample mean height will be contained in its corresponding interval.

C. About 95% of the intervals will contain the population mean height.

D. About 95% of the intervals will be identical.

3.3.32* Suppose you are calculating a 95% confidence interval for the average weight of a certain type of bag of potato chips. You collect a sample of 15 bags and find a mean weight of 10.15 oz and a SD of 0.23 oz. From this, you determine your 95% confidence interval. Which of the following individual changes in your summary statistics (without changing anything else) would result in a narrower interval? (Choose all that apply.)

A. A larger sample size

B. A smaller sample size

C. A larger sample mean

D. A smaller sample mean

E. A larger sample standard deviation

F. A smaller sample standard deviation

G. A larger confidence level

H. A smaller confidence level

3.3.33 If you are finding a 95% *t*-interval using data that has a sample size of 36, a sample mean of 4.75, and a sample standard deviation of 1.55, how many degrees of freedom do you use for the critical t^* (or multiplier)?

3.3.34* Find the critical value t^* (or multiplier) that is needed for a 90% confidence interval from a random sample of size 25. Is this larger or smaller than the z^* value for 90% confidence?

3.3.35 Find the critical value t^* (or multiplier) that is needed for a 95% confidence interval from a random sample of size 30. Is this larger or smaller than the z^* value for 95% confidence?

3.3.36* Find the critical value t^* (or multiplier) that is needed for a 99% confidence interval from a random sample of size 55.

Haircut costs

3.3.37 A random sample of 16 college students was asked to give the cost of their last haircut. The results in dollars are shown in the following dotplot. Would it be valid to use a one-sample *t*-interval to estimate the population mean haircut cost based on these data? Explain why or why not.

Haircut cost

Mothers' heights*

3.3.38 A random sample of 16 college students was asked to report their mother's height in inches and the results are shown in the following dotplot. Would it be valid to use a one-sample *t*-interval to estimate the population mean height based on these data? Explain why or why not.

Mother's height

Time Estimates

3.3.39 Student researchers wanted to know whether students at their school could accurately estimate the length of a 17-second song snippet on average. They played 17 seconds of Corinne Bailey Rae's song "Put Your Records On" to 25 students, with the results shown in the following dotplot. The mean length is 13.8 seconds and the standard deviation is 5.416 seconds.

Estimated time

a. Identify the parameter estimated by the students and the theory-based method you will use to construct a confidence interval.

b. Verify the validity conditions for the theory-based method you have chosen.

c. Construct a 95% confidence interval, showing the values that you substitute into the formula.

d. Interpret the confidence interval you obtained in the context of the problem.

e. Based on your confidence interval, do you have strong evidence that, on average, students cannot accurately estimate the length of a 17-second song snippet? Explain.

3.3.40 Repeat parts (c) and (d) from the previous exercise on time estimate, except construct a 99% confidence interval. How do the midpoints and widths of the 99% and 95% confidence intervals compare?

Reaction time*

3.3.41 Student researchers wanted to determine the average reaction time for student athletes at their school. They used a reaction time applet that had students click a button on a computer as fast as they could after they saw a light turn green on the screen. They tested 42 randomly selected varsity athletes and the results, in seconds, are shown in the following dotplot. The mean time is 0.297 seconds and the standard deviation is 0.041 seconds.

a. Identify the parameter estimated by the students and the theory-based method you will use to calculate a confidence interval.

b. Verify the validity conditions for the theory-based method you have chosen.

c. Construct a 95% confidence interval, showing the values that you substitute into the formula.

d. Interpret the confidence interval you obtained in the context of the problem.

3.3.42 Repeat parts (c) and (d) from the previous exercise on reaction time, but construct a 90% confidence interval. How do the midpoints and widths of the 90% and 95% confidence intervals compare?

Facebook friends

3.3.43 In a survey, 110 statistics students were asked how many Facebook friends they had and the results are shown in the following dotplot. The mean number is 693.4

and the standard deviation is 532.2. We will assume the 110 students surveyed are representative of all the students at the school.

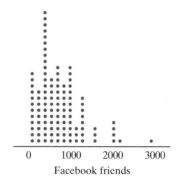

a. Identify the parameter estimated by the students and the theory-based method you will use.

b. Verify the validity conditions for the theory-based method you have chosen.

c. Construct a 95% confidence interval, showing the values that you substitute into the formula.

d. Interpret the confidence interval you obtained in the context of the problem.

3.3.44 Repeat parts (c) and (d) from the previous exercise on Facebook friends, but construct a 99% confidence interval. How do the midpoints and widths of the 99% and 95% confidence intervals compare?

Bean estimates*

3.3.45 Student researchers wanted to determine a person's abilities to estimate the number of beans in a bag. They had 1,470 beans in a clear bag for the subjects to estimate. They also showed the subjects another clear bag that contained 200 beans and told them the number in that bag. They thought this would help the subjects estimate the number of beans in the larger bag. The 40 subjects were a representative sample of the students at the researchers' school. The subjects' estimates are shown in the following dotplot. The mean estimate is 962.9 and the standard deviation is 351.7.

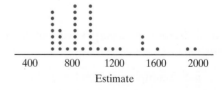

a. Identify the parameter estimated by the student researchers and the theory-based method you will use.

b. Verify the validity conditions for the theory-based method you have chosen.

c. Construct a 95% confidence interval, showing the values that you substitute into the formula.

d. Interpret the confidence interval you obtained in the context of the problem.

e. Based on your confidence interval, do you have strong evidence that students cannot accurately estimate, on average, the number of beans in the bag? Explain.

3.3.46 Repeat parts (c), (d), and (e) from the previous exercise on bean number estimates, but construct a 99% confidence interval. How do the midpoints and widths of the 99% and 95% confidence intervals compare?

Enhanced self-image

3.3.47 Do people think they look different than they actually do? In particular, do they think they look better? Researchers Epley and Whitchurch (2008) tried to answer this question by taking pictures of 27 subjects (both male and female). They then had the pictures of each subject's face morphed with that of someone who was thought to be better looking. The images were morphed in 10% increments so that the first morph was 90% the subject and 10% the better-looking person, the second was 80% subject and 20% better-looking person. This continued until the face was 50% of each person. They also did the same thing with a picture of a person that was thought to not be good looking. The researchers then had 11 pictures for each subject, one of the actual subject and 10 with various morphings. Each subject was presented with the 11 pictures, in random order, and asked which was the actual picture of their face. If they picked one that was composed of 20% of the better-looking face, their score was 20. If they picked one that was composed of 10% of the worse-looking face, their score was -10. Of course, if they picked the picture of their own face, their score was 0. The average score of the 27 subjects was 6.3 with a standard deviation of 12.45. A distribution of the results was fairly symmetric.

a. Construct a 95% confidence interval for the average score for some population of people doing this activity.

b. Based on your confidence interval, do you have strong evidence that, on average, people tend to pick a face that is more attractive than their own when they are asked to identify their own face? Explain.

SECTION 3.4

3.4.1* Recall the form of a theory-based confidence interval for a population proportion π is

$$\hat{p} \pm \text{multiplier} \times \sqrt{\hat{p}(1-\hat{p})/n}.$$

a. Remind me: What's the difference between $\hat{p}$ and π?

b. The midpoint of this interval is always equal to what?

c. What is $\sqrt{\hat{p}(1-\hat{p})/n}$ called?

d. What is multiplier $\times \sqrt{\hat{p}(1-\hat{p})/n}$ called?

3.4.2 Recall the form of a theory-based confidence interval for a population proportion π is

$$\hat{p} \pm \text{multiplier} \times \sqrt{\hat{p}(1-\hat{p})/n}.$$

a. Increasing the confidence level has what effect, if any, on the midpoint of this interval?

b. Increasing the confidence level has what effect, if any, on the margin of error of this interval?

c. Increasing the sample size, if all else remains the same, has what effect, if any, on the margin of error of this interval?

3.4.3* Name three things that affect the margin of error in a theory-based confidence interval for a population proportion, π. Which of these three things is the hardest for an investigator to control?

3.4.4 Name three things that affect the margin of error in a theory-based confidence interval for a population mean, μ. Which of these three things is the hardest for an investigator to control?

Sudoku*

3.4.5 The *2011 Statistical Abstract of the United States* includes a table reporting that a national survey in the fall of 2009 found that 11.6% of American adults had played a Sudoku puzzle in the past year. Suppose that these data are based on a sample of 1,000 randomly selected American adults.

a. Use this sample result and a theory-based approach to produce three confidence intervals (90%, 95%, 99%) for the probability that a randomly selected American adult had played a Sudoku puzzle in the past year.

b. How do the midpoints of these three intervals compare?

c. How do the widths of these three intervals compare? Is this what you expected? Explain.

d. Based on the confidence intervals, does the sample result provide strong evidence that more than 10% of all American adults had played a Sudoku puzzle in the past year? Explain.

e. Is it appropriate to use the theory-based approach to find the confidence intervals? Answer this by stating the validity condition, and explain whether or not the condition is satisfied.

3.4.6 Refer to the previous exercise to answer the following questions:

a. If the sample size had been 2,000, how would the widths of the 90%, 95%, and 99% confidence intervals be affected?

b. If the sample size had been 100, how would the widths of the 90%, 95%, and 99% confidence intervals be affected?

May 2011 Gallup poll

3.4.7 A Gallup survey of 1001 randomly selected U.S. adults conducted May 2011 asked, "In your opinion, which one of the following is the main reason why students get education beyond high school?" Fifty-three percent chose "to earn more money." Based on these data, we found the 95% confidence interval for the proportion of U.S. adults who choose "to earn more money" to be (0.499, 0.561). Suppose that the sample size was 2,002 instead, while the proportion of respondents choosing "to earn more money" was still 53%.

a. True or false? A 95% confidence interval based on these altered data would be narrower, because a larger sample size increases confidence, which in turn makes the interval narrower.

b. True or false? A 95% confidence interval based on these altered data would be narrower, because a larger sample size decreases the variability of the statistic.

c. True or false? A 95% confidence interval based on these altered data would be wider, because a larger sample size increases confidence, which in turn makes the interval wider.

d. True or false? A 95% confidence interval based on these altered data would be wider, because a larger sample size increases the variability of the statistic.

3.4.8* Looking at the formula to calculate the SD of $\hat{p}$, the "root n relationship" means that to cut the SD of $\hat{p}$ in half, you need to:

A. Multiply the sample size by 1/2

B. Multiply the sample size by 2

C. Multiply the sample size by $\sqrt{2}$

D. Multiply the sample size by 1/4

E. Multiply the sample size by 4

3.4.9 Gilbert uses a sample size of 25. Sullivan uses a sample size of 100. Gilbert's estimated SD for $\hat{p}$ will be _____ times as large as Sullivan's.

3.4.10* As n increases, the SD for $\hat{p}$ _____ (increases, decreases) more and more _____ (slowly, quickly).

Rolling dice

3.4.11 You have an ordinary six-sided die, but you suspect it may be loaded. If the die is fair, then the probability of rolling a 6 equals 1/6.

a. Let π = the probability of rolling a 6. To estimate π to within 0.01 at the 95% confidence level, you need a sample size of _____.

b. The SD for $\hat{p}$ is $\sqrt{\pi(1-\pi)/n}$. What values of π give a value of 0 for the SE? Explain why this result makes sense.

c. Compute the value of $\pi(1-\pi)$ for values of $\pi = 0, 1/4, 1/2, 3/4, 1$. Plot the points with values of π on the x-axis and join the points with a smooth curve. What value of π gives the larges possible value for SD($\hat{p}$)?

3.4.12 Ordinary dice have six equally likely sides. You can buy dice online with (A) 4 sides, (B) 6 sides, (C) 8 sides, or (D) 10 sides. Suppose you want to estimate the probability of rolling a 1 for each of dice (A)–(D).

a. Which die (A)–(D) will give an estimate for the probability of rolling a 1 with the largest SD?

b. Explain your answer in part (a).

c. Suppose the 10-sided die is in fact fair. If you roll 25 times and estimate the probability of rolling a 1, your SD for $\hat{p}$ will be _____.

d. Continue to suppose that the 10-sided die is fair. You want your estimate of π to have an SE of 0.01. How large should your sample size be?

Flipping coins*

3.4.13 You have a coin that you think is fair, with π = probability of heads = 1/2. To check, you plan to flip the coin n times.

a. Compute the SD of $\hat{p}$ for each value of n in the table below and fill in your SD values.

n	SD of $\hat{p}$
10	
20	
40	
100	
500	
1,000	

b. Plot SD($\hat{p}$) on the y-axis versus n on the x-axis and join your points with a smooth curve.

c. The SD _____ (increases/decreases) as n increases.

d. The curve becomes _____ (more, less) steep as n continues to increase.

3.4.14 You have a coin that you think is fair, with π = probability of heads = 1/2.

a. Rodgers has done 25 flips and plans to do another 25 flips. Hammerstein has done 100 flips and plans to do another 25 flips. Whose SD will go down more, Rodgers' or Hammerstein's? Explain.

b. Rodgers has done 25 flips and plans to do another 25. Hammerstein has done 100 and plans to do another 100. Whose SD for $\hat{p}$ will go down more?

School survey

In order to investigate how many hours a day students at their school tend to spend on course work outside of regularly scheduled class time, a statistics student takes a random sample of 150 students from their school by randomly choosing names from a list of all full-time students at their school that semester. The student finds that the average reported daily study hours among the 150 students is 2.23 hours. The standard deviation of the hours studied is 1.05 hours.

3.4.15 A confidence interval is constructed for the population mean hours studied. Which confidence interval would be the widest?

A. 99%   B. 95%
C. 90%   D. 85%

3.4.16 Which confidence interval would be the narrowest?

A. 99%   B. 95%
C. 90%   D. 85%

3.4.17 If the standard deviation were 0.78 hours instead of 1.05, the width of a 95% confidence interval would (increase/decrease).

3.4.18 If the standard deviation were 1.25 hours instead of 1.05, the width of a 95% confidence interval would (increase/decrease).

3.4.19 If the sample size were 15 instead of 150, the width of a 95% confidence interval would (increase/decrease).

3.4.20 If the sample size were 1,500 instead of 150, the width of a 95% confidence interval would (increase/decrease).

3.4.21 If you took repeated samples of size 150 and constructed a 95% confidence interval for the population mean study hours from each sample, what percentage of these intervals would capture the population mean study hours?

3.4.22 If you took repeated samples of size 150 and constructed a 99% confidence interval for the population mean of study hours from each sample, what percentage of these intervals would capture the population mean of study hours?

Business survey*

In order to understand why consumers visit their store, a local business conducts a survey by asking the next 100 people who visit their store to fill out a short survey. The business finds that 40 of the 100 people state that the main reason they visited the store was because the store is running a sale on coats that week. Use this information to answer Exercises 3.4.23 to 3.4.31.

3.4.23 A confidence interval is constructed for the population proportion of consumers who would visit the store because of the coat sale. Which confidence interval would be the widest?

A. 99%   B. 95%
C. 90%   D. 85%

3.4.24 Which confidence interval would be the narrowest?

A. 99%   B. 95%
C. 90%   D. 85%

3.4.25 Instead of 40, if 30 of the 100 people had stated that the main reason they had visited the store was because the store is running a sale on coats that week, the width of a 95% confidence interval would (increase/decrease).

3.4.26 Instead of 40, if 50 of the 100 people had stated that the main reason they had visited the store was because the store is running a sale on coats that week, the width of a 95% confidence interval would (increase/decrease).

3.4.27 Instead of 40, if 60 of the 100 people had stated that the main reason they had visited the store was because the store is running a sale on coats that week

a. The width of the 95% confidence interval would (increase/decrease/remain same).

b. The center of the 95% confidence interval would (increase/decrease/remain same).

3.4.28 If the sample size were 10 instead of 100, the width of a 95% confidence interval would (increase/decrease).

3.4.29 If the sample size were 1,000 instead of 100, the width of a 95% confidence interval would (increase/decrease).

3.4.30 If you took repeated samples of size 100 and constructed a 95% confidence interval for the population proportion who would shop at the store because of the coat sale from each sample, what percentage of these intervals would capture the population proportion?

3.4.31 If you took repeated samples of size 100 and constructed a 99% confidence interval for the population proportion who would shop at the store because of the coat sale from each sample, what percentage of these intervals would capture the population proportion?

Heights of students

3.4.32 Suppose we have a collection of the heights of all students at your college. Each of the 250 people taking statistics randomly takes a sample of 40 of these heights and constructs a 95% confidence interval for mean height of all students at the college. Which of the following statements about the confidence intervals is most accurate?

A. About 95% of the heights of all students at the college will be contained in these intervals.

B. About 95% of the time, a student's sample mean height will be contained in his or her interval.

C. About 95% of the intervals will contain the population mean height.

D. About 95% of the intervals will be identical.

Mean household income*

3.4.33 A 95% confidence interval is computed to estimate the mean household income for a city. Which of the following values will definitely be within the limits of this confidence interval? Circle all that apply.

A. The population mean

B. The sample mean

C. The sample standard deviation

D. The p-value

E. All the above

Foot length

3.4.34 Suppose a random sample of 50 college students are asked to measure the length of their right foot in centimeters. A 95% confidence interval for the mean foot length for students at the college is found to be 21.709 to 25.091 cm. If a 99% confidence interval were calculated instead, how would it differ from the 95% confidence interval?

A. The 99% confidence interval would be wider.

B. The 99% confidence interval would be narrower.

C. The 99% confidence interval would have the same width as the 95% confidence interval.

D. There is no way to tell if the 99% confidence interval would be wider or narrower than the 95% confidence interval.

FAQ

3.4.35 Read FAQ 3.4.1 and then answer the following question.

True or false? The standard error formulas for $\bar{x}$ and $\hat{p}$ both have $\sqrt{n}$ in the denominator.

3.4.36 Read FAQ 3.4.1 and then answer the following question.

To cut the margin of error of a confidence interval in half one must

A. Increase the sample size by a factor of 2

B. Increase the ample size by a factor of 4

C. Increase the sample size by a factor of 10

D. Increase the sample size by a factor of 100

SECTION 3.5

Coffee bars*

3.5.1 Suppose you want to compare waiting times, from getting in line to receiving the order, at two coffee bars on campus.

a. Describe what might be wrong with looking at the first 40 people who come to each of the coffee bars on a Tuesday morning.

b. Describe how you might find a more representative sample of customers at these coffee bars.

Literary Digest

3.5.2 Recall from Exploration 3.5A that the *Literary Digest* magazine conducted a very extensive public opinion poll in 1936 in order to predict the outcome of that year's presidential election. They mailed out over 10 million questionnaires to people whose names and addresses they obtained from telephone books and vehicle registration lists. They received more than 2.4 million responses, with 57% of the responses indicating an intention to vote for Republican challenger Alf Landon over the Democratic incumbent Franklin Roosevelt.

a. Use the **Theory-Based Inference** applet to produce a 99.9% confidence interval. Also interpret this interval.

b. Why is this interval so narrow, even with an extremely large confidence level of 99.9%?

c. Would you really have a lot of confidence that this interval succeeds in capturing the population proportion of American voters who intended to vote for Landon in 1936? Why or why not?

Holocaust denial*

3.5.3 In a November 1992 survey, the Roper Organization asked American adults, "Does it seem possible or does it seem impossible to you that the Nazi extermination of the Jews never happened?" The results were very surprising and widely discussed. Of the 992 adults surveyed, 22% responded that it's possible that this never happened, and 12% responded that they did not know. Therefore, only 66% of the respondents expressed certainty that the Holocaust *did* happen. What is wrong with the wording of this question that produced such surprising (and it was later shown) erroneous responses?

3.5.4 Refer to the previous exercise. When the Roper Organization conducted another survey in March of 1994, they asked, "Does it seem possible to you that the Nazi extermination of the Jews never happened, or do you feel certain that it happened?" Do you think the wording of this question is clearer than the November 1992 version? Explain why or why not.

3.5.5 Refer to the previous question. The results from the 1994 sample of 991 adults were that 91% answered that they were certain the Holocaust happened, 8% did not know, and 1% thought it possible that it never happened.

a. Produce an appropriate graph for comparing the results between the 1992 and 1994 surveys.

b. Summarize how the results differ between the two surveys.

c. For each survey, determine a 95% confidence interval for the population proportion of American adults who are certain that the Nazi extermination of the Jews happened.

d. Are these confidence intervals similar? Do they overlap?

e. Summarize the lesson to be learned from the two Roper polls.

Welfare

3.5.6 A survey question could ask for respondents' opinions about "welfare" or about "assistance to the poor." Do you think that the wording used could influence people's responses? If so, which wording would you expect to produce a higher percentage of favorable responses towards these programs?

Military strength*

3.5.7 One version of a survey question asked whether subjects agree or disagree with the statement that "the best way to ensure peace is through military strength." Another version asked subjects to choose which of two choices they agree with: "the best way to ensure peace is through military strength" or "diplomacy is the best way to ensure peace." Which version would you expect to have a larger percentage favoring military strength? Explain.

Abortion

3.5.8 Answer the following about how questions can be worded in order to bias the results:

a. How might you word a question about attitudes toward the government's relationship with abortion if the goal were to bias the results in favor of making abortions more accessible?

b. How might you word a question about attitudes toward the government's relationship with abortion if the goal were to bias the results in favor of making abortions less accessible?

Health care*

3.5.9 If you support President Obama's health care policy, would you prefer to phrase a survey question in terms of "ObamaCare" or in terms of "Affordable Care Act"? Explain.

Biased responses

3.5.10 Think of a controversial issue about which you might be interested in asking people's opinions. Describe how you could ask a survey question about that issue in as clear and unbiased a manner as possible. Then describe how you could ask the question to bias responses in one direction, and then describe how you could ask the question to bias responses in the other direction.

Interviewer effects*

3.5.11 In an article titled "Interviewer Effects in Public Health Surveys," Davis et al. (2010) argue that effects of interviewers on survey participant responses can be especially problematic when dealing with public health issues. For example, the article cited a study which found that black respondents report higher rates of alcohol and marijuana use to black interviewers than to white interviewers. Suggest another variable or issue for which you suspect that respondents might give different responses depending on the *race* of the interviewer. Justify your answer.

3.5.12 Refer to the previous exercise. The article also cited a study which found that female interviewers tended to obtain higher percentages of respondents reporting psychiatric symptoms. Suggest another variable or issue for which you suspect that respondents might give different responses depending on the *sex* of the interviewer. Justify your answer.

3.5.13 Suggest a variable or issue for which you suspect that respondents might give different responses depending on the *clothing worn* by the interviewer. Justify your answer.

3.5.14 If a survey is being conducted on the issue of whether to enact a smoking ban in a public place, how might responses be biased depending on whether or not the interviewer is smoking while asking the questions?

CNN.com polls

3.5.15 The news website CNN.com regularly posts a poll question that people who view the website can respond to. The following results were posted on January 10, 2012:

Do you surf the web while on the job?

Often	62%	69,413
Seldom	25%	27,875
Never	13%	14,652

Total votes: 111,938
This is not a scientific poll

a. Are the percentages reported in this graphic (62%, 25%, 13%) parameters or statistics? Justify your answer.

b. The margin of error for this survey is 0.003 (or 0.3%). Explain why the margin of error is so small. (*Hint:* Keep your response brief; you can use five words or less.)

c. Are you *really* confident that the proportion of all American workers who surf the Web while on the job is within 0.003 of 0.62? If not, do you suspect that the actual proportion is larger or smaller than 0.62? Explain.

3.5.16 On January 29, 2011, visitors to the CNN.com website were invited to answer a poll question. The results are shown below:

Are you exercising more in 2011?

| NO | 51% | 49,254 |
| YES | 49% | 47,232 |

Total votes: 96,486
This is not a scientific poll

A 99.9% confidence interval for the population proportion (of "yes" responses) turns out to be (0.484, 0.495).

a. Explain (using no more than 10 words, preferably no more than 5 words) why this confidence interval is so narrow.

b. The standardized z-statistic for testing the null hypothesis that 50% of American adults claim to be exercising more in 2011 turns out to be -6.52, for a p-value of 2.5×10^{-10}. Explain what this indicates about the difference between statistical significance and practical importance.

c. Even if this question could have been asked of every American adult on January 29, 2011, the results would still be questionable. Describe one reason for this.

d. Explain why you think CNN.com adds the disclaimer that "this is not a scientific poll."

At your school*

3.5.17 For each of the following variables, indicate whether you think students at your school would generally be truthful or would tend to over- or understate their honest responses. Briefly explain your answer for each.

a. Amount of sleep per night

b. Time spent on charity/volunteer work

c. Church attendance

d. Time spent studying

e. How often a seat belt is worn

3.5.18 Answer the following questions about statistical significance and practical importance:

a. Which is more appropriate to the issue of statistical significance: p-value or confidence interval?

b. Which is more appropriate to the issue of practical importance: p-value or confidence interval?

c. Explain the distinction between statistical significance and practical importance.

3.5.19 When is the distinction between statistical significance and practical importance more important to consider: with a large sample size, with a small sample size, or is sample size not relevant to the issue?

Penny flipping, spinning, tipping

3.5.20 Over several years, students of Professor Robin Lock have flipped a large number of coins and recorded

whether the flip landed heads or tails. As reported in a 2002 issue of *Chance News*, these students had observed 14,709 heads in a total of 29,015 flips.

a. What proportion of these flips resulted in heads?

b. Calculate the standardized value of this statistic for testing whether the long-run proportion of heads differs from 0.50.

c. Determine the theory-based p-value for testing whether the long-run proportion of heads differs from 0.50.

d. What conclusion would you draw at the 0.05 significance level?

e. Determine a 95% confidence interval for the long-run proportion of heads.

f. Does the confidence interval include the value 0.50? Is this consistent with your test decision in part (e)? Explain.

g. Based on the p-value and confidence interval, would you say that the difference between the sample proportion of heads and the value 0.50 is statistically significant? Would you say that the difference is practically important? Explain.

3.5.21 Refer to the previous exercise. Professor Lock's students also spun pennies on their side. The students found 9,197 heads in 20,422 spins. Answer parts (a) to (g) of the previous question with regard to penny *spinning* rather than flipping.

3.5.22 Refer to the previous two exercises. Professor Lock's students also "tipped" pennies by standing them on edge and then banging the table to see which way they would fall. The students found 10,087 heads in 14,611 tips. Answer parts (a) to (g) of the previous question with regard to penny *tipping* rather than flipping or spinning.

Pop, soda, or coke?*

3.5.23 The website www.popvssoda.com invites people to indicate whether they refer to carbonated beverages as "pop" or "soda" or "coke" or something else. As of December 30, 2013, the website had received 350,847 responses from the United States, broken down as follows:

Pop	Soda	Coke	Other	Total
131,403	149,377	54,072	15,995	350,847

a. Determine a 95% confidence interval for the population proportion who would answer "soda."

b. Based on this confidence interval, would you say that the sample proportion who answered "soda" is statistically significantly less than 0.50? Would you say that the difference is practically important? Explain your answers.

c. Based on how the sample was selected, do you have concerns about generalizing from this sample to any population? Explain.

Baseball batting power

3.5.24 Suppose that a baseball player has been a .250 hitter for his career, which means that his probability of a hit (success) has been 0.250. Then during one winter the player genuinely improves to the point that his probability of success improves to 0.333. You will investigate how likely the player is, in a sample of at-bats, to convince the manager that he has improved.

a. Open the **Power Simulation** applet. Enter 0.250 for the hypothesized value, 0.333 for the alternative value, and 20 for the sample size. Enter 200 for the number of samples, and click on **Draw Samples**. Repeat four more times to produce a total of 1,000 simulated samples. Comment on how much overlap you see between the two distributions. Does this overlap suggest that it's easy or difficult to distinguish between a .250 hitter and a .333 hitter in a sample of 20 at-bats?

b. Choose the **Level of Significance** option, and enter 0.05 for the significance level. Click on **Count**. The top graph indicates how many hits the player needs in 20 at-bats in order to produce a p-value less than 0.05 to provide convincing evidence to reject the null hypothesis that his success probability is 0.250. How many hits are needed?

c. Based on the bottom graph, in what proportion of the 1,000 samples will the player with a 0.333 probability of success obtain enough hits to reject the hypothesis that he has a 0.250 probability of success? This is the approximate power of the test.

d. Would you say that the player has a good chance of convincing the manager that he has improved in a sample of 20 at-bats? Write a summary, as if to the player.

e. What factors could be changed in order to increase the power of the test?

3.5.25 Reconsider the previous exercise. Change the sample size to 100 at-bats, and answer questions (a) to (d). Then describe the effect of increasing the sample size on the power of the test.

3.5.26 Reconsider the previous two exercises. Change the significance level to 0.10 (with a sample size of 100 at-bats), and answer Questions (a) to (d). Then describe the effect of decreasing the significance level on the power of the test.

3.5.27 Reconsider the previous three exercises. Now suppose that the player has actually become a .400 hitter. Make this change to the alternative value (with a significance level of 0.10 and a sample size of 100 at-bats), and answer Questions (a) to (d). Then describe the effect of increasing the alternative value on the power of the test.

END OF CHAPTER

Drinking water*

3.CE.1 An article, "Foul drinking water aboard airlines worsens," in *The Seattle Times* (January 2005) reported that 29 out of 169 water specimens from randomly selected passenger aircraft carrying domestic and international passengers tested positive for the presence of bacteria, thus failing to meet federal safety standards.

a. Use these data to estimate, with 95% confidence, the population proportion.

b. Interpret your answer from part (a).

Talking while driving

3.CE.2 A Pew Research (2009) survey of nationally representative 242 cell phone users, ages 16 to 17 years, found that 52% had talked on the phone while driving.

a. Use these data to estimate, with 95% confidence, the proportion of all 16- to 17-year-old cell phone users who talk on the phone while driving.

b. Do these data provide evidence that a majority of 16- to 17-year-old cell phone users talk on the phone while driving? Explain your reasoning.

c. Without performing any extensive calculations, find the 95% confidence interval for the proportion of all 16- to 17-year-old cell phone users who *do not* talk on the phone while driving.

d. Suppose that you are planning to conduct a survey in your city to estimate, with 95% confidence, the proportion of 16- to 17-year-old cell phone users who talk on the phone while driving and want the margin to be no bigger than 0.05. What should your sample size be? (*Hint:* Start by writing out the formula for the margin of error, and after plugging in appropriate values for the known quantities, solve for *n*.)

Elsa and Frank*

3.CE.3 Suppose that Elsa and Frank determine confidence intervals using the same confidence level, based on the same sample proportion. Elsa uses a larger sample size than Frank. How will midpoint and width of confidence intervals compare?

A. Same midpoint and same width

B. Same midpoint, Elsa has wider interval

C. Same midpoint, Frank has wider interval

D. Same width, Elsa has larger midpoint

E. Same width, Frank has larger midpoint

F. Elsa has larger midpoint, wider interval

G. Frank has larger midpoint, wider interval

3.CE.4 Suppose that Elsa and Frank determine confidence intervals based on the same sample proportion and sample size.

This time, Elsa uses a larger confidence level than Frank. How will midpoint and width of confidence intervals compare?

A. Same midpoint and same width

B. Same midpoint, Elsa has wider interval

C. Same midpoint, Frank has wider interval

D. Same width, Elsa has larger midpoint

E. Same width, Frank has larger midpoint

F. Elsa has larger midpoint, wider interval

G. Frank has larger midpoint, wider interval

Margin of error

3.CE.5 Recall that a margin of error for a 95% confidence interval for process probability can be approximated by the expression $1/\sqrt{n}$.

a. Evaluate this expression (to three decimal places) for the following sample sizes: 100, 400, 1,000, 2,000, 8,000, 9,000.

b. Based on your answers in part (a), produce a graph using the following axes and scales. Describe how the margin of error changes with the sample size? Does it increase, decrease, or stay the same?

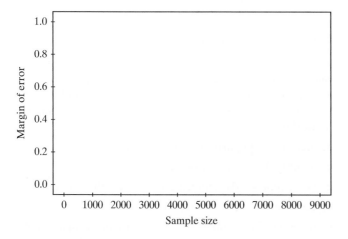

c. In order to cut the margin of error in half, by how many times must the sample size increase?

d. Which has the bigger impact on the margin of error: increasing the sample size from 100 to 500 (an increase of 400) or increasing the sample size from 8,000 to 9,000 (an increase of 1,000)? Explain.

Blood donations*

3.CE.6 Suppose that researchers in three different countries collect sample data on whether or not a person has donated blood within the past year, with the following sample results:

A. 200 blood donors in a sample of 600 people

B. 50 blood donors in a sample of 300 people

C. 250 blood donors in a sample of 1,000 people

Consider estimating the proportion of people in each country who donated blood in the previous year.

a. Explain why an interval of values is better than a single value for this estimate.

b. For which of the three countries would a 95% confidence interval be widest? For which would a 95% confidence interval be narrowest?

c. For which of the three countries would a 95% confidence interval include the value 0.2?

d. What does your answer to part (c) reveal about the p-values for testing whether the proportion of people in the country who donated blood in the previous year differs from 1/5? Explain.

3.CE.7 Suppose that researchers in three different countries collect sample data on whether or not a person has donated blood within the past year, with the following sample results:

A. 200 blood donors in a sample of 600 people

B. 50 blood donors in a sample of 300 people

C. 250 blood donors in a sample of 1,000 people

Suppose that each researcher wants to test whether the proportion of people in the country who donated blood in the previous year differs from 1/5.

a. Determine the appropriate standardized statistic for each researcher. (*Hint:* You will need to get the standard deviation of the simulated statistics from the null distribution produced by an applet, or use the theory-based formula to calculate the standard error.)

b. Based on the standardized statistics, which researcher has the strongest evidence that the population proportion differs from 1/5? Which has the least strong evidence?

American exceptionalism

3.CE.8 Do Americans believe that the United States has a unique character that makes it the greatest country in the world? This belief has been called "American exceptionalism." A Gallup poll conducted on December 10–12, 2010, asked this question of a sample of 1,019 adult Americans, with 80% responding that they do believe that the U.S. has a unique character that makes it the greatest country in the world.

a. Use the **Theory-Based Inference** applet to determine a 95% confidence interval based on this sample result. Also interpret what this interval says.

b. Would you expect values within this interval to be rejected by a two-sided significance test at the 0.05 significance level or not to be rejected by such a test? Explain. (*Hint:* Think about whether the values within the confidence interval are *plausible* values of the parameter.)

3.CE.9 Use the data described in the previous exercise to answer the following questions:

a. Investigate your answer to 3.CE.8, part (b), by using the **Theory-Based Inference** applet to test the following (null) values for the parameter: 0.76, 0.78, 0.80, 0.82, and 0.84. Report the z-statistic and (two-sided) p-value for each of these five tests.

b. Which of these five values in part (a) are rejected at the 0.05 significance level?

c. Do the values that are not rejected correspond to values that are within the 95% confidence interval?

Follow-up on subgroups*

3.CE.10 The Harris polling organization conducted a national survey in 2008, finding that 14% of the sample of 2,302 American adults had a tattoo.

a. Use the **Theory-Based Inference** applet to determine a 99% confidence interval for the population proportion of adult Americans who had a tattoo in 2008.

b. Which possible values for the population proportion would not be rejected at the 0.01 significance level? Explain how you can tell based on the confidence interval, without performing any tests.

3.CE.11 A national survey of 47,000 American households in 2006 found that 32.4% of the households included a pet cat. This survey result was reported in the *2011 Statistical Abstract of the United States*, which listed the American Veterinary Medical Association as the source. No information was provided about how the sample households were selected.

a. Conduct a theory-based test of whether one-third of all American households include a pet cat. Report the null and alternative hypotheses and the values of the z-statistic and p-value. Also state your test decision using the 0.01 significance level.

b. Explain why the p-value turned out to be so small even though the observed sample proportion appears to be quite close to 1/3.

c. Determine a 99% confidence interval for the population proportion of American households that include a pet cat.

d. Is the confidence interval *consistent* with the significance test result? How can you tell?

e. Does the confidence interval indicate that the population proportion is *much different* from 1/3? Explain.

International students

3.CE.12 An instructor wants to find the proportion of international students at his school. He contacts the registrar's office and obtains enrollment data for the year 2011. Using these data, he reports that "I am 95% confident that the proportion of international students at our school during 2011 is between 0.08 and 0.10." Is this an appropriate use of a confidence interval? Why or why not?

Confidence intervals*

3.CE.13 Higher confidence is better than lower confidence. So, why do statisticians not always use 99.99% confidence intervals?

3.CE.14 Narrower confidence intervals are better than wider confidence intervals. One way to achieve a narrower confidence interval is to use a larger sample size. So, why do statisticians interested in estimating a parameter value for the population of all adult Americans not always use a sample size of 1,000,000 people?

3.CE.15 Narrower confidence intervals are better than wider confidence intervals. One way to achieve a narrower confidence interval is to use a smaller confidence level. So, why do statisticians not always use a confidence level of 70%?

3.CE.16 Narrower confidence intervals are better than wider confidence intervals.

a. What change to sample size produces a narrower confidence interval?

b. What change to confidence level produces a narrower confidence interval?

Social networking

3.CE.17 In May of 2013, the Pew Research Center's Internet and American Life Project conducted a survey with a random sample of American adults. Of the 1,895 Internet users in the sample, 72% reported that they used social networking sites.

a. Identify the population of interest for this study.

b. Identify the parameter of interest.

c. Determine a 95% confidence interval for the parameter.

d. Interpret what this confidence interval says.

e. Based on the confidence interval, does the sample result provide strong evidence against believing that 75% of all American adult Internet users in May of 2013 used social networking sites? Explain how your conclusion follows from the confidence interval.

3.CE.18 Refer to the previous exercise. The report from the Pew Research Center also provided survey results for different age groups:

• Among those aged 18 to 29, 89% of 395 used social networking sites.

• Among those aged 30 to 49, 78% of 542 used social networking sites.

• Among those aged 50 to 64, 60% of 553 used social networking sites.

• Among those aged 65 and older, 43% of 356 used social networking sites.

a. For each age group, determine and interpret a 95% confidence interval for the relevant parameter.

b. How do the margins of error for these age-specific confidence intervals compare to the margin of error based on the entire sample (larger, smaller, or the same)? Explain why this makes sense.

Halloween spending*

3.CE.19 The National Retail Federation conducted a national survey of 8,526 consumers on September 1–9, 2009. Among the findings reported were that:

- 29.6% of those surveyed said that the state of the U.S. economy would affect their Halloween spending plans;

- the average amount that the respondents said they expect to spend on Halloween is $56.31.

a. Are these numbers parameters or statistics? Explain.

b. Determine and interpret a 95% confidence interval based on the 29.6% value given in the article.

c. What additional information would you need to determine a 95% confidence interval based on the $56.31 value given in the article?

3.CE.20 Reconsider the previous exercise.

a. Suppose the sample standard deviation of the expected spending amounts was $30. Determine and interpret a 95% confidence interval for the population mean.

b. Now suppose the sample standard deviation was $50. Recalculate a 95% confidence interval for the population mean. Comment on what's different about the confidence interval based on the larger sample standard deviation.

c. What (if anything) must be true about the distribution of the expected spending amounts in order for these confidence intervals to be valid?

Hockey goals

3.CE.21 Suppose you have very little knowledge about professional ice hockey, but you want to get a sense of how many goals are scored per game on average and what a typical margin of victory is. You decide to select a sample of games from the current season and record the total number of goals and margin of victory in each game.

a. What are the observational units and variables in this study? Are the variables categorical or quantitative?

b. Describe how you could take a simple random sample of 44 National Hockey League (NHL) games from the current season.

Feeling too lazy to take a simple random sample of games, one of the authors recorded data on all 44 NHL games played between Thursday, December 19, to Monday, December 23, 2013. The data are in the file called **Hockey** on the textbook website.

c. Examine and describe a graph of the distribution of total number of goals in the sample.

d. Based on this graph, do you think it's valid to produce a theory-based 95% confidence interval based on these data? Explain.

e. Calculate the sample mean and sample standard deviation. Report these along with the appropriate symbols.

f. Determine a 95% confidence interval for the population mean number of goals scored in an NHL game.

g. Interpret what this confidence interval says.

3.CE.22 Reconsider the previous exercise. Answer parts (c) to (g) with regard to margin of victory rather than total number of goals. Data can be found in the file called **Hockey2** on the textbook website.

Marriage ages*

3.CE.23 A student went to the local county courthouse (in Cumberland County, Pennsylvania, in June and July of 1993) to gather data on ages of soon-to-be husbands and wives who had recently applied for marriage licenses. He gathered age data on a sample of 100 couples and calculated the difference in age (husband–wife) for each couple. The results, which can be found in the file **MarriageAges** on the textbook website, are displayed in the 3.CE.23 dotplot:

a. Write a paragraph describing the distribution of differences.

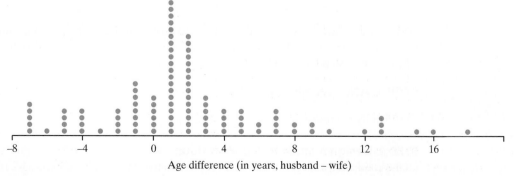

3.CE.23

b. Do you consider it valid to use a theory-based confidence interval for a population mean, based on these sample data? Explain.

c. Determine a 99% confidence interval for the population mean.

d. Interpret the interval that you calculated in part (c).

e. Based on this confidence interval, do the sample data provide strong evidence for concluding that husbands tend to be older than their wives, on average? Explain how your answer follows from the confidence interval.

f. To what population of married couples do you feel comfortable generalizing the results of this study? Explain.

3.CE.24   Reconsider the previous exercise.

a. Based on the dotplot, determine the sample proportion of married couples for whom the wife is older than the husband.

b. Is it valid to use a theory-based procedure to estimate the population proportion of married couples for which the wife is older than the husband? Justify your answer.

c. Determine and interpret a 90% confidence interval for the population proportion of married couples for whom the wife is older than the husband.

d. Based on this confidence interval, do the sample data provide strong evidence that the wife is older than the husband in less than 50% of all marriages? Explain how your answer follows from the confidence interval.

3.CE.25   Reconsider the previous two exercises. A 95% confidence interval for the population mean difference in ages (husband–wife, in years) turns out to be (0.92, 2.92). For each of the following, indicate whether the conclusion is valid or invalid:

a. We are 95% confident that at least 92% of husbands are older than their wives.

b. 95% of all husbands are between 0.92 and 2.92 years older than their wives.

c. For about 95 of the 100 married couples in this sample, the husband is between 0.92 and 2.92 years older than his wife.

d. We are 95% confident that the average difference in ages in the population is between 0.92 and 2.92 years.

Diameter of planets

3.CE.26   Suppose that you look up the diameters of the planets in our solar system and use the data to determine a 95% confidence interval. Would the resulting interval make any sense? Explain why or why not.

Emotional support*

3.CE.27   In the mid-1980s, sociologist Shere Hite undertook a study of American women's attitudes toward relationships, love, and sex by distributing 100,000 questionnaires in women's groups. One of the questions was: Do you give more emotional support to your husband or boyfriend than you receive from him? A total of 4,500 women returned the questionnaire. An ABC News/*Washington Post* poll conducted at about the same time surveyed a random sample of 767 women, asking them the same question about emotional support.

a. Which survey would you expect to obtain a more representative sample of the population? Explain briefly.

Of the 4,500 women who returned the Hite questionnaire, 96% said that they gave more emotional support than they received from their husbands or boyfriends. Of the 767 women interviewed in the ABC News/*Washington Post* poll, 44% claimed to give more emotional support than they receive.

b. Using *only* the poll corresponding to your answer to part (a), determine a 99% confidence interval for the relevant population parameter.

c. Write a sentence interpreting what your confidence interval reveals.

d. If you were to calculate the margin of error for both surveys (do not bother to actually do this calculation), which survey would have the smaller margin of error? Explain briefly.

INVESTIGATION: CELL PHONES WHILE DRIVING

Drivers today have many more distractions to deal with than drivers of a century ago. Let's focus on new drivers aged 16 to 17. Do you think a majority of drivers aged 16 to 17 have ever talked on the cell phone while driving?

STEP 1: Ask a research question.

1. Identify the research question and state it as a conjecture.

STEP 2: Design a study and collect data.   To help answer this question Pew Research (2009) conducted a survey of nationally representative 242 cell phone users ages 16 to 17 years and asked whether they had ever talked on the cell phone while driving.

2. What are the observational units?

3. What is the variable that is measured/recorded on each observational unit?

4. Describe the parameter of interest in words. (You can use the symbol π to represent this parameter.)

5. State the appropriate null and alternative hypotheses to be tested.

The survey found that 52% of the 242 16- to 17-year-olds had talked on the phone while driving.

STEP 3: Explore the data.

6. How many of the 16- to 17-year-olds in the sample have ever talked on their cell phone while driving?

STEP 4: Draw inferences. Let's use our 3S strategy to help us investigate how much evidence the sample data provide to support our conjecture that a majority of 16- to 17-year-olds have talked on their cell phone while driving.

Statistic

7. What is the statistic that you can use to summarize the data collected in the study?

8. Is the sample proportion who have talked on their cell phone while driving greater than 0.50? (If not, there's no need to conduct a simulation analysis. You will not have convincing evidence that a majority of drivers aged 16 to 17 have ever talked on the cell phone while driving.)

Simulate

9. If we assume that each driver is equally as likely to have talked on the cell phone while driving as not, what is the chance that a randomly selected individual will have talked on the cell phone while driving?

10. Is it possible that we could observe the statistic from this sample of 242 drivers even if all of the drivers were just as likely as not to have talked on the cell phone while driving? Why?

11. Use the **One Proportion** applet to simulate 1,000 repetitions of this study, assuming that every driver is just as likely to talk on the cell phone as not while driving. Report what values you input into the applet.

12. What is the center of your simulated null distribution? Does it make sense that this is the center? Explain.

Strength of evidence

13. Based on the dotplot generated using the 1,000 possible values of the statistic, what values would you consider typical values and what would you consider atypical values of the statistic when the chance model is true?

14. How do the actual study results compare to the null distribution obtained when simulating the chance model? Do you believe the study results provide convincing evidence against the "equally likely to talk on the cell phone as not" hypothesis? Why or why not?

15. Determine the approximate p-value from your simulation analysis. Also interpret what this p-value represents (i.e., the probability of what, assuming what?).

16. Summarize the conclusion that you draw from this study and your simulation analysis. Also explain the reasoning process behind your conclusion.

17. You should have seen that 0.50 is a plausible value for the true proportion of all 16- to 17-year-olds who have used their cell phones while driving. Does this prove that 0.50 is the true value?

18. Use the **One Proportion** applet to create an interval of plausible values with 95% confidence for the population proportion of drivers 16 to 17 who have ever talked on a cell phone while driving. Do this by putting different values in for π (and/or using the slider) and seeing whether or not each is plausible.

19. Now use the **One Proportion** applet to create an interval of plausible values with 95% confidence for the population proportion of drivers 16 to 17 who have ever talked on a cell phone while driving using the 2SD method with $\pi = 0.50$.

    a. What is the interval?

    b. How does your confidence interval using the 2SD method and $\pi = 0.50$ compare to the confidence interval of plausible values you found in Question 18?

    c. Without doing extensive work, find the 95% confidence interval for the proportion of drivers aged 16 to 17 who have NOT talked on the cell phone while driving.

20. Finally, use the **Theory-Based Inference** applet to find a 95% confidence interval for the population proportion of drivers 16 to 17 who have ever talked on a cell phone while driving.

    a. What is the interval?

    b. How does this interval compare to the ones you found in Questions 18 and 19a? Why would you expect that?

21. What would happen to your 95% confidence intervals if the sample size had been 1,000 instead of 242 but still 52% of your sample stated they had talked on a cell phone while driving? Use the applet to confirm your answer.

22. If you were to construct a 99% confidence interval like the 95% confidence interval you constructed in #18 by testing different values for π and seeing whether or not they are plausible, how would the width of the 99% confidence interval compare to that of the 95% confidence interval? Find this 99% confidence interval to back up your claim.

STEP 5: Formulate conclusions.

23. Now, let's step back a bit and think about the scope of our inference. What are the wider implications? Do you think that your conclusion holds true for people in general?

STEP 6: Look back and ahead.

24. Summarize your findings. If you were to repeat this study, are there any changes or improvements you would make? What additional questions might you be interested in asking?

Research Article   www.wiley.com/college/tintle

TASER   Read "Conducted Electrical Weapon (TASER) Use Against Minors: A Shocking Analysis" by Gardner, Hauda and Bozeman (*Pediatric Emergency Care*, 2012).

Causation: Can We Say What Caused the Effect?

This chapter is about *causation*, the last of the four pillars of inference: strength, size, breadth, and *cause*. What can we say about the cause of the pattern in the data? We saw in the study of organ donation in the Preliminaries that the proportion of "Yes" responses was larger when the question asked for a forced choice rather than just offering a chance to opt in. Can we conclude that it was the form of the question that *caused* the difference in proportion of "Yes" responses? The answer for that study is yes, but the conclusion is valid only because of careful planning by the investigators. (For contrast: Cities with more McDonald's restaurants record larger numbers of divorces, but it would be bad science to conclude that eating Big Macs® increases the likelihood of divorce. Or: Year by year, the larger the number of licensed amateur radio operators, the larger the number of people who are mentally ill. But that doesn't mean ... You get the idea.)

Whereas Chapters 1 and 3 were about the *logic* of statistic inference (e.g., how strong is the evidence that the difference in the proportion of "Yes" responses was not due to random chance alone and what do we estimate to be the size of the difference), cause, along with breadth (Chapter 2), are about the *scope* of inference. If we establish that the difference is "real," the breadth part of *Step 5: Formulate conclusions* tells us how broadly the conclusion applies. Finally, in this chapter, you will learn whether and when you can conclude that an observed difference is *caused* by a particular treatment.

Why do cities that sell more Big Macs have more divorces? A related variable is *city size*. The bigger the city, the more Big Macs are bought, and the more divorces there are. Section 4.1 explores such issues more formally. Section 4.2 considers how to

Alonzo Adams/AP Images

choose a study design to avoid such issues. Sections 4.3 and 4.4 further explore a couple different study designs. The key idea is to use a chance process to assign the conditions to be compared, as in the study of organ donation. This introduction of chance into the study design will play a different role than it has in previous chapters.

The main goal of this chapter is to explain when and why you can infer cause. When you can't, caution is the order of the day.

INTRODUCTION

To oversimplify, but not by much, you can think of science as a search for ***cause-and-effect*** relationships and for theories that unite them. In this section we illustrate two things to look for as part of using data to find causal relationships. The first is ***association*** between two variables. Consider smoking and cancer. Initially, scientists found that smokers had higher rates of lung cancer than did nonsmokers. Smoking and cancer were *associated*. Did that *prove* that smoking *caused* cancer? No. For example, some scientists thought there might be a gene that made people both likely to smoke and more likely to get lung cancer. Presence of the gene (yes/no) could be a *confounding* variable or *confounder*. The confounder could explain the association. To conclude that smoking causes lung cancer, you must be able to rule out the effect of possible confounders.

Is association evidence of possible causation? Yes. If smoking *causes* cancer, there has to be an association. Cancer rates will be higher for smokers. If the two are associated, one *might* cause the other. Association is necessary, but association alone is not enough to prove cause and effect.

Night Lights and Nearsightedness

Myopia, or nearsightedness, typically develops during childhood years. Recent studies have explored whether there is an association between development of myopia and the use of night lights with infants. One study (Quinn et al., 1999) interviewed parents of 479 children who were seen as outpatients in a university pediatric ophthalmology clinic. One of the questions asked whether the child typically slept with the room light on, with a night light on, or in darkness before age 2. Based on the child's most recent eye examination, the children were also separated into two groups: nearsighted or not nearsighted. They found a higher percentage of nearsighted children among those using a room light (54.7%) or with a night light (33.6%) compared to children who slept in darkness (10.5%). Pediatricians and parents became concerned that the use of light in the infants' rooms was leading to nearsightedness.

For this study, the observational units are the 479 children. We have recorded two different variables about each child: *whether the child slept with the room light, with a night light, or in darkness* and *whether or not the child was nearsighted.* These are both categorical variables. The lighting variable has three categories and the eye condition variable has two. The percentages of children with nearsightedness presented earlier are calculated *conditional* on the amount of light present in the room at night. Table 4.1 displays the data used to calculate the conditional proportions which when multiplied by 100 give percentages.

Example 4.1

4.1.1

TABLE 4.1   Data used to calculate conditional proportions of nearsightedness based on amount of light in bedroom

	Darkness	Night light	Room light	Total
Nearsighted	18	78	41	137
Not nearsighted	154	154	34	342
Total	172	232	75	479

Conditional proportions: $18/172 \approx 0.105$ (10.5%), $78/232 \approx 0.336$ (33.6%), and $41/75 \approx 0.547$ (54.7%). (These calculations will be discussed in more detail in Chapter 5.)

Notice that as the amount of light present in the room at night increases, so does the percentage of children that are nearsighted. Thus we can say that an association exists between whether or not a child is nearsighted and amount of light used in the child's room before the age of 2.

Here the two variables (amount of light and eye condition) are **associated**: Knowing the amount of light gives you information about (helps you predict) a child's later eye condition. For example, children who slept with a night light are much more likely to be nearsighted than are children who slept in the dark.

4.1.2

4.1.3

EXPLANATORY AND RESPONSE VARIABLES

Association often raises questions about possible causal relationships. After seeing the data above we might wonder, "Does sleeping with a night light *cause* a child's chance of being nearsighted to increase?" As you'll soon see, this study does *not* allow us to answer this question. As the saying goes, "Association is not causation." All the same, it is useful to have labels for the two different roles of the variables: The light condition is called the **explanatory variable**, because in this context we think of it as "explaining" the values of the other, the **response variable**, in this case, eye condition.

> ### THINK ABOUT IT
>
> Imagine that you are planning a study to look for association between overall health (good, fair, not good) and having a pet. Which variable would be explanatory, and which would be the response?

If you think having a pet increases people's happiness and likelihood to exercise, then you are considering pet ownership to be the explanatory variable and health to be the response variable. On the other hand, you may want to consider the health of the individual as an explanation for why some people are more likely to have pets than others. This would reverse the role of the explanatory and the response variable.

In another study, diet could be the explanatory variable and whether or not the person has heart disease could be the response. However, in some cases, there is not a clear distinction between the roles of the variables, such as looking at hair color and eye color—it's not as though one of these variables precedes and perhaps influences the other.

Cause and effect

In the nearsightedness study, there is an association because the percentage of nearsighted children increases as the amount of light used increases. But does this convince us that the room light and night light use is *causing* the children to develop nearsightedness? Drawing such a "**cause-and-effect**" conclusion is much different from establishing an *association* between the variables.

> ### THINK ABOUT IT
>
> Can you suggest another explanation for the higher percentage of nearsightedness in children using the room light and night light compared to those with no light?

Keep in mind that the association between amount of light in the room and eyesight condition appears to be real. If we wanted to predict whether or not a child was nearsighted, it would be worthwhile to know what type of lighting they used before the age of 2. But that is still a very different statement from saying that it was in fact the lighting condition itself that *directly impacted* the children's eye conditions.

Definition

Two variables are **associated**, or related, if the value of one variable gives you information about the value of the other variable. When comparing groups, this means that the proportions or means take on different values in the different groups.

Definitions

The **explanatory variable** is the variable we think is "explaining" the change in the response variable and the **response variable** is the variable we think is being impacted or changed by the explanatory variable. The explanatory variable is sometimes called the independent variable and the response variable is sometimes called the dependent variable.

One alternative explanation is that children who are already nearsighted are more likely to prefer to sleep with light in their rooms. This reverses the roles of the explanatory and response variables, though keep in mind that the researchers asked about light conditions before the age of two (when children don't always have as much say about their environment!) and later eye condition.

Another alternative explanation is that nearsightedness is often inherited from parents (genetics). But does this explain the observed association? It does if parents who are nearsighted are more likely to use a room light or a night light with their infants, perhaps needing the extra light to more easily navigate the room when they enter at night to check on their child. This appears to be a plausible explanation. The problem is we have no way of deciding whether this explanation is better or worse than the cause-and-effect explanation. Both explanations are consistent with the data we have and the association we observed. If the parents' eye conditions do tend to differ among the children with well-lit rooms, night lights, and darkness, then we have no way of separating out the "effects" of this variable from those of the lighting condition. In such a case, *parents' eyesight* is considered a **confounding variable**. The diagram in Figure 4.1 illustrates the confounding. The top panel shows the design of the study: Children (units) are sorted into groups according to the explanatory variable (light condition), and the response (nearsightedness) is measured. The bottom panel shows the potential confounding effect of the parents' own vision.

4.1.4

4.1.5

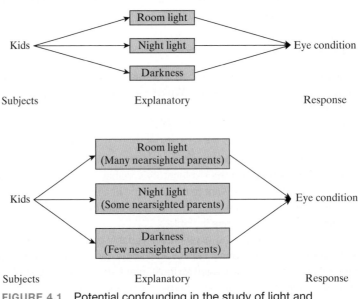

FIGURE 4.1 Potential confounding in the study of light and nearsightedness.

Definition

A **confounding variable** is a variable that is related both to the explanatory and to the response variable in such a way that its effects on the response variable cannot be separated from the effects of the explanatory variable.

Keep in mind that there will always be "other variables" floating around in any study. What we are most concerned about is these potential confounding variables that prevent us from isolating the explanatory variable as the only influence on the response variable. For example, *eye color* is another variable, but it is not likely related to eye condition or lighting use. Or maybe parents use a room light or night light more with girls than with boys. But because nearsightedness affects males and females equally, this wouldn't explain the higher percentages of nearsightedness for the children using light.

The key to discounting a cause-and-effect explanation is to identify a potential confounding variable and to explain how it is linked to *both* the explanatory variable and the response variable in a way that also explains the observed association.

Of course, this doesn't mean our explanatory variable is *not* influencing our response variable. Sometimes the explanation really is causation, as with the association between smoking and lung cancer. But we just can't feel comfortable jumping to a cause-and-effect conclusion based solely on these kinds of studies (we'll discuss this more in the next section!). In short, association does not imply causation, but sometimes it can be a pretty big hint.

Home Court Disadvantage?

Sports teams prefer to play in front of their own fans rather than at the opposing team's site. Having a sell-out crowd should provide even more excitement and lead to an even better performance, right? Well, consider the Oklahoma City Thunder, a National Basketball Association team, in its second season (2008–2009) after moving from Seattle. This team had a win-loss record that was actually worse for home games with a sell-out crowd (3 wins and 15 losses) than for home games without a sell-out crowd (12 wins and 11 losses). (These data were noted in the April 20, 2009, issue of *Sports Illustrated* in the Go Figure column.)

1. Identify the observational units and variables in this study. Also classify each variable as categorical (also binary?) or quantitative.

2. When did the Thunder have a higher winning percentage: in front of a sell-out crowd or a smaller crowd? Support your answer by calculating the proportion of sell-out games that they won and also the proportion of non-sell-out games that they won. (Write both these proportions as decimals.)

   Sell-out crowd:

   Smaller crowd:

3. Do the two variables appear to be associated?

> **Definition**
>
> Two variables are **associated** or related if the value of one variable gives you information about the value of the other variable. When comparing two groups this means that the proportions or means take different values in the two groups.

   Often, when a study involves two associated variables, it is natural to consider one the **explanatory variable** and the other the **response variable**.

4. Which would you consider the explanatory variable in this study? Which is the response? (That is, what are the *roles* of these variables in this study?)

> **Definitions**
>
> The **explanatory variable** is the variable we think is "explaining" the change in the response variable and the **response variable** is the variable we think is being impacted or changed by the explanatory variable. The explanatory variable is sometimes called the independent variable and the response variable is sometimes called the dependent variable.

   There are two possible explanations for this odd finding that the team had a better winning percentage with smaller crowds:

- The sell-out crowd *caused* the Thunder to play worse, perhaps because of pressure or nervousness.

- The sell-out crowd did *not* cause a worse performance, and some other issue (variable) explains why they had a worse winning percentage with sell-out crowds. In other words, a third variable is at play, which is related to both the crowd size and the game outcome.

   (Of course, another explanation is random chance. Using methods you will learn later, we've determined that you can essentially rule out random chance in this case.)

5. Consider the second explanation. Suggest a plausible alternative variable that would explain why the team would be less likely to win in front of a sell-out crowd than in front of a smaller crowd. (Make sure it's clear not just that your explanation would affect the team's likelihood of winning but also that the team would be less likely to win in front of a sell-out crowd compared to a smaller crowd.)

6. Identify the confounding variable based on your suggested explanation in #5. Explain how it is confounding—what is the link between this third variable and the response variable, and what is the link between this third variable and the explanatory variable? (*Hint*: Remember that this variable has to be recorded on the observational units: home games for the Thunder.)

> **Definition**
>
> A **confounding variable** is a variable that is related both to the explanatory and to the response variable in such a way that its effects on the response variable cannot be separated from the effects of the explanatory variable.

   Another variable recorded for these data was whether or not the opponent had a winning record the previous season. Of the Thunder's 41 home games, 22 were against teams that won more than half of their games. Let's refer to those 22 teams as strong opponents. Of these 22 games, 13 were sell-outs. Of the 19 games against opponents that won less than half of their games that season (weak opponents), only 5 of those games were sell-outs.

7. Was the Thunder more likely to have a sell-out crowd against a strong opponent or a weak opponent? Calculate the relevant (conditional) proportions to support your answer.

When the Thunder played a strong opponent, they won only 4 of 22 games. When they played a weak opponent, the Thunder won 11 of 19 games.

8. Was the Thunder less likely to win against a strong opponent than a weak one? Again calculate the relevant (conditional) proportions to support your answer.

9. Explain how your answers to #7 and #8 establish that strength of opponent is a confounding variable that prevents drawing a cause-and-effect conclusion between crowd size and game outcome.

10. Summarize your conclusion about whether these data provide evidence that a sell-out crowd *caused* the Thunder to play worse. Write as if to a friend who has never studied statistics. Be sure to address the fact that the Thunder had a much smaller winning percentage in front of a sell-out crowd.

Confounding explains why you cannot draw a cause-and-effect conclusion from association alone: The groups defined by the explanatory variable could differ in more ways than just the explanatory variable when confounding is present. The diagram in Figure 4.2 illustrates the confounding in the Thunder study. The top panel shows the study design: Observational units (home games) are sorted into groups according to the explanatory variable (whether or not the arena was sold out). Then the response (win/lose) was observed. The bottom panel shows the confounding: sell-out crowds tended to be against stronger opponents; weaker opponents tended not to sell out the arena.

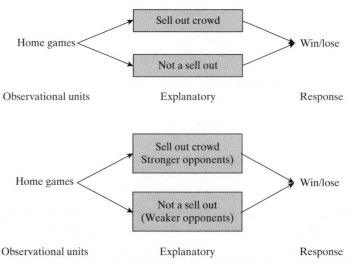

FIGURE 4.2   Confounding in the study of the home court disadvantage.

SECTION 4.1   Summary

Two variables are **associated** (related) if the values of one variable provide information about (help you predict) the values of the other variable.

Studies that involve two variables often distinguish between the roles played by the variables.

- The **explanatory variable** is the one that is suspected of possibly affecting the other.
- The **response variable** is the one that may be affected by the other.

A **confounding variable** is one whose effects on the response cannot be separated from those of the explanatory variable.

The possible presence of confounding variables is the reason that association alone does not justify a conclusion that differences in the explanatory variable *cause* differences in the response variable.

OBSERVATIONAL STUDIES VERSUS EXPERIMENTS

INTRODUCTION

Many, if not most, scientific studies involve a search for cause-and-effect relationships between variables. Studies often start by looking for an association between explanatory and response variables, but the possible presence of confounding variables prevents us from being able to draw conclusions about cause. The main challenge in designing a good study is to avoid the effect of confounding variables. If you know in advance about a particular confounding variable, you may be able to choose a design that balances the effects of that confounder. But many confounders are "lurking" variables—either not known or known but not measured. To deal with these unseen confounders, we rely on a strategy called randomization or random assignment. We use a chance device like coin tosses or drawing names from a hat to decide which subjects go into which groups. Random assignment in this way gives approximate balance for all possible confounding variables.

The importance of random assignment to avoid confounding effects leads to one of the most important distinctions in all of science: the difference between an observational study and an experimental study. In an observational study, the values of the explanatory variable are simply observed—you don't get to choose. In an experiment, you—the investigator—get to assign the conditions to the different subjects.

Lying on the Internet

4.2

Are people more likely to tell lies with e-mail than with pencil and paper? A study reported at the August 2008 meeting of the Academy of Management involved 48 graduate students in business who participated in a "bargaining" game. Researchers kept track of whether or not students misrepresented (lied about) the size of the pot when they were negotiating with other players.

STEP 1: Ask a research question. Does the Internet encourage lying? Investigators thought that the Internet might encourage users to feel anonymous, making them more likely to lie. To narrow their hypothesis, they decided to compare two groups of students playing a competitive game. Each student was randomly assigned to one of two groups. Students in one group would play on the Internet by using e-mail as their method of communication. Students in the other group would use pencil and paper as their method of communication. The researchers hypothesized that those who played on the Internet would lie more often.

STEP 2: Design a study and collect data.

> **THINK ABOUT IT**
>
> Identify the explanatory and response variables in this study. Is the study observational or experimental? How can you tell?

The explanatory variable is the communication method. The response variable is whether or not the person lied. Both variables are categorical. This was an experiment rather than an observational study because the researchers actively intervened to determine the communication method used by the students.

> **THINK ABOUT IT**
>
> Suppose there were 30 male and 18 female subjects. Imagine if you had all of the 30 men in the sample play on the Internet, and the 18 women used pencil and paper. If you were concerned that males might be more competitive and therefore more likely to lie in order to win, how would this limit your ability to draw conclusions about the initial research question from this study?

EXAMPLE

Example 4.2

4.2.1

Definitions

In an ***observational study,*** the groups you compare are "just there," that is, they are defined by what you *see* rather than by what you *do*. In an ***experiment,*** you actively create the groups by what you choose to do. More formally, you assign the conditions to be compared. These conditions may be one or more **treatments** or a **control** (a group you do nothing to).

If all of the men played on the Internet and all of the women used pencil and paper, then if we saw a difference in the two groups in terms of the proportion who lied, you would not be able to say whether it was the sex of the participant or the format of the game (Internet vs. paper and pencil) that was causing the difference.

THINK ABOUT IT

How could you address this concern?

One strategy would be to assign half the men and half the women to each group. That way, both groups will have 15 male and 9 female subjects. The groups would be balanced with respect to the sex of the subject.

KEY IDEA

A comparative study is *balanced with respect to a possible confounding variable* if the distribution of the variable is the same for each group in the study.

Note that if you have many confounders, it will be hard to balance them all. Worse yet, if you have "lurking" variables—unmeasured or unrecognized potential confounders—the challenge might seem impossible. How can you balance what you can't even see?

Fortunately, random assignment offers a solution. If you know about and measure a potential confounder in advance, you may be able to design a study that gives exact balance for that variable. If you use a chance device to assign units to groups, you may not get exact balance. In fact, most of the time you won't. But—this is the key—you will get *approximate* balance for *all* potential confounders, including the ones you don't know about. If you toss a fair coin, you tend to get half heads, half tails, or at least an outcome pretty close to that. If you use a coin toss to assign subjects to two groups, you tend to get half the men in each group and half the women in each group. You also, at the same time, tend to get half the young people in each group, half the vegetarians in each group, half the pet owners in each group, and so on.

KEY IDEA

Randomly assigning experimental units to groups tends to balance out all other variables between the groups. Any variables that could have an effect on the response should be equalized between the two groups and therefore should not be confounding.

With a randomized experiment, if you observe a difference in lying between the Internet players and the pencil-and-paper players, there are only two explanations: Either there is a cause-and-effect relationship or else the difference was just due to random chance, stemming from the random assignment process. We will be willing to assume there are no potential confounding variables to explain the difference.

The diagram in Figure 4.3 illustrates this. The top panel shows the possible confounding effect if the study design had not been randomized. We want to know whether differences in the explanatory variable cause differences in the response (dotted arrow). However, a confounding variable would affect the response variable and be associated with the explanatory variable, making it impossible to separate the effects of explanatory and confounding variable on the response. The bottom panel shows how randomization removes the effect of the potential confounders.

4.2.2

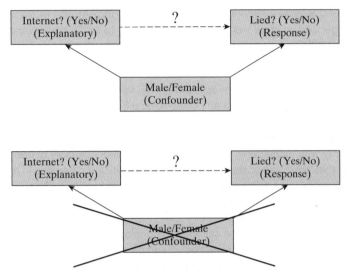

FIGURE 4.3 Randomization creates approximate balance and tends to eliminate confounding effects.

Note our change in terminology: we now will sometimes call the individuals in the study *experimental units* instead of *observational units*, because they are in an experiment instead of an observational study.

For this study each student was randomly assigned to one of two groups. Students in Group 1 used the Internet. Those in Group 2 used pencil and paper. You can think of the random assignment like drawing names out of a hat: Put all the names on slips of paper, put them in a hat, mix thoroughly, take them out one at a time, and put each of them into one of the two groups (Internet, paper, Internet, paper, etc.).

Compare this study with the two studies in the last section, Night Lights and Home Court Disadvantage. Notice that in both of those studies, it was not possible for researchers to *assign* the conditions to be compared. For the Night Lights study, each child was an observational unit. Values of the explanatory variable (level of light) were observed. They could not be chosen by the investigators. For the Home Court Disadvantage study, each home game was an observational unit. The strength of the opponent was observed, not assigned. If the home game is against the LA Lakers, there's no way you can make them be a weak team just for the sake of your research.

STEP 3: Explore the data.   The researchers found that 24 of 26 (92%) who used e-mail were guilty of lying about the pot size, compared to 14 of 22 (64%) who used paper and pencil. (We will discuss such *conditional* percentages in more detail in Chapter 5.)

STEP 4: Draw inferences beyond the data.   When you are comparing two groups like this, if you find a difference between the groups, you again need to consider several potential explanations. One possible explanation is that the people feel more comfortable lying by e-mail, perhaps because it seems anonymous. In other words, the format of the game *influenced* how people responded. But of course another important possible explanation to consider is random chance: Maybe it was just luck of the draw that led to the big difference in the proportions of liars between the two groups. We claimed that random assignment should balance out the two groups, but there is still a chance that the random assignment process itself created slightly different groups. Notice the randomness we are considering here stems from the random assignment, not random choices or random sampling. As it turns out, for this study we can rule out this explanation. Using methods you will learn in the next chapter, it's highly unlikely that the e-mailing players would lie this much more frequently, relative to the pencil-and-paper players, just by chance alone (i.e., the p-value is small, 0.015).

STEP 5: Formulate conclusions.   Now it is time to formulate our final conclusions. We found a statistically significant difference between the two groups. Does this allow us to conclude

Definitions

In a *randomized experiment*, you use a chance device to make the assignments. The units in an experiment are often called *experimental units*. The role of the random assignment is to balance out potentially confounding variables among the explanatory variable groups, giving us the potential to draw cause-and-effect conclusions.

 4.2.3

that the format of the game *influenced* how people responded? Maybe those who use e-mail tend to be younger and younger individuals are more likely to lie. Or there could be other personality traits that differ between the individuals in the e-mail group and the paper-and-pencil group. Are these potential confounding variables?

Because the study used random assignment to form the Internet group and the paper-and-pencil group, we don't expect any systematic differences between the Internet group and the pencil-and-paper group. This is because the random assignment process should create groups that are similar to each other on all respects (e.g., sex of subject, age, propensity for lying, familiarity with technology) apart from the explanatory variable of interest.

This means that when you observed a statistically significant difference in how the groups respond or behave (too large to be expected to happen by the random chance inherent in the random assignment process), then a plausible explanation is *because of* the group to which the experimental units were assigned.

In formulating our conclusions, we still want to consider the *breadth* of our study. Because the subjects in this study are business school graduate students and volunteers, we should be very cautious in generalizing these results to a larger population. See FAQ 4.2.1 and Figure 4.5 at the end of this section for more details and a helpful table.

FAQ 4.2.1   www.wiley.com/college/tintle

No random assignment, no cause-and-effect conclusions, right?

Types of experiments

We just saw that randomized experiments (experiments where the explanatory variable is manipulated by the researchers and assignment of observational units to the explanatory variable's groups is determined randomly) can potentially lead to cause-and-effect conclusions between the explanatory and response variables. What about experiments which manipulate the explanatory variable, but not randomly? These are often called **quasi-experiments**. For example, suppose we wanted to compare student learning gains when using a new curriculum to that of an old curriculum. It would be difficult to assign students *randomly* to which class they take. So the instructors might take the results from pre- and posttest from students who used the old curriculum one year and compare these to the results from pre- and posttests from students who used the new curriculum another year. Although this type of experiment may be the best option when random assignment is not feasible, there may still be reasons other than the explanatory variable (confounding variables that changed between year 1 and year 2 of the study) for the difference in outcomes between the two groups (e.g., time of day class is offered, percentage of upper-division students in the course). Therefore, even though this is considered an experiment, it is not a randomized experiment, and we should be cautious before drawing any cause-and-effect conclusions.

Also keep in mind that some explanatory variables of interest don't lend themselves to randomized experiments. For example, the sex of the participant can't be randomly imposed on individuals, and other variables, such as smoking behavior, would be unethical to manipulate!

Other considerations

THINK ABOUT IT

In this study, the subjects were randomly assigned to the Internet group and the paper-and-pencil group. Do you think the researchers told the subjects in advance that they would be assigned to one of these two groups?

In most research studies, subjects are "blind" to the other treatment conditions. In fact, they often don't know that there are multiple conditions or exactly which condition they are in. For example, suppose I want to test a new diet pill. If I give you a pill and tell you it's going to give you more energy, you may feel a positive effect even if there is no active ingredient in the pill. If one group had this psychological suggestion and not the other, then that would be a confounding variable. So the second group, the "control group," would often be given a "placebo pill" (an empty treatment) so none of the subjects knew which group they were in. In fact, for something like measuring energy, which may require subjective judgment (as opposed to heart rate), often the person making the measurements wouldn't know which group the subjects were in either, to prevent any bias creeping into their judgments as well, making the study "double blind." A "randomized, double-blind, placebo controlled experiment" has been considered by some to be the gold standard in scientific studies.

> **Definition**
>
> In a **double-blind** study, neither the subjects nor those evaluating the response variable know which treatment group the subject is in.

Have a Nice Trip

> **EXPLORATION**
>
> **4.2**

An area of research in biomechanics and gerontology concerns falls and fall-related injuries, especially for elderly people. Recent studies have focused on how individuals respond to large postural disturbances (e.g., tripping, induced slips). One question is whether subjects can be instructed to improve their recovery from such disturbances.

Suppose researchers want to compare two such recovery strategies, lowering (quickly stepping down with front leg and then raising back leg over the object) and elevating (lifting front leg over the object). Subjects will have first been trained on one of these two recovery strategies, and they will be asked to apply it after they feel themselves tripping. The researchers will then induce the subject to trip while walking (but harnessed for safety) using a concealed mechanical obstacle.

Suppose the following 24 subjects have agreed to participate in such a study:

Females: Alisha, Alice, Betty, Martha, Audrey, Mary, Barbie, Anna

Males: Matt, Peter, Shawn, Brad, Michael, Kyle, Russ, Patrick, Bob, Kevin, Mitch, Marvin, Paul, Pedro, Roger, Sam

> **Definitions**
>
> In an **observational study**, the groups you compare are "just there," that is, they are defined by what you *see* rather than by what you *do*. In an **experiment**, you actively create the groups by what you choose to do. More formally, you assign the conditions to be compared. These conditions may be one or more **treatments** or a **control** (a group you do nothing to).

1. One way to design this study would be to assign the 8 females to use the elevating strategy and the 16 males to use the lowering strategy. Would this be a reasonable strategy? Why not?

2. One way to deal with this issue is to assign 4 females and 8 males to each group. Show how the proportion of males in each group is the same.

3. Now, if you saw a difference in the proportion of trips in the two groups, could it be because of the sex of the subject? Why or why not? Could it be due to other variables, distinct from the recovery strategy? Why or why not?

4. Because there will always be more potential confounding variables which could be distributed unevenly between the groups being compared, identify a better method for deciding who uses which strategy.

Note our change in terminology: We now will sometimes call the individuals in the study *experimental units* instead of *observational units*, because they are in an experiment instead of an observational study.

> **Definitions**
>
> In a **randomized experiment**, you use a chance device to make the assignments. The units in an experiment are often called **experimental units**. The role of the random assignment is to balance out potentially confounding variables among the explanatory variable groups, giving us the potential to draw cause-and-effect conclusions.

5. Let's explore the process of random assignment to determine whether it does "work." First, let's focus on the sex (male vs. female) variable. Suppose we put each person's name on a slip, put those slips in a hat and mix them up thoroughly, and then randomly draw out 12 slips for names of people to assign to the elevating strategy. What proportion of this group do you expect will be male? What proportion of the lowering strategy do you expect will be male? Do you think we will always get an 8/8 split (8 males in each treatment group)?

6. To repeat this random assignment a large number of times to observe the long-run behavior, we will use the **Randomizing Subjects** applet. Open the applet and press the **Randomize** button. What proportion of subjects assigned to Group 1 are men? Of Group 2? What is the difference in these two proportions?

You will notice that the difference in proportions of males is shown in the dotplot in the bottom graph. In this graph, each dot represents one repetition of the random assignment process where we are recording the difference in proportions of men between the two groups.

7. Press the **Randomize** button again. Was the difference in proportions of men the same this time?

8. Change the number of replications from 1 to 198 (for 200 total), uncheck the **Animate** option, and press the **Randomize** button. The dotplot will display the difference between the two proportions of men for each of the 200 repetitions of the random assignment process. Where are these values centered?

9. Does random assignment *always* equally distribute/balance the men and women between the two groups? Is there a tendency for there to be a similar proportion of men in the two groups? Explain.

10. Prior research has also shown that the likelihood of falling is related to variables such as walking speed, stride rate, and height, so we would like the random assignment to distribute these variables equally between the groups as well. In the applet, use the pull-down menu to switch from the sex-of-participant variable to the height variable. The dotplot now displays the differences in *average* height between Group 1 and Group 2 for these 200 repetitions. In the long run, does random assignment tend to equally distribute the height variable between the two groups? Explain how you are deciding.

11. Suppose there is a "balance gene" that is related to people's ability to recover from a trip. We didn't know about this gene ahead of time, but if you select the **Reveal gene?** button and then select **gene** from the pull-down menu, the applet shows you this gene information for each subject and also how the proportions with the gene differ in the two groups. Does this variable tend to equalize between the two groups in the long run? Explain.

12. Suppose there were other "*x*-variables" that we could not measure such as stride rate or walking speed. Select the **Reveal both?** button and use the pull-down menu to display the results for the *x*-variable (X-var). Does random assignment generally succeed in equalizing this variable between the two groups or is there a tendency for one group to always have higher results for the *x*-variable? Explain.

> ### Definition
> A comparative study is *balanced with respect to a possible confounding variable* if the distribution of the variable is the same for each group in the study.

KEY IDEA

Randomly assigning experimental units to groups tends to balance out all other variables between the groups. Any variables that could have an effect on the response should be equalized between the two groups and therefore should not be confounding.

The diagram in Figure 4.4 illustrates the key idea above. The top panel shows the possible confounding effect if the study design had not been randomized. We want to know whether differences in the explanatory variable cause differences in the response (dotted arrow). However, a confounding variable would affect both the explanatory and response variables, making it impossible to separate the effects of explanatory and confounding variables on the response. The bottom panel shows how randomization removes the effect of the potential confounders.

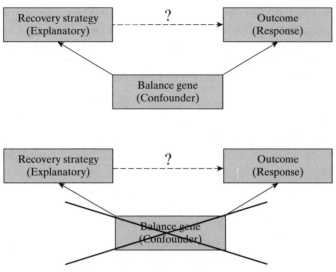

FIGURE 4.4 Randomization creates approximate balance and tends to eliminate confounding effects.

13. Suppose this study finds a statistically significant difference between the two groups. What conclusion would you draw? For what population? What additional information would you need to know?

14. As in #13, if you obtain a statistically significant result, what does that suggest about the potential for a cause-and-effect relationship? Why?

Another study: Cursive handwriting

An article about handwriting appeared in the October 11, 2006, issue of the *Washington Post*. The article mentioned that among students who took the essay portion of the SAT exam in 2005–2006, those who wrote in cursive style scored significantly higher on the essay, on average, than students who used printed block letters.

15. Identify the observational units in this study as well as the explanatory and response variables. Also classify each variable as categorical or quantitative.

Observational units:	
Explanatory variable:	Type:
Response variable:	Type:

16. Explain how you know that this was an observational study.

17. Is it reasonable to conclude that using a cursive writing style *caused* higher scores on the essay, or can you think of an alternative explanation for why students who wrote in cursive style scored higher on average than students who write with block letters? In other words, can you think of other ways in which the cursive and block letter groups might have systematically differed and identify a potential confounding variable?

The same *Washington Post* article also mentioned a different study in which the identical essay was shown to many graders, but some graders were randomly chosen to see a cursive version of the essay and the other graders were shown a version with printed block letters. The average score assigned to the essay with the cursive style was significantly higher than the average score assigned to the essay with the printed block letters.

18. How does this study differ from the original one? Explain.

19. Would you be willing to draw a cause-and-effect conclusion from this study, as opposed to the original study? Explain why.

See the Section summary for a helpful table (Figure 4.5) which summarizes the types of conclusions you can draw with and without random sampling and with and without random assignment.

The "placebo effect" has been found in numerous studies: When subjects are told something good is going to happen, they often have a positive response even if nothing is actually done to them. For this reason, subjects are often kept "blind" as to which treatment group they are placed in, for example by giving one group the actual treatment and the other group a "fake" treatment, like a placebo (an inert pill). Placebo treatments have even been used in studies about knee surgery!

Definition

In **_double-blind_** studies, neither the subjects nor those evaluating the response variable know which treatment group the subject is in.

20. Discuss why it was important in this second study for the scorers of the essays to not know that there was no difference in the essays given to different individuals other than the writing style.

21. Discuss how this study also reveals that those evaluating the response variable in a study, if it requires any subjective judgment, should be "blind" to which treatment group individuals are in.

SECTION 4.2   Summary

A well-designed **experiment** uses random assignment to determine which observational (experimental) units go into which explanatory variable groups.

- The goal of **random assignment** is to produce groups that are as similar as possible in all respects except for the explanatory variable.
- Then if the groups can be shown to differ significantly on the response variable, the difference can be attributed to a **cause-and-effect relationship** between the explanatory and response variables.

Random assignment is a very different use of randomness from random sampling, with different implications for scope of conclusions.

- Random sampling aims to select a representative sample from a population, so that results about the sample can be generalized to the larger population (Chapter 2).
- Random assignment aims to produce similar treatment groups, so that a significant difference in the response variable between groups can be attributed (causally) to the explanatory variable.

Figure 4.5 summarizes how these two types of randomness lead to a different impact on the scope of conclusions.

In a **double-blind** experiment, neither the subjects nor those evaluating the response variable know which group the subject is in. This is to guard against biases such as the placebo effect, where the mere power of suggestion can influence subjects' responses.

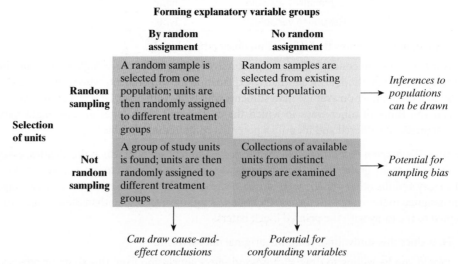

FIGURE 4.5   Study design factors and their impact on scope of conclusions (adapted from Ramsey and Schafer, _The Statistical Sleuth_).

DESIGN OF EXPERIMENTS: COMPLETELY RANDOMIZED DESIGN

SECTION 4.3

INTRODUCTION

In the previous section we looked at the differences between observational studies and experiments and introduced the need for randomized comparative experiments in order to establish a cause-and-effect relationship between an explanatory and a response variable. It was also noted that a "randomized, double-blind, placebo-controlled experiment" is considered by some to be the gold standard in scientific studies. In this section we will focus on how to design an experiment to answer a research question of interest. There are two types of experimental designs that are part of the AP Statistics curriculum: a completely randomized design and a design that incorporates **blocking** to control for potential confounding variables that are known in advance. We will focus on the completely randomized design in this section and on experimental designs that incorporate blocking in the next section.

Design of an Experiment

The design of an experiment is the overall plan for conducting the experiment. As we discussed in the previous section, a well-designed experiment involving random assignment and a control group makes it possible to (potentially) conclude a cause-and-effect relationship between our explanatory variable (treatments being imposed) and our response variable (what we are interested in measuring). We will now further explore control and random assignment, while also introducing the concept of replication with regard to a randomized experiment.

> **KEY IDEA**
>
> The key elements of a well-designed experiment include
>
> - Control
> - Random assignment
> - Replication

- ***Control***: A well-designed experiment accounts for the potential effects of variables that we are not interested in studying. (For example, making sure all the measurements are taken at the same outside temperature.) ***Comparison*** (having more than one treatment group) is the simplest form of control. By comparing two or more treatments, influences that we cannot control for, such as changes due to the passage of time, or the ***placebo effect*** (the phenomenon whereby subjects respond positively simply because they are being given a treatment) should be similar in all treatment groups. This means that observed *differences* in the treatment groups should not be due to these unwanted variables.

  Although comparison controls for the effect of extraneous variables after the treatments have been imposed, it won't help us if our treatment groups differ greatly in ways that may affect the response variable from the onset. We want the treatment groups to be as similar as possible in all respects except for the treatment that is imposed. Then, if the groups differ substantially in the response variable after the treatment is imposed, you can conclude that the explanatory variable caused that difference. This is accomplished by the next principle of a well-designed experiment: random assignment.

- ***Random Assignment***: By using a chance device to randomly assign experimental units (usually called "subjects" when they are human) to the treatment groups, the study should produce treatment groups that are similar in all respects except for the treatment imposed. In other words, random assignment to treatment groups controls for the potential effects of confounding variables, potentially allowing us to draw cause-and-effect conclusions.

> **Definition**
>
> The ***placebo effect*** is the positive psychological benefit that many people experience simply by knowing they are receiving a treatment. By giving subjects in the "placebo group" a fake or empty treatment (a *placebo*), we can balance these psychological effects across the treatment groups.

• *Replication*: In Section 1.4 you saw the impact that sample size had on our strength of evidence against the null hypothesis and in favor of the research hypothesis (larger sample sizes provide stronger evidence). We want to include sufficient experimental units in each of our treatment groups so that if we observe a difference in the treatment groups, we can rule out that the difference was just due to random chance, stemming from the random assignment process.

When describing your experimental design on the AP exam, you will want to include enough details regarding the design of your experiment so that another researcher can conduct the experiment based solely on your description. Such a description is called the **protocol** of the study. Replication of an experiment by another researcher is a way to confirm the validity of your experimental results. This type of replication, although important, does not replace the need for replication (multiple experimental units or subjects in each treatment group) in an individual experiment.

Completely Randomized Design

In a completely randomized design, the formal name for the type of experiment we introduced in the previous section, experimental units (subjects) are randomly assigned to the treatment groups (explanatory variable). Then the response variable is compared across the different treatment groups. The drawing in Figure 4.6 illustrates a completely randomized design.

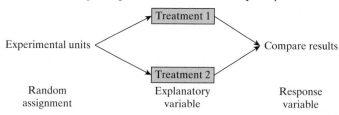

FIGURE 4.6 Graphic of a completely randomized experiment.

AP TIP

Although a graphic alone, as in Figure 4.6, would not constitute a complete answer to a question on the AP Statistics exam that asks you to design an experiment, you may find it useful as an initial first step in organizing the key components of the experiment. When you describe your study protocol after the graphic, make sure you

- Name the treatments being administered (do not just use the generic term *treatment*).
- Explain how (and how many of) the experimental units (subjects) are assigned to the treatments. Your method of random assignment should be such that another knowledgeable user of statistics would implement it in the same manner.
- Identify the response variable that you are comparing for the different treatment groups.

Example 4.3

EXAMPLE

4.3 Alternative Headache Remedies

Migraines are a well-known type of headache because of their debilitating nature and the number of people affected by them. Past studies suggest that people who suffer from chronic migraine headaches may have low magnesium levels and that taking a daily magnesium supplement can reduce the frequency of migraines with fewer potential adverse side effects. A researcher would like to conduct an experiment to compare the average number of migraine headaches during a six-month period for patients who take 400 mg of magnesium per day, patients who take 600 mg of magnesium per day, and patients who do not take any magnesium supplement but are instead given a daily placebo (a sugar pill).

THINK ABOUT IT

How would you sketch the outline of a plan that shows how to randomly assign 60 volunteers to one of three treatments?

To sketch a completely randomized design involving 60 volunteers who have been diagnosed as having chronic migraines, we can use a drawing like that in Figure 4.7.

FIGURE 4.7   Outline of migraine study.

Let's now describe in words what this plan entails: We'll put each of the volunteers' names on a separate slip of paper and place in a bag, making sure that all slips of paper are the same size. Then mix them up inside the bag. The first 20 subjects whose names are randomly selected from the bag (without replacement) will be assigned to the group that takes 400 mg of magnesium each day. The next 20 subjects whose names are randomly drawn from the bag (without replacement) will be assigned to the group that takes 600 mg of magnesium each day, and the remaining 20 subjects will be assigned to the group that takes a placebo pill each day. We'll have subjects keep track of the number of migraines they experience during the six-month period. After six months, compare the average number of migraines during the six-month period for each of the three treatment groups.

4.3.1

ALTERNATE METHODS FOR RANDOMLY ASSIGNING THE 60 SUBJECTS TO ONE OF THE THREE TREATMENT GROUPS

Using a calculator or computer: Assign each subject a unique random number between 1 and 60. Use a calculator or computer to generate 60 unique (without duplication) random numbers between 1 and 60. The subjects whose numbers match the first 20 randomly generated numbers will be assigned to the group that takes 400 mg of magnesium each day. The subjects whose numbers match the next 20 randomly generated numbers will be assigned to the group that takes 600 mg of calcium each day, and the subjects whose numbers match the remaining 20 randomly generated numbers will be assigned to the group that takes a placebo pill each day.

Using a six-sided die: For each of the 60 subjects, roll a six-sided die. If the outcome of the roll is a 1 or 2, the subject is assigned to the group that takes 400 mg of magnesium each day. If the outcome of the roll is a 3 or 4, the subject is assigned to the group that takes 600 mg of magnesium each day. If the outcome of the roll is a 5 or 6, the subject is assigned to the group that takes a placebo pill each day.

Note: This die method will not necessarily result in equal-sized treatment groups, but that is okay. What is **not** okay is to stop placing subjects in a treatment group once a group size reaches 20, because it would no longer be random assignment. If the first two groups are filled and the remaining subjects are all assigned to the third group, they may be similar in a way that could affect the response variable (e.g., the most severe cases could arrive at the clinic first).

4.3.2

4.3.3

THINK ABOUT IT

What purpose does having a group that gets a placebo each day serve?

Without the placebo, you will only know whether there is a difference in the average number of headaches for the two different levels of magnesium supplements. Including a group that does not get an active ingredient gives you information on whether taking magnesium is more effective than not. In particular, it provides a baseline average number of headaches to compare to the average number of headaches in the magnesium group. Giving them a placebo (a fake treatment) makes sure any psychological effects from believing they are receiving treatment will be balanced across the groups.

THINK ABOUT IT

Can this experiment be conducted in a double-blind manner?

As long as the person receiving the treatment does not know which treatment he or she received (the placebo pill looks and tastes just like the treatment pills) and the person administering the treatments and recording the number of headaches does not know which treatment each subject was given, the experiment is "double-blind," again guarding against any subconscious biases in favor or against the treatments

4.3.4

THINK ABOUT IT

If the difference in the average number of migraine headaches during this time period is significantly different among the three treatment groups, can we conclude a cause-and-effect relationship between the treatment received and average number of headaches experienced?

Because this was a placebo-controlled double-blind randomized experiment, any other potential confounding variables that could have an effect on the response variable (number of migraines in the six-month period) should be equalized among the three treatment groups. This means that there shouldn't be any difference among the groups other than the treatment assigned. If an analysis of the data results in a small p-value, this means that any difference we observe between the treatment groups at the end of the study is unlikely to be due to random chance from the random assignment process. Therefore, a small p-value would be evidence to conclude a cause-and-effect relationship between the explanatory variable (treatment received) and the response variable (number of migraines).

EXPLORATION 4.3 | Is a Picture Worth a Thousand Words?

How good is your memory? There are approximately 86 billion neurons in the human brain, each with multiple connections to other neurons, so humans certainly have enough space to memorize vastly large amounts of information. Why is it then that some people seem able to memorize better than others? Researchers who have studied memory and cognition definitely have suggestions on how to improve one's memory (e.g., Herculano-Houzel, 2012). Suppose that you want to investigate whether the number of items someone can remember from a list depends on whether the list consists of words or of pictures, and that 20 students from your class have volunteered to participate in the study.

1. If you were to design a study to compare the number of objects memorized from each of the two lists, what types of things might you include in your protocol? (For example, should the word list and picture list have the same items, or should they be different? Should everyone be given exactly the same amount of time to look at the list, and the same amount of time to write down their answers? Keep in mind that you want the two experimental groups to be as alike as possible, other than whether they receive a word list or a picture list.)

2. What is the explanatory variable, and what is the response variable?

3. Draw a graphic that outlines your plan of how to randomly assign the 20 students in your class to one of the two types of lists.

4. Describe how you would carry out the random assignment in your class.

5. Suppose you find a statistically significant difference in the average number of items remembered in the two lists: summarize the conclusion you would draw from the study.

- -

SECTION 4.3   Summary

In this section we examined one of the two types of experimental design that are part of the AP Statistics curriculum: a ***completely randomized design***. In a completely randomized design, experimental units are randomly assigned to the different treatment groups. Random assignment of subjects to experimental groups (treatments) guards against the problem of confounding by, on average, balancing out other variables and creating treatment groups that are similar in all ways except for the explanatory variable being studied.

- -

DESIGN OF EXPERIMENTS: RANDOMIZED BLOCK DESIGN

SECTION 4.4

INTRODUCTION

In Section 4.1 you saw that the presence of confounding variables limited our ability to draw a cause-and-effect conclusion. In Section 4.2 you learned that the role of random assignment is to balance out potential confounding variables (both known and unknown) among the explanatory variable groups, giving us the power to draw cause-and-effect conclusions (for statistically significant results). A completely randomized experiment has the advantage of minimizing the impact of any and all possible confounding variables, by making the treatment groups effectively the same before applying the treatments, thus yielding the potential for a cause-and-effect conclusion to be drawn from the study. However, when we can identify in advance potential confounding variables that may explain differences in the response variable, we can use this information to our advantage in the study design.

The ***randomized block design*** is the experimental design equivalent of stratified random sampling. Recall from Section 2.1 part 3 that stratified random sampling is used when the population is composed of several subgroups that may systematically differ from each other in the behavior or attribute (response variable) that you are studying. A stratified random sample breaks the population into subgroups or strata in such a way that the observational units within each stratum are similar in ways that may differ with respect to the response variable we are interested in measuring, and observational units in different strata are different in ways that may be associated with the response variable. An advantage to stratified sampling over simple random sampling is that the representativeness of the sample may be improved in terms of reduced sampling error. This same logic applies in experiments. Random assignment, on average, deals with confounding, but there still may be some (small) differences in confounding variable distributions between treatment groups. Blocking ensures this isn't left to "chance." Blocking helps to control for anticipated variability before we begin our experiment. A block is a group of experimental units that are similar in some way that is expected to differ on the response we are measuring. Experimental units within each block should be as similar as possible in ways that may affect the response variable, and across different blocks should be different in ways that may affect the response variable. We block on a variable because we anticipate that it may affect our response variable; then we randomly assign experimental units to treatments within each block to guard against other potential (known and unknown) confounding variables. This means that, if you can measure/identify likely confounding variables ahead of time (variables that aren't of interest but impact the response), use these as your blocking variables. There will still be confounding variables you didn't think of/can't measure easily—so we let those get balanced out by random assignment. A common statistical adage is *"Block what you can and randomize what you cannot."*

4.4 Waking Up Groggy

Example 4.4

EXAMPLE

People who use sleep aids often complain that they feel groggy the next morning and have difficulty waking up. A researcher would like to test a natural sleep aid containing melatonin (Natural Supplement) with one of the leading prescription sleep aids on the market (Prescription Drug). Thirty men and 28 women who have difficulty sleeping have volunteered to take part in the study. Volunteers will spend the night at a sleep clinic. Before being given a sleep aid, the volunteers will be given a test of their cognitive abilities. Upon being awakened in the morning, a comparable cognitive test will be administered and the difference in scores (After Taking Sleep Aid – Before Taking Sleep Aid) will be recorded. A negative difference would indicate that the volunteer scored lower on the cognitive test the morning after the sleep aid was administered. It is known that, in general, sleep aids are excreted more slowly from a woman's system than a man's, potentially making women feel groggier in the morning.

> **THINK ABOUT IT**
>
> How would you design an experiment to compare the difference in alertness as measured by the difference in cognitive test scores that takes into consideration sex-related differences in how men and women respond to sleep aids?

Because we are told that men and women may react differently to sleep aids with respect to how alert they may feel the next day, we should block on sex. First, all volunteers will be given a test of their cognitive ability before participating in the sleep aid treatment. Next we randomly assign half of the 30 men in the study to take the natural supplement and the other half of the men to take the prescription drug. This can be accomplished by writing "Group 1" on 15 slips of paper and "Group 2" on 15 slips of paper. All slips of paper will be placed into a bag and mixed up. Each male subject will be asked to randomly select a slip of paper, without replacing it. The men who select a slip of paper marked Group 1 will be given the natural supplement and the men who select Group 2 will be given the prescription drug (without the subjects knowing what drug they are receiving so the study is "blind"). When the male subjects are awakened the next morning, a comparable cognitive test will be given and the difference in scores (After – Before) will be recorded for each. The mean difference scores for the two treatment groups of men will then be compared.

4.4.1

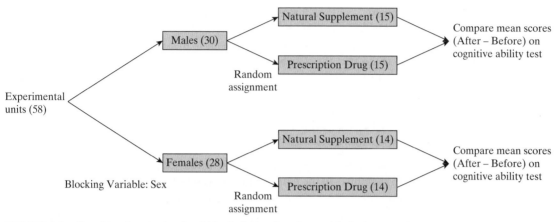

FIGURE 4.8 Graphic of a randomized block design for sleep-aid study.

We will do the same thing for the women. Half the women will be given the natural supplement and half the prescription drug. This can be accomplished by writing "Group 1" on 14 slips of paper and "Group 2" on 14 other slips of paper. The papers will be placed into a bag, shuffled, and each female subject will be asked to randomly select a slip of paper, without replacing it. The women who select a slip of paper marked Group 1 will be given the natural supplement and the women who select Group 2 will be given the prescription drug. When the female subjects are awakened the next morning, a comparable cognitive test will be given and the difference in scores (After – Before) will be recorded. The mean difference scores for the two treatment groups of women will then be compared. Figure 4.8 provides a graphic of a randomized block design for this experiment.

 4.4.2

DIGGING DEEPER (BEYOND THE AP)

Although blocking and grouping are slightly different strategies, often at the introductory level they are both called blocking.

Swim Strokes

EXPLORATION 4.4

The four most common swim strokes are: backstroke, breaststroke, butterfly, and freestyle. Suppose that you would like to design an experiment to compare these swim strokes, investigating which of the four is the fastest stroke (smallest time in seconds), which the second fastest, and so on. Sixteen students, who are a mix of eight competitive and eight recreational swimmers, have volunteered for the study, and you have been given access to a regulation 25-meter pool to conduct your study.

1. Identify the experimental units or subjects.
2. Identify the explanatory variable and the response variable.
3. What are some possible confounding variables that you should look out for?

Remember that when thinking about possible confounding variables, you want to consider what characteristics of the swimmers other than type of swim stroke could have an effect on swim time. Some such possible variables may be: whether the person is a competitive or recreational swimmer and whether the person has a personal best/better stroke, among others. So, when you randomize the assignment of treatments (in this case, swim stroke), you would like to make sure that not all competitive swimmers fall into one group and recreational in the other, or all swimmers who are better at backstroke in one group and butterfly in the other, and so on.

4. Describe how you can use blocking to take into account the effect of level of expertise between the four treatments.

To block on a potential confounding variable, you should first block or separate the experimental units into blocks or groups such that subjects within the blocks are alike on the confounding variable, and then randomize the treatments to the subjects within each block. Thus, in this study, we could take the four best competitive swimmers to form one block and the other four competitive swimmers to form a second block. Similarly, we could take the four strongest recreational swimmers to be a third block, and the four weakest swimmers to form a fourth block. We want the swimmers in each block to be as similar as possible. Then, the four swim strokes would be randomly assigned to the four swimmers within each block. This type of study design would be a **_randomized block design_**.

5. Draw a graphic and write a few sentences to illustrate/explain how you would randomly assign the 16 swimmers to the four treatments, using a randomized block design.
6. What is the role of random assignment within each block?
7. Suppose you find that the freestyle stroke is significantly faster than the other three. Summarize the conclusions you could draw from this study. Be sure to address causation and generalizability.

SECTION 4.4   Summary

In this section we examined a **_randomized block design_** that incorporates blocking to control for possible confounding variables that are known in advance. In Section 4.3 you learned that in a completely randomized design, experimental units are randomly assigned to the different treatment groups. Although random assignment of subjects to experimental groups (treatments), on average, deals with confounding, there still may be some (small) differences in confounding variable distributions between treatment groups—blocking ensures this isn't left to "chance."

A special form of block design in which there are two treatments is a matched-pairs design. In a matched-pairs design, either two subjects who are as similar as possible with respect to variables that may affect what we are measuring are paired and each is randomly assigned one of the treatments or, alternatively, a person may act as his or her own control and is administered both treatments in a random order. You will study matched-pairs designs, and how to analyze the results, in Section 7.1.

CHAPTER 4   Summary

In the first section, we saw that two variables are associated when the value of one variable provides information about (helps us predict) the value of the other variable. In a search for causal relationships, we call the possible cause variable _explanatory_ and the outcome variable the _response_. However, association alone does not prove causation because of the potential for confounding variables (variables related to both the explanatory and response variables in such a way that their effects on the response variable are intertwined with those of the explanatory variable).

In Section 4.2 we distinguished between observational and experimental studies. In an observational study, you simply record what's there. You don't get to choose which group each observational unit belongs to. In an experiment you choose and assign the conditions that define the groups to subjects or other experimental units. Ideally, this is done using a chance device like coin tosses or drawing names out of a hat. Random assignment has the advantage that it tends to ensure balance for all possible confounding variables, both known and unknown. For a properly randomized experiment, there are only two explanations for any observed difference between groups: Either the assigned explanatory variable conditions caused the difference or else the difference is a coincidence due to the random assignment. (In the next chapter you will see when and how we can find evidence against random chance as an explanation.) Not all experiments where the explanatory variable is manipulated are random. Without random assignment, conclusions about cause are not justified.

In the last two sections we looked at how to randomly assign subjects for two different types of experimental designs, and how these designs can be described verbally and graphically. The first design was a **_completely randomized design_** where all the subjects are simply randomly assigned to different treatment groups. The second was a **_randomized block design_** where subjects are first organized into blocks consisting of individuals that are similar in some way that may be related to the response and then random assignment of treatments is carried out separately with each block. This second type of design will often reduce random error.

You have now seen that there are two main "scope of inference" questions that should be asked as part of Step 5 of the statistical investigation method.

- First, is the result from the sample generalizable to a larger population? The answer is yes, if the sample is representative of the population, and we feel more comfortable believing such if the sample is a random sample from the larger population.

- Second, can we conclude that there is a cause-and-effect relationship between the explanatory and response variable? The answer is yes, if the study is a randomized experiment, meaning that the value of the explanatory variable is randomly assigned, guarding against potential confounding variables. Of course, we also need to rule out random chance from the random assignment process, which you will see how to do in the next chapter.

CHAPTER 4
GLOSSARY

association   Two variables are associated or related if the distribution of one variable differs across the values of the other variable.

block design   A study design that begins by forming blocks consisting of individuals that are similar in some way that may be related to the response. Random assignment of treatments is then carried out separately with each block.

cause and effect   In well-designed studies (randomized experiments), can conclude the explanatory variable is causing the effect (difference) seen in the response variable.

completely randomized design   A study design in which the experimental units are randomly assigned to the different treatment groups.

confounding variable   A variable that is related to both the explanatory and response variable in such a way that its effects on the response variable cannot be separated from those of the explanatory variable.

control   A *do-nothing* or placebo treatment in an experiment.

double blind   A study design where neither the subjects nor those evaluating the response know which treatment group each subject is in.

experiment   A study in which researchers actively assign subjects to treatment groups.

experimental units   What observational units are called in an experiment.

explanatory variable   The variable that, if the alternative hypothesis is true, is explaining changes in the response variable; sometimes known as the independent or predictor variable.

observational study   Study in which researchers observe individuals and measure variables of interest but do not intervene in order to attempt to influence responses.

placebo effect   The positive psychological benefit that many people experience simply by knowing they are receiving a treatment.

protocol   A detailed description of the study and its design such that another researcher is able to replicate the study.

quasi-experiments   Experiments that manipulate the explanatory variable, but not randomly.

randomized experiment   A study where experimental units are randomly assigned to two or more *treatment* conditions and the explanatory variable is actively imposed of the subjects.

response variable   The variable that, if the alternative hypothesis is true, is impacted by the explanatory variable; sometimes known as the dependent variable.

treatments   The assigned conditions in an experiment.

CHAPTER 4
EXERCISES

SECTION 4.1

GPAs and pulling all-nighters*

Exercises 4.1.1–4.1.3 refer to a study published in the January 2008 issue of *Behavioral Sleep Medicine* that involved a survey of 120 students at St. Lawrence University, a small liberal arts college in upstate New York.

4.1.1   Researchers found that students who claimed to have never pulled an all-nighter had an average GPA of 3.1, compared to 2.9 for those students who do claim to have pulled all-nighters.

a. In this context, what is the observational unit?

   A. Researcher

   B. Student

C. GPA

D. Whether or not have pulled an all-nighter

b. Which of the following is the explanatory variable?

A. Whether or not have pulled an all-nighter

B. Student

C. GPA

D. Those students who have pulled all-nighters

c. Which of the following is the response variable?

A. GPA

B. Average GPA

C. Whether or not have pulled an all-nighter

D. Students who have pulled all-nighters tend to have lower GPAs, on average.

d. The explanatory variable is _____ (categorical/quantitative).

e. The response variable is _____ (categorical/quantitative).

4.1.2 Reconsider the previous study about GPAs and pulling all-nighters. Suppose that the difference between these two averages (3.1 vs. 2.9) is shown to be statistically significant. Which of the following is a potential confounding variable and provides an alternative explanation for why the all-nighter group would have a significantly lower average GPA?

A. Students

B. Type of lifestyle choices made by student

C. Difficulty level of classes offered at St. Lawrence

D. Class sizes

4.1.3 Reconsider the previous exercise about the potential confounding variable that provides an alternative explanation for why the all-nighter group would have a significantly lower average GPA. Sketch a well-labeled diagram showing how this explanation works.

Using candy cigarettes

4.1.4 In a study published in a 2007 issue of the journal *Preventive Medicine*, researchers found that smokers were more likely to have used candy cigarettes as children than nonsmokers were. When hearing about this study, John responded, "But isn't the smoking status of the person's parents a confounding variable here?" When Karen asked what he meant, John said, "Children whose parents smoke are more likely to become smokers themselves when they become adults." What else does John need to say in order to explain how the parents' smoking status could be a confounding variable in this study?

Marriage views*

4.1.5 Do different generations view marriage differently? A 2010 survey conducted by the Pew Research Center asked the following question of each participant: "*Is marriage becoming obsolete?*" Results of this study are shown in the table below.

a. Identify the observational units.

b. Identify the explanatory and response variables. Also identify the type (categorical or quantitative) of each.

c. The conditional proportions of people who answered Yes, marriage is become obsolete, in each generation of the sample are: 0.44 (Millenial), 0.429 (Gen X), 0.350 (Boomers), and 0.322 (Age 65+). Based on these conditional proportions, does it appear that different generations tend to view marriage differently? Explain.

Heart attacks

4.1.6 Studies conducted in New York City and Boston have noticed that more heart attacks occur in December and January than in all other months. Some people have tried to conclude that holiday stress and overindulgence cause the increased risk of heart attack. Identify a confounding variable whose effect on heart attack rate might be confounded with that of the month, providing an alternative explanation for the increased risk of heart attack in December and January. Also, include a diagram showing how this explanation works.

Number of TVs and life expectancy*

Exercises 4.1.7 and 4.1.8 contain questions about an analysis of data on a sample of 22 countries that shows a strong positive association between the average life expectancy in the country and the number of TVs per 1,000 people in the country, that is, that countries that have more TVs per 1,000 people also have higher average lifetimes.

| | | Generation | | | | |
		Millennial (ages 18–29)	Gen X (ages 30–45)	Boomers (ages 46–65)	Age 65+	Total
Marriage obsolete?	Yes	236	313	401	68	1,018
	No	300	416	745	143	1,604
Total		536	729	1,146	211	2,622

EXERCISE 4.1.5

4.1.7 Based on this study, is it reasonable to conclude that by sending TVs to countries with lower life expectancies, we can increase their inhabitants' lifetimes? If yes, explain how. If no, give an alternative explanation for the association between number of TVs and life expectancy.

4.1.8 Regarding the previous question about number of TVs and life expectancy:

a. Identify the observational units.

A. People

B. Number of TVs per 1,000 people

C. Countries

D. Life expectancy

b. Identify the explanatory variable.

A. People

B. Number of TVs per 1,000 people

C. Countries

D. Life expectancy

c. The explanatory variable is _____ (categorical/quantitative).

d. Identify the response variable.

A. People

B. Number of TVs per 1,000 people

C. Countries

D. Life expectancy

e. The response variable is _____ (categorical/quantitative).

Mediterranean diet

4.1.9 Based on a four-year (2003–2007) study of over 30,000 people who were 45+ years, where all individuals were followed up regularly for diet and health changes, researchers Tsivgoulis et al. (*Neurology*, 2013) reported that the Mediterranean diet was linked to better memory and cognitive skills.

a. Identify the explanatory and response variables.

b. Identify a confounding variable whose effect on memory and cognitive skills might be confounded with that of the explanatory variable identified in part (a), providing an alternative explanation for the improved memory and cognitive skills among those on the Mediterranean diet. Also, include a diagram showing how this explanation works.

VCR ownership*

4.1.10 A Gallup poll conducted in December 2013 found that 74% of respondents who were 65 years or older owned a VCR compared to 41% of 18- to 29-year-olds.

a. Identify the explanatory variable.

A. Respondents

B. Age group

C. Whether own a VCR

D. Are older folks more likely to own a VCR?

b. Identify the response variable.

A. Respondents

B. Age group

C. Whether own a VCR

D. Are older folks more likely to own a VCR?

c. Do the results from Gallup's poll indicate that there is an association between owning a VCR and age? Explain.

Hormone therapy

4.1.11 In a study published in *Preventive Medicine* (1991), researchers Stampfer and Colditz observed that women who underwent hormone replacement therapy (HRT) showed a lower risk of coronary heart disease (CHD).

a. Identify the explanatory and response variables.

b. Identify a confounding variable that provides an alternative explanation for the reduction in CHD risk among women who underwent HRT, compared to those who didn't undergo HRT. Also, include a diagram showing how this explanation works.

Eating breakfast*

4.1.12 Based on a survey of almost 3,000 adults, researchers Wyatt et al. (*Obesity Research,* 2002) reported that those who ate breakfast regularly tended to be more successful at maintaining their weight loss.

a. Identify the explanatory and response variables.

b. Identify a confounding variable that provides an alternative explanation for the improved success rate of weight loss among regular breakfast eaters, compared to those who don't eat breakfast regularly. Also, include a diagram showing how this explanation works.

Dinner and drugs

4.1.13 In June 2012, *Time* magazine ran an article titled "Do Family Dinners Really Reduce Teen Drug Use?" Answer the following questions in this context.

a. Identify the observational units.

b. Identify the explanatory and response variables.

c. Identify a confounding variable that provides an alternative explanation for the lower drug use among teens whose families ate dinner together, compared to those whose didn't. Also, include a diagram showing how this explanation works.

Smoking while pregnant*

4.1.14 Many studies have shown that women who smoke while pregnant tend to have babies who weigh significantly less at birth, on average, than women who do not smoke while pregnant.

a. Identify the population(s) of interest in these studies.

b. Identify the explanatory variable in these studies. Also classify this variable as categorical or quantitative.

c. Identify the response variable in these studies. Also classify this variable as categorical or quantitative.

d. Socioeconomic status is potentially a confounding variable in these studies. Explain what it means for this to be a confounding variable in this context, and describe how this could provide an alternative explanation to concluding that smoking while pregnant causes lower birthweight in babies.

Spanking and IQ

4.1.15 Studies have shown that children in the U.S. who have been spanked have a significantly lower IQ score on average than children who have not been spanked.

a. Identify the explanatory variable in these studies. Also classify this variable as categorical or quantitative.

b. Identify the response variable in these studies. Also classify this variable as categorical or quantitative.

c. Identify a confounding variable that provides an alternative explanation for the lower average IQ score for children who have been spanked, compared to those who haven't.

Overweight friends*

4.1.16 In July 2013, Gallup surveyed 2,027 randomly selected U.S. adults. They found that of the 921 people who described themselves as overweight, 424 reported having some or many friends/family members who were overweight (424/921 = 0.46). Also, of the 1,106 people who described their weight as being "about right," 332 reported having some or many friends/family members who were overweight (332/1,106 = 0.30). Use the conditional proportions to explain whether the data indicate that there is an association between whether one perceives oneself as being overweight and whether they have some or many friends/family members whom they perceive as being overweight.

Children and lifespan

4.1.17 Do men with children tend to live longer than men without children? To investigate, a group of students at Cal Poly randomly sampled men from the obituaries page on the *San Luis Obispo Tribune*'s webpage between June and November 2012. For each man selected, they noted the age at which the person died and number of children under "survived by."

a. Identify the explanatory variable in this study. Also classify this variable as categorical or quantitative.

b. Identify the response variable in this study. Also classify this variable as categorical or quantitative.

c. Below is a set of dotplots displaying the data from the students' study. Based on the dotplots, is there any indication of an association between the explanatory variable and the response variable? Explain how you are deciding.

d. Identify a confounding variable that provides an alternative explanation for the overall higher lifetime values among men who have children, compared to those who don't.

Happiness and income*

4.1.18 To investigate whether there is an association between happiness and income level, we will use data from the 2002 *General Social Survey (GSS)*, cross-classifying a person's perceived happiness with their family income level. The GSS is a survey of randomly selected U.S. adults who are not institutionalized. Here are the data:

		Income			
		Above average	Average	Below average	Total
Happy?	**Very happy**	110	221	83	414
	Pretty happy	159	372	249	780
	Not too happy	21	53	94	168
	Total	290	646	426	1,362

a. Identify the explanatory variable. Is it a categorical variable or a quantitative variable?

b. Identify the response variable. Is it a categorical variable or a quantitative variable?

EXERCISE 4.1.17

c. Among above-average-income individuals 0.379 are very happy (110/290); among average income individuals 0.342 are very happy (221/646); and, among below-average-income individuals 0.195 are very happy (83/426). Do the data provide any indication of an association between happiness and income level? Why or why not?

d. Is it okay to conclude that income affects happiness? If yes, explain why. If no, then identify a confounding variable that provides an alternative explanation for the association between happiness and income level.

Sex of respondent and body image

4.1.19 A 2013 Gallup poll asked randomly selected U.S. adults whether they wanted to stay at their current body weight or change. One purpose was to investigate whether there was any difference between men and women with regard to this aspect.

a. Identify the explanatory variable. Is it a categorical variable or a quantitative variable?

b. Identify the response variable. Is it a categorical variable or a quantitative variable?

c. Of the 562 men surveyed, 43% wanted to stay at their current weight, whereas of the 477 women surveyed, 36% wanted to stay at their current weight. Do the data provide any indication of a difference between how men and women perceive their current body weight? Explain using appropriate numbers.

Political party and evolution*

4.1.20 Is there an association between political party affiliation and beliefs about human evolution? A survey of a random sample of U.S. adults by *The Pew Research Center for the People and the Press* conducted in March and April 2013 recorded each participant's political party affiliation and belief about human evolution. The table below gives the data from the Pew Research Center's study.

a. Identify the explanatory and response variables. Also identify the type (categorical or quantitative) of each.

b. Based on the table, the proportion of Republicans who believe humans have evolved over time is 0.43, the proportion of Democrats who believe humans have evolved over time is 0.67, and the proportion of Independents who share this belief is 0.65. Do the data provide any indication of an association between political party affiliation and beliefs about human evolution?

Education and the census

4.1.21 A survey of a random sample of U.S. adults by *The Pew Research Center for the People and the Press* conducted in early January 2010 recorded each participant's highest level of education completed and whether they knew that responding to the Census was required by law. Of the 973 participants who had some college or less, 27.9% (271/973) knew that responding to the Census was required by law. Of the 526 participants who had a college degree or more, 37.1% (195/526) knew that responding to the Census was required by law.

a. Identify the explanatory variable. Is it a categorical variable or a quantitative variable?

b. Identify the response variable. Is it a categorical variable or a quantitative variable?

c. Do the data provide any indication of an association between education level and the awareness that responding to the Census is required by law? Explain.

Prayer and blood pressure*

4.1.22 In August 1998, an article titled "Prayer Can Lower Blood Pressure" appeared in the *USA Today*. The article was based on the findings of a study by the National Institutes of Health Initiatives that followed 2,391 people aged 65 years or more. The article said:

"People who attended a religious service once a week and prayed or studied the Bible once a day were 40% less likely to have high blood pressure than those who don't go to church every week and prayed and studied the Bible less."

a. Identify the explanatory variable in this study. Also classify this variable as categorical or quantitative.

b. Identify the response variable in this study. Also classify this variable as categorical or quantitative.

c. Identify a confounding variable that provides an alternative explanation for the lower blood pressure among those who attended religious services regularly and studied the Bible regularly, compared to those who didn't.

		Political party affiliation		
		Republican	Democrat	Independent
Belief about human evolution	**Humans have evolved over time**	196	472	438
	Humans have existed in present form	218	190	189
	Don't know	41	43	47

EXERCISE 4.1.20

Colds and exercise

4.1.23 In November 2010, an article titled "Frequency of Colds Dramatically Cut with Regular Exercise" appeared in *Medical News Today*. The article was based on the findings of a study by researchers Nieman et al. (*British Journal of Sports Medicine*, 2010) that followed 1,002 people aged 18–85 years for 12 weeks, asking them to record their frequency of exercise (5 or more days a week? Yes or No) as well as incidences of upper respiratory tract infections (Cold during last week? Yes or No).

a. Identify the explanatory variable in this study. Also classify this variable as categorical or quantitative.

b. Identify the response variable in this study. Also classify this variable as categorical or quantitative.

c. Identify a confounding variable that provides an alternative explanation for the lower frequency of colds among those who exercised 5 or more days per week, compared to those who were largely sedentary.

Politics and gun ownership*

4.1.24 In February 2013, the Pew Research Center surveyed randomly selected U.S. adults about their opinions on gun ownership and related issues. One of the questions they asked was, "Should states be allowed to ignore federal gun laws?" Of the 366 Republicans, 57.9% (212/366) responded "yes," compared to 18.1% (85/470) of Democrats and 38.1% (230/604) of Independents.

a. Identify the explanatory variable in this study. Also classify this variable as categorical or quantitative.

b. Identify the response variable in this study. Also classify this variable as categorical or quantitative.

c. Do the data provide any indication that there is an association between political party affiliation and opinion of whether states should be allowed to ignore federal gun laws? Explain.

Red meat and heart disease

4.1.25 In March 2012, an article titled "Eating Red Meat Regularly 'Dramatically Increases The Risk Of Death From Heart Disease,'" appeared in the *Daily Mail* (www.dailymail.co.uk). The article was based on the findings of a study that followed over 120,000 men and women for almost 30 years, the data for which were analyzed by the Harvard School of Public Health in Boston.

a. Identify the explanatory variable in this study. Also classify this variable as categorical or quantitative.

b. Identify the response variable in this study. Also classify this variable as categorical or quantitative.

c. Identify a confounding variable that provides an alternative explanation for the higher risk of death from heart disease among those who ate red meat regularly, compared to those who didn't.

Chocolate and Nobel prizes*

4.1.26 Researcher F.H. Messerli published an article titled "Chocolate Consumption, Cognitive Function, and Nobel Laureates" in the October 2012 issue of the *New England Journal of Medicine*. The article shows a positive association between a country's chocolate consumption and the number of Nobel prizes won by the country (adjusted for population size).

a. Identify the observational units.

b. Identify the explanatory variable and the response variable in this study.

c. Identify a confounding variable that provides an alternative explanation for the higher number of Nobel prizes won by countries with higher chocolate consumption, compared to those with lower chocolate consumption.

Million Women study

4.1.27 The Million Women study in England followed more than 1,000,000 women aged 50–64 years beginning in 1996, tracking their living habits and maintaining records on their medical and social factors as well as cancer data. The researchers found that after around 12 years, 3.7% (217/5,877) of the South Asian women developed breast cancer, compared to 3.6% (180/4,919) of the black women and 4.4% (45,191/1,038,144) of the white women.

a. Identify the explanatory and response variables in this context. Also, identify whether each variable is categorical or quantitative.

b. Use the conditional proportions to explain whether the data indicate that there is an association between one's race and whether or not one has breast cancer?

c. Identify a possible confounding variable that provides an alternative explanation for the observed differences in breast cancer rates among the different races.

SECTION 4.2

4.2.1* Which of the following is the primary purpose of randomly assigning subjects to treatments in an experiment?

A. To produce similar (experimental) groups so any differences in the response variable can be attributed to the explanatory variable

B. To give each subject a 50–50 chance of obtaining a successful outcome

C. To produce a representative sample so results can be generalized to a larger population

D. To simulate what would happen in the long run

E. Both A and C

4.2.2 A randomized experiment allows for the possibility of drawing a cause-and-effect conclusion between _____ and _____.

A. The subjects and the treatments

B. The observational units and the variables

C. The explanatory variable and the response variable

D. Statistical significance and statistical confidence

4.2.3* Which of the following is true of experiments?

A. The researchers assign the *explanatory* variable to subjects.

B. The researchers assign the *response* variable to subjects.

C. The researchers assign *both* the explanatory and response variables to subjects.

D. The researchers assign *neither* the explanatory nor the response variable to subjects.

4.2.4 Which of the following must happen in a study to allow us to determine cause and effect?

A. Taking a random sample from a population

B. Randomly assigning the observational units to different treatment groups

C. Simulation-based inference techniques

D. Theory-based inference techniques

4.2.5* Is random sampling or random assignment the more important consideration if the research question is whether faculty tend to drive older cars than students drive on your campus?

4.2.6 Is random sampling or random assignment the more important consideration if the research question is whether Facebook users tend to have lower grade point averages than students who do not use Facebook?

4.2.7* Is random sampling or random assignment the more important consideration if the research question is whether students tend to receive higher scores on essays if they are encouraged to submit a draft than if they are not so encouraged?

4.2.8 Is random sampling or random assignment the more important consideration if the research question is whether members of one political party tend to donate more to charities than members of another political party?

4.2.9* Is random sampling or random assignment the more important consideration if the research question is whether a waitress generates higher tips by giving her name when she first greets customers?

4.2.10 Reconsider Exercises 4.2.5–4.2.9. Notice that the phrase "tend to" appears in many of the research questions. Explain what this phrase means and why it is important in these questions.

4.2.11* Can a study have both random sampling and random assignment? If so, explain what can be determined from such a study if statistical significance is found.

4.2.12 Researchers could design an experiment where there is a balance with respect to the sex of the subjects between two experimental groups by putting half the females in one group and half in the other and do the same for the males. Why don't researchers always just force variables to be balanced out between groups but often use random assignment?

4.2.13* Does random assignment *always* equally balance all the variables (except for the explanatory variable) between experimental groups? Is there a tendency for there to be a balance? Explain.

4.2.14 From which of the following studies can cause-and-effect conclusions potentially be drawn? If cause and effect can be determined, explain what may cause what.

a. From a random sample of city residents, it was found that those with higher incomes utilize the recycling services significantly more than those with lower incomes.

b. Students were randomly assigned to two groups. One group listened to music while taking a math test and one group did not. The one that did not listen to music scored significantly higher on the math test than the other.

c. A teacher gave one of his classes a math test while music was playing and another without music playing. The class that did not listen to music scored significantly higher on the math test than the other.

4.2.15* From which of the following studies can cause-and-effect conclusions potentially be drawn? If cause and effect can be determined, explain what may cause what.

a. Subjects were randomly assigned to watch one of two videos, one that was about a sad situation and one that was about a happy situation. The group that watched the sad video scored significantly lower on a quiz about their mood.

b. Students collected data on city residents shopping in their city's downtown stores and another sample from city residents that were shopping at the mall on the outskirts of the city. They found that those shopping downtown were significantly more likely to vote for the school millage than those shopping at the mall.

c. From a random sample of students, it was found that those who are members of Greek organizations have significantly lower grade point averages.

4.2.16 What is the difference between random sampling and random assignment and what types of conclusions can be drawn from each?

Smoking while pregnant*

4.2.17 Many studies have shown that babies born to women who smoked while pregnant tended to weigh less at birth than babies born to mothers who did not smoke while pregnant.

a. Are these studies observational studies or experiments?

b. Will a cause-and-effect conclusion be possible?

c. Identify the observational units in these studies.

4.2.18 Refer to the information provided in the previous question. While it's possible in principle to conduct a randomized experiment to investigate this issue, it would be unethical to do so. Explain why, as if to someone who has never studied statistics.

Why is your baby a boy?

4.2.19 Many studies have surveyed mothers and fathers about their behaviors (diet, health, etc.) at or immediately before the time of the conception of their baby in an attempt to find connections between these behaviors and the sex of the baby.

a. Are these studies observational studies or experiments?

b. Will a cause-and-effect conclusion be possible?

c. Identify the observational units in these studies.

d. Identify the explanatory variables in these studies.

e. Identify the response variable in these studies.

Classical music and intelligence*

4.2.20 Many studies have found that children who listen to classical music while in the womb or when younger tend to have higher IQs later in life. These studies are typically done by surveying parents of older children about whether or not they played classical music when the child was younger and conducting an IQ test of the child.

a. Are these studies observational studies or experiments?

b. Will a cause-and-effect conclusion be possible?

c. Identify the observational units in these studies.

d. Identify the explanatory variable in these studies.

e. Identify the response variable in these studies.

Consumer attitudes

4.2.21 A team of researchers (Singer et al., 2000) used the Survey of Consumer Attitudes to investigate whether incentives would improve the response rates on telephone surveys. A national sample of 735 households was randomly selected, and all 735 of the households were sent an "advance letter" explaining that the household would be contacted shortly for a telephone survey. However, 368 households were randomly assigned to receive a monetary incentive along with the advance letter, and the other 367 households were assigned to receive only the advance letter. Here are the data on how many households responded to the telephone survey.

		Received an incentive?		
		Yes	No	Total
Responded to the telephone survey?	Yes	286	245	531
	No	82	122	204
Total		368	367	735

a. Was this an observational study or an experiment? How are you deciding?

b. What are the observational units?

c. What are the variables recorded? For each variable, identify the type of the variable (categorical or quantitative) and the role of the variable (explanatory or response).

d. Did the study involve random *sampling*? If yes, what is the advantage of a randomly selected sample? If no, what is the disadvantage?

e. Did the study involve random *assignment* to either receive an incentive or not? If yes, what is the advantage? If no, what is the disadvantage?

f. An appropriate analysis of the data shows there is evidence that people receiving an incentive are more likely to respond to the telephone survey compared to those receiving no incentive. Is it appropriate to conclude that incentives *improve* response rates? Why or why not? Explain your reasoning.

Facebook friends*

4.2.22 Is the sex of a person making a friend request on Facebook to someone they do not know associated with whether or not the request is accepted? To answer this question, student researchers at Hope College made up fake Facebook profiles, one representing a Hope College female student and one representing a Hope College male student. The profiles were made to look as similar as possible except for a couple of pictures of the fake students, their names, and of course whether they were male or female. From a group of 219 students at the college, 118 were randomly assigned to receive the friend request from the female "student" and 101 were randomly assigned to receive the friend request from the male "student." The results of the acceptance of these requests are shown in the following table.

		Facebook profile		
		Female	Male	Total
Accepted friend request?	Yes	61	18	79
	No	57	83	140
Total		118	101	219

a. Was this an observational study or an experiment? How are you deciding?

b. What are the observational units?

c. What are the variables recorded? For each variable, identify the type of the variable (categorical or quantitative) and the role of the variable (explanatory or response).

d. Did the study involve random *sampling*? If yes, what is the advantage of a randomly selected sample? If no, what is the disadvantage?

e. Did the study involve random *assignment* to get the friend request from either the female or the male? If yes, what is the advantage? If no, what is the disadvantage?

f. An appropriate analysis of the data shows there is strong evidence that people receiving the request from the female are more likely to accept. Is it appropriate to conclude that the sex of the requestor is affecting the acceptance rates? Why or why not? Explain your reasoning.

Cuteness and aggression

4.2.23 Are cuteness and aggression related? A study done at Yale University tested this by showing people pictures of cute animals (like kittens and puppies) or pictures of older more serious looking animals. They tested the aggression of the subjects by giving them bubble wrap and letting them pop the bubbles. The subjects in the group shown the cute animals popped an average of 120 bubbles compared to 100 for the group seeing the pictures of the older animals.

a. Identify the explanatory variable in this study and tell whether it is categorical or quantitative.

b. Identify the response variable in this study and tell whether it is categorical or quantitative.

c. What should the researchers do so they have the possibility of determining that the type of picture affects how many bubbles are popped?

Power poses*

4.2.24 A research article, "Power Posing: Brief Nonverbal Displays Affect Neuroendocrine Levels and Risk Tolerance," published in *Psychological Science,* September 2010, describes a study involving 42 volunteer participants (male and female), where participants were randomly assigned to hold either low-power poses (contractive positions, closed limbs) or high-power poses (expansive positions, open limbs) for two minutes. All participants were told that the aim of this exercise was to see if their heart rate changed. After the exercise, each participant was given $2 and told that they could keep the money or roll a die for a double or nothing. Of the 20 participants who held low-power poses, 3 took the "double or nothing" bet, whereas of the 22 participants who held high-power poses, 18 took the bet. Suppose we want to know, *Are people who hold high-power poses more likely to take risks (such as the double or nothing bet) compared to those who hold low-power poses?*

a. Was this an observational study or an experiment? How are you deciding?

b. What are the observational units?

c. What are the variables recorded? For each variable, identify the type of the variable (categorical or quantitative) and the role of the variable (explanatory or response).

d. Did the study involve random *sampling*, random *assignment*, or both? How are you deciding?

e. An appropriate analysis of the data shows that there is strong evidence that people in the high-power poses are more likely to take the double or nothing bet. Is it appropriate to conclude that the pose affects likelihood of taking the bet? Why or why not? Explain your reasoning.

Skittles taste test

4.2.25 Students recruited at the cafeteria at Hope College were blindly given a single Skittles® candy to put in their mouth. They were told the five possible flavors and then were asked which flavor they had. Of the 154 healthy students tested, 78 gave the correct answer. Of the 118 students tested who had stuffy or runny noses, 44 gave the correct answer.

a. Was this an observational study or an experiment? How are you deciding?

b. What are the observational units?

c. What are the variables recorded? For each variable, identify the type of the variable (categorical or quantitative) and the role of the variable (explanatory or response).

d. Did the study involve random *sampling*, random *assignment*, both, or neither? How are you deciding?

e. An appropriate analysis of the data shows that there is strong evidence that healthy students were more likely to give the correct answer. Is it appropriate to conclude that the health of the student affects ability to taste? Why or why not? Explain your reasoning.

FAQ

4.2.26 Read FAQ 4.2.1 that discusses randomness and its implications and answer the following.

a. The FAQ discusses how the determination that smoking causes cancer was obtained from studies that did not involve random assignment. How was that possible? Was it easy to do?

b. The FAQ discusses that without random sampling, we can still sometimes generalize to a larger population if we are careful. Give an example where you think this could be done.

SECTION 4.3

4.3.1* Which of the following is NOT a key element of a well-designed experiment?

A. Control

B. Random sampling

C. Random assignment

D. Replication

4.3.2 The positive psychological benefit that many people experience simply from knowing they are receiving a treatment is known as the:

A. Placebo effect

B. Doppler effect

C. Bystander effect

D. Cause and effect

E. Pygmalion effect

4.3.3* An experiment done in such a way that neither the subjects nor the researchers know which subjects are in the treatment group and which are in the control group is called:

A. Double barreled

B. Double sided

C. Double negative

D. Double jeopardy

E. Double blind

4.3.4 Student researchers want to see whether students retain information better when they are taking notes by hand (with pen and paper) than on the computer, as some research suggests. Suppose they have 60 volunteers as their subjects. Also suppose they will be giving their subjects a 10-question quiz about the planets after they have watched a short video about the planets. Describe how they should set up and run their experiment.

4.3.5* A drug manufacturer is testing a new headache drug. It recruits 100 subjects with headaches and has them rate the severity of their headaches on a scale of 1 to 10. It gives them the new drug and one hour later has them again rate the severity of their headaches. It finds that 60% of the subjects had substantial reduction in the severity of their headaches. What fundamental component is missing in this experimental design?

4.3.6 A drug manufacturer is testing a new headache drug. It recruits 100 subjects with headaches and has them rate the severity of their headaches on a scale of 1 to 10. Based on the severity of the headache, the researchers assign 50 of them to receive the new drug and 50 to receive a placebo. One hour later the subjects again rate the severity of their headaches. The researchers find that 60% of the subjects had substantial reduction in the severity of their headaches in the treatment group compared to only 30% in the control group. What fundamental component is missing in this experimental design?

4.3.7* A drug manufacturer is testing a new headache drug. It recruits 100 subjects with headaches and has them rate the severity of their headaches on a scale of 1 to 10. The researchers randomly assign 50 of them to receive the new drug and 50 to receive a placebo. One researcher is told she will work with those that received the new drug and another researcher will work with those that received the placebo. Through an interview process each researcher determines if there has been a substantial reduction in the severity of the headache of each subject after one hour. They find that 60% of the subjects had substantial reduction in the severity of their headaches in the treatment group compared to only 30% in the control group. What fundamental component is missing in this experimental design?

4.3.8 Students completing a project for their statistics class were testing whether, when blindfolded, subjects would be more likely to identify the flavor of an orange Starburst or a lemon Starburst. The subjects were only told that they would taste two flavors of Starburst. They gave all their subjects the orange Starburst first, let them have a drink of water, and then gave them the lemon Starburst second. After each Starburst, the subjects were asked to identify its flavor. What fundamental component is missing in this experimental design and why is it important?

4.3.9* Hurricanes in the United States are given names and since 1979 both male and female names have been used, alternating between names that are typically thought of as male and those typically thought of as female. The names are chosen well ahead of hurricane season.

a. According to an article published in *Proceedings of the National Academy of Sciences* in 2014, Jung and fellow researchers claimed that hurricanes in the United States that were given male names caused significantly more deaths than hurricanes that were given female names. Based on this research, should all hurricanes be given female names so fewer deaths would occur? Explain.

b. The researchers also gave subjects a scenario including a picture of a weather map that showed a hurricane approaching their area and asked them how likely it was that they would evacuate. Half the subjects were randomly shown the map that included the name Christopher on the hurricane; the other half were shown the identical map, but the hurricane was named Christina. Those who saw the name Christopher were significantly more likely to say they would evacuate. Based on this research, does the name cause the different response? Explain.

4.3.10 The Physicians' Health Study I was a very large, randomized, double-blind, placebo-controlled study designed to "test the effects of low-dose aspirin and beta-carotene on cancer and cardiovascular disease." The subjects were 22,071 U.S. male physicians (aged 40–84 in the year 1982) who were randomly assigned to take a bi-daily low-dose aspirin or beta carotene or a placebo version of one of these.

a. Is this an experiment or an observational study? Explain how you are deciding.

b. Explain what it means for a study to be "double blind." Also, explain the purpose of using "double blinding" in this study.

c. What does it mean for this study to be "placebo-controlled" and what is the purpose of a placebo?

d. Explain how you would go about assigning the subjects to the groups. (Be clear how many groups you are assigning them to.)

4.3.11 Journal articles describing some randomized experiment will often include a table of the characteristics of the subjects after they were randomly assigned to the treatments, but before the treatments were applied. An example of part of one of those tables is shown below.

Baseline patient demographics and clinical characteristics		
Parameter	Placebo (n = 129)	Drug (n = 128)
Mean age, years	39.9	37.6
Men (%)	59.7%	54.7%
Women (%)	40.3%	45.3%
Mean disease duration (yrs)	6.3	5.5
Duration ≤1 year (%)	17.8%	21.9%
Duration >5 years (%)	39.5%	34.4%

a. What is the purpose of showing such a table and how is that related to the experimental design?

b. These types of tables also often include p-values showing the results of testing some characteristic between the two groups (e.g., deciding whether the mean age between those that will receive the placebo and those that will receive the drug is significantly different). Ideally, would you want those p-values to be large or small? Why?

SECTION 4.4

4.4.1* Consider the following two experiments concerning a teacher who wants to determine whether using a larger font size on her class tests will affect student scores.

Experiment A. She randomly determines that half of her students will receive a test prepared in typical-size font and the other half will receive the same test in a larger font. She then compares the average scores of students tested with the regular font and students with the larger font.

Experiment B. She first divides her class into two groups according to their current average grade in the class: those that are in the top 50% and those that are in the bottom 50%. She then randomly determines that half the students in the top 50% will receive the test prepared in the typical font size and the other half of the top 50% will receive the same test typed in a larger font. She repeats this process for students in the bottom 50%. She then compares the average scores of students tested with the regular font and students with the larger font.

What is true about the experimental design for these two scenarios?

A. Both Experiment A and Experiment B are completely randomized designs.

B. Neither Experiment A nor Experiment B is a randomized block design.

C. Experiment A is a completely randomized design and Experiment B is a randomized block design.

D. Experiment A is a randomized block design and Experiment B is a completely randomized design.

4.4.2 What is the main reason we would use blocking in an experiment?

A. To allow the opportunity to determine cause and effect.

B. To make sure subjects that have a certain characteristic are all placed in one experimental group and all those that don't are placed in the other.

C. To control for anticipated variability in the response variable before the experiment begins.

D. To ensure that the experimental groups are all the same size.

4.4.3* Suppose researchers want to compare the weight-loss effects of two different diets. They have 270 overweight volunteers consisting of 150 women and 120 men. They want to use body mass index (BMI) instead of weight as their measure of weight loss.

Describe how they should set up and run their experiment.

4.4.4 Suppose your research question is: Can people better memorize 10 objects if they are shown the objects in pictures or in words? Describe how you could set up and run an experiment to answer this question using a matched-pairs design with 40 subjects. (In this matched-pairs design each person should act as his or her own control; thus each person should be tested with both pictures and words.)

4.4.5* The Physicians' Health Study II was a randomized, double-blind, placebo-controlled study designed to "test alternate-day beta-carotene, alternate-day vitamin E, daily vitamin C, and a daily multivitamin, in the prevention of total and prostate cancer, cardiovascular disease, and the age-related eye diseases, cataract and macular degeneration." The subjects were 14,641 U.S. male physicians (older than 50 in the year 1997) who were randomly assigned to take a bi-daily beta-carotene, bi-daily vitamin E, daily vitamin C, daily multivitamin, or a placebo version of one of these.

a. Is this an experiment or an observational study? Explain how you are deciding.

b. Explain what it means for a study to be "double-blind." Also, explain the purpose of using "double-blinding" in this study.

c. What does it mean for this study to be "placebo-controlled" and what is the purpose of a placebo?

d. Explain how you would go about assigning the subjects to the groups. [Be clear how many groups you are assigning them to. You want the groups to consist of all the possible combinations of the drugs and the placebo version of the drug. Write out all combinations. Hint: There are 16 of them.]

4.4.6 Suppose you are designing a placebo-controlled study to test a new medicine designed to relieve the effects of ragweed allergies. You also think this drug might work differently on males than on females. You have 200 subjects (120 females and 80 male) in your study that are allergic to ragweed.

a. What variable would you block on?

b. How would you randomly assign the subjects in this study utilizing a randomized block design?

c. What is the advantage of using a randomized block design over a completely randomized design?

4.4.7* Crohn's disease involves chronic inflammation anywhere in the gastrointestinal (GI) tract. The disease is subdivided by where it occurs in the GI tract. Suppose a company is testing a new timed-release drug to help alleviate the symptoms of Crohn's disease in a placebo-controlled experiment. They recruit 200 volunteers; 120 of these have the disease in their small intestine, 100 have it in both their small intestine and colon, and 80 have it confined to just their colon.

a. What variable would you block on in this experiment?

b. How would you randomly assign the subjects in this study utilizing a randomized block design?

c. What is the advantage of using a randomized block design over a completely randomized design?

END OF CHAPTER

4.CE.1* When can you legitimately draw a cause-and-effect conclusion from a randomized experiment?

A. When the p-value is small

B. When the p-value is large

C. Always, regardless of the p-value

D. Never, regardless of the p-value

4.CE.2 Answer the following questions about explanatory and response variables.

a. Must an explanatory variable always be categorical?

b. Must a response variable always be quantitative?

Animal therapy*

4.CE.3 In a recent study of animal-assisted therapy (Cole et al., 2007), researchers investigated whether patients hospitalized with heart failure could be helped by a visit from a dog. The 76 patients in the study were randomly assigned to one of three groups: one group received a 12-minute visit from a volunteer and a dog, another group received a 12-minute visit from a volunteer only, and the third group received no visit. Many variables, including heart rate, blood pressure, and anxiety levels, were measured on the patients prior to and after the visit.

a. Identify the explanatory variable(s) in this study.

b. Identify the response variable(s) in this study.

c. Is this an experiment or an observational study? Explain.

d. Describe the purpose of randomly assigning patients to treatment groups.

e. Researchers also reported summary information on a variety of background variables such as age, sex of respondent, and smoking status. Do you think the researchers were hoping to find significant differences among the three groups on these variables? Explain why or why not.

Walking in socks

4.CE.4 In a study conducted in New Zealand, researchers Parkin et al. randomly assigned volunteers to wear either socks over their shoes (intervention) or their usual footwear (control) as they walked downhill on an inclined icy path. Researchers standing at the bottom of the inclined path would then rate how confident the participant appeared ("confident," "cautious but did not hold onto supports," or "held onto supports") and how much time (seconds) the participant took to walk down the path.

a. Was this an experiment or an observational study?

b. Identify the variables recorded. For each variable, identify the type (categorical or quantitative) and role (explanatory or response).

c. Did the study involve randomness? If so, how: random sampling, or random assignment, or both?

Cost of drugs*

4.CE.5 In a randomized, double-blind study reported in the *Journal of American Medical Association*, researchers Waber et al. (2008) administered a pill to each of 82 healthy paid volunteers from Boston, Massachusetts, but told half of them that the drug had a regular price of $2.50 per pill, whereas the remaining participants were told that the drug had a discounted price of $0.10 per pill, mentioning no reason for the discount. In the recruitment advertisement, the pill was described as an FDA-approved opioid analgesic, but in reality both groups were administered placebo pills. To simulate pain, the participants were administered electric shocks to the wrist, and the researchers recorded the proportion of subjects who reported a reduction in pain after taking the pill.

a. Identify the explanatory variable and response variable. For each variable, identify the type (categorical or quantitative).

b. Explain what "randomized" means in this study.

c. Explain what "double blind" means in this study.

d. The researchers report "pain reduction was greater for the regular-price pill (p-value < 0.001)." Explain what the researchers mean by this. Be sure to comment, with correct justification, on:

- Whether the results are statistically significant.
- Whether a cause-and-effect conclusion can be drawn.
- To whom the results of the study can be generalized.

Rebates and bonuses

4.CE.6 An article in a 2006 issue of *Journal of Behavioral Decision Making* reports on a study involving 47 undergraduate students in a class at Harvard. All of the participants were given $50, but some (chosen at random) were told that this was a "tuition rebate," while the others were told that this was "bonus income." After one week, the students were contacted again and asked how much of the $50 they had spent and how much they had saved. Those in the "rebate" group had spent an average of $22.04, while those in the "bonus" group had spent an average of $9.55.

a. Identify the explanatory and response variables in this study. Also classify each variable as categorical or quantitative.

b. Is this an observational study or an experiment? Explain.

c. Did this study make use of random *sampling*, random *assignment*, both, or neither?

d. If the difference in average spending amounts between the two groups is determined to be statistically significant, would it be legitimate to draw a cause-and-effect conclusion between what the money was called and how much was spent? Justify your answer.

e. If the difference in average spending amounts between the two groups is determined to be statistically significant, would it be legitimate to generalize the result of this study to all adult Americans? Justify your answer.

Satisfaction with attractiveness*

4.CE.7 A poll conducted by the Gallup organization asked American adults whether or not they are generally satisfied with their physical attractiveness. One goal of the study was to investigate whether men and women differ with regard to responses on this issue.

a. Identify the explanatory and response variables in this study.

b. Is this an observational study or an experiment? Explain briefly.

c. If this study were conducted well, would it have involved random *sampling*, random *assignment*, or both? Explain.

Drinking at college

4.CE.8 A study found that college students who live off-campus are significantly more likely to drink alcohol than those who live on-campus.

a. Do you suspect that this was an observational study or an experiment? Explain.

b. Is it appropriate to conclude that living off-campus causes a student to be more likely to drink alcohol? Explain why or why not.

c. Is it appropriate to conclude that being a drinker causes a student to be more likely to live off-campus? Explain why or why not.

How to name your book*

4.CE.9 Ian Ayres, the author of a popular book titled *Super Crunchers*, conducted a study to help him decide what to name his book. He placed an ad on google.com, with the ad sometimes giving the title as *Super Crunchers* and other times giving the title as *The End of Intuition*. Google provided Ayres with data on how often a person clicked on the ad to obtain more information, depending on the title given in the ad. It turned out that viewers were significantly more likely to click through on the *Super Crunchers* ad than on *The End of Intuition* ad, so that's the title that Ayres chose.

a. Was this an observational study or an experiment? Explain how you know.

b. Identify the explanatory and response variables.

c. Was Ayres justified in concluding that the name *Super Crunchers* caused a higher click-through rate than the other name? Explain why or why not.

Spanking and IQ

4.CE.10 Studies have shown that children in the U.S. who have been spanked have a significantly lower IQ score on average than children who have not been spanked.

a. Is it legitimate to conclude from this study that spanking a child causes a lower IQ score? Explain why or why not.

b. Explain why conducting a randomized experiment to investigate this issue (of whether spanking causes lower IQs) would be possible in principle but ethically objectionable.

Reading *Harry Potter**

4.CE.11   You want to investigate whether teenagers in the United Kingdom (UK) tend to have read more *Harry Potter* books, on average, than teenagers in the United States (US).

a. Identify and classify (as categorical or quantitative) the explanatory and response variable.

b. Would you ideally use random sampling for this study, or random assignment, or both? Explain.

Restaurant customer behavior

4.CE.12   Do restaurant customers tend to order more expensive meals when classical music is playing in the background than when other kinds of music are playing in the background? Describe how you could design a randomized experiment to investigate this question.

Pen color and grades**

4.CE.13   Do college professors who use a red pen to grade student essays tend to assign lower scores, on average, than professors who use a blue pen to grade student essays? Describe how you could design a randomized experiment to investigate this question.

Video games and kids

4.CE.14   Are American adults who have children significantly more likely to play video games than American adults who do not have children? Is it possible to design a randomized experiment to investigate this question? If so, describe how you would design such an experiment. If not, explain why not.

Smoking and church attendance**

4.CE.15   Are people who attend church regularly less likely to smoke than people who do not attend church regularly? Is it possible to design a randomized experiment to investigate this question? If so, describe how you would design such an experiment. If not, explain why not.

INVESTIGATION: HIGH ANXIETY AND SEXUAL ATTRACTION

Social psychologists throughout the years have shown that an aggression-sexuality link exists not only in various animal species but also in humans. Dutton and Aron (*Journal of Personality and Social Psychology*, 1974) set out to show that a more general link exists in humans, namely emotional arousal of all kinds and sexual attraction. They set up their study to compare men in a high emotional arousal situation to men in a low emotional arousal situation.

Researchers wanted to test the notion that an attractive female is seen as more attractive by males who encounter her in a fear-arousing situation than by males who encounter her in a non-fear-arousing situation. In the high emotional arousal group, men deemed to be between the ages of 18 and 35 who crossed a suspension bridge 230 feet above rocks and shallow rapids in Capilano Canyon, North Vancouver, British Columbia, Canada, and were not accompanied by a female were approached on the bridge by an attractive female interviewer. The same interviewer also approached men who fit the same criteria but crossed a solid wood bridge 10 feet above a rivulet that ran into the main river. Both groups of men were interviewed on the bridge and were told that the interview was for a psychology class project on the effects of exposure to scenic attractions on creative expression. The men filled out a short questionnaire after which the interviewer wrote her phone number down on a slip of paper and said that if they were interested in the results of the experiment they could call her. The researcher talked to 18 men on the suspension bridge and 16 men on the wooden bridge.

STEP 1: Ask a research question.   The researcher is now interested in seeing whether a higher proportion of men in the group that crossed the Capilano Canyon bridge will call her versus the proportion of calls she will receive from the group that crossed the solid wooden bridge.

STEP 2: Design a study and collect data.

1. Is this an observational study or an experiment? How are you deciding?
2. What are the observational units?

3. We have two variables: bridge type and whether the subject called or not. Which of these variables is explanatory and which is response?

   You will learn in Chapter 5 how to state null and alternative hypotheses for studies like this. Here they are for this study:

   Null: The long-run proportion of men who will call the researcher is the same under both conditions.

   Alt: The long-run proportion of men who will call the researcher is higher for those who cross the suspension bridge compared to those who cross the solid wood bridge.

   Of the 18 men on the suspension bridge that accepted her phone number, 9 called her. Of the 16 men on the solid wooden bridge that accepted her phone number, 2 called her.

STEP 3: Explore the data.

4. Fill in the two-way table with the data from the study.

	Suspension bridge	Wooden bridge	Totals
Subject called interviewer			11
Subject did not call interviewer			23
Totals	18	16	34

5. What proportion of men on the suspension bridge called the interviewer?
6. What proportion of men on the wooden bridge called the interviewer?

STEP 4: Draw inferences.   In Chapter 5, we will learn how to use the 3S strategy to help us investigate how much evidence the sample data provide to support our conjecture that the long-run probability of men who call is greater for those on the suspension bridge than for those on the wooden bridge. As a result of the simulation analysis method used in Chapter 5 we received a p-value of 0.023.

7. Use the null and alternative hypotheses stated above and the p-value of 0.023 to write a conclusion about strength of evidence in this study. (*Hint:* Even though the study design is different, the way you interpret p-values in terms of the null and alternative hypothesis is still the same.)

8. How would the p-value have changed if the alternative hypothesis was stated as: *Alt: The long-run proportion of men who will call the researcher among those who cross the suspension bridge is different from that among those who cross the solid wood bridge.*

9. Write a conclusion about the strength of evidence in the study based on the p-value from #8.

10. In studies comparing two groups, the parameter of interest is often stated as the true difference in the long-run proportions in the two groups. In this study, this is the long-run difference in the proportions of men calling the researcher comparing the men crossing the Capilano suspension bridge to the men crossing the wooden bridge. A 95% confidence interval (CI) for this parameter is 0.375 ± 0.35. Explain how the fact that the CI does not include 0 corresponds to the size of the p-value obtained in #8.

STEP 5: Formulate conclusions.

11. *Generalization.* Now, let's step back a bit and think about the scope of our inference. Was this a random sample? Does this study represent all people? How about all men? Is there any population to which we can generalize our conclusion?

12. *Causation.* What about cause-and-effect conclusions? Did the researchers use random assignment to determine which of the 34 men crossed the suspension bridge and which crossed the wooden bridge? Are we able to conclude that the cause of the difference between the two groups of men was the type of bridge they crossed?

STEP 6: Look back and ahead. The researchers acknowledged the fact that there were confounding variables involved in this study. They tried to minimize these by doing other studies to try to answer the same research question. In another study, they again interviewed subjects on the suspension bridge just as before. As a control, they interviewed subjects that had already crossed the suspension bridge at least 10 minutes earlier and were sitting or walking in the nearby park.

13. Describe the confounding variable they are trying to eliminate by completing this new study.

Let's see how this second study turned out. Of those on the suspension bridge, 13 of the 20 men called the female interviewer. Of those that had already crossed the bridge, 7 out of 23 men called the female interviewer.

14. In this study, what proportion of those on the suspension bridge called the interviewer? Of those who had already crossed the bridge?

The hypotheses are modified slightly for this new study:

Null: The long-run proportion of men who will call the researcher is the same under both conditions

Alt: The long-run proportion of men who will call the researcher is the higher among men who are approached by the female while on the suspension compared to that among men who are approached by the female after they have recently crossed the bridge.

15. Write a conclusion about the strength of evidence in this new study based on obtaining a p-value of 0.024.

16. *Generalization.* Have the researchers addressed the concerns about generalization with this new study?

17. *Causation.* Is a cause-effect conclusion possible in this new study? Why or why not?

Research Article   www.wiley.com/college/tintle

Impacting People's Willingness to Pay   Read "The Effect of Red Background Color on Willingness-to-Pay: The Moderating Role of Selling Mechanism."

Comparing Two Groups

In Unit 1 you saw the four pillars of statistical inference developed in the simplest possible situation. In almost every example, the data took the form of observed values on a single binary variable. It was possible to summarize the data using a single proportion, and to base inference on that one number. We also extended this case to another simple case: a single quantitative variable. But again, we were focused on just one outcome variable.

Now that you have experience with the basics, you are ready to apply the same ideas to more complicated situations. The chapters of Unit 2 will show you how to compare two groups using a single response variable. In Chapter 5, the response is binary, and we end up comparing two proportions, one for each group. In Chapter 6 the response is quantitative, and we end up comparing two means, one for each group. As you might guess, in many ways these two chapters are quite similar.

Chapter 7 is different. In both Chapters 5 and 6, the observational units in the two groups have nothing to do with each other; in other words they are *independent* of each other, and we get one outcome value for each unit. In Chapter 7, we get a *pair* of measurements on each observational unit, so there is a dependency built into the design of the study. The resulting paired structure has important advantages that you will learn about in Chapter 7.

Although the data structures of this unit will be somewhat more complicated, the basic ideas and methods remain the same as in Unit 1. As before, inference takes place in the framework of the six-step statistical investigation method. The 3S strategy also applies. In particular, the basic idea of the simulation step remains the same as before. You ask, "What if the null hypothesis is true: How could my statistic behave by chance alone?" Just as before, the answer requires investigating the null ("what if") distribution, and using p-value and/or standardized statistic to assess the strength of evidence against the null hypothesis. The main difference will be in the null hypothesis itself, which will typically take the form "No difference between parameters." You will also see how to construct a confidence interval to estimate the value of the population parameter, a difference in proportions or a difference in means.

UNITS 1 AND 2 DATA STRUCTURES

UNIT 1: One binary or one quantitative variable

UNIT 2: Comparing two groups

	EXPLANATORY	RESPONSE
Chapter 5	Binary	Binary
Chapter 6	Binary	Quantitative
Chapter 7	Binary	Quantitative (paired)

CHAPTER

1 2 3 4 **5** 6 7 8 9 10 11 12

Comparing Two Proportions

In the studies of Unit 1 there was only one group and only one parameter. In this chapter there will be two groups. In Chapter 1, the only parameter for Doris and Buzz was π, the probability that Buzz would be right. Our null hypothesis was $\pi = 1/2$. The value $1/2$ came from the null hypothesis that Buzz was just guessing equally between two choices.

In this chapter, one of the studies is also about dolphins: Can swimming with dolphins help patients who have been diagnosed with depression? This study uses two groups: a treatment group and a control group. For each treatment, π is the probability of substantial improvement in depression symptoms, π_1 for the dolphin (treatment) group, π_2 for the control group. The null hypothesis is that $\pi_1 - \pi_2 = 0$. Or in other words, $\pi_1 = \pi_2$: Swimming with dolphins makes no difference in the probability a subject improves. If we obtain a small p-value, and so have strong evidence against this null hypothesis, then we conclude that the difference we observed between the groups in the study did not arise from the random assignment process alone. As we saw in Chapter 4, in situations where we randomize observational units to groups we are comparing, cause-and-effect conclusions may be possible.

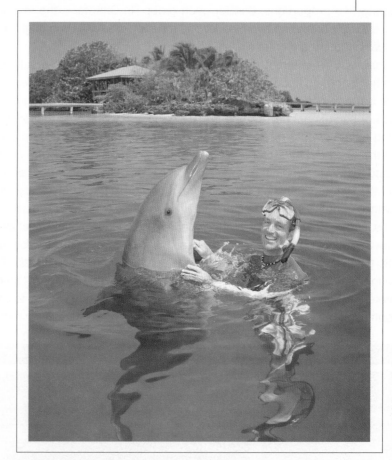

Jacom Stephens/Getty Images, Inc.

Even though having two groups is new, a lot of what we do will be familiar. The statistical investigation process follows the usual six steps. We start with a research question, design a study, and then explore the data we get. We will use the 3S strategy to measure the strength of evidence against the null hypothesis, although the statistic will be new. We will get an interval estimate for the parameter, now a difference $(\pi_1 - \pi_2)$, using the same ideas as in Unit 1. First, we simulate and use the 2SD shortcut. Then we use a theory-based method.

Section 5.1 is about exploration and description of the sample data. The main new ideas here are *conditional* proportions and something called the relative risk. Section 5.2 explains the simulation-based approach to comparing proportions while Section 5.3 introduces the theory-based approach. The chapter ends with a fourth section that takes a more detailed look at a theory-based approach to comparing two proportions.

COMPARING TWO GROUPS: CATEGORICAL RESPONSE

SECTION 5.1

INTRODUCTION

As we are now going to focus on drawing conclusions from studies involving two variables, we will start by focusing on how to summarize two categorical variables in order to make group comparisons.

Good and Bad Perceptions

5.1

Example 5.1

Student researchers were interested in how the phrasing of a question affects people's responses. In particular, they asked some students whether they were "having a good year" and other students whether they were "having a bad year." Then they recorded whether each of the 30 subjects indicated a "good perception of their year" (meaning they said either "Yes, I'm having a good year" or "No, I'm not having a bad year") or a "bad perception" (meaning they said either "No, I'm not having a good year" or "Yes, I'm having a bad year"). Which question was posed to each subject was determined in advance by randomly assigning each of the 30 subjects to get one of the two questions.

> **THINK ABOUT IT**
>
> What are the observational units in this study? How many variables were recorded on each observational unit? Identify and classify the roles of the variables (explanatory vs. response) in this study. Is this study an observational study or a randomized experiment? How do you know?

The observational units in this study are the 30 students, but now we have two variables: *whether the question wording was "having a good year" or "having a bad year" and whether the respondent's perception of their year was positive or negative.* In this study, the student researchers thought the wording of the question would help explain why some people indicated a positive perception of their year and others indicated a negative perception of their year. Thus, the roles of these variables are wording of question as the explanatory variable and perception of year as the response variable. Because the explanatory variable was randomly assigned to each subject, this is a randomized experiment.

The student researchers recorded the data by noting which version of the question was asked and how the student responded. Table 5.1 shows the *data table* that they obtained.

TABLE 5.1 Data obtained by the student researchers

Individual	Question wording	Perception of their year	Individual	Question wording	Perception of their year
1	"Good year"	Positive	16	"Good year"	Positive
2	"Good year"	Negative	17	"Bad year"	Positive
3	"Bad year"	Positive	18	"Good year"	Positive
4	"Good year"	Positive	19	"Good year"	Positive
5	"Good year"	Negative	20	"Good year"	Positive
6	"Bad year"	Positive	21	"Bad year"	Negative
7	"Good year"	Positive	22	"Good year"	Positive
8	"Good year"	Positive	23	"Bad year"	Negative
9	"Good year"	Positive	24	"Good year"	Positive
10	"Bad year"	Negative	25	"Bad year"	Negative
11	"Good year"	Negative	26	"Good year"	Positive
12	"Bad year"	Negative	27	"Bad year"	Negative
13	"Good year"	Positive	28	"Good year"	Positive
14	"Bad year"	Negative	29	"Bad year"	Positive
15	"Good year"	Positive	30	"Bad year"	Negative

Notice that in the data table each observational unit is one row, and the different columns (apart from the individual's ID number) represent the two variables.

5.1.1

However, this table does not make it simple to notice any trends or patterns in the responses. One way to organize the data is to produce a **two-way table** of counts. As the name suggests, two-way tables summarize *two* categorical variables. You may also see these tables called "contingency tables." In such a table, the entries in the table (sometimes called *cells*) indicate the number of observational units that have the specified combination of categories for the two variables. For example, Table 5.2 is a two-way table of the survey data. It shows how many students were in each of the four possible combinations (e.g., 15 students gave a "good" response to the "Are you having a good year" question) as well as the total for each category of the individual variables (e.g., 18 students were given the "Are you having a good year" version of the question).

THINK ABOUT IT

- Verify that there were four individuals in the data table (Table 5.1) who answered with a positive perception to the "Are you having a bad year" question.
- Is it reasonable to conclude from this table that there is a tendency for more positive perceptions to the "Are you having a good year" question than to the "Are you having a bad year" question?

TABLE 5.2 A two-way table summarizing the number of good and bad responses to the two different phrasings of the question. This is a *two-by-two* (2 × 2) table because each variable has two outcomes

		Question wording		
		"Good year"	"Bad year"	Total
Perception of their year	Positive	15	4	19
	Negative	3	8	11
	Total	18	12	30

An important reminder is that comparing the *counts* in individual categories may not be useful if the group sizes differ. In this case, a few more people were asked the "good year" version of the question. So we might expect a slightly higher number of positive responses to the "good year" question than to the less often asked "bad year" question for that reason alone. To take into account the sample sizes, it is much more useful to look at the ***conditional proportions*** of positive responses, where we compute the proportion of "successes" separately within each explanatory variable group. For these data, we see that $15/18 \approx 0.833$, or about 83%, of the individuals asked the "Are you having a good year" version of the question indicated a positive perception. We want to compare this to the proportion of individuals who indicated a positive perception to the "Are you having a bad year" version of the question: $4/12 \approx 0.333$. (Try to also be careful to say "higher *proportion* of positive responses" instead of the more ambiguous "more positive responses.") Keep in mind that these conditional proportions (0.833 and 0.333) are sample proportions because they have been calculated from sample data.

We can produce a picture of these data so that comparison becomes even more readily apparent. Previously, with just one categorical variable, we looked at a bar graph of the categorical variable outcomes. When exploring two categorical variables, ***segmented bar graphs*** quickly illustrate the differences among the groups. In a segmented bar graph, the total bar heights are always 100%, but each bar is broken into categories and shows the breakdown of the proportions of observational units in each category. For example, in the segmented bar graph shown in Figure 5.1, the positive response segments go to 83% and 33%.

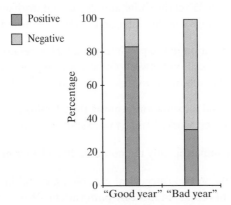

FIGURE 5.1 A segmented bar graph showing the percentage of people with good perceptions to each question.

SUMMARIZING THE DATA

These data definitely support the claim that people will have a positive perception more often to the "Are you having a good year" question than to the "Are you having a bad year" question. In other words, there is an *association* between the phrasing of the question and how people responded. We can say the proportion of positive responses was $0.833 - 0.333 = 0.500$ higher for the "good year" phrasing than the "bad year" phrasing (*Note:* We can say there was a difference of 50 percentage points, but we would not say a difference of 50% because saying one number is 50% higher than another implies multiplying by 1.50.)

Another way we can compare the two conditional proportions is to take the ratio, $0.833/0.333 \approx 2.50$, so the proportion with a positive perception is 2.50 times higher (or 150% higher) in the "good year" group than the "bad year" group. This ratio is called the ***relative risk***. This ratio is typically used in medical fields to look at the relative risk of disease or death from one treatment compared to another. Convention puts the larger of the two values in the numerator and the smaller of the two values in the denominator to yield values larger than 1.

Definition

Relative risk is the ratio of two conditional proportions. It indicates how many times greater the risk of an outcome is for one group compared to another.

For several years in the 1990s, Kristen Gilbert worked as a nurse in the intensive care unit (ICU) of the Veterans Administration Hospital in Northampton, Massachusetts. Over the course of her time there, other nurses came to suspect that she was killing patients by injecting them with the heart stimulant epinephrine. Gilbert was eventually arrested and charged with these murders. Part of the evidence presented against Gilbert at her murder trial was a statistical analysis of 1,641 eight-hour shifts during the time Gilbert worked in the ICU. For each of these shifts, researchers recorded two variables: whether or not Gilbert worked on the shift and whether or not at least one patient died during the shift.

1. Identify the observational units in this study. (*Hint:* The observational units are not people. Think about what the sample size is.)

2. Classify each variable as categorical or quantitative.

   Whether or not Gilbert worked on the shift:

   Whether or not at least one patient died during the shift:

3. Which variable would you regard as explanatory and which as response?

   Explanatory:

   Response:

4. Is this an observational study or an experiment? Justify your answer.

   So what did the researchers find when they analyzed the 1,641 eight-hour shifts? They found that Gilbert worked on 257 of the shifts, and she did not work on 1,384 of them. They also found that a patient died during 74 of the shifts, and no death occurred on the other 1,567 shifts.

5. Explain why the information in the previous paragraph does not provide any clues about whether there is an association between Gilbert working on a shift and a patient dying during the shift. What additional information do you need to know?

   Here is some additional information: Among the 74 shifts during which a patient died, 40 were shifts on which Gilbert worked and 34 were shifts on which Gilbert did not work.

6. Explain why simply comparing only the numbers 40 and 34 is not very informative.

   When analyzing data on two categorical variables, a useful first step is to organize the data into a *two-way table* of counts. In this case both variables have only two categories, so we produce a 2 × 2 table.

7. Fill in the missing counts in the following **two-way table**. (*Hint:* Start by entering 40 and 34 into the appropriate cells. Then make sure that both rows and both columns add up to the indicated totals.)

	Gilbert working on shift	Gilbert not working on shift	Total
Patient died during shift			74
No patient died during shift			1,567
Total	257	1,384	1,641

8. Suggest a better way to compare the outcomes of the shifts on which Gilbert worked and the shifts on which she did not work than simply comparing 40 to 34. Explain why your answer is more informative.

   A next step in analyzing categorical data in a two-way table is to calculate **conditional proportions**. A conditional proportion simply means that you consider the counts in only one category of the explanatory variable at a time.

9. Now let's calculate the conditional proportions.

   a. Calculate the conditional proportion of Gilbert shifts on which a patient died. (*Hint:* Put the total number of Gilbert shifts in the denominator of your fraction.)

   b. Calculate the conditional proportion of non-Gilbert shifts on which a patient died.

A *segmented bar graph* is an appropriate display for graphing data in a two-way table. Such a graph contains rectangles of total height 100% for each category of the explanatory variable. Then segments divide up each rectangle according to the conditional proportions of the response variable categories.

10. Fill in the following segmented bar graph to display the data from this study. First draw two (separated) rectangles, one for Gilbert shifts and one for non-Gilbert shifts, each with total height 100%. Then draw a line in each rectangle corresponding to the conditional proportion of shifts in which a patient died, as you calculated in #9.

11. Do the conditional proportions and segmented bar graph appear to provide evidence that at least one patient was more likely to die on a Gilbert shift than on a non-Gilbert shift? In other words, does there appear to be a tendency for Gilbert shifts to have at least one death more often than non-Gilbert shifts? Explain.

12. Without doing any further analysis, do you consider the difference between the conditional proportions to be striking, worth reporting to a jury?

   A next step is to produce a single number (statistic) to summarize the data.

13. What arithmetic operation might you perform on the two conditional proportions to obtain a single statistic?

14. Calculate the *difference* in conditional proportions of death between Gilbert and non-Gilbert shifts. Does the value of this difference strike you as noteworthy?

15. Now calculate a different statistic: the *ratio* of conditional proportions of death between Gilbert and non-Gilbert shifts. This ratio is called a *relative risk*. Write a sentence interpreting this ratio value, as the prosecution might present to a jury. Does the value of this ratio strike you as noteworthy?

16. Even if the difference between these conditional proportions of death is found to be highly statistically significant, is it reasonable to conclude from this analysis that Kristen Gilbert was responsible for (i.e., *caused*) the increased chance of death on her shifts? Explain your answer. (*Hint:* Remember your answer to #4 about what kind of study this is.)

17. Suggest an alternative explanation that the defense attorneys might use to explain the large difference in death proportions between the two groups.

> **Definition**
>
> *Relative risk* is the ratio of two conditional proportions. It indicates how many times greater the risk of an outcome is for one group compared to another.

Further analysis

18. Suppose that the data had turned out as follows:

	Gilbert working on shift	Gilbert not working on shift	Total
Patient died during shift	100	357	457
No patient died during shift	157	1,027	1,184
Total	257	1,384	1,641

   a. Calculate the conditional proportions of death for Gilbert shifts and for non-Gilbert shifts.
   b. Calculate the *difference* in these conditional proportions. How does this difference compare to the one in #14? Are they very similar?
   c. Calculate the *relative risk* of these conditional proportions. How does this ratio compare to the one in #15? Are they very similar?
   d. For which table of data, this new one or the original (real) data, would you consider the evidence against Gilbert to be more persuasive/incriminating? Explain.

19. Produce a hypothetical 2 × 2 table with the same marginal totals, but with the property that the data reveal virtually *no association* between the variables. In other words, produce a table so that the conditional proportions are very similar between the two groups.

	Gilbert working on shift	Gilbert not working on shift	Total
Patient died during shift			457
No patient died during shift			1,184
Total	257	1,384	1,641

20. What would the segmented bar graph look like for a 2 × 2 table with virtually no association between the variables? Explain your answer.

SECTION 5.1 Summary

When a study involves two categorical variables, the data can be organized into a **two-way table** of counts.

A **segmented bar graph** displays the association between two categorical variables by showing the **conditional proportions** of success and failure across the explanatory variable groups.

- If the variables have absolutely no association, then the breakdown of segments is identical across all of the bars.
- If the variables have absolutely no association, the conditional proportions are identical for all explanatory variable groups.

Comparing counts of successes between two groups is not a valid comparison, because the sample sizes in the two groups could differ substantially.

- Comparing conditional proportions is more appropriate.
- The difference between the conditional proportions in the two groups is one statistic for measuring how different the groups' responses are.
- The ratio of the conditional proportions, called the **relative risk**, can also be used as a statistic to compare the two groups. The relative risk indicates how many times more likely an outcome is in one group compared to the other.

SECTION 5.2

COMPARING TWO PROPORTIONS: SIMULATION-BASED APPROACH

INTRODUCTION

In the previous section we saw that when we have two categorical variables our interest is less on the overall "success rate" and more on comparing the success rates (conditional proportions) between groups. The previous section focused on descriptively comparing conditional proportions between two groups. We will now assess whether the difference between two sample proportions is statistically significant. We will use the same reasoning process (3S strategy) that we introduced in Chapter 1 to assess whether the two sample proportions differ enough to conclude that something other than random chance is responsible for the observed difference in groups. Once again we will evaluate the strength of evidence provided by the data based on how unlikely the observed data are to have occurred by chance alone. In this section, we will develop a new simulation approach to approximate the p-value for the group comparison. The next section, Section 5.3, will focus on a theory-based approach.

Swimming with Dolphins

EXAMPLE

Example 5.2

STEP 1: Ask a research question. Swimming with dolphins can certainly be fun, but is it also therapeutic for patients suffering from clinical depression? To answer this question, researchers wanted to focus on whether or not the presence of dolphins helps some depression patients improve at a higher rate than other individuals in similar circumstances but without dolphins.

STEP 2: Design a study and collect data. Researchers recruited 30 subjects aged 18–65 with a clinical diagnosis of mild to moderate depression. Subjects were required to discontinue use of any antidepressant drugs or psychotherapy four weeks prior to the experiment and throughout the experiment. These 30 subjects went to an island off the coast of Honduras, where they were randomly assigned to one of two treatment groups. Both groups engaged in one hour of swimming and snorkeling each day, but one group did so in the presence of bottlenose dolphins and the other group did not. (It's important to note that participants in the dolphin group and the control group experienced identical conditions except for the presence of dolphins.) At the end of two weeks, each subject's level of depression was evaluated, as it had been at the beginning of the study (Antonioli and Reveley, 2005). The response variable is defined as whether or not the subjects achieved substantial reduction (improvement) in their depression.

> **THINK ABOUT IT**
>
> Identify the observational units and the explanatory variable in this study. Classify the explanatory and response variables as quantitative or categorical. If categorical, how many categories does each variable have? Is this study an observational study or an experiment? Are the subjects in this study a random sample from a larger population?

The 30 subjects are the observational units, all with mild to moderate depression. It is difficult to imagine that they were randomly selected from some larger population and all happened to be available to go to Honduras. However, the subjects were randomly assigned to either the dolphin therapy or the control group (the explanatory variable). We also suspect that the subjects did not know there were two different groups, though at the end of the study everyone in both groups then had the opportunity to swim with the dolphins. So, this is a randomized, comparative experiment. The response variable has been coded into a binary categorical variable: whether or not there was substantial improvement in depression symptoms.

5.2.1

The researchers hoped to show the study results provide convincing evidence that swimming with dolphins is more beneficial for mild to moderately depressed subjects than simply going to Honduras. We will apply the "assume innocence" logic again from Chapter 1 and determine whether the results these researchers found are typical or not typical of what we would find if the dolphin therapy was *not* more beneficial. Let's write down the null and alternative hypotheses remembering the concept of association from Chapter 4.

> Null hypothesis: Presence of dolphins does not help; that is, whether or not someone swims with dolphins has **no association** with whether or not someone shows substantial improvement.

> Alternative hypothesis: The presence of dolphins is helpful; that is, swimming with dolphins increases the probability of substantial improvement in depression symptoms (there is an association).

If the variables are associated, this means that knowing which group someone is in (swim with dolphins, yes or no) helps us predict whether or not they will reduce their depression symptoms. This suggests another way to state the hypotheses, which focuses on the parameters in the study (probability of improvement given the dolphin therapy treatment and the probability of improving given the control treatment):

> Null: The probability of exhibiting substantial improvement after swimming with dolphins (denoted by $\pi_{dolphins}$) is the same as the probability of exhibiting substantial improvement after swimming without dolphins (denoted by $\pi_{control}$).

> Alternative: The probability of exhibiting substantial improvement after swimming with dolphins is higher than the probability of exhibiting substantial improvement after swimming without dolphins.

We can, thus, define our parameter of interest to be the difference in probabilities of substantial improvement between the two treatments, which we can symbolize with $\pi_{dolphins} - \pi_{control}$, meaning that we can restate the null and alternative hypotheses again as:

$$H_0: \pi_{dolphins} - \pi_{control} = 0$$
$$H_a: \pi_{dolphins} - \pi_{control} > 0$$

Note that the parameter of interest is the difference in the two probabilities, not the individual probabilities themselves. Stated another way, we will be analyzing a potential difference between the two treatments, not the overall probability of depression patients improving their symptoms.

The results that the researchers found are shown in Table 5.3 (a 2 × 2 table), with the explanatory variable as the columns of the table.

TABLE 5.3 A summary of the results of the experiment

	Dolphin therapy	Control group	Total
Showed substantial improvement	10	3	13
Did not show substantial improvement	5	12	17
Total	15	15	30

STEP 3: Explore the data. A segmented bar graph comparing the response variable outcomes between the two explanatory variable groups is shown in Figure 5.2.

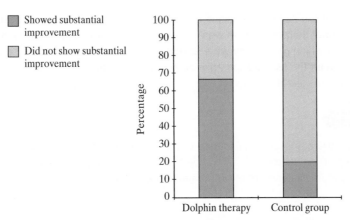

FIGURE 5.2   A segmented bar graph comparing the improvement in depression symptoms between the dolphin therapy group and the control group.

We see that subjects in the dolphin therapy group were more likely to show substantial improvement. In the dolphin therapy group, 10 of 15, or 66.67%, showed substantial improvement compared to 3 of 15, or 20%, in the control group.

What are two possible explanations for the observed difference in these conditional proportions?

This difference of 46.67 percentage points (66.67% − 20.00% = 46.67%) appears quite substantial and may reflect a genuine tendency for depressed individuals to be more likely to improve if their activities include dolphins. Still, the overall sample size (30 subjects) is rather small. Perhaps 13 subjects were going to show substantial improvement (and 17 were not) just by being participants in this experiment, regardless of which treatment group they were assigned to and we just happened, by random chance alone, to assign more of the improvers to the dolphin therapy group. We are not considering any other explanations or confounding variables because of the randomized blind nature of the study design. So, there are two possible explanations for the observed difference in these conditional proportions. Either the dolphins really helped (alternative hypothesis) or random chance alone was responsible for the observed difference (null hypothesis). We need to decide which of these explanations is more plausible based on the data from the study.

STEP 4: Draw inferences beyond the data.   As in Chapter 1, our strategy will be to determine how surprising the observed result would be if the null hypothesis were true. We can determine this by using simulation to generate a large number of "could-have-been" results under that null hypothesis and examine the null distribution of our statistic. If the observed result from our study falls in the tail of that distribution, then we have strong evidence against the null hypothesis.

APPLYING THE 3S STRATEGY

1. **Statistic:** One possible choice of statistic for comparing these two groups is the difference in the observed sample proportions who improved. In this study, $\hat{p}_{dolphins} - \hat{p}_{control} = 0.4667$. See FAQ 5.2.1 for more discussion on this choice.

FAQ 5.2.1   **www.wiley.com/college/tintle**

Which statistic?

2. **Simulation:** If the null hypothesis is true, then the dolphin therapy is no more effective than the control therapy and we were going to have 13 improvers and 17 nonimprovers regardless of which group they were assigned to. If this is true, then any differences we do see between the two groups arise solely from the randomness in the assignment to the explanatory variable groups.

KEY IDEA

To evaluate the statistical significance of the observed difference in our groups, we will investigate how large the difference in conditional proportions tends to be just from the random assignment of outcomes to the explanatory variable groups.

THINK ABOUT IT

What difference in conditional proportions would we expect to see if the null hypothesis were true?

5.2.2

5.2.3

We can perform this simulation analysis with index cards. We will let 13 blue cards represent the improvers and 17 green cards represent the nonimprovers. We are assuming these outcomes were going to happen no matter which treatment group subjects ended up in. We will simulate the random assignment process of the subjects to the two groups by shuffling the cards and putting 15 in one pile (for the dolphin therapy) and 15 in another pile (for the control group). This way an improver is equally likely to be assigned to the dolphin therapy as the control group. *Note:* We aren't saying subjects are equally likely to improve or not as we often did in Chapter 1, only that the probability of being an improver is the same for both treatments. Figure 5.3 shows the results of one such reshuffling, with Group A arbitrarily representing the dolphin therapy group and Group B the control group.

	Group A	Group B	Total
Blue cards (success)	6	7	13
Green cards (failure)	9	8	17
Total	15	15	30

FIGURE 5.3 The results of shuffling 30 cards with 13 improvers (blue cards) and 17 nonimprovers (green cards) into two groups of 15.

THINK ABOUT IT

For the simulation, why do the row totals of 13 improvers (successes) and 17 nonimprovers (failures) stay the same as the original study? Why do the column totals of 15 in the dolphin therapy group (Group A) and 15 in the control group (Group B) stay the same?

Notice the row totals are the same as in the actual study because (under the null hypothesis) we haven't changed who will improve or not. Similarly, the column totals have not changed because we are still assigning 15 subjects to each group, matching the study. But we have changed how those improvers and nonimprovers are distributed between the two groups. As expected with the random shuffling we see a more equal distribution between the two groups. This is reflected in the segmented bar group for this "could-have-been" result (Figure 5.4).

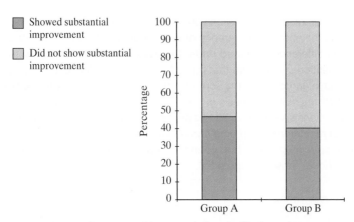

FIGURE 5.4 Segmented bar graph for shuffled results.

The conditional proportion of improvers in the dolphin therapy group (Group A) is 6/15 = 0.40 and the conditional proportion of improvers in the control group (Group B) is 7/15 ≈ 0.467, for a difference of 0.40 − 0.467 = −0.067. In fact, in this simulated trial, Group B (the control group) had a higher rate of improvers. But this can happen by random chance when there is no underlying impact from the treatment.

THINK ABOUT IT

When the null hypothesis is true, how often do you expect to see Group B with a larger conditional proportion of improvers than Group A?

If there is really no effect of dolphin therapy, then we expect Group B to have a larger proportion of improvers just as often as Group A (50% of the time). We repeated this process three more times and found 8, 5, and then 6 of the improvers in the dolphin therapy group. These results are shown in Figure 5.5.

Simulated results			
	Group A	Group B	
Success	8	5	13
Failure	7	10	17
	15	15	30
diff = 8/15 − 5/15 = 0.20			

Simulated results			
	Group A	Group B	
Success	5	8	13
Failure	10	7	17
	15	15	30
diff = 5/15 − 8/15 = −0.20			

Simulated results			
	Group A	Group B	
Success	6	7	13
Failure	9	8	17
	15	15	30
diff = 6/15 − 7/15 = −0.067			

FIGURE 5.5 The results of three more repetitions. This time we found 8, 5, and 6 improvers were randomly placed in the dolphin therapy group. These yielded differences in proportions of improvers of 0.20, −0.20, and −0.067, respectively.

Mapping this simulation to the study we find:

Null hypothesis	=	no difference in probabilities of success
One repetition	=	random assignment of response outcomes to two groups
Statistic	=	difference in conditional proportions

THINK ABOUT IT

Do any of these repetitions result in a difference in proportions of improvers that are at least as extreme as our observed study result of 0.667 − 0.20 ≈ 0.467?

5.2.4

None of the differences in proportions obtained in the four reshuffles are as extreme as or more extreme than the observed difference of 0.467, because they (−0.067, 0.20, −0.20) are all closer to 0, the difference expected under the null hypothesis, compared to 0.467. From just these four repetitions, it appears that the actual result of a difference in proportion of improvers in the dolphin group minus the control group of 0.467 is unlikely to happen by random chance alone when the null hypothesis is true. But we can't see much of a long-run pattern with only four repetitions so we repeated this process, using the **Two Proportions** applet, until we had 1000 total repetitions, each time computing the difference in proportion of improvers in the dolphin therapy group minus the proportion of improvers in the control group. We found results similar to those shown in Figure 5.6.

> **THINK ABOUT IT**
>
> What does the distribution in Figure 5.6 represent?

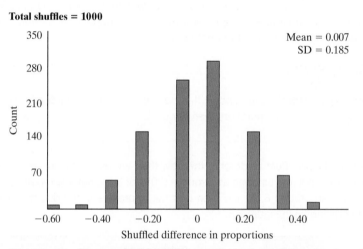

FIGURE 5.6 The results of 1,000 repetitions of simulating the dolphin therapy experiment under the null hypothesis that dolphin therapy is not more effective than the control. Each observation in this histogram represents a difference in conditional proportions.

> **THINK ABOUT IT**
>
> Does this distribution behave as you expected? In particular, where is the center and what is the shape of the distribution?

The mean of this distribution is approximately zero, which we would expect because it represents the could-have-been outcomes when there is no underlying difference in the probability of improving between the two treatments. In other words, $\pi_{dolphin} - \pi_{control} = 0$, so we expect our difference in sample proportions, generated assuming the null hypothesis is true, to reflect that and cluster around zero as well. When the null hypothesis is true, we should see that Group A has the higher proportion of improvers about half the time, and Group B has the higher proportion of improvers about half the time. We do realize there will be some random variation, but because the labeling of Group A and Group B was arbitrary, we expect the pattern of that variation to be symmetric around the mean of zero.

5.2.5

THINK ABOUT IT

How can we use the distribution shown in Figure 5.6 to evaluate whether dolphin therapy is effective?

3. **Strength of evidence:** The distribution of the difference in sample proportions, generated assuming the null hypothesis is true, does not tell us much until we see where our observed statistic falls in the distribution. We see that the statistic of 0.467 is in the tail of this null distribution. This shows that even though it's possible that the random assignment process alone could lead to such a large difference between the two groups, it's quite unlikely. In the 1,000 trials in Figure 5.6, there were 13 simulated results with a difference of 0.467 or higher, so our estimate of the p-value is 13/1,000 = 0.013. This small p-value provides strong evidence against the null hypothesis. We can also use the simulation results to standardize the statistic, as in Section 1.3. This indicates that 0.467 lies $(0.467 - 0)/0.185 \approx 2.524$ standard deviations above zero. Because this standardized statistic is larger than 2, this again demonstrates that the researcher's result is an unusual outcome when the null hypothesis is true and provides strong evidence that the data in this study did not arise from a process where there was no difference in the probability of improving between the two treatments. We have strong evidence that dolphin therapy is more effective than the control for relieving depression symptoms.

ESTIMATION

In fact, if we used a 2SD method to estimate a 95% confidence interval for the difference in the probability of substantial improvement between these two conditions using the standard deviation from the null distribution, we would find

$$0.467 \pm 2(0.185) = 0.467 \pm 0.370 = (0.097, 0.837).$$

 5.2.6

In other words, we are 95% confident that when allowed to swim with dolphins, the probability of improving is between 0.097 and 0.837 higher than when no dolphins are present. Notice that this interval is entirely positive, complementing our earlier analysis suggesting that the probability of improving is higher when swimming with dolphins than when not.

STEP 5: Formulate conclusions. When we first looked at these data, we found a substantial difference in the proportions of improvers between the two groups. After considering how much variation we might see in the difference in conditional proportions from the random assignment process when the null hypothesis is true, we confirmed that a difference this large was unlikely to occur by chance alone (p-value $\approx$ 0.013). Thus, the difference in the improvement rates between the two groups in this study is statistically significant and appears to be practically important as well [95% CI: (0.097, 0.837)].

 5.2.7

Can we say that the presence of the dolphins *caused* this improvement? Because this was a randomized experiment, and assuming everything else was identical (or balanced on average) between the two groups other than the presence of dolphins (e.g., weather, amount of time in water, diet), then we do have compelling evidence that the imposition of the explanatory variable was the cause.

However, we have some cautions in generalizing this to a larger population. We must at least restrict ourselves to mild to moderately depressed patients in this age range willing to volunteer for such a study, and even that would be risky because we don't have any evidence that random selection was used to find the original 30 subjects. See FAQ 5.2.2 for more discussion on interpreting p-values and scope of conclusions when comparing two proportions.

FAQ 5.2.2   www.wiley.com/college/tintle

Where's the randomness?

STEP 6: Look back and ahead.   There is strong evidence that the presence of the dolphins increases depression patients' probability of demonstrating substantial improvement in their depression symptoms over this time period (11–83 percentage points). Broad generalizations were difficult to make due to the convenience sample of participants. Researchers should see if they find similar results with other groups of subjects as well. Because this may not be a feasible long-term strategy to reach a large number of depression sufferers, the researchers may now want to investigate other animal care programs to see whether the effects are similar.

FOLLOW-UP ANALYSIS

THINK ABOUT IT

Suppose the actual results had found eight successes in the dolphin therapy group and five successes in the control group for these 30 subjects, what would change, if anything, about your analysis and conclusion?

Testing the same null hypothesis, we would use the same null distribution as in Figure 5.6, but this time we would see where a difference of $8/15 - 5/15 = 0.20$. Such an outcome does not fall in the tail of the distribution. In fact, we can use the **Two Proportions** applet to approximate the p-value from 1,000 repetitions of the shuffling process. This applet (with the 2×2 box checked) allows you to specify the values of your own two-way table by clicking in each cell, deleting the old value and typing in the new value, and then pressing **Use Table**. The applet (see Figure 5.7) reports an approximate p-value of 0.2320, giving us little to no evidence against the null hypothesis. This large p-value, suggesting that it would not be surprising to see a difference in sample proportions of 0.20 if the null hypothesis of no difference in the underlying probabilities was true, should make sense because the observed difference in proportions is smaller, so there is less evidence against the null hypothesis. As we saw in Chapter 1, the closer the observed value of the statistic is to the hypothesized value, the less evidence against the null hypothesis. Here the observed difference in conditional proportions is closer to zero.

FIGURE 5.7   Results for new data table shading the one-sided p-value.

FIGURE 5.7 (*Continued*).

Relative risk

Recall from Section 5.1 that the relative risk is another way to summarize the association between two binary variables. For this study, the observed relative risk is 0.667/0.200 = 3.33, meaning that individuals who swam with dolphins were 3.33 times more likely than those who did not swim with dolphins to show substantial improvement on depression symptoms. We can modify the 3S strategy in a minor way to conduct a test of significance for the relative risk.

> **THINK ABOUT IT**
>
> What would the value of the relative risk be if there was no association between swimming with dolphins and showing improvement on depression symptoms?

To state the null and alternative hypotheses, think about what value of the relative risk would mean there was no association. A relative risk of 1 means that the proportions are equal and there is no association. Thus, we can write the null and alternative hypotheses as:

Null: The relative risk of improvement on depression symptoms (computed as the ratio of the probability of exhibiting substantial improvement after swimming with dolphins to the probability of exhibiting substantial improvement after swimming without dolphins) is 1.

Alternative: The relative risk of improvement on depression symptoms (computed as the ratio of the probability of exhibiting substantial improvement after swimming with dolphins to the probability of exhibiting substantial improvement after swimming without dolphins) is larger than 1.

To apply the 3S strategy, we use the observed relative risk as the statistic and the same method of simulation.

Statistic: The observed relative risk is 0.667/0.200 = 3.33.

Simulate: We use the same simulation strategy described earlier, except that now we compute the relative risk with every shuffle. Figure 5.8 shows the results of 1,000 shuffles using the relative risk as the statistic. Notice that the null distribution is no longer symmetric but is now right skewed. However, the median of this distribution will be approximately equal to 1: half the time Group 1 has a larger proportion and half the time Group 2 has a larger proportion (with a mean larger than 1 due to the skewness to the right).

Strength of evidence: To evaluate the strength of evidence, determine how many times the observed statistic (3.33) or larger (in the direction of our alternative hypothesis) occurred in the simulations. In this case, it happened 13 out of 1,000 times, yielding a p-value of 0.013. Notice that the p-value for this test using the relative risk is the same as the one we got when using the difference in proportions. That is no accident! In fact, it will always happen. See FAQ 5.2.1 for more details.

FAQ 5.2.1   www.wiley.com/college/tintle

- -

Which statistic?

- -

We can also calculate a confidence interval for the population relative risk, but this is a bit more complicated, largely because the null distribution does not have a symmetric, bell-shaped distribution.

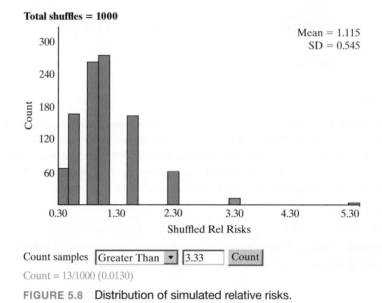

FIGURE 5.8   Distribution of simulated relative risks.

EXPLORATION 5.2 | Is Yawning Contagious?

STEP 1: Ask a research question.   Is yawning contagious? Conventional wisdom says yes: When we see someone else yawn, we're prone to let out a yawn ourselves. Has this happened to you or have you noticed it in others? Will data support this claim if we put it to a scientific test?

STEP 2: Design a study and collect data.   The folks at *MythBusters*, a popular television program on the Discovery Channel, investigated this issue by using a hidden camera. Fifty people attending a local flea market were recruited to participate. Subjects were ushered, one at a time, into one of three rooms by co-host Kari. She yawned (planting a yawn "seed") as she ushered subjects into two of the rooms, and for the other room she did not yawn. The researchers decided in advance, with a random mechanism, which subjects went to which room. As time passed, the researchers watched to see which subjects yawned.

1. Think about why the researchers made the decisions they did.
    a. Why did the researchers include a group that didn't see the yawn seed in this study? In other words, why didn't they just see how many yawned when presented with a yawn seed?
    b. Why did the researchers use random assignment to determine which subjects went to the "yawn seed" group and which to the control group?
    c. Is this an observational study or a randomized experiment? Explain how you are deciding.

d. The researchers clearly used random assignment to put subjects into groups. Do you suspect that they also use random sampling to select subjects in the first place? What would random sampling entail if the population was all flea market patrons?

2. Identify the explanatory and response variables in this study. Also classify them as categorical or quantitative.

Explanatory:	Type:
Response:	Type:

3. The two competing hypotheses to be tested are stated below. Identify which is the null hypothesis and which is the alternative hypothesis remembering that the null hypothesis is typically a statement of no effect.

Yawning is not contagious.	Yawning is contagious.

4. If yawning is not contagious, what does this say about whether or not there is an association between the explanatory and response variables?

5. If yawning is contagious, what does this say about whether or not there is an association between the explanatory and response variables?

6. State the null and alternative hypotheses in terms of association between the explanatory and response variables in this study.

An equivalent option to stating the null and alternative hypotheses for this study in terms of association is to talk about long-run probabilities.

7. There are two long-run probabilities (parameters) in this study. What are they?

8. Write the null and alternative hypotheses in terms of the two long-run probabilities in words and using appropriate symbols.

The researchers found that 11 of 34 subjects who had been given a yawn seed actually yawned themselves, compared with 3 of 16 subjects who had not been given a yawn seed.

9. Organize this information into the following 2 × 2 table:

	Yawn seed planted	Yawn seed not planted	Total
Subject yawned			
Subject did not yawn			
Total			

STEP 3: Explore the data.

10. Calculate the conditional proportion of subjects who yawned in the "yawn seed" group, and then do the same for the control group. Then calculate the *difference* between these proportions, subtracting in the direction indicated below.

Proportion who yawned in "yawn seed" group:

Proportion who yawned in control group:

Difference in conditional proportions ("yawn seed" − control):

Notice that the difference in conditional proportions is the statistic of interest now that we are comparing two groups.

11. Produce a segmented bar graph to compare the distributions of whether or not the subject yawned between the treatment (yawn seed) and control group.

12. Comment on what the graph and calculations reveal about the research question.

a. Did a larger proportion of subjects yawn who were exposed to the yawn seed, as compared to the control group?

b. Based on your analysis thus far, do you think these data provide much evidence that yawning is contagious? Explain.

STEP 4: Draw inferences beyond the data. We see that the proportion of subjects in the "yawn seed" group who yawned was greater than the proportion who yawned in the control group. But does this provide convincing evidence of a genuine difference in the long-run probabilities? To determine whether the *MythBusters* results provide convincing evidence that yawning is contagious, we will apply the same logic that we have used previously: We will use a simulation analysis to determine whether their results are typical or surprising for what we would find if yawning is not contagious.

13. As with earlier studies, there are two possible explanations for the *MythBusters* results. What are they? (*Hint:* These correspond to the null and alternative hypotheses stated earlier.)

The key to our simulation analysis is to assume that if yawning is not contagious (null hypothesis), then *the 14 yawners would have yawned regardless of whether or not they had seen the yawn seed*. Similarly, we'll assume that the 36 nonyawners would not have yawned, no matter which group they had been assigned. In other words, our simulation assumes the null hypothesis is true—that there is no association, no connection, between the yawn seed and actual yawning.

> **KEY IDEA**
>
> To evaluate the statistical significance of the observed difference in our groups, we will investigate how large the difference in conditional proportions tends to be just from the random assignment of response outcomes to the explanatory variable groups.

We cannot use coins to conduct this simulation analysis, because we have two variables to consider: whether or not the yawn seed was planted and whether or not the subject yawned. Instead of coins, we will use index cards. Here's our strategy:

- Take a set of 50 cards, with 14 blue cards (to represent the yawners) and 36 green cards (to represent those who did not yawn).
- Shuffle the cards well and randomly deal out 34 to be the yawn seed group (the rest go to the control group).
- Count how many yawners (blue cards) you have in each group and how many nonyawners (green cards) you have in each group.
- Construct the two-way table to show the number of yawners and nonyawners in each group. (Clearly nothing different happened to those in Group A and those in Group B—any differences between the two groups that arise are due purely to the random assignment process.)

14. Do this shuffling and dealing once.
    a. Report the (simulated) 2 × 2 table that your shuffling and dealing produces:

	Yawn seed planted	Yawn seed not planted	Total
Subject yawned			14
Subject did not yawn			36
Total	34	16	50

b. Calculate the conditional proportions who yawned for your simulated data and the difference in those proportions:

(Simulated) Proportion who yawned in treatment group:

(Simulated) Proportion who yawned in control group:

(Simulated) Difference in conditional proportions (treatment − control):

c. Is your simulated statistic (difference in conditional proportions) at least as large as the observed value of the statistic from the *MythBusters* study?

We need to perform a large number of repetitions (say, 1,000 or more) in order to assess whether the *MythBusters* result is typical or surprising when yawning is not contagious. To do this we will use an applet specifically designed for this purpose: the **Two Proportions** applet.

15. Open this applet and verify the two-way table, segmented bar graph, and observed difference in simulated proportions you found above.

   a. Check the **Show Shuffle Options** box. Notice how the cards have been set up: 14 blue cards, with 11 in the yawners group. Press **Shuffle** to shuffle the cards and redistribute them to the two groups. How many yawners ended up in the seeded group? What is the corresponding difference in the conditional proportions for the shuffled data?

   b. Press the **Shuffle** button four more times. Record the difference in proportions each time. Was it always the same number?

Notice that each of these values has been added to the dotplot on the right.
   (*Technical detail:* In this case, it's equivalent to looking at the *number of blue cards in the yawn group* or the *difference in conditional proportions* as the statistic of interest.)

16. Use this applet to conduct 1,000 repetitions of this simulation: Change the **Number of Shuffles** from 1 to 995 (for a total of 1,000) and press **Shuffle**. The applet produces a dotplot showing the null distribution for the difference in proportions of yawners between the two groups.

   Map this simulation to the research study:

Null hypothesis	=	
One repetition	=	
Statistic	=	

17. Look more closely at the simulated null distribution for the difference in proportions of yawners between the two groups.

   a. Is this null distribution centered around 0? Explain why this makes sense. (*Hint:* Think about the choice of statistic and about the null hypothesis, which was the basis of the simulation analysis.)

   b. Is the observed value of the statistic from the *MythBusters* study (0.136) out in the tail of this null distribution or not so much? In other words, does the observed result appear to be typical or surprising when the null hypothesis (that yawning is not contagious) is true?

   c. As you know, you can assess the strength of evidence against the null hypothesis by calculating a p-value. To calculate a p-value from this null distribution, you will count the number of repetitions that produced a simulated difference in proportions equal to _____ or _____ (choose more or less).

18. Enter the observed difference in the sample proportions in the **Count Samples** box and choose the direction from the pull-down menu and press **Count**. Check whether the shaded region of the dotplot corresponds with your answer to #17c. Then report this approximate p-value.

19. *Interpret* this p-value by filling in the following blanks:

   Under the assumption that _____, if we repeated _____ many, many times, the probability we would obtain a difference in conditional proportions as or more extreme than _____ is about _____.

20. *Evaluate* this p-value: Using guidelines for assessing the strength of evidence from p-values, would you conclude that the *MythBusters* result provides much evidence that yawning is contagious?

We have a small confession to make. We fudged the data from this study a bit. The actual data showed that 10 of the 34 subjects in the yawn seed group yawned themselves, and 4 of the 16 in the control group yawned.

21. Recalculate the conditional proportions who yawned for these data:

    Proportion who yawned in the "yawn seed" group =

    Proportion who yawned in the control group =

    Difference in conditional proportions ("yawn seed" − control) =

22. How has your observed statistic changed from the originally presented data?

Smaller	Same	Larger

23. Before you carry out the inference using this postconfession observed statistic, let's make some predictions: How do you expect the p-value and strength of evidence to change from your earlier analysis? Circle your choices below and then explain why you circled what you did.

    p-value:

Smaller	Same	Larger

    Strength of evidence:

Weaker	Same	Stronger

    Explanation:

24. Conduct a simulation analysis to check your answer predictions from the previous question. To do this, enter the new values into the four boxes of the table and press **Use Table**. Then ask for 1,000 repetitions in your simulation analysis. Enter the new observed value of the statistic and then press the **Count** button. Report the approximate p-value and summarize your conclusion in terms of strength of evidence that yawning is contagious.

Estimation

Because the *MythBusters* data did not reveal a significant difference between the groups, it's less important than usual to estimate the parameter value. But we can still use the simulation results to estimate a 95% confidence interval for the relevant parameter. Keep in mind that the relevant parameter is now the difference in the long-run probabilities between the yawn seed treatment and the no-yawn seed treatment.

25. The parameter of interest in this yawning study can be expressed in symbols as $\pi_{\text{yawn seed}} - \pi_{\text{control}}$.

    a. Describe what this parameter means in words.

    b. Report (again) the observed value of the statistic from the *MythBusters* actual data. (*Hint*: Recall that the statistic is the difference in conditional proportions between the two groups.)

    The observed value of this statistic is your best estimate of the unknown parameter value. But we should produce an interval estimate centered on this observed value. To do that we again need to consider the *chance variability* in the statistic.

    c. From the simulation analysis that you just conducted on the postconfession *Mythbusters* data, what was the standard deviation of the null distribution?

    d. Determine endpoints of a 95% 2SD confidence interval for the difference by taking the observed value of the statistic ± 2 standard deviations.

    e. Does this confidence interval include only positive values, only negative values, or zero as well as positive and negative values?

    f. Explain the importance of your answer to part (e) in terms of whether the data provide evidence that subjects who experience a yawn seed are more likely to yawn than those who do not experience a yawn seed?

STEP 5: Formulate conclusions.

26. The *MythBusters* hosts concluded from their study that there is "little doubt, yawning seems to be contagious." Based on your simulation analysis of their data, considering the issue of statistical significance, do you agree with this conclusion? Explain your answer, as if to the hosts, without using statistical jargon. Be sure to include in your answer an explanation for why you conducted the simulation analysis and what the analysis revealed about the research question.

27. If you had decided that the two groups differed significantly, would you have been justified in drawing a cause-and-effect conclusion between the yawn seed and an increased probability of yawning? Explain, based on how the study was conducted.

28. Based on how the sample was selected, to what larger population would you feel comfortable generalizing the results of this study? Justify your answer.

29. Think about the difference between these two possible conclusions:
   i. The data strongly suggest that yawning is not contagious.
   ii. The data do not provide convincing evidence to suggest that yawning is contagious.

   Explain why these conclusions are not the same. Also indicate which one is the more appropriate conclusion from your analysis and explain why.

30. As we discussed in Chapter 2, in every statistical analysis it is possible to make a Type I or a Type II error. Identify which error you might be making here, describe it in context, and briefly identify the consequences.

STEP 6: Look back and ahead.

31. Critique the design and conclusion of this study. Were there any limitations, such as how the subjects were selected or how the measurements were recorded? Was the sample size large enough? Did you observe a result of practical value? Discuss how you might address a few of these limitations. Suggest how you might design a follow-up study to investigate whether yawning is contagious. Address details such as how to ensure that the yawn seed is noticed, how long to wait for the subject's yawn to be connected to the seed, and how to select/recruit subjects.

Effect of sample size

Now let's suppose that this yawning study had involved 500 people, 10 times as many as the actual study. Let's also suppose that the conditional proportions who yawned in each group were identical to the actual study. The 2×2 table would therefore be:

	Yawn seed planted	Yawn seed not planted	Total
Subject yawned	100	40	140
Subject did not yawn	240	120	360
Total	340	160	500

32. Before you conduct a simulation analysis, indicate how you expect the following to change:
   a. Difference in conditional proportions

Smaller	Same	Larger

   b. p-value

Smaller	Same	Larger

c. Strength of evidence that yawning is contagious

Weaker	Same	Stronger

d. Test decision at the 0.05 significance level

Reject null (unlike before)	Fail to reject null (as before)

33. Use the **Two Proportions** applet, again entering the appropriate table of data first, to conduct a simulation analysis. Report the approximate p-value and summarize your conclusion in terms of strength of evidence that yawning is contagious. Also indicate whether you would find strong evidence against the null hypothesis at the 0.05 significance level.

34. Summarize how the 10-fold increase in the sample size has changed your conclusions. Do you have stronger evidence that yawning is contagious? Is the evidence now very strong that yawning is contagious?

Relative risk

In Section 5.1 we introduced you to the relative risk as an alternative statistic to summarize the relationship between two binary variables.

35. What value of the relative risk indicates no association between the two variables in this study?

36. State the null and alternative hypotheses for the yawning study in terms of the relative risk.

We will now apply the 3S strategy using the relative risk. Use the sample size of 500 people you used in #32 through #34 for the following questions.

37. **Statistic.** Calculate, and then interpret, the observed value of the relative risk by dividing the conditional proportion of yawners in the yawn seed group compared to the conditional proportion of yawners in the no-yawn seed group.

In the **Two Proportions** applet, change the statistic to "Relative risk" in the Statistic pull-down menu. Confirm that the statistic matches your answer to #37.

38. **Simulate.** If you still have your shuffles from #33 use them; otherwise generate 1,000 new shuffles. Find the p-value using the relative risk. Compare this p-value to the p-value you obtained in #33.

If you used the same simulated tables, you should have found that the p-value for the relative risk is exactly the same as for the difference in proportions! This is because there is a "one-to-one" correspondence between these statistics. See FAQ 5.2.1 for more details.

FAQ 5.2.1   www.wiley.com/college/tintle
- -
Which statistic?
- -

- -

SECTION 5.2 Summary

The 3S strategy can be used to assess whether two sample proportions differ enough to conclude that there is a genuine difference in the population proportions/process probabilities. The reasoning process of **statistical significance** is the same as with inference for a single proportion.

- The null hypothesis can be expressed as **no association** between the two variables.
  - Equivalently, the null hypothesis asserts that the population proportions (or process probabilities) are the same in the two conditions.

- The alternative hypothesis says that there is an association between the two variables.
  - The alternative hypothesis can be one-sided or two-sided, depending on whether the researchers have a particular direction in mind prior to collecting data.
- The difference in conditional proportions between the two groups is the statistic of interest.
- The key idea in simulating the null distribution of the difference in sample proportions is to shuffle the values of the response variable and reassign them to the explanatory variable groups.
  - This shuffling simulates values of the statistic under the assumption of no association.
  - With a randomized experiment, this shuffling is equivalent to re-randomizing the subjects into the two groups, assuming that the subjects' responses would have been the same regardless of which group they were assigned to.
- As always, the p-value is calculated as the proportion of repetitions in which the simulated value of the statistic is at least as extreme as the observed value of the statistic.
  - Also as always, a small p-value provides evidence against the null hypothesis.

The 2SD method can be used to produce a confidence interval for estimating the size of the difference between the two success probabilities (or population proportions).

- The most important question is whether the interval is entirely negative, is entirely positive, or includes zero.
  - If the interval does not include zero, that provides evidence that the two population proportions/process probabilities are not the same.
  - Whether the interval contains positive or negative values indicates which group has the larger population proportion and by how much.
  - If the interval contains zero, there is not convincing evidence against the null hypothesis that the two population proportions/process probabilities are equal.

Some factors that affect p-values and confidence intervals are similar to before:

- The larger the difference between the sample proportions, the stronger the evidence that the population proportions differ.
- Larger sample sizes produce stronger evidence that the population proportions differ.
- The difference in sample proportions is the midpoint of the confidence interval.
- Larger sample sizes produce narrower confidence intervals.

COMPARING TWO PROPORTIONS: THEORY-BASED APPROACH

SECTION 5.3

INTRODUCTION

In Chapter 1 we saw that we could often predict the results obtained via simulation using a theory-based approach that uses normal distributions. We could do this because, in many situations, the null distribution followed a very predictable pattern: an approximately normal distribution with a (mathematically) known average and standard deviation. Furthermore, we saw how theory-based approaches also gave us much simpler ways to generate a confidence interval for the parameter of interest. In this chapter, you may have noticed that your simulated distributions were often symmetric, bell-shaped distributions—again, it's no coincidence. In this section we will, once again, see how we can use theory-based approaches, instead of simulation, to predict the outcome of tests comparing two group proportions and to generate related confidence intervals.

5.3 — Parents' Smoking Status and their Babies' Sex

EXAMPLE

Example 5.3

An area of research that generates a lot of media coverage is examining how parents' behavior may be associated with the sex of their children. One such study (Fukuda et al., 2002) found the following:

- Of 565 births where both parents smoked more than a pack of cigarettes a day, 255 (45.1%) were boys.

- Of 3,602 births where both parents did not smoke, 1,975 (54.8%) were boys. (See Figure 5.9.)

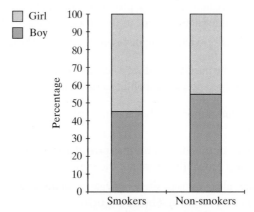

FIGURE 5.9 A segmented bar graph comparing the proportions of boys and girls born to parents that smoked with parents that didn't smoke.

The proportions of boys born to parents who smoke (0.451) and to parents who don't smoke (0.548) seem like they are considerably different. Let's compare these two proportions to see whether the difference is statistically significant. We start by stating the hypotheses.

Null hypothesis: The population proportion of boys born to smoking parents is the same as the population proportion of boys born to nonsmoking parents. There is no association between smoking status of parents and sex of child.

Alternative hypothesis: The population proportion of boys born to smoking parents is different from the population proportion of boys born to nonsmoking parents. There is an association between smoking status of parents and sex of child.

THINK ABOUT IT

Identify the two variables in this study. Would you consider one the explanatory variable and the other the response variable? What is different about how this study was conducted compared to those in Section 5.2?

The researchers are interested in whether the smoking habits of the parents might help explain the sex of the newborn. It is natural to think of smoking habit as the explanatory variable and sex as the response variable. This study was an observational study and not a randomized experiment, because the researchers did not randomly determine which parents would smoke and which would not. Therefore, even if we find the difference in these conditional proportions to be statistically significant, we will not draw any cause-and-effect conclusions from the association. Instead, we are more interested in what these sample data can tell us about the populations of smoking and nonsmoking parents. So we can state these hypotheses in terms of population parameters. Let's define $\pi_{smoking}$ as the proportion of parents where both smoke in the population who have boys and $\pi_{nonsmoking}$ as the proportion of all nonsmoking parents in the population who have boys. The null states $\pi_{smoking} = \pi_{nonsmoking}$. That is, $H_0: \pi_{smoking} - \pi_{nonsmoking} = 0$, versus $H_a: \pi_{smoking} - \pi_{nonsmoking} \neq 0$. Because these populations are quite large, applying what you learned in Chapter 2, we will consider these population proportions to be equal to the probability that a randomly selected set of parents has a boy from each population. But does this change how we assess the statistical significance of the difference in sample proportions?

SHUFFLING WITHOUT RANDOM ASSIGNMENT

In Section 5.2 we "re-randomized" the subjects to the treatment groups, shuffling the response variable outcomes to the two groups mimicking what was done in the research study (assuming those outcomes wouldn't change based on the group assignment). But here the subjects weren't randomly assigned to their explanatory variable groups, because it is an observational study. So, can we use the procedure as in Section 5.2? As it turns out, we can. To see this, note that we stated our null hypothesis as there was "no association" between parents' smoking status and the sex of the child. If we shuffle and deal the cards into two stacks (smoking and nonsmoking) then the color of the card (blue or green = girl or boy) will have no association (relationship) with which stack the card is in. In other words we will have simulated data assuming the null hypothesis is true. Thus, regardless of whether the study design involves random assignment, random sampling, both, or neither, you can simulate data assuming the null hypothesis of no association between explanatory variable and response variable using shuffling (see FAQ 5.3.1 for more details).

FAQ 5.3.1   www.wiley.com/college/tintle
- -

Which way to simulate?

- -

KEY IDEA

> Shuffling is an appropriate way to estimate a p-value for comparing groups regardless of the study design (observational study or experiment, random assignment or random sampling or neither). Of course, the study design is very important in determining the appropriate scope of conclusions. (Can you generalize to a larger population? Can you infer a cause-and-effect conclusion?)

Now let's apply the 3S strategy to these data.

1. **Statistic:** The observed difference in conditional proportions of boys born to nonsmokers and boys born to smokers is $0.548 - 0.451 = 0.097$.

2. **Simulate:** We used the **Two Proportions** applet to do our simulation. First we can type in the two-way table and press **Use Table**. Then we select the **Show Shuffle Options** box. We conducted 5,000 repetitions of randomly shuffling the 2,230 boys and 1,937 girls and "dealing them" randomly to the 565 smoking parents and 3,602 nonsmoking parents, modeling the null hypothesis to be true, and calculating the difference in proportions of boys between the two groups for all 5,000 repetitions. This random shuffling simulates the null hypothesis of no association, because shuffling and dealing ensure there is no relationship between smoking status (the pile the card is dealt to) and sex of child (the color of the card). The results are shown in Figure 5.10.

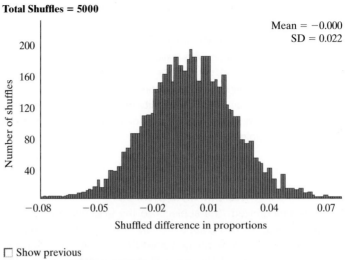

Total Shuffles = 5000

Mean = −0.000
SD = 0.022

☐ Show previous

Count samples | Beyond ▼ | .097 | Count |

Count = 0/5000 (0.0000)

FIGURE 5.10 Simulated results of the difference in proportions of boys.

3. **Strength of evidence:** We see from the graph in Figure 5.10 that nothing as extreme as our observed statistic (larger than 0.097 or smaller than −0.097) ever occurred in these 5,000 repetitions, and thus the estimated two-sided p-value is zero. The sample data provide extremely strong evidence that the population proportion of boys born to smoking parents is different from the population proportion of boys born to nonsmoking parents.

5.3.1

But notice how the null distribution is centered at zero, the value of the population parameter specified by the null hypothesis, and is bell-shaped. The applet shows a checkbox to **Overlay Normal distribution** leading to the picture in Figure 5.11. The close agreement between these two distributions in Figure 5.11 suggests that we could have calculated a p-value using the normal distribution. As we saw in Chapter 1, there are situations where the null distribution can be predicted using theoretical models and we don't have to go to the trouble of shuffling cards (by hand or using technology) to develop our null distribution. The normal distribution also reports the theory-based p-value to be approximately zero.

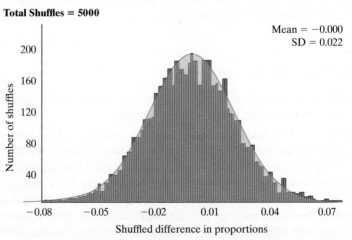

Total Shuffles = 5000

Mean = −0.000
SD = 0.022

FIGURE 5.11 A normal distribution overlaid on the simulated null distribution of differences in sample proportions.

You can also use the **Theory-Based Inference** applet to determine the theory-based p-value as shown in Figure 5.12. We first chose **Two proportions** from the top pull-down menu and then used a two-sided alternative ($\neq$). Notice that the hypotheses use the notation $\pi_1 - \pi_2$ for the difference in the population proportions. Because we input the nonsmoker data for Group 1 and the smoker data for Group 2, we are letting π_1 represent the proportion of babies that are boys in our population of nonsmokers and π_2 represent the proportion of babies that are boys in our population of smokers. We entered the two sample sizes (n) and the number of boys in each sample (count). The applet calculated the conditional proportions, the standardized statistic (z-statistic), and the corresponding (two-sided) p-value. From the standardized statistic of $z = 4.30$, we can see that our observed difference in sample proportions is more than four standard deviations above the hypothesized mean of zero. This is so far out in the tail that we don't see it showing up on the graph and we get a p-value of 0.0000 when it is rounded to four decimal places. So, just like the simulation-based result, we have very strong evidence that the population proportion of boys born to smokers is different than the population proportion of boys born to nonsmokers. *Note:* Formulas for computing z are provided at the end of this section. From our data we can also see that the sample proportion of boys is smaller for smokers.

5.3.2

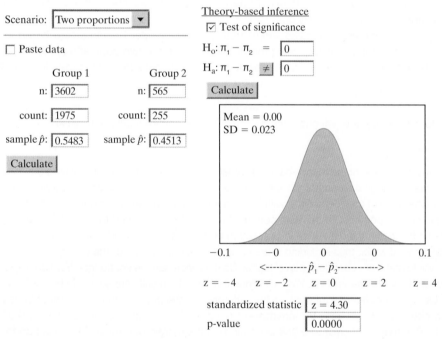

FIGURE 5.12 The results of comparing the sample proportion of boys born to smokers to the sample proportion of boys born to nonsmokers using the **Theory-Based Inference** applet.

ESTIMATION

As we discussed in Section 5.2, a natural follow-up question is "how much smaller is the population proportion of boys born to parents who smoke, compared to that born to parents who do not smoke?" In other words, if the difference in the proportions is not zero, what is it? A confidence interval will help answer this question.

Remember that when we are comparing two proportions, the population parameter we are trying to estimate is the difference in population proportions or process probabilities ($\pi_1 - \pi_2$). Because our sample difference in proportions of boys (subtracting the smoking parents' proportion from the nonsmoking parents' proportion) is 0.097, it makes sense for the interval to be centered on that number. The 2SD method (Section 5.2) tells us that a 95% confidence interval is 0.097 ± 0.044, as the simulated SD for $\hat{p}_1 - \hat{p}_2$ is 0.022 (Figure 5.10).

Of course, a theory-based approach is also available. Figure 5.13 shows the result of using the **Theory-Based Inference** applet to find a 95% confidence interval on the difference in population proportions. *Note:* Formulas for how this theory-based interval is computed are provided at the end of this section.

☑ Confidence interval

confidence level [95] % [Calculate CI]

(0.0529, 0.1411)

FIGURE 5.13 Results from the **Theory-Based Inference** applet showing a confidence interval for the difference in population proportions.

We used the same inputs (Group 1 = nonsmokers) for computing the confidence interval as we did for the test of significance. The only thing we did differently was to check the box to display the confidence interval and press **Calculate CI**. This gives us our interval of (0.053, 0.141), which is essentially the same as we obtained using the 2SD method.

Thus, we are 95% confident that the difference in population proportions ($\pi_{nonmoker} - \pi_{smoker}$) is between 0.053 and 0.141. Stated more clearly, we are 95% confident that the population proportion of males born is 0.053–0.141 higher for families where neither parent smokes as compared to families where both parents smoke. Because zero is not in this interval, zero is not a plausible value for the difference in the two population proportions—a conclusion that is consistent with the result of our significance test above (p-value < 0.001).

> **THINK ABOUT IT**
>
> How would our interval change if we changed the confidence level to 99%?

5.3.3

One advantage of the theory-based approach to finding confidence intervals is that it allows us to easily change the confidence level. We saw in earlier chapters how the level of confidence affects the width of confidence intervals for a single proportion. The same holds true for the difference in two proportions. To be more confident that we have captured the population parameter value (in this case, the difference in population proportions), we would need to make our confidence interval wider, thus including more values that are plausible for the parameter of interest. This would make our confidence level higher. So if we increase the confidence from 95% to 99%, we should see a wider interval. We have done that and the results are shown in Figure 5.14.

Our 99% confidence interval for the difference in the population proportion of boys born to smokers and boys born to nonsmokers is 0.039–0.155. We can rewrite this as 0.097 ± 0.058. This margin of error of 0.058 is larger than the margin of error of 0.044 we had for our 95% confidence interval, and the interval is wider.

confidence level [99] %

(0.0390, 0.1550)

FIGURE 5.14 When we increase the confidence level to 99% we get a wider confidence interval.

> **THINK ABOUT IT**
>
> How would our 95% confidence interval change if we were estimating $\pi_{smoker} - \pi_{nonsmoker}$, instead of $\pi_{nonsmoker} - \pi_{smoker}$?

The 95% confidence interval for $\pi_{smoker} - \pi_{nonsmoker}$, based on these data, would be (−0.141, −0.053). Even though the endpoints of the confidence interval are now flipped around and are both negative, they are giving the exact same information as they did in Figure 5.13. We are still 95% confident that the population proportion of a boys born to parents who both smoke is *lower* than that to parents who do not smoke by somewhere between 0.053 and 0.141.

VALIDITY CONDITIONS FOR THEORY-BASED APPROACH (TWO PROPORTIONS)

Just as we saw in earlier chapters, theory-based approaches that predict the characteristics of the null distribution work well most, but not all, of the time. In Chapter 1 we said that you needed a fairly large sample size in order for the theory-based approaches to work well—a similar fact is true here as well. Conservatively, the theory-based significance test and confidence interval work well if there are at least 10 observations in each of the four cells of the two-way table.

VALIDITY CONDITIONS

The theory-based test and interval for the difference in two proportions (called a *two-sample z-test or interval*) work well when there are at least 10 observations in each of the four cells of the 2 × 2 table.

For example, we have the smoking data summarized in Table 5.4. Notice that all four values in the cells (255, 310, 1,975, and 1,627) are quite a bit larger than 10 (smallest is 255), indicating that the theory-based approaches will generate results very similar to those obtained using simulation and the reported confidence interval should be valid.

TABLE 5.4 A two-way table of the smoking data

	Parents smoked at least a pack a day	Parents both nonsmokers	Total
Male	255	1,975	2,230
Female	310	1,627	1,937
Total	565	3,602	4,167

THINK ABOUT IT

What should you do if you are concerned about the validity of the theory-based approach?

Because the theory-based approach is an approximation (prediction) of what would happen if you simulated, if the validity conditions are not met you should simulate to generate a p-value.

FOLLOW-UP
As mentioned earlier, the strongly significant result in this study yielded quite a bit of press when it came out (as have other studies about variables related to parental behaviors and children's sex, like one on breakfast cereal choice). Shortly thereafter, however, other studies came out (Parazinni et al., 2004; Obel et al., 2003), which found no such relationship between smoking and sex of child. Subsequently James (2004) wrote an article arguing that confounding variables such as social factors, diet, environmental exposure, or stress were the reason why some were seeing an effect and others weren't. This, of course, is possible, because this wasn't a randomized experiment—just an observational study!

FORMULAS
Earlier, we saw that we obtained a value of the standardized statistic of 4.30. But how is this value obtained? As we've seen before the value of the standardized statistic, z, is equal to the number of standard deviations the observed statistic is away from the mean (in this case zero). However, in this case, unlike Chapters 1 and 2, the observed statistic is a difference in two proportions, instead of a single proportion, and so the resulting standardized statistic has the form

$$z = \frac{\text{observed statistic} - \text{hypothesized value}}{\text{standard error of statistic}} = \frac{\hat{p}_1 - \hat{p}_2 - 0}{\sqrt{\hat{p}(1 - \hat{p})\left(\frac{1}{n_1} + \frac{1}{n_2}\right)}}$$

where $\hat{p}$ is the overall proportion of successes for the two groups combined (total number of successes divided by the total sample size). We use this overall proportion of success because tests of significance are carried out under the assumption that the null hypothesis (that the two population proportions are the same) is true, so we combine the two groups in order to estimate the (common) population proportion of success. Sometimes you will see this overall proportion of success called a *pooled* proportion of success.

In the example shown earlier, the combined proportion of success is

$$\hat{p} = (255 + 1{,}975)/(3{,}602 + 565) = 2{,}230/4{,}167 = 0.535,$$

and so the standardized statistic is

$$z = \frac{\hat{p}_1 - \hat{p}_2}{\sqrt{\hat{p}(1 - \hat{p})\left(\frac{1}{n_1} + \frac{1}{n_2}\right)}} = \frac{0.548 - 0.451}{\sqrt{0.535(1 - 0.535)\left(\frac{1}{565} + \frac{1}{3{,}602}\right)}} = 4.30.$$

This says that the two sample proportions are more than 4 standard errors apart, which is a very large difference, producing a p-value of approximately zero.

Notice that the value for z changes as we would it expect it to. Namely, as the value of the difference between $\hat{p}_1$ and $\hat{p}_2$ increases, z gets farther from zero. Similarly, as the sample size in either (or both) groups increases, the denominator gets smaller and so the value of z gets farther from zero. This means that the strength of evidence for the alternative hypothesis increases as the difference in the conditional proportions increases and as the sample size increases.

Also, we saw that a 95% confidence interval for the difference in proportions is 0.097 $\pm$ 0.044, where 0.097 is the difference in the proportion of successes between the two groups and 0.044 is the margin of error. The formula for the margin of error is shown below:

$$\text{Margin of error} = \text{multiplier} \times \sqrt{\left(\frac{\hat{p}_1(1 - \hat{p}_1)}{n_1} + \frac{\hat{p}_2(1 - \hat{p}_2)}{n_2}\right)}$$

where the value of the multiplier is dependent upon the confidence level. For 95% confidence intervals we typically use 2 (though 1.96 would be a bit more precise), whereas for 99% confidence intervals the multiplier is 2.576, and for 90% confidence intervals it is 1.645. Notice that as the confidence level increases the value of the multiplier also increases, making the width of the confidence interval increase.

Note that, in general, the equation for margin of error for most statistical situations is defined as the multiplier $\times$ SE, where SE denotes the **standard error** of the statistic (the estimated standard deviation of the statistic). This is slightly different than the denominator of the standardized z-statistic because we are estimating the size of the difference between the population proportions under the assumption that there is a difference (rather than pooling them together as we did when we assumed the null hypothesis to be true). Thus, when finding a confidence interval for a difference in population proportions,

$$SE = \sqrt{\left(\frac{\hat{p}_1(1 - \hat{p}_1)}{n_1} + \frac{\hat{p}_2(1 - \hat{p}_2)}{n_2}\right)}.$$

EXPLORATION | Donating Blood
5.3

Blood donations from volunteers serve a crucial role in the nation's health care system. Are Americans any more or less generous about donating blood in some years than others? Are women any more or less willing to give blood than men? To investigate these questions we can analyze data from the General Social Survey, which is a national survey conducted every two years on a nationwide random sample of adult Americans.

1. Did this study make use of random sampling, random assignment, both, or neither? Also explain what your answer means in terms of the scope of conclusions that can be drawn from these data.

Let's start by comparing the years 2002 and 2004.

2. State the appropriate null and alternative hypotheses, in words and in symbols, to address the research question of whether Americans were more generous with blood donations in

one of these years than the other. (*Hint:* Remember that hypotheses are always about population parameters, and think about whether the alternative should be one- or two-sided before you see the data.)

Data from the 2002 and 2004 surveys are summarized in the following table:

	2002	2004
Donated blood in previous 12 months	210	230
Did not donate blood in previous 12 months	1,152	1,106
Total	1,362	1,336

3. For each year, calculate the (conditional) proportion of adult Americans sampled who donated blood in the previous 12 months. Use appropriate symbols to represent them. Also calculate the difference between these sample proportions (taking the 2002 proportion minus the 2004 proportion).

2002 proportion ($\hat{p}_{2002}$):

2004 proportion ($\hat{p}_{2004}$):

Difference in proportions ($\hat{p}_{2002} - \hat{p}_{2004}$):

4. Produce a segmented bar graph to display the conditional proportions who gave blood in these two years. Comment on what the graph and your calculations from #3 reveal about these two samples.

5. Use the **Two Proportions** applet to conduct a simulation analysis to approximate a p-value for testing the hypotheses that you stated in #2. You can enter the table of counts in the 2 × 2 table or type in the table in the **Sample data** box and press **Use Table**. Or you can copy the data from the text webpage and paste into the **Sample data** box and press **Use Data**. Verify the segmented bar graph that you created.

Sample data:(2×2: ☑)

	Group A	Group B	Totals
Success	210	230	440
Failure	1152	1106	2258

Sample data:(2×2: ☑)

(explanatory, response)

	2002	2004
donated	210	230
didn't	1152	1106

KEY IDEA

Shuffling is an appropriate way to estimate a p-value for comparing groups regardless of the study design (observational study or experiment, random assignment or random sampling or neither). Of course, the study design is very important in determining the appropriate scope of conclusions. (Can you generalize to a larger population? Can you infer a cause-and-effect conclusion?)

6. Check the **Show Shuffle Options** box, ask for 1000 repetitions, and press **Shuffle**.
   a. Indicate how to find the p-value from the null distribution. (*Hint:* Remember whether the alternative hypothesis is one-sided or two-sided.)
   b. Report the approximate p-value.
   c. Based on this p-value, do the sample data provide much evidence that the population proportion who gave blood in 2002 differs from the population proportion who gave blood in 2004?

7. Does the null distribution of the simulated $\hat{p}_{2002} - \hat{p}_{2004}$ values appear to follow an approximately normal distribution? Centered around what value? Also report the standard deviation of these values.

Approximately normal?	Mean:	SD:

8. Let's see what the standardized statistic tells us.
   a. Report the observed value in the sample for the statistic $\hat{p}_{2002} - \hat{p}_{2004}$.

b. How many standard deviations (based on your answer to #7) above or below zero (the hypothesized value) is the observed value of the statistic?

c. Is the strength of evidence against the null hypothesis based on this standardized statistic consistent with what the p-value revealed in #6? Explain.

Just as you learned a theory-based approach for making inferences about a single proportion in Chapter 1, so too will you now learn a theory-based approach for making inferences about comparing proportions between two groups. This theory-based approach is again based on an approximation from a normal distribution. *Note:* Formulas for these methods are given at the end of Example 5.3.

9. Check the **Overlay Normal distribution** box. Is the behavior of the two distributions similar? How do the p-values compare?

10. Check the box to compute **95% CI(s) for difference in proportions**. (This box appears if the left-hand panel when the difference is selected as the statistic.)

a. Report the endpoints of this interval.

b. Interpret this interval. Be sure to mention clearly what parameter is being estimated by this interval. (*Hint:* In other words, you are 95% confident that this interval contains what?)

c. Does this interval contain only negative values, only positive values, or does the interval include the value zero as well as both positive and negative values? Comment on the importance of what this means.

11. Another applet that can compute p-values and confidence intervals for tests of two proportions is the **Theory-Based Inference** applet. Use the pull-down menu to select **Two proportions** and enter the relevant summary information, using the 2002 sample as Group 1. Check the **Test of Significance** box and press on the **inequality** sign button until the alternative hypothesis becomes two-sided. Press **Calculate**. Verify the p-value you obtained earlier (#9) as well as the confidence interval (#10).

Validity conditions for theory-based approach (two proportions)

As with a single proportion, the theory-based inference approach for comparing two proportions is only valid when a normal distribution provides a good approximation to the distribution of the statistic $\hat{p}_1 - \hat{p}_2$. Conservatively, the theory-based significance test and confidence interval work well when there are at least 10 observations in each of the four cells of the two-way table. In other words, we require at least 10 "successes" and at least 10 "failures" in each sample in order to use this theory-based approach.

> **VALIDITY CONDITION**
>
> The theory-based test and interval for the difference in two proportions (called a *two-sample z-test or interval*) work well when there are at least 10 observations in each of the four cells of the 2 × 2 table.

12. Is it valid to use the theory-based approach for two proportions in this study? Justify your answer.

13. Is it reasonable to generalize your conclusions from this analysis to the population of all adult Americans? Explain why or why not.

14. Let's see what will happen if we switch which is Group 1 and which is Group 2.

a. Before doing any calculations, what do you think would happen to the standardized statistic, p-value, and confidence interval if you entered the 2004 sample as Group 1 and the 2002 sample as Group 2?

Standardized statistic:	p-value:
Confidence interval:	

b. Make this change in the **Theory-Based Inference** applet (i.e., switch the roles of Groups 1 and 2), and then press **Calculate**. Report the new values of the standardized statistic, p-value, and confidence interval.

Standardized statistic:	p-value:
Confidence interval:	

c. Did these change as you predicted in part (a)?

Using the General Social Survey data to classify respondents by sex and combining the years 2002 and 2004 we can construct the following table:

	Male	Female
Donated blood in previous 12 months	239	201
Did not donate blood in previous 12 months	1,032	1,226
Total	1,271	1,427

15. Analyze these data to address the question of whether American men and women differ with regard to donating blood. Include a descriptive analysis (graphs and numbers) as well as an inferential analysis (p-value and confidence interval). Use theory-based approaches, if you decide that the validity conditions are satisfied, for the inferential analysis. If you decide that men and women differ significantly, be sure to estimate by how much they differ. Write a paragraph or two summarizing your analysis and conclusions.

SECTION 5.3 Summary

Under certain circumstances, essentially when sample sizes are large enough, a theory-based approach can be used to approximate p-values and confidence intervals for the difference between two proportions.

- The standardized statistic again subtracts the hypothesized value from the observed statistic and then divides by the standard deviation (or standard error) of the statistic.
  - The statistic in this case is the difference in sample proportions, that is, $\hat{p}_1 - \hat{p}_2$.
  - $z = \dfrac{\hat{p}_1 - \hat{p}_2}{\sqrt{\hat{p}(1 - \hat{p})\left(\dfrac{1}{n_1} + \dfrac{1}{n_2}\right)}}$ where $\hat{p}$ is the overall observed proportion of successes, combining both samples.
- The confidence interval again takes the form statistic $\pm$ margin of error.
  - Statistic $= \hat{p}_1 - \hat{p}_2$
  - Margin of error $=$ multiplier $\times$ standard error of statistic
  - Standard error SE $= \sqrt{\left(\dfrac{\hat{p}_1(1 - \hat{p}_1)}{n_1} + \dfrac{\hat{p}_2(1 - \hat{p}_2)}{n_2}\right)}$
- Validity conditions: For the theory-based approach to be valid, each explanatory variable group should have at least 10 observations in each category of the response variable.
- It does not matter which group is labeled as Group 1 and which as Group 2, provided that the labeling is consistent throughout the analysis, including interpretations and conclusions.

Type of data	Name of test	Applet	Validity conditions
Two binary variables	Simulation test or interval for two proportions	Two proportions	—
	Theory-based test or interval for two proportions (two-sample z-test; interval)	Two proportions; Theory-based inference	At least 10 observations in each of the four cells of the two-way table

SECTION 5.4

CONFIDENCE INTERVAL AND SIGNIFICANCE TEST FOR A DIFFERENCE BETWEEN TWO PROPORTIONS

INTRODUCTION

In Section 1.7 you learned that when our variable of interest is a single binary variable (e.g., whether or not Buzz pushes the correct button), then, if a normal distribution is a good approximation for the distribution of the sample proportion of successes (e.g., proportion of times Buzz pushed the correct button in the study: $\hat{p}$), the appropriate theory-based approach to test hypotheses about the population proportion or long-run process proportion is called a one-proportion z-test. In Section 3.2 you saw that you can use a theory-based approach to construct an interval of plausible values for the population proportion or long-run process proportion, referred to as a one-proportion z-interval.

In the previous section, you learned about a theory-based method for comparing two groups on a binary response. As you saw with a single proportion, a normal distribution provides a good approximation for the distribution of the difference in the sample proportions $(\hat{p}_1 - \hat{p}_2)$ if you have at least 10 responses of each kind (10 successes and 10 failures) in each group. The ***theory-based test of significance*** and ***confidence interval*** for the difference in two proportions are referred to as a ***two-sample z-test*** and a ***two-sample z-interval***.

> ### KEY IDEA
>
> When the null hypothesis is of the form $H_0: \pi_1 - \pi_2 = 0$, the test statistic or ***standardized statistic for a two sample z-test*** is as follows:
>
> $$z = \frac{\text{observed statistic} - \text{hypothesized value}}{\text{standard error of statistic}} = \frac{\hat{p}_1 - \hat{p}_2 - 0}{\sqrt{\hat{p}(1-\hat{p})\left(\frac{1}{n_1} + \frac{1}{n_2}\right)}}$$
>
> where $\hat{p}_1 - \hat{p}_2$ is the difference in the sample proportions, n_1 and n_2 are the respective sample sizes, and $\hat{p}$ is the overall proportion of success for the two groups combined (total number of successes divided by the total sample size).

> ### THINK ABOUT IT
>
> Where does the overall proportion of success ($\hat{p}$) in the formula of the standardized statistic come from?

As you may remember from the previous section, the denominator of the standardized statistic represents the sampling variability in the statistic $\hat{p}_1 - \hat{p}_2$ and is called the standard error of the statistic. As noted in the previous section, we use the overall proportion of success $\hat{p}$ in the standard error calculation because tests of significance are carried out under the assumption that the null hypothesis (the two population proportions are the same) is true. If the proportions are actually the same, then combining the results from the two groups makes sense as a way to estimate the (common) population proportion of success. Sometimes you will see this overall proportion of success called a *pooled* proportion of success.

You saw in Section 3.2 that a general method, valid for any confidence level, is to estimate the parameter with

$$\text{statistic} \pm \text{multiplier} \times (\text{SE of statistic})$$

> ## KEY IDEA
>
> **Two sample z-interval for a difference in population proportions, $\pi_1 - \pi_2$:**
>
> $$\hat{p}_1 - \hat{p}_2 \pm z^* \times \sqrt{\frac{\hat{p}_1(1 - \hat{p}_1)}{n_1} + \frac{\hat{p}_2(1 - \hat{p}_2)}{n_2}}$$
>
> where $\hat{p}_1 - \hat{p}_2$ denotes the difference in the sample proportions, n_1 and n_2 are the respective sample sizes, and z^* represents the critical value from the standard normal distribution for the desired level of confidence.

Note: As we first pointed out in the previous section, the formula for the standard error of the statistic (the estimated standard deviation of the statistic) is slightly different for a confidence interval than the standard error formula in the standardized z-statistic. This is because when we are estimating the size of the difference between the population proportions, we are not making an assumption that there is no difference in the population proportions (thus we are not pooling the results from the two groups together as we did when we assumed the null hypothesis to be true).

In Section 1.7 you learned the work you must show on the AP Statistics exam for a hypothesis test. The format you learned is the same for all hypothesis tests.

1. State the hypotheses either in words or using appropriate symbols.
2. Name the test that will be used and state and verify the validity conditions for the test chosen.
3. Calculate the test statistic (standardized statistic) and corresponding p-value.
4. State your conclusion (with appropriate justification based on your p-value and stated significance level) in the context of the research question.

In Section 3.2 Part 2, you learned the work you must show on the AP Statistics exam for a confidence interval for one proportion. The format you learned is the same for all confidence intervals.

1. Identify the parameter you want to estimate and the theory-based model you will use.
2. Verify the validity conditions for the theory-based method you have chosen.
3. Construct the confidence interval, showing the values that you substitute into the formula.
4. Interpret the confidence interval you obtained in the context of the problem.

In the example and exploration below, we illustrate the four steps for both hypothesis tests and confidence intervals in the AP style.

Do Baby Simulators Impact Teenage Pregnancy?

Example 5.4

In the 1990s, the Virtual Infant Parenting (VIP) program developed *baby simulators* to help teenage girls have a realistic experience of parenting an infant and potentially impact teenage pregnancy rates. The baby simulators are essentially dolls that are battery operated and considered every bit as demanding as a real infant—crying at night, needing a diaper changed, and needing to be fed. Despite the widespread use of the VIP program, the first study to assess whether or not baby simulators have an effect on teenage pregnancy rates was not conducted until 2003 in Perth, Australia. Of the 66 schools that were eligible, 57 were enrolled in the trial, with 28 of the schools randomly assigned to the VIP program (intervention group) and the remaining 29 schools assigned to receive the standard health education curriculum (control group). Between 2003 and 2006, the VIP program was administered to 1,267 girls aged 13–15 years, while the 1,567 girls aged 13–15 years in the control group received the standard health education curriculum. In the VIP program group, 97 of the girls had at least one birth as compared to 67 girls in the control group.

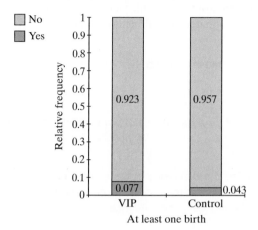

FIGURE 5.15 Segmented bar graph of observed results.

As can be seen in Figure 5.15, a larger proportion of girls had at least one birth with the VIP program (0.077 − 0.043 = 0.034). Is this evidence of a significant difference in birth rates between the two groups? Use a 5% significance level.

State the hypotheses either in words or using appropriate symbols.

Null: There is no difference in the proportion of all girls similar to those in this study that would have at least one birth if they had been in the VIP program and the proportion of all girls similar to those in this study that would have at least one birth if they had been in the control program.

$$H_0: \pi_{VIP} - \pi_{Control} = 0$$

Alternative: There is a difference in these population proportions.

$$H_0: \pi_{VIP} - \pi_{Control} \neq 0$$

Name the theory-based test that will be used and state and verify the validity conditions for the test chosen.

We will use a two-proportion z-test because we are comparing two groups on a binary response.

Now let's check the validity conditions for a two-proportion z-test

- Scope of inference: We are told that that the treatments were randomly assigned to 13- to 15-year-old girls in 57 of the 66 eligible schools in Perth, Australia. Because there was random assignment to the treatment groups (VIP or control), a cause-and-effect relationship can be attributed, though we should be cautious because the random assignment was conducted at the school level rather than for the individual females within a school. We may cautiously generalize the results to 13- to 15-year-old girls in Perth, Australia, between 2003 and 2006, provided that the girls in the study are a representative sample of girls in this age group in Perth.

- The distribution of the difference in sample proportions will be bell-shaped (approximately normal) if the counts of successes and failures in each sample or group $[n_1\hat{p}_1, n_1(1 - \hat{p}_1), n_2\hat{p}_2, n_2(1 - \hat{p}_2)]$ are all at least 10.

    97 successes and 1,170 failures in the VIP program group

    67 successes and 1,500 failures in the control group

Because the numbers of successes and failures in each of the treatment groups are much larger than 10, a two-proportion z-test is appropriate.

Calculate the test statistic (standardized statistic) and corresponding p-value.

By substituting into the appropriate formulas, we find the following:

$$\hat{p}_{VIP} = \frac{97}{1,267} \approx 0.077, \hat{p}_{Control} = \frac{67}{1,567} \approx 0.043$$

$$\hat{p} = \frac{97 + 67}{1,267 + 1,567} = \frac{164}{2,834} \approx 0.058$$

$$z = \frac{0.077 - 0.043 - 0}{\sqrt{0.058(1 - 0.058)\left(\dfrac{1}{1,267} + \dfrac{1}{1,567}\right)}} \approx 3.83$$

$$p\text{-value} \approx 0.0001$$

 5.4.1

> **CALCULATOR TIPS**
>
> You can also determine the test statistic and p-value using graphing calculators. For example:
>
> - **TI-84:** STAT → TESTS → 2-PropZTest
> - **TI-Nspire:** Statistics → Stat Tests → 2-Prop z Test

State your conclusion (with appropriate justification based on your p-value and stated significance level) in the context of the research question.

We have convincing evidence to claim that there is a genuine difference in the proportion of all girls similar to those in this study that would have at least one birth if they had been in the VIP program and the proportion of all girls similar to those in this study that would have at least one birth if they had been in the control program. Our conclusion is based on the p-value of 0.0001, which is less than our significance level of 0.05.

 5.4.2

> **DIGGING DEEPER (BEYOND AP STATISTICS)**
>
> However, we should be cautious about the strength of this p-value because, although the VIP and control programs were actually assigned to the schools, we treated the students as our observational units, using a sample size that was much bigger than the number of schools in each program. A better analysis would take this nesting into account. This also gave us a much larger sample size than when we used the schools as our units. Recall that larger sizes can make even a small difference in treatments look statistically significant.

Use the data from this study to construct a 95% confidence interval for the difference in the population proportion of all girls similar to those in this study that would have at least one birth with the VIP program minus the population proportion that would have at least one birth with the control program.

Identify the parameter you want to estimate and the theory-based model you will use.
Let $\pi_{VIP} - \pi_{Control}$ represent the difference in the population proportion of all 13- to 15-year-old girls in Perth, Australia, from 2003 to 2006 that would have at least one birth if they went through the VIP program and the population proportion that would have at least one birth if they went through the control program.

We will use a two-proportion z-interval to construct a 95% confidence interval for $\pi_{VIP} - \pi_{Control}$.

Verify the validity conditions for the theory-based method you have chosen.
The validity conditions for a two-proportion z-interval are the same as for a two-proportion z-test.

Construct the confidence interval, showing the values that you substitute into the formula.

95% C.I. for $\pi_{VIP} - \pi_{Control}$:

$$0.077 - 0.043 \pm 1.960\sqrt{\frac{0.077(1 - 0.077)}{1{,}267} + \frac{0.043(1 - 0.043)}{1{,}567}}$$

$$(0.016, 0.052)$$

CALCULATOR TIPS

You can find the confidence interval on your calculator. For example:

- **TI-84:** Stat → Tests → 2-PropInt
- **TI-Nspire:** Menu → Stat → Confidence Intervals → 2-Prop z Interval

Interpret the confidence interval you obtained in the context of the problem.

We are 95% confident that the proportion of all 13- to 15-year-old girls similar to those in this study in Perth, Australia (2003–2006), who would have at least one birth if they had received the VIP program is 0.016 to 0.052 larger than the proportion of all 13- to 15 year-old girls in Perth, Australia, who would have at least one birth during this time if they had received the control program.

5.4.3

EXPLORATION | **GMO Label—Negative Perception?**

5.4

Should all foods made from genetically modified organisms (GMO) be required to be labeled as such? An article in *Scientific American* (September 2013) made the case that, instead of providing people with useful information, mandatory GMO labels would only intensify the misconception that so-called Frankenfoods endanger people's health. Two students in an AP Statistics class undertook a study to determine whether the phrase "genetically modified" carried a stigma with students at their school and whether it would affect their likelihood of purchasing vegetables that were labeled as genetically modified. They developed two different versions of a survey question to ask students.

- Version 1: "Would you purchase vegetables that have been genetically modified?"

- Version 2: "Some vegetables are made to be drought resistant, more nutritious, or made to grow faster and larger. Would you purchase vegetables like these?"

They randomly selected 100 students from the 1,282 students at their school to take part in the study. Fifty of the students were randomly assigned to answer Version 1 (GMO wording) of the survey and the remaining 50 students were assigned to answer Version 2 (Non-GMO wording). The students who took part in the survey were unaware that two different versions of the question were being asked. The data are summarized in the two-way table below.

		Response		
		Yes	No	Total
Question wording	Version 1 (GMO)	13	37	50
	Version 2 (Non-GMO)	39	11	50
	Total	52	48	100

1. Create a graph summarizing these sample results and briefly explain what you learn from the graph.

2. Describe a method for randomly assigning the 100 students selected to take part in the survey to receive either the Version 1 (GMO) or Version 2 (Non-GMO) wording of the survey.

3. At the significance level α = 0.05, do the data provide convincing statistical evidence of a difference in proportions between students at this school who would have answered yes to purchasing vegetables for the two different versions of the questions asked? Make sure to show all work needed for a complete answer to a test of significance question on the AP Statistics exam.

   a. State the null and alternative hypotheses using either words or appropriate symbols.

   b. Name the theory-based test to be used.

   c. State and verify the validity conditions for the appropriate theory-based test.

   d. Calculate the test statistic (standardized statistic) and corresponding p-value.

   e. State your conclusion (with appropriate justification based on your p-value and stated significance level) in the context of the research question.

4. Based on your decision in #3, discuss what type of error (Type I or Type II) is possible and provide a possible consequence for this type of error in this context.

5. If there is convincing evidence of a difference in the population proportions of students at this school who would have answered yes to purchasing vegetables for the two different versions of the question asked, can you conclude a cause-and-effect relationship between the wording and how people respond? Explain.

6. Construct a 95% confidence interval for the difference in the proportion of all students at this school who would answer yes if they were given the different versions of the question. Make sure to show all work needed for a complete answer to a confidence interval question on the AP Statistics exam.

   a. Identify the parameter you will estimate and the theory-based method you will use.

   b. State and verify the validity conditions for the appropriate theory-based method.

   c. Construct the confidence interval showing the values you substitute into the formula.

   d. Interpret the confidence interval you obtained in the context of the study.

7. Explain how the interval you obtained above agrees with the decision you made for the hypothesis test that you performed in #3.

SECTION 5.4   Summary

In this section we investigated theory-based models for tests of significance for comparing two population proportions. We saw that a normal distribution provides a good approximation for the distribution of the statistic $\hat{p}_1 - \hat{p}_2$ if you have at least 10 responses of each kind (10 successes and 10 failures) in each group. The theory-based test for the difference in two population proportions is referred to as a **two-sample z-test**. In addition to the test of significance, we examined a theory-based **two-proportion z-interval** for estimating the difference in two population proportions. We saw that the work you need to show on the AP exam for both a test of significance and a confidence interval for a difference in population proportions follows the same general format as that for a single proportion.

CHAPTER 5   Summary

After this chapter, you can now apply the six steps of the statistical investigation method to comparing two groups on a binary response. In analyzing the sample data, examine and describe conditional proportions and segmented bar graphs. If you go on to an inferential analysis, state hypotheses in terms of the difference in the underlying process probabilities or population proportions. To estimate a p-value, use either the **Two Proportions** applet or, if the sample sizes are large (e.g., at least 10 successes and at least 10 failures in each of the groups), the **Theory-Based Inference** applet using the **Two Proportions** pull-down menu. The latter can also be used to find confidence intervals for any confidence level. You can also determine p-values and confidence intervals using the appropriate formulas and tables or a calculator. Remember to interpret this parameter, the difference in population proportions, carefully. Also, remember that which category of the explanatory variable is called Group 1 and which Group 2 is arbitrary; just remember to be consistent and interpret the results accordingly. Finally, consider how the data were collected to decide whether you can draw a cause-and-effect conclusion when the difference is statistically significant and to what populations you are willing to generalize the results.

In the next chapter, you will repeat this process to compare two groups on a quantitative response variable rather than a categorical response variable. In other words, the next chapter will involve comparing two means rather than two proportions.

CHAPTER 5
GLOSSARY

2 × 2 table   A two-way table where the explanatory and response variables each have two categories.

cells   Entries in two-way tables.

conditional proportion   Proportion of sucesses for a given category of the explanatory variable.

no association   General statement of the null hypothesis when two or more variables are involved indicating that two variables are not related to each other.

relative risk   The ratio of conditional proportions.

segmented bar graphs   Graphical display of conditional proportions from two-way table.

standard error   Estimate for the standard deviation of the null distribution of the statistic.

two by two (2 × 2)   A two-way table where the explanatory and response variables each have two categories.

two-sample z-interval   The theory-based confidence interval for the difference in two proportions.

two-sample z-test   The theory-based test for the difference in two proportions.

two-way table   A tabular summary of two categorical variables, also called a contingency table.

validity conditions for two-sample z-procedures   At least 10 observations in each of the cells of the 2 × 2 table.

CHAPTER 5
EXERCISES

SECTION 5.1

5.1.1*   Four 2 × 2 tables, numbered 1–4, are shown below. For each one the response is Yes/No and the explanatory variable is A/B.

1	A	B		2	A	B		3	A	B		4	A	B
Yes	10	20		Yes	10	10		Yes	20	10		Yes	20	10
No	10	20		No	20	20		No	10	20		No	20	10

a. Which two tables have the same pair of conditional proportions?

b. For which table(s) is the difference (A versus B) in conditional proportions the largest?

c. For which table(s) is the difference (A versus B) in conditional proportions the smallest?

5.1.2   Consider the following two 2 × 2 tables:

	Treatment A	Treatment B
Success	90	98
Failure	10	2
Total	100	100

	Treatment C	Treatment D
Success	40	48
Failure	60	52
Total	100	100

a. Calculate the proportion of *failures* for all four treatments.

b. Calculate the *difference* in proportions of failure between Treatments A and B. Then do the same calculation to compare Treatments C and D.

c. Calculate the *relative risk* of failure between Treatments A and B. Then do the same calculation to compare Treatments C and D.

d. Which pair of treatments do you think produce responses that are more different: A and B or C and D?

e. Which statistic reflects your answer to part (d): difference in proportions or relative risk? Explain.

Sex of respondent and playing sports*

5.1.3   Fill in the cells in the following table so there is no association between the explanatory and response variables.

		Male	Female	Total
Played sports in high school	Yes			200
	No			160
Total		150	210	360

Drinking and Greek life

5.1.4 Fill in the cells in the following table so there is no association between the explanatory and response variables.

		Member of Fraternity or Sorority		
		Yes	No	Total
Has one or more alcoholic drinks per week	Yes			152
	No			230
Total		42	340	382

School spirit*

5.1.5 Think about the proportion of students at your college who are wearing clothing that displays the college name or logo today. Also suppose that a friend of yours attends a different college, and the two of you have a recurring discussion about which college displays more school pride. You decide to measure school pride by the proportion of students at the college who wear clothing that displays the college name or logo on a particular day. You want to investigate whether this proportion differs between your college (call it Exemplary Students University, ESU) and your friend's college (call it Mediocre Students University, MSU).

a. What are the observational units in this study?

b. What is the response variable in this study? Is it categorical or quantitative?

c. Would you use random sampling to select the observational units? If so, explain why and how.

d. Would you use random assignment to create the two groups to compare? If so, explain why and how.

e. Draw and label a (blank) 2 × 2 table suitable for summarizing the data.

Medicare audits

5.1.6 The U.S. government authorizes private contractors to audit bills paid by Medicare and Medicaid. The contractor audits a random sample of paid claims and judges each claim to be either fully justified or an overpayment. Here is a 2 × 2 table that summarizes data from one such audit.

(One of the authors served as a statistical consultant in connection with this audit. For reasons of confidentiality we cannot identify the health care provider.) For this audit, all claims were divided into two sub-populations according to amount of the claim, small or medium. Two simple random samples were chosen, 30 small claims and 30 medium claims. We want to answer the question, "Does the chance that a claim is judged to be an overpayment depend on the size of the claim?"

	Small	Medium	Total
Fully justified	16	22	38
Overpayment	14	8	22
Total	30	30	60

a. What is the response variable? What is the explanatory variable?

b. What are the observational units for this study?

c. As for any 2 × 2 table, there are two pairs of conditional proportions. For this table, the two pairs are 14/30 versus 8/30 and 16/38 versus 14/22. Which pair corresponds to the question of interest?

Rattlesnakes*

5.1.7 The table below shows the numbers of male and female rattlesnakes caught at two different sites, B and G. Assume that the snakes caught at a site can be regarded as a random sample from the population of all snakes at the site.

	Site B	Site G	Total
Female	11	12	23
Male	10	21	31
Total	21	33	54

We want to know whether there is an association between site and sex. Site is the explanatory variable and sex is the response variable.

a. Explain why we use conditional proportions to evaluate the association.

b. Explain why we look at the proportion of females and proportion of males conditional on the site rather than the proportion from each site conditional on the sex.

c. Reasoning informally, do you think the data show evidence of an association between site and sex? Explain.

U.S. senators

5.1.8 The 2014 U.S. Senate consists of 80 men and 20 women. The 2014 U.S. Senate consists of 45 Republicans and 55 Democrats (counting 2 Independents as Democrats because they vote with Democrats more than with Republicans). What additional information do you need in order to produce a 2 × 2 table and investigate whether there is an association between sex and party?

5.1.9 Reconsider the previous exercise, along with this additional information: 16 senators are women Democrats.

a. Produce a 2 × 2 table that classifies senators in the 2014 U.S. Senate according to party and sex of senator.

Provide the relevant proportion(s) to answer the following questions:

b. Are most senators Republicans?

c. Are most Democrat senators women?

d. Are most women senators Democrats?

5.1.10 Reconsider the previous two exercises.

a. Produce a well-labeled segmented bar graph to display the association between party and sex of senator.

b. Does the graph reveal that there is an association between party and sex of senator in the 2014 U.S. Senate? If so, describe the association.

5.1.11 Reconsider the previous three exercises, but now ignore the real data. Invent your own fictional data that show *no association* between party and sex of senator. Provide the 2 × 2 table, calculate conditional proportions, and produce a segmented bar graph. Also explain how you invented the data to make sure that there would be no association between the variables.

Church and smoking*

5.1.12 A Gallup poll conducted in 2013 examined whether there is an association between church attendance and smoking status among American adults. The table below reports the percentage of people who classify themselves as smokers, conditional on self-described level of church attendance.

a. Is this an observational study or an experiment? Explain how you can tell.

b. Identify the explanatory variable and the response variable.

c. Produce an appropriate graph to display these percentages.

d. Summarize what these percentages reveal with regard to the question of whether there is an association between church attendance and smoking status among American adults.

e. Would you conclude from these data that attending church more often *causes* a decrease in smoking? Explain.

5.1.13 Reconsider the previous exercise.

a. Calculate the relative risk of being a smoker, comparing those who never attend church to those who attend church at least once per week. Also write a sentence interpreting what this calculation reveals.

b. Repeat (a) for the other three categories of church attendance, comparing each to the "at least once a week" category.

Breaking up digitally

5.1.14 A Pew Research study in April and May of 2013 asked single American adults whether they have ever broken up with someone by e-mail, text, or online message. Consider the following 2 × 2 table of counts:

	Female	Male	Total
Has broken up with someone by digital means	52	55	107
Has NOT broken up with someone by digital means	237	309	546
Total	289	364	653

a. Notice that there are more males (55) than females (52) who have broken up with someone by digital means. Explain why this comparison is not very useful.

b. Suggest a better comparison for investigating whether men or women are more likely to break up with someone by digital means.

c. Perform the calculation that you suggest in (b).

d. Comment on what your calculation in (c) reveals.

5.1.15 Reconsider the previous exercise. The Pew study also considered age as an explanatory variable, producing the following 2 × 2 table of counts:

	Age 18–29	Age 30–64	Total
Has broken up with someone by digital means	54	47	101
Has NOT broken up with someone by digital means	191	316	507
Total	245	363	608

Analyze these data with appropriate numerical summaries and graphical displays. Write a paragraph summarizing what you learn about whether there is an association between age

At least once per week	Almost every week	About once a month	Seldom	Never
12%	14%	22%	25%	30%

EXERCISE 5.1.12

and whether or not a person has broken up with someone by digital means.

HIV and AZT*

5.1.16 In a 1994 study, 164 pregnant, HIV-positive women were randomly assigned to receive the drug AZT during pregnancy and 160 such women were randomly assigned to a control group that received a placebo. It turned out that 40 of the mothers in the control group gave birth to babies who were HIV-positive, compared to only 13 in the AZT group.

a. Is this an observational study or an experiment?

b. Identify the explanatory and response variables.

c. Produce a 2 × 2 table of counts, with the explanatory variable in columns.

d. Calculate the proportion of babies who were born HIV-positive in each group.

e. Calculate the relative risk of a baby being born HIV-positive, comparing those in the placebo group to those in the AZT group.

f. Produce a segmented bar graph to display these data.

g. Summarize what these data reveal about the question of whether AZT is effective for reducing the HIV-positive proportion of newborn babies?

Pet CPR

5.1.17 According to a survey conducted by the Associated Press and petside.com in 2009, 63% of dog owners and 53% of cat owners would be at least somewhat likely to give CPR to their pet in the event of a medical emergency. The survey involved a nationwide sample of 1,166 pet owners.

a. Produce a well-labeled segmented bar graph to display these percentages.

b. Identify the two categorical variables displayed in the graph.

c. What additional information would you need in order to construct a 2 × 2 table?

5.1.18 Reconsider the previous exercise. The same survey found that 65% of women and 50% of men would give CPR to their pets. Answer parts (a) to (c) from the previous exercise for these data.

Student data*

5.1.19 College students were asked to indicate their sex, whether or not they drink coffee, and what letter they would use to complete the four-letter word beginning with F A I __ . Results are given in the following data table (* indicates a missing value):

ID	Sex	Coffee?	Letter?
1	Female	Yes	R
2	Female	Yes	R
3	Male	No	L
4	Female	No	*
5	Female	Yes	R
6	Male	Yes	R
7	Male	No	L
8	Male	Yes	R
9	Female	No	*
10	Female	No	*
11	Female	No	R
12	Female	Yes	R
13	Male	No	L
14	Male	Yes	R
15	Female	No	R
16	Male	No	R
17	Male	Yes	L
18	Female	No	L
19	Female	No	L
20	Male	Yes	R
21	Male	No	R
22	Female	No	L
23	Female	Yes	R
24	Female	No	R
25	Female	No	L
26	Female	Yes	L

a. Produce a 2 × 2 table of counts for investigating whether the data suggest any association between sex of respondent and coffee drinking.

b. Calculate and compare the proportions of coffee drinkers between male and female students.

c. Produce a segmented bar graph to display the data from part (a).

d. Summarize what you conclude about whether the data suggest any association between sex of respondent and coffee drinking.

5.1.20 Reconsider the data from the previous exercise. Now investigate whether there is any association between sex of respondent and the letter chosen to complete the four-letter word.

5.1.21 Reconsider the data from the previous two exercises. Now investigate whether there is any association between coffee drinking and the letter chosen to complete the four-letter word.

Trusting people

5.1.22 The following segmented bar graph was produced from data collected in the 2010 General Social Survey with regard to the question "Can people be trusted?"

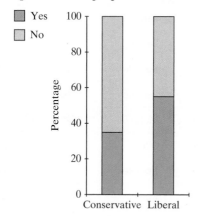

a. About what proportion of the liberals responded that people can be trusted?

b. About what proportion of the conservatives responded that people can be trusted?

c. Does the graph provide any information about what proportion of respondents were liberals?

d. Does the graph suggest that there is a relationship between political leanings and trust? Explain.

Simpson's Paradox at the hospital

5.1.23 The following two-way table classifies hypothetical hospital patients with a certain disease, according to the hospital that treated them and whether they survived or died:

	Hospital A	Hospital B
Survived	800	900
Died	200	100
Total	1,000	1,000

a. Calculate the proportion of Hospital A's patients who survived and the proportion of Hospital B's patients who survived. Which hospital saved the higher percentage of its patients?

Suppose that we further classify each patient according to a third variable: whether they were in fair condition or

poor condition prior to treatment. We obtain the following two-way tables:

Fair condition:

	Hospital A	Hospital B
Survived	590	870
Died	10	30

Poor condition:

	Hospital A	Hospital B
Survived	210	30
Died	190	70

b. Show that when the "fair" and "poor" condition patients are combined, the totals are indeed those given in the table above.

c. Among those in *fair* condition, compare the recovery rates for the two hospitals. Which hospital saved the greater percentage of its patients who had been in fair condition?

d. Among those in *poor* condition, compare the recovery rates for the two hospitals. Which hospital saved the greater percentage of its patients who had been in poor condition?

This phenomenon is called **Simpson's paradox**: An association or comparison that holds for all of several groups can reverse direction when the data are merged to form a single group.

e. Explain (arguing from the data given) the apparent "paradox" here. (*Hints:* Do fair or poor patients tend to survive more often? Does one hospital tend to treat one type of patient?)

f. Which hospital would you rather go to if you were sick with this disease? Explain.

Simpson's paradox at Berkeley*

5.1.24 In 1973 a lawsuit was filed against the University of California at Berkeley, alleging sex discrimination in its graduate admissions policies. The following table pertains to two of the graduate programs at the university. For each program, it lists the number of men accepted, the number of men denied, the number of women accepted, and the number of women denied:

	Men accepted	Men denied	Women accepted	Women denied
Program A	511	314	89	19
Program F	22	351	24	317
Combined	533	665	113	336

a. Start with the combined data. Determine the proportion of men applicants who were accepted and compare this to the proportion of women applicants who were accepted. Which proportion is larger?

b. Now consider only Program A. Did men or women have a higher proportion of applicants who were accepted? Provide calculations to justify your answer.

c. Repeat (b) for Program F.

d. Is this an example of Simpson's paradox (see the previous exercise)? Explain.

e. Explain how this paradox happens, based on the data, as if to someone who doesn't know much about statistics.

Simpson's paradox in softball

5.1.25 Show that it is possible for Simpson's paradox (see Exercise 5.1.23) to occur with two softball players. Produce a hypothetical example where one player (Amy) has a higher percentage of hits than another (Barb) in June, and Amy also has a higher percentage of hits than Barb in July. Yet when June and July are combined, Barb has a higher percentage of hits than Amy. (*Hints:* Be sure to give the two players different numbers of at-bats in the two months, and make one month easier to get a hit than the other.)

SECTION 5.2

Medicare audits*

5.2.1 Reconsider the exercise in Section 5.1 about Medicare audits (5.1.6). Of the 30 small claims, 14 were judged to be overpayments; of the 30 medium claims, 8 were judged to be overpayments. Our research question is this: "Does the chance that the claim is judged to be an overpayment tend to differ by the size of the claim?"

a. Which of the following is the appropriate null hypothesis? **Choose one.**

  A. Small claims are more likely to be judged overpayments compared to medium claims.

  B. Small claims are less likely to be judged overpayments compared to medium claims.

  C. Small and medium claims are equally likely to be judged overpayments.

  D. Small and medium claims are not equally likely to be judged overpayments.

b. Which of the following is the appropriate alternative hypothesis? **Choose one.**

  A. Small claims are more likely to be judged overpayments compared to medium claims.

  B. Small claims are less likely to be judged overpayments compared to medium claims.

  C. Small and medium claims are equally likely to be judged overpayments.

  D. Small and medium claims are not equally likely to be judged overpayments.

c. In this context, which of the following is an (are) appropriate statistic value(s) to compare small to medium claims? **Choose all that apply.**

  A. $14/60 - 8/60 = 0.10$

  B. $14/30 - 8/30 = 0.20$

  C. $14/22 - 16/38 = 0.22$

  D. $(14/30)/(8/30) = 1.75$

Suppose that we want to use cards to carry out a randomization test of the appropriate hypotheses.

d. How many cards will we need? **Choose one.**

  A. 30

  B. 52

  C. 60

  D. Doesn't matter

e. We need cards of two different colors. Let's say we decide to use red and black cards. Which of the following is an appropriate combination of red and black cards? **Choose all that apply.**

  A. 14 red and 8 black

  B. 30 red and 30 black

  C. 22 red and 38 black

  D. 38 red and 22 black

f. You shuffle the stack of red and black cards and deal them into two piles. How many cards should you place in each pile? Why?

g. What statistic should you record after you have shuffled and dealt the cards into two piles? (*Hint:* There is more than one correct answer here.)

h. Suppose that you have repeated the shuffle-and-deal many times and recorded the appropriate statistic every single time. What should you do next to find the p-value?

5.2.2 Reconsider the previous question about Medicare audits. A statistics student decides to use the **Two Proportions** applet to find a p-value to investigate whether there is an association between the size of a claim and whether it is judged to be an overpayment. Here is the output:

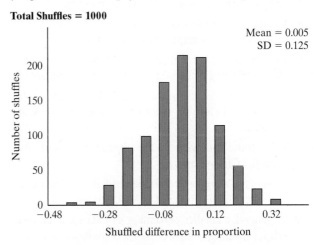

a. The above graph is a histogram of 1,000 possible values of difference in proportion of claims judged to be overpayments between small- and medium-sized claims. At what numeric value does this graph center? Explain why that makes sense.

b. The p-value is computed to be 0.184. Shade the region on the above graph that represents the p-value.

c. Interpret the p-value reported in part (b) in the context of the study.

d. Based on the p-value what would you conclude about strength of evidence?

e. Calculate an appropriate standardized statistic and interpret the standardized statistic in the context of the study.

f. Do the p-value and standardized statistic both lead you to the same conclusion?

g. Use the 2SD method to find a 95% confidence interval for the parameter of interest. Report this interval.

h. Interpret the interval reported in part (g) in the context of the study.

i. Is your conclusion from using either the p-value or the standardized statistic consistent with your finding from the 95% confidence interval? How are you deciding?

j. State a complete conclusion about this study, including significance, estimation (confidence interval), causation, and generalization. Be sure to explain how you are arriving at your conclusion.

5.2.3 Reconsider the exercise in Section 5.1 about school spirit (Exercise 5.1.3). Suppose that you find that 24% of a random sample of students at ESU wear clothing with the school name or logo, compared to 16% of a random sample of students at MSU. Our research question: *Is the observed difference in percentage of students wearing school clothing at ESU versus MSU statistically significant?*

a. Which of the following is the appropriate null hypothesis? **Choose one.**

   A. In general, a greater percentage of ESU students wear school clothing compared to MSU students.

   B. In general, a smaller percentage of ESU students wear school clothing compared to MSU students.

   C. In general, the percentage of ESU students who wear school clothing is the same as that of MSU students.

   D. In general, the percentage of ESU students who wear school clothing is different from that of MSU students.

b. Which of the following is the appropriate alternative hypothesis? **Choose one.**

   A. In general, a greater percentage of ESU students wear school clothing compared to MSU students.

   B. In general, a smaller percentage of ESU students wear school clothing compared to MSU students.

   C. In general, the percentage of ESU students who wear school clothing is the same as that of MSU students.

   D. In general, the percentage of ESU students who wear school clothing is different from that of MSU students.

c. In this context, calculate an appropriate statistic value to compare ESU students to MSU students with regard to wearing school clothing.

d. What additional information do you need in order to assess whether this difference calculated in part (c) is statistically significant?

e. Describe a scenario, involving the additional information you cited in part (d), in which you believe that this difference would be statistically significant.

f. Describe a scenario, involving the additional information you cited in part (d), in which you believe that this difference would *not* be statistically significant.

Surgery or not

5.2.4 Researchers Wilt et al. (*New England Journal of Medicine*, 2012) investigated whether surgery, compared to just observation, was (more) effective in improving men's survival chances after being diagnosed with prostate cancer. The researchers identified 731 men with localized prostate cancer who volunteered to participate. They randomly assigned 364 men to surgery and the remaining 367 to observation. All participants were followed for about 10 years. In those 10 years, 21 surgery recipients died of prostate cancer related reasons compared to 31 observation recipients.

a. Identify the observational units. **Choose one.**

   A. Men

   B. Men with prostate cancer

   C. Men with prostate cancer who underwent surgery

   D. Men with prostate cancer who received observation

b. What type of study is this? **Choose one.**

   A. Experiment

   B. Observational study

c. What is the *primary purpose* of random assignment in this type of study? **Choose one.**

   A. To ensure that subjects are representative of the population of interest

   B. To ensure that the groups are of equal sizes

   C. To create treatment groups that are alike in all aspects except for the treatment administered

   D. To improve accuracy of results

d. Identify the explanatory variable. **Choose one.**

   A. Whether or not man dies of prostate cancer related reasons

   B. Whether or not man undergoes surgery

   C. Percentage of men who die of prostate cancer related reasons

   D. The number of men who undergo surgery and the number of men who are just observed

e. Identify the response variable. **Choose one.**

A. Whether or not man dies of prostate cancer related reasons

B. Whether or not man undergoes surgery

C. Percentage of men who die of prostate cancer related reasons

D. The number of men who undergo surgery, and the number of men who are just observed

f. The explanatory variable is _____ (categorical/ quantitative).

g. The response variable is _____ (categorical/ quantitative).

h. In this context, which of the following is an (are) appropriate statistic value(s)? **Choose all that apply.**

A. $21/731 - 31/731 = -0.014$

B. $21 - 31 = -10$

C. $21/364 - 31/367 = -0.027$

D. $(31/367)/(21/364) = 1.46$

i. Give two possible explanations for the observed statistic value(s) as selected in part (h).

5.2.5 Reconsider the data from the previous exercise about investigating whether there is a relationship between undergoing surgery and whether a man dies due to prostate cancer related reasons.

a. Which of the following is the appropriate null hypothesis? **Choose one.**

A. Surgery recipients are equally likely as those just under observation to die of prostate cancer related reasons.

B. Surgery recipients are less likely than those just under observation to die of prostate cancer related reasons.

C. Surgery recipients are more likely than those just under observation to die of prostate cancer related reasons.

D. Surgery recipients are *not* equally likely as those just under observation to die of prostate cancer related reasons.

b. Which of the following is the appropriate alternative hypothesis? **Choose one.**

A. Surgery recipients are equally likely as those just under observation to die of prostate cancer related reasons.

B. Surgery recipients are less likely than those just under observation to die of prostate cancer related reasons.

C. Surgery recipients are more likely than those just under observation to die of prostate cancer related reasons.

D. Surgery recipients are *not* equally likely as those just under observation to die of prostate cancer related reasons.

Suppose that we want to use cards to perform a tactile simulation to carry out a randomization test of the appropriate hypotheses.

c. In total, how many cards will we need?

d. We need cards of different colors. How many colors do we need? How many cards of each color do we need? Explain.

e. We will shuffle the stack of cards and deal them into multiple piles. How many piles should we make and how many cards should we place in each pile? Why?

f. What statistic should we record after we have shuffled and dealt the cards into two piles? (*Hint:* There is more than one correct answer here.)

g. Suppose that we have repeated the shuffle and deal many times and recorded the appropriate statistic every single time. What should we do next to find the p-value?

h. Which of the following is the purpose of shuffling and dealing cards into two piles repeatedly and recording a chosen statistic value for each repetition?

A. To generate more samples

B. To improve accuracy of the study

C. To generate values of the statistic that could have happened by chance alone

D. All of the above

5.2.6 Reconsider the data from the previous exercise about investigating whether there is a relationship between undergoing surgery and whether a man dies due to prostate cancer related reasons.

a. Organize the counts in a well-labeled 2×2 table.

b. Use an appropriate randomization-based applet to find a p-value. Report *and* interpret the p-value in the context of the study.

c. Based on this p-value, how much evidence do you have against the null hypothesis?

d. Calculate an appropriate standardized statistic and interpret the standardized statistic in the context of the study.

e. Do the p-value and standardized statistic both lead you to the same conclusion?

f. Use the 2SD method to find a 95% confidence interval for the parameter of interest. Report this interval and interpret the interval in the context of the study.

g. Is your conclusion from using either the p-value or the standardized statistic consistent with your finding from the 95% confidence interval? How are you deciding?

h. State a complete conclusion about this study, including significance, estimation (confidence interval), causation, and generalization. Be sure to explain how you are arriving at your conclusion.

Chest-compression-only or standard cardiopulmonary resuscitation*

5.2.7 To investigate whether giving chest-compression-only (CC) instructions rather than standard cardiopulmonary resuscitation (CPR) instructions to the witness of a heart attack will improve the victim's chance of surviving, researchers Hupfl et al. (*The Lancet,* 2010) combined the results from three randomized experiments. In each experiment, the emergency services dispatcher randomly assigned either CC or CPR instructions to the bystander who was at the site where a person had just experienced a heart attack. They found that of the 1,500 cases where CC instructions had been given, 211 people had survived, whereas of the 1,531 cases where standard CPR instructions had been given, the number was 178.

Here are the data organized in a 2 × 2 table:

		CC	CPR	Total
Survived?	Yes	211	178	389
	No	1,289	1,353	2,642
Total		1,500	1,531	3,031

a. Identify the observational units. **Choose one.**

  A. Whether given CC or CPR instructions

  B. Whether heart attack victim survived or not

  C. Cases of heart attacks where emergency services were contacted

  D. Those people who survived

b. What is the *primary purpose* of random assignment in this type of study? **Choose one.**

  A. To ensure that subjects are representative of the population of interest

  B. To ensure that the groups are of equal sizes

  C. To create treatment groups that are alike in all aspects except for the treatment administered

  D. To improve accuracy of results

c. Identify the explanatory variable. **Choose one.**

  A. Whether given CC or CPR instructions

  B. Whether heart attack victim survived or not

  C. Cases of heart attacks where emergency services were contacted

  D. Those people who survived

d. Identify the response variable. **Choose one.**

  A. Whether given CC or CPR instructions

  B. Whether heart attack victim survived or not

  C. Cases of heart attacks where emergency services were contacted

  D. Those people who survived

e. The explanatory variable is _____ (categorical/quantitative).

f. The response variable is _____ (categorical/quantitative).

g. In this context, which of the following is an (are) appropriate statistic value(s)? **Choose all that apply.**

A. $211/1{,}500 - 178/1{,}531 = 0.024$

B. $211/3{,}031 - 178/3{,}031 = 0.011$

C. $211/389 - 178/389 = 0.085$

D. $(211/1{,}500)/(178/1{,}531) = 1.21$

h. Give two possible explanations for the observed statistic value(s) as selected in part (g).

5.2.8 Reconsider the data from the previous exercise about investigating whether giving chest-compression-only (CC) instructions rather than standard cardiopulmonary resuscitation (CPR) instructions to the witness of a heart attack will improve the victim's chance of surviving.

a. Which of the following is the appropriate null hypothesis? **Choose one.**

  A. Giving CC instructions is just as effective as giving CPR instructions at saving lives of heart attack victims.

  B. Giving CC instructions is more effective than giving CPR instructions at saving lives of heart attack victims.

  C. Giving CC instructions is less effective than giving CPR instructions at saving lives of heart attack victims.

b. Which of the following is the appropriate alternative hypothesis? **Choose one.**

  A. Giving CC instructions is just as effective as giving CPR instructions at saving lives of heart attack victims.

  B. Giving CC instructions is more effective than giving CPR instructions at saving lives of heart attack victims.

  C. Giving CC instructions is less effective than giving CPR instructions at saving lives of heart attack victims.

Suppose that we want to use cards to carry out a tactile simulation to investigate whether giving chest-compression-only (CC) instructions rather than standard cardiopulmonary resuscitation (CPR) instructions to the witness of a heart attack will improve the victim's chance of surviving.

c. In total, how many cards will we need?

d. We need cards of different colors. How many colors do we need? How many cards of each color do we need? Explain.

e. We shuffle the stack of cards and deal them into multiple piles. How many piles should we make and how many cards should we place in each pile? Why?

f. What statistic should you record after we have shuffled and dealt the cards into two piles? (*Hint:* There is more than one correct answer here.)

g. Suppose that we have repeated the shuffle and deal many times and recorded the appropriate statistic every single time. What should we do next to find the p-value?

h. Which of the following is the purpose of shuffling and dealing cards into two piles repeatedly and recording a chosen statistic value for each repetition?

  A. To generate more samples

  B. To improve accuracy of the study

C. To generate values of the statistic that could have happened by chance alone

D. All of the above

5.2.9 Reconsider the data from the previous exercise about investigating whether giving chest-compression-only (CC) instructions rather than standard cardiopulmonary resuscitation (CPR) instructions to the witness of a heart attack will improve the victim's chance of surviving.

a. Use an appropriate randomization-based applet to find a p-value. Report *and* interpret the p-value in the context of the study.

b. Based on this p-value, how much evidence do you have against the null hypothesis?

c. Calculate an appropriate standardized statistic and interpret the standardized statistic in the context of the study.

d. Do the p-value and standardized statistic both lead you to the same conclusion?

e. Use the 2SD method to find a 95% confidence interval for the parameter of interest. Report this interval and interpret the interval in the context of the study.

f. Is your conclusion from using either the p-value or the standardized statistic consistent with your finding from the 95% confidence interval? How are you deciding?

g. State a complete conclusion about this study, including significance, estimation (confidence interval), causation, and generalization. Be sure to explain how you are arriving at your conclusion.

5.2.10 Reconsider the context of investigating whether giving chest-compression-only (CC) instructions rather than standard cardiopulmonary resuscitation (CPR) instructions to the witness of a heart attack will improve the victim's chance of surviving. One of the randomized experiments that the researchers Hupfl et al. (*The Lancet*, 2010) looked at was by Hallstrom et al. (*New England Journal of Medicine*, 2000) where there were 35 survivors in the CC group of 240 and 29 survivors in the CPR group of 278.

a. Find the observed difference in proportion of survivors comparing those who received CC to those who received CPR.

b. Recall that in the Hupfl et al. study, where data from three studies were combined, there were 211 survivors in the CC group of 1,500 and 178 survivors in the CPR group of 1,531. Note that such a study is called a meta-analysis. Find the observed difference in proportion of survivors comparing those who received CC to those who received CPR in Hupfl et al.'s meta-analysis.

c. Compare the answers from part (a) and part (b). Which is bigger?

d. Use an appropriate randomization-based applet to find a p-value for Hallstrom et al.'s data. Report *and* interpret the p-value in the context of the study.

e. Based on this p-value, how much evidence do you have against the null hypothesis?

f. Compare the p-value from part (d) to that from Hupfl et al.'s study. Which provides stronger evidence against the null hypothesis? How are you deciding?

g. You should have found that even though the observed difference in proportion of survivors is greater for Hallstrom et al.'s study compared to Hupfl et al.'s, the p-value is smaller for Hupfl et al. Explain why that makes sense.

h. Use the 2SD method to find a 95% confidence interval for the parameter of interest based on Hallstrom et al.'s data. Report this interval and compare the midpoint and width of this interval to that based on Hupfl et al.'s data. Do the differences between the midpoints and widths of the two intervals make sense? Why?

Prenatal care for mothers with gestational diabetes

5.2.11 A baby weighing more than 4,000 g at birth is considered to be large for gestational age (LGA). Gestational diabetes in the mother is believed to be a common risk factor for LGA. In an article published in the *New England Journal of Medicine* (October 2009), researchers Landon et al. reported a study of 958 women diagnosed with mild gestational diabetes between 24 and 31 weeks of pregnancy who volunteered to participate in the study and then were randomly assigned to one of two groups: 473 to usual prenatal care (control group) and 485 to dietary intervention, self-monitoring of blood glucose, and insulin therapy, if necessary (treatment group). Of the 473 women in the control group, 68 had babies who were LGA, and of the 485 women in the treatment group, 29 had babies who were LGA.

a. Was this an experiment or an observational study? Explain how you are deciding.

b. Identify the observational units.

c. Identify the explanatory and the response variables. Also, for each variable, be sure to identify the kind of variable (categorical or quantitative).

d. Organize the data in a well-labeled 2 × 2 table. Also create a segmented bar chart with well-labeled axes to display the data. Discuss what the segmented bar chart shows with regard to a relationship between the type of prenatal care a woman with gestational diabetes receives and whether or not she has an LGA baby.

e. Find the observed difference in the conditional proportion of mothers who had LGA babies between those who received the usual prenatal care and those who received specialized care.

f. Give two possible explanations for the observed difference in conditional proportions as reported in part (e).

5.2.12 Reconsider the data from the previous study about the effect of specialized prenatal care for women with gestational diabetes. Do the data provide evidence of a relationship between the type of prenatal care a woman with gestational diabetes receives and whether or not she has an LGA baby?

a. Define (in words) the parameters of interest of this study. *Also, assign symbols* to the parameters.

b. State the appropriate null and alternative hypotheses in words.

c. State the null and alternative hypotheses in symbols.

d. Give detailed, step-by-step instructions on how one could conduct a tactile simulation to generate a p-value to test whether the observed difference in the conditional proportion of mothers who had LGA babies between those who received the usual prenatal care and those who received specialized care is statistically significant. Be sure to include details on the following:

- Would the simulation involve coins, dice, or index cards?

- How many tosses, rolls, or cards would be used?

- How many sets of tosses, rolls, or shuffles would you observe?

- What would you record after every repetition?

- How would you compute the p-value?

5.2.13 Reconsider the data from the previous study about the effect of specialized prenatal care for women with gestational diabetes. Do the data provide evidence of a relationship between the type of prenatal care a woman with gestational diabetes receives and whether or not she has an LGA baby?

a. Use an appropriate randomization-based applet to find a p-value to test whether the observed difference in the conditional proportion of mothers who had LGA babies between those who received the usual prenatal care and those who received specialized care is statistically significant. Report *and* interpret the p-value in the context of the study.

b. Based on this p-value, how much evidence do you have against the null hypothesis?

c. Calculate an appropriate standardized statistic and interpret the standardized statistic in the context of the study.

d. Do the p-value and standardized statistic both lead you to the same conclusion?

e. Use the 2SD method to find a 95% confidence interval for the parameter of interest. Report this interval and interpret the interval in the context of the study.

f. Is your conclusion from using either the p-value or the standardized statistic consistent with your finding from the 95% confidence interval? How are you deciding?

g. State a complete conclusion about this study, including significance, estimation (confidence interval), causation, and generalization. Be sure to explain how you are arriving at your conclusion.

5.2.14 Reconsider the data from the previous study about the effect of specialized prenatal care for women with gestational diabetes. Do the data provide evidence of a relationship between the type of prenatal care a woman with gestational diabetes receives and whether or not she has an LGA baby?

a. Calculate the observed value of the relative risk of having an LGA baby for the pregnant women who received usual prenatal care compared to those who received specialized prenatal care.

b. State the null and alternative hypotheses in the context of relative risk of having an LGA baby.

c. Use an appropriate randomization-based applet to find a p-value to test whether the observed relative risk (as calculated in part (a)) is statistically significant. Report *and* interpret the p-value in the context of the study. *Note:* Make sure to change the statistic to "Relative risk" when using the applet.

d. If you have a p-value from using the difference in conditional proportions as your statistic (from the previous exercise), compare that p-value to the one reported in part (c). Are they close? Explain why that makes sense.

Risk taking*

5.2.15 In the Chapter 4 exercises you read about a research article, "Power Posing: Brief Nonverbal Displays Affect Neuroendocrine Levels and Risk Tolerance," that was published in *Psychological Science*, September 2010, and describes an experiment involving 42 participants (male and female), where 20 participants were randomly assigned to hold low-power poses (contractive positions, closed limbs) and 22 to hold high-power poses (expansive positions, open limbs) for two minutes. All participants were told that the aim of this exercise was to see if their heart rate changed. After the exercise, each participant was given $2 and told that they could keep the money or roll a die for a double or nothing. The resulting data are shown below.

Research question: Are people who hold "high-power poses" more likely to take risks (such as the double or nothing bet) compared to those who hold "low-power poses"?

		Low-power pose	High-power pose	Total
Took the "double or nothing" bet?	Yes	3	18	21
	No	17	4	21
Total		20	22	42

EXERCISE 5.2.15

a. Find the observed difference in the conditional proportion of bet takers between those who held low-power poses and those who held high-power poses.

b. Give two possible explanations for the observed difference in conditional proportions as reported in part (a).

5.2.16 Reconsider the data from the study investigating whether people who hold high-power poses are more likely to take risks (such as the double or nothing bet) compared to those who hold low-power poses. For this exercise, use the difference in the conditional proportion of bet takers between those who held low-power poses and those who held high-power poses as the statistic.

a. Define (in words) the parameters of interest of this study. *Also, assign symbols* to the parameters.

b. State the null and alternative hypotheses in words.

c. State the null and alternative hypotheses in symbols.

d. Give detailed, step-by-step instructions on how one could conduct a tactile simulation to generate a p-value to test the hypotheses stated in parts (b) and (c). Be sure to include details on the following:

- Would the simulation involve coins, dice, or index cards?
- How many tosses, rolls, or cards would be used?
- How many sets of tosses, rolls, or shuffles would you observe?
- What would you record after every repetition?
- How would you compute the p-value?

5.2.17 Reconsider the data from the study investigating whether people who hold "high-power poses" are more likely to take risks (such as the double or nothing bet) compared to those who hold "low-power poses." For this exercise, for a statistic use the difference in the conditional proportion of bet takers between those who held low-power poses and those who held high-power poses.

a. Use an appropriate randomization-based applet to find a p-value. Report *and* interpret the p-value in the context of the study.

b. Based on this p-value, how much evidence do you have against the null hypothesis?

c. Calculate an appropriate standardized statistic and interpret the standardized statistic in the context of the study.

d. Do the p-value and standardized statistic both lead you to the same conclusion?

e. Use the 2SD method to find a 95% confidence interval for the parameter of interest. Report this interval and interpret the interval in the context of the study.

f. Is your conclusion from using either the p-value or the standardized statistic consistent with your finding from the 95% confidence interval? How are you deciding?

g. State a complete conclusion about this study, including significance, estimation (confidence interval), causation, and generalization. Be sure to explain how you are arriving at your conclusion.

5.2.18 Reconsider the data from the study investigating whether people who hold high-power poses are more likely to take risks (such as the double or nothing bet) compared to those who hold low-power poses.

a. Calculate the observed value of the relative risk of taking the bet for those who held high-power poses compared to those who held low-power poses.

b. State your null and alternative hypotheses in the context of relative risk of taking a bet.

c. Use an appropriate randomization-based applet to find a p-value to test whether the observed relative risk (as calculated in part (a)) is statistically significant. Report *and* interpret the p-value in the context of the study. Note: Make sure to change the statistic to "Relative risk" when using the applet.

d. If you have a p-value from using the difference in conditional proportions as your statistic (from the previous exercise), compare that p-value to the one reported in part (c). Are they close? Explain why that makes sense.

Want change?

5.2.19 A 2013 Gallup poll asked randomly selected U.S. adults whether they wanted to stay at their current body weight or change. One purpose was to investigate whether there was any difference between men and women with regard to this aspect. Of the 562 men surveyed, 242 wanted to stay at their current weight, whereas of the 477 women surveyed, 172 wanted to stay at their current weight.

a. Is this an experiment or an observational study? Explain how you are deciding.

b. Organize the data in an appropriate well-labeled 2 × 2 table.

c. Find the observed difference in the conditional proportion of those who wanted to stay at their current weight between men and women.

d. Give two possible explanations for the observed difference in conditional proportions as reported in part (c).

5.2.20 Reconsider the data from the 2013 Gallup poll that asked randomly selected U.S. adults whether they wanted to stay at their current body weight or change.

a. State the appropriate null and alternative hypotheses *in words*.

b. State the appropriate null and alternative hypotheses *in symbols*. Be sure to specify what the symbols denote.

c. Give detailed, step-by-step instructions on how one could conduct a tactile simulation to generate a p-value to test the hypotheses stated in parts (a) and (b). Be sure to include details on the following:

- Would the simulation involve coins, dice, or index cards?
- How many tosses, rolls, or cards would be used?
- How many sets of tosses, rolls, or shuffles would you observe?

- What would you record after every repetition?
- How would you compute the p-value?

5.2.21   Reconsider the data from the 2013 Gallup poll that asked randomly selected U.S. adults whether they wanted to stay at their current body weight or change.

a. Use an appropriate randomization-based applet to find a p-value. Report *and* interpret the p-value in the context of the study.

b. Based on this p-value, how much evidence do you have against the null hypothesis?

c. Calculate an appropriate standardized statistic and interpret the standardized statistic in the context of the study.

d. Do the p-value and standardized statistic both lead you to the same conclusion?

e. Use the 2SD method to find a 95% confidence interval for the parameter of interest. Report this interval and interpret the interval in the context of the study.

f. Is your conclusion from using either the p-value or the standardized statistic consistent with your finding from the 95% confidence interval? How are you deciding?

g. State a complete conclusion about this study, including significance, estimation (confidence interval), causation, and generalization. Be sure to explain how you are arriving at your conclusion.

Census awareness*

5.2.22   A survey of a random sample of U.S. adults by *The Pew Research Center for the People and the Press* conducted in early January 2010 recorded each participant's highest level of education completed and whether they knew that responding to the Census was required by law. Of the 973 participants who had some college or less, 271 knew that responding to the Census was required by law. Of the 526 participants who had a college degree or more, 195 knew that responding to the Census was required by law. Is there an association between a person's level of education and her/his Census awareness?

a. Organize the data in an appropriate well-labeled 2 × 2 table.

b. Find the observed difference in the conditional proportion of those who knew that responding to the Census was required by law between those who had a college degree or more and those with some college or less.

c. Give two possible explanations for the observed difference in conditional proportions as reported in part (b).

d. Is this an experiment or an observational study? Explain how you are deciding.

5.2.23   Reconsider the data from *The Pew Research Center for the People* survey of U.S. adults to investigate whether there is an association between a person's level of education and her/his awareness of her/his response to the Census being required by law.

a. State the appropriate null and alternative hypotheses *in words*.

b. State the appropriate null and alternative hypotheses *in symbols*. Be sure to specify what the symbols denote.

c. Give detailed, step-by-step instructions on how one could conduct a tactile simulation to generate a p-value to test the hypotheses stated in parts (a) and (b). Be sure to include details on the following:

- Would the simulation involve coins, dice, or index cards?
- How many tosses, or rolls, cards would be used?
- How many sets of tosses, rolls, or shuffles would you observe?
- What would you record after every repetition?
- How would you compute the p-value?

5.2.24   Reconsider the data from *The Pew Research Center for the People* survey of U.S. adults to investigate whether there is an association between a person's level of education and her/his awareness of her/his response to the Census being required by law.

a. Use an appropriate randomization-based applet to find a p-value. Report *and* interpret the p-value in the context of the study.

b. Based on this p-value, how much evidence do you have against the null hypothesis?

c. Calculate an appropriate standardized statistic and interpret the standardized statistic in the context of the study.

d. Do the p-value and standardized statistic both lead you to the same conclusion?

e. Use the 2SD method to find a 95% confidence interval for the parameter of interest. Report this interval and interpret the interval in the context of the study.

f. Is your conclusion from using either the p-value or the standardized statistic consistent with your finding from the 95% confidence interval? How are you deciding?

g. State a complete conclusion about this study, including significance, estimation (confidence interval), causation, and generalization. Be sure to explain how you are arriving at your conclusion.

Eating habits

5.2.25   Suppose that three high school students separately conduct polls in their city to investigate if there is an association between being a vegetarian and whether people like to eat at home or eat at restaurants.

- Sally finds that 35 out of 45 vegetarians preferred to eat at home whereas 20 out of 105 nonvegetarians preferred to eat at home.
- Tara finds that 70 out of 90 vegetarians preferred to eat at home whereas 40 out of 210 nonvegetarians preferred to eat at home.

- Uma finds that 30 out of 45 vegetarians preferred to eat at home whereas 25 out of 105 nonvegetarians preferred to eat at home.

a. Comparing Sally's study to Tara's study: Who will find stronger evidence of a difference between vegetarians and nonvegetarians with regard to preference to eat at home? Answer without doing any extensive calculations. **Choose one.**

 A. Sally

 B. Tara

 C. The strength of evidence will be similar.

 D. Cannot be answered without finding a p-value

b. Comparing Sally's study to Uma's study: Who will find stronger evidence of a difference between vegetarians and nonvegetarians with regard to preference to eat at home? Answer without doing any extensive calculations. **Choose one.**

 A. Sally

 B. Uma

 C. The strength of evidence will be similar.

 D. Cannot be answered without finding a p-value

Blood donations*

5.2.26 Have you ever donated blood? If so, how often do you donate blood? Studies have looked at who is more likely to donate blood: men or women? Suppose that three students, Eddie, Francisco, and Gina, each decide to take random samples of men and women and ask each of the participants whether they have donated blood in the past 12 months.

- Eddie finds that 20 of 100 men and 15 of 100 women in his study have donated blood in the past 12 months.

- Francisco finds that 25 of 100 men and 23 of 100 women in his study have donated blood in the past 12 months.

- Gina finds that 40 of 200 men and 30 of 200 women in her study have donated blood in the past 12 months.

a. Comparing Eddie's study to Francisco's study: Who will find stronger evidence of a difference between men and women with regard to probability of donating blood? Answer without doing any extensive calculations. **Choose one.**

 A. Eddie

 B. Francisco

 C. The strength of evidence will be similar.

 D. Cannot be answered without finding a p-value

b. Comparing Eddie's study to Gina's study: Who will find stronger evidence of a difference between men and women with regard to probability of donating blood? Answer without doing any extensive calculations. **Choose one.**

 A. Eddie

 B. Gina

 C. The strength of evidence will be similar.

 D. Cannot be answered without finding a p-value

Sexual discrimination

5.2.27 In July 2011, an Italian firm Ma-Vib was in the news for "sexual discrimination" for having chosen only its female employees to be dismissed. Before the layoffs, Ma-Vib employed 18 women and 12 men; it then fired 15 of the women and none of the men.

a. What proportion of the men were fired?

b. What proportion of the women were fired?

c. Find the difference in proportion of men and women fired.

Suppose that we want to investigate whether the proportion of females fired was significantly higher than the proportion of males fired by Ma-Vib. That is, was the difference in proportions as reported in part (c) unlikely to have happened by chance alone if nothing suspicious was going on.

d. Give detailed, step-by-step instructions on how one could conduct a tactile simulation to generate a p-value to investigate whether the proportion of females fired was significantly higher than the proportion of males fired by Ma-Vib. Be sure to include details on the following:

 - Would the simulation involve coins, dice, or index cards?

 - How many tosses, rolls, or cards would be used?

 - How many sets of tosses, rolls, or shuffles would you observe?

 - What would you record after every repetition?

 - How would you compute the p-value?

5.2.28 Recall the previous exercise, which described the Italian firm Ma-Vib that was in the news for "sexual discrimination" for having chosen only its female employees to be dismissed. Before the layoffs, Ma-Vib employed 18 women and 12 men; it then fired 15 of the women and none of the men. Using the **Two Proportions applet** for 1,000 shuffle and deals, the following output was obtained.

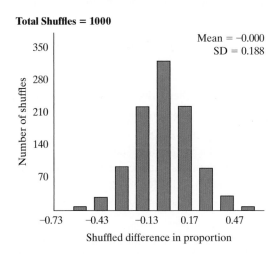

Total Shuffles = 1000

Mean = −0.000
SD = 0.188

a. The graph is a histogram of 1,000 possible values of difference in dismissals between men and women. At what numeric value does this graph center? Explain why that makes sense.

b. What value should be entered in the box next to "Beyond"?

c. Estimate *and* report the p-value from the graph. *Also,* shade the region of the graph that represents the p-value.

d. Based on the p-value reported in part (c), would it be okay to say that the proportion of women fired by Ma-Vib was significantly higher than that of men? How are you deciding?

e. Based on your findings above, would it be okay to say that Ma-Vib fired the 15 women because they were women? How are you deciding?

f. Explain why it does not make sense to calculate a confidence interval is this context. (*Hint:* What would the confidence interval be estimating?)

Do incentives work?*

5.2.29 A team of researchers (Singer et al., 2000) used the Survey of Consumer Attitudes to investigate whether incentives would improve the response rates on telephone surveys. A national sample of 735 households was randomly selected, and all 735 of the households were sent an "advance letter" explaining that the household would be contacted shortly for a telephone survey. However, 368 households were randomly assigned to receive a monetary incentive along with the advance letter, and of these 286 responded to the telephone survey. The other 367 households were assigned to receive only the advance letter, and of these 245 responded to the telephone survey.

a. Is this an experiment or an observational study? Explain how you are deciding.

b. Organize the counts in a well-labeled 2 × 2 table.

c. Find the observed difference in the conditional proportion of households that responded to the telephone survey between those who received an incentive and those who didn't receive an incentive.

d. Give two possible explanations for the observed difference in conditional proportions as reported in part (c).

5.2.30 Reconsider the data from Singer et al.'s study about whether incentives improve response rates on telephone surveys.

a. State the null and alternative hypotheses in words.

b. State the null and alternative hypotheses in symbols.

c. Give detailed, step-by-step instructions on how one could conduct a tactile simulation to generate a p-value to test the hypotheses stated in parts (a) and (b). Be sure to include details on the following:

- Would the simulation involve coins, dice, or index cards?
- How many tosses, rolls, or cards would be used?
- How many sets of tosses, rolls, or shuffles would you observe?
- What would you record after every repetition?
- How would you compute the p-value?

5.2.31 Reconsider the data from Singer et al.'s study about whether incentives improve response rates on telephone surveys.

a. Use an appropriate randomization-based applet to find a p-value. Report *and* interpret the p-value in the context of the study.

b. Based on this p-value, how much evidence do you have against the null hypothesis?

c. Calculate an appropriate standardized statistic and interpret the standardized statistic in the context of the study.

d. Do the p-value and standardized statistic both lead you to the same conclusion?

e. Use the 2SD method to find a 95% confidence interval for the parameter of interest. Report this interval and interpret the interval in the context of the study.

f. Is your conclusion from using either the p-value or the standardized statistic consistent with your finding from the 95% confidence interval? How are you deciding?

g. State a complete conclusion about this study, including significance, estimation (confidence interval), causation, and generalization. Be sure to explain how you are arriving at your conclusion.

For a song

5.2.32 In an article published in *Psychology of Music* (2010), researchers reported the results of a study conducted to investigate the effects of "romantic lyrics on compliance with a courtship request." The researchers recruited undergraduate female students who were studying social and managerial science and told them that "the purpose of the study was to discuss organic products with another participant." When a participant came in for the study, she was randomly assigned to listen to either a romantic song or a neutral song. After three minutes, she was greeted by a male "confederate" (chosen and trained by the researchers to pretend to be another participant), who while discussing the organic products also asked for her phone number so that he could call her up to ask her out.

The male confederate was kept unaware of the aim of the study and was trained to use the same script when talking to all the females.

Of the 44 women who listened to the romantic song, 23 gave their phone numbers, whereas of the 43 who listened to the neutral song, only 12 did.

a. Was this an experiment or an observational study? Explain how you are deciding.

b. Notice that neither the participants nor the male confederate were aware of the aim of the study and thus did not know who was getting what treatment. This is called double blinding. Explain why the researchers used double blinding.

c. Identify the observational units.

d. Identify the two variables recorded. Also, for each variable, be sure to identify the kind of variable (categorical or quantitative) and the role of the variable (explanatory or response).

e. Organize the counts in a well-labeled 2 × 2 table.

f. Find the observed difference in the conditional proportion of females who gave their phone number to the male confederate between those who listened to the romantic song and those who listened to the neutral song.

g. Give two possible explanations for the observed difference in conditional proportions as reported in part (f).

5.2.33 Reconsider the data from the previous study about the effects of "romantic lyrics on compliance with a courtship request."

a. Define (in words) the parameters of interest of this study. *Also, assign symbols* to the parameters.

b. State the null and alternative hypotheses in words.

c. State the null and alternative hypotheses in symbols.

d. Give detailed, step-by-step instructions on how one could conduct a tactile simulation to generate a p-value to test the hypotheses stated in parts (b) and (c). Be sure to include details on the following:

- Would the simulation involve coins, dice, or index cards?
- How many tosses, rolls, or cards would be used?
- How many sets of tosses, rolls, or shuffles would you observe?
- What would you record after every repetition?
- How would you compute the p-value?

5.2.34 Reconsider the study about the effects of "romantic lyrics on compliance with a courtship request." Recall that of the 44 women who listened to the romantic song, 23 gave their phone numbers, whereas of the 43 who listened to the neutral song, only 12 did.

a. Use an appropriate randomization-based applet to find a p-value. Report *and* interpret the p-value in the context of the study.

b. Based on this p-value, how much evidence do you have against the null hypothesis?

c. Calculate an appropriate standardized statistic and interpret the standardized statistic in the context of the study.

d. Do the p-value and standardized statistic both lead you to the same conclusion?

e. Use the 2SD method to find a 95% confidence interval for the parameter of interest. Report this interval and interpret the interval in the context of the study.

f. Is your conclusion from using either the p-value or the standardized statistic consistent with your finding from the 95% confidence interval? How are you deciding?

g. State a complete conclusion about this study, including significance, estimation (confidence interval), causation, and generalization. Be sure to explain how you are arriving at your conclusion.

FAQ

5.2.35 Read FAQ 5.2.1 about comparing the statistics difference in proportions and relative risk. In the dolphin therapy study mentioned in that FAQ there were 15 people assigned to swim with dolphins and 15 who were not (the control). We also saw that 13 people showed improvement of their depression symptoms and 17 did not. Suppose that 9 in the dolphin therapy group showed improvement.

a. How many in the dolphin therapy group did not show improvement?

b. How many in the control group showed improvement?

c. How many in the control group did not show improvement?

d. What is the difference in proportions of improvers for this scenario?

e. What is the relative risk for this scenario?

f. If we kept 15 in each group and still had 13 improvers and 17 non-improvers, could the number of improvers in the dolphin therapy group be something other than 9 and still get the same difference in proportions and relative risk that you got in parts (d) and (e)?

g. Using your answer to part (f) describe the relationship between null distributions when a difference in proportions is used as the statistic compared to when relative risk is used as the statistic.

5.2.36 Read FAQ 5.2.2 about randomness and answer the following questions.

a. Suppose we get a small p-value in an observational study comparing two proportions with no random assignment. What can we rule out as an explanation for the difference in proportions? Can we conclude there is a cause? Can we conclude what that cause is?

b. Why does random assignment allow us to determine what the cause is in a study?

c. Can you have random assignment when you are testing a single proportion? Explain.

SECTION 5.3

Hearing loss*

5.3.1 Researchers investigated whether the proportion of American teenagers with some level of hearing loss was different in 2005–2006 than in 1988–1994. They collected data on random samples of American teenagers in those two time periods. Let the symbol $\pi_{05\text{-}06}$ denote the population proportion of American teenagers with some level of hearing loss in 2005–2006 and similarly for $\pi_{88\text{-}94}$. A 95% confidence interval for the parameter $\pi_{05\text{-}06} - \pi_{88\text{-}94}$ turns out to be (0.0015, 0.0467). Which of the following is an appropriate conclusion to draw?

A. The sample data provide strong evidence that a higher proportion of American teenagers had hearing loss in 2005–2006 than in 1988–1994.

B. The sample data provide strong evidence that a higher proportion of American teenagers had hearing loss in 1988–1994 than in 2005–2006.

C. The sample data provide strong evidence that the proportion of American teenagers with hearing loss was the same in 1988–1994 as in 2005–2006.

D. The sample data provide little evidence to doubt that the proportion of American teenagers with hearing loss was the same in 1988–1994 as in 2005–2006.

5.3.2 Reconsider the previous exercise. If a 95% confidence interval had instead been produced from the same sample data for the parameter $\pi_{88\text{-}94} - \pi_{05\text{-}06}$, how would this confidence interval have turned out?

A. Same as above: (0.0015, 0.0467)

B. Negative of above: $(-0.0467, -0.0015)$

C. Impossible to say

5.3.3 Reconsider the previous exercise. If a 99% confidence interval had instead been produced from the same sample data for the parameter $\pi_{05\text{-}06} - \pi_{88\text{-}94}$, how would this confidence interval have turned out?

A. Wider than the 95% confidence interval: (0.0015, 0.0467)

B. Narrower than the 95% confidence interval: (0.0015, 0.0467)

C. Impossible to say

5.3.4 Reconsider the previous exercise. If a 99% confidence interval had instead been produced from the same sample data for the parameter $\pi_{05\text{-}06} - \pi_{88\text{-}94}$, what would be the midpoint of this confidence interval be? If the midpoint can be calculated, find it. If the midpoint cannot be calculated using only the information given, explain why not.

5.3.5 Reconsider the previous exercise. If a 99% confidence interval had instead been produced from the same sample data for the parameter $\pi_{05\text{-}06} - \pi_{88\text{-}94}$, what would the width of this confidence interval be? If the width can be calculated, find it. If the width cannot be calculated using only the information given, explain why not.

Medicare audits

5.3.6 Reconsider a previous exercise from Section 5.1 about Medicare audits. Of the 30 small claims, 14 were judged to be overpayments; of the 30 medium claims, 8 were

judged to be overpayments. Our research question is this: "Does the chance that the claim is judged to be an overpayment tend to differ by the size of the claim?"

Explain why it is not advisable to use a theory-based approach to answer this research question.

Do incentives work?*

5.3.7 Recall exercise 5.2.29 about the use of incentives to encourage people to participate in a telephone survey. A team of researchers (Singer et al., 2000) used the Survey of Consumer Attitudes to investigate whether incentives would improve the response rates on telephone surveys. A national sample of 735 households was randomly selected, and all 735 of the households were sent an "advance letter" explaining that the household would be contacted shortly for a telephone survey. However, 368 households were randomly assigned to receive a monetary incentive along with the advance letter, and the other 367 households were assigned to receive only the advance letter. Here are the data on how many households responded to the telephone survey.

		Received an incentive?		
		Yes	No	Total
Responded to the telephone survey?	Yes	286	245	531
	No	82	122	204
Total		368	367	735

a. Define the parameters of interest. Assign symbols to these parameters.

b. State the appropriate null and alternative hypotheses *in words*.

c. State the appropriate null and alternative hypotheses in symbols.

d. Explain why it would be okay to use the theory-based method (that is, normal distribution based method) to find a p-value and confidence interval for this study.

e. Use an appropriate applet to find and report the following from the data:
- The standardized statistic
- The theory-based p-value
- The theory-based 95% confidence interval

f. Include a screenshot of the applet output in your report.

g. Interpret the p-value in the context of the study.

h. Interpret the 95% confidence interval in the context of the study.

i. State a complete conclusion about this study, including significance, estimation (confidence interval), causation, and generalization. Be sure to explain how you are arriving at your conclusion.

Study of Tamoxifen and Raloxifene (STAR)

5.3.8 Researchers Vogel et al. (*JAMA*, 2006) reported the following findings about the Study of Tamoxifen and Raloxifene (STAR), a study involving postmenopausal women who were at an increased risk for invasive breast cancer. Of the 9,726 women randomly assigned to use tamoxifen daily, 163 developed invasive breast cancer sometime during the next five years, compared to 168 in the group of 9,745 who were randomly assigned to use raloxifene daily.

a. Is this an experiment or an observational study? Explain how you are deciding.

b. Identify the explanatory and response variables. Also, identify whether each is categorical or quantitative.

c. Organize the counts in a well-labeled 2 × 2 table.

d. Find the observed difference in proportion of breast cancer cases between the tamoxifen and raloxifene users.

e. State the appropriate null and alternative hypotheses *in words*.

f. Explain why it would be okay to use the theory-based method (that is, normal distribution based method) to find a p-value for this study.

g. Use an appropriate applet to find and report the following from the data.
  • The standardized statistic
  • The theory-based p-value

h. State a complete conclusion about this study, including significance, estimation (confidence interval), causation, and generalization. Be sure to explain how you are arriving at your conclusion.

5.3.9 Recall the data from the STAR study: Of the 9,726 women randomly assigned to use tamoxifen daily, 163 developed invasive breast cancer sometime during the next five years, compared to 168 in the group of 9,745 who were randomly assigned to use raloxifene daily.

a. Define the parameters of interest. Assign symbols to these parameters.

b. Explain why it would be okay to use the theory-based method (that is, normal distribution based method) to find a confidence interval for this study.

c. Use an appropriate applet to find and report the theory-based 99% confidence interval.

d. Interpret the 99% confidence interval in the context of the study.

e. Relatively speaking, is the 99% confidence interval narrow or wide? Explain why that makes sense.

5.3.10 Recall the data from the STAR study: Of the 9,726 women randomly assigned to use tamoxifen daily, 163 developed invasive breast cancer sometime during the next five years, compared to 168 in the group of 9,745 who were randomly assigned to use raloxifene daily.

a. Calculate the observed value of the relative risk of developing invasive breast cancer comparing women who took tamoxifen daily to those who took raloxifene daily.

b. Suppose that you were to calculate a 95% confidence interval for the long-run relative risk of developing invasive breast cancer comparing women who will take tamoxifen daily to those who will take raloxifene daily. Will the number 1 lie within this interval? Explain your reasoning.

Solitaire*

5.3.11 Enamored with the solitaire game on his new computer, Author A sets out to estimate his probability of winning the game and wins 25 games while losing 192 games. Anxious to outperform Author A, Author B plays 444 games of solitaire and wins 74. Author B wants to know if they are performing significantly different than Author A.

a. Do these data arise from sampling from two processes or sampling from two populations?

b. Staying consistent with your answer in part (a) define the parameters of interest. Also, assign symbols to these parameters.

c. State the appropriate null and alternative hypotheses *in words*.

d. State the appropriate null and alternative hypotheses *in symbols*.

e. Use an appropriate applet to use a simulation-based approach to find a p-value to test the hypotheses stated.

f. Explain why it would be okay to use the theory-based method (that is, normal distribution based method) to find a p-value and confidence interval for this study.

g. Use an appropriate applet to find and report the following from the data:
  • The standardized statistic
  • The theory-based p-value
  • The theory-based 95% confidence interval

h. Interpret the p-value in the context of the study.

i. How much evidence is there based on this p-value?

j. Interpret the 95% confidence interval in the context of the study.

k. Does the 95% confidence interval contain 0? How does this correspond to the p-value you obtained earlier?

l. State a complete conclusion about this study, including significance, estimation (confidence interval), causation, and generalization. Be sure to explain how you are arriving at your conclusion.

Romantic lyrics

5.3.12 Recall Exercise 5.2.32 about the study conducted to investigate the effects of "romantic lyrics on compliance with a courtship request." Of the 44 women who listened to the romantic song, 23 gave their phone numbers, whereas of the 43 who listened to the neutral song, only 12 did.

a. Define (in words) the parameters of interest of this study. *Also, assign symbols to the parameters.*

b. State, in symbols, the null and alternative hypotheses to test whether women are *more* likely to comply with a "courtship request" when they have been listening to a romantic song rather than a neutral song.

c. Explain why it is okay to use theory-based methods to test the hypotheses stated above.

$\hat{p}_1 - \hat{p}_2 = 0.244$

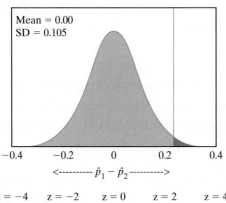

EXERCISE 5.3.12

To analyze the data, the **Theory-based Inference** applet was used and the output is shown above.

d. From the applet output, identify the following:

   i. The standardized statistic

   ii. The p-value

   iii. The 95% confidence interval

e. Interpret the p-value in the context of the study. (*Hint:* Not the conclusion, but what the p-value is a probability of.)

f. State your conclusion in the context of the study. (*Remember to address significance, estimation, causation, and generalization!*)

g. Interpret the 95% confidence interval in the context of the study.

h. Recall that the formula for the standardized statistic in this scenario is

$$z = \frac{\hat{p}_1 - \hat{p}_2}{\sqrt{\hat{p}(1 - \hat{p})\left(\dfrac{1}{n_1} + \dfrac{1}{n_2}\right)}}.$$

Plug in relevant numbers into this formula and verify the value of the standardized statistic obtained using the applet.

i. Recall that the formula for the confidence interval in this scenario is

$$\hat{p}_1 - \hat{p}_2 \pm \text{multiplier} \times \sqrt{\left(\frac{\hat{p}_1(1 - \hat{p}_1)}{n_1} + \frac{\hat{p}_2(1 - \hat{p}_2)}{n_2}\right)}.$$

Plug in relevant numbers into this formula and verify the value of the 95% confidence interval obtained using the applet.

j. Suppose a different research team wants to investigate whether type of music affects the likelihood of compliance with a courtship request. If this research team uses the same data set to explore this, what would their p-value be? Answer without carrying out the test of significance. Explain your reasoning.

Surgery and prostate cancer*

5.3.13 Recall Exercise 5.2.4 where researchers Wilt et al. (*New England Journal of Medicine*, 2012) investigated whether surgery, compared to just observation, was (more) effective in improving men's survival chances after being diagnosed with prostate cancer. The researchers identified 731 men with localized prostate cancer and randomly assigned 364 to surgery and the remaining 367 to observation. All participants were followed for about 10 years. In those 10 years, 21 surgery recipients died of prostate cancer related reasons compared to 31 observation recipients.

a. Define (in words) the parameters of interest of this study. *Also, assign symbols to the parameters.*

b. State the appropriate null and alternative hypotheses in words.

c. State the appropriate null and alternative hypotheses in symbols.

d. Explain why it is valid to use the theory-based approach to test the hypotheses stated above.

e. Use an appropriate applet to find a theory-based p-value to test the above hypotheses. Report the standardized statistic as well as the p-value.

f. Use an appropriate applet to find a theory-based 99% confidence interval and interpret the resulting interval in the context of the study.

g. Based on your findings, state a complete conclusion about the study. Be sure to address significance, estimation (confidence interval), causation, and generalization.

CPR

5.3.14 Recall Exercise 5.2.7 about investigating whether giving chest-compression-only (CC) instructions rather than standard cardiopulmonary resuscitation (CPR) instructions to the witness of a heart attack will improve the victim's chance of surviving. Researchers Hupfl et al. (*The Lancet,* 2010) combined the results from three randomized experiments. In each experiment, the emergency services dispatcher randomly assigned either CC or CPR instructions to the bystander who was at the site where a person had just experienced a heart attack. They found that of the 1,500 cases where CC instructions had been given, 211 people had survived, whereas out of the 1,531 cases where standard CPR instructions had been given, the number was 178.

a. Define (in words) the parameters of interest of this study. *Also, assign symbols to the parameters.*

b. State the appropriate null and alternative hypotheses in words.

c. State the appropriate null and alternative hypotheses in symbols.

d. Explain why it is valid to use the theory-based approach to test the hypotheses stated above.

e. Use an appropriate applet to find a theory-based p-value to test the above hypotheses. Report the standardized statistic as well as the p-value.

f. Use an appropriate applet to find a theory-based 95% confidence interval and interpret the resulting interval in the context of the study.

g. Based on your findings, state a complete conclusion about the study. Be sure to address significance, estimation (confidence interval), causation, and generalization.

Prenatal care for mothers with gestational diabetes

5.3.15 Recall Exercise 5.2.11 about the link between babies being large for gestational age (LGA) and gestational diabetes in the mother. In an article published in the *New England Journal of Medicine* (October 2009), researchers Landon et al. reported on a study of 958 women diagnosed with mild gestational diabetes between 24 and 31 weeks of pregnancy who were randomly assigned to one of two groups: 473 to usual prenatal care (control group) and 485 to dietary intervention, self-monitoring of blood glucose, and insulin therapy, if necessary (treatment group). Of the 473 women in the control group, 68 had babies who were LGA, and of the 485 women in the treatment group, 29 had babies who were LGA.

a. Define (in words) the parameters of interest of this study. *Also, assign symbols to the parameters.*

b. State the appropriate null and alternative hypotheses in words.

c. State the appropriate null and alternative hypotheses in symbols.

d. Explain why it is valid to use the theory-based approach to test the hypotheses stated above.

e. Use an appropriate applet to find a theory-based p-value to test the above hypotheses. Report the standardized statistic as well as the p-value.

f. Use an appropriate applet to find a theory-based 95% confidence interval and interpret the resulting interval in the context of the study.

g. Based on your findings, state a complete conclusion about the study. Be sure to address significance, estimation, causation, and generalization.

h. Recall that the formula for the standardized statistic in this scenario is

$$z = \frac{\hat{p}_1 - \hat{p}_2}{\sqrt{\hat{p}(1-\hat{p})\left(\frac{1}{n_1} + \frac{1}{n_2}\right)}}.$$

Plug in relevant numbers into this formula and verify the value of the standardized statistic obtained using the applet.

i. Recall that the formula for the confidence interval in this scenario is

$$\hat{p}_1 - \hat{p}_2 \pm \text{multiplier} \times \sqrt{\left(\frac{\hat{p}_1(1-\hat{p}_1)}{n_1} + \frac{\hat{p}_2(1-\hat{p}_2)}{n_2}\right)}.$$

Plug in relevant numbers into this formula and verify the value of the 95% confidence interval obtained using the applet.

5.3.16 Reconsider the data from the previous study about the effect of specialized prenatal care for women with gestational diabetes. Do the data provide evidence of a relationship between the type of prenatal care a woman with gestational diabetes receives and whether or not she has an LGA baby?

a. Calculate the observed value of the relative risk of having an LGA baby for the pregnant women who received usual prenatal care compared to those who received specialized prenatal care.

b. Suppose that you were to calculate a 95% confidence interval for the long-run relative risk of having an LGA baby for pregnant women who will receive usual prenatal care compared to those who will receive specialized prenatal care. Will the number 1 lie within this interval? Explain your reasoning.

Risk taking*

5.3.17   Recall a study from Exercise 5.2.15 , called "Power Posing: Brief Nonverbal Displays Affect Neuroendocrine Levels and Risk Tolerance," that was published in *Psychological Science*, September 2010, and describes an experiment involving 42 participants (male and female), where 20 participants were randomly assigned to hold low-power poses (contractive positions, closed limbs) and 22 to hold high-power poses (expansive positions, open limbs) for two minutes. All participants were told that the aim of this exercise was to see if their heart rate changed. After the exercise, each participant was given $2 and told that they could keep the money or roll a die for a double or nothing. Here are the data:

		Low-power pose	High-power pose	Total
Took the "double or nothing" bet?	Yes	3	18	21
	No	17	4	21
Total		20	22	42

Is it valid to use the theory-based approach to examine whether the proportion of risk takers was significantly higher in the high-power pose compared to the low-power pose? Explain your reasoning.

Change your weight

5.3.18   From Exercise 5.2.19, recall the results from a 2013 Gallup poll that asked randomly selected U.S. adults whether they wanted to stay at their current body weight or change. Of the 562 men surveyed, 242 wanted to stay at their current weight, whereas of the 477 women surveyed, 172 wanted to stay at their current weight.

a. Define (in words) the parameters of interest of this study. *Also, assign symbols* to the parameters.

b. State the appropriate null and alternative hypotheses in words.

c. State the appropriate null and alternative hypotheses in symbols.

d. Explain why it is valid to use the theory-based approach to test the hypotheses stated above.

e. Use an appropriate applet to find a theory-based p-value to test the above hypotheses. Report the standardized statistic as well as the p-value.

f. Use an appropriate applet to find a theory-based 95% confidence interval and interpret the resulting interval in the context of the study.

g. Based on your findings, state a complete conclusion about the study. Be sure to address significance, estimation (confidence interval), causation, and generalization.

Census awareness*

5.3.19   From Exercise 5.2.22, recall the survey of a random sample of U.S. adults by *The Pew Research Center for the People and the Press* conducted in early January 2010 that recorded each participant's highest level of education completed and whether they knew that responding to the Census was required by law. Of the 973 participants who had some college or less, 271 knew that responding to the Census was required by law. Of the 526 participants who had a college degree or more, 195 knew that responding to the Census was required by law. Is there an association between a person's level of education and her/his Census awareness?

a. Define (in words) the parameters of interest of this study. *Also, assign symbols* to the parameters.

b. State the appropriate null and alternative hypotheses in words.

c. State the appropriate null and alternative hypotheses in symbols.

d. Explain why it is valid to use the theory-based approach to test the hypotheses stated above.

e. Use an appropriate applet to find a theory-based p-value to test the above hypotheses. Report the standardized statistic as well as the p-value.

f. Use an appropriate applet to find a theory-based 95% confidence interval and interpret the resulting interval in the context of the study.

g. Based on your findings, state a complete conclusion about the study. Be sure to address significance, estimation (confidence interval), causation, and generalization.

Sexual discrimination

5.3.20   Recall Exercise 5.2.27 about an Italian firm Ma-Vib that was in the news for "sexual discrimination" for having chosen only its female employees to be dismissed. Before the layoffs, Ma-Vib employed 18 women and 12 men; it then fired 15 of the women and none of the men. Is it valid to use the theory-based approach to examine whether the proportion of women fired was significantly higher than the proportion of men fired? Explain your reasoning.

Cardiac disease and depression*

5.3.21 Researchers Penninx et al. (*Archives of General Psychiatry*, 2001) looked at the relationship between depression and a person's ability to survive cardiac disease. The researchers identified 450 men and women with cardiac disease, evaluated them for depression, and followed them for four years. In those four years, of the 89 patients diagnosed with minor or major depression, 26 died of cardiac disease. Of the 361 patients with no diagnosis of depression, 67 died of cardiac disease.

a. Define (in words) the parameters of interest of this study. *Also, assign symbols* to the parameters.

b. State the appropriate null and alternative hypotheses in words.

c. State the appropriate null and alternative hypotheses in symbols.

d. Explain why it is valid to use the theory-based approach to test the hypotheses stated above.

e. Use an appropriate applet to find a theory-based p-value to test the above hypotheses. Report the standardized statistic as well as the p-value.

f. Use an appropriate applet to find a theory-based 95% confidence interval and interpret the resulting interval in the context of the study.

g. Based on your findings, state a complete conclusion about the study. Be sure to address significance, estimation (confidence interval), causation, and generalization.

Cheap pill to swallow?

5.3.22 In a randomized, double-blind study reported in the *Journal of American Medical Association*, researchers Waber et al. (2008) administered a pill to each of 82 healthy paid volunteers from Boston, Massachusetts, but told half of them that the drug had a regular price of $2.50 per pill, whereas the remaining participants were told that the drug has a discounted price of $0.10 per pill, mentioning no reason for the discount. In the recruitment advertisement the pill was described as an FDA-approved "opioid analgesic," but in reality both groups were administered placebo pills.

To simulate pain, the participants were administered electric shocks to the wrist, and the researchers recorded whether subjects reported a reduction in pain after taking the pill. Of the 41 people in the regular-price pill, 35 reported a pain reduction, whereas of the 41 participants in the discount-price pill, 25 reported a pain reduction.

Is it valid to use the theory-based approach to examine whether the proportion of subjects reporting reduction in pain among those who received the regular-price pill is significantly different from the proportion of subjects reporting reduction in pain among those who received the discount-price pill? Explain your reasoning.

The Physicians' Health Study (heart attacks)*

5.3.23 The Physicians' Health Study is a very large, randomized study designed to "test the effects of low-dose aspirin… in the prevention of cardiovascular disease (CVD)." The subjects were 22,071 U.S. male physicians (aged 40–84 years, in the year 1982), who were randomly assigned to be in either the low-dose aspirin group or the placebo group. Each participant was required to take the assigned pill every other day for five years. The study was double blind. Of the 11,034 physicians who took the placebo, 189 suffered heart attacks during the study. Of the 11,037 physicians who took aspirin, 104 had heart attacks.

a. Is this an experiment or an observational study? Explain how you are deciding.

b. Identify the explanatory and response variables. Also, identify whether each is categorical or quantitative.

c. Explain what it means for a study to be "double blind." Also, explain the purpose of using "double blinding" in this study.

d. Organize the counts in a well-labeled 2 × 2 table.

e. Find the observed difference in proportion of heart attack cases between the physicians who took aspirin and those who took the placebo.

f. State the appropriate null and alternative hypotheses *in words*.

g. Use an appropriate applet to use a simulation-based approach to find a p-value to test the hypotheses stated.

h. Evaluate the strength of evidence based on the p-value.

i. Explain why it would be okay to use the theory-based method (that is, normal distribution based method) to find a p-value for this study.

j. Use an appropriate applet to find and report the following from the data:
- The standardized statistic
- The theory-based p-value

k. How do the simulation-based and theory-based p-values compare?

5.3.24 Recall the data from the Physicians' Health Study: Of the 11,034 physicians who took the placebo, 189 suffered heart attacks during the study. Of the 11,037 physicians who took aspirin, 104 had heart attacks.

a. Define the parameters of interest. Assign symbols to these parameters.

b. State the appropriate null and alternative hypotheses in symbols.

c. Explain why it would be okay to use the theory-based method (that is, normal distribution based method) to find a confidence interval for this study.

d. Use an appropriate applet to find and report the theory-based 99% confidence interval.

Interpret the 99% confidence interval in the context of the study.

e. Also, use the appropriate applet to find and report the theory-based p-value.

f. Is there *very strong evidence* of a difference in the probability of heart attacks between aspirin takers and non–aspirin takers? How are you deciding?

g. Based on your findings, state a complete conclusion about the study. Be sure to address significance, estimation (confidence interval), causation, and generalization.

h. Relatively speaking, is the 99% confidence interval narrow or wide? Explain why that makes sense.

i. Is there evidence of a *very large difference* in the probability of heart attacks between aspirin takers and non–aspirin takers? How are you deciding?

5.3.25 Recall the data from the Physicians' Health Study: Of the 11,034 physicians who took the placebo, 189 suffered heart attacks during the study. Of the 11,037 physicians who took aspirin, 104 had heart attacks.

a. Recall that the formula for the standardized statistic in this scenario is

$$z = \frac{\hat{p}_1 - \hat{p}_2}{\sqrt{\hat{p}(1 - \hat{p})\left(\frac{1}{n_1} + \frac{1}{n_2}\right)}}.$$

Plug in relevant numbers into this formula and verify the value of the standardized statistic obtained using the applet.

b. Recall that the formula for the confidence interval in this scenario is

$$\hat{p}_1 - \hat{p}_2 \pm \text{multiplier} \times \sqrt{\left(\frac{\hat{p}_1(1 - \hat{p}_1)}{n_1} + \frac{\hat{p}_2(1 - \hat{p}_2)}{n_2}\right)}.$$

Plug in relevant numbers into this formula and verify the value of the 95% confidence interval obtained using the applet.

5.3.26 Recall the data from the Physicians' Health Study: Of the 11,034 physicians who took the placebo, 189 suffered heart attacks during the study. Of the 11,037 physicians who took aspirin, 104 had heart attacks.

a. Calculate the observed value of the relative risk of heart attacks comparing physicians who took aspirin daily to those who took the placebo daily.

b. Suppose that you were to calculate a 95% confidence interval for the long-run relative risk of a heart attack comparing aspirin-taking men (like those in the study) to non-aspirin-taking men. Will the number 1 lie within this interval? Explain your reasoning.

The Physicians' Health Study (ulcers)

5.3.27 Another outcome of interest in the Physicians' Health Study was whether the subjects developed ulcers

or not. Of the 11,034 physicians who took the placebo, 138 developed ulcers during the study. Of the 11,037 physicians who took aspirin, 169 developed ulcers.

a. Identify the explanatory and response variables. Also, identify whether each is categorical or quantitative.

b. Organize the counts in a well-labeled 2 × 2 table.

c. Find the observed difference in proportion of ulcer cases between the physicians who took aspirin and those who took the placebo.

d. State the appropriate null and alternative hypotheses *in words*.

e. Use an appropriate applet to use a simulation-based approach to find a p-value to test the hypotheses stated.

f. Based on this p-value, how strong is the evidence against the null hypothesis.

g. Explain why it would be okay to use the theory-based method (that is, normal distribution based method) to find a p-value for this study.

h. Use an appropriate applet to find and report the following from the data:

- The standardized statistic
- The theory-based p-value

i. How do the simulation-based and theory-based p-values compare?

5.3.28 Recall the data from the Physicians' Health Study: Of the 11,034 physicians who took the placebo, 138 developed ulcers during the study. Of the 11,037 physicians who took aspirin, 169 developed ulcers.

a. Define the parameters of interest. Assign symbols to these parameters.

b. State the appropriate null and alternative hypotheses in symbols.

c. Explain why it would be okay to use the theory-based method (that is, normal distribution based method) to find a confidence interval for this study.

d. Use an appropriate applet to find and report the theory-based 95% confidence interval.

e. Does the 95% confidence interval contain 0? Were you expecting this? Explain your reasoning.

f. Interpret the 95% confidence interval in the context of the study.

g. Use the 95% confidence interval to state a conclusion about the strength of evidence in the context of the study.

h. Relatively speaking, is the 95% confidence interval narrow or wide? Explain why that makes sense.

5.3.29 Recall the data from the Physicians' Health Study: Of the 11,034 physicians who took the placebo, 138 developed ulcers during the study. Of the 11,037 physicians who took aspirin, 169 developed ulcers.

a. Recall that the formula for the standardized statistic in this scenario is

$$z = \frac{\hat{p}_1 - \hat{p}_2}{\sqrt{\hat{p}(1 - \hat{p})\left(\dfrac{1}{n_1} + \dfrac{1}{n_2}\right)}}.$$

Plug in relevant numbers into this formula and verify the value of the standardized statistic obtained using the applet.

b. Recall that the formula for the confidence interval in this scenario is

$$\hat{p}_1 - \hat{p}_2 \pm \text{multiplier} \times \sqrt{\left(\frac{\hat{p}_1(1 - \hat{p}_1)}{n_1} + \frac{\hat{p}_2(1 - \hat{p}_2)}{n_2}\right)}.$$

Plug in relevant numbers into this formula and verify the value of the 95% confidence interval obtained using the applet.

5.3.30 Recall the data from the Physicians' Health Study: Of the 11,034 physicians who took the placebo, 138 developed ulcers during the study. Of the 11,037 physicians who took aspirin, 169 developed ulcers.

a. Calculate the observed value of the relative risk of ulcers comparing physicians who took aspirin daily to those who took the placebo daily.

b. Suppose that you were to calculate a 95% confidence interval for the long-run relative risk of developing ulcers comparing aspirin-taking men (like those in the study) to non-aspirin-taking men. Will the number 1 lie within this interval? Explain your reasoning.

FAQ

5.3.31 Read FAQ 5.3.1 and answer the following questions.

a. When we conduct a simulation using cards, why is it that we like to fix the color of the cards (like having 17 of one color and 13 of another) and randomize which pile they get placed in?

b. If we don't have random assignment, what is the justification for shuffling cards to develop a null distribution?

SECTION 5.4

5.4.1* Suppose we have two sample proportions 40/100 = 0.40 and 120/400 = 0.30 and we want to calculate the standard error for completing a test of significance. We compute the overall proportion of success as:

A. (0.40 + 0.30)/2 = 0.35

B. 0.40 + 0.30 = 0.70

C. (40 + 120)/(100 + 400) = 160/500 = 0.32

D. 0.40 − 0.30 = 0.10

E. None of the above

5.4.2 The validity conditions for a two-sample z-test include:

A. You should have at least 10 successes and 10 failures in each group.

B. Each group should have a sample size of at least 20.

C. Your data must come from a simple random sample from some population.

D. You should have the same sample sizes in each group.

E. Your data must give significant results.

5.4.3* Which type of distribution is used in a two-sample z-test?

A. t-distribution

B. normal distribution

C. simulated null distribution

D. double proportion distribution

E. None of the above

5.4.4 The multiplier used for calculating a 90% two-sample z-interval for a difference in population proportions is:

A. 0.90

B. 1.645

C. 1.96

D. 2.576

E. 3.14

5.4.5* Suppose you are testing to see whether the proportion of males and females who voted in the last election differs. Which of the following is NOT a correct way to write out the null hypothesis?

A. The proportion of males in the population who voted in the last election is the same as the proportion of females in the population who voted in the last election.

B. $\pi_M = \pi_F$

C. $\pi_M - \pi_F = 0$

D. $\hat{p}_M = \hat{p}_F$

E. All the above are correct.

5.4.6 In a survey of college students, 50 of 80 females said they ate breakfast today, while 21 of 40 males said they ate breakfast today. Which of the following expressions gives a 95% confidence interval for the difference in the proportion of male and female students who ate breakfast today?

A. $0.100 \pm 1.96\sqrt{\dfrac{0.625(1 - 0.625)}{80} + \dfrac{0.525(1 - 0.525)}{40}}$

B. $0.100 \pm 1.96\sqrt{0.592(1 - 0.592)\left(\dfrac{1}{80} + \dfrac{1}{40}\right)}$

C. $0.100 \pm 1.96\sqrt{\dfrac{0.592(1 - 0.592)}{80} + \dfrac{0.592(1 - 0.592)}{40}}$

D. $0.100 \pm 1.645\sqrt{\dfrac{0.625(1 - 0.625)}{80} + \dfrac{0.525(1 - 0.525)}{40}}$

E. $0.100 \pm 1.645\sqrt{0.592(1 - 0.592)\left(\dfrac{1}{80} + \dfrac{1}{40}\right)}$

5.4.7* In a survey of college students, 50 of 80 females said they ate breakfast today, while 21 of 40 males said they ate breakfast today. Which of the following equations would you use to calculate the standardized statistic?

A. $z = (0.625 - 0.525)/$
$\sqrt{\dfrac{0.625(1 - 0.625)}{80} + \dfrac{0.525(1 - 0.525)}{40}}$

B. $z = (0.625 + 0.525)/\sqrt{0.592(1 - 0.592)\left(\dfrac{1}{80} + \dfrac{1}{40}\right)}$

C. $z = (0.625 - 0.525)/1.96\sqrt{0.592(1 - 0.592)\left(\dfrac{1}{80} + \dfrac{1}{40}\right)}$

D. $z = (0.625 + 0.525)/\sqrt{0.592(1 - 0.592)\left(\dfrac{1}{80} + \dfrac{1}{40}\right)}$

E. $z = (0.625 + 0.525)/\sqrt{0.592(1 - 0.592)\left(\dfrac{1}{80} + \dfrac{1}{40}\right)}$

5.4.8 Suppose a 95% confidence interval for the difference in the proportion of female and male students who regularly drink coffee is $(-0.023, 0.137)$. From this, can you conclude that you have strong evidence that there is a difference in the proportion of males and females who regularly drink coffee? Explain.

5.4.9* True or False? For each question below, indicate whether the statement is true or false. If the statement is false, briefly explain why.

a. In general, when sample sizes increase, the standard error of the statistic also increases.

b. The standard error of the difference in sample proportions is calculated the same way if you are conducting a test of significance or are calculating a confidence interval.

c. You should have at least 10 successes and 10 failures in each group for a two-proportion z-test to give you a valid p-value.

d. When comparing two proportions, 95% confidence intervals that include 0 generally correspond to two-sided p-values larger than 0.05.

5.4.10 Suppose you are getting ready to run a two-proportion z-test to see if the proportion of students who have studied statistics are more likely to always wear seatbelts in a car than those who haven't studied statistics. You find that 90 out of 100 students who have studied statistics always wear a

seatbelt and 85 out of 100 of those that haven't studied statistics always wear a seatbelt. You need to first check the validity conditions. How many successes and how many failures do you have in each of your groups? Do those numbers meet the validity condition?

5.4.11* Suppose you are conducting a test of significance in the following situations. For each of these, determine whether you should conduct a one-proportion z-test or a two-proportion z-test.

a. You want to test to see which cereal people prefer in a blind taste test, a name brand or a store brand. You find that 56% of your sample prefer the name brand and 44% prefer the store brand.

b. You want to test to see whether males and females differ in which cereal they prefer (name brand or store brand) in a taste test. You find that 62% of the females prefer the name brand and 58% of the males prefer the name brand.

5.4.12 Suppose you are conducting a test of significance in the following situations. For each of these, determine whether you should conduct a one-proportion z-test or a two-proportion z-test.

a. You want to test to see whether children and adults differ in terms of which type of chocolate they prefer (milk chocolate or dark chocolate). You find that 70% of the adults prefer dark chocolate and only 24% of the children prefer dark chocolate.

b. You want to test to see if people prefer milk chocolate or dark chocolate and find that 62% of your sample prefer dark chocolate and the other 38% prefer milk chocolate.

5.4.13* Suppose you sample from two large populations and find sample proportions of $\hat{p}_1 = 125/500$ and $\hat{p}_2 = 120/300$. Suppose you are going to complete a test of significance using these proportions to compare the population proportions.

a. Calculate and interpret the standard error of the statistic.

b. Calculate and interpret the standardized statistic.

5.4.14 Suppose you sample from two large populations and find sample proportions of $\hat{p}_1 = 125/500$ and $\hat{p}_2 = 120/300$. Suppose you are going to calculate a 95% confidence interval to estimate the difference in the population proportions.

a. Calculate and interpret the standard error of the statistic.

b. Calculate and interpret the margin of error.

c. Calculate and interpret the 95% confidence interval.

5.4.15* Through *Census at School* thousands of high school students are asked questions on a variety of topics that would be interesting to high school students. One question asks, "What is your favorite season?" Out of 468 randomly chosen high school students in Florida, 149 of them said winter, whereas 76 out of 458 randomly chosen high school students from New York said winter. We want to calculate a 95% confidence interval for the difference in the proportions of students in the populations of Florida and New York who prefer winter.

a. Describe the parameter we want to estimate and assign appropriate symbols to it.

b. What theory-based method will you use? Verify that the validity conditions are met for this method.

c. Construct the confidence interval showing the values you substitute into the formula.

d. Interpret the confidence interval you obtained in the context of the study.

5.4.16 The General Social Survey is conducted every year and asks a variety of questions to a representative sample of adults in the United States. In 2014, the survey showed that 417 out of 2,538 respondents said they read a newspaper every day. Twenty years earlier in 1994, the survey showed that 969 out of the 2,992 respondents said they read a newspaper every day. We want to calculate a 90% confidence interval for the difference in the proportions in the population who read the paper every day in 2014 compared to 1994.

a. Describe the parameter we want to estimate and assign appropriate symbols to it.

b. What theory-based method will you use? Verify that the validity conditions are met for this method.

c. Construct the confidence interval showing the values you substitute into the formula.

d. Interpret the confidence interval you obtained in the context of the study.

5.4.17* The General Social Survey is conducted every year and asks a variety of questions to a representative sample of adults in the United States. In 2014, the survey showed that 45.6% of the 2,538 respondents said they were married. Forty years earlier in 1974, the results showed that 77.8% of the 1,484 respondents said they were married. We want to calculate a 99% confidence interval for the difference in the proportions of the population that are married.

a. Describe the parameter we want to estimate and assign appropriate symbols to it.

b. What theory-based method will you use? Verify that the validity conditions are met for this method.

c. Construct the confidence interval showing the values you substitute into the formula.

d. Interpret the confidence interval you obtained in the context of the study.

5.4.18 Student researchers at Hope College were interested in cellphone usage by students on campus and how it varied during different times of the day. They observed students walking around campus during the afternoon and recorded that 48 out of 232 students observed were using their phones in some fashion. During the evening, they observed 45 out of 115 students using their phones. We will assume these are representative samples from the population of all students at this college. Is the proportion of students on their phones during the afternoon different than in the evening?

a. State the hypotheses either in words or using appropriate symbols.

b. Name the theory-based test that will be used and state and verify the validity conditions for the test chosen.

c. Calculate the test statistic (standardized statistic) and corresponding p-value.

d. State your conclusion (with appropriate justification based on your p-value and stated significance level) in the context of the research question. Be sure to address the issues of causation and generalizability as well.

5.4.19* Are metal bands used for tagging harmful to penguins? Researchers Saraux et al. (2011) reported in *Nature* the results of an investigation done to answer this question using a sample of 100 penguins near Antarctica. These penguins had already been tagged with RFID chips, and the researchers randomly assigned 50 of them to receive a metal band on their flippers in addition to the RFID chip. The other 50 penguins did not receive a metal band. Researchers found that 16 of the banded penguins were still living 4.5 years into the study and 31 of the unbanded penguins were still living. Are unbanded penguins more likely to be living after 4.5 years than banded penguins?

a. State the hypotheses either in words or using appropriate symbols.

b. Name the theory-based test that will be used and state and verify the validity conditions for the test chosen.

c. Calculate the test statistic (standardized statistic) and corresponding p-value.

d. State your conclusion (with appropriate justification based on your p-value and stated significance level) in the context of the research question. Be sure to address the issues of causation and generalizability as well.

5.4.20 Student researchers were completing a project on obedience by observing whether students would obey the instructions on a sign placed next to a bowl of candy. The sign read: "Have a great day! Please take <u>one</u>." They observed people taking candy out of the bowl from a place where they could see how many they took, but where those taking the candy didn't feel they were being observed. One of the things the researchers measured was whether the amount of candy in the bowl would affect whether people would take more than one piece of candy. When there was a large amount of candy in the bowl, 39 out of 96 people that took candy took more than one piece. When there was a small amount of candy in the bowl, 54 out of 109 people that took candy took more than one piece. Does the amount of candy in the bowl affect whether people disobey and take more than one piece?

a. State the hypotheses either in words or using appropriate symbols.

b. Name the theory-based test that will be used and state and verify the validity conditions for the test chosen.

c. Calculate the test statistic (standardized statistic) and corresponding p-value.

d. State your conclusion (with appropriate justification based on your p-value and stated significance level) in the context of the research question. Be sure to address the issues of causation and generalizability as well.

END OF CHAPTER

5.CE.1* Suppose that you collect data on two categorical variables and summarize the results in a 2 × 2 table of counts such as the following:

	Group A	Group B
Success		
Failure		

Your goal is to decide if the data provide strong evidence that Group A and Group B differ with regard to the long-run proportion of success.

a. Is it possible to investigate this question even when the sample sizes of the two groups are different? Explain your answer, as if to a friend who is skeptical.

b. Is it possible to investigate this question even when the sample sizes of the two groups are both less than 10? Explain your answer, as if to a friend who is skeptical.

5.CE.2 Reconsider the previous exercise.

a. If the observed proportion of successes turns out to be the same for both groups, would you expect the p-value to be very small, somewhat small, or not small at all? Explain.

b. If Group A results in only successes and Group B results in only failures, would you expect the p-value to be very small, somewhat small, or not small at all? Explain.

5.CE.3* Explain why the methods of this chapter are not appropriate for investigating the following research questions:

- Have teenagers in the United Kingdom read more Harry Potter books, on average, than teenagers in the United States?

- Do cows tend to produce more milk, on average, when they are spoken to by name than when they are not spoken to by name?

Praising children

5.CE.4 Psychologists investigated whether praising a child's intelligence, rather than praising his/her effort, tends to have negative consequences such as undermining their motivation (Mueller and Dweck, 1998). Children participating in the study were given a set of problems to solve. After the first set of problems, half of the children were randomly assigned to be praised for their intelligence, while the other half was praised for their effort. The children were then given another set of problems to solve and later told how many they got right. They were then asked to write a report about the problems for other children to read, including information about how many they got right. Some of the children misrepresented (i.e., lied about) how many they got right, as shown in the table below. Researchers were interested in learning whether there was a difference in the proportion of children who lied depending on how they were praised.

	Praised for intelligence	Praised for effort	Total
Misrepresented their score (lied)	11	4	15
Did not misrepresent (did not lie)	18	26	44
Total	29	30	59

a. Identify the explanatory and response variables in this study.

b. For each group, determine the proportion who lied and identify them with appropriate symbols.

c. Describe how you could use index cards to conduct a simulation analysis for determining whether the difference between these proportions is statistically significant. Include the following information in your description:

   i. How many cards you would use

   ii. How many would be marked how

   iii. How many you would deal out

   iv. Which kinds of cards you would count

   v. What you would compare the results to after you conducted a large number of repetitions

d. Use the appropriate applet to conduct a simulation with 1,000 repetitions. Sketch the resulting histogram, labeling the axes appropriately, and report the p-value from the applet.

e. Provide a complete, detailed interpretation (in one or two sentences) of what this p-value means in this context (i.e., probability of what, assuming what?)

f. Summarize your conclusion about whether the data provide evidence that praising a child's intelligence leads to more negative consequences than praising his/her effort. Be sure to address the issue of causation as well as the issue of significance.

Minority coaches*

5.CE.5 Professional baseball teams have one coach at first base and one coach at third base, with third base regarded as the more important and prestigious position. An article in the August 11, 2010, *New York Times* raised a concern that minority coaches are underrepresented at third base compared to first base. The article cited the following data:

- 27 of 60 base coaches in Major League Baseball (MLB) are members of minority groups
- 20 of the 27 minority coaches are first base coaches
- 10 of the 33 nonminority coaches are first base coaches

a. Is this an observational study or an experiment?

b. Identify the explanatory and response variables.

c. Organize these counts in a 2 × 2 table, with the explanatory variable in columns.

d. Conduct a simulation analysis and report the p-value.

e. Summarize your conclusion about whether the data provide strong evidence that minority coaches are more likely to be first base coaches than nonminorities.

f. Is drawing a cause-and-effect conclusion warranted in this study? Explain.

Nicotine lozenge

5.CE.6 A study conducted in 2002 by Shiffman, Dressler, Hajeh, and Gilburt investigated whether a nicotine lozenge is helpful for smokers trying to quit smoking. The researchers recruited smokers who were interested in quitting through advertisements near four sites in the United Kingdom and 11 sites in the United States. Those smokers who met the screening qualifications were randomly assigned to one of two groups: One group received nicotine lozenges and the other group received placebo lozenges. The subjects were compared on various background variables at the beginning of the study, and at the end of the study they were compared on whether or not they successfully abstained from smoking. Of the 459 subjects in the nicotine group, 42.9% were male. Of the 458 subjects in the placebo group, 40.2% were male.

a. Is this an observational study or an experiment?

b. Produce a 2 × 2 table of counts to represent these data.

c. Create a relevant graph to display the data.

d. Comment on whether the percentages seem to suggest a strong association between sex of participant and treatment.

e. Conduct an appropriate theory-based test to investigate whether the percentages of males differ significantly between the two groups. Report the test statistic and p-value and summarize your conclusion.

f. Do you think the researchers would be pleased with the result of this significance test. Explain why or why not.

5.CE.7 Reconsider the previous exercise. At the end of the 52-week study, 17.9% of those in the nicotine group had successfully abstained from smoking, compared to 9.6% of those in the placebo group.

a. Produce a 2 × 2 table of counts to represent these data.

b. Create a relevant graph to display the data.

c. Calculate and interpret the *difference* in the conditional proportions who had successfully abstained from smoking.

d. Calculate and interpret the *ratio* of the conditional proportions who had successfully abstained from smoking.

e. Conduct an appropriate theory-based test to investigate whether the percentages who successfully abstained from smoking differ significantly between the two groups. Report the test statistic and p-value and summarize your conclusion.

f. Do you think the researchers would be pleased with the result of this significance test? Explain why or why not.

g. Do you think a cause-and-effect conclusion (between using the nicotine lozenge and being more likely to abstain from smoking) is justified based on this study? Explain.

5.CE.8 Reconsider the previous two exercises.

a. Determine a 95% confidence interval for the difference in long-run probabilities of successfully abstaining from smoking between the two groups.

b. Interpret what this interval reveals. Be sure to address the question of whether the data provide strong evidence that the nicotine lozenge is more effective than the placebo.

5.CE.9 Reconsider the previous three exercises. Now consider only the results for the nicotine lozenge, not for the placebo.

a. Determine a 95% confidence interval for the probability that a smoker who uses a nicotine lozenge will successfully abstain from smoking for 52 weeks.

b. Based on this confidence interval, would you conclude that a smoker has a very good chance of successfully quitting if he/she uses a nicotine lozenge? Explain your answer.

Attractiveness*

5.CE.10 A survey conducted by the Gallup organization in 1999 asked American adults whether they are satisfied with their physical attractiveness or wish they could be more attractive. The survey found that 71% of women and 81% of men responded that they were satisfied with their attractiveness.

a. Could this study have involved random sampling, random assignment, or both? Explain your answer.

b. Produce a (well-labeled) segmented bar graph to display these results.

c. State the relevant null and alternative hypotheses for testing whether these proportions differ significantly.

d. What additional information do you need in order to conduct a test of these hypotheses?

5.CE.11 Reconsider the previous exercise.

a. Suppose that the study had included 100 people of each sex. Determine the test statistic and p-value for testing whether the proportions who are satisfied with their attractiveness differ significantly between the two sexes using a theory-based test.

b. Now suppose that the study had included 500 people of each sex. Reanswer (a).

c. Summarize what this reveals about the role of sample sizes in a two-proportion z-test.

Credit cards

5.CE.12 The Nellie Mae organization conducts an extensive annual study of credit card usage by college students. For their 2004 study, they analyzed credit bureau data for a random sample of 1,413 undergraduate students between the ages of 18 and 24. They found that 76% of the students sampled held a credit card. Three years earlier they had found that 83% of undergraduates sampled held a credit card. (Assume that the sample size was similar in 2001.)

a. State the appropriate null and alternative hypotheses for testing whether the proportion of undergraduate students who held a credit card differed between these two years.

b. Conduct an appropriate test of these hypotheses. Report the test statistic and p-value and summarize your conclusion.

5.CE.13 Reconsider the previous exercise.

a. Determine a 90% confidence interval for the difference in proportions of undergraduates who held a credit card between the years 2001 and 2004.

b. Repeat (a) with a 95% confidence interval.

c. Repeat (a) with a 99% confidence interval.

d. Which (if any) of these intervals include the value 0? Summarize what you conclude from this.

5.CE.14 Reconsider the previous two exercises.

a. Describe what a Type I error would mean in this context.

b. Describe what a Type II error would mean in this context.

5.CE.15 Reconsider the previous three exercises.

a. Describe what power means in this study.

b. Would you expect that you could increase the power of a test by using a larger sample size or a smaller sample size? Explain.

c. Would you expect that using a smaller (more strict) significance level would increase or decrease the power of a test? Explain.

d. Would you expect that a larger difference between the groups would increase or decrease the power of a test? Explain.

Exciting life*

5.CE.16 The General Social Survey (GSS) is a large-scale national survey conducted every two years with a representative group of American adults. The 2 × 2 table below shows results from the 2010 survey regarding sex and whether the respondent considers life to be exciting:

	Male	Female
Exciting	303	336
Routine or dull	271	356

Analyze these data to investigate the question of whether men and women differ significantly with regard to whether or not they consider life to be exciting. Write a report of your findings that includes statistics, graphs, a test of significance, and a confidence interval.

5.CE.17 Reconsider the previous exercise. Using the same data but grouping "routine" with "exciting" rather than with "dull" produces the following 2 × 2 table:

	Male	Female
Exciting or routine	540	660
Dull	34	32

Analyze these data to investigate the question of whether men and women differ significantly with regard to whether or not they consider life to be *dull*. Write a report of your findings that includes statistics, graphs, a test of significance, and a confidence interval.

INVESTIGATION: DOES VITAMIN C IMPROVE YOUR HEALTH?

In 1970 Linus Pauling, a well-known chemist and Nobel Prize winning scientist, published *Vitamin C and the Common Cold* (1970), creating a great deal of public and scientific interest. In short, Pauling argued that taking Vitamin C would reduce one's risk of the common cold. This book almost singlehandedly made Vitamin C one of the most widely used dietary supplements, a status it retains to this day (*Nutritional Supplement Review*, 2009). Subsequent to the publishing of his book, Pauling wrote a paper that appeared in the *Proceedings of the National Academy of Sciences* in 1971. In this paper he describes a study conducted by a physician in Basel, Switzerland, in the early 1960s.

Here is an excerpt from the paper explaining the study design:

The study was carried out in a ski resort with 279 skiers during two periods of 5–7 days. The conditions were such that the incidence of colds during these short periods was large enough (about 20%) to permit results with statistical significance to be obtained. The subjects were roughly of the same age and had similar nutrition during the period of study. The investigation was double-blind, with neither the participants nor the physicians having any knowledge about the distribution of the ascorbic-acid tablets (1000 mg) and the placebo tablets. The tablets were distributed every morning and taken by the subjects under observation, so that the possibility of interchange of tablets was eliminated. The subjects were examined daily for symptoms of colds and other infections. The records were largely on the basis of subjective symptoms, partially supported by objective observations (measurement of body temperature, inspection of the respiratory organs, auscultation of the lungs, and so on). Persons who showed cold symptoms on the first day were excluded from the investigation.

After the completion of the investigation, a completely independent group of professional people was provided with the identification numbers for the ascorbic-acid tablets and placebo tablets, and this group performed the statistical evaluation of the observations.

Although not stated explicitly in the paragraph above, the participants were randomly assigned to take ascorbic-acid tablets or the placebo.

STEP 1: Ask a research question.

1. State the research question.

STEP 2: Design a study and collect data.

2. Is this study an experiment or an observational study? How are you deciding?
3. What are the observational/experimental units?
4. What are the variables that are measured/recorded on each unit?
5. Describe the parameters of interest in words. (You can use the symbol π to represent these parameters.)
6. State the null and alternative hypotheses for a test of significance to see whether this experiment provides statistically significant evidence that Vitamin C prevented colds in the skiers. Use a one-sided test.
7. Of the 139 skiers assigned to take Vitamin C, 17 developed a cold. Of the 140 skiers assigned to take a placebo, 31 developed a cold. Fill in the 2 × 2 table provided.

	Vitamin C	Placebo	Total
No cold			
Cold			
Total			

8. *Incidence* is the term used to describe the percent of the sample who onset with an illness over a certain time period. In this case, the incidence rates are the same as the conditional proportions. Find the incidence rates for individuals who received Vitamin C and those who received the placebo.

STEP 3: Explore the data.

9. What is the difference in incidence rates in the two groups? Before doing a test of significance, comment on whether you think this is evidence that Vitamin C prevents colds.

STEP 4: Draw inferences. Let's use our 3S strategy to help us investigate how much evidence the sample data provide to support our conjecture that Vitamin C prevents colds.

10. What is the statistic that you can use to summarize the data collected in the study?

11. Use the **Two Proportions** applet to carry out a test of significance.

12. When you shuffle, you are simulating one of the two hypotheses (null or alternative) to be true: Which one are you simulating?

13. What is the shape of your null distribution and where is its center located? Why does it make sense for the center to be located where it is?

14. Find the p-value of your test. Is this strong enough evidence for you to conclude that Vitamin C prevented colds in the skiers? Write a sentence stating your conclusion as it applies to the question. Remember to use words pertaining to the research question.

STEP 5: Formulate conclusions.

15. Can we generalize our conclusion to the entire human population? What should be true of the 279 skiers in order for your conclusion to be drawn to the entire human population? Discuss how the sample was obtained. Are there characteristics about the sample subjects that make this an unreasonable generalization?

16. Can we make a cause-and-effect conclusion? Why or why not?

STEP 6: Look back and ahead.

17. Summarize your findings from the study. What did you like about the study design? What would you change to improve the study? What further research might you want to do to follow up or expand upon the results in this study?

There continues to be a lot of controversy regarding the use of Vitamin C both in the prevention of colds and other negative health outcomes. Recently, the Physicians Health Study II was completed. In November 2008, a paper (Sesso et al., 2008) was published in the *Journal of the American Medical Association* which reported on some of the results of the Physicians Health Study II. Consider the following excerpt from the abstract of the paper:

> *The Physicians' Health Study II was a randomized, double-blind, placebo-controlled … trial of … vitamin C that began in 1997 and continued until its scheduled completion on August 31, 2007. There were 14,641 US male physicians enrolled, who were initially aged 50 years or older.*

18. Explain what it means for the Physicians' Health Study II to be….
   a. …randomized.
   b. …double-blind.
   c. …placebo-controlled.

19. Later in the paper we find out that 619 out of 7,329 men who got Vitamin C had a "major cardiovascular event" compared to 626 out of 7,312 men who got the placebo. We also read that the p-value for a *difference* in incidence rates is 0.91. Find the incidence rates, state the null and alternative hypotheses for a test of the effectiveness of Vitamin C, and draw inferences about the effectiveness of Vitamin C in preventing major cardiovascular events in this sample.

20. In the paper it states that "In this large, long-term trial of male physicians…vitamin C supplementation [did not] reduce the risk of major cardiovascular events. These data provide no support for the use of [vitamin C] for the prevention of cardiovascular disease in middle-aged and older men." Why do you think the authors specifically qualified their conclusion to say "middle-aged and older men?"

Final Comment: There are actually well over 1,000 different experiments that have been done on Vitamin C for cold prevention, heart attack prevention, and a multitude of other health benefits. The studies reported here are merely two of the more well-known studies. Neither study is conclusive, nor is there general consensus in the scientific community as to the health benefits of supplementing your diet with Vitamin C to attain levels beyond the minimal levels necessary to prevent scurvy.

Research Article   www.wiley.com/college/tintle

The Price of Fame   Read "Death in The New York Times: The Price of Fame Is a Faster Flame" by Epstein and Epstein (*QJ Med*, 2013, 106:517–521).

CHAPTER

Comparing Two Means

CHAPTER OVERVIEW

In the previous chapter, we switched our focus to comparisons of two groups. The studies in Chapter 5 involved a binary response variable and the parameters were either probabilities or population proportions. To summarize the data numerically, we computed conditional proportions, and for graphical displays we used segmented bar charts. In this chapter, we will continue to compare groups, but for a quantitative response variable. We will expand the study of quantitative variables that we began in Chapters 2 and 3 using dotplots, histograms, or boxplots (something new!) to explore the data and means and medians to summarize the data numerically.

Despite all that is new, the big picture remains the same as in Chapter 5. Following the usual six-step method, we start with the research hypothesis and study design, then display, explore, and summarize the data. To measure strength of evidence, we simulate the null distribution of the statistic and compute a p-value. To obtain an interval estimate for a parameter, we rely on the usual approaches (e.g., statistic ± 2SD). Finally, we assess the scope of inference: Can we generalize to some larger group? Is a conclusion about cause and effect justified?

The sections of Chapter 6 echo the sections of Chapter 5. The first section (with its two parts) is about displays and summaries of our sample data. Section 6.2 sets out a simulation-based approach to inference about the larger populations or processes (p-values and confidence intervals). Section 6.3 presents theory-based shortcuts. In the final section we take a closer look at theory-based methods with an eye to what will be expected of you on the AP exam.

Monkey Business Images/Shutterstock

COMPARING TWO GROUPS: QUANTITATIVE RESPONSE

INTRODUCTION

Recall some of the research questions you have seen so far. *Do people perceive their year differently depending on how you ask the question? Is dolphin therapy beneficial to depression patients? Is yawning contagious?* Notice that all of these scenarios involved *categorical* variables. But, as we saw in the Preliminaries and in Chapters 2 and 3, when we have a quantitative variable, we summarize our data differently.

In this section, you will learn about comparing groups of data on a *quantitative* response variable. We still want to reveal patterns exhibited by the sample data and will do so by focusing on the shape, center, and variability of the **distribution(s)** of quantitative data. We will also investigate any observations that do not appear to follow the general patterns in the data (e.g., outliers).

Geyser Eruptions

Recall the Old Faithful data we explored in Example P.2. Back in the Preliminaries, we investigated times between eruptions. We even compared the times between eruptions depending on whether the previous eruption had been long or short. Now we will examine data on the times between eruptions from two different years to see whether the distributions of these times appear to have changed between the years. In particular, you will examine data on 107 eruptions occurring between 6 AM and midnight between August 1 and August 8, 1978 (from Weisberg, 1985), and data on 95 eruptions from the same week in 2003 (gathered from http://www.geyserstudy.org/geyser.aspx?pGeyserNo=OLDFAITHFUL). Thus, variables (and potential sources of variability) such as season and weather should be consistent for the two data sets. Scientists have speculated that some geological event, such as an earthquake, might have changed Old Faithful's eruption patterns between these two years.

Example 6.1

EXAMPLE

6.1

> **THINK ABOUT IT**
>
> What are the observational units in this study? What are the two variables? What types of variables are these?

6.1.1

The observational units in this study are the geyser eruptions. The variables are the year (a categorical variable) and the time until the next eruption (a quantitative variable.) The dotplots in Figure 6.1 display the distributions of inter-eruption times for the two years.

FIGURE 6.1 "Parallel" dotplots (using the same scale along the horizontal axis) of the distributions of inter-eruption times at Old Faithful in 1978 and 2003.

6.1.2 ▶

What do we see in these graphs? One difference in the distributions of inter-eruption times between the two years concerns shape: The distribution in 2003 has a few low outliers. Apart from the outliers, we might say the distribution is slightly skewed to the right. In 1978, however, the distribution is clearly bimodal. Something was going on with this process in 1978 that led to inter-eruption times lasting between roughly 50 and 60 minutes or roughly 70 and 90 minutes, with very few times between 60 and 70 minutes. Also note that the outliers of less than 60 minutes we noted in the 2003 distribution would not have been unusual in 1978.

Perhaps the most obvious difference between these two years is that the inter-eruption times were generally longer in 2003 than in 1978. A typical inter-eruption time in 2003 was about 90–100 minutes, whereas in 1978 most inter-eruption times were between 50 and 60 minutes or between 75 and 85 minutes. The variability in the times also differs noticeably between these two years: The times in 2003 had much less variability than the times in 1978.

THINK ABOUT IT

How do you expect the means of the times between eruptions to differ between the two years? Based on the dotplots, estimate the values of the means and medians.

6.1.3 ▶

The means of the times between eruptions are 71.10 minutes in 1978 and 91.20 minutes in 2003. So, the average wait time until the next eruption was slightly more than 20 minutes longer in 2003 than in 1978. The medians are 75 and 91 minutes in 1978 and 2003, respectively. Notice that the mean time in 1978 is 4 minutes smaller than the median, because the mean is pulled lower by the lower (but smaller) clump of observations.

FAQ 6.1.1   www.wiley.com/college/tintle

When should you use median rather than the mean?

THINK ABOUT IT

How do you expect the standard deviations of times between eruptions to compare between the two years? Which year do you expect to have the larger standard deviation, or do you expect the two standard deviations to be quite similar?

Definitions

The value for which 25% of the data lie below that value is called the **lower quartile** (or 25th percentile). Similarly, the value for which 25% of the data lie above that value is called the **upper quartile** (or 75th percentile). Quartiles can be calculated by determining the median of the values above/below the location of the overall median. The difference between the quartiles is called the **inter-quartile range** (IQR), another measure of variability along with standard deviation. The **five-number summary** for the distribution of a quantitative variable consists of the minimum, lower quartile, median, upper quartile, and maximum.

The standard deviations of times turn out to be 12.90 and 8.50 minutes in 1978 and 2003, respectively. Notice that the 2003 distribution has a considerably smaller standard deviation than the 1978 distribution, indicating that the times between eruptions were more consistent (closer together) in 2003 than in 1978.

Another way to summarize the distribution of a quantitative variable such as time until the next eruption is by dividing the distribution into four pieces of roughly equal size (number of observations). In other words, we can summarize the distribution by determining where the bottom 25% of the data are, the next 25%, the next 25%, and then the top 25%.

The five-number summaries for the times between eruptions turn out to be:

	Minimum	Lower quartile	Median	Upper quartile	Maximum
1978 times	42	58	75	81	95
2003 times	56	87	91	98	110

An important characteristic of the IQR is that, like the median, it is not sensitive to extreme values—unlike the SD. For example, if the two lowest wait times (56 and 58 minutes) in 2003 are removed—they are a lot different than the rest of the wait times—the IQR (11) and the median (91) don't change. However, both the mean (91.19 before, 91.90 after) and standard deviation (8.46 before, 6.87 after) do change.

KEY IDEA

IQR is a resistant measure of variability, whereas the standard deviation is sensitive to extreme values and skewness.

Notice that all of the values in the five-number summary are smaller in the 1978 distribution than the corresponding values in the 2003 distribution, reflecting that 1978 generally had smaller wait times than 2003. A visual display of the five-number summary is called a **boxplot**. Figure 6.2 shows the parallel boxplots for these two distributions.

Definition

A **boxplot** is a visual display of the five-number summary. The box displays the middle 50% of the distribution and its width (the IQR) helps us see the spread of the bulk of the distribution; the whiskers extend to the smallest and largest values in the data set.

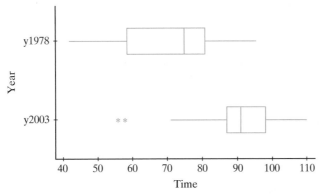

FIGURE 6.2 Parallel boxplots (using the same scale along the horizontal axis) of the distributions of inter-eruption times at Old Faithful in 1978 and 2003.

Notice in Figure 6.2 that the outliers we visually identified in 2003 are plotted separately and the whisker extends to the next observation which is not considered an outlier. (The most common criterion to identify an observation as an outlier is if it falls more than $1.50 \times$ IQR from the edge of the box. See FAQ 6.1.2 for details.)

FAQ 6.1.2   www.wiley.com/college/tintle

What is an outlier?

These boxplots give us a very quick comparison of the two distributions. We immediately see that the quickest 75% of times in 1978 were below the longest 75% of times in 2003. We also see that the length of the box (IQR) is much smaller in 2003, reflecting the smaller variability in those times. But you may also notice one disadvantage of boxplots: You can lose some important details about the shape of your distribution. For example, we wouldn't notice the two clusters of observations in 1978 that we saw in the dotplots. For this reason, we recommend examining boxplots in combination with dotplots and histograms as well.

THINK ABOUT IT

Based on the distributions of times between eruptions, in which year would you have preferred to be a tourist waiting for the next eruption of Old Faithful? Can you think of one way in which 1978 would have been preferable and a different way in which 2003 would have been preferable?

If you are a tourist who cares most about having a shorter wait for the next eruption, you would have preferred 1978 to 2003 because the average wait time in 1978 was about 20 minutes less than in 2003. But if your primary concern is being able to predict accurately when the next eruption would occur, you would have preferred 2003 to 1978 because the variability in wait times was much smaller in 2003.

EXPLORATION 6.1A | **Haircut Prices**

Do women pay more than men for haircuts? Is this a statistical tendency or always true? By how much do women spend more than men, on average? How much do haircut prices vary within a sex as well as between sexes?

To investigate these questions a professor asked students in her class to report the cost of their most recent haircut, along with their sex.

1. Which would you consider to be the explanatory variable and which the response? Also classify the type (categorical or quantitative) for each variable.

Explanatory:	Type:
Response:	Type:

2. Is this an experiment or an observational study? Explain briefly.

3. Did the professor who collected the data make use of random sampling, random assignment, both, or neither?

The following "parallel" dotplots (using the same scale along the horizontal axis) reveal the sample distributions of haircut prices for each sex:

4. Compare and contrast the distributions of haircut prices between men and women in this class. (*Hint:* As you learned in the Preliminaries, comment on center, variability, shape, and unusual observations. You should give enough detail that someone reading your comments could re-create the overall pattern of the graphs from your description. Also be sure to relate your comments to the context.)

5. Further explore the data.

   a. Explain why the right skewness of these distributions makes sense in this context.

   b. Explain why the unusual behavior at the lower end of the dotplots—several values at $0 and then a gap to the next smallest prices—makes sense in this context.

6. Based on the dotplots (without performing any calculations), make a guess for each sex's mean haircut price.

Men:	Women:

7. Based on the dotplots (without performing any calculations), which sex do you think has the larger standard deviation of haircut prices? Explain your answer.

8. Copy the haircut data, which you can access from the book's website, to the clipboard. Open the **Descriptive Statistics** applet. Check the **Stacked** check box (notice the applet assumes the explanatory variable is the first column and the response variable is the second column.) Also keep the **Includes header** box checked and press **Clear**. Paste the data into the **Sample data** box and press **Use Data**. You should see that the dotplots are similar to the ones shown previously. Check the **Actual** boxes to show the means and standard deviations (Std dev).

   a. Report the sample size, mean haircut price, and standard deviation (SD) of haircut prices for each sex. (Include appropriate symbols and measurement units.)

	Sample size	Sample mean	Sample SD
Men			
Women			

   b. Which sex has the larger mean haircut price? Is this what you predicted in #6?

   c. Which sex has the larger SD of haircut prices? Is this what you predicted in #7?

9. Would you conclude that these data show an *association* between haircut price and a person's sex? If so, describe the nature of this association.

10. Let's return to the research questions that we started with. Address these questions based on the previous graphs and statistics.

   a. Do women pay more than men for haircuts? If so, is this a statistical tendency (i.e., true on average) or always true?

   b. By how much do women spend more than men, on average?

11. Do the unequal sample sizes between the two sexes lead you to doubt whether any conclusions can be drawn from these data? Explain.

12. Based on how these data were collected, would you feel comfortable generalizing your results to the population of all college students in the U.S.? How about the population of all college students at the professor's university? Explain your answers.

13. Based on both the differences in centers and the amount of overlap in the distributions of haircut prices between men and women, do you predict that the difference will turn out to be statistically significant? (You will learn how to assess statistical significance in the next section.)

Further analyses

The individual values of the haircut prices that you have been analyzing are:

Women ($n = 37$):	0, 0, 0, 15, 15, 15, 20, 20, 20, 25, 30, 30, 35, 35, 35, 40, 45, 45, 45, 45, 50, 50, 50, 50, 55, 60, 65, 70, 70, 75, 90, 110, 120, 120, 150, 150, 150
Men ($n = 13$):	0, 0, 0, 14, 15, 15, 20, 20, 20, 22, 23, 60, 75

As you learned in Section 3.2, the median is the middle value in a data set once the values are arranged in order. The location of the median can be found by calculating $(n + 1)/2$.

14. Now let's look at the median haircut prices and compare them to the mean haircut price.

   a. Determine (by hand) the median haircut price for each sex. (You can verify your calculation by checking the **Actual** box for the **Median** in the applet.)

   Median haircut price for women:

   Median haircut price for men:

Definitions

The value for which 25% of the data lie below that value is called the *lower quartile* (or 25th percentile). Similarly, the value for which 25% of the data lie above that value is called the **upper quartile** (or 75th percentile). Quartiles can be calculated by determining the median of the values above/below the location of the overall median. The difference between the quartiles is called the *inter-quartile range* (IQR), another measure of variability along with standard deviation. The *five-number summary* for the distribution of a quantitative variable consists of the minimum, lower quartile, median, upper quartile, and maximum.

Definition

A *boxplot* is a visual display of the five-number summary. The box displays the middle 50% of the distribution and its width (the IQR) helps us compare the spread of the distribution; the whiskers extend to the smallest and largest values in the data set.

   b. Which sex has the larger median haircut price? Is this what you expected?

   c. Are the medians less than or greater than the means? Is this consistent with the right-skewed distributions of haircut prices? Explain.

One way to summarize the distribution of a quantitative variable such as haircut price is by dividing the distribution into four pieces of roughly equal size (number of observations). In other words, summarize the distribution by determining where the bottom 25% of the data are, the next 25%, the next 25%, and then the top 25%.

15. Explore the data using quartiles and the five-number summary.

   a. Calculate the lower quartile for the women's haircut prices. First note that the median is the $(37 + 1)/2 = 19$th ordered value. So, the lower quartile is the median of the bottom 18 values, which is found in position $(18 + 1)/2 = 9.50$. So, the lower quartile is the average of the 9th and 10th ordered values from the bottom.

   b. Similarly, calculate the upper quartile for the women's haircut prices.

   c. Calculate the lower and upper quartiles for the men's haircut prices.

16. Report the five-number summary for the women's haircut prices and for the men's haircut prices:

	Minimum	Lower quartile	Median	Upper quartile	Maximum
Women's haircut prices					
Men's haircut prices					

17. In the applet, check the box for **Boxplot** to overlay the two boxplots as well. Describe what the boxplots reveal about how the distributions of haircut prices compare between male and female students in the professor's class.

18. Find the IQR for both the men's and women's haircut prices.

One advantage to the IQR is that it is not sensitive to extreme values/outliers like the standard deviation is. Just like the median is not sensitive to extreme values/outliers, but the mean is.

KEY IDEA

The IQR is a resistant measure of variability, whereas the standard deviation is sensitive to extreme values and skewness.

19. Remove the male haircut price of $75 from the data and (in the applet) find the new SD and IQR. Compare them to the values you had earlier and confirm that this illustrates that the IQR is more resistant to extreme values than the SD.

More data

20. Collect data from yourself and your classmates on most recent haircut price and sex. Enter the data into the applet and examine dotplots, boxplots, and summary statistics. Write a paragraph or two summarizing what the data reveal about whether haircut price is *associated* with the sex of your classmates. Also address the research questions with which this exploration began. Finally, comment on how broadly you would be willing to *generalize* your findings.

Cancer Pamphlets

Researchers in Philadelphia investigated whether pamphlets containing information for cancer patients are written at a level that the cancer patients can comprehend (Short, Moriarty, and Cooley, 1995). They applied tests to measure the reading levels of 63 cancer patients and also the readability levels of 30 cancer pamphlets (based on such factors as the lengths of sentences and number of polysyllabic words). These numbers correspond to grade levels, but patient reading levels of under grade 3 and above grade 12 are not determined exactly.

Table 6.1 indicates the number of patients at each reading level and the number of pamphlets at each readability level.

TABLE 6.1 Comparing of pamphlet readability and patient reading levels

Patients' reading levels	<3	3	4	5	6	7	8	9	10	11	12	>12	Total
Count (number of patients)	6	4	4	3	3	2	6	5	4	7	2	17	63

Pamphlets' readability levels	6	7	8	9	10	11	12	13	14	15	16	Total
Count (number of pamphlets)	3	3	8	4	1	1	4	2	1	2	1	30

1. Explain why the way these data are presented do not allow for you to calculate the *mean* reading level of a patient.

2. Determine the *median* reading level of a patient and the median readability level of a pamphlet. (*Hint:* First note that there are 63 patients and 30 pamphlets.)

Patient:	Pamphlet:

3. How do these medians compare? Are they fairly close?

4. Does the closeness of these medians indicate that the pamphlets are well matched to the patients' reading levels? Explain.

5. What proportion of the patients in the study do not have the reading skill level necessary to read even the simplest pamphlet in the study?

6. Do you want to rethink your answer to #4 in light of your answer to #5?

This exploration reveals that measures of center (or even variability) do not always tell the whole story when you are analyzing data to address a particular research question. In this case the research question of whether pamphlets' readability levels are well-aligned with patients' reading levels requires looking at the entire distributions, not simply at measures of center.

SECTION 6.1 Summary

With **quantitative** as well as categorical variables, the first steps in exploring data are to produce graphs and calculate summary statistics.

- When comparing two groups with a quantitative response variable, *parallel dotplots* can display the distributions on the same scale.
  - Examining the centers of the dotplots and calculating means (averages) can reveal whether one group has a tendency toward larger or smaller values than the other.

- Examining the variability of the distributions and calculating standard deviations (SDs) can reveal whether one group has more variability (less consistency) than the other.
- Comparing medians between the groups can be more informative than comparing means when the distributions are skewed or when outliers are present.
  - The **inter-quartile range** (IQR) provides a resistant alternative to the standard deviation as a measure of variability.

- The **five-number summary** can be used to summarize the distribution of a quantitative variable. This summary consists of the minimum, lower quartile, median, upper quartile, and maximum.
  - **Boxplots** provide a visual display of the five-number summary. Comparing the overlap and width of the boxplots helps illuminate differences in center and spread of two or more distributions.

SECTION 6.1: Part 2

COMPARING DISTRIBUTIONS FOR A QUANTITATIVE RESPONSE VARIABLE

INTRODUCTION

In this section you will expand the study of quantitative variables that you began in Chapters 2 and 3 and continued in Part 1 of this section. You will see two other types of graphs, *stemplots* and *cumulative frequency plots*, that can also be used to explore and compare distributions of quantitative variables. You will also examine the calculations associated with boxplots in more detail, including a formal rule for identifying observations that are far from the bulk of the distribution (also see FAQ 6.1.2).

TV Viewing Habits

Example 6.1.2A

Census at School is an international classroom project in which students from grades 4–12 complete a brief online survey. One of the questions asked is, "Estimate how many hours a week you usually spend watching TV." A random sample of 25 U.S. high school students who completed the survey in 2015 was taken. The data for TV viewing hours per week by the students in this sample (sorted from smallest to largest) have been grouped by sex and listed below.

Females (self-report of number of hours of TV watched per week):

0, 1, 1, 2, 3, 3, 5, 8, 8, 10, 12, 20, 24

Males (self-report of number of hours of TV watched per week):

0, 0, 0, 0, 1, 2, 2, 4, 4, 12, 15, 15

THINK ABOUT IT

What are the observational units? What are the two variables measured on each observational unit, and are they categorical or quantitative? What is the explanatory variable? What is the response variable?

In this study, each of the 25 U.S. high school students in this random sample is an observational unit. The explanatory variable is sex (male or female), which is categorical, and the response variable is number of hours of TV watched per week, which is quantitative.

In the Preliminaries chapter, you were introduced to dotplots as a way to visualize data from a single quantitative variable. In the first part of Section 6.1, you saw that "parallel" dotplots (using the same scale along the horizontal axis) and side-by-side boxplots are useful graphical displays for comparing two groups with a quantitative response variable.

Stemplots, unlike boxplots and histograms (Chapter 2), maintain the individual numerical values of the data set. This is advantageous with smaller data sets but could become impractical for a large data set (especially where the exact numerical values may be less informative than the overall pattern).

We begin by examining just the self-reported number of hours of TV watched per week for the 13 females in our sample. A stemplot consists of a **stem**, all but the final digit of a number, and a **leaf**, the final digit. For this data set, our stem will be the tens digits and the leaves will be the ones digits. [*Note:* Depending on the level of detail in your measurements, you may want to round or truncate the data values before creating the stems and leaves.]

Because the number of hours watched for females is always less than 20, there are three "stems": 0, 1, and 2, representing observed values in the single digits, the 10s, and the 20s, respectively. We will begin by arranging the stems vertically from smallest to largest without skipping any stems, even if there are no data for a particular stem. A vertical line is drawn to the right of the stems.

```
0 |
1 |
2 |
```

Each leaf is written in the row to the right of its stem in ascending order.

```
0 | 0 1 1 2 3 3 5 8 8
1 | 0 2
2 | 0 4
```

A key is also included to indicate what a stem and leaf represent in addition to the units.

Key: 1 | 0 = 10 self-reported number of hours per week spent watching TV

THINK ABOUT IT

How would you describe the distribution of self-reported hours of TV watched per week for the females in our sample of U.S. high school students in 2015?

As we noted in previous chapters, to describe the distribution of a single quantitative variable, you should note the shape, center, variability, and any unusual features such as gaps or outliers.

But, with only three stems, the stemplot makes it a bit harder to visualize the shape, and it is also difficult to determine visually whether the values representing 20 and 24 hours of TV viewing per week (notice we can read these numerical values directly off the graph) are unusual. Is there a better way?

A stemplot with *split stems* may provide more information on the shape of the distribution and on values that may be potential outliers (similar to dividing the bin widths in a histogram in half).

Self-Reported Number of Hours of TV Watched per Week

(for a sample of 13 female U.S. high school students who completed the 2015 *Census at School* survey)

```
0 | 0 1 1 2 3 3
0 | 5 8 8
1 | 0 2
1 |
2 | 0 4
```

Key: 1|0 = 10 self-reported number of hours per week spent watching TV

Definition

A **stemplot** (also called a **stem-and-leaf plot**) is a useful method for visualizing small- to medium-sized data sets for a single quantitative response variable consisting of a stem, all but the final digit of a number, and a leaf, the final digit. (Sometimes, numbers are truncated before building the stemplot so the leaf does not consist of the final digit, but the digit immediately after the digit or digits in the stem.)

Definition

In a **split stemplot**, each stem is listed twice in the stemplot (doubling the number of stems), with data values (or "leaves") 0, 1, 2, 3, 4 on the row of the first occurrence of the stem and data values (or "leaves") 5, 6, 7, 8, 9 on the second occurrence.

6.1P2.1

This split stemplot makes commenting about the shape, center, variability, and outliers easier than the original stemplot. In particular, we notice that the distribution of self-reported hours per week spent watching TV for the 13 female U.S. high school students in our sample is skewed to the right, with the females who watch 20 and 24 hours of TV per week being a bit unusual (possible outliers).

> ### THINK ABOUT IT
>
> What if we wanted to compare the distribution of TV viewing habits for the females to that of the males in our sample of U.S. high school students: Could we use a stemplot?

Definition

In a **back-to-back stemplot**, the stems are arranged in a column with a vertical line on each side. Leaves representing one of the groups extend from the right vertical line in ascending order and leaves representing the other group extend from the left vertical line, also in ascending order. Above each set of leaves, we provide a label identifying the group (e.g., females, males).

To compare the TV viewing habits for the female and male high school students in our sample, we would use a **back-to-back stemplot**.

Split Stemplot Comparing Male and Female Self-Reported Number of Hours of TV Watched per Week

(for a sample of U.S. high school students who completed the 2015 *Census at School* survey)

```
      Males            Females
4 4 2 2 1 0 0 0 0 │ 0 │ 0 1 1 2 3 3
                  │ 0 │ 5 8 8
                2 │ 1 │ 0 2
              5 5 │ 1 │
                  │ 2 │ 0 4
```

Key: 1 | 0 = 10 estimated number of hours per week spent watching TV

6.1P2.2

To compare the distribution of hours of TV watched for the U.S. high school students in our 2015 sample from *Census at School*, we should compare the shape, center, and variability of the distributions for the two groups, and note any unusual features.

Overall, the male students in our sample tend to watch fewer hours of TV per week than the female high school students in the sample. This is supported if we calculate the medians (it's convenient that the observations have already been sorted). With 13 females, the median lands on the 7th observation (6 observations below and 6 observations above): 5 hours/week. With 12 males, the median falls between the 6th and 7th observations (6 observations below and 6 observations above) and to calculate the value of the median, we average the 6th and 7th observations: 2 hours/week.

There is a good bit of variability in the weekly hours of TV watched for both males and females, with more variability among the female students' TV viewing habits (range of 24 hours per week) than in the male students' TV viewing habits (range of 15 hours per week). The shape of both distributions is skewed to the right, with self-reported weekly viewing hours of 12 and 15 representing potential outliers for the males and 20 and 24 hours representing potential outliers for the females in the sample. Note that none of the male students sampled watched more than 15 hours of TV per week, compared to the maximum of 24 hours for the females.

6.1P2.3

AP TIP

When asked to compare one or more groups for a quantitative response variable, make sure to use comparative words such as "more," "less," or "about the same" when comparing the centers and variability of the groups. Simply listing the attributes of each group without comparing those attributes will result in losing points on the AP exam. For example, don't just say that the median for males is 2 hours/week and the median for females is 5 hours/week. Instead, point out that the median for males (2 hours/week) is smaller than the median for females (5 hours/week).

THINK ABOUT IT

What if your data set contained a large number of values? Would you want to construct a dotplot or a stemplot (particularly if you are not using technology!)?

With large data sets, the individual numerical values become less meaningful and we want to focus more on the overall pattern and comparisons across groups. Histograms and boxplots are often better suited in these cases. Boxplots were introduced in Section 6.1, and in Example 6.1.2.B you will explore the calculation details in greater depth, as well as how to identify outliers using the "1.5 IQR rule."

Who Travels More Frequently?

EXPLORATION

6.1.2A

Do male high school students travel more than females? Is this a statistical tendency or always true? What is a typical number of U.S. states visited by high school students and by how much does it vary between the two sexes?

To investigate these questions, a high school AP Statistics teacher asked the students in her class how many states in the U.S. they had visited.

Females (number of states visited):

12, 14, 15, 15, 16, 5, 17, 20, 24, 10, 12, 12, 18, 19, 19, 12, 15, 22, 15, 32, 16, 14, 9, 14

Males (number of states visited):

20, 17, 16, 12, 7, 11, 18, 22, 23, 9, 14, 16, 17, 23, 11, 15

1. What are the observational units?

2. What variables are measured on these observational units?

3. Which would you consider to be the explanatory variable and which the response? Also classify the type (categorical or quantitative) for each variable.

    Explanatory: Type:

    Response: Type:

You've already seen graphical displays called dotplots as a way to visualize data from a quantitative variable in the Preliminaries chapter and histograms in Chapter 2. Earlier in Section 6.1, you saw that "parallel" dotplots (using the same scale along the horizontal axis) and side-by-side boxplots are useful graphical displays for comparing two groups with a quantitative response variable. But both, especially boxplots, can hide some important details. So let's consider another type of graph, a *stemplot*.

Definition

A *stemplot* (also called a *stem-and-leaf plot*) is a useful method for visualizing small- to medium-sized data sets for a single quantitative response variable consisting of a stem, all but the final digit of a number, and a leaf, the final digit. (Sometimes, numbers are truncated before building the stemplot so the leaf does not consist of the final digit, but the digit immediately after the digit or digits in the stem.)

Stemplots and dotplots, unlike boxplots and histograms, maintain the individual values of the data set. To create a stemplot, we split each value in our data set into two pieces, a **stem**, all but the final digit, and a **leaf**, the final digit. For this data set, our stem will be the tens digits and the leaves will be the ones digits. [*Note:* Depending on the level of detail in your measurements, you may want to round or truncate the data values before creating the stems and leaves.]

4. Let's first construct a stemplot for the number of states *females* have visited.

   a. What is the smallest value in the data set? The largest? If we take the first digit of each of these values, what does that suggest using for the stems? (*Hint:* There should be 3 stems.)

   b. Arrange the stems vertically on the left side of the vertical line below from smallest to largest without skipping any stems, even if there are no data for a particular stem.

   c. Now attach each leaf to the appropriate stem by writing it in the same row to the right of the vertical line.

   d. Now rearrange the stems on each leaf in increasing order. (*Hint:* You can try to do (c) and (d) in one step, but make sure to cross out the values as you use them so you don't miss any!)

   e. Finally, a key is also included to indicate what a stem and leaf represent in addition to the units.

Key: 1 | 0 = _____ U.S. states visited (Use 0.10, 1.0, 10, 100)

5. How would you describe the distribution of number of states visited for the females in our sample of statistics students? (*Hint:* There are four separate characteristics you should address.)

As we noted in previous chapters, to describe the distribution of a single quantitative variable, we should note the shape, center, variability, and any unusual features such as gaps or outliers. With so few stems, you might have found it challenging to describe the shape. It is also a bit difficult to determine visually whether or not the value representing 32 states is unusual.

A stemplot with "split stems" may provide more information on the shape of the distribution and on values that may be potential outliers. This is like using histogram bins that are half as wide.

6. Construct a split stemplot for the number of states females have visited. (*Hints:* Remember to start with twice as many stems. Don't forget to include the key at the bottom.)

Key:

7. Now describe the distribution of number of states visited by females in the sample.

What if we wanted to compare the distribution of number of states female students had visited to that of the males in our sample: Could we use a stemplot? To compare the number of states visited for the female and male students in our sample, we would use a ***back-to-back stemplot***.

8. Construct a back-to-back stemplot of the number of states visited for both the females and the males in our sample.

9. Compare the distributions of number of states visited for the females and the males. Make sure to compare center, shape, and variability, and to note any unusual features.

> **Definition**
>
> In a ***back-to-back stemplot***, the stems are arranged in a column with a vertical line on each side. Leaves representing one of the groups extend from the right vertical line, in ascending order, and leaves representing the other group extend from the left vertical line, also in ascending order. Above each set of leaves, we provide a label identifying the group (e.g., females, males).

AP TIP

When asked to compare one or more groups for a quantitative response variable, make sure to use comparative words such as "more," "less," or "about the same" when comparing the centers and variability of the groups. Simply listing the attributes of each group rather than comparing them will result in a weaker response on the AP exam.

KEEP IN MIND

What if our data set contained a large number of values? Graphical displays such as dotplots and stemplots would become tedious to construct (particularly if we are not using technology!).

In the next example we will look at how the five-number summary can help us construct a modified boxplot to graphically summarize larger amounts of data.

6.1.2B

TV Viewing Habits Revisited

Example 6.1.2B

EXAMPLE

In the previous example, you used a side-by-side, split stemplot to compare the (self-reported) viewing habits of males and females.

Males		Females
4 4 2 2 1 0 0 0 0	0	0 1 1 2 3 3
	0	5 8 8
2	1	0 2
5 5	1	
	2	0 4

Key: 1 | 0 = 10 estimated number of hours per week spent watching TV

Because these data have been sorted, it would be straightforward to calculate the five-number summary for each distribution as well.

Previously, we found the medians to be 5 hours per week watching TV (females) and 2 hours per week (males), each with 6 observations falling below and 6 observations falling above the median. To find the lower and upper quartiles, we find the median of each "half" of the data set. For the 6 values below the median for the males, the median of those values falls between the 3rd and 4th observations: $(0 + 0)/2 = 0$ hours—this is the lower quartile (or 25th percentile, with 25% of the data, 3 observations, falling below that value). The upper quartile is between the 3rd and 4th values *from the maximum value*, value $= (12 + 4)/2 = 8$ hours. Notice that you need to count down from the largest values to find the upper quartile. Also notice how the stem information was used in these calculations. Combining these values with the min (0 hours) and the max (15 hours) gives us the five-number summary for the males' distribution: 0, 0, 2, 8, 15 hours.

BEYOND AP STATISTICS

Some software packages use different algorithms, but the general idea is the same.

THINK ABOUT IT

Determine the five-number summary for the females. How do the five values compare to the males'? Keep in mind that there are 13 females.

When the median falls on one of the data values (an odd number of observations), we use the values below that one to find the lower quartile. In this case, the median of the 6 values below the 5 would be $(1 + 2)/2 = 1.5$ hours and the median of the 6 values above the 5 would be $(10 + 12)/2 = 11$ hours.

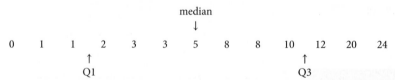

With a five-number summary of 0, 1.5, 5, 11, and 24 hours, we see again that the females tend to watch more TV. In particular, four of the five numbers in the five-number summary are larger for the females.

6.1P2.4

TABLE 6.1.1 Five-number summaries						
		Min	**Q1**	**Median**	**Q3**	**Max**
Males		0	0	2	8	15
Females		0	1.5	5	11	24

Would it make sense to look at comparative boxplots for these data?

Using the five-number summaries, we can construct boxplots for these data. Figure 6.1.1 shows these boxplots superimposed on the dotplots.

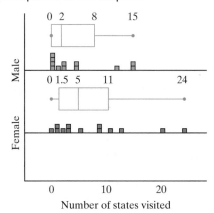

FIGURE 6.1.1 Dotplots and boxplots for the number of hours of television watched.

6.1P2.5

Note: Recall that the box displays the middle 50% of the distribution and its width (the IQR) helps us see the spread of the middle half the distribution.

THINK ABOUT IT

Why is there no left whisker for the male boxplot?

These graphs convey very similar information as the stemplots. In fact, the boxplots "reduce" our data to five observations. But these were fairly small samples to begin with! The boxplots have lost some information about grouping of the values (e.g., all integers), and both the boxplots and the dotplots prevent us from quickly seeing the exact numerical values. The boxplot also makes it difficult to highlight unusual observations. One alternative is a *modified boxplot*.

THINK ABOUT IT

What is the interquartile range (IQR) for each distribution? What are the cut-offs using the 1.5 IQR rule?

For males, IQR = 8 − 0 = 8 hours and 1.5 × 8 = 12. We will not have any low outliers because the lower quartile is the same as the min. If we extend 12 beyond the upper quartile, we land at 20 and 20 > 15 (our max), so we don't have any high outliers either.

For females, IQR = 11 − 1.5 = 9.5 hours and 1.5 × 9.5 = 14.25. If we extend 14.25 below 1.5, we are less than zero so there are no low outliers. If we extend 14.25 above 11, we land at 25.25 > 24. Therefore, neither the 20 or 24 values would be considered outliers using this criterion.

BUT WHAT IF?

What if the max in our data set had been 30 rather than 24 states. Notice that this would not change our interquartile range or the cut-off we just found, and the observation of 30 would be considered a high outlier. In this case, we could represent this outlier in our boxplots with a separate symbol, extending the whisker instead to the largest non-outlier (20, not the cut-off) as shown in Figure 6.1.2.

Definition

In a ***modified boxplot***, we display outliers with an asterisk or other identifying symbol. One mathematical rule for calculating whether an observation would be considered an outlier is to consider any data value more than 1.5 times the inter-quartile range (IQR) below the lower quartile (Q1) a ***low outlier*** (Q1 − 1.5 × IQR); and to consider any data value that is more than 1.5 times the IQR above the upper quartile (Q3) a ***high outlier*** (Q3 + 1.5 × IQR).

FIGURE 6.1.2 Modified boxplots for the number of hours of television watched.

AP TIP

On the AP exam, if a boxplot is asked for, it is understood to mean a modified boxplot.

Other than identifying the outlier from the 1.5 IQR rule, the boxplot has not really revealed any *new* information. The advantage of the stemplot was being able to see the exact numerical values (e.g., 20, 24 hours). Boxplots are often preferred for larger data sets where the comparison of interest is about the center or variability of the distributions. With technology, it's never a bad idea to look at more than one graph as they will often reveal different key features.

Another graph that you may encounter is a *cumulative frequency plot*. As with quartiles, the focus is on the percentage of observations below a value. Using the 13 sorted values for the females, we can determine the percentage of observations at or below each unique value.

Females:

0	1	2	3	5	8	10	12	20	24
1/13 ≈ 7.7%	3/13 ≈ 23%	4/13 ≈ 31%	6/13 ≈ 46%	7/13 ≈ 54%	9/13 ≈ 69%	10/13 ≈ 77%	11/13 ≈ 85%	12/13 ≈ 92%	13/13 = 100%

Similarly for the 12 males:

0	1	2	4	12	15
4/12 ≈ 33%	5/12 ≈ 42%	7/12 ≈ 58%	9/12 = 75%	10/12 ≈ 83%	12/12 = 100%

Then we can plot these percentages against the variable values, typically connecting the dots. For a comparative graph, put them both on the same scale (e.g., Figure 6.1.3).

Definition

A *cumulative frequency plot* is a plot of each unique data value and the percentage of the distribution at or below that value.

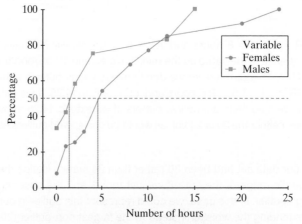

FIGURE 6.1.3 Cumulative frequency plots for males and females, with approximate median values highlighted.

6.1P2.5

6.1P2.6

THINK ABOUT IT

What do we learn from this graph?

These graphs reveal many useful features. For example, we can see that the median hours of TV watched per week for females (around 5) is larger (to the right) than the males (around 2). We see that the males' largest value is a fair bit smaller than two of the female values. In fact, at almost every position in the distribution (each percentage value), the females' values are larger, indicating a shift to the right in the females' distribution of hours of TV watched compared to the males. However, it can be a little more difficult to discern shape and variability from these graphs just at first glance. These graphs can also be very "jagged" when you have a small number of observations.

 6.1P2.7

Who Travels More Frequently? Revisited

EXPLORATION
6.1.2B

In the previous exploration, you constructed a side-by-side, split stemplot to compare the number of states visited by females and males in an AP class.

Females (n = 24)		Males (n = 16)
	0	
95	0	79
44422220	1	1124
9987665555	1	566778
420	2	0233
	2	
2	3	
	3	

Key: 0|7 = 7 states visited

Let's compare this display to comparative boxplots.

1. Use these (sorted!) data to calculate the five-number summary of the females' distribution.

   a. There are an even number of female observations, so we can divide the data set into two sets of 12 observations. What is the average of the 12th and 13th observations? Report this as the median.

   b. Now consider the 12 observations below this value:

      5, 9, 10, 12, 12, 12, 12, 14, 14, 14, 15, 15, 15

      What is the median of these 12 values? (Again, find the location between two values and then average those two values.) Report this as the lower quartile.

   c. Confirm that 25% of your data (6 observations) lie below the value you found in (b).

   d. Now consider the 12 observations above the median:

      15, 15, 16, 16, 17, 18, 19, 19, 20, 22, 24, 32

      What is the median of these 12 values? Report this as the upper quartile.

   e. Complete the table below with the five-number summary for the females.

	Min	Q1	Median	Q3	Max
Males	7	11.5	16	19	23
Females					

From the five-number summary, we can also calculate the *interquartile range = Q3 − Q1* as a measure of the variability in the distribution.

2. Calculate the IQRs for the males and for the females. Which is larger? What does this tell you?

3. Using the five-number summary, construct boxplots for the males and females using the same horizontal axis scale and being sure to label which boxplot corresponds to males and which corresponds to females.

4. What information is revealed by these boxplots that you did not see in the stemplots?

Your boxplots in #4 are probably pretty similar. In fact, the boxplots obscure some information, like the actual numerical values. One enhancement we can make to the boxplots is to display outliers separately.

5. We will use the "1.5 IQR rule" to determine whether there are any outliers in the female distribution.

   a. Calculate Q1 − 1.5 IQR for the females. Are any values smaller than this in the females' data set?

   b. Calculate Q3 + 1.5 IQR for the females. Are any values larger?

6. Redraw the boxplot for the females, using an asterisk for the large outlier(s) and extending that whisker only to the largest non-outlier.

> **AP TIP**
>
> On the AP exam, if a boxplot is asked for, it is understood to mean a modified boxplot.

Another graph that you may encounter is a *cumulative frequency plot*.

7. The *frequency table* below lists the sorted values in the female distribution and how often each value occurred. For each unique value, determine how many of the 24 observations are at or below that value. In the bottom row of the table, fill in the percentage of the 24 values at or below that value. The first few cells have been completed for you.

States	5	9	10	12	14	15	16	17	18	19	20	22	24	32
Count	1	1	1	4	3	4	2	1	1	2	1	1	1	1
% below	1/24 4%	2/24 8%	3/24 13%	7/24 29%										

8. Now, make a graph with the percentages on the vertical axis and the number of states on the horizontal axis, using a dot to represent each pair of values and then connecting the dots using the provided axes in Figure 6.1.4.

9. Repeat #7 and #8 for the males, adding the values to Figure 6.1.4, using a different type of line (e.g., dotted line) to connect the dots and differentiate the two graphs.

States	7	9	11	12	14	15	16	17	18	20	22	23
Count	1	1	2	1	1	1	2	2	1	1	1	2
% below												

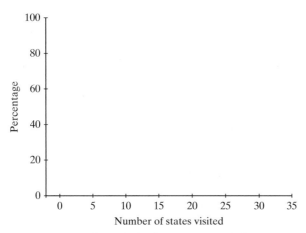

FIGURE 6.1.4   Cumulative frequency graph for number of states visited.

10. What does the cumulative frequency graph reveal about the two medians? How do you know? What does the graph reveal about the 80th percentiles (the number of states that have roughly 80% of the distribution at or below that value)?

Larger data set

11. A college professor asked the same question of her students, 61 males and 50 females. How do you think these distributions will compare to those found by the AP teacher?

Below is a frequency table of the responses to "How many states have you visited?":

No. of States Visited	1	2	3	4	5	6	7	8	9	10	11	12	13	14	15	17	18	19	20	21	23	24	25	26	28	29	35	36
male count	2	3	6	6	5	4	1	4	3	7	2	2	1	1	1	0	1	1	2	3	1	1	1	1	1	0	1	0
female count	2	3	2	5	5	3	7	4	5	3	1	4	1	0	2	1	0	1	0	0	0	1	1	0	1	1	0	1

12. What kind of graph(s) would you use to compare the male and female responses?

13. Figure 6.1.5 shows split, side-by-side stemplots, comparative boxplots, and cumulative distribution plots for these data.

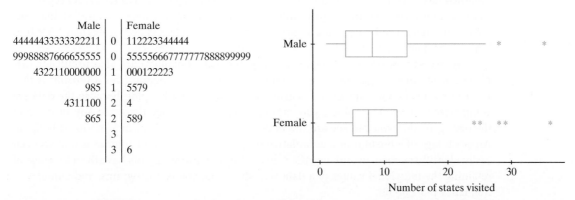

FIGURE 6.1.5   Split stemplots comparing the numbers of states visited for males and females.

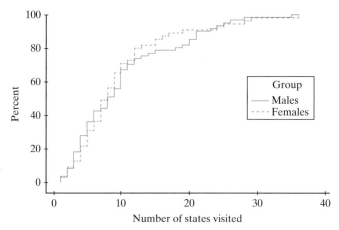

FIGURE 6.1.5 (*Continued*).

a. How would you compare the shapes, centers, and spreads of these distributions? What are the largest and smallest values? Are there any outliers? If so, how many?

b. Which graph did you use to compare the shapes?

c. Which graph did you use to determine the largest and smallest number of states visited?

d. Which graph did you use to compare the centers of the distributions?

14. How do these distributions compare to those found by the AP teacher? As you predicted?

SECTION 6.1 PART 2 Summary

In this section you examined a new graphical display, a ***stemplot***, used to display the distribution of a single quantitative variable for small- and medium-sized data sets, and a ***back-to-back stemplot*** for comparing two groups for a single quantitative response variable. You also examined ***cumulative frequency plots***, which are useful for medium to large data sets. We also saw, in more detail, how to compute the five-number summary (minimum, lower quartile, median, upper quartile, maximum) for a set of quantitative data and how to use it to describe the data distribution. You may choose to use the five-number summary to compare distributions and the interquartile range to compare variability. The five-number summary also allows you to construct a boxplot, which is often more practical than stemplots for data sets with a medium or larger number of observations. The AP exam will use ***modified boxplots*** that display individual outliers (according to the ***1.5 IQR rule***) separately so these unusual observations don't unduly influence our impressions of overall shape, center, or variability. The 1.5 IQR rule identifies outliers as any observation more than $1.5 \times$ IQR beyond the quartile.

As we saw in previous chapters, histograms (like boxplots) are also useful for displaying medium to large sets of data. An advantage of a histogram over a boxplot is that you can see peaks and gaps in the distribution, whereas in a boxplot, because the data are summarized by five key values, you cannot determine whether there are any peaks, and the only gaps that you can see are the ones resulting from outliers in a modified boxplot. An advantage of a boxplot or a cumulative frequency plot over a histogram is that you can easily identify the median and quartile values. Dotplots and stemplots have the advantage of retaining the individual values of a data set, whereas boxplots, histograms, and cumulative frequency plots do not.

COMPARING TWO MEANS: SIMULATION-BASED APPROACH

INTRODUCTION

In Section 6.1 we saw how to describe and explore data when comparing two groups on a quantitative variable. In this section, we will dig into the 3S strategy to compare two groups with a quantitative response variable and address questions about how we can assess the statistical significance of the observed difference between two groups. Instead of using proportions (as was done with categorical response variables) we will be using means (averages) for our comparisons.

Bicycling to Work

STEP 1: Ask a research question.   Does type of bicycle frame affect commuting time?

STEP 2: Design a study and collect data.   An article that appeared in the *British Medical Journal* (2010) presented the results of a study conducted by researcher Jeremy Groves, whose objective was to determine whether the type of frame of his bicycle could affect his travel time to work. On each of 56 days (from mid-January to mid-July 2010), Dr. Groves tossed a coin to decide whether he would ride the 27 miles to work on his carbon frame bicycle that was light in weight, weighing 20.90 lb, or on his steel frame bicycle that was heavier, weighing 29.75 lb. He then recorded the commute time for each trip.

Example 6.2

> ### THINK ABOUT IT
>
> What are the experimental units in this study? Identify and classify the roles (explanatory or response) of the variables in this study.

The experimental units in this study are the trips made to work on 56 different days. The explanatory variable is which bike Dr. Groves rode, and the response variable is his commute time (in minutes). Notice that the explanatory variable is categorical (binary) with two outcomes—carbon frame bicycle or steel frame bicycle—whereas the response variable is quantitative.

The data table that Dr. Groves used to collect his data started like that in Table 6.2.

TABLE 6.2   Data collected by Jeremy Groves on commuting times for his two different bikes

Date	Bike frame	Time (min)
Jan. 20	Steel	115.50
Jan. 21	Carbon	115.25
Jan. 22	Steel	116.50
Jan. 23	Carbon	114.00
Jan. 24	Carbon	119.00
...	...	...

6.2.1

Remembering the research question for this study, we can state our hypotheses as follows:

> Null hypothesis: There is no association between which bike is used and commute time. That is, commute time is not affected by which bike is used.
>
> Alternative hypothesis: There is an association between which bike is used and commute time. That is, commute time is affected by which bike is used.

Recall that in Chapter 5, when the response variable was categorical, we compared the *proportions* of successes between the two samples. Now that the response variable is quantitative, we can compare *means* between the two samples. Accordingly, we can define our parameter of interest to be the underlying difference in the long-run mean commute time for the two types of bikes. This can be represented in symbols as $\mu_{carbon} - \mu_{steel}$ where

> μ_{carbon} represents the long-run mean commute time using carbon frame (lighter) bike,
>
> μ_{steel} represents the long-run mean commute time using steel frame (heavier) bike.

Note that the Greek letter "mu" (μ) is used to denote the parameter "long-run mean." So we are distinguishing the *long-run means* that would result from Dr. Groves riding to work forever from the *sample means* that he determined in his study (see FAQ 6.2.1 for details). Using the symbols μ_{carbon} and μ_{steel} we can restate our hypotheses to be

> H_0: $\mu_{carbon} = \mu_{steel}$ OR $\mu_{carbon} - \mu_{steel} = 0$
>
> H_a: $\mu_{carbon} \neq \mu_{steel}$ OR $\mu_{carbon} - \mu_{steel} \neq 0$

FAQ 6.2.1   www.wiley.com/college/tintle

Remind me: What does "long run" mean?

Keep in mind that hypotheses are always about populations or processes, not about the sample data. We don't need to hypothesize or make inferences about the samples, because we have the data from the sample and we can see that the sample means are not identical. But we want to use these sample data to draw inferences about the long-run process or population from which the data came. That is why, as you may have already noticed, the hypotheses stated for this bike study are statements made about the general association between commute time and which bike is used, not about the sample of 56 trips.

THINK ABOUT IT

Summarize the study design used here: Is this an observational study or an experiment?

This was a randomized experiment because the researcher used random assignment (coin flip) to decide which bike he would ride on a particular day.

STEP 3: Explore the data.   To graphically display the distributions of sample commute times, separated by which bike was used, we can create parallel dotplots, as shown in Figure 6.3.

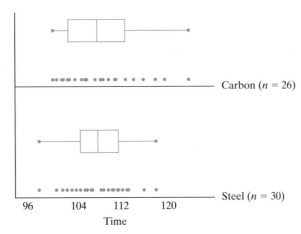

FIGURE 6.3   Graphical display of the distribution of commute times for the two bikes.

To numerically summarize the commute times, for each bike type, we can report the mean commute time, the standard deviation (SD), and the five-number summary. Recall that larger values of the standard deviation indicate more variability about the mean in the sample data. Table 6.3 reports these summary statistics for Dr. Groves' data.

TABLE 6.3 Summary statistics for commute time (in minutes) by bike type								
Bike type	Sample size	Mean	SD	Min.	First Quart.	Med.	Third Quart.	Max.
Carbon frame (lighter)	26	108.34	6.25	100.10	102.75	107.70	112.50	123.30
Steel frame (heavier)	30	107.81	4.89	97.70	104.65	107.50	111.30	117.70

STEP 4: Draw inferences beyond the data.   As can be seen from the dotplots and the numerical summaries, both the sample mean commute time and the sample variability were higher for the carbon frame (lighter) bike. This indicates that there was a tendency for longer commute times and less consistency in commute times with the carbon frame. But this difference doesn't appear to be large. Maybe he was unlucky in his random assignment and just happened to have heavier traffic on the route on the days he used the carbon frame bike? Or does this reflect a difference in the overall mean commute times between the two routes that is not typical of random chance? If so, can we estimate how much longer we think the average commute would be with the carbon frame? Is it enough longer to be willing to switch to the heavier bike permanently?

THINK ABOUT IT

Is it *possible* to have obtained a difference in sample mean commute times of 0.53 minutes (108.34 − 107.81) if, in general, commute time is not affected by type of bike used? Do you think it's *very unlikely* for such a large difference in sample means to have occurred by chance alone, due to random assignment, if commute time is not affected by type of bike used? How might you decide?

Notice that these are the same questions that we asked repeatedly in Chapter 5 when we analyzed studies with a categorical response variable. The only difference now is that the response variable is quantitative. Again, the answer to the first question is yes. Of course it's *possible* to obtain such an extreme difference in group means by chance alone. But is it *plausible*? Again, as we have done since Chapter 1, we will use simulation to investigate whether such a difference is very unlikely to have occurred by chance alone. In this case, we can consider the "chance" as arising from the random assignment process—each trip would have had the same commute time and it was simply random chance that labeled some trips as carbon frame and others as steel frame.

6.2.2

3S STRATEGY

We will now apply the 3S strategy to the sample data to evaluate how likely such an extreme difference in group means is to occur by chance alone. As we've seen before, the first step in the 3S process is to choose a statistic. In this case, because the distributions of commute times are reasonably symmetric in both groups, a reasonable choice of statistic is the difference in sample means.

6.2.3

1. **Statistic:** We calculate that the observed difference in sample mean commute times ($\bar{x}_{carbon} - \bar{x}_{steel}$) is 0.53 minutes.

2. **Simulation:** To investigate the key question of whether the observed difference in sample mean commute times is unlikely to have occurred by chance alone, we will conduct a simulation analysis. We can use $26 + 30 = 56$ index cards representing his 26 trips on the lighter carbon frame bike and 30 on the heavier steel frame bike. But now instead of color coding the cards to represent having a success/failure response as in Chapter 5, we need to incorporate the numerical values of the commute times into our analysis. We can do this by writing the 26 commute times for the lighter bike on 26 of the cards, and do the same for the 30 commute times with the heavier bike on the other 30 cards.

Now suppose the time of the commute is not associated with which bike is used. (This is what the null hypothesis says.) We can simulate this null hypothesis by shuffling all 56 cards and randomly redistributing them into two stacks: one with 26 cards (to represent the carbon frame bike) and another with 30 cards (to represent the steel frame bike), regardless of the response values (or group membership) written on the cards. We can then calculate the difference in the mean times between our two stacks of cards. By repeating this over and over again, we can develop a null distribution for the difference in the mean commute times. The table below summarizes the key aspects of the simulation:

Null hypothesis	=	Long-run mean times on each of the two bikes are the same (bike type is not associated with commute time)
One repetition	=	Rerandomizing commute times to bike type
Statistic	=	Difference in two group means

Figure 6.4(a) shows the dotplots of the data observed in the original study, with the top dotplot showing the 26 observations of carbon (lighter) bike commute times as orange circles, and the dotplot below it showing the 30 observations of steel (heavier) bike commute times as solid blue diamonds. These are equivalent to the dotplots from Figure 6.3, just without the boxplots. Figure 6.4(b) shows one possible shuffle (or rerandomization) of the commute times into the two groups. Notice that the shuffling and redistribution have resulted in some of the blue diamond (heavier bike) values ending up in the rerandomized lighter bike group, and vice versa. This shuffle produced a difference of 2.42 minutes ($109.35 - 106.93$), which is more extreme than the observed difference of 0.53 minutes, because it is farther away from 0.

FIGURE 6.4   (a) Data distribution in *Bicycling to Work;* (b) after shuffling (rerandomizing) the commute times.

6.2.4

Figure 6.5 shows the results of a second shuffle. Notice that the difference in group means here was −0.70 minutes (107.68 − 108.38), a value that (like the result of the previous shuffle) is more extreme than the observed difference of 0.53 minutes, because −0.70 is farther away from the null hypothesized difference of 0, compared to 0.53.

FIGURE 6.5   After shuffling the commute times in *Bicycling to Work* a second time.

THINK ABOUT IT

What does the value −0.70 minute imply? How can we have a negative number when we are talking about time?

Keep in mind that our statistic here is the *difference* in the two sample means. Therefore, a difference of −0.70 tells us that the mean commute time for the carbon (lighter) bike was smaller than that for the steel (heavier) bike, after the shuffling. Under the null hypothesis, we expect both positive and negative values because the longer commute times are just as likely to end up in either group. In fact, we would expect a positive difference roughly half the time and a negative difference roughly half the time.

Figure 6.6 shows the results from a third shuffle. This shuffled difference in means turned out to be 1.05 minutes (108.62 − 107.57). Is this difference more or less extreme than the observed difference of 0.53 minutes? It is more extreme because 1.05 is farther from the null hypothesized difference of 0 than 0.53 is.

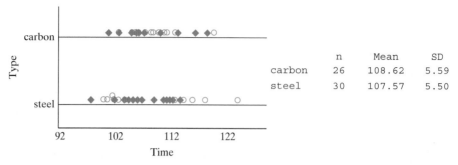

	n	Mean	SD
carbon	26	108.62	5.59
steel	30	107.57	5.50

FIGURE 6.6 After shuffling and rerandomizing the commute times in *Bicycling to Work* a third time.

To this point we've seen three separate shuffled differences in means between the two groups: 2.42, −0.70, and 1.05. In all three cases we've obtained a difference in means larger (in absolute value) than the observed value of the statistic (0.53). Of course, we really need more shuffles (or rerandomizations) to get a better sense of the long-run pattern of the difference in means by chance (random assignment) alone. To see the long-run pattern of the could-have-been differences in sample means, if the null hypothesis of no association is true, we want to repeat the shuffling many more times. Figure 6.7 shows a histogram of 1,000 possible values of the difference in sample means that could have happened if commute time was not affected by which bike was used.

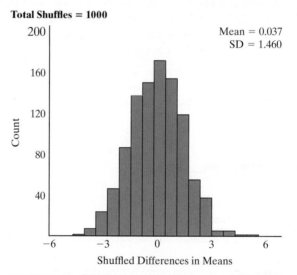

FIGURE 6.7 Distribution of 1,000 values of difference of group means that could have been observed if long-run mean commute time was the same for both bikes.

THINK ABOUT IT

At what numeric value is this histogram in Figure 6.7 centered? Why does that make sense?

Notice that the histogram in Figure 6.7 is centered at approximately 0. Remember that these values of the difference in sample means were generated assuming the null hypothesis is true, that is, the long-run means of the commute times are the same for the two bikes. If the null hypothesis is true, the difference in sample means should be around 0 (sometimes more than 0 and sometimes less than 0). The key question is how far the differences would get away from 0, which will depend on how large the sample sizes were and how variable the sample data were (the commute times for each bicycle). Notice in Figure 6.7 that all of the values of the difference in sample means fall between roughly −5 and 5 minutes.

In Dr. Groves' experiment, the observed difference in mean commute times was 0.53 minutes, and we want to find out whether this value is far enough away from 0 to provide convincing evidence that this result did not happen by chance alone and that there really is a difference between the underlying long-run mean commute times for the two bikes.

THINK ABOUT IT

Looking at the histogram in Figure 6.7, where is the observed difference of 0.53 located? If the null hypothesis were true, would a difference of 0.53 minutes be surprising? How are you deciding?

If the null hypothesis were true and the commute time is not associated with the bike chosen, it would not be at all surprising to see a difference of 0.53 minutes in the sample mean commute times just by chance. Notice that in Figure 6.7, 0.53 is not out in the tail but is quite close to the null hypothesized difference of 0. As we have done before, we can count how often the simulation produced a statistic at least as extreme as the observed value (0.53 minutes). In other words, we can use the simulation results to approximate the p-value for this study.

THINK ABOUT IT

Which values will we count in order to approximate the p-value for this study?

Because our alternative hypothesis is two-sided, we approximate the p-value by looking in *both* tails of the distribution of the differences in sample means. Figure 6.8 shows that out of the 1,000 simulated random shuffles, 732 resulted in a difference in sample means that was less than or equal to −0.53 or that was greater than or equal to 0.53, making our approximate two-sided p-value 0.732.

6.2.5

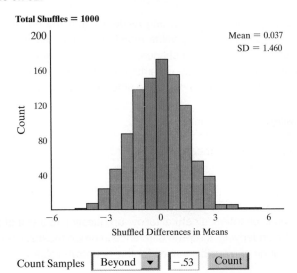

FIGURE 6.8 Histogram showing the 732 repetitions in the two tails where the rerandomization resulted in a difference in sample means that was at least as extreme as the observed difference of 0.53.

How would you interpret this p-value: the probability of what? Assuming what?

We interpret this p-value just as we have interpreted all p-values: the probability of obtaining such an extreme (or more) value for the observed statistic if the null hypothesis were true. Applied to this study: Assuming that the underlying long-run (process) mean commute times for the two bikes are the same, if we were to repeat the random assignment of the carbon frame (lighter) bike to 26 days and the steel frame (heavier) bike to 30 days, we would find the difference in sample mean commute times to differ by 0.53 minutes or even more (in either direction) in about 73.20% of the random assignments.

Based on the p-value, what is your conclusion about Dr. Groves' research question of whether the type of bike affects his commute time? Explain the reasoning process behind this conclusion.

6.2.6

3. **Strength of evidence:** A p-value of 0.732 is quite large, indicating that the observed result would not be surprising at all if the null hypothesis were true. Thus, we do not have evidence to say that type of bike affects commute time. In other words, we do not have evidence that the underlying long-run mean commute times are different for the two bikes. Even though the study was a randomized experiment, the large p-value does not let us conclude that commute time is affected by which bike is used. Of course, we are assuming that these 56 trips are representative of the underlying commuting process (vs. all occurring in winter, for example).

Based on the p-value, have we proven that Dr. Groves' two bicycles have no effect on commute time?

Remember, a large p-value is not "strong evidence that the null hypothesis is true." (See FAQ 6.2.2 for details.) This large p-value merely suggests that the null hypothesis is plausible—we shouldn't rule out random chance, because it is a reasonable explanation for the observed difference in sample mean commuting times. But it's certainly possible that there really is an effect of the bicycle on commute time that was not detected in this study.

FAQ 6.2.2   www.wiley.com/college/tintle

If we don't reject the null does that mean we accept it?

ESTIMATING A CONFIDENCE INTERVAL

As we've seen in previous chapters, a natural follow-up question to a test of significance is to estimate the size of the underlying, long-run difference in group means. We use a confidence interval to generate a range of plausible values for this unknown value.

How would you apply the 2SD method to generate a confidence interval for the difference in long-run mean commute times between the two bikes?

6.2.7

The 2SD method says that we can generate an approximate 95% confidence interval by taking two times the standard deviation of the simulated null distribution (as shown in Figure 6.8) and adding and subtracting the resulting value to the observed statistic. In this case, the standard deviation of the null distribution is 1.46 minutes (Figure 6.8). Thus, the endpoints of the 95% confidence interval for the difference in long-run mean commute times are roughly $0.53 - 2 \times 1.46 = -2.59$ to $0.53 + 2 \times 1.46 = 3.45$. In short, we are 95% confident that the difference in long-run mean commute times between the two bikes ($\mu_{carbon} - \mu_{steel}$) is between -2.59 minutes and 3.45 minutes. This means that the mean commute time with the carbon bike could be as much as 3.45 minutes longer than with the steel bike or as much as 2.59 minutes shorter.

> **THINK ABOUT IT**
>
> What are the implications of having a confidence interval that contains 0?

The fact that the confidence interval contains zero implies that it is plausible that the difference in long-run means between the two groups is zero—in other words, that the null hypothesis is plausible. Thus, the confidence interval yields a result that is consistent with the result of the test of significance.

STEP 5: Formulate conclusions.

> **THINK ABOUT IT**
>
> Can we generalize our conclusion to a larger population? Can we draw a cause-effect conclusion?

As we've seen before, there are two key questions to ask with regards to the scope of conclusions possible in this study: Was the sample randomly selected from a larger population? Were the observational units randomly assigned to treatments?

The answer to the first question is no, the sample was not randomly selected from a population. In this case, Jeremy Groves commuted on consecutive days and so if he, say, did the experiment in winter as opposed to summer, he might obtain different results. And, of course, because this is only one person and two different bikes, we certainly shouldn't generalize any further than this particular individual and his two bikes.

The answer to the second question is yes, the observational units were randomly assigned to the treatments. So, had the p-value been small, we might be inclined to say a cause-effect conclusion is plausible here (namely, that bike choice is causing a difference in his commute times). However, a serious limitation of this study is that it was not *double blind*.

In this case, the researcher knew which bike he was on for each of the commutes. Could this have influenced his performance? It could have. He stated in the article that his steel frame bike was more comfortable. Perhaps this comfort helped him pedal faster. Perhaps he likes the steel frame bike better and this prompted him to pedal faster. This implies there could have been factors apart from the type of frame that were affecting his commute time differently for the two bikes.

STEP 6: Look back and ahead.   Bicyclists are willing to pay a lot of money to reduce the weight of their bikes. Presumably they do this to increase their speed or reduce their effort in riding. Does this study show that this added expense is worth it?

The answer is no for a number of reasons. In addition to only being a single individual on two particular bikes, the lack of blinding in the study is a serious flaw in the design which could impact results. And, of course, our large p-value doesn't provide convincing evidence against the null hypothesis (that choice of bike does not affect commute time), only that it's plausible that there is no difference on average. Further studies looking at a variety of individuals, terrains, weather conditions, and bikes would be needed to make a stronger conclusion. Though difficult, a randomized experiment with blinding (e.g., make identical looking bikes except for the material of the frames; see FAQ 6.2.3 for details) would allow for stronger, more definitive conclusions. Finally, even if there is a difference in the commute times on the two different bicycles, the 95% confidence interval suggests that the difference is likely only to be at most 2–3 minutes (for a ride over 100 minutes long), on average, suggesting that the difference may not be worth the extra expense.

 FAQ 6.2.3   www.wiley.com/college/tintle

Why should I care whether studies are blind?

EXPLORATION 6.2 | **Lingering Effects of Sleep Deprivation**

STEP 1: Ask a research question.   Many students pull "all-nighters" when they have an important exam or a pressing assignment. Concerns that may arise include: *Can you really function well the next day after a sleepless night? What about several days later: Can you recover from a sleepless night by getting a full night's sleep on the following nights?*

1. What is your research conjecture about whether or not one can recover from a sleepless night by getting a full night's sleep on the following nights? What are some other related questions that you would be interested in investigating related to this issue?

STEP 2: Design a study and collect data.   Researchers Stickgold, James, and Hobson investigated delayed effects of sleep deprivation on learning in a study published in *Nature Neuroscience* (2000). Twenty-one volunteers, aged 18–25 years, were first trained on a visual discrimination task that involved watching stimuli appear on a computer screen and reporting what was seen. See Figure 6.9.

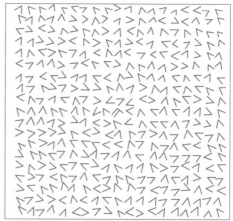

FIGURE 6.9   Subjects were flashed the screen on the left and then it was masked by the screen on the right. Then subjects were asked whether they had seen an L or a V and whether the slanted lines were placed vertically or horizontally.

After the training period, subjects were tested. Performance was recorded as the minimum time (in milliseconds) between the appearance of stimuli and an accurate response. Following these baseline measurements, one group was randomly assigned to be deprived of sleep for 30 hours, followed by two full nights of unrestricted sleep, whereas the other group was allowed to get unrestricted sleep on all three nights. Following this, both groups were retested on the task to see how well they remembered the training from the first day. Researchers recorded the *improvement* in performance as the decrease in time required at retest compared to training.

(*Note:* For example, if someone took 5 milliseconds (ms) to respond at the beginning of the study and then 2 ms to respond at the end, the improvement score is 3 ms. But if someone took 2 ms at the beginning and then 5 ms at the end, the improvement score is −3 ms.)

The goal of the study was to see whether the *improvement scores* tend to be higher for the unrestricted sleep treatment than for the sleep deprivation treatment.

2. Identify the explanatory and response variables in this study. Also classify them as either categorical or quantitative.

Explanatory:	Type:
Response:	Type:

3. Was this an experiment or an observational study? Explain how you are deciding.

4. Let $\mu_{unrestricted}$ be the long-run mean improvement on this task three days later when someone has had unrestricted sleep and let $\mu_{deprived}$ denote the long-run mean improvement when someone is sleep deprived on the first night.

   In words and symbols, state the null and the alternative hypotheses to investigate whether sleep deprivation has a negative effect on improvement in performance on visual discrimination tasks. (*Hint:* For the alternative hypothesis: Do you expect the people to do better or worse when sleep deprived? Based on your answer, what sign/direction should you choose for the alternative hypothesis?)

Here are the data, with positive values indicating better performance at retest than at training, and negative values indicating worse performance at retest than at training:

Unrestricted-sleep group's improvement scores (milliseconds):

25.20, 14.50, −7.00, 12.60, 34.50, 45.60, 11.60, 18.60, 12.10, 30.50

Sleep-deprived group's improvement scores (milliseconds):

−10.70, 4.50, 2.20, 21.30, −14.70, −10.70, 9.60, 2.40, 21.80, 7.20, 10.00

STEP 3: Explore the data.

5. To look at graphical and numerical summaries of the data from the study, go to the **Multiple Means** applet. The sleep deprivation data have already been entered into the applet.

   a. Notice that the applet creates parallel dotplots, one for each study group. Based on these dotplots alone, which group (unrestricted or deprived) appears to have had the higher mean improvement? How are you deciding?

   b. Based on the dotplots alone, which group (unrestricted or deprived) appears to have had more variability in improvement? How are you deciding?

   c. Notice also that the applet also computes numerical summaries of the data, such as the mean and standard deviation (SD) for the improvements in each group.

   i. For the *unrestricted* group, record the sample size (n), mean, and SD.

$n_{unrestricted} =$	$\bar{x}_{unrestricted} =$	$SD_{unrestricted} =$

   ii. For the *deprived* group, record the sample size (n), mean, and SD.

$n_{deprived} =$	$\bar{x}_{deprived} =$	$SD_{deprived} =$

Recall from earlier in the course that the standard deviation is a measure of variability. Relatively speaking, smaller standard deviation values indicate less variability and a distribution whose data values tend to cluster more closely together, compared to a distribution with a larger standard deviation.

d. Based on the numerical summaries reported in #5(c), which group (unrestricted or deprived) had the higher mean improvement?

e. Based on the numerical summaries reported in #5(c), which group (unrestricted or deprived) had the higher variability in improvement?

f. Notice that the applet also reports the observed difference in means for the improvements of the two groups. Record this value (and its measurement units).

$$\bar{x}_{\text{unrestricted}} - \bar{x}_{\text{deprived}} =$$

g. Before you conduct an inferential analysis, does this difference in sample means (as reported in #5(f)) strike you as a meaningful difference? Explain your answer.

STEP 4: Draw inferences.

6. What are two possible explanations for why we observed the two groups to have different sample means for improvement in performance?

7. Describe how you might go about deciding whether the observed difference between the two sample means is statistically significant. (*Hint:* Think about how you assessed whether an observed difference between two sample proportions was statistically significant in Chapter 5. Use the same strategy, with an appropriate modification for working with means instead of proportions.)

Once again the key question is how often random assignment alone would produce a difference in the groups at least as extreme as the difference observed in this study if there really were no effect of sleep condition on improvement score. You addressed similar questions in Chapter 5 when you analyzed the dolphin therapy and yawning studies. The only change is that now the response variable is *quantitative* rather than *categorical*, so the relevant statistic is the difference in group *means* rather than the difference in group *proportions*. Also once again, we use *simulation* to investigate how often such an extreme difference would occur by chance (random assignment) alone (if the null hypothesis of no difference/no effect/no association were true).

In other words, we will again employ the 3S strategy.

1. Statistic:

8. A natural statistic for measuring how different the observed group means are from each other is the difference in the mean improvement scores between the two groups. Report the value of this statistic, as you did in #5(f).

2. Simulate: You will start by using index cards to perform a tactile simulation of randomly assigning the 21 subjects between the two groups, *assuming* that sleep condition has no impact on improvement.

Because the null hypothesis asserts that improvement score is not associated with sleep condition, we will assume that the 21 subjects would have had exactly the same improvement scores as they did, *regardless* of which sleep condition group (unrestricted or deprived) the subject had been assigned.

9. a. How many index cards do you need to conduct this simulation?

b. What will you write on each index card?

To conduct *one repetition* of this simulation:

- Shuffle the stack of 21 cards well and then randomly distribute cards into two stacks: one stack with 10 cards (the unrestricted group) and one with 11 (the sleep-deprived group).
- Calculate and report the sample means for each rerandomized group:

Rerandomized unrestricted group's mean:

Rerandomized deprived group's mean:

- Calculate the difference in group means: unrestricted mean minus sleep-deprived mean. Report this value.

- Combine this result with your classmates' to create a dotplot that shows the distribution of several possible values of difference in sample means that could have happened due to pure chance if sleep condition has no impact on improvement. Sketch a dotplot on an axis like the one below, being sure to label the horizontal axis.

Label:

c. At about what value is the dotplot centered? Explain why this makes sense. (*Hint:* What are we assuming to be true when we conduct the simulation?)

d. Where is the observed difference in means from the original study (as reported in #8) on the dotplot? Did this value happen often, somewhat rarely, or very rarely? How are you deciding?

10. As before with simulation-based analyses, you would now like to conduct many, many more repetitions to determine what is typical and what is not for the difference in group means, assuming that sleep condition has no impact on improvement score. We think you would prefer to use a computer applet to do this rather than continue to shuffle cards for a very long time, calculating the difference of group means by hand. Go back to the **Multiple Means** applet, check the **Show Shuffle Options** box, select the **Plot** display, and press **Shuffle Responses**.

a. Describe what the applet is doing and how this relates to your null hypothesis from #4.

b. Record the simulated difference in sample means for the rerandomized groups, as given in the applet output. Is this difference more extreme than the observed difference from the study (as reported in #8)? How are you deciding?

c. Click on **Shuffle Responses** again and record the simulated difference in sample means for the rerandomized groups. Did it change from #10(b)?

d. Click on **Re-Randomize** again and record the simulated difference in sample means for the rerandomized groups. Did it change from #10(b) and #10(c)?

e. Now to see many more possible values of the difference in sample means, assuming sleep condition has no impact on improvement, do the following in the **Multiple Means** applet:

- Change **Number of Shuffles** from 1 to 997.

- Press **Shuffle Responses** to produce a total of 1000 shuffles and rerandomized statistics.

f. Consider the histogram of the 1,000 could-have-been values of difference in sample means, assuming that sleep condition has no effect on improvement.

i. What does one observation on the histogram represent? (*Hint:* Think about what you would have to do to put another observation on the graph.)

ii. Describe the overall shape of the null distribution displayed in this histogram.

iii. Where does the observed difference in sample means (as reported in #8) fall in this histogram: near the middle or out in a tail? Are there a lot of observations that are even more extreme than the observed difference, assuming sleep condition has no impact on improvement? How are you deciding?

g. To estimate a p-value, continue with the **Multiple Means** applet.

- Type in the observed difference in group means (as reported in #8) in the **Count Samples** box (for the one-sided alternative hypothesis) and press **Count**.

- Record the approximate p-value.

h. Fill in the blanks of the following sentence to complete the interpretation of the p-value.

The p-value of _____ is the probability of observing _____
_____ assuming _____.

3. Strength of evidence:

11. Based on the p-value, evaluate the strength of evidence provided by the experimental data against the null hypothesis that sleep condition has no effect on improvement score: not much evidence, moderate evidence, strong evidence, or very strong evidence?

12. *Significance*: Summarize your conclusion with regard to strength of evidence in the context of this study.

13. *Estimation*:

   a. Use the 2SD method to approximate a 95% confidence interval for the difference in long-run mean improvement score for subjects who get unrestricted sleep minus the long-run mean improvement score for subjects who are sleep deprived. (*Hints*: Remember the observed value of the difference in group means and obtain the SD of the difference in group means from the applet's simulation results. The interval should be observed difference in means ± 2SD, where SD represents the standard deviation of the null distribution of the difference in group means.)

   b. Interpret what this confidence interval reveals, paying particular attention to whether the interval is entirely positive, entirely negative, or contains zero. (*Hint*: Be sure to convey "direction" in your interpretation by saying how much larger improvement scores are on average for the treatment you find to have the larger long-run mean: I'm 95% confident that the long-run mean improvement score is _____ to _____ higher with the _____ treatment as opposed to the _____ treatment.)

STEP 5: Formulate conclusions.

14. *Generalization*: Were the participants in this study randomly selected from a larger population? Describe the population to which you would feel comfortable generalizing the results of this study.

15. *Causation*: Were the participants in the study randomly assigned to a sleep condition? How does this affect the scope of conclusion that you can draw?

Another statistic

Could we have chosen a statistic other than the difference in group means to summarize how different the two groups' improvement scores were? Yes, for example we could have used the difference in group *medians*. Why might we do this? For one reason, the median is less affected by outliers than the mean (see Section 3.2).

To analyze the difference in group medians, we carry out the 3S strategy as before, except:

- We calculate the observed value of the difference in *medians* as the statistic.
- After we conduct the rerandomizing, we calculate the difference in medians for the rerandomized data. Then we repeat this process a large number of times.
- We determine the p-value by counting how many of the simulated statistics are at least as large as the observed value of the difference in *medians*.

16. Return to the **Multiple Means** applet and use the **Statistic** pull-down menu (on the left) to select **Difference in Medians**.

   a. From the **Summary Statistics** for the original data, record the median improvement score for each group. Also record the difference between the medians (unrestricted median minus deprived median).

Unrestricted median:	Deprived median:
Difference (unrestricted − deprived):	

   b. Enter 1000 for **Number of Shuffles** and press **Shuffle Responses**. Describe the resulting null distribution of difference in group medians. Does this null distribution appear to be centered near zero? Does it seem to have a bell-shaped distribution?

c. To calculate a p-value based on the difference in medians, enter the observed value in the **Count samples** box. Then press **Count**. Report both the value that you enter into the applet and the resulting p-value.

d. Does this p-value indicate strong evidence that sleep deprivation has a harmful effect on improvement score? Explain how you are deciding.

e. With which statistic (difference in *means* or difference in *medians*) do the data provide *stronger* evidence that sleep deprivation has a harmful effect on improvement score? Explain how you are deciding.

17. **STEP 6: Look back and ahead.**

Looking back: Did anything about the design and conclusions of this study concern you? Issues you may want to critique include:

- Any mismatch between the research question and the study design
- How the experimental units were selected
- How the treatments were assigned to the experimental units
- How the measurements were recorded
- The number of experimental units in the study
- Whether what we observed is of practical value

Looking ahead: What should the researchers' next steps be to fix the limitations or build on this knowledge?

SECTION 6.2 Summary

The 3S strategy can be used to assess whether two sample means differ enough to conclude that there is a genuine difference in the population means or long-run means of processes. The reasoning process of statistical significance is the same and the simulation process is very similar to that used for comparing two proportions.

- The null hypothesis can be expressed as no association between the two variables.
  - Equivalently, the null hypothesis asserts that the two population means are the same, or in the case of processes, the two long-run means are the same.
- The alternative hypothesis says that there is an association between the two variables.
  - The alternative hypothesis can be one-sided or two-sided, depending on whether the researchers have a particular direction in mind prior to collecting data.
- The difference in sample means between the two groups is often the statistic of interest.
- The key idea in simulating the null distribution of the difference in sample means is to shuffle the values of the response variable and redistribute at random to the explanatory variable groups.
  - This shuffling generates simulated values of the difference in sample means under the assumption of no association to help us see how much these sample means tend to differ from each other by random chance alone.
  - With a randomized experiment, this shuffling simulates rerandomizing the subjects into the two groups, assuming that the subjects' numerical responses would have been the same regardless of which group they were assigned.
- As always, the p-value is calculated as the proportion of repetitions of the simulation in which the simulated value of the statistic is at least as extreme as the observed value of the statistic.
  - Also as always, a small p-value provides evidence against the null hypothesis.

The 2SD method can be used to produce a confidence interval for estimating the size of the difference between the two population means or two long-run process means.

- As with comparing two proportions, an important question is whether the interval is entirely negative, is entirely positive, or includes zero.
  - If the interval does not include zero, that confirms that our test of significance will reject the null hypothesis that the two population means, or in the case of processes the two long-run means, are not the same.
  - Whether the interval contains positive or negative values indicates which population (or long-run) mean of the two is estimated to be larger and by how much.
  - If the interval contains zero, there is not convincing evidence against the null hypothesis that the two population means or the two long-run process means are equal.

An alternative to comparing the means between two groups is to compare the medians. The 3S strategy works just as well with comparing medians as with comparing means.

SECTION 6.3

COMPARING TWO MEANS: THEORY-BASED APPROACH

INTRODUCTION

Earlier we saw that under certain conditions a normal distribution provides a reasonable model for the null distribution of a sample proportion (Chapters 1–3) and for the null distribution of a difference in group proportions (Chapter 5), whereas a t-distribution provides a reasonable model for the null distribution of a standardized sample mean (Chapter 2). In these cases we don't have to simulate, we can instead use these theory-based predictions to anticipate what would happen (the distribution of the statistic or standardized statistic) if we were to simulate.

Maybe you already noticed that in Section 6.2 the shape of the distribution of possible values of the difference in two group means was somewhat bell-shaped and centered at zero. If that makes you think "Here we go again…" you're absolutely right. In this section we will, once again, look at a theory-based approach to predict the distribution of our statistic, leading to t-procedures: the two-sample t-test and the two-sample t-interval. It should be no surprise that this approach will work well most of the time, but not all of the time—only when certain validity conditions are met.

Breastfeeding and Intelligence

Example 6.3

EXAMPLE

An article by researchers Jacobson, Chiodo, and Jacobson published in the journal *Pediatrics* (1999) studied whether and how children who were breastfed during infancy differed from those who weren't breastfed. The study involved 323 white children who were recruited at birth in 1980–1981 from four Western Michigan hospitals. After some initial exploration, the researchers deemed that the participants in the study were representative of the community in terms of social class, maternal education, age, marital status, and sex of infant. These children were revisited at age four years and assessed on the McCarthy Scales of Children's Abilities. The General Cognitive Index (GCI)—an overall measure of the child's present level of intellectual functioning—was recorded for each child, as was whether or not the child had been breastfed during infancy.

> **THINK ABOUT IT**
>
> What kind of study is this: experiment or observational? Identify and classify the explanatory and response variables.

This was an observational study because the researchers were not involved at all with determining which children would be breastfed. The explanatory variable is whether or not the baby was breastfed during infancy (categorical), and the response variable is the baby's GCI measure at age four (quantitative). Because the study was not a randomized experiment, we cannot consider drawing a *cause-and-effect* conclusion between breastfeeding and higher cognitive functioning.

Because the researchers were interested in any differences in GCI scores between children who were breastfed and those who weren't, they formulated their null and alternative hypotheses as shown here:

> Null hypothesis: There is no underlying association between breastfeeding during infancy and GCI at age four.

> Alternative hypothesis: There is an association between breastfeeding during infancy and GCI at age four.

Alternatively, we can define our parameter of interest to be $\mu_{breastfed} - \mu_{not}$ where

$\mu_{breastfed}$ = Population mean GCI value at age four for the population of children who are breastfed

μ_{not} = Population mean GCI value at age four for the population of children who are not breastfed

Using these symbols we can restate our hypotheses to be

H_0: $\mu_{breastfed} = \mu_{not}$ OR $\mu_{breastfed} - \mu_{not} = 0$

H_a: $\mu_{breastfed} \neq \mu_{not}$ OR $\mu_{breastfed} - \mu_{not} \neq 0$

Table 6.4 gives the summary statistics for GCI at age four years by whether or not the child was breastfed during infancy.

TABLE 6.4 Summary statistics for GCI at age four by whether or not breastfed during infancy			
Group	Sample size, n	Sample mean	Sample SD
Breastfed	237	105.30	14.50
Not breastfed	85	100.90	14.00

Based on the summary statistics given in Table 6.4, the distribution of GCI values was simulated and the results are graphed in Figure 6.10.

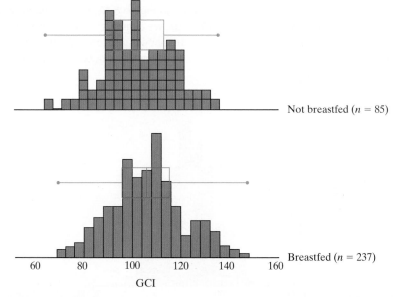

FIGURE 6.10 Histograms/boxplots showing the distribution of GCI values by whether or not breastfed.

From the summary statistics and histograms/boxplots, we can see that the variability in GCI values was similar for the two groups (SD = 14.50 and SD = 14.00), but the mean GCI value for the breastfed group was higher than the mean GCI value for the non-breastfed group (105.30

compared to 100.90). Thus, in the study, the mean GCI values of the two groups differed by 4.40 (105.30 − 100.90). *Is this difference unlikely to have happened by chance alone, that is, if breastfeeding is not associated with GCI at age four and children who are breastfed and those who aren't breastfed have the same population mean GCI at age four?* How do we answer this?

Using the same approach as in Section 6.2, we could use the **Multiple Means** applet to simulate what the difference in sample means could have been by random chance, assuming breastfeeding was not associated with GCI at age four. As we discussed in Chapter 5, even though this is not a randomized experiment (it is an observational study), we can still use shuffling to redistribute the observed GCI values for the two groups, assuming the null hypothesis of no association, and then approximate a p-value from the simulation results. Figure 6.11 shows the simulated null distribution of the difference in sample means after 1000 shuffles.

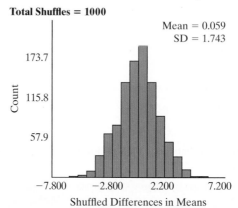

FIGURE 6.11   Distribution of difference in sample mean GCI values, generated assuming breastfeeding is not associated with GCI at age four.

Figure 6.12 circles those shuffles which resulted in values of the difference in sample means that were at least as extreme as that observed in the study, that is, 4.40. It turns out that 6 of the 1,000 shuffles resulted in values of difference in group means less than or equal to −4.40, and 4 shuffles resulted in values of difference in group means larger than or equal to 4.40. Adding up the two circled regions as shown in Figure 6.12, we get the approximate two-sided p-value to be 0.006 + 0.004 = 0.010. Thus, we estimate a 0.010 probability of observing a difference in sample mean GCI values for breastfed and non-breastfed children of at least 4.40, just by chance, if breastfeeding were not associated with GCI at age four.

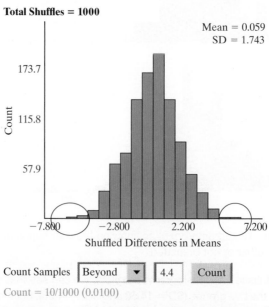

FIGURE 6.12   Display of the p-value (circled regions).

A quick 2SD confidence interval would be $4.40 \pm 2(1.743)$ or $(0.914, 7.886)$. We are about 95% confident that the population mean GCI score is 0.914 to 7.886 points higher for breast-fed babies than babies that aren't breastfed (about a 5%–10% increase).

> **THINK ABOUT IT**
>
> What do you notice about the overall shape, center, and variability of the distribution of difference in sample means as shown in Figure 6.12?

Notice that the shape of the distribution appears to be somewhat like a normal curve, with a mean of approximately 0 (which was the difference hypothesized in the null hypothesis!) and standard deviation of 1.743.

> **THINK ABOUT IT**
>
> How many standard deviations away from the hypothesized difference of 0 is the observed difference of 4.40? How are you deciding?

Recall that we use a standardized statistic (e.g., z-statistic or t-statistic) to measure how far away the observed statistic is from the hypothesized value of the parameter as given by the null hypothesis, taking into account the standard deviation of the statistic. When the sample sizes were large, the standardized statistic was also utilized to find a probability based on the area under a normal or a t-distribution curve. We can use a similar strategy here. Because the sample sizes in our study are considered large enough ($n_1 = 237, n_2 = 85$), we can use the theory-based approach to predict the distribution of the standardized statistic using a mathematical model and hence the p-value from that model.

6.3.1

In the **Multiple Means** applet, if we use the pull-down menu to select **t-statistic**, the applet reports the observed t-statistic to be 2.46. (This may not match your calculation exactly because above you used the estimated value of the standard error from the simulation rather than the theory-based formula shown at the end of this section.) You should remember t-statistics from Chapter 3. Similar to the standardized z-statistic for the difference in sample proportions, this two-sample t-statistic is a standardized statistic for the difference in sample means. Typically the distribution of this t-statistic is bell-shaped and symmetric, but it is not exactly normally distributed, being less peaked with fatter tails. As the sample size increases, the distribution of the standardized statistic becomes more normal. At the end of this section we provide a few more details about how this statistic is calculated when comparing two means. As before, the standardized statistic (e.g., $t = 2.46$) is telling us that the observed difference in sample means of 4.40 is 2.46 standard deviations away from the hypothesized difference of 0.

The applet allows us to overlay the theoretical t-distribution on top of the shuffled t-statistics and find the theory-based p-value as shown in Figure 6.13. (*Note:* You could also use the **Theory-Based Inference** applet to perform this calculation.) This standardized statistic produces an approximate p-value of 0.0150.

6.3.2

> **THINK ABOUT IT**
>
> Based on the p-value, what conclusion would you draw? Is there statistically significant evidence of a difference between the mean GCI values of the two populations? Can you conclude that breastfeeding improves the mean GCI at age four? To what larger population(s) would you be comfortable generalizing these results?

A p-value of 0.015 is usually considered small enough to provide strong evidence against the null hypothesis. If there were really no association between breastfeeding and GCI values, there would only be a 0.015 chance of obtaining, by random chance alone, sample means as far apart or even farther apart as was found in this study. Thus, we have statistically significant evidence that there is a genuine difference in mean GCI at age four between children who are breastfed during infancy and those who are not. Considering that the study was not a randomized experiment, we cannot conclude any cause-and-effect relationship between breast-feeding and GCI at age four. Also, the participants in this study were all white children born in Western Michigan. This limits the population to whom we can generalize these results. The association between breastfeeding and GCI observed in this study may not hold true for people of other races/ethnicities.

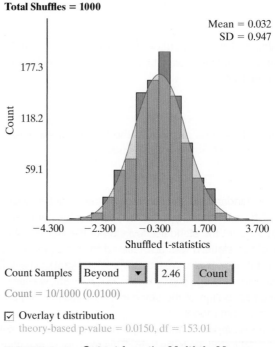

Total Shuffles = 1000

Mean = 0.032
SD = 0.947

Count Samples [Beyond ▼] [2.46] [Count]

Count = 10/1000 (0.0100)

☑ Overlay t distribution
theory-based p-value = 0.0150, df = 153.01

FIGURE 6.13   Output from the **Multiple Means** applet, showing the shuffled *t*-statistics and theory-based p-value for the breastfeeding study.

Notice that the p-value approximated by the theory-based method (0.015) very closely matches the p-value approximated by simulation (0.010). The p-values are both small enough and close enough to lead you to the same conclusion.

THINK ABOUT IT

So, we were unable to conclude a cause-and-effect relationship between breastfeeding and GCI at age four. What might be an alternative explanation for the significant difference in mean GCI values of children who were breastfed compared to those who weren't?

Alternative explanations for the difference in mean GCI values of children who were breastfed compared to those who weren't could be characteristics of the mothers, such as their level of education. Perhaps better-educated mothers are more likely to breastfeed their children and are also more likely to have children of high intellectual functioning. Then this variable, maternal education level, would qualify as a confounding variable, because its effects on intellectual functioning could not be distinguished from the effects of breastfeeding. In that case we cannot say whether the higher GCI values in the breastfeeding group are due to the breastfeeding or due to the mother's education, or perhaps a combination of both, or perhaps neither and some other confounding variable is the real cause. But what the significance test does allow is for us to essentially rule out random chance as a plausible explanation for the large observed difference between the two samples.

How could you design a different study that would allow for drawing a cause-and-effect conclusion if a significant difference were found between the groups? Would it be feasible/ethical to conduct such a study?

In order to draw a cause-and-effect conclusion, you would have to perform a randomized comparative experiment. This would mean using random assignment to determine which mothers would breastfeed their babies and which would not. The random assignment would aim to balance out all other variables, such as mother's education level, between the two groups. Then if the group that was breastfed performed significantly better than the other group, we could legitimately conclude that the breastfeeding *caused* the higher intellectual functioning. But conducting such a study would not be feasible or ethical, because such a personal decision as whether to breastfeed a baby cannot be imposed on mothers.

In earlier chapters we have discussed the factors that are associated with the size of the p-value. For the most part, these factors are the same. In particular, increasing the sample size still decreases the variability in the null distribution, which in turn reduces the p-value if nothing else changes. Now that the statistic is the difference in group means, if this difference between the two groups increases, then the p-value will decrease. As in Chapter 2, with quantitative data another aspect that also impacts size of the p-value is the underlying data variability, as measured by the standard deviations within each group. In this case the standard deviations are 14.00 and 14.50 in the two groups. If they were larger, the variability in the null distribution would be larger and so the p-value would be larger as well.

ESTIMATION

When you show the *t*-statistic and overlay the theoretical distribution, you can also check a box on the far left of the applet to display the 95% confidence *t*-interval.

☑ 95%CI(s) for difference in means   Breastfed - Not breastfed: (0.8699, 7.9302)*

Notice that this interval is similar to what we found with the 2SD method earlier. The asterisk indicates that zero is not contained within the confidence interval.

Does the 95% confidence interval contain the value 0? What does that imply?

Recall that a confidence interval is an interval of plausible values for the parameter of interest. In this case, the parameter of interest is $\mu_{breastfed} - \mu_{not}$, where $\mu_{breastfed}$ was defined to be the mean GCI at age four for the population of all children who are breastfed during infancy and μ_{not} to be that for children who aren't breastfed during infancy. The 95% theory-based confidence interval for $\mu_{breastfed} - \mu_{not}$ is calculated by the applet to be (0.8699, 7.9302). Notice that this interval contains only positive values and does not contain 0. Thus, we are 95% confident that the difference in mean GCI values between children who are and are not breastfed is *not* 0. More specifically, we are 95% confident that the mean GCI at age four for all children who are breastfed during infancy is 0.8699 to 7.9302 points higher than the mean GCI for children who aren't breastfed. (Please keep in mind that the same cautions as mentioned above with regard to not drawing a cause-and-effect conclusion and about the relevant population to which these results apply also need to be heeded when interpreting the findings from a confidence interval.) Note that, as we've seen before, increasing the sample size, decreasing the confidence level, or decreasing the data variability (standard deviation) will decrease the width of the confidence interval. The observed value of the statistic (difference in group means) will determine the midpoint of the interval.

The theory-based approach presented above (for both tests of significance and confidence intervals) is valid if *either one* (or both) of the following conditions are met:

VALIDITY CONDITIONS

The quantitative variable should have a symmetric distribution in both groups or you should have at least 20 observations in each group and the sample distributions should not be strongly skewed.

In the breastfeeding example discussed here, the validity conditions are met (see FAQ 6.3.1 for more details). The sample sizes in each group are larger than 20 (237 and 85) and there is not strong skewness (in fact, the data are fairly symmetric; see Figure 6.10). This is why the p-value and confidence interval obtained from the theory-based approach are so similar to those obtained from simulation.

FAQ 6.3.1   www.wiley.com/college/tintle

What are the validity conditions when comparing two means?

FORMULAS

Earlier you saw how when we applied the theory-based approach we could predict the value of the p-value and the confidence interval for the difference in two means using the standardized *t*-statistic (see FAQ 6.3.1 for why it's named "t") instead of through simulation. We'll now show a few details of how this works.

First, the value of the *standardized t-statistic* is obtained using

$$ t = \frac{\text{statistic} - \text{hypothesized value}}{SE(\text{statistic})} = \frac{\bar{x}_1 - \bar{x}_2 - 0}{\sqrt{\dfrac{s_1^2}{n_1} + \dfrac{s_2^2}{n_2}}} $$

where, $\bar{x}_1$, s_1, and n_1 are the sample mean, sample standard deviation (SD), and sample size of the data in group 1, with the subscript "2" indicating the same quantities in group 2. Notice that there are a lot of similarities between this equation and the equation for the standardized *z*-statistic shown in Section 5.3—namely, the numerator is the difference in group means (larger difference means larger *t*-statistic) and the denominator includes the sample sizes (larger sample sizes mean larger *t*-statistic). The difference here is that the standard deviations of the quantitative variable in each group also impact the value of the *t*-statistic: namely, larger values of the sample standard deviations decrease the value of the *t*-statistic. Note that in this case our hypothesized value is 0, but we could use nonzero hypothesized values just as easily.

In many cases sample sizes are large enough that we can use the same approximate guidelines we had for the standardized *z*-statistic to understand the meaning of the *t*-statistic. In particular, values of *t* larger than 2 generally correspond to p-values less than 0.05 for two-sided tests.

YOU MAY BE THINKING

Why do you call the statistic *t* instead of *z* if they are the same?

As you may recall from Chapter 3, the null distributions of the two standardized statistics are not exactly the same. As it turns out, the null distribution of the *t*-statistic is symmetric, bell-shaped, and centered at zero—but it is not normal—its peak in the middle is shorter, and its tails are longer (heavier). The difference between the normal (or *z*) and *t*-distributions goes away when the sample size gets larger, and so, most times, interpreting a *t*-statistic like a *z*-statistic is fine.

A theory-based confidence interval for $\mu_1 - \mu_2$ is also similar to the approach used in Chapter 5 for estimating $\pi_1 - \pi_2$. In particular, the confidence interval is obtained as

Statistic $\pm$ margin of error

which is

$$(\bar{x}_1 - \bar{x}_2) \pm \text{multiplier} \times \sqrt{\frac{s_1^2}{n_1} + \frac{s_2^2}{n_2}}.$$

When the sample size in each group is large, the multiplier is approximately equal to 2 for 95% confidence intervals, 1.645 for 90% confidence intervals, and 2.576 for 99% confidence intervals. The actual value of the multiplier from the *t*-distribution depends not only on the confidence level but also on the sample sizes involved.

In the example shown earlier, the *standard error* of $\bar{x}_1 - \bar{x}_2$ is calculated as

$$\sqrt{\frac{s_1^2}{n_1} + \frac{s_2^2}{n_2}} = \sqrt{\frac{14.00^2}{85} + \frac{14.50^2}{237}} = 1.7869$$

So, the margin of error for the 95% confidence interval is approximately equal to $2 \times 1.7869 = 3.57$. Thus, the 95% confidence interval is approximately equal to 4.40 ± 3.57, alternatively written as (0.83, 7.97). *Note:* The difference between what we show here and the results from the applet are because the applet uses 1.9756 as the multiplier instead of 2.

Note: In Chapters 1 and 5, when dealing with categorical data, we discovered that when we increased the sample size(s) we increased the evidence against the null if all else remained the same. This is true when dealing with quantitative data as well. However, when dealing with quantitative data, we also notice that standard deviations of the sample data play a role in assessing strength of evidence. Let's look at this intuitively. Figure 6.14 shows two pairs of dotplots.

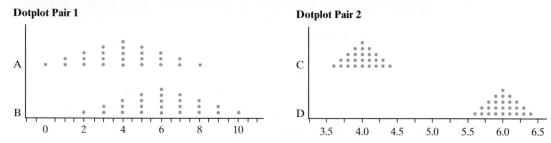

Dotplot Pair 1   **Dotplot Pair 2**

FIGURE 6.14   These dotplots are designed to show that for the same difference in means, the strength of evidence is increased when standard deviations are smaller.

The distributions in dotplot Pair 1 have group means of 4 and 6, two units apart. The distributions in dotplot Pair 2 have identical group means as dotplot Pair 1. This indicates that the variability *between* groups in dotplot Pair 1 is the same as the variability between groups in dotplot Pair 2. What is different, however, is the variability *within* the groups. The standard deviations for the samples in dotplot Pair 1 are much larger than those in dotplot Pair 2. Now suppose you wanted to show, using tests of significance, that the population means were different in each of the two cases. Which one would have stronger evidence? Hopefully you can see that there is a lot of overlap with the two distributions in dotplot Pair 1, and it could be difficult to convince us that the population means are different using these data. However, the distributions in dotplot Pair 2 are completely separated. There is no overlap at all. It would appear that using these data it would be easy to convince us that the two corresponding population means differ. This all implies that as sample standard deviations decrease (all else the same), the strength of evidence of a difference in population means increases.

Close Friends

EXPLORATION

6.3

How many close friends do you have? You know, the kind of people you like to talk to about important personal matters. Do men and women tend to differ on the number of close friends? And if so, by how much do men and women differ with regard to how many close friends they have? One of the questions asked of a random sample of adult Americans on the 2004 General Social Survey (GSS) was:

From time to time, most people discuss important matters with other people. Looking back over the last six months—who are the people with whom you discussed matters important to you? Just tell me their first names or initials.

The interviewer then recorded how many names each person gave, along with keeping track of the person's sex. The GSS is a survey of a representative sample of U.S. adults who are not institutionalized.

1. Identify the variables recorded. Also classify each as either categorical or quantitative, and identify each variable's role: explanatory or response.
2. Did this study make use of random assignment, random sampling, both, or neither?
3. Was this an experiment or an observational study? Explain how you are deciding.
4. In words, state the null and the alternative hypotheses to test whether American men and women *differ* with regard to how many friends they have.
5. Define the parameters of interest and assign symbols to them.
6. State the null and the alternative hypotheses in symbols.

The survey responses are summarized in the Table 6.5 (and the data can be found in expanded form in the file **CloseFriends**).

TABLE 6.5 Number of close friends reported by sex								
Number of close friends reported	**0**	**1**	**2**	**3**	**4**	**5**	**6**	**Total**
Men	196	135	108	100	42	40	33	654
Women	201	146	155	132	86	56	37	813

7. Now you will obtain numerical summaries (statistics, such as mean and SD) of the survey data using the **Multiple Means** applet.
   - Open the data file **CloseFriends** to access the raw data. Copy the data (e.g., CTRL-A and CTRL-C).
   - Open the **Multiple Means** applet and press **Clear**. Click inside the **Sample data** box and paste (e.g., CTRL-V). Then press **Use Data**.
   a. Report the sample size, sample mean, and sample SD of the number of close friends reported for each sex. Based on the sample statistics, who tends to have more close friends, on average: men or women? How are you deciding?
   b. Based on the sample statistics, who tends to have more variability with respect to how many close friends they have: men or women? How are you deciding?
   c. Based on the data as presented in Table 6.5, are the distributions of number of close friends symmetric or skewed? If skewed, in which direction?
   d. Calculate the observed difference in the mean number of close friends between these two groups (men − women). (Verify your calculation by checking the **Observed diff** output.)
   e. Notice that the value recorded in (d) is a negative number. Well, number of friends can only be 0 or more. Why is the number recorded in (d) less than 0?

The question we want to answer is, *Is the difference in mean number of close friends between men and women, as seen in the GSS sample data, something that could plausibly have happened by chance, by random sampling alone, if, on average, men and women have the same number of close friends?*

8. Using the same approach as in Section 6.2 with the **Multiple Means** applet, you can use this applet to generate possible values of the difference in sample means under the null

hypothesis by shuffling which response values go with which explanatory variable values. Check the **Show Shuffle Options** box and enter 1,000 for the **Number of Shuffles**. Press the **Shuffle Responses** button (there will be a pause; this is a large data set!). The histogram on the right is the simulated null distribution for the difference in sample means.

Enter the observed difference in sample means in the **Count Samples** box and press **Count**.

a. Record your estimated p-value.

b. Fill in the blanks of the following sentence, to complete the interpretation of the p-value.

The p-value of _____ is the probability of observing _____ assuming _____.

9. If the difference in means was larger (more different than 0), how would this impact the size of the p-value?

10. How would increasing the sample size (all else remaining the same) change the p-value? Why?

11. How would increasing the standard deviation of the number of close friends for both males and females (all else remaining the same) change the p-value? Why?

As we saw earlier, another measure of the strength of evidence against the null hypothesis would be to *standardize* the statistic by subtracting the hypothesized value and dividing by the standard error of the statistic.

12. On the left side of the applet (below the **Sample data** window) use the **Statistic** pull-down menu to select the **t-statistic** (again, there will be a pause). Record the value of the t-statistic that is computed for your data. Write a one-sentence interpretation of this value.

Notice that the standardized statistic uses the letter t (the one you should remember from Chapter 3) instead of the z (from Chapters 1 and 5) we saw when testing proportions. This is because the theoretical distribution used is now a t-distribution instead of a normal distribution. These t-distributions are very similar to normal distributions especially when sample sizes are large. The t-statistic, like the z-statistic, tells us how many standard deviations our sample difference is above or below the mean and it can be judged in the same manner. More details about the t-statistic are given earlier in this section and in the Calculation Details appendix.

13. In light of the value of the standardized statistic, should you expect the p-value to be large or small? How are you deciding?

14. The histogram on the far right now displays the null distribution of simulated t-statistics. Describe the behavior of this distribution.

15. Below the null distribution check the box **Overlay t distribution**. Does the t-distribution appear to adequately predict the behavior of the shuffled t-statistics? What do you think this suggests about whether the validity conditions will be met for these data?

16. Enter the observed value of the t-statistic in the **Count Samples** box and press **Count**. (Remember to use the pull-down menu to specify what direction(s) you want to consider more extreme based on the alternative hypothesis.) How does the p-value from the t-distribution (in orange) compare to the simulation-based p-value (from #8(a))?

Validity conditions

The *validity conditions* required for this theory-based approach (a "two-sample t-test") to be valid are shown in the box.

> The quantitative variable should have a symmetric distribution in both groups or you should have at least 20 observations in each group and the sample distributions should not be strongly skewed.

17. Do the validity conditions appear to be satisfied for these data? Justify your answer.

18. Based on the above analysis, state your conclusion in the context of the study. Be sure to comment on the following.

   a. *Statistical significance:* Do the data provide evidence that the mean number of close friends that men have is different from the mean number of friends women have? How are you deciding?

   b. *Causation:* Do the data provide evidence that how many friends one has is *caused* by one's sex? How are you deciding?

   c. *Generalization:* To whom can you apply the results of this study? All people? All adults? How are you deciding?

19. *Estimation:* When you have selected the *t*-statistic and the theory-based overlay, you can also use this applet for estimating the parameter of interest. (You can also go directly to the **Theory-Based Inference** applet which will also allow you to change the confidence level.) Check the box next to **95% CI(s) for difference in means.**

   a. Identify, in words related to the context of this study, the relevant parameter to be estimated here.

   b. Report the 95% confidence interval for this parameter.

   c. Does the 95% confidence interval calculated from the GSS sample data contain the value 0? What does that imply? (*Hint:* Recall that a confidence interval is an interval of *plausible* values for the parameter of interest, and the interval is calculated using the sample statistics.)

   d. Does the 95% confidence interval agree with your conclusion in #16? How are you deciding?

   e. Fill in the blanks of the sentence below to complete the interpretation of the 95% confidence interval:

   > We are _____% confident that the mean number of close friends men have is
   > _____ than the mean number of close friends that women have,
   > by between _____ and _____ friends.

   f. How would the width of the interval change if you increased the confidence level to 99%? Why?

   g. How would the width of the interval change if you increased the sample size? Why?

   h. How would the width of the interval change if the variability of the number of close friends increased for both males and females? Why?

20. **Step 6: Look back and ahead.**

   Looking back: Did anything about the design and conclusions of this study concern you? Issues you may want to critique include:

   - The match between the research question and the study design
   - How the observational units were selected
   - How the measurements were recorded
   - The number of observational units in the study
   - Whether what we observed is of practical value

   Looking ahead: What should the researchers' next steps be to fix the limitations in this study and/or build on this knowledge?

SECTION 6.3   Summary

Under certain circumstances, essentially when sample sizes are large enough, a theory-based approach can be used to approximate p-values and confidence intervals for the difference between two means.

- The standardized statistic again subtracts the hypothesized value from the observed statistic and then divides by the standard deviation of the statistic.
  - The statistic in this case is the difference in sample means, that is,

$$\bar{x}_1 - \bar{x}_2.$$

- The standardized statistic for a hypothesized difference of zero is

$$t = \frac{\bar{x}_1 - \bar{x}_2 - 0}{\sqrt{\dfrac{s_1^2}{n_1} + \dfrac{s_2^2}{n_2}}}.$$

  - This standardized statistic is called a t-statistic rather than a z-statistic.
- The confidence interval again takes the form statistic $\pm$ margin of error.

$$\text{Statistic} = \bar{x}_1 - \bar{x}_2$$

$$\text{Margin of error} = \text{multiplier} \times \text{standard error of statistic}$$

$$\text{Standard error } SE = \sqrt{\frac{s_1^2}{n_1} + \frac{s_2^2}{n_2}}$$

- Validity conditions for the theory-based approach to be valid are that both sample sizes are large (generally considered to be at least 20 with no strong skewness) or the data are distributed symmetrically in both groups.
- It does not matter which group is labeled as Group 1 and which as Group 2, provided that the labeling is consistent throughout the analysis, including interpretations and conclusions.

Some factors that affect p-values and confidence intervals are also similar to before:

- A larger difference between the sample means provides stronger evidence that the population means differ.
- Larger sample sizes produce stronger evidence that the population means differ.
- Larger within-group variability decreases evidence that the population means differ.
- The difference in sample means is the midpoint of the confidence interval.
- Larger sample sizes produce narrower confidence intervals.
- Larger confidence levels produce wider confidence intervals.
- Less within-group variability produces narrower confidence intervals.

Type of data	Name of test	Applet	Validity conditions
Two groups compared on a quantitative variable	Simulation test for comparing two groups on quantitative variable	Multiple means	—
	Theory-based test or interval for comparing two means (two-sample t-test; interval)	Multiple means; Theory-based inference	At least 20 observations in each group without strong skewness, or symmetry in distribution of quantitative variable in each group

CONFIDENCE INTERVAL AND SIGNIFICANCE TEST FOR A DIFFERENCE BETWEEN TWO INDEPENDENT MEANS

INTRODUCTION

In Section 2.2 you learned that when the variable of interest is a single quantitative variable (e.g., estimated length of a short song snippet), then, provided that a bell-shaped distribution is a good approximation for the distribution of the sample mean $\bar{x}$, the appropriate theory-based approach is called a one-sample t-test. Then you extended your work with a single quantitative variable in Section 3.3 to investigate a theory-based approach for constructing an interval of plausible values for a population mean, referred to as a one-sample t-interval.

In the previous section, you examined a theory-based method for comparing two groups on a quantitative response. As with a single mean, a t-distribution provides a good approximation for the distribution of the difference in two sample means, provided certain validity conditions are met. The ***theory-based test*** and ***interval*** for the difference in two population means are referred to as a ***two-sample t-test*** and a ***two-sample t-interval***, respectively.

In Section 2.2, Part 3, you learned that the t-distribution is actually an entire family of distribution curves, similar in shape to the normal distribution but characterized by a number called the **degrees of freedom** (abbreviated df). You also saw that for a one-sample t-test or one-sample t-interval, the degrees of freedom are equal to the sample size minus one ($n - 1$).

The degrees of freedom for a two-sample t-test or two-sample t-interval are actually quite complicated to compute, as seen below:

$$df = \frac{\left(\dfrac{s_1^2}{n_1} + \dfrac{s_2^2}{n_2} \right)^2}{\dfrac{1}{n_1 - 1}\left(\dfrac{s_1^2}{n_1} \right)^2 + \dfrac{1}{n_2 - 1}\left(\dfrac{s_2^2}{n_2} \right)^2}$$

Note: Fortunately, you will ***never*** have to compute this formula for the AP exam. You can obtain the appropriate degrees of freedom from your graphing calculator or statistical software. In the absence of technology, a conservative estimate uses the smaller of $n_1 - 1$ and $n_2 - 1$ as the degrees of freedom and, in practice, works just as well as the complicated formula above.

Below are the validity conditions that you will need to verify when conducting a two-sample t-test or two-sample t-interval on the AP exam.

Validity conditions for a two-sample t-test and a two-sample t-interval

- Data are from two independent random samples from the populations of interest, or from two groups in a randomized experiment.

- Both population distributions are approximately normally distributed or the sample sizes for both groups are large enough for the central limit theorem to apply (e.g., n_1 and $n_2 \geq$ 30, but different texts may give slightly different cut-offs).

  - For smaller samples where the population shapes are unknown, graph the sample data and comment on whether it is reasonable to assume that the sample data from each group came from populations that are fairly symmetric (recall from Section 2.2 , Part 2, that when the shape of the population distribution is fairly symmetric, the distribution of sample means will tend to become bell-shaped fairly quickly, even for small sample sizes). Occasionally, you may also have other reasons to suspect the population distribution is close to normally distributed (e.g., historical evidence).

As we saw in the previous section, for a **two-sample t-test**, when the null hypothesis is of the form $H_0: \mu_1 - \mu_2 = 0$, the standardized statistic has the form

$$t = \frac{\text{observed statistic } - \text{ hypothesized value}}{\text{standard error of statistic}} = \frac{\bar{x}_1 - \bar{x}_2 - 0}{\sqrt{\dfrac{s_1^2}{n_1} + \dfrac{s_2^2}{n_2}}}$$

where, $\bar{x}_1$, s_1, and n_1 are the sample mean, sample standard deviation (SD), and sample size of the data in Group 1, with the subscript "2" indicating the same quantities in Group 2. Notice that there are a lot of similarities between this formula and that for the standardized z-statistic shown in Section 5.3, namely, the numerator is the difference in group means (larger difference means larger t-statistic) and the denominator includes the sample sizes (larger sample sizes mean larger t-statistic). The standard deviations of the quantitative variable in each group also appear in the denominator of the t-statistic, such that larger values of the sample standard deviations decrease the value of the t-statistic. Note that in this case, our hypothesized difference is zero, but we could use nonzero hypothesized values just as easily (i.e., we can test a null hypothesis of the form $H_0: \mu_1 - \mu_2 = D$, where D is a value other than 0).

In Section 1.7 you learned the work you must show on the AP Statistics exam when a hypothesis test is called for. The format you learned is the same for all hypothesis tests.

a. State the hypotheses in either words or using appropriate symbols.

b. Name the test that will be used and state and verify the validity conditions for the test chosen.

c. Calculate the test statistic (standardized statistic) and corresponding p-value.

d. State your conclusion (with appropriate justification based on your p-value and stated significance level) in the context of the research question.

Recall from Section 2.2, Part 3, that when you want to look up the p-value corresponding to a t-statistic, you can use either your graphing calculator or Table B on the AP^{TM} formula sheet that is included with the exam. If you use the calculator, it will calculate the degrees of freedom for you. If you are using Table B, remember that for the two-sample t-test, a conservative estimate of the degrees of freedom uses the smaller of $n_1 - 1$ and $n_2 - 1$.

> **AP TIP**
>
> If you are using your calculator to calculate the p-value, then you must use the corresponding degrees of freedom from the calculator, not the conservative estimate (the smaller of $n_1 - 1$ and $n_2 - 1$).

You saw in Section 3.2 that a general method, valid for any confidence level, is to estimate the parameter with

$$\text{statistic} \pm \text{multiplier} \times (\text{SE of statistic})$$

As we saw in the previous section, a confidence interval estimating the difference in population means is given by

$$(\bar{x}_1 - \bar{x}_2) \pm t_{df}^* \times \sqrt{\frac{s_1^2}{n_1} + \frac{s_2^2}{n_2}}$$

where t_{df}^* represents the critical value from the t-distribution with the appropriate degrees of freedom (see above) for the confidence level desired. Recall that in Section 3.3, Part 2, you learned how to use either your graphing calculator or Table B on the AP^{TM} formula sheet to find t^*.

In Section 3.2, Part 2, you learned the work you must show on the AP Statistics exam when a confidence interval is called for. The format you learned is the same for all confidence intervals.

a. Identify the parameter you want to estimate and the theory-based model you will use.

b. Verify the validity conditions for the theory-based method you have chosen.

c. Construct the confidence interval, showing the values that you substitute into the formula.

d. Interpret the confidence interval you obtained in the context of the problem.

6.4 — Visual Spatial Memory

Example 6.4

EXAMPLE

Spatial memory is a part of the memory that records one's surroundings and forms a cognitive map, which is a mental representation of one's surroundings. We use this mental picture formed by our visual spatial memory to navigate through familiar environments, such as our homes, schools, or even cities. Not only does our visual spatial memory help us navigate through our environments, but it also provides an aid in remembering where we have placed something (Myers, D. G., *Myers' Psychology for AP*. 2nd Ed. New York: Worth, 2014).

Two students in an AP Statistics class conducted a study to investigate whether a difference exists in visual spatial memory between ninth-grade females and ninth-grade males at their school. To conduct their study, they randomly selected 19 females and 22 males from the current ninth-grade class to take part in their study. The selected students were given a drawing that consisted of a turtle, a couple of paint cans, and a couple of paint brushes on a counter that was splattered with paint. They were allowed to study the picture for 30 seconds. After 30 seconds, the drawing was taken away and the students were then given a drawing very similar to the first but with several small changes made. For example, names on the paint cans changed and one of the paint brushes moved. Participants were given 60 seconds to circle any differences in the second drawing from the original one they had studied. Their score was the correct number of differences found between the two images.

Here are the scores for the female students and the male students:

Female: 3, 4, 4, 5, 5, 5, 6, 6, 6, 6, 6, 7, 7, 7, 8, 8, 8, 9, 9

Male: 3, 3, 4, 4, 4, 4, 4, 4, 5, 5, 5, 5, 5, 5, 5, 6, 6, 6, 6, 7, 7, 8

These data from the study can be organized as given in Table 6.6 as a "frequency distribution."

TABLE 6.6   Number of correct reported changes by sex

Score	3	4	5	6	7	8	9	Total
Female	1	2	3	5	3	3	2	19
Male	2	6	7	4	2	1	0	22
Total	3	8	10	9	5	4	2	41

Do these data provide convincing evidence of a difference in the mean score on the visual spatial memory test for the populations of female and male ninth-grade students at this high school? Use a 5% significance level.

THINK ABOUT IT

What are the observational units? What are the variables? What are the parameters of interest? What are the relevant hypotheses?

The 41 ninth-grade students in this study are the observational units. The explanatory variable is whether the student is a male student or a female student, which is a categorical variable. The response variable is each student's score on the visual spatial memory test, and this is a quantitative variable. The parameters of interest are μ_F and μ_M, representing the population mean visual spatial memory test score for the female and male ninth-graders, respectively, at this high school.

Recall that on the AP exam you are expected to show the following work, illustrated in four parts:

a. **State the hypotheses in either words or using appropriate symbols.**

Null: There is no difference in the mean visual spatial memory test score for the populations of female and male ninth-grade students at this high school.

$$H_0: \mu_F - \mu_M = 0$$

Alternative: There is a difference in these population means.

$$H_a: \mu_F - \mu_M \neq 0$$

b. **Name the theory-based test that will be used and state and verify the validity conditions for the test chosen.** We will use a ***two-sample t-test*** because we are comparing two groups on a quantitative response.

Now let's check the validity conditions for a two-sample t-test.

- Generalizability: We are told that the students were randomly selected from ninth-grade students at this school. We should be able to generalize the results to all ninth-grade students at this school, provided that the students in the study are a representative sample of ninth-grade students from this school. The responses of the males and females should be independent of each other.

- We do not know the shapes of the populations of scores on the test for female and male students at this school, and because our samples of 19 female and 22 male students are not large enough to meet the sample size condition based on the central limit theorem (how many would be required for that?), we need to graph the sample data.

    Dotplots of the scores for both the sampled female and male students on the visual spatial memory test are fairly bell-shaped, so it is reasonable to assume that the population distributions of scores for both female and male ninth-grade students at this high school are approximately normal. The distribution of the differences in sample means for samples of these sizes should therefore be bell-shaped, so it is reasonable to conduct a two-sample t-test.

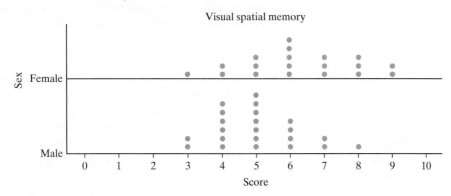

c. **Calculate the test statistic (standardized statistic) and corresponding p-value.** By substituting into the appropriate formula, we find the following.

$$\bar{x}_F = 6.263 \qquad \bar{x}_M = 5.045$$
$$s_F = 1.695 \qquad s_M = 1.290$$
$$n_F = 19 \qquad n_M = 22$$

$$t = \frac{6.263 - 5.045 - 0}{\sqrt{\dfrac{1.695^2}{19} + \dfrac{1.290^2}{22}}} \approx 2.557 \qquad \text{p-value} \approx 0.015$$

The calculator used 33.37 df to determine the p-value, you may also use Table B with 18 df (using the conservative estimate—the smaller of $n_1 - 1$ and $n_2 - 1$). The corresponding two-sided p-value (using the conservative estimate for degrees of freedom) is between $0.005 \times 2 = 0.01$ and $0.01 \times 2 = 0.02$.

d. **State your conclusion (with appropriate justification based on your p-value and stated significance level) in the context of the research question.** We have convincing evidence to conclude that there is a difference in the population mean scores on the visual spatial memory test for the population of female and male ninth-grade students at this high school. Our decision is based on our obtained p-value of 0.015, which is less than our significance level of 0.05.

THINK ABOUT IT

How would you interpret the p-value that you obtained in part (c)?

When applied to this study, we interpret the p-value as follows: Assuming that the students in the sample were representative of the population of ninth-grade students at this school, and that male and female ninth-graders have the same mean score on the visual spatial memory test, the probability of obtaining a difference in sample mean scores of 1.218 points or even larger (in either direction) is about 1.5%.

THINK ABOUT IT

Summarize the study design used here: Is this an observational study or an experiment? How would the answer to this question affect your scope of inference?

6.4.1

This was an observational study because the students could not be randomly assigned to a sex (female or male). We can say that there is an association between sex and score on the visual spatial memory test, but we cannot attribute a cause-and-effect relationship.

Next, let's use the data from this study to construct a 95% confidence interval for the difference in the population mean score on the visual spatial memory test for female ninth-grade students at this school minus the population mean for male ninth-grade students at this school.

Recall that on the AP exam you are expected to show the following work, illustrated in the four parts that follow:

a. **Identify the parameter you want to estimate and the theory-based model you will use.** Let $\mu_F - \mu_M$ represent the difference in the population mean scores on the visual spatial memory test for ninth-grade female and male students at this school.

We will use a two-sample *t*-interval to construct a 95% confidence interval for $\mu_F - \mu_M$.

b. **Verify the validity conditions for the theory-based method you have chosen.** The validity conditions for a two-sample *t*-interval are the same as for a two-sample *t*-test that we already checked above.

c. **Construct the confidence interval, showing the values that you substitute into the formula.**

95% C.I. for $\mu_F - \mu_M$:

$\bar{x}_F = 6.263$ $\bar{x}_M = 5.045$
$s_F = 1.695$ $s_M = 1.290$
$n_F = 19$ $n_M = 22$

$$6.263 - 5.045 \pm t^*_{33.4}\sqrt{\frac{1.695^2}{19} + \frac{1.290^2}{22}}$$

$(0.249, 2.187)$

> **CALCULATOR TIPS**
>
> You can find the confidence interval on your calculator. For example:
>
> - **TI-84:** Stat → Tests → 2-SampTInt
> - **TI-Nspire:** Menu → Stat → Confidence Intervals → 2-Sample t Interval

d. **Interpret the confidence interval you obtained in the context of the problem.** We are 95% confident that the mean score for all ninth-grade females at this school who would take the visual spatial memory test is 0.249 to 2.187 points higher than the mean score for all ninth-grade males at this school who would take the test (assuming that the sample was representative of all ninth-grade students at this school).

> **THINK ABOUT IT**
>
> What are the implications of having a confidence interval that does not contain zero?

The fact that the confidence interval does not contain zero implies that it is not plausible that the difference in mean scores for female and male ninth-grade students on the visual perception memory test is zero—in other words, that the null hypothesis is not plausible and that there is convincing evidence to support our research (alternative) hypothesis. Thus, not only does the confidence interval yield a result that is consistent with the result of the test of significance, but it gives us even more information by estimating the size of the difference between the population mean scores.

 6.4.2

Ready to Learn Math?

 EXPLORATION 6.4

The Educational Research Institute of America recently conducted a study to evaluate the effectiveness of the *Ready* Instructional Program to improve student reading and mathematics knowledge. The study was conducted by comparing the New York State Test performance of schools that used the *Ready* program for instruction in both English Language Arts and Mathematics to the performance of schools that had not used the *Ready* program. Students' performance on the 2014 New York State Mathematics Test was used as one measure of program effectiveness.

Table 6.7 provides summary statistics based on the schoolwide performance of eighth-graders who took the 2014 New York State Mathematics Test. Summary statistics are separated by whether a school used the *Ready* program or not. The observational units are the schools, and the variable of interest is the average score for the students at each school.

TABLE 6.7 Comparison of eighth-grade school scores on New York State Mathematics Test for Grade 8 *Ready* users and non-users

	Number of Schools	Mean Score	Standard Deviation
Non-users	759	293	19.1
Ready users	273	297	17.4

1. Is there convincing evidence of a difference in the mean score on the New York State Mathematics Test for schools using the *Ready* program (*Ready* users) and schools not using the *Ready* program (non-users) at the 5% significance level? (*Hint:* Recall that on the AP Statistics exam when a hypothesis test is called for, you must show the following work.)

   a. State the hypotheses in either words or using appropriate symbols.

   b. Name the test that will be used and state and verify the validity conditions for the test chosen.

   c. Calculate the test statistic (standardized statistic) and corresponding p-value.

   d. State your conclusion (with appropriate justification based on your p-value and stated significance level) in the context of the research question.

2. Students were not randomly assigned to the two different programs. If there is convincing evidence of a difference between the mean New York Mathematics State Test scores for the two populations (Grade 8 non-users and Grade 8 *Ready* users), can you conclude a cause-and-effect relationship exists between the mathematics program a school uses (non-user or *Ready* user) and their students' average score on the New York State Mathematics Test? Justify your response.

3. Use the data from this study to construct and interpret a 95% confidence interval for the difference in mean scores between Grade 8 *Ready* users and Grade 8 non-users on the New York Mathematics State Test. (*Hint:* Recall that on the AP Statistics exam when a confidence interval is called for, you must show the following work.)

   a. Identify the parameter you want to estimate and the theory-based model you will use.

   b. Verify the validity conditions for the theory-based method you have chosen.

   c. Construct the confidence interval, showing the values that you substitute into the formula.

   d. Interpret the confidence interval you obtained in the context of the problem.

4. Is zero in your confidence interval? What does this imply about the difference in the population mean mathematics test scores for the Grade 8 *Ready* users and non-users?

SECTION 6.4 Summary

In this section you investigated theory-based methods for tests of significance and confidence intervals for comparing two population means. You saw that a t-distribution provides a good approximation for the distribution of the statistic $\bar{x}_1 - \bar{x}_2$ if the population distributions are bell-shaped or the sample sizes are large enough for the central limit theorem to apply. The theory-based test for the difference in two population means is referred to as a **two-sample t-test**. In addition to the test of significance, you examined a theory-based **two-sample t-interval** for estimating the difference in two population means. You saw that the work you need to show on the AP exam for both a test of significance and a confidence interval for a difference in population means follows the same general format as that for a single mean.

CHAPTER 6 Summary

In this chapter we looked at approaches to consider potential differences in the center and/or variability of a quantitative variable between two independent groups. We started by learning how parallel dotplots can be used to examine potential differences in the quantitative variable between the two groups. Comparing centers (e.g., means) and variability (e.g., SDs, IQRs) can tell us a lot, but when the data are skewed or outliers are present, using the median may be more appropriate than the mean, as the median is more resistant to skewness and outliers than is the mean. We also learned that the five-number summary (minimum, lower quartile, median, upper quartile, and maximum) and boxplots can be used to summarize the distribution of a quantitative variable. We also saw how stemplots and cumulative frequency plots can be used to graph and compare a the distribution of a quantitative response variable.

We then learned that we can apply the 3S strategy in a manner very similar to the one we saw in Chapter 5 to assess whether two sample means differ enough to conclude that there is a genuine difference in the population means or long-run means of processes. Similarly, we can use the 2SD method to generate a 95% confidence interval on the difference in population or long-run means. This approach also can be used to compare the medians of two independent groups. As we've seen before, when certain validity conditions are met, in this case when both sample sizes are large (generally considered to be at least 20) or the data are distributed symmetrically in both groups, a theory-based approach can be used to approximate p-values and confidence intervals for the difference between two means. In this case the standardized statistic is called a t-statistic, the theory-based test is called a two-sample t-test and the confidence interval is called a two-sample t-interval.

CHAPTER 6
GLOSSARY

A stemplot (also called a stem-and-leaf plot) is a useful method for visualizing small to medium-sized data sets for a single quantitative response variable consisting of a stem, all but the final digit of a number, and a leaf, the final digit. (Sometimes, numbers are truncated before building the stemplot so the leaf does not consist of the final digit, but the digit immediately after the digit or digits in the stem.)

back-to-back stemplot A stemplot used to compare two groups with a quantitative response where stems are arranged in a column with a vertical line on each side. Leaves representing one of the groups extend from the right vertical line in ascending order and leaves representing the other group extend from the left vertical line, also in ascending order. Above each set of leaves, we provide a label identifying the groups.

boxplot A visual display of the five-number summary, summarizing the behavior of a quantitative variable.

cumulative frequency plot A plot of each unique data value and the percentage of the distribution at or below that value.

degrees of freedom (abbreviated df) A number that is used to describe a t-distribution. As the number of degrees of freedom increases, the tails of the t-distribution get lighter and the t-distribution gets closer to the shape of a normal distribution.

five-number summary Minimum, lower quartile, median, upper quartile, maximum.

inter-quartile range (IQR) The difference between the upper quartile and the lower quartile.

lower quartile The value for which 25% of the data lie below.

modified boxplot A boxplot where the outliers are displayed with an asterisk or other identifying symbol. A value is considered an outlier if it is more than 1.5 times the inter-quartile range (IQR) below the lower quartile (Q1) or more than 1.5 times the IQR above the upper quartile (Q3).

split stemplot A stemplot in which each stem is listed twice (doubling the number of stems), with data values (or 'leaves') 0, 1, 2, 3, 4 on the row of the first occurrence of the stem and data values (or 'leaves') 5, 6, 7, 8, 9 on the second occurrence.

two-sample t-interval The theory-based confidence interval for the difference in two population means.

two-sample t-test The theory-based test of significance for the difference in two population means.

upper quartile The value for which 25% of the data lie above.

validity conditions for two-sample t-test The quantitative variable should have a symmetric distribution in both groups, or you should have at least 20 observations in each group and the sample distributions should not be strongly skewed.

CHAPTER 6
EXERCISES

SECTION 6.1

6.1.1* Which of the following is true about the inter-quartile range?

A. It represents the range of approximately the middle quarter of a data set.

B. It represents the range of approximately the middle 50% of a data set.

C. If a value above the upper quartile is increased, the inter-quartile range will also increase.

D. It a value below the lower quartile is decreased, the inter-quartile range will also decrease.

6.1.2 Which of the following is NOT true about quartiles?

A. The lower quartile is always smaller than the upper quartile.

B. Quartiles can be calculated by determining the median of the values above/below the location of the overall median.

C. Approximately 50% of the numbers in a data set lie between the lower and upper quartiles.

D. The lower quartile is the same as the 25th percentile.

6.1.3* Approximately what does the box portion of a boxplot display?

A. The middle quarter of the data

B. The middle half of the data

C. The lower quarter of the data

D. The upper quarter of the data

6.1.4 What are the five parts of the five-number summary?

6.1.5* On a data set that is bell-shaped, which will typically be larger, its standard deviation or its inter-quartile range?

Rattlesnakes

6.1.6 The following dotplot gives the ages of 21 male rattlesnakes. Which of the following would be true if one of the rattlesnakes whose age is given as 13 years is actually 15 and that change is made in the data set. (There may be more than one correct answer.)

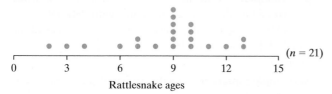

Rattlesnake ages

A. The median would increase.

B. The mean would increase.

C. The inter-quartile range would increase.

D. The standard deviation would increase.

TV watching*

6.1.7 The following histogram is the distribution of the amount of time, in minutes, that some statistics students said they watched television the previous day. Using this graph to estimate the mean and median age for the amount of television watching time, we can conclude:

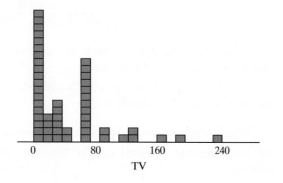

TV

A. The mean is smaller than the median.

B. The mean is larger than the median.

C. The mean and the median have the same value.

D. You can't tell which is larger without the actual data.

Quiz scores

6.1.8 The following set of scores was obtained from a quiz: 4, 5, 8, 9, 11, 13, 15, 18, 18, 18, 20. The teacher computes the usual descriptive measures of central tendency and spread for these data and then discovers that an error was made. One of the 18s should have been a 16. Which of the following measures will NOT need to be changed from the original computations? (There may be more than one correct answer.)

A. Mean

B. Median

C. Standard deviation

D. IQR

E. They all will need to be changed.

Changing exam scores*

6.1.9

a. Suppose an instructor decides to add five points to every student's exam score in a class. What effect would this have on the five-number summary? On the inter-quartile range? Explain.

b. Suppose an instructor decides to add five points only to the exam score for the highest-scoring student in the class. What effect would this have on the five-number summary? On the inter-quartile range? Explain.

c. Suppose an instructor decides to add five points only to the exam score for the lowest-scoring student in the class. What effect would this have on the five-number summary? On the inter-quartile range? Explain.

Student heights

6.1.10 A sample of heights (in inches) of 20 female statistics students is as follows:

67, 64, 67, 65, 64, 65, 67, 64, 65, 60, 67, 67,
72, 65, 70, 63, 67, 65, 67, 70

a. Find the median height.

b. Find the first and third quartiles.

c. Find the inter-quartile range.

d. Construct a boxplot by hand for the data.

States visited*

6.1.11 An instructor collected data on the number of states that 50 students in her class had visited in the U.S. The results are shown in the 6.1.11 dotplot.

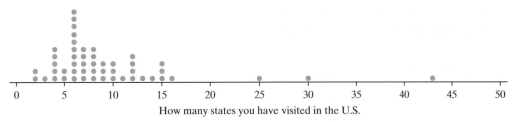

EXERCISE 6.1.11

a. Use the dotplot to find and report the median value for the number of states visited by the students in this study.

b. Use the dotplot to determine the lower and upper quartile values and the inter-quartile range for the number of states visited by the students in this study.

c. Would the mean value for these data be smaller than, larger than, or the same as the median, as reported in part (a)? Explain your reasoning.

6.1.12 Reconsider the data in the dotplot in the previous question about the number of states that students had visited. Suppose the observation recorded as 43 states is a typo and was meant to be 34. If we corrected this entry in the data set, how would the following numerical statistics change, if at all?

Mean: Smaller	Same	Larger
Median: Smaller	Same	Larger
Standard deviation: Smaller	Same	Larger
Inter-quartile range: Smaller	Same	Larger

Monthly temperatures

6.1.13 The 6.1.13 dotplot shows the average monthly temperatures (°F) for San Francisco, CA, and Raleigh, NC.

a. What are the observational units here? (*Hint:* The observational units are not cities.)

b. Identify the response variable and whether it is categorical or quantitative.

c. Would the mean be a reasonable measure of center for these data? Why or why not?

d. The yearly mean temperature for Raleigh is 59.25°F and the yearly mean temperature for San Francisco is 57.25°F. Since these values are rather close, is it fair to say the cities are similar *with respect to average monthly temperatures?*

e. Will the standard deviation for Raleigh be larger or smaller than the standard deviation for San Francisco? How are you deciding?

6.1.14 Reconsider the data in the dotplots from the previous question about average monthly temperatures for San Francisco and Raleigh.

a. Determine the median temperature for each city. What do these numbers tell us about the two data sets?

b. Determine the inter-quartile range for each city. What do these numbers tell us about the two data sets?

Study hours*

6.1.15 In a survey of introductory statistics students, an instructor asked students to report how many hours they had spent studying in a typical week during the last term and their sex. The data appears in the 6.1.15 dotplot.

Describe what the graph tells us about any similarities and differences between men and women when it comes to how much time they report spending studying

EXERCISE 6.1.13

EXERCISE 6.1.15

every week. Be sure to compare and contrast the shape, center, and spread for study hours' distributions for males and females.

6.1.16 Reconsider the data in the previous question about number of hours spent studying.

a. Find the median number of study hours for both males and females. What do these numbers tell us about the two data sets?

b. Find the inter-quartile range for the number of study hours for both males and females. What do these numbers tell us about the two data sets?

c. Construct parallel boxplots by hand for the two data sets.

Gettysburg Address

6.1.17 The graph below displays the distribution of word lengths (number of letters) in the Gettysburg Address, which you explored in Exploration 2.1A.

$\mu = 4.29$
$\sigma = 2.12$

Letters

a. Describe the shape of this distribution.

b. Based on this shape, do you expect the median to be less than the mean, greater than the mean, or very close to the mean? Explain.

The following table lists how often each of the word lengths appears for these 268 words.

Word length	1	2	3	4	5	6	7	8	9	10	11
Number of words	7	49	54	59	34	27	15	6	10	4	3

c. Determine the median word length of these 268 words.

d. The mean word length is 4.29 letters per word. Is the median greater than, less than, or very close to the mean? Does this confirm your answer to part (b)?

e. Calculate the five-number summary of the word lengths.

College student bedtimes*

6.1.18 In a survey, 30 college students were asked what their usual bedtime was and the results are shown in the 6.1.18 dotplot in terms of hours after midnight. Negative responses are hours before midnight.

a. Determine the five-number summary for the bed times.

b. What is the inter-quartile range?

c. The earliest bedtime is 11:30 PM (represented by −0.50 on the graph). If that person's usual bedtime is actually 9:00 PM and that change was made in the dotplot, does that change the inter-quartile range? Would it change the standard deviation?

Candy bars

6.1.19 Weights of 20 Mounds® candy bars and 20 PayDay® candy bars, in grams, are shown in the 6.1.19 dotplots.

a. Describe how the distributions of weights of the two types of candy bars differ in both variability and center.

b. Based on your answers to part (a), which set of candy bar weights has the lowest standard deviation? Which has the lowest mean?

c. Would you say there is an association between the type of candy bar and the weight? Why or why not?

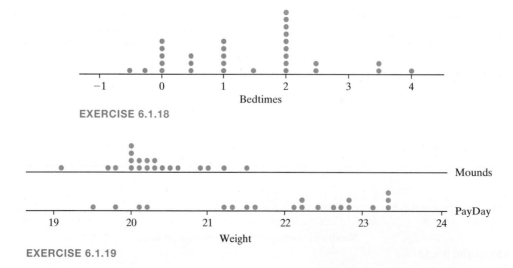

Bedtimes

EXERCISE 6.1.18

Weight

EXERCISE 6.1.19

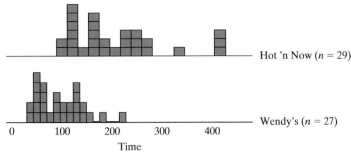

Hot 'n Now (n = 29)

Wendy's (n = 27)

EXERCISE 6.1.21

6.1.20 Using the candy bar weight data shown in the previous exercise, do the following:

a. Find the five-number summary for both sets of candy bar weights.

b. Construct parallel boxplots for both sets of candy bar weights.

Fast food wait times*

6.1.21 Students compared drive-through times at a couple of fast food restaurants in their town. They kept track of the time (in seconds) for people to go through the drive-through at Wendy's® and Hot 'n Now® from the time of ordering until they exited the pick-up window during lunch time. The results are shown in the 6.1.21 histograms.

a. The medians for the two sets of times are 85 and 173 seconds. Which belongs to which restaurant?

b. The inter-quartile ranges for the two sets of times are 75 and 116.50 seconds. Which belongs to which restaurant?

c. For each restaurant is the mean larger or smaller than the median?

6.1.22 Reconsider the drive-through times (in seconds) for a Wendy's and a Hot 'n Now restaurant from the previous question.

a. The means for the two sets of times are 93.70 and 203.00 seconds. Which belongs to which restaurant?

b. The standard deviations for the two sets of times are 46.70 and 89.60 seconds. Which belongs to which restaurant?

Time in the bathroom

6.1.23 Students collect the time (in seconds) for men and women to use the restroom at a mall in Michigan. The results are shown in the 6.1.23 histograms.

a. One data set (male or female) has both the larger mean and median. Which one is that?

b. Do you think the median is larger, smaller, or about the same as the mean for each data set?

c. One data set has a larger standard deviation but a smaller inter-quartile range than the other. Which one is that? Explain why.

TV watching*

6.1.24 Statistics students were asked how many minutes of television they watched on the previous day. The results, in minutes, are shown in the 6.1.24 histograms, for the males in the top histogram and the females in the bottom histogram.

a. In which direction is each distribution skewed?

b. Will the mean be larger, smaller, or about the same as the median for each distribution?

c. Do you think that there is likely an association between TV watching and a person's sex? Explain.

Car crashes and exercise

6.1.25 As part of a survey of statistics students, they were asked if they had ever been in a car crash while they were

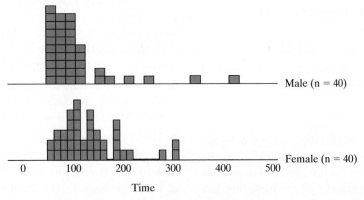

Male (n = 40)

Female (n = 40)

EXERCISE 6.1.23

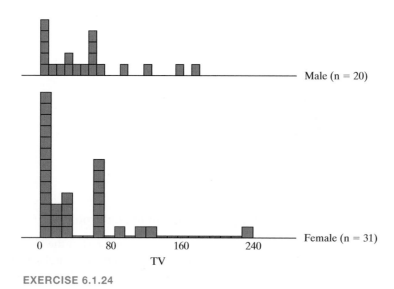

EXERCISE 6.1.24

driving and how many minutes of exercise they had on the previous day. The data file **CarCrashExercise.txt** has these results. Copy and paste this data set into the **Descriptive Statistics** applet.

a. Based on just how the distributions look, do you think there is an association between being in a car crash while driving and exercise? Is so, in what way? Explain.

b. Find the mean of number of minutes of exercise for those that have been in car crashes while driving and those that have not. With this added information, do you think there is an association between being in a car crash while driving and exercise? Explain.

c. Find the median number of minutes of exercise for those that have been in car crashes while driving and those that have not. With this added information, do you think there is an association between being in a car crash while driving and exercise? Explain.

6.1.26 Reconsider the previous exercise where students responded to a survey where they were asked if they had ever been in a car crash while they were driving and how many minutes of exercise they had on the previous day. The data file **CarCrashExercise.txt** has these results. Copy and paste this data set into the **Descriptive Statistics** applet and display boxplots for the data.

a. Is the data skewed to the right or the left?

b. Describe how you can see the skewedness you described in the part (a) when looking at the boxplots.

Sugar in cereals*

6.1.27 Statistics students found the sugar content of breakfast cereals, in grams per serving, for those placed on the high shelves of the store versus the low shelves. The data file **CerealSugar.txt** has these results. Copy and paste this data set into the **Descriptive Statistics** applet.

a. If you want to compare the sugar content of cereals on high versus low shelves, what would be the explanatory variable and what would be the response.

b. Based on just how the distributions look, do you think there is an association between where the cereal is located and its sugar content? If so, in what way? Explain.

c. Find the mean grams of sugar per serving for the cereal on the low shelves and the mean for those on the high shelves. With this new information, do you think there is an association between where the cereal is located and its sugar content? Explain.

d. Find the median grams of sugar per serving for the cereal on the low shelves and the median for those on the high shelves. With this new information, do you think there is an association between where the cereal is located and its sugar content? Explain.

e. Are the median sugar contents between high and low shelved cereal farther apart or closer together than the means are?

Coffee and height

6.1.28 You may have heard someone say that drinking coffee will stunt your growth. To test this, college students were asked their heights and if they were coffee drinkers. The data file **CoffeeHeight.txt** has the results. Copy and paste this data set into the **Descriptive Statistics** applet.

a. Based on just how the distributions look, do you think there is an association between height and drinking coffee? Is so, in what way? Explain.

b. Notice there are two peaks (or what is called bimodal) in the distribution of heights for the non–coffee drinkers? Why do you think the distribution has this feature?

c. Find the mean height for the coffee drinkers and the non–coffee drinkers. With this added information, do you think there is an association between drinking coffee and height? Explain.

d. Find the median height for the coffee drinkers and the non–coffee drinkers. With this added information, do you think there is an association between drinking coffee and height? Explain.

e. If you could find that coffee drinkers were significantly shorter than non–coffee drinkers in a study like this, would this show there is a tendency for coffee to stunt a person's growth? Explain.

FAQ

6.1.29 Read FAQ 6.1.1 and answer the following question: When should you use the median as a summary statistic instead of the mean?

6.1.30 Read FAQ 6.1.2 and answer the following question: The IQR is calculated as

A. Q1 − Q3   B. Mean − median

C. Min − max   D. Q3 − Q1

E. Median − mean   F. Max − min

6.1.31 Read FAQ 6.1.2 and answer the following question: True or false, a data point that is labeled an outlier is beyond 1.5 IQRs of either Q1 or Q3.

6.1.32 Read FAQ 6.1.2 and answer the following question: Which measure of spread is more resistant to outliers, SD or IQR?

SECTION 6.1: Part 2

6.1.33* Suppose you are making a stemplot of people's heights that range from 48″ to 84″. For the height of 74″:

A. The 7 would be the stem and the 4 would be the leaf.

B. The 4 would be the stem and the 7 would be the leaf.

C. It doesn't matter as long as you are consistent with the other entries.

D. Because 74″ is a large height, both the 7 and the 4 would be in the stem.

E. None of the above

6.1.34 When you want to make a stemplot to compare two distributions (i.e., you have a binary explanatory variable and a quantitative response), what type of stemplot do you use?

A. An inverted stemplot

B. A double stemplot

C. A back-to-back stemplot

D. A Tukey-Tukey stemplot

6.1.35* In the stemplot below, 0|5 = 5, the estimated number of hours doing school work at home each week for high school students. What is the median of this data set?

A. 0
B. 1
C. 5
D. 10
E. 25

```
0 | 0 0 1 2
0 | 5 5
1 | 0 0 0 0 0 4
1 |
2 | 0 0 5
```

6.1.36 In the stemplot below, 0|5 = 5, the estimated number of hours doing school work at home each week for high school students. What is the IQR of this data set?

A. 2
B. 5
C. 10
D. 12
E. 14

```
0 | 0 0 1 2
0 | 5 5
1 | 0 0 0 0 0 4
1 |
2 | 0 0 5
```

6.1.37* Suppose you have a data set with the following summary statistics: lower quartile = 18, median = 22, upper quartile = 28. Which of the following numbers would be outliers according to the 1.5 IQR rule? (Choose all that apply.)

A. 1
B. 4
C. 40
D. 45
E. 46

6.1.38 The following figure is a cumulative frequency plot for the number of small Tootsie Roll candies 45 college students could pick up with one hand. Based on the graph, what appears to be the median number of candies that could be picked up?

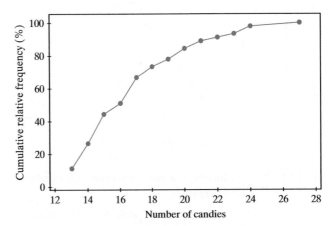

A. 14
B. 16
C. 18
D. 20
E. 80

6.1.39* The following figure is a cumulative frequency plot for the ages of the 100 U.S. senators in October 2017. Based on the graph, roughly what percentage of the senators are older than 60?

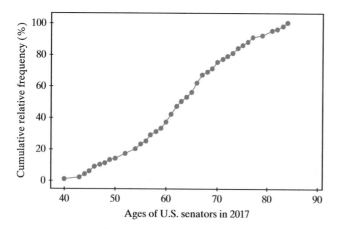

Ages of U.S. senators in 2017

A. 21%

B. 37%

C. 50%

D. 63%

E. 82%

6.1.40 Based on the cumulative frequency plot below of the heights of 124 college students, answer the questions that follow.

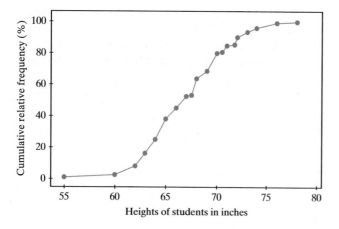

Heights of students in inches

a. A height of 65 inches is at what percentile? (Estimate to the nearest 10th percentile.)

b. A height of 70 inches is at what percentile? (Estimate to the nearest 10th percentile.)

6.1.41* The student heights from the previous exercise are displayed in the following cumulative frequency plot, but are split up so there is one graph of the female heights and a separate graph of the male heights.

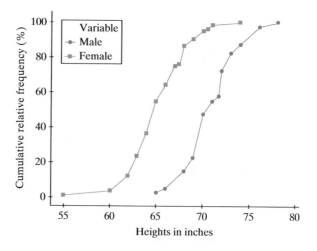

Heights in inches

a. From the graph, can you determine whether all the male heights are greater than all the female heights or not? Explain.

b. From the graph, can you determine whether all the numbers in the five-number summary for the male heights are greater than the corresponding numbers in the five-number summary for the female heights? Explain.

c. Explain, using the graph, how you would determine the approximate difference between the median male and median female heights.

d. Explain, using the graph, how you would determine the approximate difference in the percentiles for a female height that is 70″ and a male height that is 70″.

6.1.42 Thirty college students were asked how many states in the United States they have been to and the results are shown below.

1, 3, 3, 5, 6, 8, 10, 10, 10, 12, 12, 12, 13, 14, 15, 15, 16, 16, 19, 21, 23, 23, 25, 25, 27, 28, 30, 30, 30, 32

a. Find the five-number summary for this data set.

b. Would you say the data set is fairly symmetric, skewed left, or skewed right? Explain.

6.1.43* Twenty college students were asked how many texts they send on a typical day and the results are shown below.

3, 4, 5, 10, 10, 10, 20, 20, 30, 30, 30, 50, 50, 55, 75, 75, 100, 150, 200, 250

a. Find the five-number summary for this data set.

b. Would you say the data set is fairly symmetric, skewed left, or skewed right? Explain.

6.1.44* For the previous question on students sending texts, are there any outliers in the distribution according to the 1.5 IQR rule? If so, which ones?

6.1.45 A study done by Jung et al. (2014) looked at hurricane names and their perceived threat. They thought that if hurricanes in the U.S. had male names, they would be perceived as more dangerous. In one part of the research, the subjects were given a weather map showing a hurricane moving toward the area where they lived. Half the 142 subjects saw the map with the hurricane named Christina and half the subjects saw the map with the hurricane named Christopher. They were then asked to rate how likely it was they would evacuate, with 1 being to definitely evacuate immediately and 7 to definitely not evacuate. The results are shown in the following boxplots.

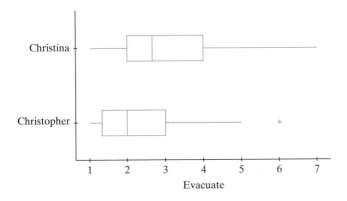

a. Compare the five-number summaries for each hurricane name.

b. Based on the boxplots, is there preliminary evidence that people are more likely to evacuate if the hurricane is given a male name (in this case Christopher)? Explain.

6.1.46* Recall the previous exercise about hurricane names and the perceived threat. The researchers also gave 274 subjects a weather map showing a hurricane, with about a third of the subjects seeing the hurricane named Victor, about a third seeing the hurricane named Victoria, and about a third seeing an unnamed hurricane. They also read a statement about the uncertainty of the future intensity of the hurricane. The subjects were asked to rate the riskiness of the hurricane, with 1 being not at all risky and 7 being very risky. The results are shown in the following boxplots.

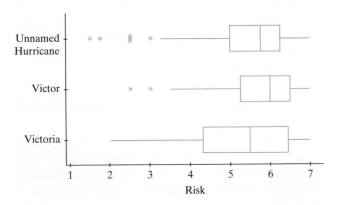

a. Compare the five-number summaries for each hurricane name.

b. Based on the boxplots, is there preliminary evidence that people are more likely to perceive the hurricane that is given a male name (in this case Victor) as more risky? Explain.

6.1.47 As part of a study, 45 college students picked up as many small Tootsie Roll candies as they could with one hand. The results are shown in the following stemplot.

```
1 | 33333
1 | 444444455555555
1 | 6667777777
1 | 88899
2 | 00011
2 | 23
2 | 44
2 | 7            Key:  1|3 = 13 candies picked up
```

a. Is this data set skewed to the large numbers (right) or small numbers (left) of candies? Does the shape make sense in this context?

b. What is the median number of Tootsie Rolls students were able to pick up?

c. What are the lower and upper quartiles for the number of Tootsie Rolls students were able to pick up?

d. Why do you think we decided to split up the stems in the way we did? (*Hint:* Explain the process and what the stemplot would have looked like without splitting.)

6.1.48* *Census at School* is an international classroom project in which students from Grades 4–12 complete a brief online survey. Through the Census at School website, we obtained a random sample of the time, in minutes, it took high school students to get to school, surveying 22 students who rode a bus and 22 students who took a car. The results are shown in the following split stemplot. (The shortest time for someone riding in a car was 1 minute.)

a. What is the median time for those that rode a bus? For those that took a car? Which is larger? What does this tell you?

b. What is the IQR for those that rode a bus? For those that took a car? Which is larger? What does this tell you?

c. What interesting feature about many of these data values jumps out to you in the stemplot, and why does it make sense in this context?

Bus		Car
4	0	12
75	0	5788888
300000	1	00022
5	1	55
00000	2	000
5	2	
0000	3	00
5	3	5
	4	
5	4	Key: 0|1 = 1 minute travel time

6.1.49 Listed below are temperatures, in degrees Fahrenheit, for the 20 largest cities in the United States based on population (New York, Los Angeles, Chicago, Houston, Philadelphia, Phoenix, San Antonio, San Diego, Dallas, San Jose, Austin, Jacksonville, San Francisco, Indianapolis, Columbus, Fort Worth, Charlotte, Detroit, El Paso, Seattle) on the afternoon of December 27, 2016.

58, 71, 30, 82, 60, 70, 74, 67, 70, 54, 74, 75, 38, 56, 41, 76, 67, 32, 55, 55

a. Construct a stemplot of the temperatures. (*Hint:* Remember the final leaves should be sorted.)

b. Briefly summarize what you learn about the distribution from this graph.

c. Find the median, quartiles, and IQR for the temperatures. Provide a one-sentence interpretation of the IQR.

d. Are there any outliers in the data set according to the 1.5 IQR method?

e. Construct a modified boxplot for the temperatures.

f. Is the distribution of temperatures symmetric, skewed to the large numbers, or skewed to the small numbers? Which graph (the stemplot or the boxplot) is more useful in helping you see this shape?

6.1.50* Listed below are the number of cups of coffee students in a college statistics class said they drink per week.

1, 14, 4, 13, 10, 14, 10, 5, 18, 21, 26, 20, 10, 6, 1 ,7, 10, 1, 12, 2, 3, 16, 14, 5, 7

a. Construct a stemplot of the number of cups using split stems. [*Hint:* Remember to include a key.]

b. Find the median, quartiles, and IQR for the number of cups. Provide a one-sentence summary of the IQR.

c. Are there any outliers in the data set according to the 1.5 IQR method?

d. Construct a modified boxplot for the number of cups.

e. Is the distribution of number of cups of coffee symmetric, skewed to the large numbers, or skewed to the small numbers? Which graph (the stemplot or the boxplot) is more useful in helping you see this shape? Does this shape make sense for this variable? Explain.

6.1.51 Student researchers tested to see whether listening to music while memorizing words would interfere with a person's ability to do so. Their subjects were randomly assigned to either listen to music or not. Everyone was shown 40 five-letter words for 90 seconds. The words were taken away and they were asked to write down as many words as they could remember. The results are in the file **WordsMemorized**.

a. Is this an experiment or an observational study?

b. What is the explanatory variable? Is it categorical or quantitative?

c. What is the response variable? Is it categorical or quantitative?

d. Construct back-to-back stemplots of the data using split stems. Write a brief comparison of the two distributions.

e. Which group, music or not, tended to remember more words? How did you decide? Does this provide preliminary evidence in favor of the students' research conjecture?

6.1.52 Reconsider the word memorizing study from the previous exercise.

a. Find the median, quartiles, and IQR for each group (while listening to music or not). A higher median number of words remembered corresponds to which group (music or not)? Does this provide preliminary evidence in favor of the students' research conjecture?

b. Are there any outliers in the data sets according to the 1.5 IQR method?

c. Construct parallel modified boxplots using the data.

d. Write a brief comparison of the two distributions based on the boxplots.

6.1.53* Student researchers at Hope College conducted an experiment to determine whether there is a difference in the memorization ability of students when they take notes on paper by hand versus taking notes on a computer. They randomly assigned 20 students to the paper-based note-taking group and 20 students to the computer-based note-taking group. They showed all their subjects a 12-minute video about the sun, asking students to take notes using the method assigned. After the video was over, the notes were collected and the students were given a 10-question quiz on information about the sun given in the video, with the instructor recording the number of correct responses out of 10. The quiz results are found in the file **NoteTaking**.

a. Is this an experiment or an observational study?

b. What is the explanatory variable? Is it categorical or quantitative?

c. What is the response variable? Is it categorical or quantitative?

d. Construct back-to-back stemplots of the data. Write a brief comparison of the two distributions.

e. Which group, paper or computer, tended to have higher scores on the quiz? How did you decide? Does this provide preliminary evidence in favor of the students' research conjecture?

6.1.54* Reconsider the note-taking study from the previous exercise.

a. Find the median, quartiles, and IQR for each group (computer and paper). Which group, computer or paper, has a higher median quiz score? Does this provide preliminary evidence in favor of the students' research conjecture?

b. Are there any outliers in the data sets according to the 1.5 IQR method?

c. Construct parallel boxplots using the data.

d. Write a brief comparison of the two distributions based on the boxplots.

6.1.55 The following set of dotplots with overlaid boxplots gives the number of pairs of flip-flops students in a statistics class, 13 males (top) and 37 females (bottom), said they owned. The smallest number of pairs of flip-flops a male had was 1 and for females it was 2.

a. What is the median number of pairs of flip-flops for the males? For the females?

b. Although the female boxplot clearly has two whiskers on each side of the box and clear, separate lines for the two quartiles and the median, why doesn't the male boxplot have a lower whisker and those same three separate lines?

c. The boxplots are drawn so as not to show any outliers. Summary statistics are also included. Are there any outliers in either data set? If so, which ones? (Explain how you determined this.)

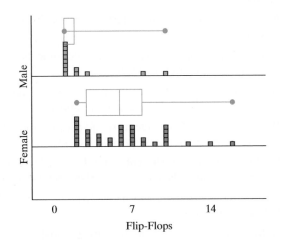

The five-number summary for the number of flip-flops owned, by sex, for these students is

	Minimum	Lower Quartile (Q1)	Median	Upper Quartile (Q3)	Maximum
Females	2	3	6	8.5	16
Males	1	1	1	2.5	10

6.1.56* The following set of dotplots with overlaid boxplots gives the cost of the most recent haircut for 20 male college students (top) and 20 female college students (bottom) in a statistics class. Summary statistics are also given. (Note: This is a different dataset than was used in Exploration 6.1A)

a. Which group has the higher median haircut cost?

b. For which group is there more variability in haircut costs?

c. The female boxplot clearly has three separate lines for the two quartiles and the median; why doesn't the male boxplot have those same three separate lines?

d. The boxplots are drawn so as not to show any outliers. Are there any outliers in either data set? (Explain how you determined this.)

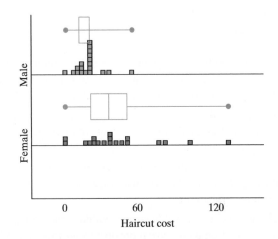

The five-number summary for the cost of a haircut, by sex, for these students is

	Minimum	Lower Quartile (Q1)	Median	Upper Quartile (Q3)	Maximum
Females	$0	$21	$35	$50	$130
Males	$0	$13.5	$20	$20	$54

SECTION 6.2

Haircut prices*

6.2.1 As seen in Exploration 6.1, an instructor collected data on prices (in dollars) paid by students for their most recent haircut, also recording each student's sex, to test whether females in the population paid more on average for their most recent haircut than males. Which of the following are appropriate sets of hypotheses? (Circle all that apply.)

A. H_0: There is no association between a person's sex and haircut prices.

H_a: There is an association between a person's sex and haircut prices with females tending to pay more than males.

B. H_0: Males and females in the population pay the same price on average for their last haircut.

H_a: Males in the population pay less on average than females for their last haircut.

C. H_0: $\mu_{female} - \mu_{male} = 0$

H_a: $\mu_{female} - \mu_{male} > 0$

D. H_0: $\mu_{female} = \mu_{male}$

H_a: $\mu_{female} > \mu_{male}$

E. $H_0: \bar{x}_{female} = \bar{x}_{male}$

$H_a: \bar{x}_{female} > \bar{x}_{male}$

F. H_0: There is no association between a person's sex and haircut prices.

H_a: There is an association between a person's sex and haircut prices.

G. $H_0: \mu_{female} = \mu_{male}$

$H_a: \mu_{female} \neq \mu_{male}$

6.2.2 Reconsider the previous exercise about haircut prices. The p-value for the appropriate test turns out to be 0.0022. What would you conclude? (Circle all that apply.)

A. The sample data provide *strong* evidence that females in the population paid more on average than males for their most recent haircut.

B. The sample data provide *little* evidence that females in the population paid more on average than males for their most recent haircut.

C. The sample data provide strong evidence that females in the population paid *much* more on average than males for their most recent haircut.

6.2.3 Reconsider the previous two exercises about haircut prices. The sample mean prices were $21.85 for males and $54.05 for females, a difference of $32.20. Which are appropriate interpretations of the p-value of 0.0022? (Circle all that apply.)

A. There's a 0.22% chance that women in the population did not pay more on average than males for their most recent haircut.

B. If there were no difference in the population between what females and males paid for their most recent haircut, then there's a 0.22% chance that the sample mean price for females would have been at least $32.20 higher than the sample mean price for males.

C. If there were no difference in the population between what females and males paid for their most recent haircut, then 0.22% of all random shuffles based on the sample data would produce the shuffled mean price for females being at least $32.20 higher than the shuffled mean price for males.

Biking and sleep deprivation

6.2.4 Reconsider the bicycle commuting time study (Example 6.2) and the sleep deprivation study (Exploration 6.2).

a. In what primary way do these studies differ from the dolphin therapy and yawning studies from Chapter 5?

b. Are both of these studies (sleep deprivation and bicycle commuting time) randomized experiments, are both observational studies, or is there one of each type (if so, which is which)?

c. Did we use simulation-based or theory-based methods to analyze these studies?

d. Which, if any, of these two studies uses a two-sided alternative?

e. With which of these two studies did we find strong evidence that there was a cause-and-effect relationship between the variables?

Study hours*

6.2.5 In a survey of introductory statistics students, an instructor asked her students to report how many hours they spent studying in a typical week during the last term and their sex. Suppose that the intent is to compare reported study habits of male students to those of female students.

a. Is this an experiment or an observational study? Explain how you know.

b. Identify the observational units.

c. Identify the explanatory and response variable. Also, identify whether each is quantitative or categorical.

d. Identify the appropriate null hypothesis from the following set of five choices.

A. Male students and female students are equally likely to study.

B. On average, male students and female students spend an equal amount of time studying.

C. On average, female students spend a greater amount of time studying compared to male students.

D. On average, female students spend a lesser amount of time studying compared to male students.

E. On average, female students differ from male students when it comes to how much time they spend studying.

e. Identify the appropriate alternative hypothesis from the following set of five choices.

A. Male students and female students are equally likely to study.

B. On average, male students and female students spend an equal amount of time studying.

C. On average, female students spend a greater amount of time studying compared to male students.

D. On average, female students spend a lesser amount of time studying compared to male students.

E. On average, female students differ from male students when it comes to how much time they spend studying.

How many Facebook friends do you have?

6.2.6 In a survey of introductory statistics students, an instructor asked her students to report how many Facebook friends they had. Suppose that the intent is to study whether there is an association between number of Facebook friends and a person's sex.

a. Identify whether the study is an experiment or an observational study. Explain.

b. Identify the observational units.

c. Identify the explanatory and response variables. Also, for each variable identify whether it is categorical or quantitative.

d. Which of the following is the appropriate null hypothesis? Circle one.

   A. There is an association between a person's sex and the number of Facebook friends.

   B. There is no association between a person's sex and the number of Facebook friends.

   C. On average, men have more Facebook friends than women.

   D. On average, men have fewer Facebook friends than women.

e. Which of the following is the appropriate alternative hypothesis? Circle one.

   A. There is an association between a person's sex and the number of Facebook friends.

   B. There is no association between a person's sex and the number of Facebook friends.

   C. On average, men have more Facebook friends than women.

   D. On average, men have fewer Facebook friends than women.

Here are a few summary statistics about the data:

	Sample size	Sample mean	Sample median	Sample SD
Women	35	594.30	532	309.80
Men	13	405.60	485	228.40

f. In this context, which of the following is an (are) appropriate statistic value(s) to compare men to women? Circle all that apply.

   A. $35 - 13 = 22$

   B. $594.30 - 405.60 = 188.70$

   C. $532 - 485 = 47$

   D. $309.80 - 228.40 = 81.40$

Suppose that we want to use cards to carry out a randomization test of the appropriate hypotheses.

g. How many cards will we need? Circle one.

   A. 35   B. 13

   C. 48   D. Doesn't matter

The following is output from carrying out the randomization test using the **Multiple Means** applet.

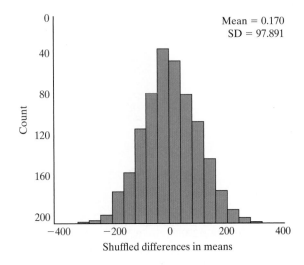

h. On the histogram above, shade the region that depicts the p-value. (*Hint:* Is your alternative hypothesis one-sided or two-sided?)

6.2.7 Reconsider the previous exercise about the study of whether there is an association between number of Facebook friends and a person's sex.

a. Use the information available in the previous exercise to find a standardized statistic to test whether the average number of Facebook friends men have is different from that of women.

b. Based on the standardized statistic, what is the strength of evidence against the null hypothesis?

6.2.8 Reconsider the previous exercises about the study of whether there is an association between number of Facebook friends and a person's sex. The p-value for the randomization-based test of whether the average number of Facebook friends men have is different from that of women turns out to be 0.0520.

a. Interpret this p-value in the context of the study.

b. Based on the p-value, what is the strength of evidence against the null hypothesis?

6.2.9 Reconsider the previous exercises about the study of whether there is an association between number of Facebook friends and a person's sex.

a. Use the 2SD method and the information available in the previous exercises to find a 95% confidence interval for the difference in average number of Facebook friends that men have and that women have.

b. Interpret the confidence interval reported in part (a) in the context of the study.

6.2.10 Reconsider the previous exercises about the study of whether there is an association between number of Facebook friends and a person's sex. The following is output with shuffled differences in medians from carrying out the randomization test using the **Multiple Means** applet.

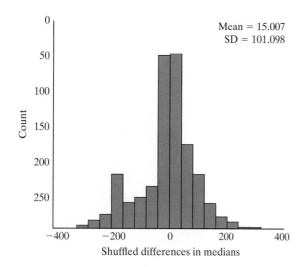

Mean = 15.007
SD = 101.098

Recall that the summary statistics about the data are as follows:

	Sample size	Sample mean	Sample median	Sample SD
Women	35	594.30	532	309.80
Men	13	405.60	485	228.40

a. On the above histogram, shade the region that depicts the p-value. (*Hint:* Pay close attention to the label on the x-axis. What is the statistic of interest here?)

b. Use the information available to find and report the standardized statistic in this context.

How many flip-flops do you have?*

6.2.11 In a survey of introductory statistics students, an instructor asked her students how many flip-flops they have. Suppose that the intent is to study whether there is an association between number of flip-flops and a person's sex.

a. Identify whether the study is an experiment or an observational study. Explain.

b. Identify the observational units.

c. Identify the explanatory and response variables. Also, for each variable identify whether it is categorical or quantitative.

d. Which of the following is the appropriate null hypothesis? Circle one.

A. There is an association between a person's sex and the number of flip-flops.

B. There is no association between a person's sex and the number of flip-flops.

C. On average, men have more flip-flops than women.

D. On average, men have fewer flip-flops than women.

e. Which of the following is the appropriate alternative hypothesis? Circle one.

A. There is an association between a person's sex and the number of flip-flops.

B. There is no association between a person's sex and the number of flip-flops.

C. On average, men have more flip-flops than women.

D. On average, men have fewer flip-flops than women.

Here are a few summary statistics about the data:

	Sample size	Sample mean	Sample median	Sample SD
Women	37	6.22	6.00	3.58
Men	13	2.54	1.00	2.96

f. In this context, which of the following is an (are) appropriate statistic value(s) to compare men to women? Circle all that apply.

A. $37 - 13 = 24$

B. $6.22 - 2.54 = 3.68$

C. $6 - 1 = 5$

D. $3.58 - 2.96 = 0.62$

Suppose that we want to use cards to carry out a randomization test of the appropriate hypotheses.

g. How many cards will we need? Circle one.

A. 37   B. 13

C. 50   D. Doesn't matter

The following is output from carrying out the randomization test using the **Multiple Means** applet.

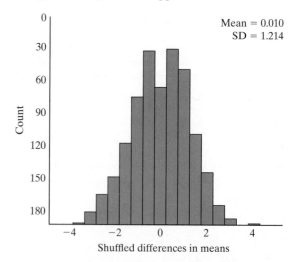

Mean = 0.010
SD = 1.214

h. On the histogram above, shade the region that depicts the p-value. (*Hint:* Is your alternative hypothesis one-sided or two-sided?)

6.2.12 Reconsider the previous exercise about the study of whether there is an association between number of flip-flops and a person's sex.

a. Use the information available in the previous exercise to find a standardized statistic to test whether the average number of flip-flops men have is different from that of women. Report the standardized statistic and interpret it in the context of the study.

b. Based on the standardized statistic, how much evidence do you have against the null hypothesis?

6.2.13 Reconsider the previous exercises about the study of whether there is an association between number of flip-flops and a person's sex. The p-value for the randomization-based test of whether the average number of flip-flops men have is different from that of women turns out to be 0.001.

a. Interpret this p-value in the context of the study.

b. Based on this p-value, how much evidence do you have against the null hypothesis?

6.2.14 Reconsider the previous exercises about the study of whether there is an association between number of flip-flops and a person's sex.

a. Use the 2SD method and the information available in the previous exercises to find a 95% confidence interval for the difference in average number of flip-flops that men have and that women have.

b. Interpret the confidence interval reported in part (a) in the context of the study.

c. Do the conclusions from this confidence interval agree with the conclusions from the p-value of 0.001 reported in the previous exercise? Explain your reasoning.

6.2.15 Reconsider the previous exercise about the study of whether there is an association between number of flip-flops and a person's sex. The following is output from carrying out the randomization test using the **Multiple Means** applet.

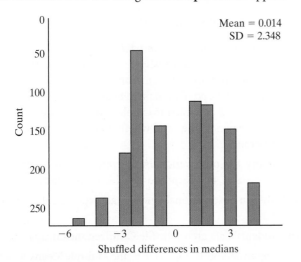

Shuffled differences in medians

Mean = 0.014
SD = 2.348

Recall that the summary statistics about the data are as follows:

	Sample size	Sample mean	Sample median	Sample SD
Women	37	6.22	6.00	3.58
Men	13	2.54	1.00	2.96

a. On the histogram, shade the region that depicts the p-value. (*Hint:* Pay close attention to the label on the x-axis. What is the statistic of interest here?)

b. Use the information available to find and report the standardized statistic in this context.

The anchoring phenomenon

6.2.16 Anchoring is "the common human tendency to rely too heavily, or 'anchor,' on one trait or piece of information when making decisions." (Source: *Wikipedia.*) A group of students taking an introductory statistics course at a four-year university in California were asked to guess the population of Milwaukee, Wisconsin. Some of the students were randomly chosen to be told that the nearby city of Chicago, Illinois has a population of about 3 million people, while the rest of the students were told that the nearby city of Green Bay, Wisconsin, has a population of about 100,000. Previous studies have shown that these numbers serve as a psychological anchor, so people told about Chicago tend to guess a higher population for Milwaukee than people told about Green Bay. (For more about this phenomenon, see the book *Nudge: Improving Decisions about Health, Wealth, and Happiness* by Richard H. Thaler and Cass R. Sunstein.) The purpose in analyzing the data is to see if we find strong evidence of this phenomenon among students like the ones in this study.

a. Identify the observational units.

b. Identify the explanatory variable and the response variable in this study. Also classify each as categorical or quantitative.

c. Is this an observational study or an experiment? Explain.

d. Were the subjects in this study randomly selected from a population? Explain.

e. Were the subjects in this study randomly assigned to groups? Explain.

The data set is titled **Milwaukee**. The first column contains the city mentioned to subjects, and the second column contains the guesses for the population of Milwaukee (in thousands, to the nearest thousand).

f. Using an appropriate applet (e.g., the **Multiple Means** applet) find and record the following summary statistics for the guesses made about Milwaukee's population by the city which they were told about:

	Sample size	Sample mean	Sample SD
Chicago			
Green Bay			

g. Find and report the difference in the average guess made by those told about Chicago and those told about Green Bay.

h. Give two possible explanations for the observed difference in average guesses for the population of Milwaukee reported in part (g).

6.2.17 Reconsider the study mentioned in the previous exercise about guessing the size of Milwaukee's population. **Our research question:** *On average, will students like the ones in the study tend to guess a higher population size for Milwaukee if they are told about Chicago's population size rather than told Green Bay's population size?*

a. Define (in words) the parameters of interest of this study. *Also, assign symbols to the parameters.*

b. Express the null and alternative hypotheses for testing whether the class data give strong evidence in support of the anchoring phenomenon described above. Use words only.

c. Express the null and alternative hypotheses for testing whether the class data give strong evidence in support of the anchoring phenomenon described above. Use the symbols defined in part (a).

d. Give detailed, step-by-step instructions on how one could conduct a tactile simulation to generate a p-value, keeping in mind that you want to investigate whether there is strong evidence of the anchoring phenomenon among students like the ones in this study. Be sure to include details on the following:

   • Would the simulation involve coins, dice, or index cards?

   • How many tosses, rolls, or cards would be used?

   • How many sets of tosses, rolls, or shuffles would you observe?

   • What would you record after every repetition?

   • How would you compute the p-value?

6.2.18 Reconsider the study mentioned in the previous exercise about guessing the size of Milwaukee's population. Do the data provide evidence of the anchoring phenomenon among students like the ones in this study? That is, our research question is: *On average, will students like the ones in the study tend to guess a higher population size for Milwaukee if they are told about Chicago's population size rather than told Green Bay's population size?*

Recall that the data set is titled **Milwaukee** and that the first column contains the city mentioned to subjects and the second column contains the guesses for the population of Milwaukee (in thousands, to the nearest thousand).

a. Use an appropriate randomization-based applet to find a p-value to test whether there is strong evidence of the anchoring phenomenon among students like the ones in this study. Report *and* interpret the p-value in the context of the study.

b. Use the p-value to indicate the strength of evidence against the null hypothesis.

c. Calculate an appropriate standardized statistic and interpret the standardized statistic in the context of the study.

d. Use the 2SD method to find a confidence interval for the parameter of interest. Report this interval and interpret the interval in the context of the study.

e. Do the results from the 95% confidence interval agree with your conclusion in part (b)? How are you deciding?

f. Give a full conclusion, including significance, estimation, causation, and generalization.

6.2.19 Reconsider the study mentioned in the previous exercise about guessing the size of Milwaukee's population. Do the data provide evidence of the anchoring phenomenon among students like the ones in this study? Suppose that instead of comparing the average guess for Milwaukee's population (Chicago vs. Green Bay), we wanted to compare the *median* guesses.

Recall that the data set is titled **Milwaukee** and that the first column contains the city mentioned to subjects and the second column contains the guesses for the population of Milwaukee (in thousands, to the nearest thousand).

a. Use an appropriate randomization-based applet to find a p-value to test whether there is strong evidence of the anchoring phenomenon among students like the ones in this study. Report *and* interpret the p-value in the context of the study.

b. Use the p-value to indicate the strength of evidence against the null hypothesis.

c. Calculate an appropriate standardized statistic and interpret the standardized statistic in the context of the study.

d. Use the 2SD method to find a confidence interval for the parameter of interest. Report this interval and interpret the interval in the context of the study.

e. Do the results from the 95% confidence interval agree with your conclusion in part (b)? How are you deciding?

f. Give a full conclusion, including significance, estimation, causation, and generalization.

Children and lifespan*

6.2.20 *Do men with children tend to live longer, on average, than those without?* To investigate, a group of Cal Poly students randomly sampled men from the obituaries page on the *San Luis Obispo Tribune*'s webpage between June and November 2012. For each man selected, they noted the age at which the person died and whether or not the person had any children.

a. Identify the observational/experimental units, explanatory variable, and response variable in this study.

b. Is this an observational study or an experiment? Explain briefly.

The students' data are in the file **ChildrenandLifespan**.

c. Using an appropriate applet (e.g., the **Multiple Means** applet) find and record the following summary statistics for the lifespan of men by whether or not the man had children:

	Sample size	Sample mean	Sample SD
Had children			
No children			

d. Find and report the difference in the average lifespan of men with versus without children.

e. Give two possible explanations for the observed difference in average lifespan reported in part (d).

6.2.21 Reconsider the study mentioned in the previous exercise about an investigation of whether men with children tend to live longer, *on average,* than men without children.

a. Define (in words) the parameters of interest of this study. *Also, assign symbols* to the parameters.

b. Express the null and alternative hypotheses for testing whether men with children tend to live longer, *on average,* than men without children. Use words only.

c. Express the null and alternative hypotheses for testing whether men with children tend to live longer, *on average,* than men without children. Use the symbols defined in part (a).

d. Give detailed, step-by-step instructions on how one could conduct a tactile simulation to generate a p-value to test the hypotheses stated in parts (b) and (c). Be sure to include details on the following:

- Would the simulation involve coins, dice, or index cards?
- How many tosses, rolls, or cards would be used?
- How many sets of tosses, rolls, or shuffles would you observe?
- What would you record after every repetition?
- How would you compute the p-value?

6.2.22 Reconsider the study mentioned in the previous exercises about an investigation of whether men with children tend to live longer, *on average,* than men without children. The data are in the file **ChildrenandLifespan**.

a. Use an appropriate randomization-based applet to find a p-value to test whether men with children tend to live longer, *on average,* than men without children. Report *and* interpret the p-value in the context of the study.

b. Use the p-value to indicate the strength of evidence against the null hypothesis.

c. Calculate an appropriate standardized statistic and interpret the standardized statistic in the context of the study.

d. Use the 2SD method to find a confidence interval for the parameter of interest. Report this interval and interpret the interval in the context of the study.

e. Do the results from the 95% confidence interval agree with your conclusion in part (c)? How are you deciding?

f. Give a full conclusion, including significance, estimation, causation, and generalization.

6.2.23 With randomization techniques we are able to analyze any statistic we desire. What if we wanted to look at whether the *median* lifespan of men with children was higher than men without children? Using the **Multiple Means** applet and the **Median** option on it, answer parts (a) through (f) of the previous exercise looking at the difference in median lifespans.

Mercury levels in tuna

6.2.24 Rising mercury levels due to industrial pollution is a recent concern. Many fish have high levels of mercury. Data were collected on random samples of tuna from 1991 to 2010 and are available in the file **Tuna**. Each row in the data set represents the mercury level of a different fish. *Do fresh Yellowfin tuna have different levels of mercury on average compared to fresh Albacore tuna?* Use the fresh tuna data to answer the following questions.

a. Is this an experiment or an observational study? Explain how you know.

b. Identify the observational units.

c. Identify the explanatory and response variable. Also, identify whether each is quantitative or categorical.

d. Define (in words) the parameters of interest of this study. *Also, assign symbols* to the parameters.

e. State the null and alternative hypotheses in words as well as using symbols.

f. What statistic will you use?

g. Use an appropriate applet to carry out a simulation analysis. Report the p-value and strength of evidence.

h. Use the 2SD rule to determine a 95% confidence interval. Interpret the interval, making sure it is clear which parameter (in context) the 95% confidence interval is estimating.

i. Give a full conclusion, including significance, estimation, causation, and generalization.

6.2.25 With randomization techniques we are able to analyze any test statistic we desire. What if we wanted to look at whether there was a difference in the *median* values of mercury in the Yellowfin tuna compared to the Albacore tuna? Using the **Multiple Means** applet and the **Median** option on it, answer parts (f) through (i) of the previous exercise looking at the difference in median mercury levels.

Bike commuting*

6.2.26 Recall Example 6.2 about the bike commuting times. On each of 56 days (from mid-January to mid-July 2010), researcher Jeremy Groves tossed a £1 coin to decide whether he would be biking the 27 miles to work on his carbon frame (lighter) bicycle that weighed 20.90 lb or on his steel frame (heavier) bicycle that weighed 29.75 lb. He then recorded the commute time (given in minutes) for each trip. The summary statistics were reported to be:

Bike type	Sample size	Sample average	Sample SD
Carbon frame (lighter)	26	108.34 min	6.25 min
Steel frame (heavier)	30	107.81 min	4.89 min

In Example 6.2 you read about conducting a randomization-based test to investigate whether the average commute time differs by bike type.

a. Suppose we suspect that the lighter carbon frame bike will be less stable, especially in inclement weather conditions, and will have a higher variability in commute times, compared to the heavier steel frame bike. Is there any indication from the data in support of this suspicion? Explain how you are deciding.

To investigate whether the variability in commute times will be higher with the lighter carbon frame bike than the heavier steel frame one, we can examine the ratio of the SDs, such that Ratio = $SD_{carbon} \div SD_{steel}$. (*Note:* $\div$ is "divided by.")

b. In theory, what numeric values can this ratio take?

c. For the observed data, what is the numeric value of the statistic Ratio?

d. Describe in detail how you would use simulation (with pennies, dice, spinners, cards, etc.) to find a p-value to test whether the variability in commute times is *higher* with the lighter carbon frame bike than the heavier steel frame one.

Here is a histogram from an appropriately conducted simulation:

Ratio

e. As per the above histogram, what numeric values are most common for Ratio from the simulation? Why does that make sense?

f. Indicate, on the above histogram, the region that depicts the p-value in the context of the study, being sure to include appropriate numbers.

g. Which of the following appears to be the approximate p-value? No explanations needed. **Choose one.**

A. 1.00
B. 0.10
C. 0.01
D. < 0.01

h. Which of the following is an appropriate statement to make based on the above histogram? **Circle one.**

A. There is not convincing evidence of the variability in commute times being higher with the lighter carbon frame bike than the heavier steel frame one because the distribution of Ratio is not centered at 0.

B. There is some evidence of the variability in commute times being higher with the lighter carbon frame bike than the heavier steel frame one because the distribution of Ratio is centered not at 0 but at 1.

C. There is not convincing evidence of the variability in commute times being higher with the lighter carbon frame bike than the heavier steel frame one because the distribution of Ratio is not normal but skewed right.

D. None of the above.

FAQ

6.2.27 Read FAQ 6.2.1 and answer the following question: True or false, the parameter is fixed and unknown, while the statistic is the parameter plus a random error.

6.2.28 Read FAQ 6.2.3 and answer the following question: True or false, in a blind study, the subjects do not know which treatment they are receiving.

6.2.29 Read FAQ 6.2.2 and answer the following question: True or false, the statements "do not reject" and "accept" mean the same thing in a statistical conclusion.

SECTION 6.3

Time online*

6.3.1 Suppose that randomly sampled college students are asked how many hours they typically spend online each day. You conduct a two-sided test of the null hypothesis that $\mu_{females} - \mu_{males} = 0$, and you also calculate a 95% confidence interval for $\mu_{females} - \mu_{males}$.

a. Describe (in words) what the parameter $\mu_{females} - \mu_{males}$ means here.

b. Now suppose that your friend analyzes the same data but with the order of subtraction reversed (males − females, rather than females − males). Describe the impact (if any) on each of the following. In other words, describe how your friend's findings will compare to yours with regard to each of the following.

i. Distribution of simulated statistics under the null hypothesis

ii. Standard deviation of the simulated statistics under the null hypothesis

iii. Observed value of the statistic (difference in sample means)

iv. Approximate p-value from simulation

v. Value of t-test statistic

vi. p-Value from t-test

vii. Midpoint of confidence interval

viii. Endpoints of confidence interval

ix. Width of confidence interval

c. What is the bottom line: Will you and your friend reach the same conclusions even though you disagreed about the order in which to perform the subtraction (males − females or females − males)? Explain.

Haircut prices

6.3.2 Reconsider Exercise 6.2.1 in which an instructor collected data on prices (in dollars) paid by students for their most recent haircut, also recording each student's sex. A 95% confidence interval for $\mu_{female} - \mu_{male}$ turned out to be (12.17, 52.23). For each of the following, indicate whether it provides a correct or incorrect interpretation/conclusion from this interval.

a. Between 12.17% and 52.23% of females in the population paid more than males for their haircut.

b. About 95% of all females in the *population* paid between $12.17 and $52.23 more than males for their haircut.

c. About 95% of all females in the *sample* paid between $12.17 and $52.23 more than males for their haircut.

d. We can be 95% confident that the *probability* is between 12.17% and 52.23% that females in the population pay more than males for their haircut.

e. We can be 95% confident that the *average* price paid for a haircut in this population is between $12.17 and $52.23.

f. We can be 95% confident that the *average* price paid for a haircut by a female in this population is higher than the average price paid by males in this population by between $12.17 and $52.23.

g. We can be 95% confident that *all* females in the population paid more than all males for their haircut by between $12.17 and $52.23.

h. We can be 95% confident that *most* females in the population paid more than most males for their haircut by between $12.17 and $52.23.

i. We can be 95% confident that females in the population paid more *on average* than males for their haircut by between $12.17 and $52.23.

6.3.3 Reconsider the previous exercise about haircut prices. Suppose that the instructor wants to test whether females in the population paid more on average for their most recent haircut than males. Which kind of test might be appropriate? (Circle all that apply.)

a. Simulation-based test comparing proportions

b. Simulation-based test comparing means

c. One-sided test

d. Two-sided test

e. z-test for single proportion

f. z-test for comparing two proportions

g. t-test for comparing means

Too scared to fall asleep?*

6.3.4 Selvi et al. (2012) conducted a study on university medical students in Turkey to investigate whether and how sleep habits were associated with having nightmares. During the study, these students were engaged in lecture-based learning with no hospital duties. All participants were given initial surveys, the results of which were used to determine who among them had "early bird" sleep habits and who "night owl" habits. Next, the students were given the Van Dream Anxiety Scale (VDAS) assessment, which involved questions regarding nightmare frequency and dream anxiety due to frightening dreams during the last 30 days. Here are the summary statistics on nightmare frequency by "early bird" and "night owl." Note that higher scores indicate higher nightmare frequency.

	Sample size	Sample average	Sample SD
Diagnosed early bird	67	1.23	0.93
Diagnosed night owl	59	2.10	0.99

Analyze the data using a theory-based approach (use the **Theory-based Inference** applet) to determine whether early birds differ from night owls with respect to average nightmare frequency. The data are not strongly skewed within each group. Be sure to include the appropriate hypotheses, a statement about validity conditions, as well as numerical evidence (including p-value) in support of your conclusion with regard to the hypotheses. In your conclusion, include comments about statistical significance, estimation (95% confidence interval (include interpretation)), causation, and generalization.

6.3.5 Reconsider the previous exercise. How, if at all, would your analysis and conclusions change if the sample sizes had been larger and all else had remained the same? Be sure to refer to the test statistic, p-value, and confidence interval as well as give your conclusion.

6.3.6 Reconsider the previous two exercises. How, if at all, would your analysis and conclusions change if the sample means had been closer together and all else had remained the same as in the original question? Be sure to refer to the test statistic, p-value, and confidence interval as well as give your conclusion.

6.3.7 Reconsider the previous three exercises. How, if at all, would your analysis and conclusions change if the sample standard deviations had been larger and all else had remained the same as in the original question? Be sure to refer to the test statistic, p-value, and confidence interval as well as give your conclusion.

6.3.8 Refer to the previous exercises. The researchers also gave each participant a score for "Fear of sleeping because of anticipated nightmares." Given in the table below are the summary statistics for these scores. Note that higher scores indicate higher fear and that the data are not strongly skewed in either group.

	Sample size	Sample average	Sample SD
Diagnosed early bird	67	1.22	0.99
Diagnosed night owl	59	1.49	1.19

Analyze the data using a theory-based approach to determine whether early birds differ from night owls with respect to fear of sleeping in anticipation of nightmares. Be sure to include the appropriate hypotheses, a statement about validity conditions, and numerical evidence (including p-value) in support of your decision with regard to the hypotheses. In your conclusion, include comments about statistical significance, estimation (95% CI for parameter of interest), causation, and generalization.

Anchoring

6.3.9 Recall the study about anchoring from Exercise 6.2.16, in which students estimated the population of Milwaukee after some had been told about Chicago and others about Green Bay.

a. Describe in words the parameter(s) of interest in the context of this study.

b. In the context of the parameter(s) described in part (a), express the null and alternative hypotheses for testing whether the class data give strong evidence in support of the anchoring phenomenon described above. *If you use symbols, make sure to define them.*

c. Check whether the conditions for the validity of the theory-based *t*-test to compare two means are satisfied here.

d. Use appropriate technology (an applet or a statistical software package) to conduct a *t*-test of significance of the hypotheses that you stated in part (b). Report the test statistic and p-value.

e. State your conclusion in the context of the study, being sure to comment on statistical significance.

f. Determine *and* interpret the 95% confidence interval using a theory-based approach for the parameter(s) of interest in the context of the study.

g. Comment on causation and generalization for this study.

Left-right confusion*

6.3.10 Left-right confusion (LRC) is the term used to describe the difficulty of distinguishing between left and right. In a study related to LRC, researchers Ocklenburg et al. (2011) gave a mental rotation test (MRT) to 91 neurologically healthy men and women. The MRT involved picking two images that were rotated versions of a target figure from a list of fives images. Each correct answer led to one point. Here are the summary statistics on the scores for the men and women. Note that the data within each group is not strongly skewed.

	Sample size	Sample average	Sample SD
Men	41	14.10	3.78
Women	50	9.56	3.97

Analyze the data to determine whether men differ from women with respect to the long-run average MRT score. Use a theory-based approach. Be sure to include the appropriate hypotheses as well as numerical evidence in support of your decision with regard to the hypotheses (p-value). Find and interpret a 95% confidence interval. Include comments about causation and generalization. Comment on adherence to validity conditions for use of the theory-based methods.

Downhill walking

6.3.11 In a study conducted in New Zealand, Parkin et al. randomly assigned volunteers to either wear socks over their shoes (intervention) or wear usual footwear (control) as they walked downhill on an inclined icy path. Researchers standing at the bottom of the inclined path measured the time (in seconds) taken by each participant to walk down the path. Here are the summary statistics. Note that the data are fairly symmetric in both groups.

	n	Mean	SD
Intervention	14	37.7	9.36
Control	15	39.6	11.57

The research question to be addressed through the following questions is: Do the data provide evidence that people wearing socks over their shoes will take a shorter time to walk down an icy, steeply inclined road, on average, compared to those wearing usual footwear?

a. Describe the parameter(s) of interest in the context of this study.

b. State the null and the alternative hypotheses in the context of the study.

c. Name the appropriate theory-based method you would use to test the hypotheses stated in part (b).

d. State the validity conditions that have to be met to be able to perform the test named in part (c). Are these conditions met? How are you deciding?

e. Regardless of your answer to part (d), perform the theory-based test proposed in part (c). Be sure to report a test statistic value and a p-value.

f. Determine a 95% confidence interval for comparing the walking time between the two groups.

g. Summarize your conclusions about the research question of the study. Be sure to comment on statistical significance, confidence/estimation, causation, and generalization.

Pricing pills*

6.3.12 In a randomized, double-blind study reported in the *Journal of American Medical Association*, researchers Waber et al. (2008) administered a pill to each of 82 healthy paid volunteers from Boston, Massachusetts, but told half of them that the drug had a regular price of $2.50 per pill, whereas the remaining participants were told that the drug had a discounted price of $0.10 per pill, mentioning no reason for the discount. In the recruitment advertisement the pill was described as an FDA-approved "opioid analgesic," but in reality both groups were administered placebo pills.

To simulate pain, the participants were administered electric shocks to the wrist. These shocks were calibrated to each participant's pain tolerance, *prior* to administering the pills. In the article, the researchers present the summary statistics on the calibrated maximum tolerance for the participants for the two groups. Researchers wondered if evidence exists for a difference in average pain tolerance between the two groups. The distribution of maximum tolerance scores are not strongly skewed in either group.

	n	Mean	SD
Regular-price pill	41	51.80 volts	18.70 volts
Discount-price pill	41	54.90 volts	23.30 volts

a. Explain why the researchers want to compare the pain tolerance of the treatment groups.

b. State the appropriate null and the alternative hypotheses in the context of the study.

c. Name the appropriate theory-based method you would use to test the hypotheses stated in part (b).

d. State the validity conditions that have to be met to be able to perform the test named in part (c). Are these conditions met? How are you deciding?

e. Regardless of your answer to part (d), perform the theory-based test proposed in part (c). Be sure to include a test statistic value and a p-value in your answer.

f. Interpret your p-value in the context of the study.

g. Determine a 95% confidence interval for comparing the tolerance levels between the two groups.

h. Summarize your conclusions about the research question of the study. Be sure to comment on statistical significance, confidence/estimation, causation, and generalization.

Perceived wealth

6.3.13 Do people tend to spend money differently based on perceived changes in wealth? In a study conducted by Epley et al. (2006), 47 Harvard undergraduates were randomly assigned to receive either a "bonus" check of $50 or a "rebate" check of $50. A week later, each student was contacted and asked whether they had spent any of that money, and if yes, how much. In this exercise we will focus on how much money they recalled spending when contacted a week later. It turned out that those in the "bonus" group spent an average of about $22, compared to $10 in the "rebate" group.

a. Identify the observational units.

b. Identify the explanatory and response variables. Identify each as either categorical or quantitative.

c. State the appropriate null and alternative hypotheses in the context of the study.

Scenario		Sample sizes	Sample means	Sample SDs	t-statistic	p-value
1	Bonus	24	22	5		
	Rebate	23	10	5		
2	Bonus	24	22	10		
	Rebate	23	10	10		
3	Bonus	30	22	5		
	Rebate	17	10	5		
4	Bonus	30	22	10		
	Rebate	17	10	10		

EXERCISE 6.3.13

d. In the article that appeared in the *Journal of Behavioral Decision Making*, the researchers reported neither the sample size nor the sample SD of each group. In this exercise you will explore whether and how the strength of evidence is impacted by the sample size and sample SD. Complete the following table by finding the *t*-statistic and a p-value for a theory-based test of significance comparing two means under each of the four different scenarios.

e. Summarize what your analysis has revealed about the effects of the sample size breakdown and the sample standard deviations on the values of the *t*-statistic and p-value.

Nostril breathing and cognitive performance*

6.3.14 In an article titled "Unilateral Nostril Breathing Influences Lateralized Cognitive Performance" that appeared in *Brain and Cognition* (1989), researchers Block et al. published results from an experiment involving assessments of spatial and verbal cognition when breathing through only the right versus left nostril.

The subjects were 30 male and 30 female right-handed introductory psychology students who volunteered to participate in exchange for course credit. Initial testing on spatial and verbal tests revealed the following summary statistics. Note that the scores on the spatial task can range from 0 to 40, whereas those on the verbal task can go from 0 to 20. The distributions are not strongly skewed on either scale or for males or females.

Sex	Spatial		Verbal	
	Mean	SD	Mean	SD
Male	10.20	2.70	10.90	3.00
Female	7.80	2.50	15.10	3.40

a. Consider comparing males to females with regard to performance on the spatial assessment task. State the appropriate null and alternative hypotheses in the context of the study.

b. Explain why it is valid to use the theory-based method for producing a p-value to test the hypotheses stated in part (a).

c. Carry out the appropriate test to produce a p-value to test the hypotheses stated in part (a) and interpret the p-value.

d. Find a 95% confidence interval for the difference in mean scores of males and females with regard to performance on spatial assessments. Interpret the interval.

e. Based on your p-value, state a conclusion in the context of the study. Be sure to comment on statistical significance, estimation (confidence interval), causation, and generalization.

f. Repeat the investigation comparing males and females, this time on verbal performance. Be sure to address the questions asked in parts (a)–(e).

6.3.15 Reconsider the previous exercise. In this question, we will focus on comparing 10 males who were randomly assigned to breathe only through their left nostril to 10 who were randomly assigned to breathe only through their right nostril while they took the spatial and verbal tests. *Note:* Ten of the 30 total males were not assigned to either condition considered here. Here are the summary statistics on the spatial test performance; the data are fairly symmetric in both groups.

Condition	Spatial test	
	Mean	SD
Left nostril breathing	8.90	2.80
Right nostril breathing	11.40	2.00

a. Describe the parameter(s) of interest in the context of this study.

b. State the null and the alternative hypotheses (two-sided test) in the context of the study.

c. Name the appropriate theory-based method you would use to test the hypotheses stated in part (b).

d. State the validity conditions that have to be met to be able to perform the test named in part (c). Are these conditions met? How are you deciding?

e. Regardless of your answer to part (d), perform the theory-based test proposed in part (c). Be sure to include a test statistic value and a p-value in your answer.

f. Based on your p-value, state your conclusion in the context of the study. Be sure to comment on statistical significance, 95% confidence interval, causation, and generalization.

g. Without performing any additional calculations, explain how, if at all, the p-value reported in part (f) would change if each condition was implemented on 30 males in each group instead of 10 males in each group but the means and SDs stayed the same.

h. Without performing any additional calculations, explain how, if at all, the p-value reported in part (f) would change if the mean for "left" condition was 10.9 and that for "right" was 13.4 but the sample sizes and SDs stayed the same.

i. Without performing any additional calculations, explain how, if at all, the p-value reported in part (f) would change if SDs for both conditions were 2.00 but the sample sizes and means stayed the same.

6.3.16 Reconsider the previous two exercises. In this question, we will focus on comparing 10 males who breathe only through their left nostril to 10 males who breathe only through their right nostril while they perform a verbal task. Assume that the verbal scores in each group are fairly symmetric.

a. When the average scores on the verbal task obtained by the males in the study were compared using a two-sided alternative hypothesis and two-sample *t*-test, the p-value turned out to be 0.0162. Use this p-value and a 1% level of significance to state an appropriate conclusion in the context of the study. Explain your reasoning.

b. How, if at all, would your conclusion in part (a) change if you were to use a 5% level of significance?

c. In the context of this study and the related data results, which of the following statements are true?

   i. The 95% confidence interval for the difference in the mean scores between males in the "population" who perform a verbal task while breathing through only the left nostril versus only the right nostril will contain 0 because the p-value is less than 5%.

   ii. The 95% confidence interval for the difference in the mean scores between males in the "population" who perform a verbal task while breathing through only the left nostril versus only the right nostril will *not* contain 0 because the p-value is less than 5%.

   iii. The 99% confidence interval for the difference in the mean scores between males in the "population" who perform a verbal task while breathing through only the left nostril versus only the right nostril will contain 0 because the p-value is greater than 1%.

   iv. The 99% confidence interval for the difference in the mean scores between males in the "population" who perform a verbal task while breathing through only the left nostril versus only the right nostril will *not* contain 0 because the p-value is greater than 1%.

Drive-through times

6.3.17 Reconsider the data from Exercise 6.1.21 and corresponding statistics from Exercise 6.1.22 about drive-through times at two fast food restaurants. Conduct a two-sample *t*-test of whether the sample data provide strong evidence that the population mean drive-through times differ between the two restaurants. Be sure to check whether the validity conditions are satisfied, state the hypotheses, report the test statistic and p-value, and summarize your conclusion.

6.3.18 Reconsider the previous exercise. Determine a 95% confidence interval for comparing the population mean drive-through times between the two fast food restaurants. Also interpret what this interval says. Finally, comment on whether the confidence interval is consistent with the conclusion of your significance test in the previous exercise.

Restroom times*

6.3.19 Reconsider the data from Exercise 6.1.23 about times spent in a public restroom by men and women in a Michigan mall. The average time in the bathroom was 106.65 (SD = 79.611) for the 40 men and 133.5 (SD = 62.369) for the 40 women. The data are not strongly skewed in either group. Conduct a two-sample *t*-test of whether the sample data provide strong evidence that the population mean restroom times differ between the two sexes. Be sure to check whether the technical conditions are satisfied, state the hypotheses, report the test statistic and p-value, and summarize your conclusion.

6.3.20 Reconsider the previous exercise. Determine a 95% confidence interval for comparing the population mean restroom times between the two sexes. Also interpret what this interval says. Finally, comment on whether the confidence interval is consistent with the conclusion of your significance test in the previous exercise.

Pen color

6.3.21 A psychology study (Rutchick, Slepian, and Ferris, 2010) investigated whether using a red pen causes people to assign lower scores than using a blue pen. A group of 128 students in an introductory undergraduate psychology class were asked to grade an eighth grader's essay on a scale of 0–100. Half of the student graders were randomly assigned to use a red pen while grading the essay, and the other half were randomly assigned to use a blue pen. The researchers reported that the group using a red pen gave an average score of 76.20, and the SD of the scores was 12.29. For the group using blue pens, the average score was 80.00, and the SD of the scores was 9.36.

a. State the null and alternative hypotheses to be tested.

b. Without having access to the 128 scores that were assigned to the essays, can you feel comfortable in applying a two-sample *t*-test using the summary statistics? Explain.

c. What additional information is needed to apply a two-sample *t*-test using the summary statistics?

d. Make a reasonable guess for the missing information and conduct a two-sample *t*-test. Report the values of the test statistic and p-value.

e. Summarize your conclusion from this test.

f. Is it legitimate to draw a cause-and-effect conclusion based on these data and your test result? Explain why nor why not.

g. What would you advise the researchers about how broadly they can generalize the conclusions of this study? For example, would you feel comfortable in generalizing the results of this study to eighth-grade teachers or to college professors? Explain.

h. Do you think the study's conclusions would be stronger if the subjects had been actual teachers or college professors? Why do you think the researchers used introductory students as their subjects?

Got a tip?*

6.3.22 Can waitresses increase their tips simply by introducing themselves by name when they greet customers? A waitress collected data on two-person parties that she waited on during Sunday brunch (with a fixed price of $23.21) at a Charley Brown's restaurant in southern California. For each party the waitress used a random mechanism to determine whether to give her name as part of her greeting or not. Then she kept track of how much the party gave for a tip at the end of their meal.

a. Is this an observational study or a randomized experiment? Explain.

b. Identify and classify the explanatory and response variables.

c. State the null and alternative hypotheses in symbols and in words for testing the waitress' conjecture.

The sample mean tip amount for the 20 parties to which the waitress gave her name was $5.44, with a standard deviation of $1.75. These statistics were $3.49 and $1.13, respectively, for the 20 parties to which the waitress did not give her name. The data were not strongly skewed in either group.

d. Use appropriate symbols for the six numbers reported in this paragraph.

e. Are the validity conditions met? Explain.

f. Use these summary statistics to calculate the test statistic and p-value using an appropriate theory-based test.

g. What test decision would you reach at the 0.05 significance level? Explain what this decision means in the context of this study.

6.3.23 Reconsider the previous exercise.

a. Calculate a 95% confidence interval for the difference in population mean tip amounts between the two experimental treatments (giving name or not).

b. Interpret what this interval means in this context.

c. Is this confidence interval consistent with the test decision from the previous exercise? Explain how you know.

d. Summarize your conclusions from this test. Be sure to comment on issues of causation and generalization as well as significance and confidence.

6.3.24 Reconsider the previous two exercises.

a. If you change the confidence level to 98%, what impact would you expect this to have on the midpoint and width of the confidence interval?

b. Make this change, from part (a), and report the new confidence interval. Was the impact what you expected?

6.3.25 Reconsider the previous exercises.

a. If the waitress had used larger sample sizes (say, 40 in each group) and the sample means and SDs had turned out the same as they did in the study originally, what impact would you expect this to have on the test statistic, p-value, and confidence interval?

b. Make this change and report the new test statistic, p-value, and confidence interval. Was the impact what you expected?

6.3.26 Reconsider the previous exercises.

a. If the sample responses had shown more variability in each group (say, SD of 2 in each group) and all else had remained the same as originally, what impact would you expect this to have on the test statistic, p-value, and confidence interval?

b. Make this change and report the new test statistic, p-value, and confidence interval. Was the impact what you expected?

FAQ

6.3.27 Read FAQ 6.3.1 and answer the following question: Explain how the validity conditions of 'at least 20 in each group' and 'not strong skewness' are not to be implemented as precise rules to follow in practice.

SECTION 6.4

6.4.1* If we have two independent samples of a quantitative variable and one is size 42 and the other 36, what is the conservative estimate for the degrees of freedom that you would use?

A. 35

B. 36

C. 41

D. 42

E. 78

6.4.2 When testing two independent means, we use:

A. A normal distribution

B. A t-distribution that is a bit wider (or heavier in the tails) than a normal distribution

C. A t-distribution that is a bit narrower (or lighter in the tails) than a normal distribution

D. Either a normal or a t-distribution as they are the same

E. None of the above

6.4.3* Suppose we are testing two means using a two-sided test and get a p-value of 0.03. We also construct a 95% confidence interval from the same data. We would expect:

A. 0.03 to be in the confidence interval

B. 0.03 to not be in the confidence interval

C. 0 to be in the confidence interval

D. 0 to not be in the confidence interval

E. There is no way to expect any specific value to be in or not in the confidence interval.

6.4.4 Suppose you are doing a test to see whether there is a significant difference in the average weight of white-breasted nuthatches (w) and red-breasted nuthatches (r). Which of the following is the correct way to write the alternative hypothesis?

A. $\bar{x}_W \neq \bar{x}_R$

B. $\hat{p}_W \neq \hat{p}_R$

C. $\pi_W \neq \pi_R$

D. $\mu_W \neq \mu_R$

E. $s_W \neq s_R$

6.4.5* A two-sample *t*-test gives more valid p-values with:

A. Larger sample sizes and sample distributions that are fairly bell-shaped

B. Larger sample sizes and sample distributions that are fairly skewed

C. Smaller sample sizes and sample distributions that are fairly bell-shaped

D. Smaller sample sizes and sample distributions that are fairly skewed

E. Any sample size with any shaped sample distributions

6.4.6 *Census at School* is an international classroom project in which students from Grades 4–12 complete a brief online survey. Through the Census at School website, we obtained a random sample of the time, in minutes, it took students in the United States to get to school surveying 22 high school students who rode a bus and 22 high school students who took a car. The results are shown in the following split stem-plot. Do you consider the validity conditions met for using two-sample *t*-procedures to compare these two groups? Explain why or why not.

Bus		Car
4	0	12
75	0	5788888
300000	1	00022
5	1	55
00000	2	000
5	2	
0000	3	00
5	3	5
	4	
5	4	4|5 = 45 minutes

6.4.7* The following set of dotplots with overlaid boxplots gives the number of pairs of flip-flops students in a statistics class, 13 males (top) and 37 females (bottom), said they owned. Do you consider the validity conditions met for using two-sample *t*-procedures to compare these two groups? Explain why or why not.

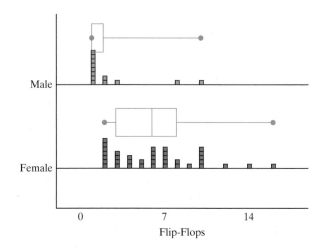

6.4.8 Suppose you sample from two large populations with sample statistics of $\bar{x}_1 = 6.2$, $s_1 = 0.7$, and $n_1 = 35$ from one sample and sample statistics of $\bar{x}_2 = 5.2$, $s_2 = 1.1$, and $n_2 = 36$ from the other sample. Suppose you are going to use the difference in sample means to calculate a 95% confidence interval to estimate the difference in the population means.

a. (By hand) calculate and interpret the standard error of the statistic.

b. (By hand) calculate and interpret the margin of error.

c. (By hand) calculate and interpret the 95% confidence interval.

6.4.9* Suppose you sample from two large populations with sample statistics of $\bar{x}_1 = 34.2$, $s_1 = 2.7$, and $n_1 = 40$ from one sample and sample statistics of $\bar{x}_2 = 26.2$, $s_2 = 3.1$, and $n_2 = 50$ from the other sample. Suppose you are going to use the difference in sample means to calculate a 99% confidence interval to estimate the difference in the population means.

a. (By hand) calculate and interpret the standard error of the statistic.

b. (By hand) calculate and interpret the margin of error.

c. (By hand) calculate and interpret the 99% confidence interval.

6.4.10 Researchers Dumas and Dunbar (2016) wanted to see whether stereotypes related to creativity can influence the creativity of a subject. The 64 subjects were randomly placed into two groups of 32 each. One group was told to imagine that they were rigid librarians and another group was to imagine they were eccentric poets. As a measure of their creativity, they were then shown 10 items and asked to generate as many different uses for these items as possible. The "rigid librarians" averaged 60.34 total uses for the objects (SD = 24.38 uses) and the "eccentric poets" averaged 92.16 total uses (SD = 36.99 uses). Is there convincing evidence of a stereotype effect here? That is, is there a significant difference in average creativity (as measured by finding multiple uses for objects) between the "rigid librarians" and "eccentric poets"?

a. State the hypotheses either in words or using appropriate symbols.

b. Name the theory-based test that will be used and state and verify the validity conditions for the test chosen.

c. Calculate the test statistic (standardized statistic) and corresponding p-value.

d. State your conclusion (with appropriate justification based on your p-value and stated significance level) in the context of the research question. Be sure to address the issues of causation and generalizability as well.

e. Would a statistically significant difference establish that real poets are more creative than real librarians?

6.4.11* Similar to the previous question, researchers Dumas and Dunbar wanted to compare the creativity of students with different majors at their university. As a measure of their creativity, they were shown 10 items and asked to generate as many different uses for these items as possible. The 24 biology majors averaged 69.97 total uses for the objects (SD = 24.24 uses) and the 24 theater majors averaged 85.71 total uses (SD = 38.78 uses). Graphs of the total uses for the objects for both the biology and theater majors showed no extreme skewness or outliers.

a. Calculate and interpret the 95% confidence interval for the difference in average creativity (as measured by finding multiple uses for objects) between the biology majors and theater majors.

b. Based on your confidence interval, is there strong evidence of a difference in the mean number of uses for the objects between biology and theater majors? Explain how you determined this.

c. Does your answer to (b) establish that being a theater major causes someone to be more creative? Or that more creative people are more likely to become theater majors than biology majors?

6.4.12 Researchers Holdgate et al. (2016) studied the walking behavior of elephants in North American zoos. They put GPS loggers on 33 African elephants and 23 Asian elephants and measured the distance the elephants walked per day. The African elephants walked an average 5.4 kilometers per day (SD = 1.5 km) and the Asian elephants walked an average 5.3 kilometers per day (SD = 3.4 km). Is there a significant difference in the average distance walked per day between captive African and Asian elephants? Graphs of the data showed no strong skewedness or outliers.

a. State the hypotheses either in words or using appropriate symbols.

b. Name the theory-based test that will be used and state and verify the validity conditions for the test chosen.

c. Calculate the test statistic (standardized statistic) and corresponding p-value.

d. State your conclusion (with appropriate justification based on your p-value and stated significance level) in the context of the research question. Be sure to address the issues of causation and generalizability as well.

6.4.13 Recall the previous question about comparing distances traveled by captive African and Asian elephants.

a. Calculate a 95% confidence interval for the difference in the mean distance traveled by the two kinds of elephants.

b. Explain what your interval from part (a) means in context.

c. Based on your interval, is there strong evidence of a difference in the mean distance traveled by captive African and Asian elephants? Explain how you know this.

6.4.14* Student researchers at Hope College conducted an experiment to determine whether students memorize material better if they take notes on paper by hand as opposed to taking notes on a computer. They randomly assigned 20 students to the paper-based note-taking group and 20 students to the computer-based note-taking group. The researchers showed all their subjects a 12-minute video about the sun and they were allowed to take notes in the method assigned. After the video was over, the notes were collected and the students were given a 10-question quiz on information about the sun given in the video. Do students tend to memorize better using handwritten notes? (The results are in the file **NoteTaking**.)

a. State the hypotheses either in words or using appropriate symbols.

b. Name the theory-based test that will be used and state and verify the validity conditions for the test chosen.

c. Calculate the test statistic (standardized statistic) and corresponding p-value.

d. State your conclusion (with appropriate justification based on your p-value and stated significance level) in the context of the research question. Be sure to address the issues of causation and generalizability as well.

6.4.15* Recall the previous question about comparing quiz scores between students taking notes on paper versus the computer.

a. Calculate a 95% confidence interval for the difference in mean difference quiz scores between the two types of note-taking groups.

b. Explain what your interval from part (a) means in context.

c. Based on your interval, is there strong evidence of a difference in the mean difference in quiz scores between the two types of note-taking groups? Explain how you know this.

6.4.16 To investigate an association between violent video games and aggressive behavior, British researchers Hollingdale and Greitemeyer (2014) randomly assigned 49 university students to play *Call to Duty: Modern Warfare* (a violent video game) and 52 students to play *LittleBigPlanet 2* (a non-violent/neutral video game). After 30 minutes of playing the video games, the subjects were asked to complete a marketing survey investigating a new hot chili sauce recipe. They were told to prepare some chili sauce for a taste tester and that the taste tester "couldn't stand hot chili sauce but was taking part due to good payment." The subjects were then presented with what appeared to be a very hot chili sauce and asked to spoon what they thought would be an appropriate amount into a bowl for a new recipe. The amount of chili sauce was weighed in grams after each participant left the experiment. The amount of chili sauce was used as a measure of aggression; the more chili sauce, the greater the subject's aggression. The results are in the file **VideoAgression**. Do people tend to put more chili sauce into the recipe (and thus be more aggressive) after they play a violent video game as opposed to a non-violent one?

a. State the hypotheses either in words or using appropriate symbols.

b. Name the theory-based test that will be used and state and verify the validity conditions for the test chosen.

c. Calculate the test statistic (standardized statistic) and corresponding p-value.

d. State your conclusion (with appropriate justification based on your p-value and stated significance level) in the context of the research question. Be sure to address the issues of causation and generalizability as well.

6.4.17 Recall the previous question on aggression and video games. Calculate and interpret the 90% confidence interval for the difference in the mean amount of chili sauce that would be used between those who played the violent video game and those who played the non-violent game.

6.4.18* Student researchers tested to see whether listening to music would interfere with a person's ability to memorize words. Their subjects were randomly assigned to either listen to music or not. They were then shown 40 five-letter words for 90 seconds. The flashcards showing the words were taken away and the subjects were asked to write down as many words as they could remember. The results can be found in the file **WordsMemorized**. Does listening to music tend to hinder people's abilities to memorize words?

a. State the hypotheses either in words or using appropriate symbols.

b. Name the theory-based test that will be used and state and verify the validity conditions for the test chosen.

c. Calculate the test statistic (standardized statistic) and corresponding p-value.

d. State your conclusion (with appropriate justification based on your p-value and stated significance level) in the context of the research question. Be sure to address the issues of causation and generalizability as well.

6.4.19* Recall the previous question in which a group listening to music was asked to memorize a list of words compared to a group not listening to music.

a. Calculate a 90% confidence interval for the difference in the mean number of words memorized between the two groups.

b. Explain what your interval from part (a) means in context.

c. Based on your interval, is there a significant difference, at the 10% significance level, in the mean number of words memorized between the two groups? Explain how you know this.

6.4.20 Statistics students wanted to see whether there was an association between whether or not students eat breakfast daily and their grade point average (GPA). They surveyed 106 students at their college and asked them if they usually eat breakfast and what their current GPA was. The results are in the file **BreakfastGPA**. Is there an association between eating breakfast or not and a student's GPA?

a. State the hypotheses either in words or using appropriate symbols.

b. Name the theory-based test that will be used and state and verify the validity conditions for the test chosen.

c. Calculate the test statistic (standardized statistic) and corresponding p-value.

d. State your conclusion (with appropriate justification based on your p-value and stated significance level) in the context of the research question. Be sure to address the issues of causation and generalizability as well.

6.4.21* A study by Jung et al. (2014) looked at hurricane names and their perceived threat. They thought that if hurricanes in the U.S. had male names, they would be perceived as more dangerous. In one part of the research, the subjects were given a weather map showing a hurricane moving toward the area where they lived. Half the 142 subjects saw the map with the hurricane named Christina and half the subjects saw the map with the hurricane named Christopher. They were then asked to rate how likely it is they would evacuate, with 1 being to definitely evacuate immediately and 7 to definitely not evacuate. The 71 people who saw the hurricane named Christina gave it an average rating of 2.94 (SD = 1.54) and the 71 people who saw the hurricane named Christopher gave it an average rating of 2.34 (SD = 1.21). Is there a significant difference in the average ratings for how likely it is they would evacuate between the hurricane named Christina and the one named Christopher?

a. State the hypotheses to test this either in words or using appropriate symbols.

b. Name the theory-based test that will be used and state and verify the validity conditions for the test chosen.

c. Calculate the test statistic (standardized statistic) and corresponding p-value.

d. State your conclusion (with appropriate justification based on your p-value and stated significance level) in the context of the research question.

6.4.22* Recall the hurricane name study from the previous question.

a. Calculate a 95% confidence interval for the difference in the mean difference in evacuation ratings between the female-named hurricane (Christina) and the male-named hurricane (Christopher).

b. Based on your confidence interval, are people significantly more likely to evacuate for one type of name? Explain.

END OF CHAPTER

Harry Potter books*

6.CE.1 Suppose that a random sample of teenage boys and girls are asked how many Harry Potter books they have read. You conduct a two-sided test of the null hypothesis that $\mu_{girls} - \mu_{boys} = 0$ and you also calculate a 95% confidence interval for $\mu_{girls} - \mu_{boys}$.

a. Describe (in words) what the parameter $\mu_{girls} - \mu_{boys}$ means here.

b. Now suppose that your friend analyzes the same data but with the order of subtraction reversed (boys − girls, rather than girls − boys). Describe the impact (if any) on each of the following. In other words, describe how your friend's findings will compare to yours with regard to each of the following.

   i. Distribution of simulated statistics under the null hypothesis

   ii. Standard deviation of the simulated statistics under the null hypothesis

   iii. Observed value of the statistic (difference in sample means)

   iv. Approximate p-value from simulation

   v. Value of t-test statistic

   vi. p-Value from t-test

   vii. Midpoint of confidence interval

   viii. Endpoints of confidence interval

   ix. Width of confidence interval

c. What is the bottom line: Will you and your friend reach the same conclusions even though you disagreed about the order in which to perform the subtraction (boys − girls or girls − boys)? Explain.

Flexibility

6.CE.2 Data were gathered on 98 female college students and 81 male college students to see on average which sex was more flexible after participating in a physical wellness class and are available in the file **FlexibilityPost**.

a. State the research question.

b. How is the study designed: observational study or randomized experiment?

c. State the hypotheses.

d. Check validity conditions. Can you use the theory-based approach or should you use randomization methods?

e. Regardless of your answer to part (d) use a simulation analysis to generate a p-value and 95% CI.

f. Regardless of your answer to part (d) use a theory-based approach to generate a p-value and 95% CI.

g. Based on your answer to part (d) compare the p-values and 95% CIs received in parts (e) and (f).

h. Is zero in the confidence intervals? How does that fit with inference based on the p-values?

NFL referees*

6.CE.3 Recall from Exercise P.2.5 the data on duration of NFL football games in 2012 for the first three weeks of the season, when replacement referees officiated the games, and for the next three weeks when the regular referees returned

EXERCISE 6.CE.3

to officiate the games. Dotplots of these data are reproduced in the 6.CE.3 dotplots. The data appear in the file **Referees**.

a. Identify the observational units and variables in this graph. Also identify which variable is explanatory and which is response and classify the variables as categorical or quantitative.

b. Did the data collection for this study make use of random sampling, random assignment, or neither? Explain.

c. Before you conduct an inferential analysis, what do the dotplots suggest with regard to the question of whether game durations differed for the two types of referees?

d. State the appropriate hypotheses for testing whether the long-run average game duration is different for games played with replacement referees as compared to games played with regular referees.

e. Use an applet to simulate a randomization test for testing the hypotheses in part (d) and find the p-value.

f. Interpret what this p-value means in this context.

g. Use the simulation results to produce a 95% confidence interval for the relevant parameter.

h. Interpret this confidence interval.

i. Summarize your conclusions from these data. Make sure you address significance, confidence, generalization, and causation.

Elasticity of balsa wood

6.CE.4 Student researchers investigated whether balsa wood is less elastic after it has been immersed in water. They took 44 pieces of balsa wood and randomly assigned half to be immersed in water and the other half not to be. They measured the elasticity by seeing how far (in inches) the piece of wood would project a dime into the air.

a. Identify the observational units, explanatory variable, and response variable in this study.

b. Is this an observational study or an experiment? Explain briefly.

c. Express the appropriate null and alternative hypotheses, in the context of the study, for testing the student researchers' conjecture that balsa wood is less elastic after it has been immersed in water.

The students' data are in the file **Balsawood**.

d. Examine graphical displays and summary statistics to compare the elasticity measurements between the two groups. Write a paragraph comparing and contrasting the distributions of elasticity measurements between the two groups.

6.CE.5 Reconsider the previous exercise.

a. Give detailed, step-by-step instructions on how one could conduct a tactile simulation to generate a p-value to test the hypotheses stated in part (c). Be sure to include details on the following:

- Would the simulation involve coins, dice, or index cards?
- How many tosses, rolls, or cards would be used?
- How many sets of tosses, rolls, or shuffles would you observe?

b. Use an appropriate applet or other technology to find a simulation-based p-value to test the hypotheses stated in the previous exercise. Report the p-value.

c. Interpret the p-value reported in part (b), being sure to explain what the number means in the context of how the simulation-based method generated this p-value.

d. Summarize your conclusion from the p-value.

6.CE.6 Reconsider the previous two exercises.

a. Use a theory-based method to determine the test statistic and p-value.

b. Investigate and comment on whether the validity conditions of the theory-based method are satisfied.

c. Does the p-value obtained using the simulation-based method agree with that obtained using the randomization/simulation-based method?

d. Summarize your conclusion from this study, addressing whether the data provide strong evidence to support the students' conjecture.

6.CE.7 Reconsider the previous three exercises.

a. Determine a 95% confidence interval for the difference in mean elasticity (as measured by distance dime is projected) between treated and untreated balsa wood. Use the theory-based approach to find the interval. Be sure to also include an interpretation of the obtained 95% confidence interval.

b. Do the results from the 95% confidence interval agree with your conclusion in the previous exercise? How are you deciding?

c. Address the scope of conclusions for this study by discussing generalization and cause and effect in this study.

Sentence lengths*

6.CE.8 A student investigated whether popular novelist John Grisham uses shorter sentences in his books aimed at teenage readers than in his more general books. She took a sample of sentences from two of his books: *The Confession*, aimed at general readers, and *Theodore Boone: Kid Lawyer*, aimed at teenage readers. She then recorded the length (number of words) in each sentence. The sorted data appear below and in the file **GrishamSentences**.

The Confession (55 sentences)

2 2 3 3 4 4 6 7 8 8 8 8 9 9 9

9 9 10 10 10 10 11 11 12 12 12 13 13 13 13

13 14 14 14 15 15 15 15 15 15 16 17 18 19 21

21 21 23 23 24 29 29 32 34 39

Theodore Boone: Kid Lawyer (29 sentences)

3 4 4 7 7 8 11 11 12 12 13 13 14 14 14

15 16 16 17 19 19 20 20 20 22 25 29 30 47

a. Determine the five-number summary for each group.

b. Construct boxplots to compare the two distributions.

c. Comment on what the five-number summaries and boxplots reveal about the question of whether Grisham tends to use shorter sentences for his books aimed at teenage readers than in his books aimed at a general audience.

6.CE.9 Reconsider the previous question.

a. State the appropriate null and alternative hypotheses for testing whether Grisham tends to use shorter sentences for his books aimed at teenage readers than in his books aimed at a general audience.

b. Calculate the sample mean and SD of the sentence lengths for each group.

c. Explain why the calculations in part (b) indicate that there's no reason to proceed with testing the hypotheses stated in part (a).

Two tests

6.CE.10

a. Explain the difference between a two-*sample* test and a two-*sided* test.

b. Is it legitimate to use a one-sided test with a two-sample test? If so, give an example. If not, why not?

c. Is it legitimate to use a two-sided test with a one-sample test? If so, give an example. If not, why not?

SAT coaching*

6.CE.11 Suppose that 5,000 students are randomly assigned to either take an SAT coaching course or not, with the following results in their improvements in SAT scores:

	Sample size	Sample mean	Sample SD
Coaching group	2,500	46.20	14.40
Control group	2,500	44.40	15.30

a. Use technology to conduct a test of whether the sample data provide evidence that SAT coaching is helpful. State the hypotheses and report the test statistic and p-value. Draw a conclusion in the context of this study.

b. Use technology to produce a 99% CI for the difference in population mean improvements between the two groups. Interpret this interval.

c. Are the test conclusion and CI consistent with each other? Explain.

d. Do the sample data provide *very* strong evidence that SAT coaching is helpful? Explain whether the p-value or the CI helps you to decide.

e. Do the sample data provide strong evidence that SAT coaching is *very* helpful? Explain whether the p-value or the CI helps you to decide.

f. Comment on what this exercise reveals about the distinction between statistical significance and practical importance.

Runs scored in MLB

6.CE.12 Suppose that a professional baseball fan wants to investigate whether teams in one league (National or American) tend to score more runs on average than teams in the other league. The fan waits until the end of the season, records the number of runs scored by all 30 teams, and classifies the teams as National or American League.

a. Describe the population of interest in this study.

b. Explain how you know that this study involves neither random sampling nor random assignment.

c. Is it legitimate to perform a significance test and calculate a p-value based on the data that this baseball fan collected, even though the fan gathered data on the entire population of all 30 Major League Baseball teams? Explain your thinking.

INVESTIGATION: MEMORIZING LETTERS?

Can people better memorize letters if they are presented in recognizable groupings than if they are not? Students in an introductory statistics class were the subjects in a study that investigated this question. These students were given a sequence of 30 letters to memorize in 20 seconds. Some students (25 of them) were given the letters in recognizable three-letter groupings such as JFK-CIA-FBI-USA-.... The other students (26 of them) were given the exact same letters in the same order, but the groupings varied in size and did not include recognizable chunks, such as JFKC-IAF-BIU- … The instructor decided which students received which grouping by random assignment. After 20 seconds of studying the letters, students recorded as many letters as they could remember. Their score was the number of letters memorized correctly before their first mistake. The instructor conjectured that students in the JFK-CIA-… group would memorize more letters, on average, than students in the JFKC-IAF-… group.

STEP 1: Ask a research question.

1. State the research question.

STEP 2: Design a study and collect data.

2. Is this a randomized experiment or an observational study? Explain how you know.
3. What are the observational units?
4. What variables are measured/recorded on each observational unit?
5. Is there an explanatory/response relationship for these variables? Classify the variable in this study as categorical or quantitative.
6. State the null and alternative hypotheses to be investigated with this study. (You can use the symbol μ to represent these parameters if you want.)

Go to the textbook website and download the data for this investigation. Paste the data into the **Multiple Means** applet.

STEP 3: Explore the data.

7. Report the following:
   Mean number of letters memorized in recognizable groups_____
   SD of number of letters memorized in recognizable groups_____
   Mean number of letters memorized when not in recognizable groups_____
   SD of number of letters memorized when not in recognizable groups_____
   Difference in means_____

Is the difference in the direction conjectured by the instructor (i.e., did the group expected to do better actually do better)?

STEP 4: Draw inferences.

8. Conduct a simulation analysis with 1000 shuffles. Indicate how to determine the approximate p-value from the simulation results and report that p-value.
9. Give a conclusion about the strength of evidence against the null, in context, based on the p-value you obtained in #8.
10. Use the 2SD rule to generate a 95% confidence interval on the long-run difference in means between the two groups.
11. Interpret the 95% confidence interval you obtained in #10.

STEP 5: Formulate conclusions.

12. If the evidence against the null were strong, would you be justified in concluding that you have found strong evidence of a cause-and-effect relationship between recognizable groupings and better memory performance for this study? Why?
13. What broader population are you willing to generalize your findings to, if any? Explain.

An alternative approach: Theory-based inference

14. Explain whether a theoretical approach to computing the p-value and confidence interval would be valid for these data.

15. Now, use the **Theory-Based Inference** applet to generate a test statistic, p-value, and confidence interval. Report these, and compare them to what you determined from the simulation analysis. Explain how they are similar or different in light of your answer to #14.

STEP 6: Look back and ahead.

16. Provide a short paragraph (three- or four-sentence) summary of your findings. Make sure to include limitations of the study design. Also indicate at least one possible follow-up study that you now want to conduct.

Research Article   www.wiley.com/college/tintle

Physical fitness and urbanicity   Read "Does Living in Urban or Rural Settings Affect Aspects of Physical Fitness in Children? An Allometric Approach" by Tsimeas et al. (2005), 39:671–674 in the *British Journal of Sports Medicine*.

1 2 3 4 5 6 **7** 8 9 10 11 12

Paired Data: One Quantitative Variable

The main focus in this chapter is on analyzing paired data. The paired data sets of this chapter have a structure with two features:

1. There is one *pair* of response values for each observational unit.

2. There is a built-in *comparison*: One number in each pair is for Condition A, the other for Condition B.

Studies leading to paired data are often more efficient—better able to detect differences between conditions—because you have controlled for a source of variation (individual variability among the observational units). In this chapter, we turn to how to formally analyze and draw inferences from paired data. Most of the analysis is not new: You will continue to use the six-step statistical investigation method and the 3S strategy. In particular, the basic idea of the simulation step remains the same as before. You ask, "What if the null hypothesis is true? How will my statistic behave?" Just as before, the answer takes the form of the null ("what if") distribution, and you assess how unlikely the observed result would be if the null hypothesis were true, and you use a p-value to assess the strength of evidence against the null hypothesis.

Just as in Chapter 5, you can think of the null hypothesis in terms of an association between the response and a binary explanatory variable (Condition A or Condition B). To generate the null distribution, you *break the association*

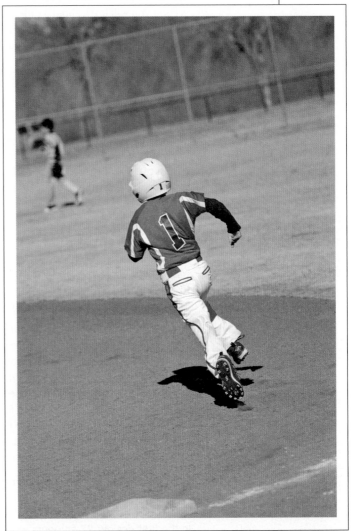

tammykayphoto/Shutterstock

509

and create data sets by shuffling. (Here, because of the pairing, the right way to break the association will be different, but the general idea remains the same.) Section 7.1 focuses on the paired study design. Section 7.2 explains the simulation-based approach and Section 7.3 explains the theory-based shortcut. Finally, in Section 7.4, the theory-based approach for tests and confidence intervals for paired data is further explored focusing on how to communicate these analyses for the AP exam.

By the end of the chapter, you will see several examples of the efficiency that can be gained from paired designs.

SECTION 7.1   PAIRED DESIGNS

INTRODUCTION

So far in this unit all the studies have compared whole *groups* of individuals: mildly depressed patients randomly assigned to swim with dolphins or without dolphins, students randomly assigned to be sleep deprived or get unrestricted amounts of sleep and then see how well they score on a visual learning task. All of these studies used an ***independent groups design***—there were no systematic connections relating individuals in one group to individuals in another group. In this section you will learn about a different study design based on pairs of units. For many situations, such ***paired designs*** allow more focused comparisons. As a result, these designs lead to more powerful tests for differences and narrower confidence intervals (see FAQ 7.1.1 for details).

FAQ 7.1.1 www.wiley.com/college/tintle

Why do we pair?

Your main goal in Section 7.1 should be to learn to tell the difference between an independent subjects design and a paired design. The reason is this: The analysis of the data follows the design of the study that was used. If you are wrong about the design that was used, your analysis will be wrong. In other words, your p-values and confidence intervals may be misleading.

Can You Study with Music Blaring?

Example 7.1

EXAMPLE

Many students like to study while listening to music. They seem to think that it doesn't hurt their ability to focus on their work. Is that really true? What does the research say? The following excerpt is from "Checking It Out: Does Music Interfere with Studying?" (Strauss 2009):

So what happens when your child studies for a science test with Jay-Z pouring from an iPod? According to Stanford University Professor Clifford Nass, the human brain listens to song lyrics with the same part that does word processing, which is the same part that supposedly is being employed for studying, he said. Something has to give, and it is the ability your child has to do the work he or she is supposed to be doing. Instrumental music is another story. For the most part, it is processed on the other side of the brain from the part that is processing language. "So if you are reading and listening to instrumental music you get virtually no interference," Nass said. "The music would not, in fact affect you, unless you are thinking deeply about the music, like, 'I wonder why Chopin chose the F sharp.'"

Consider the following two experimental designs:

EXPERIMENT 1—RANDOM ASSIGNMENT TO TWO SEPARATE GROUPS

In the first design, 27 students would be randomly assigned to one of two groups: a group that will listen to music with lyrics and a group that will listen to music without lyrics. While students are listening to the music, they will play a memorization game: They will study a list of 25 common five-letter words for 90 seconds. Then, the students will write down as many of the words as they can remember.

EXPERIMENT 2—PAIRED DESIGN USING REPEATED MEASURES

In the second design, instead of randomly assigning students to each of the two groups, each student will play the memorization game twice: once listening to the song with lyrics and once without lyrics. This is called a *paired design*.

> ### THINK ABOUT IT
>
> Identify the explanatory variable and the response variable in this study (regardless of how we design it). Are there any advantages or disadvantages to the two designs?

The response variable in this study is the number of words memorized (quantitative). We would like to compare the outcomes of this variable between the two conditions, with lyrics and without lyrics (the explanatory variable). However, there is probably a fair bit of variability in the scores from person to person because different people tend to have different memorization abilities. This variability may make it difficult to see differences between performances under the two conditions, especially if those differences are small. For these reasons, the paired design has a couple of obvious advantages. First, instead of focusing on the number of words memorized by each individual, we can instead focus on the *difference* in the number of words memorized between the two versions of the song by each individual. The variable *difference in number of words memorized* may well have less variability than the actual number of words memorized because there will probably be more consistency in how many more words people can remember with and without the lyrics than in the number of words remembered by different people. Focusing on the differences will provide us with a clearer picture of the "lyrics effect," in particular, increasing the power (see Chapter 2), compared to an independent groups design, to find an effect if there really is one.

It is important to remember that "randomness" will still play an important role in paired study designs. For example, here we would randomize which version of the song the student listened to first. Otherwise, if everyone listened to the song without lyrics second but tended to perform better, we wouldn't know whether that improvement was due to the absence of lyrics or to having previously heard the song and played the memory game.

Why does the distinction between these two study designs matter? There are two main reasons.

- *When a paired design is possible, you typically get more informative results* because units within a pair tend to be similar to each other. When pairing is effective, differences within each pair on the response variable tend to be due mainly to the explanatory variable.

- *The right way to analyze the data depends on the study design*. The analyses for the two designs are not the same. If you get the design wrong, you get the analysis wrong, and your p-value and confidence interval estimate will be wrong.

You will learn more about the advantages of paired designs and how to use simulation- and theory-based methods for inference from paired data in later sections. For now, we focus mainly on differences between the paired design and the independent groups design.

When should we pair?

We should use a paired design when we expect a strong association between repeated observations within the pair (e.g., on the same individual). In the example above, pairing was a good idea because we expect that some students are better memorizers than others, so when students play the game multiple times their memorization scores are strongly associated. FAQ 7.1.2 talks more about this issue.

 7.1.1

Definitions

For a *paired design*, response values come in pairs, with one response value in the pair for Group 1 and the other for Group 2. Sometimes the pairs come from matching similar individuals to create groups of two (we call this *paired design using matching*); sometimes the pairs come from measuring the same individual twice, once under each condition (we call this *paired design using repeated measures*). For an *independent groups design*, each individual in a group is unrelated to all the other individuals in the study. Each individual provides only one response value.

 7.1.2

FAQ 7.1.2   www.wiley.com/college/tintle

Should we always use pairs?

Do we ever have pairing in observational studies?

Yes, absolutely. There are many cases where this comes up. For example, if you are interested in whether a diet program works you can evaluate the difference between the pre- and postdiet weights of the same individuals. Did most people lose weight? How much? This is a type of paired design where the response variable focuses on the weight difference. Another example would be if you wanted to compare prices at two different grocery stores. You would have one list of products and then both prices for each product at the two stores. On average is there a price difference? By how much?

Do pairs have to be the same observational unit?

Imagine we want to see whether there is a difference in the average hours spent watching TV by married men and women. One option is to randomly sample some married men and randomly sample some married women and compare the differences in the average hours spent on watching TV between the two groups. However, we might expect a fairly strong association between husband-wife pairs in terms of TV watching, because they might often be watching together. Thus, sampling husband-wife pairs and then testing to see whether the average difference in hours spent watching TV is different from zero will likely be a better study design. In this kind of a study design, the pair becomes the observational unit.

   Note: We say here that a pair is an observational unit because we think this is the most intuitive way to understand the difference between an independent groups design and a paired design. However, the standard theory of experimental design says that each pair in a paired design is a *pair of units*. Each response value corresponds to a unit. For now, you can continue to think of the pair as the observational unit, but if you take more statistics, you may need to change your definition.

> **THINK ABOUT IT**
>
> Suppose that we gave each subject a pretest to see how many words they could remember with no music. How could you use pretest scores to create pairs of individuals for a paired design?

EXPERIMENT 3—PAIRED DESIGN USING MATCHING

So far, we have created the pairs by measuring the same observational unit twice. For example, in the memorization game, each student played the memorization game twice, once under each condition. We got the pairs by "repeated measures." Another way to create pairs could use a pretest to rank students according to how many words they could memorize and use the results to create pairs. The top two students (memorized the most words) would be Pair 1, the next two would be Pair 2, and so on. Once we had the pairs, we would randomly assign one person in each pair to each condition. We are still expecting there to be less variability in the responses for the two individuals in each pair than among pairs.

   Both paired designs are quite different from the first design for which the two groups are independent. For this particular context, the second design (repeated measures) is better because you get two response values from the exact same subject. Sometimes, however, it is not possible or not a good idea to use repeated measures to create pairs. If you are comparing two different surgeries, for example, you can't expect each patient to have two surgeries. In this case, matching can be useful if you have good criteria (i.e., related to the response variable) on which to base the matching to try to create pairs where the individuals in each pair are likely to be very similar to each other. As we will see, both paired designs have some distinct advantages over the independent samples design.

Rounding First Base

Imagine you are at the plate in baseball and have hit a hard line drive. You want to try to stretch your hit from a single to a double. Does the path that you take to "round" first base make much of a difference? For example (see Figure 7.1), is it better to take a "narrow angle" or a "wide angle" around first base? (This exploration is based on an actual study reported in a master's thesis by W. F. Woodward in 1970.)

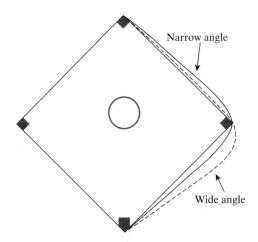

FIGURE 7.1 Two methods of rounding first base when a player plans to run to second base.

Think about designing a study to investigate this question.

1. Identify the explanatory and response variables in this study.

   Explanatory:

   Response:

2. How would you design an observational study to investigate this question? Explain why an observational study would not allow you to decide which base-running angle is better than the other.

3. Suppose 20 baseball players volunteered to participate in an experiment. Suppose that you also plan to assign a single angle, either wide or narrow, to each player. How would you decide which player ran with which base-running angle?

A reasonable experimental design would be to randomly assign 10 of the 20 players to run with the wide angle and the other 10 to run with the narrow angle.

4. Some runners are faster than others. Explain how random assignment controls for this, so that speed is not likely to be a confounding variable in this study.

   Even though random assignment tends to balance out other variables (such as speed) between the two groups, there's still a chance that most of the fast runners could be in one group and most of the slow runners in the other group. More importantly, there's likely to be a good bit of variability in the runners' speeds, and that variability would make it harder to spot a difference between the base-running angles even if one angle really is superior to the other.

5. Suggest a different way of conducting the experiment to make sure that speed is completely balanced between the two groups.

In this study each runner can use *both* base-running angles. That way we can be sure that neither treatment has more of the fast or slow runners, and we can also expect that *differences* in times for each runner will show considerably less variability than individual running times.

Definitions

For a ***paired design***, response values come in pairs, with one response value in the pair for Group 1 and the other for Group 2. Sometimes the pairs come from matching individuals to create groups of two (we call this ***paired design using matching***); sometimes the pairs come from measuring the same individual twice, once under each condition (we call this ***paired design using repeated measures***). For an ***independent groups design***, each individual in a group is unrelated to all the other individuals in the study. Each individual provides only one response value.

6. What aspect of this experiment should be determined randomly? (*Hint:* The treatment is not determined randomly, because each runner experiences both treatments. But what other factor could still have an effect on the response unless it was randomized?)

7. What do you suggest using as the variable to be analyzed with this paired-design experiment? (*Hint:* Think of a better option than simply analyzing the set of times with the wide angle and the set of times with the narrow angle separately the way you would for an independent groups design of the sort described in #3 and #4.)

   With a paired design, we analyze the *differences* in the response between the two treatments. In this case we would calculate the difference in running times between the wide and narrow angles for each player and then analyze the sample of differences. You will learn how to do this in Sections 7.2 and 7.3.

   The order in which the players run with the two angles should be determined randomly; otherwise, the order could be a confounding variable. Perhaps players would be slower with their second angle because of fatigue or perhaps they would be faster with their second angle if they were slow to get warmed up. Randomizing the order takes away any worries about an order effect.

8. So far you have seen three designs for this study. The first (#2) was observational. The second (#3 and #4) was a randomized experiment with independent groups. The third (#5 and #6) used a paired design with pairs created by repeated measures. Consider a fourth design: Suppose you have 20 players, as before, and you have the time for each player in a 100-yard dash. Explain how you could use this information to create pairs of runners that you expect to be similar and how you would assign one runner in each pair to the narrow angle and the other to a wide angle.

9. Of the four designs (observational with independent groups, experimental with independent groups, paired design using repeated measures, and paired design using matching), which do you think is best for this context? Explain why. (*Hint:* Pairing works best when the units in a pair are as similar to each other as possible.)

10. As noted in #9, pairing works best when the two units in a pair are as similar as possible. When the units in a pair are not similar, pairing will not be effective. Invent and describe an example where you think pairing will be effective. Give the response and explanatory variable, how you would create the pairs, and why you think pairing will be effective.

11. Invent and describe an example where you think pairing will not be effective. Again, give the response and explanatory variable, how you would create the pairs, and this time why you think pairing will not be effective.

12. For some contexts, the strategy of using repeated measures to create pairs is either impossible or a bad idea. Invent and describe such a context.

13. Pairing can also be used in the design of an observational study. Revisit the observational study in #2, and suppose also that you have times in the hundred yard dash for each of the 20 players. Explain how you could use those times to create pairs. (Suppose that, of the 20 players, 12 used the wide angle and only 8 used the narrow angle. This means you can create only 8 pairs.)

SECTION 7.1 Summary

In **paired designs**, response values come in pairs, with one response value in the pair belonging to each explanatory variable group. Sometimes the pairs come from matching individuals and sometimes the pairs come from measuring the same individual twice. In studies with an **independent groups design**, each individual in a group is unrelated to all the other individuals in the study. Each individual provides only one response value.

- When a paired design is possible, you typically get more informative results because units within a pair tend to be similar to each other. When pairing is effective, subsequent differences within each pair on the response variable tend to be due mainly to the explanatory variable.

- *The right way to analyze the data depends on the study design.* The analyses for the two designs are not the same. If you get the design wrong, you get the simulation wrong, and your p-values and confidence intervals will be wrong.

SIMULATION-BASED APPROACH TO ANALYZING PAIRED DATA

SECTION 7.2

INTRODUCTION

In Chapter 6 you learned how to compare two groups on a quantitative response. The data arose either from a randomized experiment or from independent random samples. In Section 7.1, you studied a different experimental design that called for collecting *paired* data. Now you will learn how to analyze data that arise from a matched pairs design. In this section, you will see how to use randomization-based methods to conduct a test of significance for paired data.

Rounding First Base (*continued*)

7.2

Recall the study from Exploration 7.1 that explored whether taking a "narrow angle" or a "wide angle" while rounding first base would increase your time to second base. (See Figure 7.2.)

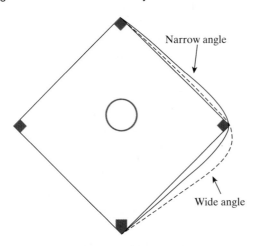

Narrow angle

Wide angle

FIGURE 7.2 Two methods of rounding first base when a player plans to run to second base.

Example 7.2

EXAMPLE

In Woodward's study, he used a stopwatch to time 22 different runners going from a spot 35 feet past home to a spot 15 feet before second. He had each runner use each method, with a rest period in between.

> **THINK ABOUT IT**
>
> Why did he use a stopwatch? Why did he use the "middle" of the route instead of the entire distance from home to second? Why did he have each runner use each method? How should he decide which method the runners use first? Why was there a rest period in between?

Keep in mind that we are always trying to minimize other sources of variability in our data so we can more directly compare the treatments we are interested in. In this study, we can use accurate timing devices and consistent definitions to help minimize some of that extraneous variability. But we can also use an experimental design that has that goal as well. You should recognize Woodward's study as a *matched pairs design* as discussed in Section 7.1. This design is advantageous because it controls for the runner-to-runner variability: Some runners are faster than others. By having each runner use both methods, we will have a more direct comparison of the effects *of the base-running strategies* on the time to second base. The order of the methods used by each runner was determined randomly. The rest period is intended to eliminate fatigue as a confounding variable. If each runner first ran the narrow angle and then the wide angle, we wouldn't be able to separate the fatigue/learning effects from the base-running strategy effect.

> **KEY IDEA**
>
> As discussed in Section 7.1, in a matched pairs experimental design, it is important to randomize the order of the treatments.

Although pairing should make it easier to help us separate out any treatment effect from other variables, pairing is not always feasible or helpful. In this study, especially with the rest period in between, pairing is very feasible. Next, we'll investigate whether it was beneficial.

The data in Table 7.1 show the times (seconds) for the first 10 runners, and Figure 7.3 shows dotplots of the times for all 22 runners for the two methods.

TABLE 7.1   The running times (seconds) for the first 10 of the 22 subjects

Subject	1	2	3	4	5	6	7	8	9	10	
Narrow angle	5.50	5.70	5.60	5.50	5.85	5.55	5.40	5.50	5.15	5.80	...
Wide angle	5.55	5.75	5.50	5.40	5.70	5.60	5.35	5.35	5.00	5.70	...

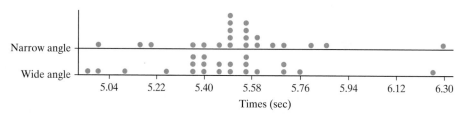

FIGURE 7.3 The running times for a sample of 22 runners.

One thing to notice in these results is that there is a lot of overlap in the two distributions (narrow mean: 5.534 sec, wide mean: 5.459 sec) and a fair bit of variability (narrow SD: 0.260 sec, wide SD: 0.273 sec). The slowest times took over 6 seconds, whereas the fastest times were just under 5 seconds. As you saw in Chapter 6, it will be difficult to detect a difference between the two methods when there is so much natural variation in the running times.

However, these data are clearly *paired*. As discussed earlier, such data should *not* be treated as coming from two **independent samples**. Instead, we will focus our analysis on the *difference* in times for each runner between the two methods.

Paired response variable: time difference in running to second (narrow angle − wide angle).

Keep in mind that the direction of subtraction here does not make a difference as long as you are consistent for each pair and throughout the analysis. Table 7.2 shows the differences for the first 10 runners and Figure 7.4 is a dotplot of the differences for all 22 runners.

Subject	1	2	3	4	5	6	7	8	9	10	
TABLE 7.2	**Last row is difference in times for each of the first 10 runners (narrow – wide)**										
Narrow angle	5.50	5.70	5.60	5.50	5.85	5.55	5.40	5.50	5.15	5.80	...
Wide angle	5.55	5.75	5.50	5.40	5.70	5.60	5.35	5.35	5.00	5.70	...
Difference	−0.05	−0.05	0.10	0.10	0.15	−0.05	0.05	0.15	0.15	0.10	...

FIGURE 7.4 Dotplot of differences in running times (narrow − wide), $\bar{x}_d = 0.075$ sec, $s_d = 0.0883$ sec.

The distribution of the differences might be considered slightly skewed left. The mean difference in running times is 0.075 seconds with a standard deviation of 0.0883 seconds. Notice that the mean of the differences (0.075) is equal to the difference in the means between the two methods (5.534 − 5.459). But the standard deviation of the differences (0.0883) is much smaller than the original standard deviations of the running times (0.260 and 0.273). This stems from the fact that although there is considerable runner-to-runner variability, the runners are fairly consistent in how much time they take—typically between 0.05 and 0.20 longer with the narrow method. Whereas we saw differences of up to a second between runners (less than 5 to more than 6 seconds), we did not see any one runner having a difference between the two routes of longer than 0.20 seconds. Figure 7.5 shows the original dotplots but with each observation paired between the two base-running strategies.

FIGURE 7.5 Dotplots of the running times for each method with lines connecting each runner's times.

7.2.1

What we notice is that the faster runners with the narrow angle tend to be the faster runners with the wide angle. The slowest runner with the narrow angle is also the slowest runner with the wide angle. So by looking at the differences in running speeds of the runners, we are able to account for a lot of the (runner-to-runner) variability in the data. Plus we see that most of the connecting lines slant from left to right, indicating a tendency for longer times with the narrow angle. This "leaning" would be difficult to pick up if we just treated them as unrelated dotplots.

So now we can ask whether this mean difference of 0.075 seconds is significantly different from zero. We can define our parameter of interest to be

μ_d = the long-run mean difference in running times for runners when using the narrow angle instead of the wide angle.

Note that the subscript "d" in μ_d is added to emphasize that we are looking at an average of *differences* in times. Then, the relevant hypotheses are

H_0: $\mu_d = 0$ (on average, the time to second base does not differ between the two methods)

H_a: $\mu_d \neq 0$ (there is a difference in running times between the two methods, on average)

> ### KEY IDEA
>
> When the parameter of interest is the long-run mean difference or population mean difference, the corresponding statistic is the sample mean difference.

The statistic $\bar{x}_d = 0.075$ is above zero, but we need to ask the same question we've asked before: *Is it surprising to see such a large average difference in running times by chance alone, even if the base-running strategy has no genuine effect on the times?*

> ### THINK ABOUT IT
>
> What should you use to measure how surprising the observed results would be if the null hypothesis were true? Suppose you want to use simulation-based methods to find an approximate p-value, what will you assume to be true in carrying out the simulation? What is the statistic whose could-have-been values you will generate? And then what do you do next to find a p-value?

Another way to think about this question: If the base-running strategy doesn't make a difference in general, then the two times for each runner were going to be the same two times regardless of which strategy was being used. Any difference in times for each person was just by chance, perhaps which one they ran first. So it doesn't matter which one we call the "wide-angle" time and which we call the "narrow-angle" time—the two times are completely interchangeable. In other words, we can consider the pair of measurements for each subject to be "swappable."

To model this using simulation, we will assume the same two times for each runner, but we will randomly decide which time goes with the narrow method and which goes with the wide method. In other words, for each runner we randomly decide whether to swap the two values or leave them as is. Then we see how much variability this creates in the sample mean difference from repetition to repetition. To decide which time comes first, we can use a coin flip. This is equivalent to using the coin flip to determine which pairs of times to swap and which to leave as is. We will let heads tell us to swap the times and tails tell us to not swap the times. We did this once and the results for the first 10 runners are shown in Table 7.3.

TABLE 7.3	Runners whose responses were swapped are in bold type									
Subject	1	2	3	4	5	6	7	8	9	10	
Narrow angle	**5.55**	5.70	**5.50**	5.50	**5.70**	**5.60**	5.40	5.50	5.15	**5.70**	...
Wide angle	**5.50**	5.75	**5.60**	5.40	**5.85**	**5.55**	5.35	5.35	5.00	**5.80**	...
Difference	**0.05**	−0.05	**−0.10**	0.10	**−0.15**	**0.05**	0.05	0.15	0.15	**−0.10**	...

As a result of this one repetition, we ended up with an average difference of $\bar{x}_d = -0.025$ seconds. Note that our observed average difference of 0.075 is larger and farther away from the hypothesized long-run mean difference of zero than the average difference found in the simulated results. But we need to repeat this process many times and find many simulated sample mean differences to construct a null distribution. This is how we could really tell whether our original sample mean difference is surprising when there is no connection between the times and which base-running strategy was being used. The table below summarizes the key aspects of the simulation:

Null hypothesis	=	Long-run average difference in times is 0
One repetition	=	Rerandomizing (potentially swapping) narrow- and wide-angle run times within runners
Statistic	=	Average difference in run times in the sample

To do this we will use the **Matched Pairs** applet. If you check the **Randomize** box and then press **Randomize**, the applet simulates flipping a coin for each runner. If the coin lands "heads" we swap that runner's wide angle times with his narrow angle time; if "tails," no change is made. After this is done for each of the 22 runners, the average of the time differences for each of the 22 runners is recorded. This process is then repeated a large number of times. Figure 7.6 shows the mean differences from 1,000 such repetitions.

7.2.2

> **THINK ABOUT IT**
>
> Consider Figure 7.6. The distribution of the simulated sample mean difference appears to be centered at about 0. Does that make sense?

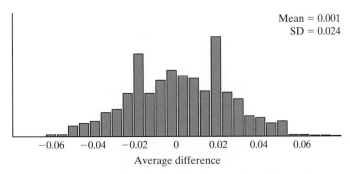

Mean = 0.001
SD = 0.024

Average difference

FIGURE 7.6   Simulated mean differences for 1,000 repetitions where for each repetition a coin is flipped for each runner to decide whether the runners' times are swapped.

As can be seen in Figure 7.6, the distribution of the simulated sample mean difference appears to be centered around 0 seconds. This makes sense because the simulation is based on the assumption that the null hypothesis is true, and the time to get to second base with the two methods is the same, on average. Figure 7.6 also shows that the SD of the mean difference is 0.024 seconds—an estimate of repetition-to-repetition variability in the mean difference by random chance alone (the coin-tossing random assignment).

> **THINK ABOUT IT**
>
> Consider Figure 7.6. With 1,000 simulated values of the sample mean difference, is the observed mean difference from the actual study unlikely to have occurred assuming the null hypothesis to be true? How are you deciding?

In the actual study, the mean difference in running times was observed to be 0.075 seconds. We can see from Figure 7.7 that this falls in the upper tail of the distribution. We can use the applet to count whether there are any mean differences beyond 0.075 or −0.075 to estimate a two-sided p-value.

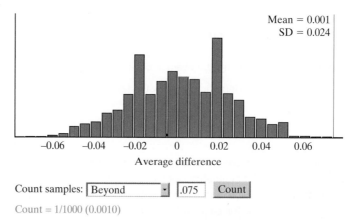

Count samples: [Beyond ▾] [.075] [Count]

Count = 1/1000 (0.0010)

FIGURE 7.7   The simulated statistics that are at least as extreme
as 0.075 (in either direction) are marked.

We see just one of the 1,000 repetitions of random swappings gave us an $\bar{x}_d$ value at least as extreme as what Woodward found in his study. We can also standardize the 0.075 by dividing by the applet's estimate for the SD of the mean differences (approximately 0.024). We note that 0.075 is just over 3 standard deviations from zero (e.g., 0.075/0.024 is 3.1215), another indication that the observed result would be unlikely to occur by random chance alone.

> **THINK ABOUT IT**
>
> How would you interpret the p-value?

Assuming the running time is the same with a wide angle or a narrow angle, on average, if we were to randomly decide whether to swap which value was recorded for which strategy, we would find a sample mean difference in times of 0.075 seconds or more extreme in about 0.1% of such repetitions.

> **THINK ABOUT IT**
>
> Based on the p-value and standardized statistic, what is your conclusion about the hypotheses? Is there evidence against the null hypothesis? How are you deciding? What are your conclusions about causation and generalization?

This small p-value provides very strong evidence against the null hypothesis and in favor of the alternative hypothesis that runners such as those in this study tend to (on average) take different times getting from home to second when comparing these two running angles. We can draw a cause-and-effect conclusion about the study because the researcher used random assignment between the two methods for each runner (and the small p-value eliminates random chance as a plausible explanation). However, we don't have much information about how these 22 runners were selected to decide whether we can generalize to a larger population.

To estimate how much slower the narrow-angle route tends to be, we can approximate a 95% confidence interval for μ_d using the standard deviation of the null distribution:

$$0.075 \pm 2(0.024) = (0.027, 0.123) \text{ seconds}$$

We are 95% confident that, on average, the narrow-angle route takes 0.027 to 0.124 seconds longer than the wide-angle route. Because every (fraction of a) second counts, we would recommend that all base runners, at least like those in this study, use a wide angle when rounding the bases.

As you may have already noticed, the strategy we used to find the p-value for this study is the same 3S strategy that is found in Step 4 of our statistical investigation method and has been used in analyses involving one or two proportions and two means:

1. **Statistic:** Compute the statistic in the sample. In this case, the statistic we looked at was the observed mean difference (narrow – wide) in running times.

2. **Simulate:** Identify a chance model that reflects the null hypothesis. We tossed a coin for each runner, and if it landed heads we swapped the two running times recorded for that runner—interchanging the wide-angle and narrow-angle times. If the coin landed tails, we did not flip the times. We repeated this process 1,000 times, recording the simulated mean difference in running times each time and thus obtained a distribution of the mean differences that could have happened when the null hypothesis is true.

3. **Strength of evidence:** We found that in just one of our 1,000 repetitions, the mean difference turned out to be at least as extreme as the observed difference of 0.075 seconds. This gave us a p-value of 0.001, which provided very strong evidence to say that running times for the narrow-angle path and wide-angle path are different, on average.

Did pairing matter? An incorrect analysis

THINK ABOUT IT

What do you think would happen if we wrongly analyzed the data using a two-independent-samples procedure? In other words, what if the researcher had treated the 22 observations from the narrow method and the 22 observations from the wide method as coming from two different sets of 22 runners, instead of accounting for the paired nature of the observations? Would the p-value stay the same, increase, or decrease?

We can use the **Multiple Means** applet to simulate what would happen if we were to incorrectly analyze the data using a two-independent-samples procedure. Figure 7.8 gives the output from the applet, and the approximate p-value is 0.3470, much larger than that obtained from the paired samples analysis.

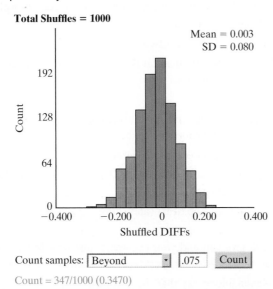

FIGURE 7.8 **Multiple Means** applet output when incorrectly analyzing the base-running data using a two-independent-samples method.

This analysis, which assumes no connections between the times within runners, does not detect a significant difference between the two base-running strategies. The larger standard deviation of the differences in group means (0.080) comes from not accounting for the runner-to-runner variability we saw back in Figure 7.3. Therefore, the researcher was very wise to use a matched pairs design for this experiment, because otherwise he likely would not have detected that the wide-angle method is significantly faster than the narrow-angle method.

EXPLORATION 7.2 | Exercise and Heart Rate

Raising your heart rate is one of the major goals of exercise. Do some exercises raise your heart rate more than others? Which common exercise, jumping jacks or bicycle kicks, raises your heart rate more? In this exploration, you are going to compare heart rates of you and your classmates doing jumping jacks and bicycle kicks. If you don't want to collect your own data, you may use data already collected on a class where jumping jacks were compared to bicycle kicks. The data set can be found on the textbook website and is titled, **JJvsBicycle**.

Below are links to YouTube videos explaining how to do each of these exercises.

- Jumping jack: http://www.youtube.com/watch?v=dmYwZH_BNd0
- Bicycle kicks: http://www.ehow.com/video_2369096_basic-exercises-bicycle-kicks.html

After you do the exercise for 30 seconds, you will measure your heart rate. For instructions on how to measure your heart rate, visit the National Emergency Medicine Association website (http://www.nemahealth.org/index.php/heart-rate-or-pulse-2) and follow the link for "How to measure your pulse."

It is very important that you follow these protocols carefully so we have high-quality data to analyze. Although it is best to have the largest sample size possible, if you feel uncomfortable doing any of these exercises, please don't feel you have to.

1. You will first randomize the order (jumping jacks first or bicycle kick first) in which you measure your heart rate.

   - Flip a coin.
     - If "heads"
       - Do jumping jacks for 30 seconds. Then, measure your **jumping jack heart rate** _____ beats per minute.
       - Sit down and take a break for two minutes.
       - Now do bicycle kicks for 30 seconds. Then, measure your **bicycle kick heart rate** _____ beats per minute
     - If "tails"
       - Do the bicycle kick exercise for 30 seconds. Then, measure your **bicycle kick heart rate** _____ beats per minute
       - Sit down and take a break for two minutes.
       - Now do jumping jacks for 30 seconds. Then, measure your **jumping jack heart rate** _____ beats per minute.
   - Find the difference in your two heart rates (jumping jack heart rate–bicycle kick heart rate). _____
   - Your instructor will give you and your classmates instructions on where to record your jumping jack heart rate, bicycle kick heart rate, and difference (jumping jacks–bicycle kick).

2. Explain why it is reasonable to say that the two heart rates you collected should *not* be treated as **independent** data.

3. Why do you think we randomized the order of jumping jacks and bicycle kicks before measuring heart rates?

As seen in Chapter 6, we can summarize the quantitative data on heart rates using averages or means. But, because the data are *paired*, instead of comparing mean jumping jack heart rate to mean bicycle kick heart rate, we will instead look at the mean *difference* in heart rate between doing jumping jacks and bicycle kick. Thus, we can define our parameter of interest to be

μ_d = long run mean *difference* in heart rate when doing jumping jacks and
bicycle kicks in the population of interest.

Note that the subscript "*d*" in μ_d is used to denote that we are looking at an average of *differences*.

4. State the null and alternative hypotheses (using μ_d) to test whether the mean difference in heart rate between the two exercises is not 0.

KEY IDEA

When the parameter of interest is the long-run mean difference or population mean difference, the corresponding statistic is the sample mean difference.

5. Find the average of the differences between the two heart rates for the entire class. This is the statistic we will use to summarize the data.

Your null hypothesis should essentially state that there is no difference in the heart rates between the two exercises, on average. If that is the case, it doesn't really matter if we swap someone's jumping jack heart rate with his or her bicycle kick heart rate. This is how we will model the null to develop a null distribution. To randomly swap some of the values we can just use a coin flip. If the coin lands heads you will swap the two heart rates. If the coin lands tails you won't swap the heart rates.

6. Flip a coin for each pair of heart rates and switch the appropriate ones. Recalculate the difference in heart rates and find the new simulated mean difference. Plot this value on the board in the classroom along with those from the rest of the class. Where does the actual statistic you found in #5 fit in this null distribution? Is it out in the tail?

7. As you know, it would be better to have many more simulations than what your class just did. We will do this by using an applet.
   - Go to the **Matched Pairs** applet.
   - Press **Clear** to erase the default data and then copy and paste the data (both columns— jacks and kicks) into the **Data** window. Then press **Use Data**.
   - Notice that the applet graphs the individual heart rates in each group, along with the means and standard deviations for the two groups.
   - Below that, the applet provides a dotplot of the differences in the heart rates in the sample. Please note that these difference values can be negative numbers because you are looking at *change* or *difference* in heart rates. The "Differences" graph also shows the mean of the differences and the standard deviation of the differences.
   - Write down these values in the following table:

Condition	Sample mean, $\bar{x}$	Sample SD, s
Jumping jacks	$\bar{x}_{jj} =$	$s_{jj} =$
Bicycle kicks	$\bar{x}_{bicycle} =$	$s_{bicycle} =$
Diff = JJ – BK	$\bar{x}_d =$	$s_d =$

8. The **Matched Pairs** applet will perform the simulation similar to what you did with flipping a coin.
   - Check the **Randomize** box.
   - Set the number of times to **Randomize** to 1 and press **Randomize**.
   - Once the coin tosses have determined which heart rate will be in which column, the applet displays the rerandomized data (the colors show you the original column for each observation, so you should see a mix in each group now).

- This could-have-been value for the mean difference is added to the Average Difference graph.
- Write down these could-have-been values for the re-randomized data:

Condition	Rerandomized sample mean, $\bar{x}$	Rerandomized sample SD, s
Jumping jacks	$\bar{x}_{jj} =$	$s_{jj} =$
Bicycle kicks	$\bar{x}_{bicycle} =$	$s_{bicycle} =$
Diff = JJ – BK	$\bar{x}_d =$	$s_d =$

a. How does the actual mean difference compare to your simulated mean difference. Choose one.

More extreme Less extreme Similar

b. How are you deciding?

9. Update the number of times to **Randomize** to 99 (for a total of 100 repetitions), and press **Randomize**. Consider the graph "Average Difference" that the applet has created ...

a. How many dots are in this graph?

b. What does each dot represent?

The table below summarizes the key aspects of the simulation:

Null hypothesis	=	Long-run average difference in heart rates is 0
One repetition	=	Rerandomizing (possibly swapping) exercise heart rates within students
Statistic	=	Average difference in heart rates in the sample

10. To see many more possible values of mean difference in sample means that could have been, IF jumping jacks and bicycle kick rates were *swappable*, update the number of times to **Randomize** to 900 and press **Randomize** (for a total of 1,000 repetitions). Describe the updated "Average Difference" graph with the 1,000 samples or repetitions, with regard to the following features.

a. Shape:

b. About what number is this graph centered? Explain why you were expecting this.

c. This graph also reports a value for standard deviation, SD. Report this value and give a simple *interpretation* of this value, as in, "What is this value measuring?"

11. You now should have generated 1,000 possible values of the mean difference in jumping jacks and bicycle kick heart rates that were simulated assuming the null hypothesis was true and these rates were the same, on average. How does the observed mean difference from your data (as reported in #5 and #7) compare to these simulated values? Is an average difference in heart rates like that observed in the actual study unlikely to happen by chance alone if jumping jacks and bicycle kick heart rates are the same, on average? How are you deciding?

12. To quantify the strength of evidence against the null hypothesis, you can find the p-value.

- Go back to the **Matched Pairs** applet.
- In the **Count Samples** box, make an appropriate selection from the drop-down menu (*Hint:* In what direction does your alternative hypothesis look?) and enter the appropriate number in the box (*Hint:* At least as extreme as what number?).
- Report the approximate p-value.

13. Use the p-value to state a conclusion in the context of the problem. Be sure to comment on statistical significance. Can you conclude that there is strong evidence that jumping jack heart rate and bicycle kick heart rate differ? Why or why not? Can you draw a cause-and-effect conclusion? To what population are you willing to generalize the results?

14. Alternatively, you can summarize the strength of evidence using a standardized statistic. Find the standardized statistic and confirm that the strength of evidence you receive from the p-value is approximately the same as with the standardized statistic.

15. We can again use the 2SD method to approximate a 95% confidence interval for the mean difference in heart rates between those that do the two exercises. The overall structure of the formula is the same:

$$\text{statistic} \pm 2\,(\text{SD})$$

where the statistic is the sample mean difference in heart rates for your class and SD is the standard deviation of your null distribution when you did 1,000 repetitions in the applet (NOT the standard deviation from the data). Use these numbers to find an approximate 95% confidence interval for the mean difference in heart rates for those that do the two exercises your class did.

16. Provide an interpretation of this confidence interval, being sure to explain the parameter in this context.

As you may have already noticed, the strategy we used to find the p-value for this study is the same 3S strategy that is found in Step 4 of our statistical investigation method and has been used in analyses involving one or two groups:

1. **Statistic:** Compute the statistic in the sample. In this case, the statistic you looked at was the observed mean difference in heart rates.

2. **Simulate:** Identify a chance model that reflects the null hypothesis. To simulate what could have been if the null hypothesis is true, you can toss a coin for each student, and if it lands heads, swap the two heart rates recorded for that student. If the coin lands tails, do not swap the heart rates. Repeat this process 1,000 times, recording the mean difference in heart rates each time and thus obtaining a distribution of these mean differences that were simulated assuming the null hypothesis were true.

3. **Strength of evidence:** If your actual observed statistic falls in the tail of the null distribution, then you have strong evidence that there is a genuine difference in the average heart rates between the two exercises.

Note: The heart rates from both exercises were *paired* on the same individuals, and so you used a simulation method that lets you use this information.

Let's check out how things would have worked had we ignored the pairing and analyzed the data as if the jumping jacks heart rates and bicycle kicks heart rates had come from two totally different samples that were independent of each other.

17. Go to the **Multiple Means** applet and analyze the data as though we have two independent samples, as you did in Chapter 6. (The heart rate data are unstacked, meaning the heart rates for the two exercises are given in two columns. Make sure you have the unstacked box checked before you paste in your data.)

    - With regard to the graph of the distribution of "Shuffled Differences in Means":

      - Mean = _____
      - SD = _____
    - Find and report the approximate p-value. _____

18. Compare the SD of the null distribution obtained using the *two-independent-samples* method to that obtained using the *paired samples* method. Which SD is larger?

19. Compare the p-value obtained using the *two-independent-samples* method to that obtained using the *paired samples* method. Which p-value is smaller and hence provides stronger evidence against the null hypothesis of no difference?

Note: Using a paired samples method will often give a smaller p-value and hence stronger evidence against the null hypothesis than the two-independent-samples method. Perhaps this is what you found in Question 19. This would happen if students with high heart rates after doing jumping jacks tended to have high heart rates after doing bicycles, and students with low heart rates after doing jumping jacks tended to have low heart rates after doing bicycles.

This would make the variability of the differences in heart rates small. However this may not have happened for students in your class. If the variability within your jumping jack data or within your bicycle data is small but there is a lot of variability in the differences, you could get a smaller p-value using the two-independent-samples method.

SECTION 7.2 Summary

In this section, you learned about analyzing paired samples. In particular, you learned how to use a randomization approach to investigate whether the mean difference in response obtained from paired samples is statistically significant. The null hypothesis said that there was no difference in responses, on average. To simulate what could have happened if this null hypothesis were true, we tossed a coin for every observational unit in our sample and swapped their responses if the coin landed heads and did not swap the responses if the coin landed tails. After every repetition, we recorded the mean difference that was obtained by chance alone. This process of shuffling and redistributing was repeated many (about 1,000) times to get an idea of what could happen in the long run when the null hypothesis is true, and then we compared this long-run pattern to the observed mean difference in the actual study. When the observed mean difference is unlikely to have happened by random chance, we declare the observed mean difference to be statistically significant. How you decide on what is considered unlikely or unusual is done exactly the same way as you did in the previous chapters. The interpretation of the p-value and what you can conclude from it maintains the same essence it did in earlier chapters. All that has changed is that instead of dealing with one set of responses from one sample or one set of responses from each of two independent samples, you are now dealing with two sets of responses paired on the same set of observational units.

SECTION 7.3 THEORY-BASED APPROACH TO ANALYZING DATA FROM PAIRED SAMPLES

INTRODUCTION

In Section 7.2 you probably noticed that the shape of the simulated null distribution tends to be somewhat bell-shaped—something we've seen before! As we've discussed in earlier chapters, when certain validity conditions are met, simulation isn't needed, and we can use theory-based methods to conduct the analysis. We'll look at a theory-based approach, with its validity conditions, for paired data in this section.

How Many M&Ms Would You Like?

Example 7.3

EXAMPLE

Does your bowl size affect how much you eat? Food psychologist Brian Wansink (www.mindlesseating.org) ran an experiment with a group of undergraduates from the University of Illinois at Urbana-Champaign to investigate whether bowl size would affect how many M&Ms® candy pieces students took. In this example, we will analyze some of the data collected as part of that study. The study was conducted over several days. At one of the sessions, some participants were assigned to receive either a small bowl or a large bowl and allowed to take as many M&Ms as they planned on eating during the study session. At a following session, the bowl sizes were switched, with those who received small bowls at a previous session now receiving large bowls, and vice versa.

> **THINK ABOUT IT**
>
> What are the observational units in this study? What will you consider the response variable and explanatory variable in this study? Is each variable quantitative or categorical?

We will use the data from these undergraduates (the observational units) to test whether bowl size (the explanatory variable, categorical) affects how much we eat, as measured by number of M&Ms taken (the response variable, quantitative), in this case. Thus, we can state our hypotheses as:

Null hypothesis: There is no association between bowl size and how much we eat, as measured by number of M&Ms taken, in the population.

Alternative hypothesis: When large bowls are presented, people tend to select more M&Ms.

THINK ABOUT IT

Was this an observational study or an experiment? What implications might this have with regard to potential conclusions that can be drawn?

You should have noticed that this was a randomized experiment, and the order in which each participant received a small bowl or a large bowl was randomly assigned. This means that if we find a statistically significant difference we will be able to draw a cause-and-effect conclusion between the size of the bowl and the number of M&Ms taken.

Data on the number of M&Ms taken by the 17 participants who attended both sessions is shown in Table 7.4. Note that the data are ordered by participant ID; that is, the number of M&Ms taken from the small bowl is matched up with the number of M&Ms taken by that individual from the large bowl, regardless of which bowl the student was given first.

TABLE 7.4   Number of M&Ms taken based on whether they were given a small bowl or a large bowl

Subject	1	2	3	4	5	6	7	8	9	10	11	12	13	14	15	16	17
Small bowl	33	24	35	24	40	33	88	36	65	38	28	50	26	34	51	25	26
Large bowl	41	92	61	19	21	35	42	50	11	104	97	36	43	62	33	62	32

Because the data are paired and quantitative, we will be looking at the difference in the number of M&Ms taken when a small bowl is used compared to when a large bowl is used. Thus, we can define our parameter of interest to be

μ_d = Long-run mean difference in the number of M&Ms taken when using a small bowl minus a large bowl.

Using μ_d, we can restate our hypotheses as

$H_0: \mu_d = 0$ (that is, bowl size makes no difference, on average, with regard to number of M&Ms taken)

$H_a: \mu_d < 0$ (that is, bowl size does make a difference, with fewer M&Ms taken on average from a small bowl)

Table 7.5 and Figure 7.9 show the summary statistics and a dotplot of the distribution of the differences (small bowl – large bowl).

TABLE 7.5   Summary statistics, including the difference (small – large) in the number of M&Ms taken between the two bowl sizes

Bowl size	Sample size, n	Sample mean	Sample SD
Small	17	$\bar{x}_s = 38.59$	$s_s = 16.90$
Large	17	$\bar{x}_l = 49.47$	$s_l = 27.21$
Difference = small − large	17	$\bar{x}_d = -10.88$	$s_d = 36.30$

FIGURE 7.9 Dotplot of differences (small − large) in number of M&Ms taken between the two bowl sizes.

From Figure 7.9 and Table 7.5, you can see, based on the sample mean and on the bulk of negative differences, that, on average, when students used a small bowl, they took about 11 fewer M&Ms than when they used a large bowl. However, there is a fair bit of variability in these differences, with some students taking 40–60 more M&Ms with the small bowl and some taking almost 70 more with the large bowl.

As done in Section 7.2, the **Matched Pairs** applet can be used to run a simulation of what could have happened when the null hypothesis is true. Figure 7.10 gives a screenshot of the applet output.

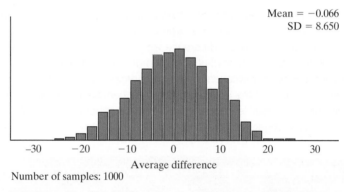

FIGURE 7.10 Distribution of mean difference in M&Ms taken, generated assuming bowl size makes no difference.

Figure 7.11 denotes (shaded to the left of the line) those rerandomizations that resulted in a mean difference less than −10.88, the mean difference observed in the study. Thus, the approximate p-value is = 122/1,000 = 0.122. If bowl size makes no difference to how many M&Ms are taken, on average, there is about a 12.2% chance of seeing a sample mean difference of −10.88 M&Ms or less.

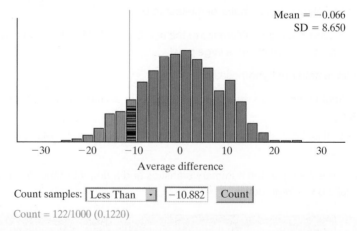

FIGURE 7.11 Distribution of mean differences in M&Ms taken, generated assuming bowl size makes no difference; area corresponding to p-value shaded red (to left of the line).

As expected, the null distribution in Figure 7.11 is centered at about zero (mean = −0.066). We also note that the null distribution is approximately normal and the standard deviation of the differences is 8.65 candies.

THINK ABOUT IT

How many standard deviations away from the hypothesized difference of 0 is the observed mean difference of −10.88 candies? How are you deciding?

The observed difference, −10.88 candies, is approximately 1.26 standard deviations below 0 [−1.26 = (−10.88 − 0)/8.65]. Thus, the observed mean difference is only 1.26 standard deviations below the mean, which does not put our observed statistic out in the tail of the null distribution—not a rare occurrence. The conclusion from this standardized statistic agrees with the not small p-value of 0.122.

THEORY-BASED APPROACH

 7.3.1

When the sample size is *large enough*, the overall shape of the null distribution of paired differences is approximately normal. With quantitative data, we said we could safely apply the theory-based methods if the response variable was symmetrically distributed or you had at least 20 observations in (each) sample and the sample distribution has no strong skewness. We will apply these same criteria to our sample of differences: We want at least 20 differences without severe skewness or outliers in the sample distribution or we want the population distribution of the differences to be symmetric.

VALIDITY CONDITIONS

Validity conditions for theory-based analysis of paired data: Theory-based methods of inference will work well for paired data if the population distribution of differences has a symmetric distribution or you have at least 20 pairs (i.e., at least 20 differences) and the distribution of the sample differences is not strongly skewed. This test is known as a ***paired t-test***.

Thus, if the sample size is large enough or if the differences themselves follow a normal distribution, then the null distribution of the sample mean difference has these properties:

- The shape of the null distribution is approximately normal.
- The null distribution is centered at the hypothesized value of the population mean difference.
- The variability of the null distribution depends on the sample size (larger samples will have less variability by chance) and on the variability in the sample differences (the more variability in the differences, the more variability in the null distribution).

As in earlier chapters, we can use this information about the distribution of the sample mean difference in responses (with regard to shape, center, and variability) to estimate p-values and find confidence intervals.

In this case, because there are fewer than 20 pairs (only 17), we look for symmetry. Figure 7.9 illustrates the symmetry of the sample differences and so we will consider the validity conditions to be met for these data.

It is for this reason that the null distribution we obtained when doing the simulation-based method (see Figure 7.11) looked fairly normal. Now, let's run the theory-based test and compare the p-value to the one we obtained from simulation.

 7.3.2

Once we have found the differences for each observational unit, the theory-based approach we use is simply the one-sample *t*-procedure (see Section 2.2 for more details) applied to the differences. Figure 7.12 shows the results of using the **Theory-Based Inference** applet to assess the strength of evidence we have against the null hypothesis of no difference.

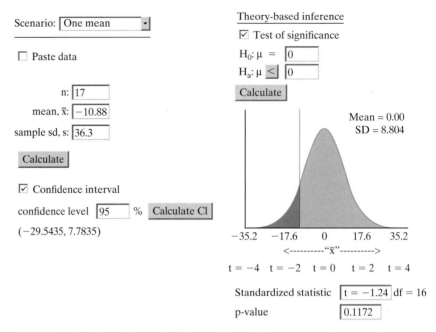

FIGURE 7.12 Output from the **Theory-Based Inference** applet, showing standardized statistic, p-value, and 95% confidence interval for the M&Ms study.

From Figure 7.12, you can see that "One mean" is being compared to a hypothesized value of 0 and that the hypotheses have been adjusted to match our hypotheses (comparing to zero, one-sided). The applet produces a standardized statistic of $t = -1.24$ and a p-value of 0.1172. Notice that this standardized statistic and p-value are very close to what we found with the simulation-based analysis.

> **THINK ABOUT IT**
>
> Based on the p-value, what is your conclusion? Do the data provide evidence that bowl size matters with regard to number of M&Ms taken? To what larger population(s) would you be comfortable generalizing these results? Can you draw a cause-and-effect conclusion?

Because our p-value is not small, we do not find strong evidence from these data that the bowl size influences the number of candies taken, on average. We must restrict our conclusions to university students like those in the study attending review sessions.

CONFIDENCE INTERVAL

The **Theory-Based Inference** applet output also produces a 95% confidence interval for μ_d (small – large).

> **THINK ABOUT IT**
>
> What parameter is this confidence interval estimating? Does the 95% confidence interval contain 0? What does that imply?

Recall that a confidence interval is an interval of plausible values for the parameter of interest. In this case, the parameter of interest is μ_d, the mean difference in the amount of M&Ms that would be taken from a small bowl versus that taken with a large bowl for the population of students like those in this study. The 95% confidence interval for μ_d is calculated by the applet to be (−29.54, 7.78). We are 95% confident that, on average in the long run, students take up to 29.54 fewer candies with a small bowl or up to 7.78 more candies with a small bowl. (Zero is contained in our confidence interval, confirming what we learned from the test in that we can't declare a clear winner here.)

CONCLUSIONS

A p-value of 0.1172 is not considered small enough to provide strong evidence against the null hypothesis. Thus, we do not have evidence to conclude that, on average, bowl size matters with regard to number of M&Ms taken. Even though the study was a randomized experiment, the lack of statistically significant results prevents us from concluding any cause-and-effect relationship between bowl size and number of M&Ms taken. Also, the data are from undergraduates at a large university. We do not have information on the participants' backgrounds. This limits the population to whom we can generalize these results. These results may or may not be extendable to other age groups.

> ### THINK ABOUT IT
>
> So, we were unable to find evidence to conclude a cause-and-effect relationship between bowl size and number of M&Ms taken. Why might have this happened? What are some possible explanations?

We can think of the following as possible explanations:

- Perhaps, in reality, bowl size does not affect how much we eat.
- Or maybe, in reality, bowl size does affect how much we eat, but the sample size was not big enough to detect the difference, especially considering how much variability there was in the differences of number of M&Ms taken (low power).
- Maybe bowl size does affect how much we eat of other food, but we looked at data for M&Ms, which is considered a snack. Perhaps people don't treat snacks the same way as they would a bowl of soup or pasta.

FORMULAS

The formula used to calculate the t-statistic, to test the above null hypothesis, is

$$t = \frac{\bar{x}_d - 0}{s_d / \sqrt{n}}$$

where $\bar{x}_d$ is the mean of the paired sample differences, zero is the hypothesized value of the mean difference for the population, s_d is the sample standard deviation of the observed differences, and n is the sample size. The numerator for the t-statistic is essentially comparing the observed mean difference to a hypothesized population mean difference of 0. The denominator $s_d / \sqrt{n}$ is a measure of the sample-to-sample variability of the sample mean difference and is called the **standard error (SE)** of the sample mean difference. The SE combines information on how much variability there was in the differences in response among observational units in each pair (the sample variability in the differences s_d) and how many observational units (pairs) are in the sample (n). When the sample size is large enough (e.g., at least 20) and the distribution of the sample differences is not strongly skewed, or the population distribution of differences follows a normal distribution, then this standardized statistic follows a t-distribution with $n - 1$ degrees of freedom. (More about the t-distribution was discussed in FAQ 2.2.2.)

| FAQ 2.2.2 | www.wiley.com/college/tintle |

Why do we use z for π but t for μ?

When the sample sizes are large enough, we can also find an approximate 95% confidence interval for μ_d, as follows:

$$\bar{x}_d \pm multiplier \times \frac{s_d}{\sqrt{n}}$$

where the multiplier is approximately 2 for 95% confidence intervals (the actual value of the multiplier comes from the *t*-distribution and depends on the confidence level and the number of observational units *n*).

As before, the formula for confidence interval is *statistic* ± *margin of error*. In the context of paired data with a quantitative response, the statistic is the observed sample mean difference. The margin of error, as before, accounts for (i) the confidence level and (ii) the sample-to-sample variability in the statistic.

EXPLORATION 7.3 | Comparing Auction Formats

An economist at Vanderbilt University devised a study to compare different types of online auctions. In one experiment he compared a *Dutch* auction to a *first-price sealed bid* auction. In the Dutch auction the item for sale starts at a very high price and is lowered gradually until someone finds the price low enough to buy. In the first-price sealed bid auction each bidder submits a single sealed bid before a particular deadline. After the deadline, the person with the highest bid wins. The researcher auctioned off collectible trading cards from the game *Magic: The Gathering*. He placed pairs of identical cards up for auction; one would go into the Dutch auction and the other to the first-price sealed bid auction. He then looked at the difference in the prices he received on the pair. He repeated this for a total of 88 pairs.

1. Before we look at the data that were collected and start the analysis, let's make sure you understand the study design.

   a. Explain why the price data should be analyzed using paired samples as opposed to two independent samples.

   b. What makes a pair?

   c. What is the explanatory variable? Is it categorical or quantitative?

   d. What is the response variable? Is it categorical or quantitative?

2. State the relevant hypotheses in words. (Use a two-sided alternative.)

   Null hypothesis:

   Alternative hypothesis:

3. Define the parameter of interest and give the symbol that should be assigned to it.

4. State the relevant hypotheses in symbols.

   H_0:

   H_a:

5. The data for the auction, **Auction**, can be found on the textbook website. The selling prices for the Dutch auction are labeled *Dutch* and the prices for first-price sealed bid auction are labeled *FP*. Paste these data into the **Matched Pairs** applet and answer the following questions.

   a. What is the sample mean price for the Dutch auction?

   b. What is the sample mean price for the first-price sealed bid auction?

   c. What are the mean and standard deviation for the difference in the two prices?

   d. Determine a p-value using the applet. Explain how you did so.

Notice that the simulated null distribution is bell-shaped. This is no coincidence. A theory-based method exists that predicts this to occur when certain validity conditions are met.

VALIDITY CONDITIONS

Validity conditions for theory-based analysis of paired data: Theory-based methods of inference will work well for paired data if the distribution of differences has a symmetric distribution, or you have at least 20 pairs (i.e., at least 20 differences) and the distribution of the sample differences is not strongly skewed. This test is known as a ***paired t-test***.

6. Are the validity conditions met for these data? Explain.

7. Because the sample is large enough without strong skewness in the distribution of differences, we can use a theory-based approach. We will do this by using the **Theory-Based Inference** applet. To do this:

   - Open the **Theory-Based Inference** applet.
   - Choose **One mean** from the pull-down menu.
   - Enter the sample size, sample mean, and sample standard deviation for the differences as you found in #5.
   - Check the box for **Test of Significance**.
   - Enter the appropriate information for the hypotheses.
     - Make sure the appropriate sign for the alternative hypotheses is chosen.
   - Press **Calculate**.

   a. What is the value of the standardized statistic? What does that number tell you?
   b. In the light of the value of the standardized statistic, do you expect the p-value to be small or not small? How are you deciding?
   c. What is the value of the p-value? Is it similar to the p-value found using the simulation-based method?

8. Recall that the **Theory-Based Inference** applet can also produce confidence intervals for the parameter of interest.

   - Go to the applet, check the **Confidence interval** box and let the **confidence level** be 95%.
   - Press **Calculate CI**.

   a. Report the 95% confidence interval.
   b. Interpret the 95% confidence interval in context.
   c. Does the 95% confidence interval agree with your conclusion when using the p-value? How are you deciding?

9. Based on the above analysis, state your conclusion in the context of the study. Be sure to comment on:

   - *Statistical significance:* Do the data provide evidence that selling cards in a Dutch auction differ than when sold in a first-price sealed bid auction on average? How are you deciding?
   - *Estimation:* Find and interpret a 95% confidence interval.
   - *Causation:* Can you conclude causation? If yes, what causes what? If not, how are you deciding?
   - *Generalization:* Can you extend the results of this study? Other kinds of cards? Other types of items? Anything sold in an auction format on the Internet? How are you deciding?

SECTION 7.3 Summary

Under certain circumstances, essentially when sample sizes are large enough and/or skewness in the sample (of differences) is minimal, a theory-based approach can be used to approximate p-values and confidence intervals for the population mean difference with a matched pairs design.

- Once again, the standardized statistic subtracts the hypothesized value from the observed statistic and then divides by the standard deviation of the statistic.
  - The statistic in this case is the sample mean difference, that is, $\bar{x}_d$.
  - The standardized statistic is $t = \dfrac{\bar{x}_d}{s_d/\sqrt{n}}$ where s_d is the standard deviation of the differences and n is the number of pairs.

- The confidence interval takes the form statistic ± margin of error.
  - Statistic $= \bar{x}_d$.
  - Margin of error = multiplier × standard error of statistic.
  - Standard error of the statistic (SE) $= \dfrac{s_d}{\sqrt{n}}$.

- **Validity conditions for the theory-based approach** for matched pairs data (**paired *t*-test**) are that the sample size (of pairs) is large (say at least 20) and the distribution of the sample differences is not strongly skewed, or the differences in the population follow a normal distribution. You can judge this latter possibility by viewing the distribution of the sample differences to check whether it is symmetric.

- The order of subtraction does not matter provided that the labeling is consistent throughout the analysis, including interpretations and conclusions.

Type of data	Name of test	Applet	Validity conditions
Paired observations of a quantitative variable	Simulation test for paired data	Matched pairs	—
	Theory-based test or interval for paired data (paired *t*-test; paired *t*-interval)	Matched pairs; Theory-based inference	At least 20 pairs without strong skewness or symmetry in distribution of differences

---

SECTION 7.4

CONFIDENCE INTERVAL AND SIGNIFICANCE TEST FOR A DIFFERENCE BETWEEN TWO MEANS (PAIRED DATA)

INTRODUCTION

Definition

For a **one-sample *t*-test (paired data)**, the standardized statistic has the form

$$t = \frac{\bar{x}_d - 0}{s_d/\sqrt{n}}$$

where $\bar{x}_d$ denotes the sample mean difference (the mean of the sample of differences), s_d denotes the standard deviation of the sample differences, and n is the sample size (the number of differences).

In Section 2.2 you learned that when the variable of interest is a single quantitative variable (e.g., the estimated length of a short song snippet), then, if validity conditions are met, the appropriate theory-based approach to test hypotheses about the population mean of the variable of interest is called a one-sample *t*-test. You extended your work with a single quantitative variable in Section 3.3 to investigate a theory-based approach for constructing an interval of plausible values for a population mean, referred to as a one-sample *t*-interval. And in the previous section (7.3) you saw that you could use a one-sample *t*-test and a one-sample *t*-interval to approximate p-values and confidence intervals for the population mean difference from a **matched-pairs design**. Now you will see how to summarize the results of an analysis of paired quantitative data in AP Statistics exam style.

In Section 1.7 you learned the work you must show on the AP Statistics exam when a hypothesis test is called for. The format you learned is the same for all hypothesis tests.

1. State the hypotheses either in words or using appropriate symbols.

2. Name the test that will be used and state and verify the validity conditions for the test chosen.

3. Calculate the test statistic (standardized statistic) and corresponding p-value.

4. State your conclusion (with appropriate justification based on your p-value and stated significance level) in the context of the research question.

In Section 3.2, Part 2, you learned the work you must show on the AP Statistics exam when a confidence interval is called for. The format you learned is the same for all confidence intervals.

1. Identify the parameter you want to estimate and the theory-based model you will use.
2. Verify the validity conditions for the theory-based method you have chosen.
3. Construct the confidence interval, showing the values that you plug into the formula.
4. Interpret the confidence interval you obtained in the context of the problem.

Now, let's see how to apply these formats for hypothesis tests and confidence intervals for theory-based tests of a population mean difference from a matched pairs design.

> **Definition**
>
> A **one-sample t-interval (paired data)** has the form
>
> $$\bar{x}_d \pm t^*_{df=n-1}(s_d/\sqrt{n})$$
>
> where $\bar{x}_d$ denotes the sample mean difference (the mean of the sample of differences), s_d denotes the standard deviation of the sample differences, n is the sample size (the number of differences), and df is the degrees of freedom.

Pulse Rates

Example 7.4

Does it make a difference whether your pulse rate is taken in a sitting or a standing position? A high school statistics teacher conducted an experiment with her class to determine whether students' pulse rates when sitting tended to be different than when standing. First, she placed 16 slips of paper in a bag. Eight of the slips of paper had the word *sit* on them and the other eight had the word *stand*. She then had each student randomly select a slip of paper from the bag without replacing it. Students who drew a slip of paper that had *sit* on it took their seated pulse rate, while students whose slip of paper had *stand* on it took their pulse rate while standing. The students then reversed roles so that each of the 16 students took their pulse rate in both sitting and standing positions. The data for the pulse rates in beats per minute are given in Table 7.6.

TABLE 7.6   Pulse rates in beats per minute (bpm) of 16 students taken while sitting and standing

Student	1	2	3	4	5	6	7	8
sitting pulse (bpm)	60	76	56	79	96	52	60	80
standing pulse (bpm)	68	80	60	80	94	60	60	92
sit-stand pulse (bpm)	−8	−4	−4	−1	2	−8	0	−12

Student	9	10	11	12	13	14	15	16
sitting pulse (bpm)	68	66	76	64	56	44	64	76
standing pulse (bpm)	72	68	72	68	68	56	68	76
sit-stand pulse (bpm)	−4	−2	4	−4	−12	−12	−4	0

THINK ABOUT IT

Do the data provide convincing evidence at a significance level of $\alpha = 0.05$ to support the teacher's suspicion that high school students' pulse rates when sitting tend to be different than when standing, on average? How will you decide?

Let's look at how one could answer this question according to the AP Statistics style.

STEP 1: State the hypotheses in either words or using appropriate symbols. Let $\mu_{\text{sit-stand}}$ represent the mean difference in high school students' pulse rates (sitting − standing). We want to decide whether we are convinced that sitting pulse rates tend to be different than standing pulse rates, on average. Thus, the hypotheses can be stated in symbols as

H_0: $\mu_{\text{sit-stand}} = 0$

H_a: $\mu_{\text{sit-stand}} \neq 0$ or in words as

Null: In the population of students similar to those in this study, there is no difference in pulse rates (sitting − standing), on average

Alternative: In the population of students similar to those in this study, there is a difference in pulse rates (sitting − standing), on average

STEP 2: Name the test that will be used and state and verify the validity conditions for the test chosen. We will use a one-sample t-test for paired data because we are conducting a test on a single mean (mean of the differences in pulse rates sitting minus standing). The pulse rates for the two positions are paired for each student and the population standard deviation of the differences in pulse rates is not known.

Now let's check the validity conditions (from Section 2.2) for a one-sample t-test.

7.4.1

- The order in which the students took their pulse rates (sitting first or standing first) was randomly assigned, so if the results are significant, a cause-and-effect relationship between the student's position and his or her difference in pulse rates can be concluded. The students were not randomly selected from a larger population, so we can only generalize our results to other students who may be similar to these students.

- We do not know the shape of the population of differences in pulse rates (sitting − standing) for students similar to those in this study, and because our sample of 16 students is not large enough to appeal to the central limit theorem, we need to graph the sample data.

  Note: Because we are interested in the differences in pulse rates (sitting − standing), we need to check that the distribution of differences is fairly symmetric. It would not be appropriate to examine separate graphs of the sitting and standing pulse rates.

A dotplot of our sample data of the differences in pulse rates (sitting − standing) for students in this class appears to be fairly symmetric with no extreme skewness or outliers present, so it is reasonable to assume that the population distribution of differences for students at this high school is approximately symmetric. The distribution of sample mean differences for samples of this size should therefore be approximately bell-shaped, so it should be reasonable to conduct a one-sample t-test on the differences.

STEP 3: Calculate the test statistic (standardized statistic) and corresponding p-value. By substituting into the appropriate formulas, we find the following:

$\bar{x}_{\text{sit-stand}} = -4.31$

$s_{\text{sit-stand}} = 4.95$

$n = 16$

$df = 16 - 1 = 15$

$t = \dfrac{-4.31 - 0}{4.95/\sqrt{16}} = -3.49$

p-value ≈ 0.003

From AP Table B with df = 15, we find the two-sided p-value is between 0.002 and 0.005.

STEP 4: State your conclusion (with appropriate justification based on your p-value and stated significance level) in the context of the research question. The p-value we obtained (0.003) is smaller than the significance level of 0.05. Therefore, we have sufficient evidence to claim that sitting pulse rates tend to be different than standing pulse rates, on average, in this population. Because a controlled, randomized experiment was conducted, we can attribute a cause-and-effect relationship between the position in which a student's pulse is taken (sitting or standing) and his or her pulse rate. Because the students were not selected randomly from some population, we should only generalize these results to students who may be similar to those in our study.

 7.4.2

THINK ABOUT IT

How would you use the data from this study to construct a 95% confidence interval for the mean difference in pulse rates (sitting – standing) for the population of students similar to those in our study?

Let's look at a solution in the AP Statistics style.

STEP 1: Identify the parameter you want to estimate and the theory-based model you will use. Let $\mu_{\text{sit-stand}}$ represent the mean difference in pulse rates (sitting – standing) for the population of students similar to those in our study.

We will use a one-sample t-interval for paired differences to construct a 95% confidence interval for $\mu_{\text{sit-stand}}$.

STEP 2: Verify the validity conditions for the theory-based method you have chosen. The validity conditions for a one-sample t-interval are the same as for a one-sample t-test that we checked above.

STEP 3: Construct the confidence interval, showing the values that you substitute into the formula.

95% C.I. for $\mu_{\text{sit-stand}}$

$\bar{x}_{\text{sit-stand}} = -4.31$

$s_{\text{sit-stand}} = 4.95$

$n = 16$

$df = 16 - 1 = 15$

$t^*_{15} = 2.131$

$-4.31 \pm 2.131 \, (4.95/\sqrt{16})$

$(-6.95, -1.68)$

STEP 4: Interpret the confidence interval you obtained in the context of the problem. We can be 95% confident that the difference in mean pulse rates (sitting – standing) for the population of students similar to those in our study is between −6.95 bpm and −1.68 bpm (assuming the sample is indeed representative of this entire population). Because an experiment was performed, we can conclude that it is plausible that sitting pulse rates, on average, cause a 1.68 bpm to 6.95 bpm drop in pulse rate compared to standing.

> ### THINK ABOUT IT
>
> Can you make connections between your 95% confidence interval and the test of significance you completed on the same data? Does the confidence interval you obtained above agree with the decision you made in your hypothesis test.? How are you deciding?

7.4.3

Based on our p-value of 0.003 at an alpha-level of 0.05, we had sufficient evidence to claim that sitting pulse rates tend to be different than standing pulse rates, on average. Because our entire 95% confidence interval is below zero, this agrees with our claim that zero is not a plausible value for the mean difference (sitting − standing), and that students' pulse rates when sitting tend to be different than when standing. In particular, pulse rates are lower when sitting than when standing by an average of 1.68 bpm to 6.95 bpm.

EXPLORATION 7.4 | Popping Balloons—Does Color Matter?

Red is often thought of as a color of caution and may influence people to take fewer risks. In a 2015 study, German researchers Gnambs, Appel, and Oeberst (*PloS ONE* 10(7)) set up an experiment in which people would earn points for playing a computer game that involved pumping up virtual balloons by clicking on a computer mouse. The balloons had an increasing (though not always the same) probability of popping the more they were pumped up. The players would earn more points for more "air" in the balloons, but if the balloon popped, they received no points. Each of the 142 players had 30 balloons to pump up, of which 15 were red and 15 were blue. The two colors of balloons were presented to the players in random order. Afterward, each player received a score for the blue balloons and a score for the red balloons. The researchers wanted to determine whether players would be more cautious with the red balloons, thus filling them with less air and popping fewer of them. The summary statistics for this experiment are given in Table 7.7, where a player's red score is the number of points assigned by the computer based on the amount of air pumped into the red balloons that did not pop; similarly, the blue score is for the blue balloons.

TABLE 7.7 Color risk data showing the mean and standard deviation of points scored

Balloon color	Mean	SD	n
Blue score	6.127	2.370	142
Red score	5.775	2.445	142
Blue score − Red score	0.352	2.226	142

1. Using a significance level of $\alpha = 0.05$, do the data provide convincing evidence that players would be more cautious with the red balloons and thus, on average, have the computer put less air into the red balloons than blue balloons?

Answer this question by completing (a)–(d) in the AP Statistics exam format.

   a. State the hypotheses using either words or symbols.

   b. Name the theory-based test you will use and verify validity conditions for that test.

   c. Calculate the test statistic (standardized statistic) and corresponding p-value.

   d. State your conclusion (with appropriate justification based on your p-value and stated significance level) in the context of the research question.

2. If there is statistically significant evidence of a nonzero difference in mean scores, can a cause-and-effect relationship be attributed to the color of the balloon and the score that would be attained in this computer game? Justify your response.

3. Use the data from this study to compute a 95% confidence interval for the mean difference in scores for the two colors that would be attained by players who play this computer game.

Answer this question by completing (a)–(d) in the AP Statistics exam format.

    a. Identify the parameter you are trying to estimate and the theory-based method you will use.

    b. Verify validity conditions for the theory-based method.

    c. Compute the confidence interval, showing values you will substitute into the formulas.

    d. Interpret the confidence interval in the context of the problem.

4. Explain how the confidence interval you obtained in #3c agrees with the decision you made in your hypothesis test.

SECTION 7.4　Summary

In this section you saw how one-sample t-procedures that you learned in Chapter 2 could be used for analyzing paired differences. You saw that the theory-based test for a population mean difference from a **matched-pairs design** is a one-sample t-test (often called a ***matched pairs t-test***). In addition to the test of significance, you examined a theory-based one-sample t-interval for estimating the population mean difference for paired data. You saw that the work you need to show on the AP exam for both a test of significance and a confidence interval for a population mean difference from a matched-pairs design follows the same general format as that for a single mean.

CHAPTER 7　Summary

In this chapter we saw how a paired design differs from an independent groups design. A key component of a paired design is to create pairs (or repeated observations on the same observational unit) that should be similar to each other in all respects except for the explanatory variable. This more direct comparison accounts for some of the variability in the data. Ideally the variability of the differences will be smaller than the variability in the response variable, making it more likely (greater power) that we will correctly detect population differences that exist and giving us a smaller margin of error.

- When designing a matched pairs experiment, randomization is used to determine the order of the treatments.

- After pairing, it is important to adjust the analysis to recognize the paired nature of the data. We do this by computing the differences in the response for each pair. The order of subtraction does not matter provided that the labeling is consistent throughout the analysis, including interpretations and conclusions.

    You then learned how to use a randomization approach to investigate whether the observed mean difference obtained from paired samples is statistically significantly different from zero. This simulation replicated the swapping of the observations within each pair under the null hypothesis that the response would not change depending on the explanatory variable. This allowed us to create a null distribution of mean differences from which we can assess the chance variability in the statistic and approximate a p-value.

    The interpretations of the p-value, standardized statistic, confidence interval, and what you can conclude from them maintain the same essence as in earlier chapters. All that has changed is that instead of dealing with one set of responses from one sample, or one set of responses from each of two independent samples, you are now dealing with two sets of responses paired on the same set of observational units.

    You also saw how one-sample t-procedures that you learned in Chapter 2 (in this context, known as *paired t-tests* or *matched pairs t-tests* and *paired t-intervals* or *matched pairs t-intervals*) on the differences can be used as a theory-based approach when the validity conditions are met.

- The statistic in this case is the sample mean difference, that is, $\bar{x}_d$.
- The standardized statistic is $t_{df=n-1} = \dfrac{\bar{x}_d - 0}{s_d/\sqrt{n}}$
- The confidence interval is $\bar{X}_d \pm t^*_{df=n-1}(s_d/\sqrt{n})$

Validity conditions for the theory-based approach (paired *t*-test and interval) are that the sample size (of pairs) is large (we will consider this to be at least 20) without strong skewness or that the differences in the population follow a normal distribution. (Check this last case by examining the distribution of differences in the sample.)

CHAPTER 7
GLOSSARY

μ_d Population or long-run average of the differences.

independent groups design Each individual in a group is unrelated to all the other individuals in the study. Each individual provides one response value.

independent samples The data recorded on one sample are unrelated to those recorded on the other sample. In other words, if the data within the samples can be rearranged without losing information then the samples are independent.

paired design Study design that allows for the comparison of two groups on a response variable but by comparing two measurements within each pair instead of on completely separate groups of individuals. This typically serves to reduce variability in the response variable (now the differences).

paired design using matching Pairs are created by matching up two very similar observational units and randomly assigning each to a different condition.

paired design using repeated measures Pairs are created by measuring each observational unit twice under different conditions where the order of the conditions is randomly assigned.

paired t-test (or matched pairs t-test) A theory-based test for paired data.

standard error of $\bar{X}_d$ (SE) The standard deviation of the sample average differences.

validity conditions for theory-based test of paired data A sample size of at least 20 pairs without strong skewness in the distribution of differences, or a symmetric distribution of differences. This test is known as a *paired t-test*.

$\bar{X}_d$ Observed sample average of the differences.

CHAPTER 7
EXERCISES

SECTION 7.1

7.1.1* Which of the following statements are true and which are false?

a. In a paired design, each pair of observations *always* consists of measuring the same individual twice.

b. In a paired design, each pair of observations *often* consists of measuring the same individual twice.

c. In an independent groups design, each individual in a group is unrelated to all the other individuals in the study.

d. When a paired design is possible, you typically get more informative results because units within a pair tend to be similar to each other.

7.1.2 Which of the following statements are true and which are false?

a. After you collect the data, you can then decide whether or not to use a paired design or independent samples design.

b. The simulations for paired design and independent groups design are the same. Just how the data are collected is different.

c. Paired designs can only be done in experiments and not observational studies.

d. In a paired design with repeated measures, you can use random assignment because each individual is measured twice.

7.1.3* For the following scenarios, determine whether or not they represent paired designs.

a. Reaction times for students taken at 8:00 A.M. compared to reaction times for the same students taken at 10:00 P.M.

b. Change in weight for those on the Atkins diet compared to the change in weight for those on the Paleo diet.

c. Times for skiers to complete a downhill skiing race course on skis treated with Wax A with times for the same skiers to complete the course on skis treated with Wax B.

7.1.4 For the following scenarios, determine whether or not they represent paired samples.

a. Test scores for students in a biology class taught by Professor Quick are being compared to test scores in a different section of the biology class taught by Professor Quack.

b. Pulse rates for students at the beginning of class are being compared to pulse rates for the same students at the end of class.

c. The weights of 10-year-olds in 2009 are being compared to the weights of 10-year-olds in 1994.

7.1.5* For each of the following, indicate whether or not a *paired* analysis would be appropriate.

a. To investigate the claim that first-year college students tend to gain weight during their first term, you take a random sample of 20 first-year students and weigh them at the beginning and end of their first term.

b. You wonder whether students on your campus tend to drive newer cars than faculty. You take a random sample of 20 students and a random sample of 10 faculty members and ask each person how old their car is.

7.1.6 For each of the following, indicate whether or not a *paired* analysis would be appropriate.

a. A school cafeteria offers a vegetarian and a nonvegetarian option for lunch every day. For a period of two weeks, you record how many calories are in the vegetarian option and how many calories are in the nonvegetarian option. Your goal is to see if vegetarian options tend to differ with regard to average number calories from nonvegetarian options.

b. A farmer investigates whether talking to cows by name leads to producing more milk. He randomly selects 30 of his cows and randomly assigns 15 to talk to by name and the other 15 not to.

7.1.7* What is the difference between paired design using repeated measures and paired design using matching?

Testing students

7.1.8 Which of the following is an example of a paired design?

A. A teacher compares the pretest and posttest scores of a group of students.

B. A teacher compares the scores of students using a computer-based method of instruction with the scores of other students using a traditional method of instruction.

C. A teacher compares the scores of students in her class on a standardized test with the national average score.

D. A teacher calculates the average scores for students on a pair of tests and tests to see if this average is significantly larger than 80%.

Teaching with technology*

7.1.9 Which of the following is an example of a paired design?

A. A teacher taught one class a lesson using technology and another class without technology. Their scores on a quiz were then compared.

B. A teacher taught a lesson using technology and then compared the class scores on a quiz to the national average score.

C. A teacher teaches a lesson using technology and then gives her students a pair of quizzes and compares these results to those from her class the previous year.

D. Pairs of students were matched by similar IQs. One of the pair was taught a lesson using technology and one without technology. Their scores on a quiz were then compared.

Football kicking

7.1.10 Suppose that you want to determine whether there is a difference between the distances traveled by an air-filled football and by a helium-filled football, and that you have managed to recruit 12 punters of varying abilities to participate in the study.

a. Describe, in detail, the design of an experiment that does not utilize pairing.

b. Next, describe, in detail, the design of an experiment that does utilize pairing.

c. Which study design (a) or (b) do you think is a better study design for the purpose of this study or does it not matter? Explain your reasoning.

Golf drives*

7.1.11 Suppose that you want to determine whether there is a difference between the distances traveled by two different brands of golf balls. You use the 30 people on your golf league to participate in the study.

a. Describe, in detail, the design of an experiment that does not utilize pairing.

b. Next, describe, in detail, the design of an experiment that does utilize pairing.

c. Which study design (a) or (b) do you think is a better study design for the purpose of this study or does it not matter? Explain your reasoning.

Caffeine and the long jump

7.1.12 Suppose an instructor wants to study the association between caffeine intake and performance in the long jump. The instructor asks her students to suggest ways to collect data to investigate this question. For each of the suggestions, identify:

- Whether the study is an experiment or an observational study
- Whether or not the data will be paired

a. Lara suggests the instructor record everyone's performance on a long jump and then ask each of them to report their caffeine intake from earlier in the day.

b. Mimi suggests the students be paired by height and then one student in each pair is randomly assigned to caffeine while the other isn't.

c. Nia suggests all students be given both a caffeine pill and a placebo but the order be randomized. Students' performances on both these occasions should then be recorded.

Sleep and memorization*

7.1.13 Suppose an instructor wants to see if there is an association between the amount of sleep students get and their ability to memorize words. The instructor asks her students to suggest ways to collect data to investigate this question. For each of the suggestions, identify:

- Whether the study is an experiment or an observational study
- Whether or not the data will be paired

a. Julia suggests the instructor have each student do two trials: one where they are told to get at least 7 hours of sleep the night before they take the memorization test and one where they are told to limit their sleep to at most 4 hours before they take the memorization test. The trials are a week apart and the students are randomly assigned which they do first.

b. Lindsey suggests half the students (chosen at random) should be told to get at least 7 hours of sleep before the memorization test and the other half should be told to get at most 4 hours of sleep before the test. They all then take the memorization test on the following day.

c. Mikaela suggests all students are given the memorization test and then are asked how many hours of sleep they got the night before.

Reaction times

7.1.14 To test reaction times, a computer program will display a red circle. When it changes to yellow, the users click the mouse as fast as they can. The program will then display the reaction time. Students want to compare reaction times between people using their dominant hand and nondominant hand on the mouse.

a. Suppose you had 20 subjects participating in this study. Describe how you would conduct this study with a paired design with repeated measures.

b. If you found a significant difference in reaction times, could you conclude that the hand being used caused the difference?

7.1.15 Reconsider the reaction time study in the previous question.

a. Describe how you would conduct this study with an independent samples design?

b. Which design, paired with repeated measures or independent samples, would you say is more appropriate for this study? Explain why.

7.1.16 Reconsider the reaction time study in the previous questions

a. Describe how you would conduct this study with a paired design using matching?

b. Which design, paired with repeated measures or paired with matching, would you say is more appropriate for this study? Explain why.

Exercise and memorization*

7.1.17 Students wanted to see if exercising (in particular doing jumping jacks) would help people memorize a list of 10 words that were read to them. They wanted to compare this with the same test of memorizing words while the subjects were sitting down.

a. Suppose you had 20 subjects participating in this study. Describe how you would conduct this study with a paired design with repeated measures.

b. If you found a significant difference in the number of words memorized, could you conclude exercising caused the difference?

7.1.18 Reconsider the memorization and exercise study in the previous question.

a. Describe how you would conduct this study with an independent samples design?

b. Which design, paired with repeated measures or independent samples, would you say is more appropriate for this study? Explain why.

7.1.19 Reconsider the memorization and exercise study in the previous questions.

a. Describe how you would conduct this study with a paired design using matching?

b. Which design, paired with repeated measures or paired with matching, would you say is more appropriate for this study? Explain why.

Chewing gum and memorizing

7.1.20 Students wanted to see if chewing gum would help people memorize words from a given list of 25 words compared to trying to memorize words when not chewing gum.

a. Suppose you had 20 subjects participating in this study. Describe how you would conduct this study with a paired design with repeated measures.

b. If you found a significant difference in the number of words memorized, could you conclude gum chewing caused the difference?

7.1.21 Reconsider the chewing gum and memorization study in the previous question.

a. Describe how you would conduct this study with an independent samples design?

b. Which design, paired with repeated measures or independent samples, would you say is more appropriate for this study? Explain why.

7.1.22 Reconsider the chewing gun and memorization study in the previous questions.

a. Describe how you would conduct this study with a paired design using matching?

b. Which design, paired with repeated measures or paired with matching, would you say is more appropriate for this study? Explain why.

Caffeine and running*

7.1.23 Researches wanted to see if using a caffeine supplement would make runners faster in a 5-kilometer run.

a. Suppose you had 30 subjects participating in this study. Describe how you would conduct this study with a paired design with repeated measures.

b. If you found a significant difference in running times, could you conclude caffeine caused the difference?

7.1.24 Reconsider the caffeine and running time study in the previous question.

a. Describe how you would conduct this study with an independent samples design?

b. Which design, paired with repeated measures or independent samples, would you say is more appropriate for this study? Explain why.

7.1.25 Reconsider the caffeine and running time study in the previous questions.

a. Describe how you would conduct this study with a paired design using matching?

b. Which design, paired with repeated measures or paired with matching, would you say is more appropriate for this study? Explain why.

FAQ

7.1.26 Read FAQs 7.1.1 and 7.1.2 and then answer the following questions:

a. Suppose I want to compare two blood pressure medicines with a paired design. Describe how to carry out the study using repeat observations on each subject.

b. Suppose instead I decide to pair individuals. Do you recommend that I pair subjects by current weight or current height?

c. Which design, the one in (a) or the one in (b), would you recommend? Justify your answer.

SECTION 7.2

7.2.1* Suppose you are testing the hypotheses $H_0: \mu_d = 0$ and $H_a: \mu_d \neq 0$ in a paired-design and obtain a p-value of 0.21. Which one of the following could be a possible 95% confidence interval for μ_d?

A. -2.30 to -0.70

B. -1.20 to 0.90

C. 1.50 to 3.80

D. 4.50 to 6.90

7.2.2 Suppose you are testing the hypotheses $H_0: \mu_d = 0$ and $H_a: \mu_d \neq 0$ in a paired-design test and obtain a p-value of 0.02. Also suppose you computed confidence intervals for μ_d. Based on the p-value which of the following is true?

A. Both a 95% confidence interval and a 99% confidence interval will contain 0.

B. A 95% confidence interval will contain 0, but a 99% confidence interval will not.

C. A 95% confidence interval will not contain 0, but a 99% confidence interval will.

D. Neither a 95% confidence interval nor a 99% confidence interval will contain 0.

7.2.3* What does one outcome in a null distribution made by the **Matched Pairs** applet represent?

A. It is a simulated mean difference under the assumption there is no association between the explanatory and response variables in the study.

B. It is a simulated mean difference under the assumption there is an association between the explanatory and response variables in the study.

C. It is a simulated difference in proportions under the assumption there is no association between the explanatory and response variables in the study.

D. It is a simulated difference in proportions under the assumption there is an association between the explanatory and response variables in the study.

7.2.4 In the matched pairs tests done in this section:

A. The explanatory and response variables are categorical.

B. The explanatory and response variables are quantitative.

C. The explanatory variable is categorical and the response variable is quantitative.

D. The explanatory variable is quantitative and the response variable is categorical.

7.2.5* Match the appropriate *test of significance* to each of the following research questions.

1. Testing a single proportion
2. Testing a single mean
3. Comparing two proportions
4. Comparing two means (independent)
5. Testing a mean difference (paired data)

   a. Do a minority of males think cigars smell good?

   b. Are males more likely to donate blood compared to females?

   c. Is the average body temperature of females higher than that for males?

   d. Is there an improvement from the pretest scores students take before a lesson to their posttest scores after the lesson?

7.2.6 Match the appropriate *test of significance* to each of the following research questions.

1. Testing a single proportion
2. Testing a single mean
3. Comparing two proportions
4. Comparing two means (independent)
5. Testing a mean difference (paired data)

   a. Is the average body temperature higher than 98.6°F?

   b. Will rats go through a maze faster after given caffeine compared to the same rats without caffeine?

   c. Is there an association between a person's sex and GPA?

   d. Is there an association between a person's sex and whether or not a person gets the flu?

7.2.7* A researcher measures body flexibility in college students. She suspects that females will be more flexible than males.

a. State the null and alternative hypotheses.

b. Identify the explanatory and response variables.

c. Identify whether the study uses an independent groups design or a paired study design.

7.2.8 A researcher takes a sample of sibling-pairs from two-child families. All individuals are given a test of their impatience, hypothesizing that older siblings tend to have higher levels of impatience.

a. State the null and alternative hypotheses.

b. Identify the explanatory and response variables.

c. Identify whether the study uses an independent groups design or a paired study design.

7.2.9* The **Matched Pairs** applet displays parallel dotplots of the response variable for two different conditions of a study. It also displays a dotplot for the differences. Which is the more useful dotplot to look at to help you determine whether the test of significance will give you significant results? Explain.

7.2.10 What is the coin flip accomplishing in the **Matched Pairs** applet and why is it doing it?

Weight gain in college*

7.2.11 Suppose the table below represents statistics about the weights of female college students during their first two years of college. You are interested in trying to show that female college students gain weight between their first and second years in college. Explain what in this summary tells you that they should get a smaller p-value when you run your test by doing a matched paired test than if you did an independent samples test.

	Freshmen	Sophomore	Difference
Mean	130 lb	135 lb	5 lb
Standard deviation	25 lb	27 lb	2 lb

Marriage ages

7.2.12 To investigate whether or not people tend to marry spouses of similar ages or whether husbands tend to be older than their wives, a student gathered age data from a sample of 24 couples, taken from marriage licenses filed in Cumberland County, PA, in June and July 1993. The data file **MarriageAges** contains the data.

a. Here's a *scatterplot* of the ages of the husbands and their wives (one dot for each husband-wife pair). What does the scatterplot reveal?

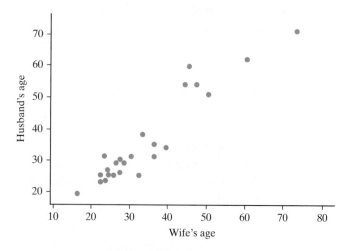

b. Explain why it is reasonable to say that the marriage age of the husband and the marriage age of the wife should *not* be treated as *independent* observations.

Because the data are *paired*, instead of comparing ages of husbands and wives, we should instead look at the *difference* in age between husbands and wives.

c. Define the appropriate parameter of interest in the context of the study.

d. State the appropriate null and alternative hypotheses in the context of the study.

e. Use the **Matched Pairs** applet to produce appropriate graphical displays (dotplot) and summary statistics (sample size, mean, and SD) for the data. Comment on whether this descriptive analysis of the data suggests whether or not husbands tend to be older than their wives.

f. Use the **Matched Pairs** applet to find an approximate p-value.

g. Interpret the p-value in the context of the study. That is, what is the p-value a probability of?

h. Give a conclusion about the strength of evidence based on the p-value.

7.2.13 In the previous exercise the statistic used was the mean of the difference in ages (husband's age − wife's age). Explain how the following things would change (or not) if you used the mean of the wife's ages − husband's ages as your statistic when you conducted this test?

a. Observed statistic

b. Alternative hypothesis

c. p-value

d. Conclusion

Memorizing and listening to music*

7.2.14 Does listening to music affect how many words you can memorize? Student researchers tried to answer this question by having 20 subjects listen to music while trying to memorize words and also had the same 20 subjects try to memorize words when not listening to music. They randomly determined which condition was done first for each of their subjects. Here are their hypotheses:

Null: The average of the difference in number of words memorized (no music − with music) is 0 ($\mu_d = 0$).

Alternative: The average of the difference in number of words memorized (no music − with music) is greater than 0 ($\mu_d > 0$).

The students found the following results in terms of number of words memorized:

	No music	With music	Difference
Mean	12.80	10.50	2.30
Standard deviation	3.38	3.15	3.76

a. What is the explanatory variable in this study? Is it categorical or quantitative?

b. What is the response variable in this study? Is it categorical or quantitative?

c. What is the observed statistic in this study?

d. Assuming a true null hypothesis, we simulated this study and found 1,500 mean differences that are shown in the null distribution below. Based on where the observed statistic lies in this distribution, does the p-value appear to be fairly small?

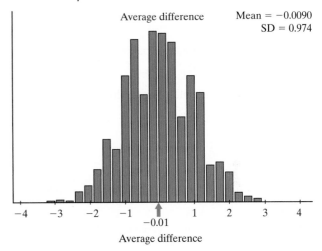

e. The standard deviation of the null distribution is 0.974. Use this to find the standardized statistic for this test.

f. Based on your standardized statistic from part (e), is there strong evidence that people can memorize words better when music is not playing compared to when it is? Explain.

7.2.15 Reconsider the previous exercise about memorization with and without music.

a. The standard deviation of the null distribution shown is 0.974. Use this to find an approximate 95% confidence interval for the mean difference in the number of words memorized (no music − music) for the population of interest.

b. Based on your confidence interval from part (a), is there strong evidence that people can memorize words better when music is not playing compared to when it is? Explain.

7.2.16 Reconsider the previous exercises about memorization with and without music. The statistic used was the mean of the difference in words memorized (no music − music). Explain how the following things would change (or not) if we used the mean of the (music − no music) as the statistic when the test was conducted?

a. Observed statistic

b. Alternative hypothesis

c. p-value

d. Confidence interval

Reaction time of day

7.2.17 Student researchers wanted to see whether a person's reaction time is affected by the time of day. They had a computer program that would display a red circle. When it changed to yellow, the subjects were to click the mouse as fast as they could and the computer would calculate the reaction time. The researchers had their subjects perform this test at 10:00 AM and again at 10:00 PM, recording the reaction time for each student at each time. They randomly determined which time of day was done first for each of their subjects. Here are their hypotheses.

Null: There is no association between time of day and reaction times ($\mu_d = 0$).

Alternative: There is an association between time of day and reaction times ($\mu_d \neq 0$).

The students found the following results for reaction times in seconds:

	Morning	Night	Difference
Mean	0.244	0.306	−0.062
Standard deviation	0.052	0.082	0.084

a. What is the explanatory variable in this study? Is it categorical or quantitative?

b. What is the response variable in this study? Is it categorical or quantitative?

c. What is the observed statistic in this study?

d. Assuming a true null hypothesis, we simulated this study and found 1,000 mean differences that are shown in the null distribution below. Based on where the observed statistic lies in this distribution, does the p-value appear to be fairly small?

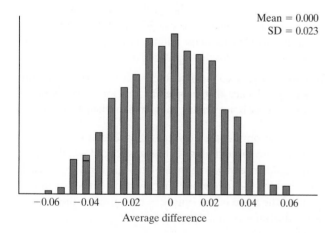

Mean = 0.000
SD = 0.023

Average difference

e. What is the standardized statistic for this test?

f. Based on your standardized statistic from part (e), is there strong evidence that reaction times differ between morning and night? Explain.

7.2.18 Reconsider the previous exercises about reaction times and time of day.

a. Find an approximate 95% confidence interval for the mean difference in the reaction times (morning − night) for the population of interest.

b. Based on your confidence interval, from part (a), is there strong evidence that reaction times differ between morning and night? Explain.

7.2.19 Reconsider the previous exercises about reaction times and time of day. The statistic used was the mean of the difference in reaction times (morning − night). Explain how the following things would change (or not) if we used the mean of the (night − morning) as the statistic when the test was conducted?

a. Observed statistic

b. Alternative hypothesis

c. p-value

d. Confidence interval

Exercise and memory*

7.2.20 Students wanted to see whether exercising (in particular doing jumping jacks) would help or hinder people's ability to memorize a list of 10 words that were read to them. This would be compared to the same test of memorizing words while the subjects were sitting down. The number of words memorized for the 31 subjects can be found in the data file **ExerciseMemorize**.

a. What is the explanatory and what is the response variable in this study?

b. Write down the hypotheses in either words or symbols.

c. Put the data into the **Matched Pairs** applet. What is the value of the statistic that will be used in the study and what does it represent.

d. Randomize at least 1,000 times to develop a null distribution and determine a p-value.

e. Is there strong evidence that exercising while trying to memorize a list of words helps or hinders the process?

Memorization delay

7.2.21 Student researchers wanted to see whether a short delay between seeing a list of words and when people were asked to recall them would hinder memorization. The subjects were shown a list of words to memorize for 1 minute and were then given 1 minute to recall as many words as they could. Each subject did this once with no delay between memorizing and recall and another time with a 30-second wait between memorizing and recall. They were randomly assigned the order of the two conditions. The number of words memorized under each condition can be found in the data file **MemorizationDelay**.

a. What is the explanatory and what is the response variable in this study?

b. Write down the hypotheses in either words or symbols.

c. Put the data into the **Matched Pairs** applet. Just by looking at the graphs in the applet, does it appear that the delay significantly hinders memorization? Explain.

d. What is the value of the statistic that will be used in the study and what does it represent.

e. Randomize at least 1,000 times to develop a null distribution and determine a p-value.

f. Is there strong evidence that a short delay hinders the memorization process?

7.2.22   Reconsider the previous exercise on memorization with and without a delay. If you haven't already done so, put the data file **MemorizationDelay** into the **Matched Pairs** applet and do at least 1,000 randomizations.

a. What is the standardized statistic in this study?

b. Based on the standardized statistic is there strong evidence that a short delay hinders the memorization process? Explain why or why not.

7.2.23   Reconsider the previous exercises on memorization with and without a delay. If you haven't already done so, put the data file **MemorizationDelay** into the **Matched Pairs** applet and do at least 1,000 randomizations.

a. Determine an approximate 95% 2SD confidence interval for the mean difference in the number of words memorized (without delay − delay).

b. Explain what your confidence interval from part (a) means. In other words, we are 95% confident of what?

c. Based on your confidence interval is there strong evidence that a short delay hinders the memorization process? Explain why or why not.

Reaction times and handedness*

7.2.24   Student researchers wanted to see if a person's reaction time is slower if they use their nondominant hand to click a computer mouse compared to using their dominant hand. The researchers had a computer program that would display a red circle. When it changed to yellow, the subjects were to click the mouse as fast as they could and the computer would calculate the reaction time. Researchers had their subjects find their reaction time with their dominant hand (e.g., right hand for right handers) and also with their nondominant hand. They randomly determined which hand was tested first. The reaction times (in seconds) for the subjects for each condition can be found in the data file **ReactionTimes**.

a. What is the explanatory and what is the response variable in this study?

b. Write down the hypotheses in either words or symbols.

c. Put the data into the **Matched Pairs** applet. Just by looking at the graphs in the applet, does it appear that reaction time is significantly slower with the nondominant hand? Explain.

d. What is the value of the statistic that will be used in the study and what does it represent.

e. Randomize at least 1,000 times to develop a null distribution and determine a p-value.

f. Is there strong evidence that reaction times are slower when people use their nondominant hand?

7.2.25   Reconsider the previous exercise on handedness and reaction time. If you haven't already done so, put the data file **ReactionTimes** into the **Matched Pairs** applet and do at least 1,000 randomizations.

a. What is the standardized statistic in this study?

b. Based on the standardized statistic is there strong evidence that using the nondominant hand results in slower average reaction times? Explain why or why not.

7.2.26   Reconsider the previous exercises on handedness and reaction time. If you haven't already done so, put the data file **ReactionTimes** into the **Matched Pairs** applet and do at least 1,000 randomizations.

a. Determine an approximate 95% confidence interval using the 2SD rule for the mean difference in the reaction times (dominant − nondominant).

b. Explain what your confidence interval from part (a) means. In other words, we are 95% confident of what?

c. Based on your confidence interval is there strong evidence that using the nondominant hand results in slower average reaction times? Explain why or why not.

SECTION 7.3

7.3.1   Design your own experiment: Develop the plan for the investigation of a research question that would be best answered using paired data.

a. State the research question.

b. Explain how pairing will be used.

c. Identify the response and explanatory variables.

d. Describe how randomization (random sampling, random assignment, or both) will be used.

e. State the appropriate null and alternative hypotheses in words.

f. Describe when it will be appropriate to use a theory-based method to test the hypotheses stated above.

Marriage ages*

7.3.2   Refer to Exercise 7.2.12 where a student wanted to investigate whether or not people tend to marry spouses of similar ages and so gathered age data from a sample of 24 couples taken from marriage licenses filed in Cumberland County, PA, in June and July 1993.

a. Define, in words, the appropriate parameter(s) of interest in the context of the study. Also, state the appropriate symbol(s) to denote the parameter(s).

b. State, in words, the appropriate null and alternative hypotheses in the context of the study.

c. State, using the symbol(s) described in part (a), the appropriate null and alternative hypotheses in the context of the study.

d. Check whether the validity conditions for the theory-based test are satisfied here.

e. Use appropriate technology (such as the **Matched Pairs** or **Theory-Based Inference** applet, or a statistical software package) to conduct the theory-based test of significance to find *and* report the test statistic and p-value.

f. Interpret the p-value from part (e) in the context of the study and then draw a conclusion about statistical significance.

g. Find *and* interpret the 95% confidence interval for the parameter(s) of interest in the context of the study.

h. State your conclusion in the context of the study, being sure to comment on statistical significance, estimation, causation, and generalization.

Perception of child's size

7.3.3 In a study of parents' perceptions of their children's size, researchers Kaufman et al. (*Current Biology*, 2013) asked parents to estimate their youngest child's height. The researchers hypothesized that parents tend to underestimate their youngest child's size because the youngest child is the baby of the family and everybody else is the family appears bigger compared to the baby. The sample of 39 parents who were surveyed underestimated their youngest child's height by 7.50 cm, on average; the standard deviation for the difference in actual heights and estimated heights was 7.20 cm and the data are not strongly skewed.

a. Which of the following is an appropriate null hypothesis for this study?

A. Parents' estimate of their youngest child's height is accurate, on average.

B. Parents tend to overestimate their youngest child's height, on average.

C. Parents tend to underestimate their youngest child's height, on average.

b. Which of the following is an appropriate alternative hypothesis for this study?

A. Parents' estimate of their youngest child's height is accurate, on average.

B. Parents tend to overestimate their youngest child's height, on average.

C. Parents tend to underestimate their youngest child's height, on average.

c. Identify the observational units in this study.

A. Children

B. Parents

C. Actual heights

D. Estimated heights

d. Identify the parameter in this study.

A. The probability that parents will overestimate their youngest child's height, π

B. The probability that parents will underestimate their youngest child's height, π

C. The probability that parents will correctly estimate their youngest child's height, π

D. The average amount by which parents' guess of their youngest child's height will differ from the actual height, μ

e. Explain why the simulation-based method cannot be used to analyze the available information, to investigate whether parents tend to overestimate their youngest child's height.

f. Explain why a theory-based approach is valid.

7.3.4 Refer to the previous exercise about the study of parents' perceptions of their children's size by researchers Kaufman et al. (*Current Biology*, 2013). Recall that the sample of 39 parents underestimated their youngest child's height by 7.50 cm, on average; the standard deviation for the difference in actual heights and estimated heights was 7.20 cm.

a. Is there evidence that youngest children's heights tend to be underestimated by their parents? Carry out a theory-based test using an appropriate applet or statistical software. Find and report a p-value as well as a standardized statistic.

b. Interpret the p-value in the context of the study.

c. Using an appropriate applet or statistical software, find a 95% confidence interval for the difference. Interpret the confidence interval in the context of the study.

d. Summarize your findings, being sure to include a discussion of statistical significance, estimation (confidence), causation, and generalization in your answer.

e. What assumption do you have to make about the data in order for the validity conditions of the appropriate theory-based test to be satisfied?

7.3.5 Refer to the previous exercises about the study of parents' perceptions of their children's size. The researchers Kaufman et al. (*Current Biology*, 2013) also surveyed a sample of 38 parents about their eldest child's height. The parents overestimated their eldest child's height by 0.40 cm, on average; the standard deviation for the difference in actual heights and estimated heights was 5.60 cm without strong skewness in the data.

a. Is there evidence that parents tend to either over- or underestimate eldest children's heights? Carry out a theory-based test using an appropriate applet or statistical software. Find and report a p-value as well as a standardized statistic.

b. Using an appropriate applet or statistical software, find a 95% confidence interval for the difference. Interpret the confidence interval in the context of the study.

c. Summarize your findings, being sure to include a discussion of statistical significance, causation, and generalization in your answer.

d. What assumption do you have to make about the data in order for the validity conditions of the appropriate theory-based test to be satisfied?

Infant behavior*

7.3.6 Researchers Hamlin et al. (*Nature*, 2007) conducted a study with 16 infants that involved an assessment of infants' expectations of a climber toy's attitude towards a "helper" (a toy figure that helped the climber climb a hill) and a "hinderer" toy (a figure that had hindered the climber's progress up a hill) and whether infants tend to watch the climber's confrontation with the hinderer for a longer time than that with the helper. Each of the sixteen 10-month-olds was shown a new display where the climber would alternately approach the helper and the hinderer, of which the latter was considered to be a surprising event, because such an action was perceived as "violation of the expectation paradigm." The lengths of time that each infant spent watching the climber approach the helper and the hinderer was recorded, and it was noted that in the study the infants looked longer at the approach of the climber towards the hinderer than the helper. (Wonder if the infants were expecting the climber to punch the hinderer, and that held their interest longer!) Given below are some summary statistics for the difference (hinderer − helper) in looking times (seconds). Note that the distribution of differences is fairly symmetric.

	n	Mean	SD
Difference = $\text{Time}_{\text{Hinderer}} - \text{Time}_{\text{Helper}}$	16	1.140 sec	1.752 sec

Do infants tend to look at surprising events or behavior for longer times, on average, compared to uninteresting ones?

a. What are the pairs?

b. What are the two conditions?

c. What is the response variable?

d. State, in words, the appropriate null and alternative hypotheses in the context of the study.

e. Explain why, with the available information, one cannot use a simulation-based method to test the hypotheses.

7.3.7 Refer to the previous exercise about investigating whether infants tend to look at surprising events or behavior for longer times, on average, compared to uninteresting ones?

a. Define, in words, the appropriate parameter(s) of interest in the context of the study. Also, state the appropriate symbol(s) to denote the parameter(s).

b. State, using the symbol(s) described in part (a), the appropriate null and alternative hypotheses in the context of the study.

c. State the validity conditions that have to be met to be able to perform a theory-based test to test the hypotheses stated in part (b). Are these conditions met? How are you deciding?

d. Regardless of your answer to part (c), perform a theory-based test to test the hypotheses stated in part (b). Be sure to report a test statistic value and a p-value in your answer.

e. Interpret your p-value in the context of the study.

f. Find and interpret a 95% confidence interval for the parameter of interest in the context of the study.

g. Give a full conclusion with regards to statistical significance, estimation (confidence), causation, and generalization.

7.3.8 Refer to the previous exercises about investigating whether infants tend to look at surprising events or behavior for longer times, on average, compared to uninteresting ones? Given below are the summary statistics for the difference (hinderer − helper) in looking times (seconds).

	n	Mean	SD
Difference = $\text{Time}_{\text{Hinderer}} - \text{Time}_{\text{Helper}}$	16	1.140 sec	1.752 sec

Suppose the summary statistics had been:

	n	Mean	SD
Difference = $\text{Time}_{\text{Hinderer}} - \text{Time}_{\text{Helper}}$	32	1.140 sec	1.752 sec

How, if at all, would the values of the following (using the theory-based method) be different?

a. p-value: Same   Larger   Smaller

b. Standardized statistic: Same   Larger   Smaller

c. Midpoint of the 95% confidence interval: Same   Larger   Smaller

d. Width of the 95% confidence interval: Same   Larger   Smaller

7.3.9 Refer to the previous exercises about investigating whether infants tend to look at surprising events or behavior for longer times, on average, compared to uninteresting ones? Given below are the summary statistics for the difference (hinderer − helper) in looking times (seconds).

	n	Mean	SD
Difference = $\text{Time}_{\text{Hinderer}} - \text{Time}_{\text{Helper}}$	16	1.140 sec	1.752 sec

Suppose the summary statistics had been:

	n	Mean	SD
Difference = $\text{Time}_{\text{Hinderer}} - \text{Time}_{\text{Helper}}$	16	2.280 sec	1.752 sec

How, if at all, would the values of the following (using the theory-based method) be different?

a. p-value: Same   Larger   Smaller

b. Standardized statistic: Same   Larger   Smaller

c. Midpoint of the 95% confidence interval: Same   Larger   Smaller

d. Width of the 95% confidence interval: Same   Larger   Smaller

7.3.10 Refer to the previous exercises about investigating whether infants tend to look at surprising events or behavior for longer times, on average, compared to uninteresting ones? Given below are the summary statistics for the difference (hinderer − helper) in looking times (seconds).

	n	Mean	SD
Difference = $\text{Time}_{\text{Hinderer}} - \text{Time}_{\text{Helper}}$	16	1.140 sec	1.752 sec

Suppose the summary statistics had been:

	n	Mean	SD
Difference = $\text{Time}_{\text{Hinderer}} - \text{Time}_{\text{Helper}}$	16	1.140 sec	0.752 sec

How, if at all, would the values of the following (using the theory-based method) be different?

a. p-value: Same   Larger   Smaller

b. Standardized statistic: Same   Larger   Smaller

c. Midpoint of the 95% confidence interval: Same   Larger   Smaller

d. Width of the 95% confidence interval: Same   Larger   Smaller

Cholesterol levels

7.3.11 The Cholesterol Level data sets give cholesterol levels of heart attack patients. Cholesterol measures are taken 2, 4, and 14 days after a patient has suffered a heart attack. *Is there a significant difference between day 2 cholesterol measures and day 4 cholesterol measures?* Carry out a theory-based test and find a 95% confidence interval for the difference. Use the data set **CholesterolLevel_day2-4**. Summarize your findings, being sure to include a discussion of statistical significance, estimation (confidence interval), causation, and generalization in your answer. Make sure to confirm that validity conditions are met.

7.3.12 The Cholesterol Level data sets give cholesterol levels of heart attack patients. Cholesterol measures are taken 2, 4, and 14 days after a patient has suffered a heart attack. *Is there a significant difference between day 2 cholesterol measures and day 14 cholesterol measures?* Carry out a theory-based test and find a 95% confidence interval for the difference. Use the data set **CholesterolLevel_day2-14**. Summarize your findings, being sure to include a discussion of statistical significance, estimation (confidence interval), causation, and generalization in your answer. Make sure to confirm that validity conditions are met.

7.3.13 The Cholesterol Level data sets give cholesterol levels of heart attack patients. Cholesterol measures are taken 2, 4, and 14 days after a patient has suffered a heart attack. *Is there a significant difference between day 4 cholesterol measures and day 14 cholesterol measures?* Carry out a theory-based test and find a 95% confidence interval for the difference. Use the data set **CholesterolLevel_day4-14**. Summarize your findings, being sure to include a discussion of statistical significance, estimation (confidence interval), causation, and generalization in your answer. Make sure to confirm that validity conditions are met.

Estimating energy expenditure*

7.3.14 How many calories do you think you burn or expend with 60 minutes of walking on the treadmill? An article that appeared in the *American Journal of Men's Health* (2010) presented the results of a study conducted by researchers Harris and George, whose objective was to evaluate how accurately men can estimate their energy expenditure (EE) as measured in kilocalories (kcal).

Eighty normal-weight and overweight male participants, ages 21–45 years, were recruited from a large, urban university in South Florida. During one session, each participant was made to walk for 60 minutes on a treadmill, and their actual EE was calculated. After they had completed the task, each participant was asked to estimate the number of calories they burned during the task. A summary of the results are shown in the following table.

	Sample size	Sample average (kcal)	Sample SD (kcal)
Difference = Estimated − Actual	80	$\bar{x}_d = 129$	$s_d = 393.50$

The researchers wanted to see whether men tended to overestimate or underestimate their EE.

a. On average, did the men in the study significantly overestimate or underestimate their EE? How do you know?

b. Explain why a matched pairs test would be appropriate to analyze these data.

c. Give the null and alternative hypotheses.

d. What assumption do you need to make about the data in order to use the theory-based approach to analyze these data?

e. Use the **Theory-Based Inference** applet to find the standardized statistic and p-value for this test.

f. Use the **Theory-Based Inference** applet to find a 95% confidence interval. Interpret the 95% confidence interval in the context of the study.

g. Explain how the confidence interval corresponds to the conclusion reported in part (e).

h. Provide a full (four-part) conclusion, including comments on significance, estimation, causation, and generalization.

7.3.15 Recall the previous exercise about estimating energy expenditure (EE). The previous exercise also reports the summary statistics for the difference in EE (estimate − actual).

a. Use the formula of the standardized statistic $\left(t = \dfrac{\bar{x}_d - 0}{s_d/\sqrt{n}} \right)$ to calculate its value. Interpret the value of the standardized statistic in the context of the study.

b. Use the formula for the confidence interval $\left(\bar{x}_d \pm multiplier \times \dfrac{s_d}{\sqrt{n}} \right)$ to calculate the 95% confidence interval.

7.3.16 Recall the previous exercises about estimating energy expenditure. Previously you carried out a theory-based matched pairs test to investigate whether, on average, men in the study significantly overestimated or underestimated their EE. Here are a few more summary statistics.

	Sample size	Sample average (kcal)	Sample SD (kcal)
Estimated	80	$\bar{x}_e = 411$	$s_e = 505.70$
Actual	80	$\bar{x}_a = 282$	$s_a = 44.70$
Difference = Estimated − Actual	80	$\bar{x}_d = 129$	$s_d = 393.50$

a. Use the **Theory-Based Inference** applet to carry out a test for two independent means. Report the standardized statistic and p-value for this test.

b. Use the **Theory-Based Inference** applet to find a 95% confidence interval for the difference between two independent means.

c. Explain how the p-value and 95% confidence interval reported in parts (a) and (b) correspond to those reported in the previous exercise.

d. While the analysis you conducted in parts (a) and (b) is the "wrong" analysis, explain what it suggests about the effectiveness of pairing in this study.

7.3.17 Recall the previous exercises about estimating energy expenditure. The summary statistics on the difference between estimated EE and actual EE were as follows:

	Sample size	Sample average (kcal)	Sample SD (kcal)
Difference = Estimated − Actual	80	$\bar{x}_d = 129$	$s_d = 393.50$

Suppose the summary statistics had been:

	Sample size	Sample average (kcal)	Sample SD (kcal)
Difference = Estimated − Actual	40	$\bar{x}_d = 129$	$s_d = 393.50$

How, if at all, would the values of the following (using the theory-based method) be different?

a. p-value: Same Larger Smaller

b. Standardized statistic: Same Larger Smaller

c. Midpoint of the 95% confidence interval: Same Larger Smaller

d. Width of the 95% confidence interval: Same Larger Smaller

7.3.18 Recall the previous exercises about estimating energy expenditure. The summary statistics on the difference between estimated EE and actual EE were as follows:

	Sample size	Sample average (kcal)	Sample SD (kcal)
Difference = Estimated − Actual	80	$\bar{x}_d = 129$	$s_d = 393.50$

Suppose the summary statistics had been:

	Sample size	Sample average (kcal)	Sample SD (kcal)
Difference = Estimated − Actual	80	$\bar{x}_d = 64.50$	$s_d = 393.50$

How, if at all, would the values of the following (using the theory-based method) be different?

a. p-value: Same Larger Smaller

b. Standardized statistic: Same Larger Smaller

c. Midpoint of the 95% confidence interval: Same Larger Smaller

d. Width of the 95% confidence interval: Same Larger Smaller

7.3.19 Recall the previous exercises about estimating energy expenditure. The summary statistics on the difference between estimated EE and actual EE were as follows:

	Sample size	Sample average (kcal)	Sample SD (kcal)
Difference = Estimated − Actual	80	$\bar{x}_d = 129$	$s_d = 393.50$

Suppose the summary statistics had been:

	Sample size	Sample average (kcal)	Sample SD (kcal)
Difference = Estimated − Actual	80	$\bar{x}_d = 129$	$s_d = 93.50$

How, if at all, would the values of the following (using the theory-based method) be different?

a. p-value: Same   Larger   Smaller

b. Standardized statistic: Same   Larger   Smaller

c. Midpoint of the 95%
   confidence interval: Same   Larger   Smaller

d. Width of the 95%
   confidence interval: Same   Larger   Smaller

Rounding first base

7.3.20 Recall Exploration 7.1 and Example 7.2 about the time needed to round first base, using the narrow angle versus the wide angle. Here are the summary statistics on the difference in times (narrow − wide) for the 22 players:

	Sample size	Sample average (sec)	Sample SD (sec)
Difference = Narrow − Wide	22	0.075	0.088

a. Use an appropriate theory-based method to investigate whether the choice of angle affects the running time. Be sure to find and report a standardized statistic and p-value.

b. Use an appropriate theory-based method to find and report a 95% confidence interval for the parameter of interest.

c. Provide a full (four-part) conclusion, including comments on significance, estimation, causation, and generalization.

7.3.21 Recall Exploration 7.1 and Example 7.2 about the time needed to round first base using the narrow angle versus the wide angle. The previous exercise reports the summary statistics for the difference in times (narrow − wide).

a. Use the formula of the standardized statistic $\left(t = \dfrac{\bar{x}_d - 0}{s_d / \sqrt{n}} \right)$ to calculate its value. Interpret the value of the standardized statistic in the context of the study.

b. Use the formula for the confidence interval $\left(\bar{x}_d \pm multiplier \times \dfrac{s_d}{\sqrt{n}} \right)$ to calculate the 95% confidence interval.

M&Ms*

7.3.22 Recall Example 7.3 about the number of M&Ms taken with small versus large bowls. The example uses the following parameter of interest:

μ_d = Long-run mean difference for the number of M&Ms that will be taken when using a small bowl minus a large bowl.

The hypotheses are H₀: $\mu_d = 0$ versus Hₐ: $\mu_d < 0$. The example reports the theory-based p-value to be 0.1172 and the 95% confidence for μ_d to be $(-29.54, 7.78)$. Suppose we defined the parameter of interest to be

μ_{new} = Long-run mean difference for the number of M&Ms that will be taken when using a large bowl minus a small bowl.

a. State the hypotheses in terms of μ_{new}.

b. Without doing any calculations, report what the p-value would be for the hypotheses stated in part (a). Explain your reasoning.

c. Without doing any calculations, report what the 95% confidence interval μ_{new} would be. Explain your reasoning.

Tomoxetine

7.3.23 In a study of the effect of tomoxetine as an alternative treatment for attention deficit hyperactivity disorder (ADHD), researchers Spencer et al. (*The American Journal of Psychiatry*, 1998) recruited men and women diagnosed with ADHD. All participants were administered tomoxetine and a placebo—each for three weeks in a random order and with a week of washout period between the two treatments. The researchers noted that the average increase in standing heart rate when on tomoxetine compared to when on the placebo was 11 beats per minute, with a standard deviation of 15.05 beats per minute, for a sample of 18 individuals. The distribution of differences in standing heart rate is approximately symmetric.

a. Define, in words, the appropriate parameter(s) of interest in the context of the study. Also, state the appropriate symbol(s) to denote the parameter(s).

b. State, using the symbol(s) described in part (a), the appropriate null and alternative hypotheses to test whether the use of tomoxetine causes an increase in standing heart rate.

c. State the validity conditions that have to be met to be able to perform a theory-based test to test the hypotheses stated in part (b). Are these conditions met? How are you deciding?

d. Regardless of your answer to part (c), perform a theory-based test to test the hypotheses stated in part (b). Be sure to report a test statistic value and a p-value in your answer.

e. Interpret your p-value in the context of the study.

f. Find a 95% confidence interval for the parameter of interest.

g. Provide a full (four-part) conclusion, including comments on significance, estimation, causation, and generalization.

Effect of oxytocin*

7.3.24 The "Reading the Mind in the Eyes Test" (RMET) measures the ability of a person to infer the mental state of another from looking at facial expressions. Researchers Domes et al. (*Biological Psychiatry*, 2007) conducted a study on the effect of oxytocin (a hormone often linked with bonding, trust, and empathy) on people's performance on the RMET. Thirty healthy male volunteers (ages 21–30 years) were administered oxytocin and a placebo—each as a nasal spray, in a random order and with a week of washout period between the two treatments. Forty-five minutes after administering each treatment, participants were given the RMET. The researchers noted that the average increase in RMET score when on oxytocin compared to when on the placebo was 3 points, with a standard deviation of 7.54 points. The differences in RMET scores were not strongly skewed.

a. Define, in words, the appropriate parameter(s) of interest in the context of the study. Also, state the appropriate symbol(s) to denote the parameter(s).

b. State, using the symbol(s) described in part (a), the appropriate null and alternative hypotheses to test whether the use of oxytocin causes an increase in ability to infer the mental state of others, as measured by the RMET score.

c. State the validity conditions that have to be met to be able to perform a theory-based test to test the hypotheses stated in part (b). Are these conditions met? How are you deciding?

d. Regardless of your answer to part (c), perform a theory-based test to test the hypotheses stated in part (b). Be sure to report a test statistic value and a p-value in your answer.

e. Interpret your p-value in the context of the study.

f. Find a 95% confidence interval for the parameter of interest.

g. Provide a full (four-part) conclusion, including comments on significance, estimation, causation, and generalization.

7.3.25 Refer to the previous exercise about the effect of oxytocin on the ability to infer the mental state of others, as measured by the RMET score. Recall that for the sample of 30 participants, the researchers noted that the average increase in RMET score when on oxytocin compared to when on the placebo was 3 points, with a standard deviation of 7.54 points.

a. Use the formula of the standardized statistic $\left(t = \dfrac{\bar{x}_d - 0}{s_d/\sqrt{n}} \right)$ to calculate its value. Interpret the value of the standardized statistic in the context of the study.

b. Use the formula for the confidence interval $\left(\bar{x}_d \pm multiplier \times \dfrac{s_d}{\sqrt{n}} \right)$ to calculate the 95% confidence interval.

SECTION 7.4

7.4.1* Which of the following is an appropriate way to write out the null hypothesis in symbols for a one-sample *t*-test for paired data?

A. $H_0: \bar{x}_d = 0$

B. $H_0: \hat{p}_d = 0$

C. $H_0: \pi_d = 0$

D. $H_0: \mu_d = 0$

E. $H_0: \alpha_d = 0$

7.4.2 The number of degrees of freedom for the *t*-distribution used for a one-sample *t*-test for paired data is:

A. the sample size minus 1

B. the sample size plus 1

C. the mean minus 1

D. the mean plus 1

E. the standard deviation plus 1

7.4.3* Which of the following is the correct way to calculate the standardized test statistic for a one-sample *t*-test for paired data with $\bar{x}_d = 2.3$, $s_d = 1.8$, and $n = 35$?

A. $t = \dfrac{2.3}{1.8/\sqrt{35}}$

B. $t = \dfrac{1.8}{2.3/\sqrt{35}}$

C. $t = \dfrac{2.3}{1.8/35}$

D. $t = \dfrac{2.3}{\sqrt{1.8/35}}$

E. $t = \sqrt{\dfrac{2.3}{1.8/35}}$

7.4.4 Which of the following is the correct way to calculate the 95% confidence interval for paired data with $\bar{x}_d = 3.5$, $s_d = 2.4$, and $n = 40$?

A. $2.4 \pm 2.023(3.5/\sqrt{40})$

B. $2.4 \pm 2.023\sqrt{3.5/40}$

C. $3.5 \pm 2.023\sqrt{2.4/40}$

D. $3.5 \pm 2.023(2.4/40)$

E. $3.5 \pm 2.023(2.4/\sqrt{40})$

7.4.5* Suppose you are calculating a 95% confidence interval for paired data to compare the number of words memorized by people while listening to music compared to the number of words memorized while not listening to music. The observed mean difference is $\bar{x}_{no\ music\ -\ music}$ and you calculate your interval to be $(-0.5, 1.8)$. This interval means that we are 95% confident that in the population:

A. The mean number of words memorized with no music is between 0.5 and 1.8 words more than the mean number of words memorized with music.

B. The mean number of words memorized with music is between 0.5 and 1.8 words more than the mean number of words memorized with no music.

C. The mean number of words memorized with no music is between 0.5 less to 1.8 words more than the mean number of words memorized with music.

D. The mean number of words memorized with music is between 0.5 less to 1.8 words more than the mean number of words memorized with no music.

E. The mean number of words memorized with no music is between 0.5 and 1.8 words less than the mean number of words memorized with music.

7.4.6 True or false?

a. With paired data, the mean of the differences, $\bar{x}_d$, is equal to the difference of the means of the two original data sets.

b. With paired data, the standard deviation of the differences, s_d, is equal to the difference of the standard deviations of the two original data sets.

7.4.7* Suppose we have the following summary statistics from the results of a paired study: $\bar{x}_d = 2.2$, $s_d = 4.9$, and $n = 34$.

a. Using these summary statistics, calculate the standardized statistic, t.

b. Find the p-value if the alternative hypothesis is $H_a: \mu_d > 0$.

7.4.8 Suppose we have the following summary statistics from the results of a paired study: $\bar{x}_d = 2.1$, $s_d = 4.5$, and $n = 29$.

a. Using these summary statistics, calculate the standardized statistic, t.

b. Find the p-value if the alternative hypothesis is $H_a: \mu_d \neq 0$.

7.4.9* Suppose we have the following summary statistics from the results of a paired study: $\bar{x}_d = 1.7$, $s_d = 0.7$, and $n = 24$. We want to construct a 95% confidence interval for the parameter, μ_d.

a. What is the value of $t^*_{df=n-1}$?

b. What is the value of the margin of error?

c. What are the endpoints of the confidence interval?

7.4.10* Repeat #7.4.9 except compute a 99% confidence interval. How does the margin of error compare?

7.4.11 Student researchers wanted to see whether listening to music would affect the time it takes people to complete a

Stroop test. A Stroop test is a test in which words of colors are shown printed in a color that does not correspond to the word. For example, BLUE is written in orange letters. The subjects have to say the color of the letters and not the word. The researchers had 38 subjects do the test once while listening to music and then again without music (the order was randomly determined). The results, time in seconds for 25 words, are in the file **StroopMusic** and a summary of the statistics are shown below.

	Mean ($\bar{x}$)	SD (s)	n
No Music	21.956	4.351	38
Music	20.303	3.335	38
Difference	1.654	2.657	38

a. State the hypotheses either in words or using appropriate symbols.

b. Name the test that will be used and state and verify the validity conditions for the test chosen.

c. Calculate the test statistic (standardized statistic) and corresponding p-value.

d. State your conclusion (with appropriate justification based on your p-value and stated significance level) in the context of the research question.

7.4.12 Recall the previous question about music and the Stroop test.

a. Construct a 95% confidence interval, showing the values that you substitute into the formula.

b. Interpret the confidence interval you obtained in the context of the problem.

c. Based on your confidence interval, do you have strong evidence that listening to music has an effect on the length of time to complete a Stroop test, on average? Explain how you are determining this and, if it is significant, indicate which condition results in more time to take the test.

7.4.13* Is there a difference in a person's ability to memorize objects if he or she is shown the objects in pictures that are in color or pictures in black and white? That is what student researchers wanted to explore. They printed out pictures of 10 objects, where 5 were in color and 5 in black and white. The 50 subjects each had 15 seconds to look at the pictures and then had to write down as many as they could remember. The results for the number of objects they could recall are in the file **PicturesColor** and the summary statistics are shown in the following table. We will investigate this question using a confidence interval.

	Mean	SD	n
Black and White	3.680	0.957	50
Color	3.500	1.015	50
Difference	0.180	1.574	50

a. Identify the parameter you want to estimate and the theory-based method you will use.

b. Verify the validity conditions for the theory-based method you have chosen.

c. Construct a 95% confidence interval, showing the values that you substitute into the formula.

d. Interpret the confidence interval you obtained in the context of the study.

e. Based on your confidence interval, do you have strong evidence that there is a difference, on average, in the number of objects people can recall when shown pictures in color compared to when shown pictures in black and white? Explain how you are determining this and, if significant, which condition tends to have the higher recall rate.

7.4.14 Researchers at Arizona State University (McNabb & Gray, 2016) explored the effects of various types of cell phone use on driving. In particular, they were interested in comparing the effects between text-based media and picture-based media. The researchers had their subjects use a driving simulator and requested that they stay 2 seconds behind the car in front of them. The car in front travelled between 55 and 65 mph and was programmed to come to a complete stop 8 times during the simulation. One of the variables they measured was the reaction time for the subjects to brake when the car in front stopped. They measured this when the subjects were instructed to scroll through Facebook messages that just consisted of text. They also measured this when the subjects were instructed to scroll through Instagram pictures that did not contain any text. The order of the conditions was randomized. The results, in seconds, are in the file **BrakeReactionTime**. We want to decide whether there is a difference in the average braking reaction time when looking at text (Facebook) versus looking at pictures (Instagram) on the phone.

a. State the hypotheses either in words or using appropriate symbols.

b. Name the test that will be used and state and verify the validity conditions for the test chosen.

c. Calculate the test statistic (standardized statistic) and corresponding p-value.

d. State your conclusion (with appropriate justification based on your p-value and stated significance level) in the context of the research question.

7.4.15 Recall the previous question in which researchers explored the effects of various types of cell phone use on driving. In particular, they were interested in comparing the effects of text-based media and picture-based media. They had their subjects use a driving simulator and follow the car in front of them, which was programmed to travel at various speeds between 55 and 65 mph. Time headway is the time between the front of the car directly ahead of you and the front of your car; the subjects were instructed to keep their time headway at 2 seconds. The researchers measured the variability in this time over the course of the study. A variability number of 0 would mean they kept the time at a constant 2 seconds, and the higher the variability, the more difficulty the subject had at maintaining this distance. The researchers measured the time headway data when the subjects were instructed to scroll through Facebook messages that just consisted of text. They also measured this when the subjects were instructed to scroll through Instagram pictures that did not contain any text. The order of these conditions was randomized. The results, in seconds, are in the file **TimeHeadwayVariability**. We want to decide whether there tends to be a difference in the headway variability between looking at text (Facebook) or pictures (Instagram) by constructing a 99% confidence interval.

a. Identify the parameter you want to estimate and the theory-based method you will use.

b. Verify the validity conditions for the theory-based method you have chosen.

c. Construct a 99% confidence interval, showing the values that you substitute into the formula.

d. Interpret the confidence interval you obtained in the context of the problem.

e. Based on your confidence interval, do you have very strong evidence (at the 1% level) that there is a difference, on average, in the variability number between scrolling through texts compared to pictures? Explain how you are determining this and, if significant, which condition has the higher variability rate.

7.4.16* Student researchers wanted to see whether listening to music with lyrics would decrease a person's ability to memorize words compared to listening to music without lyrics. They recruited 31 people for this test. The subjects looked at 10 common words for 1 minute. The list was taken away and they then had 30 seconds to list all the words they could remember. They did this once while listening, through headphones, to music that contained words (lyrics) and once while listening to music without words (instrumental). These conditions were applied in random order. The results are in the file **MemorizeMusic**.

a. State the hypotheses either in words or using appropriate symbols.

b. Name the theory-based test that will be used and state and verify the validity conditions for the test chosen.

c. Calculate the test statistic (standardized statistic) and corresponding p-value.

d. State your conclusion (with appropriate justification based on your p-value and stated significance level) in the context of the research question.

7.4.17 Is basketball players' ability to make free throws different when they get their own rebound or when someone else gets their rebound for them? This is what student researchers wanted to explore. The researchers used students (20 females and 20 males) taking a college physical education class as their subjects. The students each attempted 10 shots from the free-throw line where they had to get their own rebound, and 10 shots where someone else got their rebound and passed the ball back to them while they stayed on the free-throw line. The results are found in the file **Rebound**. We want to estimate the mean difference in the number of baskets made between the two conditions by calculating a 95% confidence interval.

a. Identify the parameter you want to estimate and the theory-based method you will use.

b. Verify the validity conditions for the theory-based method you have chosen.

c. Construct a 95% confidence interval, showing the values that you plug into the formula.

d. Interpret the confidence interval you obtained in the context of the study.

e. Based on your confidence interval, do you have strong evidence that there is a difference, on average, in the number of free throws made depending on whether players get their own rebounds or have someone else do it for them? Explain how you are determining this and, if significant, which condition tends to have the higher free-throw rate.

7.4.18* A study done by Jung et al. (2014) looked at hurricane names and each storm's perceived threat. They thought that hurricanes in the U.S. with male names would be perceived as more dangerous. In one part of the research, 346 subjects were shown five male names (Arthur, Cristobal, Omar, Kyle, Marco) and five female names (Bertha, Dolly, Fay, Laura, Hanna) from the official 2014 Atlantic hurricane names and were asked to predict each hurricane's intensity (1 = not intense at all, 7 = very intense, 1 = not strong at all, 7 = very strong). The average rating for the male names was 4.386 (SD = 0.822) and the average rating for the female names was 4.160 (SD = 0.907), for a difference of 0.226 (SD = 0.925). The data are available in the file **Hurricane**. Do male-named hurricanes tend to be rated as more intense or strong?

a. State the hypotheses either in words or using appropriate symbols.

b. Name the theory-based test that will be used and state and verify the validity conditions for the test chosen.

c. Calculate the test statistic (standardized statistic) and corresponding p-value.

d. State your conclusion (with appropriate justification based on your p-value and stated significance level) in the context of the research question.

7.4.19* Recall the previous question about comparing ratings of intensity for male-named hurricanes and female-named hurricanes.

a. Construct a 95% confidence interval for the mean difference in the ratings.

b. Based on your confidence interval from part (b), do you have strong evidence that hurricanes with male names will be rated as more intense, on average, than female-named hurricanes? Explain.

7.4.20 Do people think bottled water tastes better than tap water? In a blind taste test, student researchers asked their 31 subjects to rate the taste of two waters, one bottled and one tap, on a scale of 1 to 7, with 7 being great-tasting and 1 being awful. The average rating for the tap water was 4.03 (SD = 1.74), the average rating for the bottled water was 4.06 (SD = 1.50), and the differences had a mean of −0.03 (SD = 1.98). You can also find the data in the file **BottledWater**.

a. State the hypotheses either in words or using appropriate symbols for the research question.

b. Name the theory-based test that will be used and state and verify the validity conditions for the test chosen.

c. Calculate the test statistic (standardized statistic) and corresponding p-value.

d. State your conclusion (with appropriate justification based on your p-value and stated significance level) in the context of the research question.

END OF CHAPTER

7.CE.1* Match each question with the proper significance test (from (A) − (D)) needed to answer the question.

a. _____ Do a majority of students at your college prefer chocolate soft serve ice cream to vanilla?

b. _____ Is the proportion of females at your college who participate in varsity athletics different from the proportion of males who participate in varsity athletics?

c. _____ Is the average study time per week for seniors at your college different from the average study time per week for freshmen?

d. _____ On average, is there a significant difference in one's heart rate before using chewing tobacco and after using chewing tobacco?

A. Single proportion test of significance

B. Paired samples test of significance

C. Two-sample mean test of significance

D. Two-proportion test of significance

7.CE.2 Does your bowl size influence how much you eat? To investigate, researchers recruited undergraduates from a large university to participate in a study that was conducted over several days. The participants were not told about the goal of the study until the very end of the data collection process. At the first session, the researchers assigned some participants to receive either a small bowl or a large bowl.

After that, each participant was allowed to scoop as many M&Ms into their bowl as they planned on eating that day, and then during the session they counted how many M&Ms their bowl contained. When the data from the first session were analyzed by comparing the average M&Ms count for the "small-bowl" group to the average M&Ms count for the "large-bowl" group, the p-value was found to be 0.40.

a. Based on the results of the first session, is it okay to say that bowl size influences how much you eat? Why or why not?

b. At the next session, the size of the bowls was switched: Those who received small bowls at the first session now received large bowls, and vice versa. So, at the end of the second session, each participant had an M&M count for small bowl and an M&Ms count for large bowl. How should the researchers analyze the updated data? *Briefly explain.*

7.CE.3* *Clearly describe* what, if anything, is incorrect about each of the following hypotheses.

a. $H_0: \hat{p}_1 - \hat{p}_2 = 0$ versus $H_a: \hat{p}_1 - \hat{p}_2 \neq 0$

b. $H_0: \mu = 40$ versus $H_a: \mu < 30$

c. $H_0: \pi_1 - \pi_2 = 0$ versus $H_a: \pi_1 - \pi_2 < 0$

7.CE.4 For each of the following studies, indicate whether the data were collected in a paired manner and therefore require a paired analysis.

a. A farmer wants to know whether hand-milking or machine-milking tends to produce more milk from cows. He examines records of how much milk the cows have produced in the past, and orders them from most to least productive. For the top two milk producers, he randomly assigns one to hand-milking and the other to machine-milking. He does the same for the next two and the next two and so on.

b. A reporter for a local newspaper wants to compare prices of grocery items at two stores. She selects 30 grocery items that are sold at both stores and records the price of each item at each store.

c. Are some diet programs easier to stick to than others? Researchers randomly assigned overweight people to one of four popular diets, and they recorded how many in each diet successfully completed the program for one year.

d. Does catnip have a negative effect on cats' social interactions with other cats? A student went to the local animal shelter and observed a dozen cats. She counted how many negative interactions each cat had in a 15-minute period. Then she exposed each cat to catnip and counted how many negative interactions the cat had in the following 15-minute period.

Smoke alarms*

7.CE.5 Some smoke alarms for homes with children now use a recording of the mother's voice calling the child by name, as opposed to the beeping sound of conventional smoke alarms.

a. Describe how you could design a matched pairs study to investigate whether the new smoke alarms reduce the time needed for a child to wake up and leave the house.

b. Explain why a matched pairs design is likely to be helpful, as compared to a completely randomized design, in this study.

c. Explain why it's important to randomize the order in which the children receive the treatments.

Music at the restaurant

7.CE.6 Suppose that a restaurant owner wants to investigate whether the type of music played in the background affects how much customers spend on their meals. The owner plans to play classical music on some evenings and contemporary music on other evenings for a total of two weeks, comparing the amounts spent by customers on those evenings. The owner is considering three ways to design the study:

- Plan 1: Flip a coin for each evening. If the coin lands heads, play classical music. If the coin lands tails, play contemporary music.

- Plan 2: Write "classical" on seven index cards and "contemporary" on seven index cards. Shuffle the cards well. Record the order of "classical" and "contemporary" on the cards and play the music in that order over the 14 days.

- Plan 3: Flip a coin for each evening of the first week. If the coin lands heads, play classical music. If the coin lands tails, play contemporary music. Then for each day in the second week, play the other kind of music from what was played on that day in the first week.

a. Identify the explanatory and response variables in this study. Also classify the variables as categorical or quantitative.

b. Is this an observational study or an experiment? Explain how you know.

c. Which of these plans is a matched pairs design?

d. Why might the matched pairs design be better than a completely randomized design in this context?

Marriage ages*

7.CE.7 Suppose that a student wants to gather data to investigate whether husbands tend to be older, on average, than their wives. The student obtains a sample of 200 marriage licenses that report the ages of both the husband and wife. The student randomly selected 100 of the marriage licenses and recorded the husbands' age from the license, and then the student recorded the wife's age from the other 100 licenses.

a. Explain why a paired analysis would not be appropriate for the student's data.

b. How could the student's data collection method from the 200 marriage licenses be improved so the data would be paired?

c. Why is it reasonable to believe that pairing would be helpful in this situation?

Water proofing boots

7.CE.8 Suppose that a company has developed a new method of waterproofing boots that it wants to compare in an experiment against a standard method.

a. Describe how to conduct a randomized experiment without pairing to compare the two methods of waterproofing boots.

b. Describe how to conduct a matched pairs experiment to compare the two methods of waterproofing boots. (*Hint:* Try to think of a very natural way to do the pairing.)

Flexibility*

7.CE.9 During one semester of a healthy living class taught at Hope College, students measured how flexible they were in terms of inches reached while sitting. Flexibility was measured at the beginning of the semester and again at the end of the semester. We will consider this a representative sample of all students taking this class around this time.

a. In Chapter 6 we carried out a test to see if the posttest flexibility scores were different for males and females. We found that they were. Carry out a test to confirm that pretest flexibility scores are significantly different for males and females as well. (Use **FlexibilityPre**.)

b. How would you test to see if there was a significant gain in flexibility for all students who might take the class? Describe how this test is different than the tests to compare the pretest flexibility and posttest flexibility between males and females.

c. Now, carry out the six-step method to test if there is an average gain in flexibility for all students taking the healthy living class. (Use **Flexibility**.)

d. What if you wanted to see whether or not there was a significant difference between males and females as far as their average flexibility gain from this class. Describe what the two variables are that you would use in your analysis and what kind of a test you would use.

e. Carry out the six-step method to test whether or not there is a significant difference in the average flexibility gain between males and females. (Use **Flexibility Pre and Post**; *Note:* You will need to create a new variable in order to do this analysis.)

Body fat percentage

7.CE.10 During one semester of a healthy living class taught at Hope College, students were weighed (in kilograms), were weighed under water (in kilograms), and had their body fat percentage calculated. These were all done at the beginning of the semester and again at the end of the semester. We will consider this a representative sample of all students taking this class around this time. The data are available in **Weight**, **WaterWeight**, and **BodyFat**.

a. Complete *three* theory-based tests to determine whether or not Hope students' weight, underwater weight, and body fat percentage are different at the end of the semester when compared to the beginning. Make sure validity conditions hold before conducting the test. When running the tests, find the mean difference, produce a dotplot of the differences, write out the hypotheses, determine the p-value, and write a conclusion.

b. If the result is significant, determine the direction of the change. Can you explain the differences in these directions?

Chimpanzee collaboration*

7.CE.11 Humans are able to collaborate on projects to accomplish their goals. What about chimpanzees? Do chimpanzees know when they need to recruit help in order to solve a problem and when they are able to solve it on their own? Researchers placed a food platform outside of the chimpanzee's cage. They threaded a rope through metal loops at either end of the platform with the rope ends extending into the cage. If the chimp pulled on only one rope, it would unthread through the platform and the chimp would not be able to get the food. If both ends of the rope were pulled simultaneously, the food platform would move toward the cage and eventually the chimp could reach it. Two different conditions were presented to eight chimpanzees. In the collaboration condition, the food platform was wide enough that one chimp couldn't reach both ends of the rope at the same time to successfully pull the food platform toward them. They needed to recruit another chimp to pull one end while they pulled the other. In the solo condition the food platform width was such that a single chimp could reach both ends of the rope and unassisted successfully pull the food platform to the cage. For both of these conditions there was an adjacent cage containing another chimp available to help solve the problem. The test chimp had the ability to unlock a sliding door to let the other chimp into their cage to assist them in the retrieval of the food platform. Each of the eight chimps performed several trials of each condition. Data were gathered as the percentage of trials the test chimp opened the door to the adjacent cage for each of the two conditions. Are chimps more likely to recruit a collaborator in the collaboration condition than in the solo condition? (Use data **Chimps**.)

a. State the null and alternative hypotheses.

b. If you compared the average percent of trials the cage was opened in the collaborative condition to the average percent of trials the cage was opened in the solo condition, what piece of information are you ignoring? How would this affect your analysis?

c. Carry out a randomization analysis of these data to see if chimps are more likely to collaborate in the collaboration condition than in the solo condition. Remember, the same chimp is performing in each of these different conditions.

Running the bases, revisited

7.CE.12 Reconsider the baseball data from Example 7.2 (**FirstBase**). Suppose for now that the data had been from 44 different players rather than paired data on the same 22 players. Test whether one of the methods is significantly different than the other.

a. Perform a simulation of a randomization test to compare the two groups (assuming that the data had been from 44 different players). Report the p-value. What conclusion would you reach?

b. How do the p-value and conclusion change from this analysis, as compared to the paired analysis conducted in Example 7.2?

c. Explain how this exercise demonstrates the value of having conducted a matched pairs experiment to investigate the question of whether one method of running the bases is better than the other method.

7.CE.13 Reconsider again the baseball data from Example 7.2.

a. Perform the appropriate (theory-based) matched pairs *t*-test. Report the hypotheses, test statistic, and p-value. Summarize your conclusion.

b. Now suppose that the data had been from 44 different players rather than the same 22 players. Perform a two-sample *t*-test. Report the hypotheses, test statistic, and p-value. Summarize your conclusion.

c. Comment on how different your answers to parts (a) and (b) are. What does this indicates about the usefulness of using a matched pairs design for this study?

7.CE.14 Reconsider again the baseball data from Example 7.2.

a. Repeat the previous exercise, this time producing a 95% confidence interval first based on the actual matched pairs data and then based on assuming that the data were from 44 different players rather than the same 22 players.

b. Comment on how the midpoints and widths of the confidence intervals in part (a) compare. Explain why your answers make sense.

Catnip*

7.CE.15 A student who did volunteer work at an animal shelter wanted to see if cats really respond aggressively to catnip (Jovan, *Stats* magazine, 1999). Using a sample of 15 cats, she recorded how many "negative interactions" (such as hissing or clawing) each cat engaged in during a 15-minute period prior to being given a teaspoon of catnip

and also in the following 15-minute period. Her conjecture was that the number of negative interactions would increase after the introduction of the catnip. Her data follow:

Cat name	Negative interactions before catnip	Negative interactions after catnip
Amelia	0	0
Bathsheba	3	6
Boris	3	4
Frank	0	1
Jupiter	0	0
Lupine	4	5
Madonna	1	3
Michelangelo	2	1
Oregano	3	5
Phantom	5	7
Posh	1	0
Sawyer	0	1
Scary	3	5
Slater	0	2
Tucker	2	2

a. Explain how you know that these data came from a matched pairs design.

b. State the relevant null and alternative hypotheses for testing the student's conjecture.

c. Conduct a simulation analysis to produce a p-value. Report the p-value, and interpret what it means (probability of what, assuming what?).

d. Summarize your conclusion about strength of evidence against the null hypothesis.

7.CE.16 Reconsider the previous exercise.

a. Comment on whether the conditions for applying a theory-based paired *t*-test are satisfied.

b. Regardless of your answer to part (a), conduct a theory-based paired *t*-test. Report the test statistic and p-value.

c. Summarize your conclusion about strength of evidence against the null hypothesis.

7.CE.17 Reconsider the previous two exercises.

a. Use the simulation analysis to produce a 95% confidence interval for the relevant parameter. Interpret what the interval reveals.

b. Determine a 95% theory-based paired *t*-interval for the relevant parameter. Interpret what the interval reveals.

7.CE.18 Reconsider the previous three exercises.

a. Even though it's not an appropriate analysis, perform a two-sample *t*-test (rather than the appropriate paired *t*-test) on the data. Report the hypotheses, test statistic, and p-value. Summarize the conclusion that you would draw if this were the correct analysis.

b. How has the p-value changed from the paired test?

c. Does this analysis indicate that the pairing was useful in this study? Explain.

INVESTIGATION: FILTERING WATER IN CAMEROON

Students and professors in the Nursing and Engineering Departments at Hope College went to the central African country of Cameroon to help improve drinking water quality and community health in rural communities by installing water filters in or near homes in one village. The families living in this village had no electricity, had no water distribution system, and got their water from streams. The filters they installed contained a diffuser plate, fine sand, coarse sand, and gravel. Using the new filters, family members were expected to gather their water and filter it before drinking, instead of drinking directly from the stream as was common practice.

Students working on this project examined the quality of the filters by looking at many different variables, including general observations, filter observations, microbiology observations, household practice observations, user perceptions, and water source observations. It should be noted, when making inferences, the water filters in this data set should be treated as a sample of all filters that could be constructed if this pilot project were expanded to other villages. Thus, inference is to an as-yet-unbuilt, larger population of filters.

PART 1

STEP 1: Ask a research question. There are several research questions we will ask in this investigation. The first one is: On average, is there a significant difference in the *E. coli* counts between the water that has just been filtered and water that is sitting in the bottom of a filter after it was filtered the previous day? The data set we will use contains results from 14 water filters each giving *E. coli* counts (per 100 mL) on the first day and the second day after the water was filtered.

STEP 2: Design a study and collect data.

1. What are the observational units?
2. What variables are measured/recorded on each observational unit?
3. Identify the role of these variables (explanatory, response). Classify the variables in this study as categorical or quantitative.
4. Are the samples of the first *E. coli* count independent or dependent of the samples of the second *E. coli* count? Explain. Based on your answer, is this an independent samples or paired design?
5. Could the sample size of 14 be large enough to give a valid p-value from a theory-based test of significance?
6. State the null and alternative hypotheses to be investigated with this study in symbols or in words.

See data file **Ecoli-time**.

STEP 3: Explore the data.

7. What are the average *E. coli* counts for each day? Did the *E. coli* in the sample increase or decrease on average from Day 1 to Day 2? Explain. Also give the standard deviations for the *E. coli* counts for each day.

8. What is the average of the difference (Day 1 – Day 2) in *E. coli* counts? Does the sign of this average correspond to your answer of increasing or decreasing between Day 1 and Day 2 in the previous question? Explain. Also give the standard deviation for the differences in *E. coli* counts.

STEP 4: Draw inferences.

9. Carry out an appropriate test of significance to see whether, on average, there is a genuine difference between the first *E. coli* count and the second *E. coli* count. Report your p-value and a 95% confidence interval.

STEP 5: Formulate conclusions.

10. Based on your p-value and confidence interval, what conclusions can you draw from this test?

11. Can generalizations be made to a larger population? Is there a cause-effect relationship between the variables?

STEP 6: Look back and ahead.

12. Discuss the study design. Why does pairing make sense here? What would you do differently to improve upon this study? What further research would you propose based on your findings from this study?

PART 2

As mentioned earlier, sand is used in the filter. Different filters had different amounts of sand. The students split the filters into two groups: those that had more than 2 inches of sand and those that had less. We will explore whether this difference results in different *E. coli* counts when filtering the water. In this sample, we have results from 19 filters, 14 with more than 2 inches of sand and 5 with less than 2 inches of sand. (See data file **Ecoli-sand**.)

13. Identify the explanatory and response variables in this study. Classify the variables in this study as categorical or quantitative.

14. What are the average *E. coli* counts for each sand level? Are the counts higher or lower with the higher level of sand in the filter? Also give the standard deviations for the *E. coli* counts for each sand level.

15. Are the samples of the first *E. coli* count independent or dependent of the samples of the second *E. coli* count? Explain.

16. Is the sample large enough to use a theory-based test?

17. Carry out an appropriate test of significance to see whether on average there is a difference in the *E. coli* counts between filters with more than 2 inches of sand and those with less. Report your p-value, a 95% confidence interval, and your conclusion.

PART 3

Let's look at one last research question. As a general rule, the flow rate of a water filter in good working condition should be around 1,000 mL/min. Let's test to see whether these water filters had an average flow rate that is significantly different than 1,000 mL/min. (See data set **Ecoli-flow**.)

18. List some similarities and differences between this research question and our first research question looking at the average difference in first and second *E. coli* counts.

19. Use the **Descriptive Statistics** applet to create a dotplot of the flow rates. Include average and standard deviation for the flow rate. What do you observe?

20. Carry out an appropriate test of significance to see whether the Cameroon water filters (population) tend to flow at a rate different than 1,000 mL/min, or is an average of 1,000 mL/min plausible? State your hypotheses, 95% confidence interval, p-value, and conclusions.

21. You should have found that 1,000 mL/min is a plausible value for average flow rate for the population of all similar water filters. Does this mean that all the filters have flow rates of about 1,000 mL/min? Is testing a single mean here really telling us what we need to know about these filters? Why or why not?

Research Article   www.wiley.com/college/tintle

Lie Detection   Read "The Eyes Don't Have It: Lie Detection and Neuro-Linguistic Programming" by Wiseman et al. (2012), 7(7), e40259, in the journal *PLoS One*.

Analyzing More General Situations

So far our data sets have been fairly simple in their structure. That's a good way to start, but life is not always simple. The next three chapters extend what you have seen to more general situations.

UNIT 1–3 DATA STRUCTURES

UNIT 1: One Binary or One Quantitative Variable

UNIT 2: Comparing Two Groups

	EXPLANATORY	RESPONSE
Chapter 5	Binary	Binary
Chapter 6	Binary	Quantitative
Chapter 7	Binary	Quantitative (paired)

UNIT 3: Association Between Variables

	EXPLANATORY	RESPONSE
Chapter 8	Categorical	Categorical
Chapter 9	Categorical	Quantitative
Chapter 10	Quantitative	Quantitative

Although the data structures in Unit 3 are new, and they vary from one chapter to the next, most of what you have already seen will still apply. We will still use the six-step statistical investigation method to structure a scientific investigation. We will still use the 3S Strategy for testing hypotheses. The statistic will be different for different chapters, but apart from that, the simulation step will be the same. As before, we ask, "What if the null hypothesis is true: How could the statistic behave?" As before, the answer takes the form of a null distribution for the statistic and again we use a p-value to assess the strength of evidence. We will also consider how to follow-up a statistically significant test with confidence intervals to further explore the associations we are analyzing.

Common Null and Alternative Hypotheses

But wait: There's more! For Chapters 8, 9, and 10 (except for Section 8.4) there is a single generic way to think about the hypotheses. Abstractly, we will always be testing the same null hypothesis, namely, that there is *no association between the response variable and the explanatory variable* and the alternative is simply that *there is an association*. This way to think about the hypotheses can help you deepen your understanding of how the various chapters and methods are connected. Not only can you state the null hypothesis generically ("no association") but you can think of the 3S strategy in generic terms: You typically want a statistic that is small when there is no association, but large when the association is strong. To simulate the values of the statistic under the null hypothesis, you break the association by shuffling the response variable (reassigning the values at random to the explanatory variable values) to get the null distribution. As always, a tiny p-value indicates strong evidence of a genuine association, too strong to be attributed just due to random chance.

Issues in Multiple Testing

Chapters 8 and 9 are similar to Chapters 5 and 6. The main difference is that now (in Chapters 8 and 9) the categorical explanatory variables might have multiple categories instead of being binary (as in Chapters 5 and 6). Thus, Chapter 8 deals with multiple proportions and Chapter 9 deals with multiple means.

You might think that to compare multiple proportions (or multiple means), one simply conducts all the possible two-sample comparisons between the groups using the methods you learned in Chapters 5 and 6. For example, with four groups, we could test all the different ways we could pair them up. If our groups are labeled A, B, C, and D our comparisons are A vs. B, A vs. C, A vs. D, B vs. C, B vs. D, and C vs. D, giving us six tests of significance to perform. Suppose each of these tests is tested at the 5% significance level (i.e., rejecting the null hypothesis if the p-value is smaller than 0.05). Now suppose the null hypotheses in these tests are all true (all four of the group parameters are actually the same). This means that for each test there is a 5% chance that we will make a mistake and reject the null hypothesis even though each statistic actually did happen by chance alone. In Section 2.3 this was defined as a **Type I error**, or false alarm. Each time we do a test, we have a chance of making a Type I error, which we control through the level of significance. The problem is, these Type I errors "accumulate" when we do more and more tests on the same data. (For an analogy, suppose that every time you ski down a certain run, there's a 5% chance you will fall. If you ski down the run 15 times, what's the chance you will fall at least once?) If we conduct six tests each at the 5% significance level, our overall Type I error rate (the probability of rejecting at least one of the six null hypotheses that are all actually true) jumps to more than 26%.

An alternative approach is to use one test that compares all four parameters at once. If we fail to reject the null hypothesis, say at the 5% level, we are "done," in that we will conclude that we don't have evidence that the long-run parameters differ. By constructing a statistic that compares all sample proportions or sample means at once, we can perform just one test and thus we can keep the probability of a Type I error as small as we want. But, to do this, we need to find a single statistic that measures the differences in all our proportions (or means) at once so we can run one overall test. We'll use the Mean Absolute Difference (MAD) statistic in both Chapters 8 (differences in proportions) and 9 (differences in means) to do this. We'll also see the commonly used theory-based alternatives: the chi-square test and ANOVA. In these cases we'll also explore a follow-up method that allows us to begin to construct a more detailed picture of the nature of the relationship, when evidence exists that there is a relationship.

Comparing More Than Two Proportions

In Chapter 5 you learned how to compare two groups using proportions. In this chapter, we will show you how to compare more than two groups. In Chapter 5 you worked with data in the form of 2 × 2 tables. Here we'll work first with 2 × 3 tables and eventually with larger tables. Recall before Chapter 1, in the Preliminaries chapter, we looked at a study that explored the best way to recruit people to become organ donors. The data from that study could have been summarized in a 2 × 3 table like that shown here.

		Default option		
		Opt in	Opt out	Neutral
Organ donor	Yes	23	41	44
	No	32	9	12

Just as in Chapter 5, the response variable is binary. However, in Chapter 5, the explanatory variable was always binary and here our explanatory variable (default option) has three categories. With three or more groups, we can often state the null hypothesis to be that all groups have the same probabilities of success. If any one sample proportion differs significantly from the others, there is evidence against the null. Another equivalent way to state the null hypothesis is that there is no association between the explanatory variable (default option) and the response variable (whether agree to be an organ donor). This kind of test is called an *overall test* because it tests all three probabilities at once.

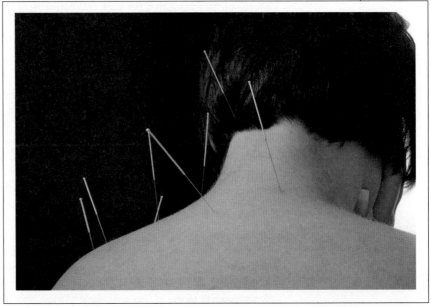

Piotr Rzeszutek/Shutterstock

Many things will be the same as in Chapter 5. As always, inference will take place as part of the six-step method. You will use segmented bar graphs to display conditional proportions, just as before. You will use the 3S strategy to compute p-values by simulation. When the overall test tells you that group differences are statistically significant, you can follow up using pairwise tests and intervals to pin down where the population differences are. For these pairwise comparisons, you'll use the same methods as in Chapter 5. (But you can think of the overall test as preventing us from doing all these comparisons when it is not necessary; see the Unit 3 Introduction for some discussion about this.)

Chapter 8 has four sections. Section 8.1 takes a simulation-based approach—but we need to think carefully about what to use as our statistic. Section 8.2 shows how one choice of statistic leads to a theory-based shortcut. This latter statistic also easily extends to any number of categories for both the explanatory variable and/or the response variable. Section 8.3 elaborates on the theory-based method shown in Section 8.2. Finally, Section 8.4 shows how to compare observed data (e.g., single categorical variable) to a prescribed model.

SECTION 8.1 | COMPARING MULTIPLE PROPORTIONS: SIMULATION-BASED APPROACH

INTRODUCTION

In Chapter 5 we saw how to use simulation-based methods to investigate the statistical significance of the difference between two conditional proportions. This was accomplished by taking the difference in the two conditional proportions as our statistic and shuffling (re-randomizing) the response outcomes to the explanatory variable groups to simulate the null distribution under the null hypothesis of no association between the response and explanatory variables. This allowed us to compare the observed difference in the sample proportions to these simulated differences in conditional proportions in order to draw a conclusion about strength of evidence.

Would that approach work when comparing categorical variables that have more than two categories? Yes, but the key question is first defining a reasonable statistic to measure the degree of the association between two categorical variables with multiple categories.

Coming to a Stop

Example 8.1

Students at Virginia Tech studied which vehicles come to a complete stop at an intersection with four-way stop signs. They looked at several factors to see which (if any) were associated with coming to a complete stop. (They defined a complete stop as "the speed of the vehicle will become zero at least for an [instant]"). Some of these variables included the age of the driver, how many passengers were in the vehicle, and type of vehicle. The variable we are going to investigate is the arrival position of vehicles approaching an intersection all traveling in the same direction. They classified this arrival pattern into three groups: whether the vehicle arrives alone, is the lead in a group of vehicles, or is a follower in a group of vehicles. The students studied one specific intersection in northern Virginia at a variety of different times. Because random assignment was not used, this is an observational study. Also note that no vehicle from one group is paired with a vehicle from another group. In other words, there is independence between the different groups of vehicles.

You should have seen in Chapters 5 and 6 that we can often state our null and alternative hypotheses in terms of "no association" (null) and "association" (alternative). In this case, the null and alternative hypotheses are:

Null hypothesis: There is no association between the arrival position of the vehicle and whether or not it comes to a complete stop.

Alternative hypothesis: There is an association between the arrival position of the vehicle and whether or not it comes to a complete stop.

ANOTHER WAY TO WRITE THE HYPOTHESES

THINK ABOUT IT

What does "no association" mean in this context? Specifically, what does no association imply about the similarity or differences in the conditional probabilities that stop for the three stopping positions? What should be true about the segmented bar graph if there is no association?

As we discussed in Chapter 5, no association implies that the probabilities for each of the explanatory variable conditions are the same. The difference in this example compared to what we saw in Chapter 5 is that now there are three probabilities of stopping (single, lead, or following vehicle). If the null hypothesis (no association) is true, then these three probabilities are all actually equal. Therefore, in the samples, we would expect the three bars of a segmented bar graph comparing the sample proportions to be shaded similarly. *Note:* This doesn't mean that the shaded areas within each bar will be the equally sized (e.g., 50/50) but that the portions of the bars with each color are the same across the bars. Here is another way to write the null hypothesis that reflects this:

Null hypothesis: The probability that a single vehicle will stop is *the same as* the probability a lead vehicle will stop, which is *the same as* the probability that a following vehicle will stop. In other words all three probabilities are actually the same.

Here is the null hypothesis written in symbols:

H_0: $\pi_{Single} = \pi_{Lead} = \pi_{Follow}$ where π represents the probability a vehicle will stop.

One more way to think about this is that the null hypothesis means that regardless of what the arrival position is, the chance the vehicle will stop is the same.

We've already stated the alternative hypothesis: There is an association between arrival position and whether or not the vehicle stops. Now let's translate that into what it means for the conditional probabilities.

THINK ABOUT IT

What does "there is an association" mean in this context? Specifically, what does "an association" imply about the similarity or differences in probabilities of stopping across the arrival position categories?

Saying there "is an association" is a very generic, all-purpose kind of statement because "an association" can mean several different things. In short, it means that the null hypothesis is not true—at least one of the pairs of probabilities of stopping is not equal. Here is the alternative hypothesis in words:

H_a: At least one of the three probabilities of stopping is different from the others.

A common student mistake is to think that the alternative hypothesis means that *all* of the probabilities must be different from each other. But, even if just one of the probabilities is different from the others, that's an association between the two variables.

EXPLORE THE DATA

The results for this study are shown in Table 8.1 and Figure 8.1.

	Single vehicle	Lead vehicle	Following vehicle	Total
TABLE 8.1 A two-way table showing the number (and conditional percentage) of vehicles that came to a complete stop for three different arrival positions to the intersection				
Complete stop	151 (85.8%)	38 (90.5%)	76 (77.6%)	265
Not complete stop	25 (14.2%)	4 (9.5%)	22 (22.4%)	51
Total	176	42	98	316

We also put the data into the **Multiple Proportions** applet and produced a segmented bar graph. (See Figure 8.1.)

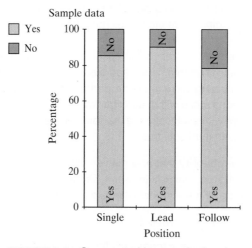

FIGURE 8.1   Segmented bar graph showing the proportion of vehicles that came to a complete stop (yes) for the three different arrival positions to the intersection.

We see from Table 8.1 that a vehicle was most likely to stop (90.50%) if it was leading a group of vehicles as it approached the intersection, followed by single vehicles (85.80%), and then by following vehicles (77.60%). Although these percentages are all different, are they different enough to be statistically significant? Are they different enough to convince us that the differences didn't arise just by random chance? In other words, do these sample proportions provide convincing evidence that any of the probabilities of stopping differ for the different arrival positions of vehicles at this intersection?

APPLYING THE 3S STRATEGY

The first step in the 3S strategy is to specify a statistic. The statistic should be a single number that summarizes all the evidence for the alternative hypothesis based on the sample data.

> **THINK ABOUT IT**
>
> Propose a formula to determine a single number (statistic) that summarizes how different the conditional proportions are in our sample. That is, how might we measure the discrepancies in these conditional proportions across the three groups with one numerical value? What types of values for that statistic (e.g., large or small, positive or negative) would you consider evidence against the null hypothesis?

There are many different statistics you can use. Let us take a look at a few possible statistics. Keep in mind that the alternative hypothesis simply says at least two of the probabilities differ from each other. So if we have any pair of proportions with a large difference, that is evidence against the null hypothesis and in favor of the alternative hypothesis. One approach is to examine each pair of differences. Let's start by computing the three differences in proportions.

$\hat{p}_S$ = proportion of single vehicles that stopped = 0.858

$\hat{p}_L$ = proportion of lead vehicles that stopped = 0.905

Difference in conditional proportions = 0.858 − 0.905 = −0.047

$\hat{p}_F$ = proportion of following vehicles that stopped = 0.776

$\hat{p}_S$ = proportion of single vehicles that stopped = 0.858

Difference in proportions = 0.776 − 0.858 = −0.082

$\hat{p}_L$ = proportion of lead vehicles that stopped = 0.905

$\hat{p}_F$ = proportion of following vehicles that stopped = 0.776

Difference in proportions = 0.905−0.776 = 0.129

We now have three numbers (−0.047, −0.082 and 0.129) measuring the differences in the pairs of sample proportions. Whereas we could evaluate each of these differences separately, this has the potential to inflate the overall Type I error rate by doing multiple tests (see the Unit 3 introduction for more about this as well as FAQ 8.1.1). The null hypothesis we want to test is an *overall* test of no association, so the statistic must be a single number to test this single overall hypothesis.

 8.1.1

| FAQ 8.1.1 | www.wiley.com/college/tintle |

What's wrong with conducting multiple tests?

THINK ABOUT IT

How can we combine the three separate differences in proportions into a single number that summarizes the entire strength of evidence for the alternative hypothesis?

One option is to subtract the smallest group proportion from the largest: 0.129. This represents the largest of the differences. However, this doesn't tell us much about the *average difference*.

Another option is to simply average these three numbers: [−0.047 + (−0.082) + 0.129]/3 = 0. Uh-oh. That's not good. We certainly wouldn't say there are no differences in the conditional proportions in this sample. The differences in proportions "cancelled out" because some were negative and some were positive. Also if we subtracted the proportions in different orders, we would come up with a different statistic, so this method does not work well. To get around this, one option is to make all the differences positive by taking the absolute value before averaging them. You could also square the numbers to make them positive or, as we will discuss in the next section, standardize and square to yield a *chi-square* statistic.

1. **Statistic — Mean absolute difference:** One single number that summarizes the sample evidence for the alternative hypothesis is (0.047 + 0.082 + 0.129)/3 = 0.258/3 = 0.086. This is the average (or mean) of the (absolute value of the) differences in the conditional proportions, which we will refer to as the **MAD** statistic. It provides a measure of how far apart these sample proportions are on average.

 8.1.2

8.1.3

> **THINK ABOUT IT**
>
> What would have to be true for the average of the absolute differences to equal 0? Could the average of absolute differences ever be negative? What types of values of this statistic (e.g., large or small) would provide evidence in favor of the alternative hypothesis?

The average of the absolute differences is equal to 0 when each pairwise difference is 0. This only happens when all of the sample proportions are the same. So, small values of the MAD offer weak evidence against the null. Conversely, large values of the MAD offer strong evidence against the null hypothesis and in support of the alternative that at least one of those probabilities is different from the others. The absolute value of a difference will always be nonnegative. If we average several nonnegative numbers we will always get a nonnegative number. So the MAD statistic is always going to be nonnegative (zero or positive), with larger and larger values indicating stronger and stronger evidence against the null hypothesis.

2. **Simulate:** We know that the next step in the 3S strategy is to simulate the null distribution of the statistic.

> **THINK ABOUT IT**
>
> How can we simulate MAD values assuming the null hypothesis of no association? Could we do this with playing cards?

We've seen already that the null hypothesis of "no association" means that the value of the explanatory variable (the arrival position of the vehicle) has no impact on, or no relationship with, the outcome of the response variable (whether or not the car comes to a complete stop). To simulate this with cards, we could let black cards represent the vehicles that stopped in our sample and red represent vehicles that did not stop. Specifically we would have 265 black cards to represent the stoppers and 51 red cards to represent the nonstoppers. Simulating the null hypothesis of no association means that we can shuffle all the cards and no matter which group they are dealt into (lead, follow, single) they will always stop if they are a stopper (black card) and always not stop if they are a nonstopper (red card). So then we would:

1. Deal 176 of the cards to represent the single group, 42 to represent the lead group, and 98 to represent the following group.
2. Determine the proportion of black cards in each group to calculate the simulated proportions of stoppers under the assumption that the null is true. From these simulated proportions we can now calculate a simulated MAD statistic.

8.1.4

We can also think of this simulation done not with cards but with the raw data. To simulate "no association" using the data table, we can shuffle the observed outcomes of the response variable (stopping or not) and reassign each to an existing outcome of the explanatory variable (vehicle arrival position). This accomplishes the same thing as the simulation done with cards. We will do this with the **Multiple Proportions** applet. Figure 8.2 shows part of the spreadsheet for the observed data from the study, the conditional proportions for the vehicles that stopped, a segmented bar graph for the sample data, and the observed value of our statistic, 0.086.

The table below summarizes the key aspects of the simulation:

Null hypothesis	=	Proportions are the same in each population
One repetition	=	Re-randomizing cars to the order they arrived without changing whether or not they stopped
Statistic	=	Mean absolute difference in proportions between the three groups

FIGURE 8.2 The sample data are pasted into the applet and the display shows a segmented bar graph of the sample as well as our observed value of the statistic, the mean of the absolute values of all pairwise differences (MAD).

First we will shuffle the response variable one time. The results from the applet are shown in Figure 8.3.

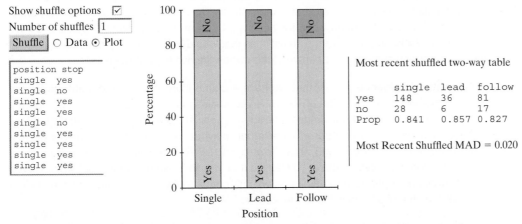

FIGURE 8.3 The results after one shuffling of the response variable. Part of the shuffled data is shown on the left (using the **Data** option) along with a segmented bar graph (using the **Plot** option) for these shuffled data and the mean of absolute differences for the shuffled data.

When viewing the **Most Recent Shuffle** output, you can see the outcomes for the explanatory variable did not change whereas the outcomes for the response variable were reassigned to those outcomes. The segmented bar graph and the conditional proportions also reflect the results from the shuffled data. One last thing to note is the sum of the absolute values for the shuffled data is 0.020. This outcome shows that for this shuffle we obtained three sample proportions that were a bit closer than they were for the original data, because this shuffled MAD value is lower than the observed MAD of 0.086. Will this always be the case? Let's shuffle some more and find out.

We used the applet to conduct 1,000 shuffles of the data, which yielded 1,000 values of the simulated values of the MAD statistic as shown in Figure 8.4.

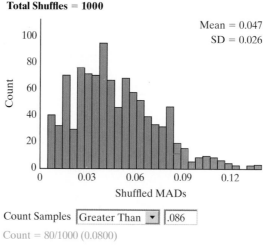

Count Samples [Greater Than ▼] [.086]

Count = 80/1000 (0.0800)

FIGURE 8.4   Distribution of the simulated values of the MAD statistic when there is no association between arrival position of the vehicle and whether or not it comes to a complete stop at the intersection.

THINK ABOUT IT

Why is the simulated distribution of the statistic not a bell-shaped curve centered at zero like we are used to seeing?

8.1.5

By making all of the differences in the proportions nonnegative (by taking the absolute value), we cannot get a negative value of the statistic. The result is a right-skewed distribution of statistics that could happen when the null hypothesis of "no association" is true. We have fewer and fewer large values for the statistic, as that would indicate a larger difference among the groups, which shouldn't happen very often when the null hypothesis is true.

3. **Strength of evidence:**   Now that we have a distribution of simulated statistics for the null hypothesis and the value of the observed statistic from our data, we can compute a p-value as a measure of the strength of evidence against the null hypothesis. In the past we have used the way we've phrased our alternative hypothesis to determine whether the test is one-sided or two-sided and, thus, how to calculate the p-value (one tail or both tails). But in this case, values of the MAD statistic that are more extreme than what we observed will always be larger positive values, so we only care about values that are equal to or even larger than the observed value of the statistic.

As always, the p-value will be the probability, assuming the null is true, that we obtain a statistic value as extreme as or more extreme than what we observed in our sample. In this case the p-value turns out to be 0.080 because we saw a MAD value of 0.086 or greater occur 80 times (out of 1,000) when simulating the null hypothesis. To see this, look back at Figure 8.4.

With a p-value of 0.080 we have moderate evidence against the null hypothesis, but this evidence is not extremely strong. So, these sample data provide only moderate evidence that the probability of coming to a complete stop is related to the arrival position of the vehicle. It is probably unwise to generalize these results to intersections beyond the one in northern Virginia that the students studied. Each intersection probably has many different factors that would influence someone to come to a complete stop or not. We also would not want to draw any cause-and-effect conclusions between arrival position and coming to a complete stop, because this is an observational study and not a randomized experiment.

If we had found more evidence of a difference in the groups, we might then proceed to examine confidence intervals to help us see which arrival positions' stopping probabilities are significantly different from each other. This idea will be discussed in more detail with theory-based methods in the next section.

 8.1.6

Recruiting Organ Donors

In Example P.1 we considered a study that investigated how to encourage people to be more likely to become organ donors. At the time, we did not formally analyze the data from the study. Now we are studying methods for comparing three groups, so we can further analyze the data and draw inferential conclusions from this study.

Recall that researchers asked volunteer subjects to imagine they moved to a new state, applied for a driver's license, and needed to decide whether or not to become an organ donor. Researchers created three different versions of the survey, each with a different donor recruiting strategy. Subjects were randomly assigned to one of the three types of recruiting strategies:

- The default option is to be an organ donor, and individuals have to *opt out* of organ donation (opt-out group)
- The default option is to not be an organ donor, and individuals have to *opt in* to organ donation (opt-in group)
- There is no default option, and individuals have to choose whether or not they will be an organ donor (neutral group)

1. What are the observational units? What are the variables? Are the variables categorical or quantitative? If categorical, how many categories do they have? Also, identify the roles (explanatory or response) of the variables.

Observational units:	
Explanatory variable:	Type:
Response variable:	Type:

2. Did this study make use of random sampling, random assignment, both, or neither? Also describe the implication of your answer in terms of scope of conclusions that can potentially be drawn from this study.

3. Did this study pair subjects in one group with subjects in another group or are the subjects in the different recruiting groups independent of each other?

4. Let's write out the hypotheses.

   a. Write the appropriate null and alternative hypotheses (in words) using the language of association between the explanatory and response variables.

   b. Express the null hypothesis in symbols. (*Hint*: Remember that hypotheses are always about parameters, so define and use appropriate symbols for parameters.)

5. Researchers found that 23 of 55 subjects in the opt-in group chose to be organ donors, 41 of 50 in the opt-out group chose to be organ donors, and 44 of 56 in the neutral group chose to be organ donors.

   a. Based on these counts, produce a two-way table of counts, putting the explanatory variable in columns. (*Hint*: You have seen this table earlier in this chapter!)

   b. For each of the three groups, calculate the conditional proportion who agreed to become an organ donor.

   c. Produce a segmented bar graph (by hand or with the **Multiple Proportions** applet) to compare these conditional proportions across the three groups.

d. Comment on what your calculations and graph reveal about whether the default option used in the question appears to affect how likely the person is to become an organ donor.

We see some differences in the sample proportions of individuals who chose to be organ donors across the three treatments, but are these differences large enough to be statistically significant? In other words, do these data provide strong evidence of an association between donor recruiting strategy (opt-in, opt-out, neutral) and choosing to become an organ donor in the population?

6. Suggest two possible explanations for how these observed proportions could have turned out to be as different from each other as they are. (*Hint:* Think about what our null and alternative hypotheses are.)

Applying the 3S strategy

To investigate, we will see how we can apply the 3S strategy to these data. Because researchers are attempting to minimize (or at least control) the probability of Type I errors, in cases with multiple groups they first do an overall test (see the Unit 3 introduction for more discussion on this). However, this requires computing a single statistic and considering the null distribution of that statistic. Let's look at this approach now.

1. Statistic

7. What statistic would you propose?

a. Propose a formula for a statistic that could be used to measure how different the three sample proportions are. (*Hint:* The key here is that the statistic needs to provide a *single* number that somehow focuses on differences between/among the observed sample proportions.)

b. For the statistic you propose, would a large value or small value give evidence for the alternative hypothesis that at least one recruiting strategy has a different probability of someone agreeing to be a donor?

When we compared *two* proportions in Chapter 5, we used the difference in two proportions as the statistic. In this chapter, though, there are multiple proportions. There are actually several reasonable ways of summarizing the differences among the groups in one number. Once you have settled on a statistic, you apply the 3S strategy as before—simulate the distribution of the statistic under the null hypothesis and then see where the observed value of the statistic falls in that distribution.

8. One possible statistic is $\hat{p}_{max} - \hat{p}_{min}$. Review the conditional proportions you determined in #5(b) and calculate the observed value of this statistic for these data. Why might this be a less than satisfactory choice?

However, this statistic ignores some of the groups. Another reasonable statistic to calculate is the mean of the absolute values of differences for each pair. (We could call this statistic **MAD** for mean of absolute differences.)

9. Let's construct the MAD statistic for these data by going through the following steps.

a. Review the conditional proportions of organ donors you determined in #5(b) and calculate the differences in these proportions for each pair:

Opt-out minus opt-in:

Opt-out minus neutral:

Opt-in minus neutral:

b. Calculate the mean of the absolute values of these differences.

So which statistic should you use? And how can you use the statistic to estimate a p-value? We'll consider those questions in the following sections.

2. **Simulation:** In Chapter 5 we first saw how we can simulate a null hypothesis of no association by shuffling the response variable outcomes across the explanatory variable groups. This models the random assignment process used in the data collection process, and, assuming the null hypothesis is true, "breaks any potential association" between the response and explanatory variables. We modeled this with playing cards in Chapter 5.

10. Describe how you would model a simulation of the null hypothesis with red and black playing cards now that there are three explanatory variable groups instead of two. Make sure to tell how many black cards you would need and how many red ones. Also tell what each color of cards would represent. How many cards would you deal out to each group? What would you calculate after dealing them out?

11. Now let's use the **Multiple Proportions** applet to simulate a null distribution of these MAD statistics. This null distribution is again used to measure the strength of evidence provided by the observed statistic against the null hypothesis. Open the **Organ Donor** data file and paste the two columns (with column names) into the applet and press **Use Data**. (Or enter/paste in the two-way table of counts in the **Sample data** window and press **Use Table**.) Check the **Show table** box and verify that the sample proportions of organ donors match your answers from #5(b) and the observed MAD statistic shown matches your answer from #9(b). If you cannot see the whole table, click on the lower right corner and drag it to make the table larger.

   a. Now check **Show Shuffle Options** and leave **Number of Shuffles** at 1. Press **Shuffle Response** to perform one shuffle of the response variable values. You should see the shuffled response variable, the new two-way table for the simulated data, and the value of the simulated statistic (Most Recent Shuffled MAD) which is also placed in blue on the graph on the right. Select the **Plot** radio button to see the shuffled segmented bar graph. How does the distribution across the groups for the shuffled data compare to the original data? Is the simulated MAD statistic value closer to zero than the observed value of the MAD statistic?

   b. Now enter 999 for the **Number of Shuffles** and press **Shuffle Responses**. This repeats the shuffling of the response variable 999 more times for a total of 1,000 repetitions. You should see a graph of a null distribution of the MAD statistics. What is the shape of this distribution? Why is it not a bell-shaped curve centered at zero?

3. Strength of evidence

12. To estimate a p-value, determine how often the observed value of the statistic, or something even larger, occurred in the null distribution. (*Hint:* Enter the observed value for the MAD statistic from the research study in the **Count Samples** box and press **Count**.)

13. Based on the p-value, summarize the strength of evidence that the sample data provide against the null hypothesis.

Generalization

14. Comment on how the sample was obtained and to which population your conclusion can be generalized.

Causation

15. Comment on how the study was designed and whether a cause-and-effect conclusion is warranted from this study.

Look back and ahead

16. Summarize your conclusion for the researchers. Do you have any concerns about the study design? Any comments on sample size? Are there other limitations that you feel need to be addressed? Are there specific improvements you would suggest to make this study better? Based on what you concluded from this study, can you suggest one or two follow-up studies that could be carried out?

SECTION 8.1 Summary

The 3S strategy for simulation-based inference can be applied to comparing proportions across multiple groups. Neither the explanatory nor the response variable has to be binary. The key is choosing a formula for the statistic that reasonably summarizes the overall evidence against the null hypothesis.

- This approach provides an *overall* test of the multiple groups simultaneously, as opposed to testing each pair of groups separately, in order to guard against inflating the Type I error rate.
- The null hypothesis is that there is no association between the two variables in the population.
  - This is equivalent to saying that the probabilities of the response variable outcomes are identical for all categories of the explanatory variable.
- The alternative hypothesis is that there is an association between the two variables in the population.
  - No direction is specified for the association in the alternative hypothesis.
  - The alternative hypothesis can be expressed as saying that at least one population proportion (or probability) differs from the others.

The choice of a statistic to measure how different the groups are is not straightforward. Many reasonable statistics can be used.

- One reasonable statistic is to calculate the difference in sample proportions for each pair of groups and then take the **mean of the absolute differences (MAD)**.
  - Larger values of the MAD statistic indicate a greater difference in sample proportions across the groups.
- Another statistic is the largest sample proportion minus the smallest sample proportion; however, this statistic may be less powerful than the MAD in many cases.
- Other statistics also exist. The key thing to remember is that a single number is needed and that the general approach of the 3S strategy works regardless.

The simulation method is to shuffle the values (outcome categories) of the response variable and redistribute to the explanatory variable categories.

- This shuffling method simulates the results of the study under the assumption of no association between the variables (the response variable outcomes were going to be the same regardless of which group they are assigned to).
- As we've seen before, the p-value is calculated as the proportion of repetitions in which the simulated value of the statistic is at least as extreme as the observed value of the statistic.
  - As always, a small p-value provides evidence against the null hypothesis.
- As before, we will often use this shuffling method to obtain a p-value even with random sampling and studies with no randomness in the study design.

SECTION 8.2 COMPARING MULTIPLE PROPORTIONS: THEORY-BASED APPROACH

INTRODUCTION

As we've seen numerous times already, simulation methods are quite flexible because they work in many situations, but they do require a computer to perform enough repetitions to understand the long-run pattern of the null distribution. Theory-based approaches avoid the need for simulation but only work under certain conditions—which must be met in order to accurately predict the null distribution that would have occurred if you were to simulate.

In the past three chapters, our simulated null distributions were bell-shaped and centered at zero. Because of the way we constructed our statistics in the previous section, we saw that our null distribution was no longer bell-shaped or centered at zero. Unfortunately, the theory to accurately predict the variability of the null distribution for the MAD statistic is challenging.

As it turns out, if we use a slightly different statistic (the *chi-square statistic)*, instead of the MAD statistic, we can accurately predict the behavior of the null distribution by a mathematical model, called a chi-square distribution. In this section we will see how to use the chi-square statistic and chi-square distribution instead of simulation to conduct a theory-based test in order to evaluate the strength of evidence for an association between two categorical variables with multiple (two or more) categories.

Sham Acupuncture

Example 8.2

EXAMPLE

8.2

Increasingly, health insurers, federal agencies, medical organizations, and others are insisting on the use of evidence-based medicine in making health care decisions. Evidence-based medicine means only using medical treatments where evidence (measured using statistics, most typically based on randomized experiments) exists that a particular treatment is both effective and better than other available treatments.

Recently, a randomized experiment was conducted exploring the evidence for the effectiveness of acupuncture in the treatment of chronic lower back pain (Haake et al., 2007). Acupuncture involves the insertion of needles into the skin of the patient at specific locations (acupuncture points) around the body to treat a variety of ailments.

In the experiment, there were three treatment groups of interest: (1) verum acupuncture practiced according to traditional Chinese medicine principles; (2) sham acupuncture where needles were inserted into the skin but not at acupuncture points and not very deep (this is often used as a control in experiments involving acupuncture); and (3) traditional (nonacupuncture) therapy consisting of a combination of drugs, physical therapy, and exercise. A total of 1,162 patients were randomly assigned to each of the three treatment groups, yielding 387 patients in Groups 1 and 2 and 388 patients in Group 3.

THINK ABOUT IT

What are the explanatory and response variables in this study? Is there any pairing in the design of the study? If we find an effect, are we able to draw cause/effect conclusions?

The explanatory variable is the type of treatment. It is a categorical variable with three categories: verum acupuncture, sham acupuncture, and traditional therapy. The response variable is also categorical. It has two categories: whether or not there was significant relief from lower back pain. There wasn't any pairing of subjects between the treatment groups; rather the subjects in the three different treatment groups are independent of each other.

THINK ABOUT IT

What are the null and alternative hypotheses being tested in this study?

HYPOTHESES

The null hypothesis is that there is no association between the type of treatment received (real, sham, or no acupuncture) and whether or not someone in this population shows substantial reduction in back pain. In other words, the probability of improvement is the same across the three treatments. The alternative hypothesis is that there is an association between these two variables in the population. In other words, at least one of the probabilities of improvement is different from the others.

The data gathered on the 1,162 subjects are presented in Table 8.2 along with the conditional proportions comparing the treatment groups to whether or not patients showed a substantial reduction in lower back pain.

TABLE 8.2 Two-way table of pain reduction by acupuncture group

	Real acupuncture	Sham acupuncture	Nonacupuncture	Total
Substantial reduction in pain	184 (0.475)	171 (0.442)	106 (0.273)	461
Not a substantial reduction in pain	203 (0.525)	216 (0.558)	282 (0.727)	701
Total	387	387	388	1,162

We also put the two-way table into the **Multiple Proportions** applet (pressing **Use Table**) and produced the conditional proportions of those that had substantial reduction in pain (better) or not as well as a segmented bar graph. (See Figure 8.5.)

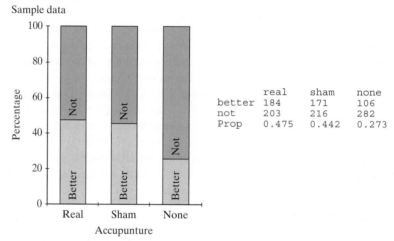

FIGURE 8.5 Segmented bar graph of pain reduction by acupuncture group and the conditional proportions for those that had substantial pain reduced (better) or not.

Both Table 8.2 and Figure 8.5 illustrate that real acupuncture showed the highest percentage of patients with reduction in pain symptoms—but is it significantly better than the other treatments?

SIMULATION-BASED APPROACH

In Section 8.1 we learned how to take a simulation-based approach to the analysis by applying the 3S strategy to test the statistical significance of an association between two categorical variables. Initially in that section, our choice of statistic was the mean of the absolute values of the differences in the conditional proportions between the groups (the MAD statistic).

1. **Statistic:** The absolute value of the differences in proportions of improvement comparing all three groups is:

 Real vs. sham: $0.475 - 0.442 = 0.033$

 Real vs. none: $0.475 - 0.273 = 0.202$

 Sham vs. none: $0.442 - 0.273 = 0.169$

 Thus, the observed statistic is MAD = $(0.033 + 0.202 + 0.169) = 0.404/3 = 0.135$

2. **Simulate:** We can use the **Multiple Proportions** applet to shuffle the response variable (equivalent to re-randomizing the subjects to treatments, assuming their responses will not change) and recompute the value of the statistic for each of the shuffled data sets. We repeated this process 1,000 times to obtain the null distribution shown in Figure 8.6.

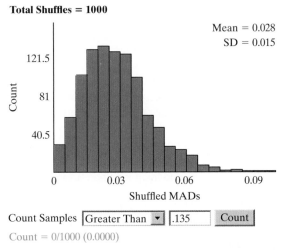

Total Shuffles = 1000

Mean = 0.028
SD = 0.015

Count Samples [Greater Than ▼] [.135] [Count]
Count = 0/1000 (0.0000)

FIGURE 8.6 Null distribution for acupuncture study.

3. **Strength of evidence:** The p-value in this study is approximately 0, because a statistic of 0.135 or larger never occurred in this simulation that assumes the null hypothesis is true. This gives us very strong evidence against the null hypothesis. We don't think it's plausible that the observed differences in conditional proportions that we saw in this study arose solely from the random chance in the random assignment process. We have very strong evidence that the treatment (type of acupuncture) used is genuinely associated with pain reduction.

ALTERNATE CHOICE OF STATISTIC—CHI-SQUARE

The MAD statistic focuses on how all pairs of proportions compare to each other. Another option is to consider how the proportions compare to some *average proportion*. As it turns out, this new statistic, called a ***chi-square statistic***, has the advantage of being well predicted by a mathematical model and thus is commonly used in practice for these types of problems. It also can be used on larger sized tables (two categorical variables, with any number of categories each; see Exploration 8.2B).

 8.2.1

> **THINK ABOUT IT**
>
> Reconsider Table 8.2. What is the overall proportion in the sample of 1,162 subjects that experienced substantial reduction in pain? What would we expect to be true about each of the group proportions if there really is no difference among the treatments?

If we ignored the type of treatment, then 461/1,162, or about 39.70%, of the patients experience substantial reduction in pain. If the different treatments really don't differ in their effectiveness, then we would expect this same percentage in each of the three categories.

> **THINK ABOUT IT**
>
> How could we compare each group proportion to this overall proportion? How could we *standardize* each comparison?

In general, when we standardize, we take the observed statistic, subtract the "typical" (average) value, and divide by the standard deviation. So, similar to standardized z-statistics that we have calculated before, we could standardize each group proportion ($\hat{p}_i$) by comparing it to this overall proportion ($\hat{p}$) and dividing by the standard deviation of the group proportion for that sample size assuming the null is true ($\sqrt{\hat{p}(1 - \hat{p})/n_i}$, where n_i is each individual group's sample size). We do so as follows.

Real	Sham	None
$\dfrac{0.475 - 0.397}{\sqrt{0.397(1 - 0.397)/387}} = 3.14$	$\dfrac{0.442 - 0.397}{\sqrt{0.397(1 - 0.397)/387}} = 1.81$	$\dfrac{0.273 - 0.397}{\sqrt{0.397(1 - 0.397)/388}} = -4.99$

This gives us *standardized statistics* which tell us how different each group proportion is from the average (overall) proportion. In particular, notice that both the real group and the none group are quite a bit different from the overall proportion because their standardized statistics are greater than 2 or less than -2.

So how do we combine these into one overall standardized statistic? We could just add them together, but again we don't want the positive and negative values to cancel each other out. This time we will square them before we add them together: $3.14^2 + 1.81^2 + (-4.99)^2 \approx 38.04$.

$$\chi^2 = \left[\left(\frac{0.475 - 0.397}{\sqrt{0.397(1 - 0.397)/387}}\right)^2 + \left(\frac{0.442 - 0.397}{\sqrt{0.397(1 - 0.397)/387}}\right)^2 \right.$$
$$\left. + \left(\frac{0.273 - 0.397}{\sqrt{0.397(1 - 0.397)/388}}\right)^2 = 38.04\right]$$

[See the Formulas section for an alternate (and more generalizable) way to do this calculation.]

> **THINK ABOUT IT**
>
> What value would this statistic have if the group proportions had all been the same? What types of values will this statistic have if there is a strong association between the explanatory variable and the response variable?

The calculation just performed is a special case of the **chi-square statistic**. The smallest value this statistic can be is zero, which would only happen if all the group proportions had been exactly the same. Larger values of the chi-square statistic indicate stronger evidence against the null hypothesis. To decide whether this chi-square statistic is larger than we would expect by chance, we need to see how it performs in repeated shuffles. Figure 8.7 shows a simulated null distribution for the chi-square statistic for these data. (Like with the MAD statistic, we only need to worry about values larger than our observed statistic to be considered *more extreme* for this always positive statistic.)

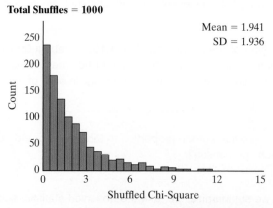

FIGURE 8.7 Null distribution of chi-square statistic.

Not surprisingly, the results are similar to when we used the mean of the absolute differences in proportions as the statistic. The null distribution is skewed to the right and the observed value of the statistic (38.05) is very far in the tail of the distribution. Similar to what we found with the MAD statistic, our observed statistic is not even close to the largest simulated values, giving us very strong evidence against the null hypothesis, in favor of the alternative hypothesis.

HOW DO WE DECIDE WHICH STATISTIC TO USE?

See FAQ 8.2.1 for more details, but the chi-square statistic does have some advantages. It is a standardized statistic in that it takes into account the sample sizes in our groups. In fact, looking at the individual components of the chi-square sum (think of them as mini z-statistics) helps us identify which cells have the largest discrepancy from what the null hypothesis would predict. Furthermore, chi-square statistics can more directly be compared to other chi-square statistics from different studies (as long as the tables are similar in size).

FAQ 8.2.1	www.wiley.com/college/tintle

Which test statistic?

Another huge advantage is that the chi-square statistic is often well predicted by a mathematical model—that is, it can be used to obtain a theory-based p-value. Yet another advantage to the chi-square statistic is that it easily generalizes to a categorical response variable with more than two categories (see Exploration 8.2B for details).

THEORY-BASED APPROACH: THE CHI-SQUARE TEST

8.2.2

Instead of actually simulating data (shuffling) to generate a null distribution, can we use mathematical theory to predict the results that would occur by simulation? For the $\hat{p}_{max} - \hat{p}_{min}$ and MAD statistics, the answer is no. However, if we use the chi-square statistic, the answer is yes. Figure 8.8 shows the theoretical *chi-square distribution* overlaid on the simulated chi-square statistics. This appears to be a close match to the simulated distribution.

FIGURE 8.8 A chi-square distribution used to predict our simulated null distribution for the acupuncture study.

This also predicts the p-value for the test of no association to be 0.0000, which is comparable to what we obtained through simulation.

The applet can also display more details about the chi-square statistic calculations and output for the theory-based test if you check the **Show χ^2 output** box (Figure 8.9).

```
          Chisq Cell Contributions
                  real   sham   none
          better  6.05   1.99   14.92
          not     3.98   1.31    9.82

          Sum = 38.05
          df = 2
```
Show χ² output: ☑   `p-value = 0.0000`

FIGURE 8.9 Chi-square Test from **Multiple Proportions** applet.

Note: The **Chisq Cell Contributions** show the components being summed together for the other version of the formula as shown in the Formulas section. The cell contribution values are useful for helping you detect where larger differences arise (e.g., much of the relationship here comes from the smaller than expected number of participants who felt better without acupuncture and the larger than expected number who did not feel better without acupuncture).

VALIDITY CONDITIONS

Of course, this theory-based approach only works well when certain validity conditions are met. When the conditions are not met, the simulation-based method still gives accurate estimates of the p-value, whereas the theory-based approach does not. When the validity conditions are met, then the results will be similar regardless of the method (simulation- or theory-based) you choose.

Like we have seen with other theory-based tests, the **validity condition for a chi-square test** is that we need large sample sizes. When we were comparing two proportions, we said we had large sample sizes if the number of successes and failures were both at least 10 in each explanatory variable group. We will use the same guideline here. If each cell of the two-way table contains at least 10 observations, then we will consider our sample sizes to be large enough for the theory-based chi-square test to work well. (*Note:* This is a rather conservative guideline and if your data do not satisfy it, you might still consider the theory-based approach. See the Calculation Details appendix for more details and alternative validity conditions.)

Did we have large enough sample sizes in our acupuncture example? Yes. The smallest number of observations back in Table 8.2 was 106. So our overall sample size was plenty large for the chi-square model to provide a good approximation of the null distribution of the chi-square statistic.

> ### YOU MIGHT BE THINKING
>
> So, I found evidence of an association—what now? How do I follow up a chi-square test? How do I decide which groups differ significantly from which others and by how much?

Although there is no conventional method for following up a chi-square test, one approach is to simply follow up a statistically significant chi-square test (based on a specific level of significance) by looking at all the pairwise comparisons between the groups. We can do that by producing theory-based confidence intervals for the difference in proportions for each pair of groups. We can calculate these intervals by checking the **Compute 95% CI(s) for difference in proportions** box (when the chi-square statistic has been chosen).

☑ Compute 95% CI(s) for difference in proportions
real-sham: (−0.0366, 0.1038)
real-none: (0.1356, 0.2689)*
sham-none: (0.1022, 0.2351)*

These results tell us that we do not have convincing evidence of a difference between the sham and real acupuncture (because that interval contains 0); it is plausible that there is no additional effect of real acupuncture as compared to sham acupuncture. However, because the other two intervals do not contain 0 there is a significant difference for pain reduction between real acupuncture and none as well as between sham acupuncture and none.

Conserving Hotel Towels

EXPLORATION 8.2A

If you have stayed at a hotel recently, you may have noticed how guests are increasingly encouraged to practice conservation habits by not having their towels washed every day—instead hanging them back on the rack to be reused. A recent study (Goldstein et al., 2008) conducted a randomized experiment to investigate how different phrasings on signs placed on bathroom towel racks impacted guests' towel reuse behavior. In particular, the researchers were interested in evaluating how messages that communicated different types of social norms impacted towel reuse. One week prior to a guest staying in the room, rooms at a particular hotel were randomly assigned to receive one of the following five messages on a sign hung on the towel bar in the room:

> Message 1: HELP SAVE THE ENVIRONMENT. You can show your respect for nature and help save the environment by reusing your towels during your stay. (No social norm)
>
> Message 2: JOIN YOUR FELLOW GUESTS IN HELPING TO SAVE THE ENVIRONMENT. In a study conducted in fall 2003, 75% of the guests participated in our new resource savings program by using their towels more than once. You can join your fellow guests in this program to help save the environment by reusing your towels during your stay. (Guest identity norm)
>
> Message 3: JOIN YOUR FELLOW GUESTS IN HELPING TO SAVE THE ENVIRONMENT. In a study conducted in fall 2003, 75% of the guests who stayed in this room (#xxx) participated in our new resource savings program by using their towels more than once. You can join your fellow guests in this program to help save the environment by reusing your towels during your stay. (Same room norm)
>
> Message 4: JOIN YOUR FELLOW CITIZENS IN HELPING TO SAVE THE ENVIRONMENT. In a study conducted in fall 2003, 75% of the guests participated in our new resource savings program by using their towels more than once. You can join your fellow citizens in this program to help save the environment by reusing your towels during your stay. (Citizens norm)
>
> Message 5: JOIN THE MEN AND WOMEN WHO ARE HELPING TO SAVE THE ENVIRONMENT. In a study conducted in fall 2003, 76% of the women and 74% of the men participated in our new resource savings program by using their towels more than once. You can join the other men and women in this program to help save the environment by reusing your towels during your stay." (Gender identity norm)

Data were collected on 1,595 instances of potential towel reuse. For each of the 1,595 instances, room attendants recorded whether or not the hotel guest reused their towels.

1. In your own words, state the research question of interest in this study.
2. Identify the explanatory and response variables in this study, along with their types (categorical or quantitative). For the explanatory variable, indicate how many categories it involves.

Explanatory:	Type:
Response:	Type:

3. Did the study design make use of any pairing of subjects or are the subjects who receive the different signs independent of each other?

4. State the appropriate null and alternative hypotheses for testing the researchers' conjecture using both words and symbols.

5. Paste the two-way table from the **Towels** file into the **Multiple Proportions** applet, then in the Sample Data box and press **Use Table**.

   a. Check the box next to **Show Table** in order to present the two-way table of counts and calculate conditional proportions of those who reused towels. (You can grab the bottom right corner of the table in the applet to extend it.) Report these five proportions.

   b. Looking at the segmented bar graph as well as the conditional proportions, conjecture on whether you think there will be a significant difference among the five groups with regard to towel reuse.

Applying the 3S strategy

6. Let's apply the 3S strategy.

   a. *Statistic:* Report the observed value of the MAD (mean absolute difference) statistic for this study, as given by the applet.

   b. *Simulate:* Use the applet to conduct 1,000 shuffles of the response variable. (First check **Show Shuffle Options** and then enter 1,000 for the **Number of Shuffles**. Press **Shuffle Responses**.) Then enter the observed value of the MAD statistic in the **Count Samples** box and press **Count**. Report the p-value.

   c. *Strength of evidence:* Based on the p-value, evaluate the strength of evidence provided by the data against the null hypothesis. Summarize your conclusion in the context of this study.

Another choice of statistic: Chi-square statistic

The MAD statistic is fairly easy to understand but is not widely used in part because it cannot be easily predicted theoretically. A more commonly used statistic is called a ***chi-square*** (χ^2) ***statistic***. You can think of this statistic as measuring how far the group proportions of success are from the overall proportion of success. These (standardized) deviations from the overall proportion are then squared and summed together across all of the explanatory variable groups. We'll do this calculation now.

7. Determine the overall proportion, $\hat{p}$, of rooms that reused towels.

8. We will calculate the standard error of a group proportion by computing $\sqrt{\hat{p}(1-\hat{p})/n_i}$ where $\hat{p}$ is the overall proportion found in #7 and n_i is the sample size for the ith group. Find the standard error of the group proportion for each of the five groups.

9. Create a standardized z-statistic for each conditional proportion compared to this overall proportion. To do this take each of the five group proportions, subtract the overall proportion (#7), and then divide the result by the standard deviation you found for that group in #8.

10. Which of the five standardized statistics are larger than 2 or smaller than –2, suggesting strong evidence that the group proportion is significantly different than the overall proportion?

11. Square each of these values and sum them to calculate the chi-square statistic.

12. What kinds of values (large, small, positive, negative) will the chi-square statistic have if the null hypothesis is true? What kinds of values will provide evidence against the null hypothesis?

From the **Statistic** pull-down menu, select χ^2. What does the applet report for the observed value of the chi-square statistic? Confirm that this matches your answer to the previous questions. (*Note:* You may be a bit different due to rounding.)

13. The applet will also now display the null distribution for the χ^2 statistic rather than the MAD statistic. Determine the p-value based on the simulated χ^2 statistics. (*Hint*: Change the value in the **Count Samples** box to the observed value of the χ^2 statistic.)

14. How does the p-value based on the χ^2 statistic compare to the one based on the MAD statistic? Are they similar? Is your conclusion about strength of evidence provided by the data against the null hypothesis similar?

Theory-based approach

The primary advantage of using the χ^2 statistic is that its null distribution can be predicted well by a theoretical distribution. So, once again a theory-based approach could be used without conducting a simulation in the first place.

15. Below the graph of the simulated chi-square statistics, check the box to **Overlay Chi-square distribution**. Does the theoretical distribution match the distribution of simulated statistics reasonably well? How does the theory-based p-value compare to what you found in #13? Does it lead you to a similar conclusion about strength of evidence?

Validity conditions

Like all theory-based tests, this one also comes with the condition of having a large sample size. We will (very conservatively) consider a sample size large if the sample data include at least 10 observations in each cell of the two-way table.

16. Go back to the applet and make sure the **Show Table** box is checked.
    a. How many cells are in this table? In other words, how many counts need to be checked that they are at least 10?
    b. Is the validity condition for a theory-based chi-square test satisfied for these data? Justify your answer.

Follow-up analysis

When a chi-square test produces a significant result, we conclude that at least one probability or population proportion differs from at least one of the others. A sensible next step is to try to identify *which* group proportion differs significantly from which others. We can do this by producing confidence intervals for pairwise differences in population proportions.

17. Below the p-value output, check the box to **Compute 95% CI(s) for difference in proportions**.
    a. How many intervals are produced?
    b. Which conditions are significantly different from each other? How are you deciding?
    c. For one of the intervals you identified in part (b), write a one-sentence interpretation of the interval, being very clear what is supposed to be captured inside the interval and which condition has a more positive effect on towel use and by how much.

Scope of conclusions

18. Is this an observational study or a randomized experiment?
19. Explain how the conclusions of this study are limited by conducting the study at a single hotel.

Look back and ahead

20. Summarize your conclusion for your analysis of the data from this study. Include a recommendation for the hotel manager about whether it matters what message is used, which

message should be used, and how large of an impact the best message would be expected to have. Think about the study and its design. Were there any limitations you feel need to be addressed? Did the design match the research question? Can you suggest a better sampling method of hotel guests—a better way to collect data on towel use? Share some ideas for a logical next study.

EXPLORATION 8.2B | Nearsightedness and Night Lights Revisited

Recall Example 4.1, which described a study investigating whether there is a relationship between use of night lights in a child's room before age 2 and the child's eyesight condition a few years later. In Chapter 4, we presented a two-way table of counts from the study examining whether or not the child was nearsighted as the response variable:

	Darkness	Night light	Room light
Nearsighted	18	78	41
Not nearsighted	154	154	34
Total	172	232	75

The conditional proportions of nearsightedness in the three lighting groups are 0.105, 0.336, and 0.547, respectively, which suggest that the more light used in the child's room, the more likely the child is to become nearsighted. Now we know how to calculate a standardized statistic and estimate a p-value to measure the strength of evidence provided by these sample data for the conjecture that eyesight is associated with the type of lighting used in the child's room.

1. State null and alternative hypotheses in terms of population proportions.
2. State null and alternative hypotheses in terms of association between variables.
3. Are the validity conditions necessary for a chi-square test met for these data? Explain.

Alternative formula for chi-square statistic

Another popular and more general way to formulate the chi-square statistic is in terms of observed and expected cell counts. The **observed counts** are what you actually observed in the study. The *expected cell counts* are what you would expect for the count in a cell if the null hypothesis were true.

4. To find out how many children we expect to be in the (darkness, nearsighted) cell of the table do the following:
   a. Find the overall proportion of children who were nearsighted in the sample.
   b. How many children in the sample slept in darkness?
   c. Multiply these two numbers together to find the "expected" number of children who would be nearsighted in the "slept in darkness" group if the null hypothesis were true (the probability of nearsightedness is the same in each condition).
   d. How different is this expected cell count from what was observed for that cell? What does this suggest about the strength of evidence against the null hypothesis?

A similar calculation is performed to find the expected cell count for each of the six cells of the table. The chi-square statistic is obtained by squaring the differences in the observed and expected counts, dividing by the expected count (a form of standardizing), and then summing the six values. This can be thought of as $(O - E)^2/E$, where O = observed count and E = expected count. See the Formulas section at the end of this exploration for the complete details.

5. Enter the two-way table of counts into the **Multiple Proportions** applet (remember to use one-word variable names and to not include the totals). Press **Use Table** and check the box to **Show χ^2 output**. Report the chi-square statistic and theory-based p-value. What conclusion do you draw about the statistical significance of the sample results?

6. Examine the **Chisq Cell Contributions** (remember you can expand that table by pulling out the lower right corner). (Verify that the first term in the table is the square of [18 − the number you calculated in #4(c)]/number from #4(c).) These six values are added together to yield the chi-square statistic; in other words, they are the six $(O − E)^2/E$ values. Which cell contributions are largest and so are contributing the most to the chi-square statistic value? According to the segmented bar graph, how are the observed counts in these cells deviating from what the null hypothesis would predict? (In other words, which is larger, the observed count or the expected count? How does that relate to our research question?)

The original research study actually classified the response variable into three categories of eyesight, as shown in the following table:

	Darkness	Night light	Room light
Nearsighted	18	78	41
Normal refraction	114	115	22
Farsighted	40	39	12

One advantage to the more general chi-square statistic formula using observed and expected counts is that it works for any size table (any number of categories for the explanatory variable and the response variable).

7. Create a segmented bar graph to summarize this table. Discuss what the graph reveals, including what this graph tells you that we did not learn from the previous table showing only nearsighted vs. not nearsighted.

8. With this new table, do you need to change your null and alternative hypotheses from #2?

9. Are the validity conditions for the chi-square test met for this table?

10. Enter this table into the **Multiple Proportions** applet and carry out the chi-square test. Report the chi-square statistic and p-value. Is the strength of evidence of a genuine association between the variables in the population stronger, weaker, or essentially the same as before? Explain your answer.

11. Carry out a randomization test (shuffling) for this table using the chi-square statistic. Overlay the chi-square distribution on the simulated null distribution of chi-square statistic values. Does it appear to be a reasonable model for the null distribution?

12. Examine the cell contributions. Is the pattern of deviations from the null similar to before?

13. Does this study suggest that use of night lights and room lights *causes* an increase to the chance that a child is nearsighted? Why or why not?

Formulas: Details of the chi-square statistic and distribution

In calculating the chi-square statistic when you had a binary response variable (Example 8.2 and Exploration 8.2A), you used the formula

$$\sum \frac{(\hat{p}_i - \hat{p})^2}{\hat{p}(1 - \hat{p})/n_i}$$

where the overall proportion $\hat{p}$ came from assuming the null hypothesis was true and we expect the same probability of success in each group, so we estimate that common probability by pooling all the groups together. The goal was to compare each group proportion to this common proportion. In Exploration 8.2B we saw an alternate approach that used observed and expected cell counts. Observed counts were what we actually observed in the study, and expected counts were what we would get, on average, if the null hypothesis were true.

For example, in the night light study:

Observed counts	Darkness	Night light	Room light	Total
Nearsighted	18	78	41	137
Normal refraction	114	115	22	251
Farsighted	40	39	12	91
Total	172	232	75	479

The null hypothesis says we expect a similar proportion to be nearsighted in each lighting group. We can estimate the proportion of nearsighted children using $137/479 \approx 0.286$. Similarly, we expect about $251/479$, or 52.4%, to have normal refraction and $91/479$, or about 19%, to be farsighted.

We need to work with the proportions instead of the counts because we have different sample sizes in our explanatory variable groups. By multiplying these proportions by the respective samples sizes we get a table of *expected counts*—the expected count of children in the cell if the null hypothesis were true. Verify that these expected counts would produce the same segmented bar graph for each lighting category.

Expected counts	Darkness	Night light	Room light	Total
Nearsighted	$172 \times 0.286 = 49.192$	$232 \times 0.286 = 66.352$	$75 \times 0.286 = 21.45$	137
Normal refraction	$172 \times 0.524 = 90.128$	$232 \times 0.524 = 121.568$	$75 \times 0.524 = 39.3$	251
Farsighted	$172 \times 0.19 = 32.68$	$232 \times 0.19 = 44.08$	$75 \times 0.19 = 14.25$	91

Notice that the *expected* counts need not be integers but that each column will still sum to the column total and each row will sum to the row total.

By comparing the observed counts to the expected counts we get a sense of how much evidence there is against the null hypothesis. To do this, each expected count is subtracted from each observed count and then squared. This squared difference is then divided by the expected count to "standardize" the value, ensuring that bigger differences count more if the cell count wasn't expected to be very large. All of the standardized, squared differences are added up to yield the chi-square statistic as shown below.

$$\chi^2 = \sum_{i=1}^{\substack{\text{Total number of cells} \\ \text{in the two-way table}}} \frac{(observed - expected)^2}{expected} = \sum_{i=1}^{\substack{\text{Total number of cells} \\ \text{in the two-way table}}} \frac{(O_i - E_i)^2}{E_i}$$

$$= \frac{(18 - 49.19)^2}{49.19} + \frac{(78 - 66.35)^2}{66.35} + \frac{(41 - 21.45)^2}{21.45}$$

$$+ \frac{(114 - 90.13)^2}{90.13} + \frac{(115 - 121.57)^2}{121.57} + \frac{(22 - 39.3)^2}{39.3}$$

$$+ \frac{(40 - 32.68)^2}{32.68} + \frac{(39 - 44.08)^2}{44.08} + \frac{(12 - 14.25)^2}{14.25}$$

$$= 19.78 + 2.04 + 17.82 + 6.32 + 0.36 + 7.62 + 1.64 + 0.58 + 0.35 = 56.51$$

The terms being summed together, one from each cell, are often called the *cell contributions*. They are often useful in identifying which cells have the largest discrepancies between the observed and expected counts.

In order to use the chi-square statistic to estimate a p-value you also need to know the *degrees of freedom* of the test. The degrees of freedom are computed by multiplying the number of categories in the explanatory variable minus 1 by the number of categories in the response variable minus 1. It turns out that the mean of this distribution equals the degrees of freedom. We expect larger values in the distribution as we are summing the results for more cells together.

In our case, that is $(3 - 1) \times (3 - 1) = 4$. Thus, we have a test with 4 degrees of freedom.

In general, the chi-square distribution changes as the degrees of freedom increases. Notice in Figure 8.10 that the distribution is often right skewed.

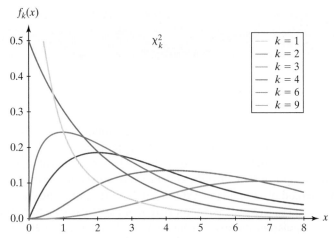

FIGURE 8.10 Chi-square distributions with various degrees of freedom (k).

SECTION 8.2   Summary

A theory-based approach can be used to test association between two categorical variables under certain conditions.

- This procedure is called a **chi-square test**.
- The statistic for theory-based inference is called a **chi-square statistic**.
- With a binary response variable, this statistic is: $\sum\limits_{i\,groups} \left(\dfrac{\hat{p}_i - \hat{p}}{\sqrt{\hat{p}(1 - \hat{p})/n_i}} \right)^2$.

  More generally, this statistic is $\sum\limits_{all\,cells} \dfrac{(observed - expected)^2}{expected}$, where "observed" refers to the observed cell counts and "expected" refers to the expected cell counts, computed assuming the null hypothesis to be true. To find the expected cell counts multiply the row total times the column total and divide by the table total.

  - This chi-square statistic becomes larger as the discrepancies in the sample proportions become larger.
  - Larger values of the chi-square statistic provide stronger evidence against the null hypothesis.
  - Software produces the contribution to the chi-square statistic for each cell of the table.
    - Cells with larger contributions indicate the greatest discrepancy between what was observed and what would have been expected if there were no association between variables.
- The validity condition for applying the chi-square test is that all cells of the two-way table should each have at least 10 observations.

When a chi-square test reveals strong evidence that at least one of the population proportions differs from the others, confidence intervals for the difference in population proportions can be calculated for pairs of groups.

- Confidence intervals that do not include zero indicate which pairs of sample proportions differ significantly.

SECTION 8.3

CHI-SQUARE TESTS FOR HOMOGENEITY OF PROPORTIONS AND INDEPENDENCE

INTRODUCTION

Definition

A **chi-square test of independence** examines one group of individuals classified according to two categorical variables. It tests the null hypothesis that there is no association between the two categorical variables in the population of interest.

Definition

A **chi-square test of homogeneity** compares the distribution of proportions for two or more groups on the same categorical response variable. Independent random samples are taken from each population of interest or the individuals (experimental units) are randomly assigned to treatments in an experiment. It tests the null hypothesis that there is no difference in the distribution of a categorical variable for several populations or treatments.

Earlier in Section 8.2 you saw that when we compare proportions across multiple groups (i.e., when we have two categorical variables), the appropriate theory-based approach is a chi-square test. In this section you will look at two versions of the chi-square test for two-way tables, called **chi-square tests of independence** and **chi-square tests of homogeneity of proportions**. The method of sampling or experimentation (i.e., how the data were collected) determines which of these two tests is appropriate in a particular situation. If our sample is taken from a single population and two categorical variables are measured for each individual, then our null hypothesis is framed as a statement of **independence** between the two variables. On the other hand, if samples are taken from different populations or assigned randomly to treatment groups, then the null hypothesis is framed as a statement of **homogeneity** (sameness) **of proportions** among the populations.

As we saw earlier in Section 8.2, the standardized statistic for a chi-square test is found by comparing the observed sample counts in a two-way table, with the counts that would be expected if the null hypothesis is true. Here is the equation for the chi-square statistic:

$$\chi^2 = \sum \frac{(\text{Observed Count} - \text{Expected Count})^2}{\text{Expected Count}}$$

where the sum (indicated by Σ) is over all cells of the two-way table. The terms being summed together, one from each cell of the table, are often called the **cell contributions**.

Both tests calculate the chi-square statistic the same way. The difference lies in how you frame our hypotheses and the conclusion you make based on those hypotheses.

As you've seen before, the AP exam sometimes requires slightly different versions of the validity conditions from those that we've seen in previous sections. Earlier in Section 8.2 we talked about a sample size requirement as the primary validity condition. For the AP exam, you are expected to be a bit more specific—stating information about both the study design and also about expected cell counts (sample size), as shown in the box below.

> **AP TIP**
>
> **Validity conditions for conducting a chi-square test**
>
> 1. Randomness in the data collection:
>   - Test of Independence: Data are from a random sample from the population of interest.
>   - Test of Homogeneity: Data are from independent random samples or a randomized experiment.
> 2. All **expected** cell counts are at least 5.

As you saw earlier in Section 8.2, the degrees of freedom for a chi-square test of independence and for a chi-square test of homogeneity of proportions are computed by multiplying the number of categories in the explanatory variable minus one by the number of categories in the response variable minus one. In other words, for data arranged in a two-way table with r rows and c columns, the degrees of freedom $= (r - 1)(c - 1)$. On the AP exam you should also state the degrees of freedom when you state your chi-square statistic and the corresponding p-value.

In Section 1.7 and in many sections since, you learned the work you must show on the AP Statistics exam when a hypothesis test is called for. The format you learned is the same for all hypothesis tests.

1. State the hypotheses either in words or using appropriate symbols.
2. Name the test that will be used and state and verify the validity conditions for the test chosen.
3. Calculate the test statistic (standardized statistic) and corresponding p-value.
4. State your conclusion (with appropriate justification based on your p-value and stated significance level) in the context of the research question.

Happy, Healthy, or Rich?

Are males and females different in how they respond to the question, "Would you rather be happy, healthy, or rich?" *Census at School* is an international classroom project in which students from grades 4–12 complete a brief online survey. Through Census at School, we obtained a random sample of 217 U.S. high school students who answered this question, and also noted whether their sex was male or female. The results are shown in the following table.

 Example 8.3A

	Female	Male	Total
Happy	83	54	137
Healthy	19	11	30
Rich	15	35	50
Total	117	100	217

> **THINK ABOUT IT**
>
> What is the explanatory variable? Is it quantitative or categorical? What is the response variable? Is it quantitative or categorical? Was this an observational study or an experiment? Does the study design call for a test of homogeneity or a test of independence?

The explanatory variable is the sex of the student surveyed. It is a categorical variable. The response variable is the student's response to the question, "Would you rather be happy, healthy, or rich?" It is also a categorical variable. This was an observational study as no treatment was imposed. Because we have one random sample, in which each individual was asked both questions on the survey, this calls for a test of independence. (If we had taken independent random samples of males and of females, that would call for a test of homogeneity.)

Let us compare the conditional distributions of responses to the question posed between female students and male students both numerically and graphically.

 8.3.1

> **THINK ABOUT IT**
>
> Numerically, what are the appropriate statistics to calculate in order to compare groups on a categorical response?

Calculating the conditional proportions of female response to the question posed (happy, healthy, rich) will numerically describe the females who responded to the survey:

Proportion of females who chose happy = 83/117 ≈ 0.71
Proportion of females who chose healthy = 19/117 ≈ 0.16
Proportion of females who chose rich = 15/117 ≈ 0.13

Calculating the conditional proportions of male response to the question posed (happy, healthy, rich) will numerically describe the males who responded to the survey:

Proportion of males who chose happy = 54/100 = 0.54
Proportion of males who chose healthy = 11/100 = 0.11
Proportion of males who chose rich = 35/100 = 0.35

THINK ABOUT IT

What would be an appropriate graphical display to compare the responses to the question posed between females and males in this survey?

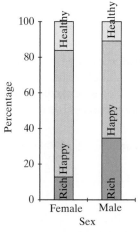

FIGURE 8.11 Segmented bar graph of life choices by sex.

We used the **Multiple Proportions** applet to make Figure 8.11, which shows a segmented bar graph comparing the female distribution of responses to the question posed to the male distribution of responses. A majority of both sexes chose being happy, with a higher percentage of females making this choice (71% to 54% for males). Being healthy was the next highest choice for females, whereas the next highest choice for males was being rich. More than twice as many of the male high school students chose being rich (0.35) as the female high school students (0.13). From the segmented bar graph it appears that there may be a relationship between the sex of a student and his or her response to the question posed, as those two conditional distributions do not look very similar.

THINK ABOUT IT

What steps would you need to take to carry out a test using the AP format to decide whether there is convincing evidence of a relationship between the sex of a student and his or her response to the question posed for U.S. high school students?

We need to complete a test of significance, showing the work outlined in the following four steps:

1. **State the hypotheses either in words or using appropriate symbols.**

   Null: There is no association between a student's sex and his or her response to the question posed in the population of high school students.

Alternative: There is an association between a student's sex and his or her response to the question posed.

2. **Name the theory-based test that will be used and state and verify the validity conditions for the test chosen.**

   Now let's check the validity conditions for a chi-square test of independence.

   a. Generalizability: We are told that that the students were randomly selected from U.S. high school students who completed the *Census at School* survey. We can probably generalize the results to U.S. high school students, provided that the students surveyed are a representative sample of U.S. high school students.

   b. In order to use a chi-square test, the expected counts in each cell must be at least 5. The expected cell counts are given in parentheses in the table below beside the corresponding observed counts. All expected counts are much greater than 5, so a chi-square test of independence is appropriate.

	Female	Male	Total
Happy	83 (73.9)	54 (63.1)	137
Healthy	19 (16.2)	11 (13.8)	30
Rich	15 (27.0)	35 (23.0)	50
Total	117	100	217

   To find out how many females we expect to be in the cell that corresponds to choosing the response *happy* to the question posed (happy, healthy, rich), do the following:

   a. Find the overall proportion of students that answered *happy* to the question posed. 137/217.

   b. How many females responded to the survey? 117

   c. Multiply these two numbers together to find the "expected" number of females surveyed who would respond *happy* to the question posed if the null hypothesis were true (the probability of choosing the response *happy* is the same for each sex). $(137/217 \times 117 \approx 73.9)$

   Expected count = (row total $\times$ column total)/(table total) = $(137 \times 117)/217 \approx 73.9$

   $$\text{stat. ExpMatrix} \quad \begin{bmatrix} 73.8664 & 63.1336 \\ 16.1751 & 13.8249 \\ 26.9585 & 23.0415 \end{bmatrix}$$

CALCULATOR TIPS

You can determine the table of expected counts as well as the test statistic and p-value using graphing calculators. For example:

- **TI-84:** Enter observed counts into a matrix and name the matrix. Specify the chi-square test, the matrix where the observed counts are found, and the matrix where the expected counts will be stored. The calculator will display the chi-square statistic, the p-value, and the appropriate degrees of freedom for the test. To see the expected counts, go to the home screen and enter the name of the matrix you designated for storing the expected counts.

- **TI-Nspire:** Enter observed counts into a matrix and name the matrix. Select chi-square 2-Way Test from the statistics test menu. The calculator will display the chi-square statistic, the p-value, and the appropriate degrees of freedom for the test in addition to "ExpMatrix" "[…]" and "CompMatrix" "[…]". To display the expected matrix, hit the var key and choose *stat.expmatrix*. To display the components that make up the chi-square statistic, choose *stat.compmatrix*.

3. **Calculate the test statistic (standardized statistic) and corresponding p-value.**

By substituting into the appropriate formula, we find the following:

$$\chi^2 = \frac{(83 - 73.8664)^2}{73.8664} + \cdots + \frac{(35 - 23.0415)^2}{23.0415} \approx 15.0325 \quad \text{p-value} \approx 0.00054$$

From Table C, with $(3 - 1)(2 - 1) = 2$ degrees of freedom, we find the p-value is between 0.0005 and 0.001.

TABLE C χ^2 **critical values**

					Tail probability p							
df	.25	.20	.15	.10	.05	.025	.02	.01	.005	.0025	.001	.0005
1	1.32	1.64	2.07	2.71	3.84	5.02	5.41	6.63	7.88	9.14	10.83	12.12
→2	2.77	3.22	3.79	4.61	5.99	7.38	7.82	9.21	10.60	11.98	13.82	15.20
3	4.11	4.64	5.32	6.25	7.81	9.35	9.84	11.34	12.84	14.32	16.27	17.73
4	5.39	5.99	6.74	7.78	9.49	11.14	11.67	13.38	14.86	16.42	18.47	20.00

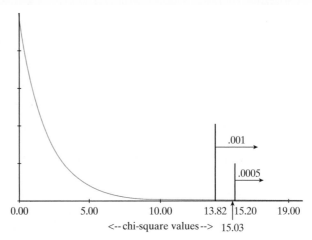

Note: The p-value of 0.00054 was obtained from carrying out the chi-square test on the calculator.

4. **State your conclusion (with appropriate justification based on your p-value and stated significance level) in the context of the research question.**

We have convincing evidence of an association in this population between the sex of a high school student and his or her response to the question. Our decision is based on obtaining a p-value of 0.00054, which is less than a significance level of 0.05.

8.3.2

EXPLORATION | **Choice of Superpower**
8.3A

Do male and female high school students wish they had different superpowers? Through Census at School, we obtained a random sample of 200 U.S. high school students and their answers to the question, "Which of the following superpowers would you most want to have?" The results are shown in the following table, separating female and male responses.

	Female	Male	Total
Fly	23	19	42
Telepathy	43	18	61
Invisibility	16	17	33
Freeze Time	34	30	64
Total	116	84	200

1. What is the explanatory variable? Is it quantitative or categorical?
2. What is the response variable? Is it quantitative or categorical?
3. Was this an observational study or an experiment?
4. Calculate the conditional proportions for superpower choice (fly, telepathy, invisibility, freeze time) for the females who responded to the survey.
5. Calculate the conditional proportions for superpower choice (fly, telepathy, invisibility, freeze time) for the males who responded to the survey.
6. Construct an appropriate graphical display to compare the distribution of superpower choices for females to those of males in this survey. Write a few sentences to describe the relationship between the sex of a student and his or her superpower choice in this sample.
7. Is there convincing evidence of a relationship between the sex of a high school student and his or her superpower choice, for all U.S. high school students? (*Hint:* Keep in mind that when a hypothesis test is called for on the AP Statistics exam, you must complete the work outlined in the following four steps:

STEP 1: State the hypotheses either in words or using appropriate symbols.

STEP 2: Name the test that will be used and state and verify the validity conditions for the test chosen.

STEP 3: Calculate the test statistic (standardized statistic) and corresponding p-value.

STEP 4: State your conclusion (with appropriate justification based on your p-value and stated significance level) in the context of the research question.)

Heart Disease and Baldness

To investigate a possible relationship between heart disease and baldness, researchers asked a random sample of 663 male heart patients to classify their degree of baldness on a 5-point scale (Lasdko et al., 1993). They also asked a random sample of 772 men who were not suffering from heart disease (control group) to do the same baldness assessment. The results are summarized in the following table.

Example 8.3B

	None	Little	Some	Much	Extreme	Total
Heart Disease	251	165	195	50	2	663
Control	331	221	185	34	1	772
Total	582	386	380	84	3	1,435

> **THINK ABOUT IT**
>
> Would it be valid to carry out a chi-square test on these data? Would this be a test of independence or a test of homogeneity? Explain.

Because the researchers used independent random samples of men with and without heart disease, the appropriate theory-based analysis would be a test of homogeneity. In order to use a chi-square test, the expected counts in each cell must be at least 5. Let's calculate the expected count for men classifying themselves as having *extreme baldness* and having *heart disease*.

8.3.3

To find out how many men with *extreme baldness* we expect to be in the cell that corresponds to having *heart disease*, do the following:

a. Find the overall proportion of men with *heart disease*. 663/1,435

b. How many men have extreme baldness? 3

Multiply these two numbers together to find the "expected" number of men with *extreme baldness* that would have *heart disease* if the null hypothesis were true (the probability for each hair loss rating is the same for the heart disease and control groups).

$(663/1{,}435 \times 3 \approx 1.39)$

Expected count = (row total × column total)/(table total) = $(663 \times 3)/1{,}435 \approx 1.39$

As we have at least one expected count below 5, we would be hesitant to carry out a chi-square test on these data.

> **THINK ABOUT IT**
>
> When you have a table where some cells have very small counts, one approach is to combine some of the rows or columns together. Which categories would it make sense to combine together here?

Because so few men categorized themselves as having extreme hair loss, the expected counts for these cells do not meet the validity condition. Because "much" hair loss and "extreme" hair loss are similar with respect to amount of baldness, it would make sense to combine these two categories.

Below we create a new two-way table that classifies the baldness levels of much and extreme as "much or extreme."

	None	Little	Some	Much or Extreme	Total
Heart Disease	251	165	195	52	663
Control	331	221	185	35	772
Total	582	386	380	87	1,435

> **THINK ABOUT IT**
>
> Would it be valid to carry out a chi-square test on this table? (What is the smallest expected cell count?)

The smallest expected cell count is for men with heart disease who classified themselves as having much or extreme hair loss (the smallest row and column totals). The expected cell count is $(663 \times 87)/1{,}435 \approx 40.2$. So it would be valid to carry out the test because all the expected cell counts are greater than 5.

8.3.4

> **THINK ABOUT IT**
>
> Based on the new table, is there convincing evidence of a difference in the distribution of baldness ratings for the heart disease population and the control population?

We need to complete a test of significance as outlined in the following four steps:

1. **State the hypotheses either in words or using appropriate symbols.**

   Null: There is no difference in the distribution of baldness ratings for men in the heart disease and control populations.

   Alternative: There is a difference in the distribution of baldness ratings for men in the heart disease and control populations.

2. **Name the theory-based test that will be used and state and verify the validity conditions for the test chosen.**

   Now let's check the validity conditions for a chi-square test of homogeneity of proportions.

   a. Generalizability: We are told that a random sample of heart patients and an independent random sample of men not suffering from heart disease were taken. We can probably generalize the results to men similar to those in the two groups (heart disease and control).

   b. In order to use a chi-square test, the expected counts in each cell must be at least 5. The matrix of expected cell counts is given below. All expected counts are much greater than 5, so a chi-square test of homogeneity of proportions is appropriate.

$$\text{stat. ExpMatrix} \begin{bmatrix} 268.896 & 178.34 & 175.568 & 40.1958 \\ 313.104 & 207.66 & 204.432 & 46.8042 \end{bmatrix}$$

CALCULATOR TIPS

You can determine the table of expected counts as well as the test statistic and p-value using graphing calculators. For example:

- **TI-84:** Enter observed counts into a matrix and name the matrix. Specify the chi-square test, the matrix where the observed counts are found, and the matrix where the expected counts will be stored. The calculator will display the chi-square statistic, the p-value, and the appropriate degrees of freedom for the test. To see the expected counts, go to the home screen and enter the name of the matrix you designated for the expected counts to be stored.
- **TI-Nspire:** Enter observed counts into a matrix and name the matrix. Select chi-square 2-Way Test from the statistics test menu. The calculator will display the chi-square statistic, the p-value, and the appropriate degrees of freedom for the test in addition to "ExpMatrix" "[…]" and "CompMatrix" "[…]". To display the expected matrix, hit the var key and choose *stat.expmatrix*. To display the components that make up the chi-square statistic, choose *stat.compmatrix*.

---

3. **Calculate the test statistic (standardized statistic) and corresponding p-value.**

   By substituting into the appropriate formula, we find the following:

$$\chi^2 = \frac{(251 - 268.896)^2}{268.896} + \cdots + \frac{(35 - 46.8042)^2}{46.8042} \approx 14.5102 \quad \text{p-value} \approx 0.0023$$

   From Table C, with degrees of freedom = $(4 - 1)(2 - 1) = 3$, we find the p-value is between 0.001 and 0.0025

TABLE C χ^2 **critical values**

						Tail probability p						
df	.25	.20	.15	.10	.05	.025	.02	.01	.005	.0025	.001	.0005
1	1.32	1.64	2.07	2.71	3.84	5.02	5.41	6.63	7.88	9.14	10.83	12.12
2	2.77	3.22	3.79	4.61	5.99	7.38	7.82	9.21	10.60	11.98	13.82	15.20
→3	4.11	4.64	5.32	6.25	7.81	9.35	9.84	11.34	12.84	14.32	16.27	17.73
4	5.39	5.99	6.74	7.78	9.49	11.14	11.67	13.38	14.86	16.42	18.47	20.00

4. **State your conclusion (with appropriate justification based on your p-value and stated significance level) in the context of the research question.**

   We have convincing evidence of a difference in the distribution of baldness ratings for men in the heart disease and control populations. Our decision is based on our obtained p-value of 0.0023, which is less than our significance level of 0.05.

 8.3.5

In Exploration 8.1 we considered a study that investigated how to encourage people to be more likely to become organ donors. We used the MAD statistic to calculate the difference in sample proportions for each pair of groups. In this section we will revisit the study using the chi-square statistic.

Recall that researchers asked volunteer subjects to imagine they moved to a new state, applied for a driver's license, and needed to decide whether or not to become an organ donor. Researchers created three different versions of the survey, each with a different donor recruitment strategy. Subjects were randomly assigned to one of the three types of recruitment strategies:

- The default option is to not be an organ donor, and individuals have to opt in to organ donation (opt-in group).
- The default option is to be an organ donor, and individuals have to opt out of organ donation (opt-out group).
- There is no default option, and individuals have to choose whether or not they will be an organ donor (neutral group).

The data for the study are given in the table below.

| | | Default Option | | | |
		Opt in	Opt out	Neutral	Total
Organ donor	Yes	23	41	44	108
	No	32	9	12	53
	Total	55	50	56	161

1. What is the explanatory variable? Is it quantitative or categorical?
2. What is the response variable? Is it quantitative or categorical?
3. Was this an observational study or an experiment?
4. Is there convincing evidence of a difference in the distribution of organ donations for the different donor recruitment strategies? (*Hint:* Keep in mind that when a hypothesis test is called for on the AP Statistics exam, you must complete the work outlined in the following four steps:

   STEP 1: State the hypotheses either in words or using appropriate symbols.

   STEP 2: Name the test that will be used and state and verify the validity conditions for the test chosen.

   STEP 3: Calculate the test statistic (standardized statistic) and corresponding p-value.

   STEP 4: State your conclusion (with appropriate justification based on your p-value and stated significance level) in the context of the research question.)

SECTION 8.3 Summary

In this section we investigated theory-based models for tests of significance for comparing proportions across multiple groups. We looked at two versions of the chi-square test for two-way tables: the chi-square test of independence and chi-square test of homogeneity of proportions. We saw that the calculations for both tests are the same; what differs is how we frame our null hypothesis, which is determined by the method of sampling or experimentation. If our sample is taken from a single population and two categorical variables are measured for each individual, then our null hypothesis is framed as a statement of *independence* between the two variables. On the other hand, if samples are taken from different populations or individuals are assigned randomly to treatment groups, then the null hypothesis is framed as a statement of *homogeneity* (sameness) *of proportions* among the populations. In addition, we saw that the work you need to show on the AP exam for a chi-square test of significance follows the same general format as that for the other hypothesis tests you have encountered in previous chapters.

CHI-SQUARE GOODNESS-OF-FIT TEST

SECTION 8.4

INTRODUCTION

The *chi-square goodness-of-fit test* is a theory-based test of significance that compares observed data to a prescribed model. In this course, you will use goodness-of-fit tests to compare the distribution of a categorical variable to a hypothesized distribution. For example, in Chapter 1, you conducted tests to evaluate questions like "When playing the game rock-paper-scissors (see Example 1.2), do novice players play scissors less than 1/3rd of the time in the long run?" These tests evaluated whether sample data provided evidence that the probabilities associated with a categorical variable with *two* categories (*scissors* or *not scissors*) differed from hypothesized probabilities (π and $1 - \pi$). However, at that time you were limited to only evaluating categorical variables with two categories. As you've been exploring in Chapter 8, it is often the case that categorical variables have more than two categories. So, for example, maybe you want to test whether the way novice players make choices when playing the game rock-paper-scissors is such that all three options are chosen equally often in the long run (1/3, 1/3, 1/3). Similarly, we could ask: Are birthdays equally distributed across the seven days of the week? Do certain pea plants produce three times as many purple flowers as white flowers? We'll see how to evaluate these types of questions in the following examples and explorations.

To answer these questions, we will explore the chi-square goodness-of-fit test. When executing a chi-square goodness-of-fit test, we compare observed counts in each of the categories of our variable to counts we would expect to see if the null hypothesis is indeed true. The chi-square statistic and distribution we will use in this section are the same as those we used earlier in Chapter 8 when we compared multiple proportions with theory-based methods. We will, however, first introduce this process using simulation-based techniques with a MAD-type statistic like what we used to compare multiple proportions and multiple means.

Fair Die?

A statistics student wondered whether rolling six-sided dice by pushing them off a 2-inch ledge was a fair way of rolling dice.

8.4

Example 8.4

EXAMPLE

> **THINK ABOUT IT**
>
> What would it mean to be "fair" in this context?

In this case, for a die roll to be fair, it means that all six sides are equally likely to occur. In other words, if we were to repeatedly roll the die by pushing it off a 2-inch high ledge, then we would expect each of the 6 numbered faces of the die to appear on top an equal number of times in the long run. If we rolled the die 120 times, we would expect to see each of the 6 different numbers rolled about 20 times. After rolling the die 120 times, if we observe our data to have deviated substantially from what we expected to see from a fair die (~20 times each), we may have evidence that our rolling method is not "fair."

The student decided to conduct a study to check her hypothesis. The student placed the die on the ledge the same way each time—the 6 was facing up and the 3 was facing the ledge. Five dice were pushed off the ledge 24 times for a total of 120 rolls. The hypotheses we are testing follow:

H_o: The method of rolling is fair (Each face is equally likely to appear or $\pi_1 = \pi_2 = \pi_3 = \pi_4 = \pi_5 = \pi_6 = 1/6$.)

H_a: The method of rolling is not fair (Not all faces are equally likely to appear, that is, at least one of the π_i is different from 1/6.)

where π_i represents the long-run proportion of times the number i would appear, $i = 1, 2, ..., 6$. Notice how this hypothesis looks familiar—testing the equality of several probabilities—but a key difference is that we are now specifying a specific numerical value for each π_i (and those values must sum to 1).

The number of times each face appeared in the student's trials are recorded below in Table 8.3, and graphically displayed in the bar graph in Figure 8.12.

TABLE 8.3 Summary of the number of times each face occurred in sample						
Value	1	2	3	4	5	6
Observed count	19	10	31	17	15	28

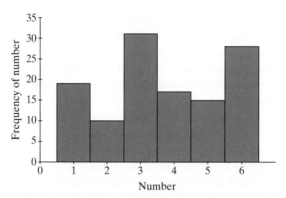

FIGURE 8.12 A bar graph of the number of times each face occurred in the sample.

From this observed distribution, it would appear that there are many more threes and sixes than twos and fives.

> THINK ABOUT IT
>
> If the die-rolling method was fair, what would be the expected count of rolling a 1? Rolling a 5?

8.4.1

Remember if the die-rolling method was fair, we would expect each face to be rolled 20 ($= 1/6 \times 120$) times. But we didn't obtain each face 20 times. Some faces rolled fewer than 20 times (e.g., 2 appeared only 10 times) and some faces rolled more than 20 times (e.g., 3 appeared 31 times). Could this difference just be from random chance? How likely is it that we would get a distribution of number of times each face is rolled that looks at least as extreme as the one from the sample data if the method is really fair? These questions can be answered, just as before, by comparing what was observed in the sample to what could have happened by random chance alone. And, just as before, a null distribution of an appropriate statistic can give us an idea of what could have happened by random chance. We can accomplish all of this by using what is called a ***goodness-of-fit test***.

> **Definition**
>
> A ***goodness-of-fit test*** is used to compare observed counts for a categorical variable to hypothesized probabilities.

Simulation-based goodness-of-fit test

Let us first see how we can use simulation to investigate whether the data provide evidence that this "pushing off the ledge" method of tossing dice is not fair. Remember that first we need to come up with a statistic that will measure how far away our observed data are from what we would expect if the null hypothesis was true. One choice for a statistic is to compare the observed counts to the expected counts for each category, where expected counts are what we would expect to happen if the null hypothesis was true (the die rolling method was fair).

One way to do this is similar to what we used in Section 8.1—the ***mean absolute difference*** (or MAD). But here, instead of finding the difference between two categories, we will compare each category to the hypothesized value. Because this is just one sample, we can work with the counts rather than the proportions. We will find the absolute values of the difference in the observed and expected counts, and then average those differences. In the calculation, absolute values of the differences will be taken so that the order of subtraction does not matter, and positive and negative values do not cancel each other out. In this case, the MAD gives the average distance the observed counts are away from the expected counts. Thus the MAD statistic for our data is

$$\text{MAD} = \frac{|19-20| + |10-20| + |31-20| + |17-20| + |15-20| + |28-20|}{6} = 6.33$$

So our observed counts (or frequencies) of the numbers rolled for the dice being pushed off the 2-inch ledge are, on average, 6.33 units away from what is expected.

YOU MAY BE THINKING

Earlier we were subtracting proportions, and now we are using counts. Can we not use proportions anymore?

Sure, you can still work with proportions. If you used proportions, you would subtract the observed proportions from the hypothesized proportions (in this case, 1/6 or 0.167 for each face) and average the absolute value of the differences. You can check that this value turns to be about 0.053 (6.33/120). And if you did decide to use the MAD statistic with the proportions, you would need to make sure that when you generated the null distribution, you used proportions, too.

THINK ABOUT IT

Let's go back to the MAD statistic that used the counts. How do we decide whether a MAD statistic of 6.33 is surprising or extreme enough to convince us that the dice-rolling method is not fair?

Now we need to simulate similar results of 120 throws of a die *from a process we know to be fair*, compute the MAD statistic for each result, and repeat this process many, many times to develop a null distribution. We could actually use real dice to conduct our simulation! We would have to roll 120 dice or one die 120 times (assuming that throwing is a fair process, whereas pushing them off a shelf may not be), compute the MAD statistic, and repeat this many, many times. Instead of going through this long process, we will turn to technology and use the **Goodness of Fit** applet to make things go faster.

Figure 8.13 shows output from the **Goodness of Fit** applet where we have entered the table of counts and pressed Use Table. Then we checked the Show Sampling Options box, entered the hypothesized probabilities (separating the values by commas), and generated one random sample from the hypothesized probability distribution. The panel on the right shows the counts for each face for this "could-have-been" random sample from a perfectly fair die-rolling process.

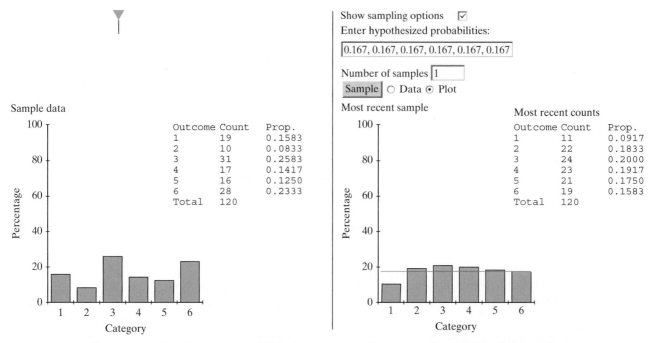

FIGURE 8.13   One simulated random sample of 120 dice rolls under the assumption that the dice are fair.

For this first random sample, taken from a process with fair die rolls, let's calculate the MAD statistic:

$$\text{MAD} = \frac{|11 - 20| + |22 - 20| + |24 - 20| + |23 - 20| + |21 - 20| + |19 - 20|}{6} = 3.33$$

This MAD statistic of 3.33, which is not as extreme as our observed statistic of 6.33 because it is not as far from 0 as 6.33 is, becomes one value in our null distribution. We repeat this step 999 more times to generate a total of 1,000 values of the MAD statistic that could have happened as a result of the fair die-rolling process. This gives us the simulated null distribution shown in Figure 8.14. Note that a MAD statistic of 0 represents throwing each of the six faces exactly 20 times when rolling the dice 120 times. Although a MAD of 0 could appear in our null distribution a few times, typically there is more variability in our outcomes.

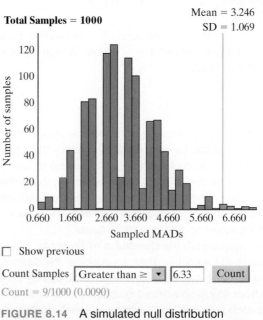

FIGURE 8.14   A simulated null distribution representing 1,000 MAD statistics computed from the outcomes of tossing 120 fair dice.

You can see that the observed MAD statistic of 6.33 is quite far out in the tail of this simulated null distribution. In fact, a MAD statistic of 6.33 or greater occurred only 9 times out of 1,000, and thus our estimate of the p-value is 0.009.

8.4.2

YOU MAY BE THINKING

Couldn't we have used the chi-square statistic here instead of the MAD statistic?

Yes, we can absolutely use the chi-square statistic, and as you may remember, one advantage of using the chi-square statistic instead of the MAD is that the distribution of a chi-square statistic is easily predicted by a theory-based distribution, whereas that's not the case for the MAD statistic.

Before we use a theory-based method, let us take a quick look at how to use the chi-square statistic instead of the MAD in the simulation. Recall that the chi-square statistic (like the MAD) gives a measure of how far apart our observed counts are from the expected counts. This is done by finding the difference between the observed and expected counts, squaring that difference, then dividing that quantity by the corresponding expected count. This is done for each of the categories in the model and then the sum of these components is found. This is shown in the following formula:

$$\chi^2 = \Sigma \frac{(\text{Observed Count} - \text{Expected Count})^2}{\text{Expected Count}}$$

Recall that when the observed counts are close to the corresponding expected counts, a small chi-square test statistic is found. When these counts are far apart, a large (e.g., larger than the corresponding degrees of freedom) chi-square test statistic is found. Therefore, relatively speaking, a large chi-square test statistic will support the idea that the method is not fair (the alternative hypothesis), just as a large MAD statistic would. In our dice example, each expected count from 120 attempts is 20. We then do the following to compute the chi-square test statistic:

$$\chi^2 = \frac{(19 - 20)^2}{20} + \frac{(10 - 20)^2}{20} + \frac{(31 - 20)^2}{20} + \frac{(17 - 20)^2}{20} + \frac{(15 - 20)^2}{20} + \frac{(28 - 20)^2}{20}$$

$$= 0.05 + 5 + 6.05 + 0.45 + 1.25 + 3.2$$

$$= 16$$

THINK ABOUT IT

How do we decide whether a chi-square statistic of 16 is surprising or extreme enough to convince us that the dice-rolling method is not fair?

Using the same **Goodness of Fit** applet with 1,000 repetitions of 120 fair die rolls, we can also compute the chi-square statistic each time and the results are shown in Figure 8.15.

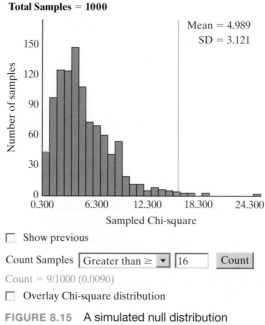

FIGURE 8.15 A simulated null distribution representing 1,000 chi-square statistics computed from the outcomes of tossing 120 fair dice.

8.4.3

Where does our observed chi-square statistic lie in this distribution? You can see it is quite far out in the tail, just as the MAD statistic was. A chi-square statistic of 16 or greater occurred only 9 times out of 1,000, and thus our simulation-based p-value is 0.009.

Theory-based goodness-of-fit test

From Figure 8.16, you can see that the shape of the simulated null distribution of the chi-square statistic can be predicted using the theoretical chi-square distribution.

FIGURE 8.16 A theoretical chi-square distribution.

Our theory-based p-value 0.0068 is very similar to both of our simulation-based p-values. From this we can conclude we have strong evidence that pushing dice off a 2-inch ledge is not a fair way of tossing dice.

> **NOTE**
>
> You may use your calculator to obtain your test statistic and corresponding p-value.
>
> - **TI-84:** To obtain the p-value, DISTR → χ^2 cdf (*lower, upper, df*). In the dialog box, enter the value of your chi-square statistic for the lower bound, a very large value such as 10,000 for the upper bound, and the appropriate degrees of freedom).
> - **TI-Nspire:** Enter your observed and expected values into two lists in a List and Spreadsheet page. Statistics → Stat Tests → χ^2 GOF. In the dialog box, use the drop-down menu to select the names of your observed and expected lists, type in the appropriate degrees of freedom, and then press Enter.

As in our other theory-based tests, this one comes with validity conditions as well. The validity conditions for a chi-square goodness-of-fit test are that all expected counts are at least 5 and, as usual, that the data are representative of a larger population or long-run process.

> **AP TIP**
>
> **Validity conditions for conducting a theory-based chi-square goodness-of-fit test**
> - Data (single categorical variable) are a random sample from the population or process of interest.
> - All **expected** cell counts are at least 5.

> **THINK ABOUT IT**
>
> Do you think that the data (die roll outcomes) are a random sample from the population or process of interest? For that matter, what is the population or process of interest? Are these results generalizable to all dice?

 8.4.4

The study design is fairly well controlled because the same ledge was used for each trial, the same lineup of dice was used for each trial, and the same person did the pushing of the dice each trial. Thus, it seems reasonable to believe that the method of dice rolling, pushing them off a 2-inch ledge, is the cause of the faces not being rolled equally likely. We weren't, however, told whether our five dice were a random sample of all dice. It is plausible that they were taken from a generic board game. Then we could argue they are representative of all game board dice of the same size and thus say that this method of dice rolling is not fair for all game board dice of this size. We need more information, though, to extend our conclusions beyond the five dice and 2-inch height used. Additionally, we would need the assurance that these five dice weren't loaded prior to conducting our study!

 8.4.5

Are Birthdays Equally Distributed Throughout the Week?

EXPLORATION

8.4

Are the days of the week that women give birth distributed equally throughout the week? Is someone just as likely to be born on a Tuesday as a Saturday? In this Exploration, you will investigate whether there is convincing evidence that birthdays are NOT distributed equally throughout the week. You will be using a chi-square goodness-of-fit test to help make your conclusion.

STEP 1: Ask a research question.

1. State your research question.

Definition

A *goodness-of-fit test* is used to compare observed counts for a categorical variable to hypothesized probabilities.

STEP 2: Design a study and collect data.

2. What's the categorical variable of interest, and what are the possible categories?

3. State the null and alternative hypotheses.

4. Write down your own birthday (month/day/year) and those of up to nine of your family members or friends. (Try not to write down a birthday that someone else in the class would write down.)

5. Do an Internet search for "day of birth calculator." Use the calculator to find out on what day of the week each of your family members/friends was born. Summarize your results in the table below.

Day	Sun	Mon	Tues	Wed	Thurs	Fri	Sat	Total
Observed Count								

6. Combine your results with those for the rest of the class and enter those results in the following table.

Day	Sun	Mon	Tues	Wed	Thurs	Fri	Sat	Total
Observed Count								

STEP 3: Explore the data.

7. If the null hypothesis is true and birthdays are distributed equally over the seven days in a week, then the expected count for each day will just be the total number of birthdays divided by 7. Find the expected count for each day. Is the validity condition of all expected cell counts being at least 5 met? If not, what can you do so it is met?

Day	Sun	Mon	Tue	Wed	Thurs	Fri	Sat	Total
Expected Count								

8. Comparing the observed and expected counts, does it seem that the data gathered would be likely, assuming the birthdays are distributed equally?

STEP 4: Draw inferences.

Simulation-based goodness-of-fit test: Using the MAD statistic

9. You will now conduct a simulation analysis using the mean absolute difference (MAD) statistic to investigate whether the data provide evidence that birthdays are not equally likely on all seven days of the week.

   a. **Statistic:** Here, we will use a MAD-type statistic to compare the observed and expected counts. To find the MAD statistic value for your data, complete the following table:

Day	Sun	Mon	Tue	Wed	Thu	Fri	Sat	Total
Observed Count minus Expected Count								
Absolute value of the difference in Observed and Expected counts								

   b. The MAD statistic is obtained by finding the average of the absolute values of the differences in observed and expected counts.

   MAD =

Sure, you can still work with proportions. If you used proportions, your MAD statistic would subtract the observed proportions from the hypothesized proportions (in this case, 1/7 or 0.143 for each day) for each day of the week and then average the absolute values of those differences.

c. **Simulation:** You could spin a spinner with 7 equal sections to find out what values of the MAD statistic could happen by chance alone, or you can use an applet. Open the **Goodness of Fit** applet.

- Press the **Clear** button, enter two column names (e.g., category count), and then specify each day of the week followed by a space and the count from your sample (e.g., Mon 16). Hit return and repeat for each day of the week. Then press **Use Table**. This should update the bar graph under "Sample Data."
  - In the right panel, check the box next to **Show Sampling Options** and enter the hypothesized probabilities to three decimal places, separated by commas.
- Set the **Number of Samples** to be 1 and push **Sample**.
- What is the resulting "Most Recent Sample MAD"? Is this value more or less extreme than the one from the observed data? How are you deciding?
- Now change the **Number of Samples** to be 999, for a total of 1,000 samples, and push **Sample**. This will produce a simulated null distribution of 1,000 MAD statistics.

d. **Strength of evidence:**
- Where does your observed MAD statistic lie on the simulated null distribution of MAD statistics? Does the observed MAD statistic appear surprising and unlikely to have happened by chance alone, that is, if the null hypothesis of all days being equally likely were to be true? How are you deciding?
- To find the p-value to quantify the strength of evidence against the null hypothesis, enter the observed value of the MAD statistic in the **Count Samples** box and press **Count**.

10. Based on the p-value you obtained above, do you have strong evidence against the null hypothesis? How are you deciding?

Simulation-based goodness-of-fit test: Using the chi-square statistic

11. In this situation you can also conduct a simulation analysis using the chi-square statistic to investigate whether the data provide evidence that birthdays are not equally likely on all seven days of the week.

a. **Statistic:** To find the chi-square statistic value for your data, complete the following table:

Day	Sun	Mon	Tue	Wed	Thu	Fri	Sat	Total
Observed Count − Expected Count								
Square the difference								
Divide the squared difference by the expected count								

Recall that the chi-square statistic is given by the formula

$$\chi^2 = \sum \frac{(\text{Observed Count} - \text{Expected Count})^2}{\text{Expected Count}}$$

Thus, the chi-square statistic is the Total from the last row of the table above.

Chi-square statistic =

b. **Simulation:** Just as you ran the simulation using the MAD statistic, you can follow the same steps this time using the **Statistic** pull-down menu to select the chi-square statistic (χ^2). Create a null distribution for the chi-square statistic.

c. **Strength of evidence:**

  • Where does the observed chi-square statistic lie on the simulated null distribution of the chi-square statistic? Does it appear surprising and unlikely to have happened by chance alone, that is, if the null hypothesis of all days being equally likely were to be true? How are you deciding?

  • Find the corresponding p-value. How does it compare to what you found with the MAD statistic?

12. Based on the p-value reported in #11c from the simulated null distribution for a chi-square statistic, do you have strong evidence against the null hypothesis? How are you deciding?

STEP 5: Formulate conclusions.

13. State your complete conclusions. In particular, to what population are you willing to generalize your conclusions?

14. If you found convincing evidence that birthdays are not equally distributed throughout the week, which days seemed to be different than the others and why do you think that is the case?

STEP 6: Look back and ahead.

15. If you did not find convincing evidence that birthdays are not distributed equally throughout the week, what could you do differently in a follow-up study to try to support your case?

REVISITING STEP 4: Draw inferences.

Theory-based chi-square goodness-of-fit test

Earlier, for Step 4, you used simulation to find a p-value using the chi-square statistic. Recall that one advantage of using the chi-square statistic (instead of the MAD) is that the distribution of the chi-square statistic can be predicted by a theory-based distribution called the chi-square distribution.

16. Go back to the **Goodness of Fit** applet, and picking up where you left off above, check the "Overlay chi-square distribution" box under the null distribution for the chi-square statistics. Report the "theory-based p-value."

17. How does the theory-based p-value compare to the one from the simulation-based p-value using the chi-square test statistic? Do you still arrive at the same conclusion about whether there is convincing evidence that not all seven days of the week are equally likely to be birthdays?

Remember that there are always certain checks to be made before you can decide that it is valid to use a theory-based method to test hypotheses.

> **AP TIP**
>
> **Validity conditions for conducting a theory-based chi-square goodness-of-fit test**
> • Data (single categorical variable) are a random sample from the population or process of interest.
> • All *expected* cell counts are at least 5.

18. Does the theory-based chi-square goodness-of-fit test appear to be valid in this context? Explain how you are deciding.

One of the authors collected data on which day of the week each of her 49 students was born. The data appear in the table below.

Day	Sun	Mon	Tues	Wed	Thurs	Fri	Sat	Total
Observed Count	4	7	7	7	8	6	10	49

19. Do you think these data will provide more or less evidence against the null hypothesis than the data you collected? Explain your reasoning.

   We will use the data from this class to determine whether there is convincing evidence that not all seven days of the week are equally likely to be birthdays, following the AP style.

20. Using a significance level of $\alpha = 0.05$, do the data provide convincing evidence that the days of the week that women give birth are not equally distributed throughout the week? Answer this question by completing (a)–(d) in the AP Statistics exam format.

   a. State the hypotheses using either words or symbols

   b. Name the theory-based test you will use and verify validity conditions for that test.

   c. Calculate the test statistic (standardized statistic) and corresponding p-value.

   d. State your conclusion (with appropriate justification based on your p-value and stated significance level) in the context of the research question.

   e. If there is not sufficient evidence to support the research hypothesis that all seven days of the week are not equally likely to be birthdays, is this proof that birthdays are evenly distributed throughout the days of the week? Explain.

   f. Were these data stronger or weaker evidence against the null hypothesis than the data you observed? Is this what you predicted?

   g. Based on your conclusion in (d), are you potentially making a Type I or Type II error? Explain the potential consequences of this type of error in this context.

SECTION 8.4   Summary

In this section you saw how the chi-square procedures that you learned about earlier in this chapter could be used to compare the observed distribution of a categorical variable to a hypothesized distribution through simulation- and theory-based methods. For the simulation-based approach, you used the mean absolute difference statistic and the chi-square statistic. You saw that the theory-based test for comparing the distribution of a single categorical variable to a hypothesized distribution uses the chi-square statistic and is called a chi-square goodness-of-fit test. You saw that the work you need to show on the AP exam for a chi-square goodness-of-fit test follows the same general format as the tests of significance you encountered in previous chapters.

CHAPTER 8   Summary

In this chapter we saw that the 3S strategy for simulation-based inference can be applied to comparing proportions across multiple groups (two categorical variables). Neither the explanatory nor the response variable has to be binary. This approach provides an *overall* test of the multiple groups simultaneously, as opposed to testing each pair of groups separately. (Something you will see again in Chapter 9 when we compare multiple means.)

   Because comparing more than two groups is a bit more complicated than just two, the choice of a statistic to measure how different the groups are is not straight forward. We saw that a reasonable statistic to use is the MAD, or the mean of the absolute differences. Using this statistic, it is easy to see that larger values of the MAD statistic indicate a greater difference in sample proportions across the groups. (Again, this is something you will see repeated in Chapter 9 with multiple means.)

   The $\hat{p}_{max} - \hat{p}_{min}$ and MAD statistics are fairly easy to understand but are not widely used. A more commonly used statistic is called a chi-square (χ^2) statistic. We also saw that the chi-square statistic has some similar properties to that of the MAD statistic. This statistic is used as the basis for the theory-based test, appropriately called the chi-square test.

   When a chi-square test reveals strong evidence that at least one of the population proportions or probabilities differs from the others, confidence intervals for these differences can be calculated for pairs of groups. Confidence intervals that do not include zero indicate which pairs of sample proportions differ significantly. (This, again, is something we will see repeated in Chapter 9 when we compare multiple means.)

We also saw that the chi-square test of association we looked at in Section 8.2 can be thought of as two different tests, though identical methods are used to compute the p-values. The first of these tests is the *chi-square test of independence* that examines one group of individuals classified according to two categorical variables. It tests the null hypothesis that there is no association between the two categorical variables in the population of interest. The second is the *chi-square test of homogeneity* that compares the distribution of proportions for two or more groups on the same categorical response variable. Independent random samples are taken from each population of interest or the individuals (experimental units) are randomly assigned to treatments in an experiment. It tests the null hypothesis that there is no difference in the distribution of a categorical response variable for several populations or treatments.

Finally, we explored the *chi-square goodness-of-fit test* that is used to compare observed counts for a categorical variable to a complete set of hypothesized probabilities. Although the process of computing the chi-square test statistic is the same as the previous tests, what you are testing is quite different.

Type of data	Name of test	Applet	Validity conditions
A categorical explanatory variable with 2 or more categories and a categorical response variable with 2 or more categories	Simulation test for multiple proportions	Multiple proportions	—
	Theory-based chi-square test of independence (Sample comes from a single population)	Multiple proportions	At least 5 expected counts in each cell
	Theory-based chi-square test of homogeneity (Samples come from a multiple populations)		
A single categorical variable with 2 or more categories	Simulation test for goodness of fit	Goodness of fit	—
	Theory-based chi-square goodness-of-fit test	Goodness of fit	At least 5 expected counts in each cell

CHAPTER 8
GLOSSARY

cell contributions Contribution of cell in two-way table to the chi-square statistic; helpful in determining where large differences between *observed data* and what would be expected if the null hypothesis were true, exist.

chi-square distribution A nonnegative, right-skewed distribution used in all the theory-based chi-square tests.

chi-square goodness-of-fit test A theory-based test used to compare observed counts for a categorical variable to a complete set of hypothesized probabilities.

chi-square statistic A standardized statistic for summarizing the relationship between two categorical variables which has a predictable null distribution, making it a popular theory-based test.

chi-square test of homogeneity A theory-based test that compares the distribution of a categorical response variable for two or more groups. Independent random samples are taken from each population of interest or the individuals (experimental units) are randomly assigned to treatments

in an experiment. It tests the null hypothesis that there is no difference in the distribution of the categorical variable response variable for several populations or treatments.

chi-square test of independence A theory-based test that examines one group of individuals classified according to two categorical variables. It tests the null hypothesis that there is no association between the two categorical variables in the population of interest.

expected counts The predicted outcomes for the cells of the table assuming the null hypothesis is true.

MAD A statistic testing an association between two categorical variables of more than two categories; (M)ean of the (A)bsolute values of the (D)ifferences in the conditional proportions.

observed counts The values in the cells of the table from the study.

validity conditions for chi-square tests The expected counts in each cell of a table must be at least 5.

CHAPTER 8

EXERCISES

SECTION 8.1

8.1.1* Which of the following are true about the MAD statistic? There may be more than one statement that is true.

a. The MAD statistic can never be negative.

b. The MAD statistic is the average distance sample proportions are from each other.

c. The MAD statistic is the average of a group of sample proportions.

d. A MAD statistic of zero means that all the proportions are the same distance apart.

e. As the MAD statistic increases, the p-value decreases.

8.1.2 As observed proportions move farther apart:

A. Both the MAD statistic and the p-value will decrease.

B. Both the MAD statistic and the p-value will increase.

C. The MAD statistic will increase and the p-value will decrease.

D. The MAD statistic will decrease and the p-value will increase.

8.1.3* Null distributions using the MAD statistic will be:

A. Symmetric and centered at zero.

B. Symmetric and centered at the MAD statistic.

C. Skewed right.

D. Skewed left.

8.1.4 What has to be true about the observed proportions if the MAD statistic is zero?

8.1.5* Given the three sample proportions 0.25, 0.30, and 0.35, determine the MAD statistic.

8.1.6 Given the four sample proportions 0.66, 0.45, 0.73, and 0.44, determine the MAD statistic.

8.1.7* Consider the MAD statistic. What would happen if you did not take absolute values before calculating the sum of differences between group proportions? Why would this not be a useful calculation without taking absolute values?

New law

8.1.8 Suppose a poll is done to see if voters agree with a new law passed in Congress. The results are summarized in the 8.1.8 table along with the voters' party affiliation. You plan to test to see whether there is an association between party affiliation and agreement with the new law.

a. Determine the proportion of each political group that agrees with the new law.

b. Determine the MAD statistic.

Giving blood and political party*

8.1.9 Suppose that you want to compare proportions of registered Democrats, Independents, and Republicans who have donated blood within the past year.

a. Which would be appropriate for this study: random sampling, random assignment, both, or neither? Explain.

b. If you find that the sample proportions who have donated blood are 0.20, 0.15, and 0.12, what more information would you need to determine if these proportions differ significantly?

Giving blood and state

8.1.10 Suppose you want to compare proportions of adults who have donated blood within the past year among California, Iowa, Massachusetts, and Michigan residents. You take a random sample of 200 adults from each state.

a. Which of the following sets of sample proportions (A, B, or C) would produce the *smallest* p-value? Explain.

b. Which of the following sets of sample proportions (A, B, or C) would produce the *largest* p-value? Explain.

	California proportion	Iowa proportion	Massachusetts proportion	Michigan proportion
A	0.30	0.25	0.28	0.22
B	0.40	0.15	0.18	0.37
C	0.35	0.20	0.23	0.30

Sex and phone type*

8.1.11 Suppose 100 students are asked if the cellphone they use is a smartphone or a basic phone and the 8.1.11 two-way table summarizes the results.

		Republican	Democrat	Independent	Total
Agree with a new law?	**Yes**	125	201	178	504
	No	233	156	184	573
	Total	358	357	362	1,077

EXERCISE 8.1.8

	Male	Female	Total
Smartphone	25	30	55
Basic phone	25	20	45
Total	50	50	100

EXERCISE 8.1.11

a. Find the proportion of males that own smartphones and the proportion of females that own smartphones.

b. Determine the MAD statistic.

c. When comparing two proportions, you could use the difference in the proportions or the MAD as the statistic. How do these two statistics compare in this example? Will they always have the same relationship as in this example? Explain.

d. Put the data from the table in the **Multiple Proportions** applet and make null distributions using both the difference in proportions and the MAD statistic. Describe how these distributions are different.

e. Based on your answer from part (c), explain why a distribution of MAD statistics is skewed right when the distribution of differences in proportions is bell-shaped.

Generation and marriage views

8.1.12 Do different generations view marriage differently? A 2010 survey of a random sample of adult Americans conducted by the Pew Research Center asked the following question of each participant: *"Is marriage becoming obsolete?"* The results from the survey are shown in the 8.1.12 table below.

a. Find and report appropriate numerical statistics to describe the association, if any, between generation and opinion about marriage.

b. Calculate the MAD statistic for these data.

c. Create a well-labeled graph to display the above data. Also, describe in one or two sentences what this graph tells you about the association between generations and whether marriage is viewed as becoming obsolete. Does it appear that generations tend to view marriage differently, and if so, how?

8.1.13 Reconsider the previous question on how different generations view marriage. The results are shown in the

table in the previous exercise and can also be found in the file **MarriageViews.**

a. Identify the observational units.

b. Identify the variables recorded. For each variable, identify the role (explanatory or response) and the type (categorical or quantitative).

c. Give two ways in which this study is different from the *"Is yawning contagious?"* study which was introduced in Exploration 5.2.

d. Describe the parameter(s) of interest and assign appropriate symbol(s) to the parameter(s).

e. State in words the appropriate null and alternative hypotheses in the context of the study.

f. State in symbols the appropriate null and alternative hypotheses in the context of the study.

g. Use a simulation-based approach to test the hypotheses stated in parts (e) and (f). Use the **Multiple Proportions** applet and paste the table located in the file **Marriage Views** and press **Use My Table**.

Be sure to report the following:

• The name and the observed value of the statistic (from the study)

• The p-value

• Your conclusion in the context of the study (Be sure to comment on significance, causation, and generalization.)

8.1.14 Reconsider the previous exercises. If the different generations *did not* view marriage differently what would you expect the cell counts in the 8.1.14 table to be? (That is, there is no association between the age groups and whether or not someone thinks marriage is obsolete.) Complete the table.

Heart disease and baldness*

8.1.15 Many studies have been done to look at the relationship between heart disease and baldness. In one study, researchers selected a sample of 663 heart disease male patients and a control group of 772 male patients not suffering from heart disease from hospitals in eastern Massachusetts and Rhode Island. Each was asked to classify their degree

		Generation				
		Millennial (ages 18–29)	Gen X (ages 30–45)	Boomers (ages 46–65)	Age 65+	Total
Marriage obsolete?	Yes	236	313	401	68	1,018
	No	300	416	745	143	1,604
	Total	536	729	1,146	211	2,622

EXERCISE 8.1.12

	Generation				
	Millennial (ages 18–29)	Gen X (ages 30–45)	Boomers (ages 46–65)	Age 65+	Total
Marriage obsolete? Yes					1,018
No					1,604
Total	536	729	1,146	211	2,622

EXERCISE 8.1.14

of baldness. The results are given in the following table. Use these data to answer the following questions.

		Baldness				
		None	Little	Some	Much	Total
Heart disease	Yes	251	165	195	52	663
	No	331	221	185	35	772
	Total	582	386	380	87	1,435

Notice the degree of baldness uses ordered categories. This makes it possible to reduce the 2 × 4 table to a simpler one:

a. Of those in the control group, what percent claimed to have:

i. Little or no baldness?

ii. Some or much baldness?

b. Of those with heart disease, what percent claimed to have:

i. Little or no baldness?

ii. Some or much baldness?

c. At this stage in the investigation, state whether you think there is a relationship between heart disease and baldness. Explain your answer.

We are now going to run a test of significance on these data using all four degrees of baldness. Use the data set **HeartDiseaseAndBaldness**.

d. State the null and alternative hypotheses you would use to test whether there is an association between heart disease and baldness.

e. Use a simulation-based approach to test the hypotheses stated in part (d).

Be sure to report the following:

• The name and the observed value of the statistic (from the study)

• The shape of the null distribution and the p-value

• Your conclusion in the context of the study (Be sure to comment on significance, causation, and generalization.)

Note: Save your results. You will need them for Exercise 8.CE.20

Night lights and vision

8.1.16 In Exploration 8.2B, we will look at a study that was done to determine if there is an association between the amount of light in infants' bedrooms at night (darkness, night light, room light) and whether or not the child was nearsighted when they were older. A summary of the data from that study is shown in the following table. We are interested in determining if there is an association between the type of light in the room and whether or not the child is nearsighted.

	Darkness	Night light	Room light	Total
Nearsighted	18	78	41	137
Normal vision	154	154	34	342
Total	172	232	75	479

a. What is the explanatory variable in this study? Is it categorical or quantitative?

b. What is the response variable in this study? Is it categorical or quantitative?

c. Write out the null and alternative hypotheses for this study.

d. Compute the observed proportions of children that are nearsighted for each lighting condition.

e. Compute the MAD statistic.

f. A null distribution was generated for this data set and is shown. Based on this distribution along with the MAD statistic, what can you say about the value of the p-value?

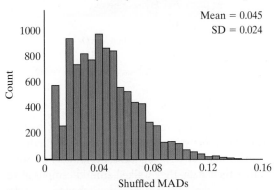

g. What is your conclusion based on this p-value?

Political jokes*

8.1.17 Researchers at the University of Pennsylvania studied the humor of late-night comedians Jon Stewart, Jay Leno, and David Letterman. Between July 15 and September 16, 2004, they performed a content analysis of the jokes made by Jon Stewart during the "headlines" segment of *The Daily Show* and by Jay Leno and David Letterman during the monologue segments of their shows. (We will consider this a random sample of all their jokes.) We want to determine if there is an association between the comedian and the political nature of their jokes. A summary of the data they gathered was:

- Leno: 315 of the 1,313 jokes were of a political nature
- Letterman: 136 of the 648 jokes were of a political nature
- Stewart: 83 of the 252 jokes were of a political nature

a. Organize the data into a two-way table, with the explanatory variable as the columns and the response variable as the rows.

b. What is the explanatory variable in this study? Is it categorical or quantitative?

c. What is the response variable in this study? Is it categorical or quantitative?

d. Write out the null and alternative hypotheses for this study.

e. For each comedian, calculate the conditional proportion of his jokes that were political in nature.

f. Compute the MAD statistic.

g. A null distribution was generated for this data set and is shown. Based on this distribution along with the MAD statistic, what can you say about the value of the p-value?

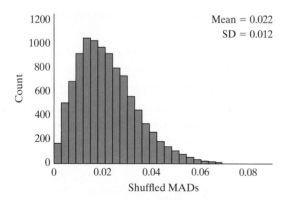

h. What is your conclusion based on this p-value?

Contagious yawning

8.1.18 Student researchers wanted to see if it there was an association between the time of day and whether or not someone would yawn right after seeing another person yawn. To gather their data, they walked around campus at various times of day yawning at people and watched to see if the subjects yawned. The results are shown in the following table.

		Time of Day				
		8–11a	11a–2p	2–5p	5–8p	Total
Subject yawned?	Yes	25	38	15	29	107
	No	14	28	18	15	75
	Total	39	66	33	44	182

a. What is the explanatory variable in this study? Is it categorical or quantitative?

b. What is the response variable in this study? Is it categorical or quantitative?

c. Write out the null and alternative hypotheses for this study.

d. What time period did the highest proportion of the subjects yawn?

e. What time period did the lowest proportion of subjects yawn?

f. The table for these results can be found in the file **Yawn-Time**. Put that table in the **Multiple Proportions** applet (make sure you click on **Use Table**). What is the value of the MAD statistic?

g. Do at least 1,000 repetitions and find a p-value.

h. Based on your p-value, do you have strong evidence that there is an association between the time of day and whether or not someone will yawn after they see a yawn?

8.1.19 Reconsider the previous exercise about contagious yawning and time of day. The results of this test are not significant. If this study were redone, what suggestions do you have that would help make the results significant?

Stop and frisk*

8.1.20 In a February 2013 Quinnipiac University poll the following question about a typical practice of the New York Police Department was asked to a random sample of New York City voters: *"As you may know, there is a police practice known as 'stop and frisk', where police stop and question a person they suspect of wrongdoing and, if necessary search that person. Do you approve or disapprove of this police practice?"* The results from the poll are shown in the following table by age groups.

	Age			
	18–34	35–54	55+	Total
Approve	68	128	173	369
Disapprove	164	204	165	533
Total	232	332	338	902

a. What proportion in each age category approves of stop and frisk?

b. Does there seem to be an association with age and whether or not someone approves of stop and frisk? If so, describe the association.

c. Write out the null and alternative hypotheses for this study.

d. The table for these results can be found in the file **FriskAge**. Put that table in the **Multiple Proportions** applet (make sure you click on **Use Table**). What is the value of the MAD statistic?

e. Do at least 1,000 repetitions and find a p-value.

f. Based on your p-value, do you have strong evidence that there is an association between age and whether or not someone approves of the stop and frisk practice?

8.1.21 Reconsider the previous problem on approval of stop and frisk. Complete a test of significance to determine if there is an association between age category and whether or not someone approves or disapproves of the police practice known as stop and frisk using $\hat{p}_{max} - \hat{p}_{min}$ as the statistic. Make sure you give the hypotheses, your p-value, and a conclusion.

Health care reform

8.1.22 In a January 2014 Quinnipiac University poll the following question was asked to a random sample of U.S. voters: *"Do you support or oppose the health care law passed by Barack Obama and Congress in 2010?"* The results from the poll are shown in the following table by age groups.

	Age				
	18–29	30–49	50–64	65+	Total
Support	128	236	213	153	730
Oppose	122	367	331	247	1,067
Total	250	603	544	400	1,797

a. What proportion in each age category supports the health care law?

b. Which age category is most supportive of the health care law? Which age category is the least supportive?

c. Write out the null and alternative hypotheses for this study.

d. The table for these results can be found in the file **HealthcareAge**. Put that table in the **Multiple Proportions** applet (make sure you click on **Use Table**). What is the value of the MAD statistic?

e. Do at least 1,000 repetitions and find a p-value.

f. Based on your p-value, how much evidence is there against the null hypothesis?

g. Comment on the ability to generalize and draw cause-and-effect conclusions from these data.

Cellphone ownership*

8.1.23 In a September 2013 poll conducted by the Pew Research Center, they asked a random sample of U.S. adults if they owned a cellphone. The results are shown in the following table by race.

		White	Black	Hispanic	Total
Own a cellphone?	Yes	3,801	611	614	5,026
	No	422	53	68	543
	Total	4,223	664	682	5,569

a. What proportion in each race category owns a cellphone?

b. Does there seem to be an association between race and whether or not someone owns a cellphone?

c. Write out the null and alternative hypotheses for this study.

d. The table for these results can be found in the file **CellphoneRace**. Put that table in the **Multiple Proportions** applet (make sure you click on **Use Table**). What is the value of the MAD statistic?

e. Do at least 1,000 repetitions and find a p-value.

f. Based on your p-value, do you have strong evidence that there is an association between race and whether or not someone owns a cellphone?

8.1.24 Reconsider the previous problem on cellphone use. Complete a test of significance to determine if there is an association between race and whether or not someone owns a cellphone using $\hat{p}_{max} - \hat{p}_{min}$ as the statistic. Make sure you give the hypotheses, your p-value, and a conclusion.

8.1.25 In a September 2013 poll conducted by the Pew Research Center, they asked a random sample of U.S. adults if they owned a smart phone. The results are shown in the following table by race.

		White	Black	Hispanic	Total
Own a smartphone?	Yes	2,238	372	382	2,992
	No	1,985	292	300	2,577
	Total	4,223	664	682	5,569

a. What proportion in each race category owns a smartphone?

b. Does there seem to be an association between race and whether or not someone owns a smartphone?

c. Write out the null and alternative hypotheses for this study.

d. The table for these results can be found in the file **SmartphoneRace**. Put that table in the **Multiple Proportions** applet (make sure you click on **Use Table**). What is the value of the MAD statistic?

e. Do at least 1,000 repetitions and find a p-value.

f. Based on your p-value, write a complete conclusion. Be sure to include to whom you can generalize the result.

8.1.26 Reconsider Exercises 8.1.23 and 8.1.25 on cellphone and smartphone ownership. We considered our population to be that of all adults in the U.S. Now suppose we want the population to be all the cellphone users in the U.S.

a. Combine the results in the tables from these two exercises so you have a new two-way table where race is the explanatory variable and the response variable is whether or not someone owns a smartphone given that they own a cellphone.

b. What proportion of the cellphone owners of each race own smartphones?

Political party survey

8.1.27 Suppose two surveys are done to see if Democrats, Independents, and Republicans differ on their agreement with a certain issue and the results are shown in the following two tables.

Survey A

	Dem	Ind	Rep	Total
Agree	30	25	20	75
Disagree	70	75	80	225
	100	100	100	300

Survey B

	Dem	Ind	Rep	Total
Agree	300	250	200	750
Disagree	700	750	800	2,250
	1,000	1,000	1,000	3,000

a. Input the table for Survey A in the **Multiple Proportions** applet and report the MAD statistic.

b. Do at least 1,000 shuffles to find a null distribution for Survey A. Report your p-value and standard deviation of the null distribution.

c. Input the table for Survey B in the **Multiple Proportions** applet and report the MAD statistic.

d. Do at least 1,000 shuffles to find a null distribution for Survey B. Report your p-value and standard deviation of the null distribution.

e. You should have found the MAD statistics are the same for both surveys. Explain why they are the same.

f. You should have also found the p-value from Survey B was much smaller than that for Survey A. Explain why this makes sense intuitively.

g. Even though the MAD statistics are the same, explain why the p-value for Survey B is smaller based on the two null distributions.

Coming to a stop*

8.1.28 In Example 8.1 you used the MAD statistic to evaluate the strength of evidence for association between the order in which a car arrived at an intersection and whether or not it came to a complete stop.

a. Complete a test of significance to determine if there is an association between order of car and whether or not it came to a complete stop using $\hat{p}_{max} - \hat{p}_{min}$ as the statistic. Make sure you give the hypotheses, your p-value, and a conclusion.

b. Compare and contrast the null distribution you found with the $\hat{p}_{max} - \hat{p}_{min}$ statistic vs. the MAD statistic.

c. Compare and contrast the strength of evidence using $\hat{p}_{max} - \hat{p}_{min}$ vs. MAD on this data set.

Recruiting organ donors

8.1.29 In Exploration 8.1 you used the MAD statistic to evaluate the strength of evidence for association between the way a question was asked and whether or not someone chose to be an organ donor.

a. Complete a test of significance to determine if there is an association between survey type and whether or not someone chose to become an organ donor using $\hat{p}_{max} - \hat{p}_{min}$ as the statistic. Make sure you give the hypotheses, your p-value, and a conclusion.

b. Compare and contrast the null distribution you found with the $\hat{p}_{max} - \hat{p}_{min}$ statistic vs. the MAD statistic.

c. Compare and contrast the strength of evidence using $\hat{p}_{max} - \hat{p}_{min}$ vs. MAD on this data set.

FAQ

8.1.30 Read FAQ 8.1.1 and then reconsider Exercise 8.1.29 based on Exploration 8.1, where you investigated whether there was evidence of an association between the type of default option and whether a person chooses to be an organ donor.

a. What would be a danger of conducting three separate tests, comparing two groups at a time rather than one overall test?

b. In Exploration 8.1 you should have found strong evidence of an association between the type of default option and whether a person chooses to be an organ donor. Now to conduct follow-up tests, suppose that we wanted to control the familywise error rate at 5%. Would the adjusted Type I error rate for any one of the three tests be larger than, smaller than, or the same as 5%?

8.1.31 Read FAQ 8.1.1 and then reconsider Exercise 8.1.12 about whether different generations view marriage differently.

a. If you were to compare two generations at a time, how many separate comparisons would you need to make?

b. Suppose that your chance of making a Type I error was 6% for each one of these comparisons. What would be the approximate probability of making at least one Type I error across all the possible comparisons? What is this number called?

c. Suppose that you wanted to keep the familywise error rate to 6%, to what would each individual comparison's Type I error rate have to be adjusted?

SECTION 8.2

8.2.1* Consider the chi-square statistic.

a. Can the value of this statistic be negative? Why or why not?

b. When will the chi-square statistic be 0?

c. Which of (A)–(C) describes the shape of the distribution of the chi-square statistic:

  A. Symmetric

  B. Skewed toward high values (long right tail)

  C. Skewed toward low values (long left tail)

d. Give an intuitive explanation of why you expect the shape of distribution of the chi-square statistic to be what you described in part (c).

HIV intervention programs

8.2.2 Researchers Jemmott III et al. (*Journal of American Medical Association*, 1998) reported a study in which a group of inner-city African American adolescents from Philadelphia were randomly divided into three groups as part of an experiment to assess the effectiveness of different HIV prevention programs. One group was given "abstinence HIV intervention," the next group was given "safer-sex HIV intervention," and the third group was given "health promotion intervention," which was to serve as a control. One outcome that was measured was whether subjects who were sexually active during a three-month period reported consistent condom use. The 8.2.2A table shows the summarized data.

a. Is this an experiment or an observational study? How are you deciding?

b. Identify the observational units.

c. Identify the explanatory and response variables. Also, for each variable, identify whether it is categorical or quantitative.

d. Define the parameters of interest. Assign symbols to these parameters.

e. State the appropriate null and alternative hypotheses.

f. Find the table of expected cell counts; that is, complete the 8.2.2B table, assuming the null hypothesis is true.

g. Describe how one might use everyday items (for example, coins, dice, cards, etc.) to conduct a tactile simulation-based test of the hypotheses. Be sure to clearly describe how the p-value will be computed from the simulation.

8.2.3 Refer to the previous exercise about the study of different HIV intervention programs.

a. State the appropriate null and alternative hypotheses *in words*.

b. Explain why it would be okay to use the theory-based method to find a p-value for this study.

c. Use an appropriate applet (for example, the **Multiple Proportions** applet) to find and report the following from the data.

  • The name of the statistic and its numeric value

  • The theory-based p-value

d. Comment on the strength of evidence based on the p-value.

e. Comment on causation and generalization. Be sure to explain how you are arriving at your conclusion.

f. Explain why it is not particularly useful to look at confidence intervals for the parameter(s) of interest in this study.

		Abstinence intervention	Safer-sex intervention	Control	Total
Consistent condom use?	Yes	14	20	21	**55**
	No	20	12	20	**52**
	Total	**34**	**32**	**41**	**107**

EXERCISE 8.2.2A: **Observed counts**

		Abstinence intervention	Safer-sex intervention	Control	Total
Consistent condom use?	Yes				55
	No				52
	Total	**34**	**32**	**41**	**107**

EXERCISE 8.2.2B: **Expected counts**

8.2.4 Refer to the previous exercise about the study of different HIV intervention programs. Show how to calculate the chi-square statistic by setting up the formula with appropriate numbers.

8.2.5 Refer to the previous exercise about the study of different HIV intervention programs. Suppose that the observed cell counts were actually twice as big as those reported in the original study.

For parts (a)–(c): How, if at all, would the values of the following change?

a. The expected cell
counts: Increase Decrease Stay the same

b. The chi-square
statistic: Increase Decrease Stay the same

c. The p-value: Increase Decrease Stay the same

d. Would the evidence in support of an association between type of HIV intervention program and consistent condom usage among adolescents such as the ones in the study be stronger or weaker compared to the original study? Explain how you are deciding.

Views of marriage*

8.2.6 Recall Exercise 8.1.12 about whether different generations view marriage differently. The corresponding data are available in the file **MarriageViews**.

a. State the appropriate null and alternative hypotheses *in words*.

b. Explain why it would be okay to use the theory-based method to find a p-value for this study.

c. Use an appropriate applet (for example, the **Multiple Proportions** applet) to find and report the following from the data.

- The name of the statistic and its numeric value
- The theory-based p-value

d. Comment on the strength of evidence based on the p-value.

e. Comment on causation and generalization. Be sure to explain how you are arriving at your conclusion.

f. Use an applet to find and report a set of confidence intervals appropriate for the context. Also, interpret the confidence intervals in the context of the study.

Sleep apnea and hypertension

8.2.7 In a study of the relationship between sleep apnea and hypertension (*New England Journal of Medicine*, 2000), researchers Peppard et al. categorized the participants by the severity of sleep apnea at the beginning of the study, and four years later recorded whether or not the participant had hypertension. Here is the table of the summarized data:

		Severity of sleep apnea				
		Not	Somewhat	Severe	Very	Total
Severe hypertension?	Yes	32	142	63	40	**277**
	No	155	365	69	27	**616**
	Total	**187**	**507**	**132**	**67**	**893**

a. Is this an experiment or an observational study? How are you deciding?

b. Identify the observational units.

c. Identify the explanatory and response variables. Also, for each variable, identify whether it is categorical or quantitative.

d. Define the parameters of interest. Assign symbols to these parameters.

e. State the appropriate null and alternative hypotheses in symbols.

f. Find the table of expected cell counts; that is, complete the table below, assuming the null hypothesis were true.

		Severity of sleep apnea				
		Not	Somewhat	Severe	Very	Total
Severe hypertension?	Yes					277
	No					616
	Total	187	507	132	67	893

g. Describe how one might use everyday items (for example, coins, dice, cards, etc.) to conduct a tactile simulation-based test of the hypotheses. Be sure to clearly describe how the p-value will be computed from the simulation.

8.2.8 Refer to the previous exercise about the study of the relationship between sleep apnea and hypertension.

a. State the appropriate null and alternative hypotheses *in words*.

b. Explain why it would be okay to use the theory-based method to find a p-value for this study.

c. Use an appropriate applet (for example, the **Multiple Proportions** applet) to find and report the following from the data.

- The name of the statistic and its numeric value
- The theory-based p-value

d. Interpret the p-value in the context of the study.

e. State a complete conclusion about this study, including significance, causation, and generalization. Be sure to explain how you are arriving at your conclusion.

f. If relevant, use an applet to find and report a set of confidence intervals appropriate for the context. Also, interpret the confidence intervals in the context of the study. If not relevant, explain why it is not particularly useful to look at confidence intervals for the parameter(s) of interest in the context of this study.

8.2.9 Refer to the previous exercise about the study of the relationship between sleep apnea and hypertension. Show how to calculate the chi-square statistic by setting up the formula with appropriate numbers.

8.2.10 Refer to the previous exercise about the study of the relationship between sleep apnea and hypertension. Suppose that the observed cell counts were actually three times as big as those reported in the original study.

For parts (a)–(c): How, if at all, would the values of the following change?

a. The expected cell
counts: Increase   Decrease   Stay the same

b. The p-value: Increase   Decrease   Stay the same

c. The chi-square
statistic: Increase   Decrease   Stay the same

d. Would the evidence in support of an association between sleep apnea and hypertension for people such as the ones in the study be stronger or weaker compared to the original study? Explain how you are deciding.

Heart disease and baldness?*

8.2.11 Recall Exercise 8.1.15 about the relationship between heart disease and baldness. The data are provided in the file **HeartDiseaseAndBaldness**.

a. Identify the observational units.

b. Describe the parameter(s) of interest and assign appropriate symbol(s) to the parameter(s).

c. State in words the appropriate null and alternative hypotheses in the context of the study.

d. State in symbols the appropriate null and alternative hypotheses in the context of the study.

e. Use a theory-based approach to test your hypotheses from the previous question. Report the p-value and state your complete conclusion. Discuss your scope of conclusions: whether your results necessarily mean that heart disease is caused by baldness or baldness is caused by heart disease and whether you can extend your conclusions to a broader population.

8.2.12 Refer to the previous exercise about the relationship between heart disease and baldness. The data are provided in the file **HeartDiseaseAndBaldness**.

a. Compute the conditional proportions of heart disease given each degree of baldness.

b. There are six pairwise differences. Which two are the largest? Which one is the smallest?

c. Use the **Theory-Based Inference** applet to compute p-values and confidence intervals for the two largest differences and the smallest difference.

d. Are the results from the theory-based approach valid for the data in this study? State the validity conditions and explain how you are deciding whether or not these conditions are met.

Physical activity and aging

8.2.13 An eight-year cohort study of 3,454 initially disease-free men and women (ages around 60 years or more) recorded the extent of physical activity the participants engaged in and whether or not they were showing signs of "healthy aging" (*British Journal of Sports Medicine*, 2013). Here is the table of summarized counts at the conclusion of the study:

| | | Activity level | | | |
		Inactive	Moderate	Vigorous	Total
Healthy aging?	Yes	55	345	265	**665**
	No	598	1,347	844	**2,789**
	Total	**653**	**1,692**	**1,109**	**3,454**

a. Is this an experiment or an observational study? How are you deciding?

b. Identify the observational units.

c. Identify the explanatory and response variables. Also, for each variable, identify whether it is categorical or quantitative.

d. State the appropriate null and alternative hypotheses.

e. Describe how one might use everyday items (for example, coins, dice, cards, etc.) to conduct a tactile simulation-based test of the hypotheses. Be sure to clearly describe how the p-value will be computed from the simulation.

8.2.14 Refer to the previous exercise about the study of the relationship between level of physical activity and aging.

a. Explain why it would be okay to use the theory-based method to find a p-value for this study.

b. Use an appropriate applet (for example, the **Multiple Proportions** applet) to find and report the following from the data: (i) the name of the statistic and its numeric value and (ii) the theory-based p-value.

c. Interpret the p-value in the context of the study.

d. State a complete conclusion about this study, including significance, causation, and generalization. Be sure to explain how you are arriving at your conclusion.

e. If relevant, use an applet to find and report a set of confidence intervals appropriate for the context. Also, interpret the confidence intervals in the context of the study. If not relevant, explain why it is not particularly useful to look at confidence intervals for the parameter(s) of interest in the context of this study.

8.2.15 Refer to the previous exercise about the study of the relationship between level of physical activity and aging. Show how to calculate the chi-square statistic by setting up the formula with appropriate numbers.

8.2.16 Refer to the previous exercise about the study of the relationship between level of physical activity and aging. Suppose that the observed cell counts were actually half as small as those reported in the original study.

a. Without carrying out any extensive calculations, say whether the p-value would increase, decrease, or stay the same. Explain your reasoning.

b. Without carrying out any extensive calculations, say what the value of the chi-square statistic would be. Explain your reasoning.

c. Would the evidence in support of an association between physical activity and healthy aging for people such as the ones in the study be stronger or weaker compared to the original study? Explain how you are deciding.

Politics and taxes*

8.2.17 Given below is a table of summarized data from a 2013 study of a nationally representative sample of U.S. adults by the Gallup organization, where participants were asked about their political leaning as well as their opinion on whether there should be a tax on unhealthy food/soda.

a. Is this an experiment or an observational study? How are you deciding?

b. Identify the observational units.

c. Identify the explanatory and response variables. Also, for each variable, identify whether it is categorical or quantitative.

d. Define the parameters of interest. Assign symbols to these parameters.

e. State the appropriate null and alternative hypotheses in symbols.

f. State the appropriate null and alternative hypotheses in words.

g. Explain why it would be okay to use the theory-based method to find a p-value for this study.

h. Use an appropriate applet (for example, the **Multiple Proportions** applet) to find and report the following from the data: (i) the name of the statistic and its numeric value and (ii) the theory-based p-value.

i. Interpret the p-value in the context of the study.

j. State a complete conclusion about this study, including significance, causation, and generalization. Be sure to explain how you are arriving at your conclusion.

k. If relevant, use an applet to find and report a set of confidence intervals appropriate for the context. Also, interpret the confidence intervals in the context of the study. If not relevant, explain why it is not particularly useful to look at confidence intervals for the parameter(s) of interest in the context of this study.

Fish and cancer

8.2.18 In an article published in *Lancet* (2001), researchers shared their findings from a study where they followed 6,272 Swedish men for 30 years to see whether there was an association between the amount of fish in the diet and likelihood of prostate cancer. The results are presented in the following two-way table:

		Large	Moderate	Small	None	Total
Prostate cancer?	Yes	42	209	201	14	466
	No	507	2,769	2,420	110	5,806
	Total	549	2,978	2,621	124	6,272

a. Is this an experiment or an observational study? How are you deciding?

b. Identify the observational units.

c. Identify the explanatory and response variables. Also, for each variable, identify whether it is categorical or quantitative.

d. Define the parameters of interest. Assign symbols to these parameters.

e. State the appropriate null and alternative hypotheses in symbols.

		Political leaning			
		Republican	Democrat	Independent	Total
Favor tax on unhealthy food/ soda?	Yes	127	273	246	646
	No	403	334	500	1,237
	Total	530	607	746	1,883

EXERCISE 8.2.17

f. State the appropriate null and alternative hypotheses *in words*.

g. Explain why it would be okay to use the theory-based method to find a p-value for this study.

h. Use an appropriate applet (for example, the **Multiple Proportions** applet) to find and report the following from the data: (i) the name of the statistic and its numeric value and (ii) the theory-based p-value.

i. Interpret the p-value in the context of the study.

j. State a complete conclusion about this study, including significance, causation, and generalization. Be sure to explain how you are arriving at your conclusion.

k. If relevant, use an applet to find and report a set of confidence intervals appropriate for the context. Also, interpret the confidence intervals in the context of the study. If not relevant, explain why it is not particularly useful to look at confidence intervals for the parameter(s) of interest in the context of this study.

A person's sex and breakfast*

8.2.19 In a survey of 50 students in an introductory statistics students, data were collected on an individual's sex and breakfast eating habits. Here is a table of the summarized data:

		Females	Males	Total
	Every morning	21	5	26
Eat breakfast?	Most mornings	7	4	11
	Some mornings	7	3	10
	Never	2	1	3
	Total	37	13	50

a. Is this an experiment or an observational study? How are you deciding?

b. Identify the observational units.

c. Identify the explanatory and response variables. Also, for each variable, identify whether it is categorical or quantitative.

d. State the appropriate null and alternative hypotheses *in words*.

e. Explain why it would NOT be okay to use the theory-based method to find a p-value for this study.

f. Describe how one might use everyday items (for example, coins, dice, cards, etc.) to conduct a tactile simulation-based test of the hypotheses. Be sure to clearly describe how the p-value will be computed from the simulation.

g. Use an appropriate applet (for example, the **Multiple Proportions** applet) to find and report the following

from the data: (i) the name of a statistic and its numeric value and (ii) the simulation-based p-value.

h. Interpret the p-value in the context of the study.

i. State a complete conclusion about this study, including significance, causation, and generalization. Be sure to explain how you are arriving at your conclusion.

Design your own study

8.2.20 Design your own study: Develop the plan for the investigation of a research question that can be answered using a chi-square test.

a. State the research question.

b. Will you conduct an experiment or an observational study? How are you deciding? Also, describe how the randomization (random sampling, random assignment, or both) will be carried out.

c. Identify the observational units.

d. Identify the response and explanatory variables. Also, identify whether each is categorical or quantitative.

e. State the appropriate null and alternative hypotheses in words.

f. Describe when it will be appropriate to use a theory-based method to test the hypotheses stated above.

Cocaine treatment*

8.2.21 Researchers Gawin et al. (*Journal of American Medical Association Psychiatry,* 1989) reported a study where each of 72 cocaine abusers were randomly assigned to receive one of three treatments for six weeks: 24 subjects received the antidepressant drug desipramine hydrochloride, 24 subjects received lithium carbonate (the usual treatment), and the remaining 24 received a placebo. Forty-one percent of the desipramine group had a relapse during the six-week period, compared to 75% for the lithium carbonate and 83% for the placebo.

a. Use the above information to create a well-labeled table of observed cell counts.

b. Is this an experiment or an observational study? How are you deciding?

c. Identify the observational units.

d. Identify the explanatory and response variables. Also, for each variable, identify whether it is categorical or quantitative.

e. State the appropriate null and alternative hypotheses *in words*.

f. Explain why it would NOT be okay to use the theory-based method to find a p-value for this study.

g. Describe how one might use everyday items (for example, coins, dice, cards, etc.) to conduct a tactile simulation-based test of the hypotheses. Be sure to clearly describe how the p-value will be computed from the simulation.

h. Use an appropriate applet (for example, the **Multiple Proportions** applet) to find and report the following from the data: (i) the name of a statistic and its numeric value and (ii) the simulation-based p-value.

i. Interpret the p-value in the context of the study.

j. State a complete conclusion about this study, including significance, causation, and generalization. Be sure to explain how you are arriving at your conclusion.

Happiness and income

8.2.22 To investigate whether there is an association between happiness and income level, we will use data from the 2002 General Social Survey (GSS), cross-classifying a person's perceived happiness with their family income level. The GSS is a survey of randomly selected U.S. adults who are not institutionalized.

		Not too happy	Pretty happy	Very happy	Total
	Above average	21	159	110	290
Income?	Average	53	372	221	646
	Below average	94	249	83	426
	Total	168	780	414	1,362

a. State the appropriate null and alternative hypotheses *in words*.

b. Explain why it would be okay to use the theory-based method to find a p-value for this study.

c. Use an appropriate applet (for example, the **Multiple Proportions** applet) to find and report the following from the data: (i) the name of the statistic and its numeric value and (ii) the theory-based p-value.

d. Interpret the p-value in the context of the study.

e. State a complete conclusion about this study, including significance, causation, and generalization. Be sure to explain how you are arriving at your conclusion.

Demographics of treatment groups*

8.2.23 Often research articles include tables of comparisons for demographics of experimental groups. In one such article (*Psycho-Oncology*, 2006) reporting a study investigating the effect of art therapy on women diagnosed with cancer, researchers Monti et al. randomly assigned women to either the "mindfulness-based art therapy" treatment group or the "wait-list" control group. The researchers report the counts for race for the control group and the treatment group.

		Control group	Treatment group	Total
	Caucasian	38	45	83
	African-American	13	10	23
Race?	Asian	1	1	2
	Hispanic	2	0	2
	Other	1	0	1
	Total	55	56	111

a. Is this an experiment or an observational study? How are you deciding?

b. State the appropriate null and alternative hypotheses *in words*.

c. Explain why it would NOT be okay to use the theory-based method to find a p-value for this study.

d. Use an appropriate applet (for example, the **Multiple Proportions** applet) to find and report the following from the data: (i) the name of a statistic and its numeric value and (ii) the simulation-based p-value.

e. Explain why providing such a table would be in the best interest of the researchers. What does the p-value tell you about the distribution of race in the control group compared to the treatment group? Be sure to explain how you are arriving at your conclusion.

Estimating energy expenditure and energy intake

8.2.24 How good are you at estimating how many calories you expend? Researchers Harris et al. (*American Journal of Men's Health*, 2010) conducted a study where 80 males (ages 21–45 years) were first given a test to identify whether they had high or low dietary restraint. Dietary restraint measures the conscious control over food intake. After a session of exercising, each participant was asked how many calories they thought they had expended, and according to their response they were classified into one of the three categories: underestimation, within 50% estimation, or overestimation. Here are the summarized data:

	High restraint	Low restraint	Total
Underestimation	7	10	17
Within 50% estimation	29	10	39
Overestimation	12	12	24
Total	48	32	80

a. State the appropriate null and alternative hypotheses *in words*.

b. Explain why it would NOT be okay to use the theory-based method to find a p-value for this study.

c. Use an appropriate applet (for example, the **Multiple Proportions** applet) to find and report the following from the data: (i) the name of the statistic and its numeric value and (ii) the simulation-based p-value.

d. Interpret the p-value in the context of the study.

e. State a complete conclusion about this study, including significance, causation, and generalization. Be sure to explain how you are arriving at your conclusion.

8.2.25 Refer to the previous exercise about the study of the relationship between dietary restraint and energy expenditure. Another response variable the researchers were interested in was the estimation of energy intake. After a session of exercising, each participant was given a meal and then asked how many calories they thought they had consumed, and according to their response they were classified into one of the three categories: underestimation, within 50% estimation, or overestimation. Here are the summarized data:

	High restraint	Low restraint	Total
Underestimation	18	17	35
Within 50% estimation	28	13	41
Overestimation	2	2	4
Total	48	32	80

a. State the appropriate null and alternative hypotheses *in words*.

b. Explain why it would NOT be okay to use the theory-based method to find a p-value for this study.

c. Use an appropriate applet (for example, the **Multiple Proportions** applet) to find and report the following from the data: (i) the name of a statistic and its numeric value and (ii) the simulation-based p-value.

d. State a complete conclusion about this study, including significance, causation, and generalization. Be sure to explain how you are arriving at your conclusion.

Harvesting alligators

8.2.26 Alligators have become a big concern in Florida. Here are some gator data.

Lake	Year 2000	2005	2010	Total
Pierce	12	8	16	36
Marian	30	50	90	170
Hatchineha	36	71	135	242
Blue Cypress	31	66	128	225
Seminole	16	25	16	57
Total	125	220	385	730

The rows are for five small Florida lakes. They stretch along a line from the west coast near Tampa to the east coast. The columns are for years, spaced half a decade apart. The counts tell the numbers of alligators harvested. (Data source: *myfwc.com/media·1357388·Alligator_Annual_Summaries.pdf.*)

Look first at the column totals: Is there a trend over time? Then look at row totals: How do lakes compare? Finally, think about association. Is the pattern over time pretty much the same for all five lakes?

8.2.27 Referring to the previous exercise, two possible data tables are shown in the 8.2.27 table. Which one has the observational units right? Why?

8.2.28 Referring to the previous exercises, If both variables are categorical, you have two choices for segmented bar graphs. Either one of the two variables can go on the x-axis,

ID	Lake	Year	Harvest
1	Pierce	2000	12
2	Pierce	2005	8
3	Pierce	2010	16
4	Marian	2000	30
5	Marian	2005	50
6	Marian	2010	90
7	Hatch	2000	36
8	Hatch	2005	71
9	Hatch	2010	135
10	Blue	2000	31
11	Blue	2005	66
12	Blue	2010	128
13	Seminole	2000	16
14	Seminole	2005	25
15	Seminole	2010	16

ID	Year	Lake
1	2000	Pierce
:	:	:
12	2000	Pierce
13	2005	Pierce
:	:	:
20	2005	Pierce
21	2010	Pierce
:	:	:
36	2010	Pierce
37	2000	Marian
:	:	:
:	:	:
:	:	:
730	2010	Seminole

EXERCISE 8.2.27

with percentages for the other on the *y*-axis. Here are both segmented bar graphs for the gator data. Tell what you learn from both taken together.

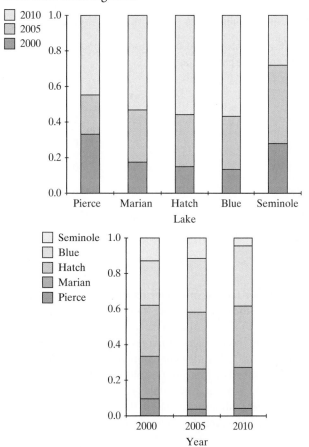

Segmented bar graphs for the gator data

8.2.29 Referring to the previous exercises, sometimes a categorical variable comes from a quantitative variable. For the gator data, the year can be regarded as quantitative. Here's a plot that takes advantage of that quantitative underpinning. What do you see in this plot that was harder to see in the two bar graphs? Try to name at least two or three systematic patterns. Do keep in mind that small changes are likely due to chance. Large patterns are the ones that matter.

Timeplot of Numbers of Alligators for Five Lakes

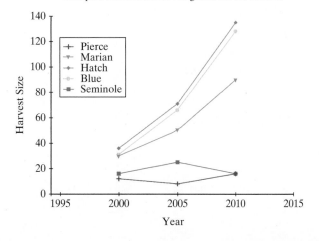

8.2.30 Referring to the previous exercises, lakes Pierce and Seminole have smaller harvests that show little or no evidence of a time trend.

OBS	2000	2005	2010	Total
Pierce	12	8	16	36
Seminole	16	25	16	57
Total	28	33	32	93

Is it reasonable to treat them as a group? Use the **Multiple Proportions** applet to compare the two lakes using segmented bar graphs and to conduct an appropriate test of whether the pattern over time differs for the two lakes.

8.2.31 Referring to the previous exercises, the other three lakes have larger harvests that show steep increases over time:

OBS	2000	2005	2010	Total
Marian	30	50	90	170
Hatchineha	36	71	135	242
Blue Cypress	31	66	128	225
Total	97	187	353	637

Here are values of $(O - E)^2/E$, the contribution to chi-square, for each cell.

$(O - E)^2/E$	2000	2005	2010	Total
Marian	0.65	0.00	0.19	0.84
Hatchineha	0.02	0.00	0.01	0.03
Blue Cypress	0.31	0.00	0.09	0.40
Total	0.98	0.00	0.29	1.27

Based on these values, is it reasonable to regard the time trend for these three lakes as essentially the same?

8.2.32 As we hope you agree, there seem to be two kinds of lakes. Two (Pierce and Seminole) have small harvests that don't show a time trend. The other three lakes have much bigger harvests that increase steeply (and similarly) over time. Use the **Multiple Proportions** applet to compare the two groups over time and to test the strength of evidence that the two groups differ.

Lake Group	Year			
	2000	2005	2010	TOTAL
Pierce and Seminole	28	33	32	93
The other three	97	187	353	637
TOTAL	125	220	385	730

8.2.33 Referring to the previous exercise, what can you say about cause and effect and generalization based on the gator data?

FAQ

8.2.34 Read FAQ 8.2.1 and answer the following: True or false? When analyzing data from 2 × 2 tables, the choice of statistic ($\hat{p}_{max} - \hat{p}_{min}$, MAD, and chi-square) doesn't matter.

8.2.35 Read FAQ 8.2.1 and answer the following: True or false? When comparing more than two groups on a categorical response, the choice of statistic ($\hat{p}_{max} - \hat{p}_{min}$, MAD, and chi-square) doesn't matter.

8.2.36 Read FAQ 8.2.1 and answer the following: True or false? When using a theory-based test to analyze data from 2 × 2 tables, the choice of statistic ($\hat{p}_{max} - \hat{p}_{min}$, MAD, and chi-square) doesn't matter.

8.2.37 Read FAQ 8.2.1 and answer the following: True or false? When comparing many groups on a categorical response, the choice of statistic ($\hat{p}_{max} - \hat{p}_{min}$, MAD, and chi-square) has no bearing on the power of the test.

SECTION 8.3

8.3.1* College students were asked to rate their abilities as drivers and how often they text while driving, with the results shown in the following table. If a chi-square test of independence was to be performed with the data, how many degrees of freedom would be used?

	Text Frequently	Text Sometimes	Text at Stop Light	Text Never	Total
Above-Average Driver	3	13	28	6	50
Average Driver	1	15	32	14	62
Below-Average Driver	1	2	5	4	12
Total	5	30	65	24	124

A. 2

B. 6

C. 12

D. 20

E. 123

8.3.2 In previous question about driving ability and texting, are the validity conditions met to perform a chi-square test of independence?

A. Yes, because the sample size, 124, is larger than 30.

B. Yes, because the table has more than 10 cells.

C. No, because the response variable isn't binary.

D. No, because not all the expected counts are at least 5.

E. No, because it is clear that the data did not come from a normal population.

8.3.3* The results of a survey of college students, in which they were asked if they were a coffee drinker or not and if they had taken a nap in the past 3 days or not, are shown in the following table. What is the expected count in the cell that contains the count for the number of students that do not drink coffee and have taken a nap in the past 3 days?

	Nap	No Nap	Total
Not a Coffee Drinker	43	22	65
Coffee Drinker	42	18	60
Total	85	40	125

A. 40.8

B. 42

C. 43

D. 44.2

E. 45

8.3.4 In the previous question about coffee drinkers and naps, suppose you were going to complete a test of association on the data. In doing so, what is the value of the chi-square statistic?

A. 0

B. −0.0025

C. 0.2121

D. 5.76

E. 125.21

8.3.5* College students were asked if they were regular coffee drinkers or not, and the following segmented bar graph shows the results of a comparison of males to females from this sample of 125. If a chi-square test of independence was done on these data, it would result in:

A. A small chi-square statistic and a small p-value

B. A small chi-square statistic and a large p-value

C. A large chi-square statistic and a small p-value

D. A large chi-square statistic and a large p-value

E. It is impossible to tell just by looking at the graph

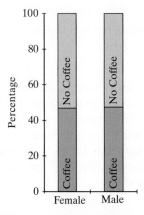

8.3.6 In running a chi-square test of association on the data from the graph in the previous question about comparing coffee drinking between males and females, which of the following is the appropriate way to write out the null hypothesis?

A. There is no association between students' sex and whether or not they are regular coffee drinkers in the population.

B. There is an association between students' sex and whether or not they are regular coffee drinkers in the population.

C. The average number of females that drink coffee in the population is the same as the average number of males that drink coffee in the population.

D. The average number of females that drink coffee in the population is different than the average number of males that drink coffee in the population.

E. The proportion of females that drink coffee in the population is different than the proportion of males that drink coffee in the population.

8.3.7* Completing a chi-square test on a two-by-two table is equivalent to what other type of test (with a two-sided alternative)?

A. One-proportion z-test

B. Two-proportion z-test

C. One-sample t-test

D. Two-sample t-test

E. One-sample t-test for paired data

8.3.8 How does a chi-square test of independence differ from a chi-square test of homogeneity?

A. They use different ways of calculating the chi-square statistic. In a test of homogeneity, you don't divide by the expected count.

B. They use different ways of calculating the degrees of freedom. For a test of independence, you don't subtract 1 from the row and column totals before multiplying.

C. The test of independence compares two variables on one sample, while a test of homogeneity compares distributions from more than one sample.

D. The expected counts are calculated differently.

E. The independence test is two-sided, while the test of homogeneity is one-sided.

8.3.9* Data in the following table come from a random sample of high school students from the 2017 *Census at School* database. The sample was selected to compare males and females on whether or not they have any allergies. Calculate the expected values for the table assuming there was no association between students' sex and whether or not they have allergies.

	Female	Male	Total
Allergies? No	22	30	52
Allergies? Yes	16	12	28
Total	38	42	80

8.3.10* Calculate the chi-square statistic from the data in the previous question about comparing males and females and whether or not they have allergies.

8.3.11 Data in the following table comparing males and females and which of their feet is the longest (or they are of the same length) come from a random sample of high school students taken from the 2017 *Census at School* database. Calculate the expected values for the table assuming there was no association between students' sex and which foot is longest (or they are both the same).

	Female	Male	Total
Left foot	11	6	17
Right foot	12	9	21
Same length	16	33	49
Total	39	48	87

8.3.12 Calculate the chi-square statistic from the data in the previous question about comparing males and females and their foot lengths.

8.3.13* Are college students more likely to be on their cellphones at certain times of day than others as they walk across their campus? Student researchers explored this question. Of the 221 students they observed in the morning, 44 were using their phone; of the 232 students they observed in the afternoon, 48 were using their phone; and of the 115 students they observed in the evening, 45 were using their phone.

a. What is the explanatory variable in this study? Is it categorical or quantitative?

b. What is the response variable in this study? Is it categorical or quantitative?

c. Put the counts in a two-way table where the explanatory variable is in the columns and the response in the rows.

d. Make a table of expected counts assuming the population proportion of students on their cellphones is the same for different time periods (morning, afternoon, evening) while walking on campus.

e. Name the appropriate theory-based test to use and check whether the validity conditions are met with these data.

f. State the hypotheses.

g. Calculate the test statistic and corresponding p-value.

h. State your conclusion (with appropriate justification based on your p-value and stated significance level) in the context of the research question.

8.3.14* In the previous question about cellphone use, what if the question was, "Are students more likely to be on their cellphones in the evening as they walk across campus than during the daytime?" How would you analyze the data now? Re-analyze the data by naming the test you will use, state the hypotheses, determine a p-value, and state your conclusion.

8.3.15 Do high school students in Michigan have a different favorite season from Florida students? Through Census at School, a random sample of 200 Michigan high school students and 200 Florida high school students was taken and we will look at their answers to the question, "Which is your favorite season?" The results are shown in the following table.

	Michigan	Florida	Total
Winter	24	55	79
Spring	31	20	51
Summer	84	69	153
Fall	61	56	117
Total	200	200	400

a. What is the explanatory variable in this study? Is it categorical or quantitative?

b. What is the response variable in this study? Is it categorical or quantitative?

c. Make a table of expected counts assuming the distribution of favorite seasons is the same between Michigan and Florida students.

d. Name the appropriate theory-based test to use and check whether the validity conditions are met with these data.

e. State the hypotheses.

f. Calculate the test statistic and corresponding p-value.

g. State your conclusion (with appropriate justification based on your p-value and stated significance level) in the context of the research question.

8.3.16* When surveys are administered, it is hoped that the respondents give accurate answers. Does the mode of survey delivery affect this? American researchers investigated this question (Schober et al., 2015). They selected 634 people who agreed to be interviewed on an iPhone and each was randomly assigned one of the four interview modes (Human Voice, Human Text, Automated Voice, Automated Text). One question that was asked was whether the participants exercise less than once per week in a typical week (an example of a question in which a yes would be considered socially undesirable). The results of the answers to this question are shown in the table.

	Human Text	Automated Text	Human Voice	Automated Voice	Total
Yes	34	46	21	20	121
No	124	111	139	139	513
Total	158	157	160	159	634

a. Make a table of expected counts if the probability of answering yes is the same across the interview modes.

b. Name the appropriate theory-based test to use and check whether the validity conditions are met with these data.

c. State the hypotheses.

d. Calculate the test statistic and corresponding p-value.

e. State your conclusion (with appropriate justification based on your p-value and stated significance level) in the context of the research question.

8.3.17* Refer to the previous question on accuracy in surveys. Another way to measure accuracy of responses is whether people round when giving numerical answers. The researchers considered a number to be rounded if it ended in a 0 or a 5. One question in which the subjects had to give a numeric answer was "How many movies have you seen in the past 12 months?" They found that 17.1% of those that got the survey via a human text rounded their answers, 12.1% of those that got the survey via an automated text rounded their answers, 24.4% of those that got the survey via a human voice rounded their answers, and 18.2% of those that got the survey via an automated voice rounded their answers.

a. Produce a table of observed *counts* comparing whether the subjects rounded or not across the modes of survey. The totals for each interview mode are the same as in the table in the previous question.

b. Make a table of expected counts assuming the probability of answering yes is the same across the interview modes.

c. Name the appropriate theory-based test to use and check whether the validity conditions are met with these data.

d. State the hypotheses.

e. Calculate the test statistic and corresponding p-value.

f. State your conclusion (with appropriate justification based on your p-value and stated significance level) in the context of the research question.

8.3.18 Researchers in Brazil explored the relationship between overconfidence and accuracy among Brazilian accountants (Cardoso, 2016). Based on a pre-survey, the researchers classified their subjects as being overconfident in their decision-making skills or not. They also presented participants with data displayed in various formats that described people entering and exiting a store. The participants then had to determine the time (to the minute) when the largest number of people were entering the store and the time (to the minute) when the largest number of people were exiting the store. The following table shows the number that got neither question (entering/existing) correct, one correct, and both correct.

	Overconfident	Not Overconfident	Total
Neither Correct	18	21	39
One Correct	22	15	37
Both Correct	150	69	219
Total	190	105	295

a. Make a table of expected counts assuming there is no association between the confidence level and the number of questions answered correctly.

b. Name the appropriate theory-based test to use and check whether the validity conditions are met with these data.

c. State the hypotheses.

d. Calculate the test statistic and corresponding p-value.

e. State your conclusion (with appropriate justification based on your p-value and stated significance level) in the context of the research question.

8.3.19* Does the color of a sign that asks someone to do something make a difference in a person's obedience to that sign? This is what a student researcher investigated. There are double doors at the entrance of her college's library. She put a sign in the door on the right as you exit the library. The sign read, USE OTHER DOOR with an arrow pointing to the door on the left. She counted students as they exited the library to see what proportion used the door on the left when the sign was printed on red paper, printed on yellow paper, and (as a control) no sign at all. The results are shown in the following table.

	No Sign	Yellow	Red	Total
Left Door	13	14	24	51
Right Door	42	40	29	111
Total	55	54	53	162

a. Make a table of expected counts assuming the proportion of people that would obey the signs is the same for all conditions (no sign, yellow, red).

b. Name the appropriate theory-based test to use and check whether the validity conditions are met with these data.

c. State the hypotheses.

d. Calculate the test statistic and corresponding p-value.

e. State your conclusion (with appropriate justification based on your p-value and stated significance level) in the context of the research question.

8.3.20 Two samples of Facebook users collected by the Pew Research Center (one in 2016 and one in 2013) were asked how often they visited or used Facebook. The results are shown in the following table. We will assume this sample is representative of all American adults for the two given years. Is there a difference in the distribution of how often U.S. adults in 2016 versus 2013 used Facebook?

	2016	2013	Total
Several times a day	292	384	676
About once a day	117	230	347
A few times a week	80	221	301
Total	489	835	1,324

a. Name the appropriate theory-based test to use and check whether the validity conditions are met with these data.

b. State the hypotheses.

c. Calculate the test statistic and corresponding p-value.

d. State your conclusion (with appropriate justification based on your p-value and stated significance level) in the context of the research question.

SECTION 8.4

8.4.1* Given that the null hypothesis is that all the population proportions are the same, which of the following data sets DO NOT meet the validity conditions for a chi-square goodness-of-fit test? (There may be more than one correct answer.)

A.

Category	A	B	C	D	Total
Observed Count	5	9	10	4	28

B.

Category	A	B	C	D	Total
Observed Count	7	8	5	5	25

C.

Category	A	B	C	D	E	F	Total
Observed Count	7	5	6	4	3	4	29

D.

Category	A	B	C	D	Total
Observed Count	4	6	4	4	18

E.

Category	A	B	C	Total
Observed Count	5	6	7	18

8.4.2 A chi-square goodness-of-fit test is going to be used on data that fall into three categories and have a sample size of 26. How many degrees of freedom should be used?

A. 2

B. 3

C. 23

D. 25

E. 26

8.4.3* The flavors of a certain kind of candy are supposed to be distributed as follows: 50% cherry, 30% lemon, and 20% orange. You randomly sample 180 of these candies to run a chi-square goodness-of-fit test. What are the expected counts of the cherry, lemon, and orange flavors?

A. 60, 60, 60

B. 50, 30, 20

C. 95, 57, 38

D. 90, 54, 36

E. None of the above

8.4.4 Which of the following is the proper way to write out the **_alternative_** hypothesis for the test from the previous question on candy flavor distribution?

A. The long-run proportions of candies are distributed 50% cherry, 30% lemon, and 20% orange.

B. The long-run proportions of candies are not distributed 50% cherry, 30% lemon, and 20% orange.

C. The long-run proportions of candies are not distributed evenly.

D. $\pi_{cherry} = \pi_{lemon} = \pi_{orange}$

E. $\pi_{cherry} \neq \pi_{lemon} \neq \pi_{orange}$

8.4.5* Using the data in the following table, what is the chi-square test statistic?

Category	A	B	C	D	Total
Observed Count	10	51	39	20	120
Expected Count	15	45	45	15	120

A. 0.93

B. 4.93

C. 5.38

D. 8.13

E. 484.93

8.4.6 Suppose you are running a chi-square goodness-of-fit test on a data set that has five categories and you calculate a chi-square test statistic of 7.46. What is the corresponding p-value?

A. 0.189

B. 0.113

C. 0.048

D. 0.065

E. 0.073

8.4.7* The following distributions represent colors of 100 candies. You want to run a chi-square goodness-of-fit test with the null hypothesis that the distribution of colors is evenly distributed. Which of the following distributions will give you the smallest p-value?

A.

B.

C.

D.

8.4.8 Match the following descriptions with the appropriate chi-square test (independence, homogeneity, goodness of fit).

a. A sample of a fruity cereal is taken and the researchers want to see if this cereal does not consist of an equal proportion of each flavor.

b. A sample of college students is taken and the researchers want to see if there is a relationship between their major area of study and the pressure to succeed in school (none, some, a lot).

c. A sample of students at one high school is asked what pressure they feel to succeed at school (none, some, a lot) and that distribution is compared with the results from a sample of students at a different high school.

8.4.9* What data type is used in a chi-square goodness-of-fit test? How does that compare with the type of data used in a chi-square independence test?

8.4.10 Calculate the chi-square test statistic for the following data sets and null hypotheses.

a. $H_0: \pi_A = \pi_B = \pi_C = 1/3$

Category	A	B	C	Total
Observed Count	12	16	8	36

b. $H_0: \pi_A = \pi_B = \pi_C = 1/3$

Category	A	B	C	Total
Observed Count	23	34	24	81

8.4.11* Calculate the chi-square test statistic for the following data sets and null hypotheses.

a. H_0: The population is distributed in a ratio of 1:2:1 for the categories A, B, and C, respectively.

Category	A	B	C	Total
Observed Count	14	22	15	51

b. H_0: The population is distributed in a ratio of 1:2:1 for the categories A, B, and C, respectively.

Category	A	B	C	Total
Observed Count	24	34	26	84

8.4.12 Consider doing a chi-square goodness-of-fit test with the null hypothesis of $\pi_1 = \pi_2 = \pi_3 = 1/3$ on two different sets of data. For categories 1, 2, and 3, respectively, data set A has observed values of 10, 15, 10, whereas data set B has observed values of 100, 150, 100.

a. What are the observed ratios (e.g., 1:2:1) for each of the data sets and how do they differ?

b. Based on the observed ratios, would you say one data set would provide stronger evidence against the null hypothesis than the other? Explain.

c. Calculate the chi-square test statistic for each data set.

d. Based on the chi-square test statistics, which data set provides stronger evidence against the null hypothesis? Explain why that makes sense.

Census at School*

8.4.13 A random sample of 100 high school students was taken from the *Census at School* database and the following table gives a summary of their responses when they were asked what their favorite season is. We are interested in testing to see if the distribution of favorite seasons of high school students in the database is not distributed evenly.

Season	Winter	Spring	Summer	Fall
Count	20	12	25	43

a. What are the expected frequencies for each season?

b. Name the appropriate theory-based test to use and check whether the validity conditions are met with these data.

c. Write out the hypotheses.

d. Calculate the test statistic and appropriate p-value.

e. State your conclusion (with appropriate justification based on your p-value and stated significance level) in the context of the research question.

8.4.14 A random sample of 95 high school students was taken from the *Census at School* database and the following table gives a summary of their birth months. We are interested in testing to see if the distribution of birth months is not distributed evenly.

Month	Jan	Feb	Mar	Apr	May	Jun	Jul	Aug	Sep	Oct	Nov	Dec
Count	10	10	3	8	8	8	5	9	6	8	11	9

a. What are the expected frequencies for each month?

b. Name the appropriate theory-based test to use and check whether the validity conditions are met with these data.

c. Write out the hypotheses.

d. Calculate the test statistic and appropriate p-value.

e. State your conclusion (with appropriate justification based on your p-value and stated significance level) in the context of the research question.

Fair dice

8.4.15 In addition to having dice pushed off a 2-inch ledge, as in the example in this section, the researchers also pushed dice off a 4-inch-high ledge with the following results.

Value	1	2	3	4	5	6
Observed Count	26	24	19	12	18	21

Is this an unfair way to "roll" dice? In other words, is there strong evidence that the results will not be equally distributed in the long run?

a. What are the expected frequencies for each value on the die if the results would be equally distributed in the long run?

b. Name the appropriate theory-based test to use and check whether the validity conditions are met with these data.

c. Write out the hypotheses.

d. Calculate the test statistic and appropriate p-value.

e. State your conclusion (with appropriate justification based on your p-value and stated significance level) in the context of the research question.

Random number—phone*

8.4.16 One of the authors' cellphones recently became able to state a random number when asked, The author wondered whether the phone's method of picking a random number was truly random. He asked his phone to pick a random number between 1 and 5 fifty times and the results are shown in the following table.

Value	1	2	3	4	5
Observed Count	9	13	7	11	10

a. What are the expected frequencies for each value, assuming the five values are equally distributed in the long run? (What we would expect for the outcomes if the phone method of picking a number was truly random.)

b. Name the appropriate theory-based test to use and check whether the validity conditions are met with these data.

c. Write out the hypotheses.

d. Calculate the test statistic and appropriate p-value.

e. State your conclusion (with appropriate justification based on your p-value and stated significance level) in the context of the research question.

f. You should have obtained a large p-value. Does this mean you have strong evidence that the phone's method of picking a number is truly random?

g. The sample size is not huge here. Suggest another way to investigate these outcomes in which it would be more valid to use the theory-based test.

Eye color

8.4.17 Do female models have eye colors that are distributed differently than those of the population of their country? That is a question that UK researchers were interested in exploring (Forti, 2016). They sampled from 400 profiles of females registered as commercial models in the United Kingdom and found that 187 had blue eyes, 120 had brown eyes, and 93 other colors. They reported that another study showed that 71.5% of female UK residents are thought to have blue eyes, 21% have brown eyes, and 7.5% other colors.

a. What are the expected frequencies for each eye color of the 400 models, assuming the eye colors are distributed in the same way as those of all female UK residents?

b. Name the appropriate theory-based test to use and check whether the validity conditions are met with these data.

c. Write out the hypotheses.

d. Calculate the test statistic and appropriate p-value.

e. State your conclusion (with appropriate justification based on your p-value and stated significance level) in the context of the research question.

8.4.18 Recall the previous question on commercial models and their eye colors. The researchers also explored the eye colors of registered commercial models in Brazil. They sampled from 400 profiles of females registered as commercial models in Brazil and found that 76 had blue eyes, 210 had brown eyes, and 114 other colors. They reported that another study showed that 8% of female Brazil residents are thought to have blue eyes, 74% have brown eyes, and 18% other colors.

a. What are the expected frequencies for each eye color of the Brazilian models if the eye colors are distributed in the same way as those of all female Brazil residents?

b. Name the appropriate theory-based test to use and check whether the validity conditions are met with these data.

c. Write out the hypotheses.

d. Calculate the test statistic and appropriate p-value.

e. State your conclusion (with appropriate justification based on your p-value and stated significance level) in the context of the research question.

Benford's Law*

8.4.19 In 1938 Dr. Frank Benford, a physicist at General Electric, noticed that, given a list of numbers, more numbers started with the digit 1 than any other digit. He analyzed 20,222 sets of numbers including areas of rivers, baseball statistics, numbers in magazine articles, and street addresses. He concluded that the probability of the numeral d appearing as the first digit was log $(1 + 1/d)$ and this property is known as Benford's Law. The probabilities are shown below.

d	1	2	3	4	5	6	7	8	9
Probability the leading digit starts with d	0.301	0.176	0.125	0.097	0.079	0.067	0.058	0.051	0.046

A textbook was analyzed to see whether the pattern of leading digits of the numbers in the book differed from that predicted by Benford. Pages were randomly selected and the leading digits of the numbers on those pages are shown in the following table.

Leading digit	1	2	3	4	5	6	7	8	9
Frequency	47	32	10	8	10	10	8	4	3

a. What are the expected frequencies for each leading digit if they are distributed in the long run according to Benford's Law?

b. Name the appropriate theory-based test to use and check whether the validity conditions are met with these data.

c. Write out the hypotheses.

d. Calculate the test statistic and appropriate p-value.

e. State your conclusion (with appropriate justification based on your p-value and stated significance level) in the context of the research question.

Random number—students

8.4.20 Eighty statistics students were asked to write down a random number between 1 and 10. They gave the following results.

Number	1	2	3	4	5	6	7	8	9	10
Count	3	10	8	8	3	8	19	13	5	3

If the students were picking a number truly randomly, the digits chosen shouldn't deviate too much from being distributed equally. Are they?

a. What are the expected frequencies for each number if the 10 numbers are distributed equally in the long run?

b. Name the appropriate theory-based test to use and check whether the validity conditions are met with these data.

c. Write out the hypotheses.

d. Calculate the test statistic and appropriate p-value.

e. State your conclusion (with appropriate justification based on your p-value and stated significance level) in the context of the research question.

Mendel's peas*

8.4.21 In one set of Mendel's pea experiments, he crossed a round-green pea with a wrinkled-yellow pea (Mendel, 1866). The result of this cross gave him a round-yellow pea. He then crossed two of these round-yellow peas together and got the results shown in the following table. He conjectured that this type of crossing should result in a 9:3:3:1 ratio with the pea types in the order shown in the table. Do we have convincing evidence that the proportions of pea types are not distributed in this 9:3:3:1 ratio? Test as follows: (a) State the hypotheses in words or in symbols. (b) Name the theory-based test you will use. (c) State and verify the validity conditions for the test chosen. (d) Calculate the test statistic, degrees of freedom, and p-value. (e) State your conclusion in the context of the research question.

Category	Round-yellow	Wrinkled-yellow	Round-green	Wrinkled-green	Total
Observed Count	315	101	108	32	556

8.4.22 Mendel used 315 seeds from the round-yellow peas he obtained from the experiment given in the previous question and planted them. Fourteen of the plants did not grow or did not produce seeds. Of the remaining 301 plants, he grew pea plants that had peas with the distribution shown in the table below. (Note that most plants had peas with different characteristics. For example, 65 plants had some round-yellow and some round-green peas.) Do we have convincing evidence that the proportions of pea types are not distributed in this 1:2:2:4 ratio? Test as follows: (a) State the hypotheses in words or in symbols. (b) Name the theory-based

test you will use. (c) State and verify the validity conditions for the test chosen. (d) Calculate the test statistic, degrees of freedom, and p-value. (e) State your conclusion in the context of the research question.

8.4.23 In another set of Mendel's pea experiments, he crossed a purple-flowered pea plant with a white-flowered pea plant. This resulted in plants that were all purple-flowered. He then took these purple-flowered pea plants and pollinated them with themselves. Seeds from these plants were planted and in these Mendel counted 705 purple-flowered plants and 224 white-flowered plants. He conjectured that this type of crossing should result in a 3:1 ratio with the larger number being purple-flowered. Do we have convincing evidence that the proportions of pea flower types are not distributed in this 3:1 ratio? Test as follows: (a) State the hypotheses in words or in symbols. (b) Name the theory-based test you will use. (c) State and verify the validity conditions for the test chosen. (d) Calculate the test statistic, degrees of freedom, and p-value. (e) State your conclusion in the context of the research question.

Kidney disease

8.4.24 Patients with kidney disease often undergo a procedure known as dialysis, which cleans their blood because their kidneys can't properly do this. This procedure is often done three days per week, with Monday, Wednesday, and Friday often being those days. In terms of dialysis treatments, these days are all the same except for the gap of two off days before the Monday treatment. Does this gap make a difference? Cardiac arrest and sudden death for patients undergoing dialysis for kidney disease are a concern. In recent years, it has been noted that these types of patients are apt to have cardiac arrests on Mondays more often than what would be expected if the three days were equally likely. A study published in *Kidney International* (Karnik et al., 2001) looked at 205 dialysis patients who had cardiac arrests on Monday, Wednesday, or Friday, the same days they underwent dialysis. They found that 93 of these happened on a Monday, 54 on a Wednesday, and 58 on a Friday. Do we have convincing evidence that the probability of death is not the same among the three days? Test as follows: (a) State the hypotheses in words or in symbols. (b) Name the theory-based test you will use. (c) State and verify the validity conditions for the test chosen. (d) Calculate the test statistic, degrees of freedom, and p-value. (e) State your conclusion in the context of the research question.

Category	round-yellow	round-yellow, round-green	round-yellow, wrinkled-yellow	round-yellow, round-green, wrinkled-yellow, wrinkled-green	Total
Observed Count	38	65	60	138	301

EXERCISE 8.4.22

8.4.25 Recall the previous question about dialysis patients dying of heart attacks. The researchers also looked at patients that had their dialysis done on Tuesday, Thursday, and Saturday and experienced cardiac arrest on the same day they had dialysis. They found that 65 of these events happened on a Tuesday, 68 on a Thursday, and 57 on a Saturday. Do we have convincing evidence that the probability of death is not distributed evenly among the three days? Test as follows: (a) State the hypotheses in words or in symbols. (b) Name the theory-based test you will use. (c) State and verify the validity conditions for the test chosen. (d) Calculate the test statistic, degrees of freedom, and p-value. (e) State your conclusion in the context of the research question.

Heart attacks*

8.4.26 A study done in Germany (Willich et al., 1993) looked at which days of the week people had heart attacks. One subgroup the researchers looked at were those who were employed. They found that the 884 heart attack victims had heart attacks distributed as shown in the following table. They wanted to know whether heart attacks are distributed evenly across the days of the week in the long run. Test as follows: (a) State the hypotheses in words or in symbols. (b) Name the theory-based test you will use. (c) State and verify the validity conditions for the test chosen. (d) Calculate the test statistic, degrees of freedom, and p-value. (e) State your conclusion in the context of the research question.

Day	Sun	Mon	Tue	Wed	Thur	Fri	Sat
Number of heart attacks	106	160	123	115	141	107	132

(f) Compare the observed counts to the expected counts to identify which days differ the most from what we would expect if the days were equally likely. Does your comparison make sense for individuals who are employed? Explain.

8.4.27 Recall the study in the previous question on which days of the week people experienced heart attacks. Another subgroup the researchers looked at were those who were not employed. They found that the 1,191 heart attack victims had heart attacks distributed as shown in the following table. They wanted to know whether or not heart attacks are distributed evenly across the days of the week in this population. Test as follows: (a) State the hypotheses in words or in symbols. (b) Name the test you will use. (c) State and verify the validity conditions for the test chosen. (d) Calculate the test statistic, degrees of freedom, and p-value. (e) State your conclusion in the context of the research question.

Day	Sun	Mon	Tue	Wed	Thur	Fri	Sat
Number of heart attacks	168	180	157	169	180	169	168

(f) Compare your conclusion to that in the previous question. Did your conclusions differ? If so, why do you think this happened?

The traveling salesperson problem

8.4.28 The task of the traveling salesperson problem is to find the shortest path when traveling through a series of points. For example, on a baseball diamond the shortest path from home plate that touches all the bases is to either go to first, second, then third base, or the reverse (third, second, then first base). Researchers (Miyata et al., 2015) wanted to see what sort of routes young children would take in completing such a task. They set up a computer program where a dog could be moved to collect three bones. The pattern they set up was just like a baseball diamond, where the dog was at home plate and the bones were at the three bases. The researchers categorized all the possible routes into three different groups: rounding (where they would go from first to second to third or from third to second to first), crossing (where they would go first to third to second or third to first to second), and G2 first (where they would go to second and the other two bases after that in either order). One of the questions the researchers were interested in was whether children are equally likely to pick each of the three routes. One subgroup they tested was young children 3 to 5 years old. They found that 11 of these children selected the crossing route, 5 did the rounding, and 12 did the G2 first. Do young children have the same probability of picking each of these routes? Test as follows: (a) State the hypotheses in words or in symbols. (b) Name the theory-based test you will use. (c) State and verify the validity conditions for the test chosen. (d) Calculate the test statistic, degrees of freedom, and p-value. (e) State your conclusion in the context of the research question.

8.4.29 Recall the previous question about the distribution of routes chosen by young children tasked with getting a dog to three bones on a computer screen. The three route types were rounding, crossing, and G2 first. The researchers also tested adults on this same task. They found that 8 of the adults selected the crossing route, 16 did the rounding, and 0 did the G2 first. Do adults have the same probability of picking each of these routes? Test as follows: (a) State the hypotheses in words or in symbols. (b) Name the theory-based test you will use. (c) State and verify the validity conditions for the test chosen. (d) Calculate the test statistic, degrees of freedom, and p-value. (e) State your conclusion in the context of the research question.

8.4.30* Consider the question of whether sick days in a company are equally likely to occur Monday through Friday.

a. State the null and alternative hypotheses using symbols.

b. If we conduct a chi-square goodness-of-fit test, what are the degrees of freedom for this chi-square test?

c. In the **Goodness of Fit** applet, enter some fake sample data (50 observations) for each of the five days of the week. It's easiest to use a format like below and press Use Table.

Day	Count
Mon	10
Tues	10
Wed	10

Your choice of observed counts is not important in this problem! All you are really doing is telling the applet the number of categories and the sample size. Use the Statistic pull-down menu to select the chi-square statistic. Then check Show Sampling Options and enter the hypothesized probabilities.

Enter hypothesized probabilities:

```
.2, .2, .2, .2, .2
```

Now generate 10,000 samples. In the null distribution, assuming 0.05 as the level of significance, use trial and error to determine a reasonable rejection region (to the nearest hundredth). What is the approximate probability of your making a Type I Error? Include a screen capture.

d. Suppose the actual probabilities were 0.26, 0.16, 0.16, 0.16, 0.26. Check the "Alternative" box and enter these alternative probabilities. Draw a random sample. Which distribution (the null or the alternative) do these observations seem to be coming from? [*Hint:* Use the Plot radio button.]

e. Generate 10,000 samples and then count how many are in the rejection region from (c). This estimates the power of the test. Include a screen capture.

f. Write a sentence describing what the proportion from (e) means in the context of the problem.

g. Repeat (c) and (e), changing (and documenting) the appropriate settings, to find the power for the following alternative probabilities: 0.32, 0.12, 0.12, 0.12, 0.32. Should the power be larger or smaller? Why? Is it?

h. Repeat (c) and (e) for the MAD statistic. Is the power for the MAD statistic larger or smaller than for the chi-squared statistic?

i. Repeat (h) for the Max-Min statistic. Which of the three statistics seems to have the least power? Does this make sense? Explain.

END OF CHAPTER

Coffee consumption*

8.CE.1   Suppose that you want to investigate whether men and women differ with regard to coffee consumption. You plan to ask people to indicate their sex and also to say whether they drink coffee every day, sometimes, or almost never.

a. Identify the two variables in this study. Also classify each variable as categorical or quantitative. For the categorical variable(s), also report how many categories are involved.

b. Could this study involve random sampling, random assignment, or both? Explain.

Suppose that you collect survey responses on these questions for a sample of 70 students at your school. You then give the responses to your friend to ask him to tally them. He reports the following results back to you:

Sex: 38 men, 32 women

Coffee consumption: 22 every day, 22 sometimes, 26 almost never

c. Does this provide enough information for you to investigate whether the sample data provide strong evidence that men and women differ with regard to coffee consumption? If not, describe what additional information is needed.

8.CE.2   Reconsider the previous exercise about sex and coffee consumption. The sample data could be organized in a two-way table as follows:

	Men	Women	Total
Every day			22
Sometimes			22
Almost never			26
Total	38	32	70

a. Fill in the table with counts (which you make up) in such a way that there's almost *no association* between sex and coffee consumption. Also draw the appropriate graph to display what your made-up data reveal.

b. Now fill in the table with counts (which you make up) in such a way that there's a *strong association* between sex and coffee consumption. Again draw the appropriate graph to display what your made-up data reveal.

8.CE.3   Reconsider the previous two exercises. Students at Cal Poly collected data from their classmates and produced the following two-way table of counts:

	Men	Women	Total
Every day	7	15	22
Sometimes	12	10	22
Almost never	19	7	26
Total	38	32	70

a. Produce a segmented bar graph to display these data. Comment on what the graph reveals.

b. Perform a simulation-based analysis using the chi-square statistic. Submit a screen capture of the simulated null distribution and report the approximate p-value.

c. Based on the approximate p-value from the simulation analysis, would you conclude (at the 0.05 significance level) that there is an association between sex and coffee consumption?

d. Summarize your conclusions from this analysis.

8.CE.4 Reconsider the data from the previous exercise. Check whether the validity conditions for a theory-based analysis are met. Regardless of your answer, conduct such a theory-based analysis. Report the test statistic and p-value. Summarize your conclusions.

8.CE.5 Reconsider the data from the previous two exercises. Suppose that the sample size had been twice as large, with the counts for every cell in the table also being twice as large.

a. What effect would this change have on the segmented bar graph?

b. What effect would this change have on the p-value? (Do not bother to perform any analysis to answer this question.)

c. What effect would this change have on the strength of evidence of an association between sex and coffee consumption?

Giving blood

8.CE.6 The General Social Survey asked a random sample of adult Americans about their political viewpoint and also about whether they had given blood in the previous year. The sample results for the 2012 survey are organized in the following two-way table of counts:

	Liberal	Moderate	Conservative
Gave blood	41	33	48
Did not give blood	317	411	368

a. For each political viewpoint, determine the sample proportion who claimed to have given blood in the past year.

b. Calculate the value of the MAD statistic for these sample data.

c. Express the null hypothesis to be tested with these data.

d. Conduct a simulation-based analysis of these data based on the MAD statistic. Submit a screen capture of the null distribution and shade the area in the null distribution that corresponds to the p-value.

e. Report the p-value from the simulation analysis. Also write a sentence interpreting what this p-value represents (probability of what, assuming what?).

f. At the 0.05 significance level, do the sample proportions who gave blood differ enough among the three political groups to consider the observed association to be statistically significant? Explain how you determine the answer.

8.CE.7 Reconsider the previous exercise. Conduct a theory-based analysis, including a check of validity conditions, and summarize your conclusion.

8.CE.8 Reconsider the data from the previous two exercises. Use what you learned in the first three chapters to address the following questions. Provide a complete analysis and summary of conclusions for both questions.

a. Do the sample data provide convincing evidence that more than 10% of adult Americans gave blood in the year preceding the survey?

b. Estimate with 95% confidence the proportion of adult Americans who gave blood in the year preceding the survey.

Trusting people*

8.CE.9 The 2010 General Social Survey asked a random sample of Americans about whether they generally trust people. The 8.CE.9 table classifies responses by the highest educational degree achieved by the person:

a. Identify the explanatory and response variables in this study.

b. For each category of educational attainment, calculate the proportion indicating they generally trust people. Also produce a graph to display these proportions. Comment on what the calculations and graph reveal.

	Less than high school	High school	Junior college	Bachelor's	Graduate
Trusts people	29	183	28	121	97
Does not trust people	181	490	63	124	56
Total	210	673	91	245	153

EXERCISE 8.CE.9

c. State the null hypothesis to be tested from these data.

d. Calculate the value of the MAD statistic for these sample data.

e. Conduct a simulation-based analysis using the MAD statistic. Submit a screen capture of the null distribution and report the approximate p-value.

f. Interpret what the p-value says in this context.

g. Would you reject the null hypothesis at any reasonable significance level?

h. State your conclusion about the strength of evidence.

8.CE.10 Reconsider the previous exercise. Conduct a theory-based analysis. Report the test statistic and p-value and summarize your conclusions. Also, compute 95% confidence intervals as a follow-up, including these in your summary.

8.CE.11 Reconsider the previous two exercises. There were actually three categories of the response variable. The response "it depends" had been classified as not trusting people in Exercise Table 8.CE.9 but is separated out into its own category in the 8.CE.11 table.

Perform a chi-square test on these data. Report the test statistic and p-value and summarize your conclusion. Also comment on whether the analysis is very different from the previous exercise when two of the response categories had been combined, as well as whether you have any concerns about using the chi-square test for the data as presented in this exercise.

Drinking at college

8.CE.12 A study of drinking habits of college students at a particular college produced the two-way table of counts shown in Exercise Table 8.CE.12.

Analyze these data with appropriate descriptive and inferential methods. Write a short report summarizing and justifying your conclusions.

School goals*

8.CE.13 Students (grades 4–6) in the Lansing, Michigan, area were asked, "What is the most important goal in school: getting good grades, being popular, or excelling in sports." The data are tabled below. (The raw data is in the **Goals** file.)

	Boy	Girl
Grades	117	130
Popular	50	91
Sports	60	30

a. What proportion of boys believes that getting good grades is the most important goal?

b. What proportion of girls believes that getting good grades is the most important goal?

c. What proportion of boys believes that being popular is the most important goal?

d. What proportion of girls believes that being popular is the most important goal?

e. What proportion of boys believes that excelling in sports is the most important goal?

f. What proportion of girls believes that excelling in sports is the most important goal?

g. What is the (marginal) proportion of students who believe that getting good grades is the most important goal?

	Less than high school	High school	Junior college	Bachelor's	Graduate
Trusts people	29	183	28	121	97
"It depends"	9	32	11	12	11
Does not trust people	172	458	52	112	45
Total	210	673	91	245	153

EXERCISE 8.CE.11

	Reside on campus	Reside off campus, not with parents	Reside off campus, with parents	Total
Abstain from drinking	46	17	43	106
Light or moderate drinking	126	72	68	266
Heavy drinking	130	52	32	214
Total	302	141	143	586

EXERCISE 8.CE.12

h. What is the (marginal) proportion of students who believe that being popular is the most important goal?

i. What is the (marginal) proportion of students who believe that excelling in sports is the most important goal?

j. Based on your answers for parts (a)–(i), do you think that boys and girls in the fourth to sixth grades have different goals? Explain your reasoning.

8.CE.14 Reconsider the previous exercise. Carry out a theory-based test to investigate whether the sample data provide strong evidence of an association between the sex and goals of fourth to sixth graders. Follow up, if applicable, with confidence intervals for any differences you may find. Be sure to include the following in your report:

- The appropriate null and alternative hypotheses
- The statistic you are using as well as its observed value
- The p-value
- An appropriate conclusion that comments on significance, estimation, causation, and generalization in the context of the study

Social norms

8.CE.15 What happens when you break social norms? Pedestrians walking on sidewalks typically follow the same traffic patterns as cars driving in the streets. What happens if you walk on the wrong side of the sidewalk? Do sex, location, and speed of walker affect the number of people in the oncoming traffic that run into you?

Data were collected using both a male experimenter and a female experimenter and are given in the data file **SocialNormsSex**.

a. Is there an association between whether you collide with oncoming pedestrians and the sex of the experimenter? Calculate appropriate descriptive statistics (*Hint*: percent collisions by the sex of experimenter) and create segmented bar graphs. Write a few sentences (two or three) about what these numerical and graphical summaries reveal to you. Explain how you are deciding.

b. Carry out a simulation-based test of significance to test whether there is evidence of an association between whether you collide with oncoming pedestrians and the sex of the experimenter. State the hypotheses and an appropriate conclusion and be sure to include your reasoning for your conclusion.

8.CE.16 Recall the previous exercise about social norms. Data were also collected in a hallway inside a building and on a sidewalk outside in a park and are given in the data file **SocialNormsLocation**. Is there an association between whether you collide with oncoming pedestrians and location?

a. State the appropriate null and alternative hypotheses in the context of the study.

b. Choose either a simulation-based approach or a theory-based approach to test your hypotheses from part (a).

- If you have chosen to use a theory-based approach, be sure to explain why you think this is a valid approach. That is, state the validity conditions and explain how you are deciding whether or not these conditions are met.
- Analyze the data using technology (either an applet or statistical software). Be sure to report the following: the name of the statistic you are using and its value (from the study) and the p-value.
- State your conclusion in the context of the study.

8.CE.17 Recall the previous exercises about social norms. Data were also collected on whether the experimenter was walking at a slow speed or was walking at a fast speed and are given in the data file **SocialNormsSpeed**. Is there an association between whether you collide with oncoming pedestrians and your speed, as measured by the speed of experimenter and whether the experimenter was in a collision?

a. State the appropriate null and alternative hypotheses in the context of the study.

b. Choose either a simulation-based approach or a theory-based approach to test your hypotheses from part (a).

- If you have chosen to use a theory-based approach, be sure to explain why you think this is a valid approach. That is, state the validity conditions and explain how you are deciding whether or not these conditions are met.
- Analyze the data using technology (either an applet or statistical software). Be sure to report the following: the name of the statistic you are using and its value (from the study) and the p-value.
- State your conclusion in the context of the study.

Bonus or rebate?*

8.CE.18 Do people tend to spend money differently based on perceived changes in wealth? In a study conducted by researchers Epley et al. (2006), 47 Harvard undergraduates were randomly assigned to receive either a *bonus* check of $50 or a *rebate* check of $50. A week later, each student was contacted and asked whether they had spent any of that money, and if yes, how much. In this exercise we will focus on whether or not they had spent any of that money as the response variable of interest. It turned out that 36% of those in the bonus group spent none of the money, compared to 73% in the rebate group.

a. Identify the observational units.

b. Identify the explanatory variable. Is it categorical or quantitative?

c. Recall that in this exercise our response variable of interest is whether or not each student had spent any of the money given to him or her. Is the response variable categorical or quantitative?

d. State the appropriate null and alternative hypotheses in the context of the study.

8.CE.19 Reconsider the previous exercise. In the article that appeared in the *Journal of Behavioral Decision Making*, the researchers did not report the sample size of each group. The following 2 × 2 table gives a set of observed counts that are consistent with the rest of the study data. This table can be found in the file **Rebate**.

	Bonus	Rebate	Total
Saved	9	16	25
Spent	16	6	22
Total	25	22	47

a. Use the **Two Proportions** applet to test the hypotheses stated in the previous question. Be sure to specify the statistic you used and its value (from the study). Also, find and report the p-value.

b. Next, use the **Multiple Proportions** applet to test the hypotheses stated in the previous question. Be sure to specify the statistic you used and its value (from the study). Also, find and report the p-value.

c. How do the p-values from parts (a) and (b) compare? Are they about the same or very different? Explain why.

Heart disease and baldness

8.CE.20 The study used for exercises in Sections 8.1 and 8.2 actually included a fifth degree of baldness, extreme. Here is a table that summarizes the full data set:

Counts	None	Little	Some	Much	Extreme	Total
Yes	251	165	195	50	2	663
No	331	221	185	34	1	772
Total	582	386	380	84	3	1,435

What stands out about the new category is the tiny sample size: only three patients with extreme baldness. This exercise explores what can happen when a category has so few observational units. Use the data set **HeartDiseaseAndBaldness2**.

Simulation-based test using MAD.

a. Use the **Multiple Proportions** applet to find the MAD, its simulation-based null distribution, and the p-value.

b. Compare the null distribution with the null distribution you obtained in Exercise 8.1.15 (re-create it if you need to). What are the main differences? How do you account for these differences?

c. Compare the conclusions from the two simulation-based analyses using the MAD. Which conclusion do you consider more trustworthy? Why?

Simulation-based test using chi-square.

d. Use the **Multiple Proportions** applet to find the chi-square statistic, its simulation-based null distribution, and the p-value.

e. Compare the shape of the distribution for chi-square with the shape of the simulation-based distribution in part (a).

f. Compare the conclusions from the simulation-based analysis using MAD in part (c) above and using chi-square. Which conclusion do you consider more trustworthy? Why?

Theory-based test using chi-square.

g. Use the applet to find the p-value and contributions to chi-square for a theory-based test.

h. Is the theory-based test trustworthy? Why or why not?

The bottom line.

i. Which analysis do you consider more persuasive: the one based on four degrees of baldness or the one based on all five? Justify your answer.

j. A third approach to the data analysis would be to omit the extreme category. What results do you expect from this analysis? Explain your reasoning.

Which test?

k. What lesson should you take away from your comparison of the three tests?

INVESTIGATION: WHO YIELDS TO PEDESTRIANS?

Researchers from the University of California, Berkeley wondered whether upper-class individuals behave more unethically than lower-class individuals. To further investigate this question, they studied behaviors of drivers in different makes and models of cars. The cars were a surrogate measure for the drivers' class status. According to California Vehicle Code, cars must yield to a pedestrian if said pedestrian is crossing within any marked crosswalk. Data were collected from an intersection in the San Francisco Bay Area on three weekdays between 2:00 PM and 5:00 PM in June of 2011. A coder, positioned near the crosswalk, rated the approaching car on a scale from 1 to 5 based on make, age, and physical appearance of the car. The lowest status received a code of 1 and the highest status a code of 5. The coder also recorded whether or not the approaching car yielded to the pedestrian (a confederate of the study) waiting to cross. There were 152 drivers who were scored.

STEP 1: Ask a research question.

1. State the research question.

STEP 2: Design a study and collect data.

2. What are the observational/experimental units?
3. Is this a randomized experiment or an observational study? Explain how you know.
4. State the two variables measured on each unit.
5. Is there an explanatory/response relationship for these variables? Classify the variables in this study as categorical or quantitative.
6. State the null and alternative hypotheses to be investigated with this study. (You may use the symbol π to represent these parameters.)

The following table provides descriptive statistics on the 152 drivers:

	Status				
	1	2	3	4	5
Did yield	5	20	41	25	7
Didn't yield	0	8	20	20	6
Total	5	28	61	45	13

STEP 3: Explore the data.

7. Calculate the conditional proportions of those who didn't yield to the pedestrian for each level of status.
8. Calculate the MAD (mean absolute value of the differences) for these data.

STEP 4: Draw inferences.

9. Use the appropriate applet to construct a simulated null distribution using the MAD statistic. Mark the observed MAD statistic calculated in the previous question on this graph.
   a. Paste a screenshot or draw your null distribution below with the observed MAD marked and the approximate p-value shaded in.
   b. Is the observed statistic out in the tail of this null distribution or is it a fairly typical result?
   c. What is the p-value from your simulation? Based on this simulation analysis, would you conclude that the experiment provides *strong* evidence against the null hypothesis and conclude that there is a genuine difference in at least one of the probabilities of not yielding for the five different status groups? Explain your reasoning.
10. Are the validity conditions met to complete a theory-based chi-square test for these data? Explain. Whether the conditions are met or not, use a theory-based chi-square test to find a p-value for this test. How does this p-value compare to the p-value your found using the randomization method?
11. Are the validity conditions met so we can perform follow-up analysis (pairwise comparisons) using theory-based techniques? Explain.
12. Regardless of your answer to #11, find confidence intervals for each pair of differences in the probabilities of not yielding. Comment on how this shows where differences can be established and where it is plausible there are no differences between probabilities.

STEP 5: Formulate conclusions.

13. Are you able to conclude that the cause of any differences was due to the class status of the driver? Explain.

14. What generalizations are you willing to make? Explain.

STEP 6: Look back and ahead.

15. Summarize the findings from the study. What worked well in this study design? What would you change? What are some follow-up research questions you would like to explore based on the findings from this study?

Reference: http://www.pnas.org/content/109/11/4086.full?sid=6d9e4159-8d2c-4979-a63c-62a204f42158

Research Article   www.wiley.com/college/tintle
- -

Organ Donation   Read "Attitudes toward Strategies to Increase Organ Donation: Views of the General Public and Health Professionals" by Barnieh et al. (2012), 7:1956–1963 in the *Clinical Journal of the American Society of Nephrology*.

- -

CHAPTER

① ② ③ ④ ⑤ ⑥ ⑦ ⑧ ⑨ ⑩ ⑪ ⑫

Comparing More Than Two Means*

CHAPTER OVERVIEW

In Chapter 6 you learned how to compare two groups using means. Chapter 9 will show you how to compare more than two groups on a quantitative response. This chapter very much parallels Chapter 8 and also follows from Chapter 6. In Chapter 6 you learned simulation-based and theory-based methods for determining p-values and confidence intervals for comparing two means from independent samples. In this chapter you will extend those approaches to compare more than two groups. Many of the details (statement of hypotheses, interpretation of p-values and confidence intervals, scope of conclusions) are virtually unchanged. What does need to change is determining a statistic we can calculate from our sample data that summarizes the information we have about how the group means differ. Once we have such a formula, we can easily assess the statistical significance of an observed value using the same 3S strategy. As described in the Unit 3 introduction, we will do a single test instead of multiple comparisons of two groups to minimize the impact of Type I errors on our analysis.

Chapter 9 has two sections. Section 9.1 explores the simulation-based approach and then Section 9.2 explores the theory-based approach for a particular choice of statistic.

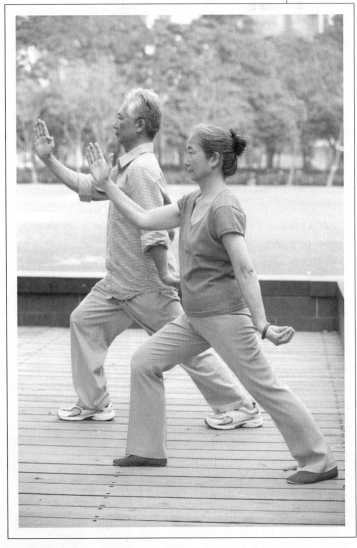

© monkeybusinessimages/iStockphoto

*Because the content found in Chapter 9 is not part of the topic outline for the AP® Statistics course, and thus not part of the AP® exam, it is not provided in this print version. Should you wish to see that content, you can access it free of charge on the Student Companion Site for *Introduction to Statistical Investigations, AP® Edition* located at <u>wiley.com/go/highschool</u>.

① ② ③ ④ ⑤ ⑥ ⑦ ⑧ ⑨ ⑩ ⑪ ⑫

Two Quantitative Variables

In Chapters 5–9 the focus was on comparing two or more groups. Chapter 10 is different. Until now the explanatory variable has been binary or categorical. In Chapter 10 both variables are quantitative. This allows us to address questions about an association between two quantitative variables and to predict the value of one variable based on the other variable (including explanatory outcomes not observed in our study).

Graphical summaries will use a new kind of plot called a *scatterplot*. These are like the dotplots we've been using throughout the book, except that they now tell you information about two (quantitative) variables at once. In describing these graphs, we will focus on the *form*, *direction*, and *strength* of the relationship. Here are some quick examples: (1) You measure the heights of classmates, first in centimeters, then in inches. Graphing the height in centimeters on the *y*-axis vs. the height in inches along the *x*-axis, the dots will fall along a straight line. The direction of the relationship is positive: *y* goes up as *x* goes up. The relationship cannot be stronger, because the points lie exactly on the line and we can perfectly predict one variable from the other. (2) You measure shoe size and height of your classmates.

Taller people tend to have bigger feet (the relationship is positive), but there is a lot of variability (the relationship is not as strong). (3) You plot age and height for one person each year on her birthday, from year 1 to year 60. This relationship is *not* linear—people stop getting taller, and the plot flattens out. (4) You plot age and height for a sample of adults. There may be no systematic relationship. Once we stop getting taller, age and height for a sample of adults are unrelated.

Chapter 10 has six sections, with one having three parts. The first section uses scatterplots to

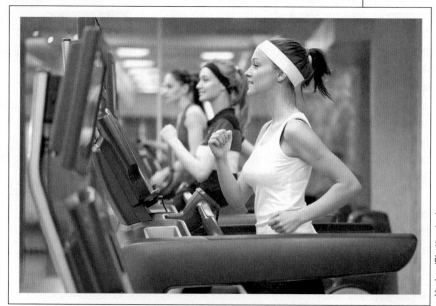

YanLev/Shutterstock

explore form, direction, and strength of the relationship between two quantitative variables. This section also introduces a new statistic, the correlation coefficient, which measures direction and strength of a linear association on a scale from -1 to 1, with 0 indicating no linear relationship. (Heads up: The strength of a relationship is not the same as the strength of evidence that a relationship exists.) Section 10.2 illustrates how to conduct simulation-based tests based on the correlation coefficient.

Section 10.3 indicates how to fit a line to give a quantitative description of a linear relationship. The slope of the fitted line might tell us, for example, that between the ages of 8 and 13 kids tend to get taller by about 2 inches per year. The second part of Section 10.3 takes a more in-depth look at linear regression models and residual plots while the third part explores how non-linear data sets can be transformed so they better fit linear models. Section 10.4 uses simulation to test a null hypothesis of no association using the slope as the statistic. Finally, Sections 10.5 and 10.6 present theory-based approaches for both the regression slope and the correlation coefficient.

It is important to keep in mind throughout this chapter that *association does not necessarily imply causation*. Beware of confounding variables. For a sample of children in grades K–12, kids with larger feet tend to drink more diet soft drinks, but drinking diet soda won't make your feet grow. State by state, there is a strong positive relationship between the number of McDonald's restaurants and the number of cases of lung cancer, but Big Macs do not cause lung cancer.

TWO QUANTITATIVE VARIABLES: SCATTERPLOTS AND CORRELATION

SECTION 10.1

INTRODUCTION

Do you think there is an association between a student's grade point average and the number of classes they skip per semester? How about the fuel efficiency of cars and their weight? These questions are different from what we have studied so far, because both variables are *quantitative*. But we will follow the same general strategy as before—first producing graphical summaries that can illuminate the relationship exhibited in the sample and then numerical summaries or statistics that measure the strength of the association. In the next section (10.2), we will draw inferences, again using simulation to compare the observed statistic of association to what we might expect to see by chance alone. These inferential techniques employ the same reasoning process as techniques we used in previous chapters. We start, however, by spending some time with scatterplots and the correlation coefficient before moving into simulation-based inference techniques.

Exam Times and Exam Scores

Is there an association between the time it takes a student to take an exam and their score on the exam? One of the authors wondered about this question and decided to collect data from one of his mathematics classes.

EXAMPLE

10.1

Example 10.1

> **THINK ABOUT IT**
>
> What are the two variables here? Which do you consider the explanatory variable and which the response variable?

Even though this was not an experiment, it makes sense to consider the time spent on the test as the explanatory variable, helping to explain why some scores were higher and some were lower. It also makes sense to think of predicting test score (response) from time spent on test (explanatory). *Note:* With this goal, we often call the explanatory variable a **predictor** variable.

EXPLORING THE DATA: GRAPHICAL SUMMARY

To examine an association between these variables graphically, it would not be helpful to make separate dotplots of time spent on test and score on test. Doing so would tell us nothing about the *relationship* between the two variables. Instead, a **scatterplot** shows the two values for each observational unit. In constructing a scatterplot we put the explanatory variable on the horizontal axis and the response variable on the vertical axis. (If you don't have a clear explanatory/response variable distinction, then this choice is more arbitrary.) Then each dot on the scatterplot shows the values for both variables on that observational unit. The results for 27 students are shown in Figure 10.1.

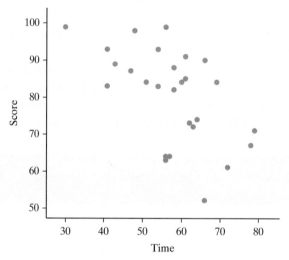

FIGURE 10.1   A scatterplot showing the association between students' scores on a mathematics test and the time it took them to take the test.

> ### THINK ABOUT IT
>
> Based on the graph, approximate the score and time for the student who was first to turn in his or her exam. Also describe what you learn about the research question from the scatterplot.

When describing a scatterplot we look for three aspects of association: direction, form, and strength. The **direction** of the association in Figure 10.1 is negative because larger values on one variable correspond to smaller values on the other variable. This shows that the longer it takes students to finish the test, the lower their scores tend to be. (This is not a hard-and-fast rule, of course; some students who took longer scored higher, but overall there is this tendency.)

In describing the **form** of an association, we describe whether it follows a linear pattern or some more complicated curve. For the test time and score data, it appears that a line would do a reasonable job of summarizing the overall pattern in the data, so we say that the association between score and time is linear. We will see lots of examples in which the form is fairly linear. Occasionally, however, the form is clearly not linear and that will be very important to note.

In describing the **strength** of association revealed in a scatterplot, we see how closely the points follow a pattern. If you imagine a line through the test time and score scatterplot, the data points all fall pretty close to that line, so we say that the association is reasonably strong.

It is also important to consider any **unusual observations** that do not follow the overall pattern. In this example, the fastest student finished in about 30 minutes and scored 100 on the exam. Even though this time is smaller than all the rest and might be considered an outlier if looking at the time variable alone (no one else finished in less than 40 minutes!), this (time, score) combination appears consistent with the overall pattern of the sample. However, if we saw a student that finished in 30 minutes and only received a score of 60, we might try to follow up on the data and make sure there wasn't an error recording their score, their time, or some other issue.

KEY IDEA

Association between quantitative variables can be described with direction, form, and strength.

- If above-average values of one variable tend to correspond to above-average values of the other variable, the **direction** is positive. If, however, above-average values of one variable are associated with below-average values of the other, the **direction** is negative.
- The **form** of the association is whether the data follow a linear pattern or some more complicated pattern.
- The **strength** of an association refers to how closely the data follow a particular pattern. When an association is strong, the value of one variable can be accurately predicted from the other.
- Also look for, and investigate further, any **unusual observations** that do not fit the pattern of the rest.

EXPLORING THE DATA: NUMERICAL SUMMARY

We can also summarize the association between two quantitative variables numerically. The **correlation coefficient** measures the strength and the direction of a *linear* association between two quantitative variables. The correlation coefficient, which is a unitless quantity usually denoted by the letter r, has the property that $-1 \leq r \leq 1$. If the correlation coefficient is close to -1 or 1, then the variables are highly correlated, revealing a strong linear association. In fact, if $r = 1$ or $r = -1$, the data all fall exactly in a straight line. If the correlation coefficient is close to 0, then the data points do not have a linear association. If the correlation coefficient is positive, then there is a positive linear association between the two variables. If the correlation coefficient is negative, then there is a negative linear association between the two variables.

 10.1.3

 10.1.4

KEY IDEA

The correlation coefficient uses a rather complex formula (see the Calculation Details appendix for specifics) that is rarely computed by hand; instead, people almost always use a calculator or computer to calculate the value of the correlation coefficient. But you should be able to apply the above properties to interpret the correlation coefficient that is found.

The correlation coefficient between test time and score is approximately $r = -0.56$. The negative value indicates that students with longer times tend to have lower test scores. The magnitude of the -0.56 correlation appears to indicate a fairly strong linear association between time and test score, so you could predict a student's test score reasonably well knowing only how long he or she took on the test. Be aware that evaluating the strength of the association will be subjective, especially across different research areas. A correlation of −0.56 might be considered extremely strong for a psychologist trying to predict human behavior but very weak for a physicist trying to predict how far a particle will travel. (To help develop your judgment for how a scatterplot looks for various correlation values, you can play the **Correlation Guessing Game** applet.)

10.1.5

> ### KEY IDEA
>
> The correlation coefficient is only applicable for data which have a linear form; nonlinear data is not summarized well by the correlation coefficient. In fact, we could say that the correlation coefficient is a numerical summary of the strength and direction of a *linear* association between two quantitative variables.

10.1.6

CAUTION: INFLUENTIAL OBSERVATIONS

We haven't been completely honest in presenting our test time and score data set. There were three additional students in the class, the last three students to turn in their tests. Their times were 93, 96, and 100 minutes. These three students also scored very well on the exam: 93, 93, and 97, respectively. We added these scores to the scatterplot shown in Figure 10.2.

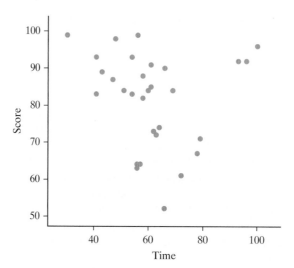

FIGURE 10.2 A scatterplot of the score on a math test and the time (in minutes) it took to complete the test after the last three tests turned in were added for all 30 students.

The three added scores can be seen on the far right side of the graph. These three students took a long time and had high scores, so they go against the general tendency that students who took longer tended to score lower. Without these three students we would view the relationship differently than we do with these students. For this reason, these unusual observations are called ***influential observations***. They are influential because the addition of just these three points changes the correlation coefficient dramatically (and our perception of the strength of the relationship), from −0.56 (a fairly strong negative correlation) to −0.12 (a weak negative correlation). Influential points tend to be ones that are far to the right or left on the graph, having extreme values for the explanatory variable like these three. The amount of influence of even just one observation can sometimes be dramatic. For example, if the person that finished the test in 30 minutes would have scored 50 instead of 100, the correlation coefficient would switch from negative to positive (0.12).

Note: There are two kinds of unusual observations seen in scatterplots: influential observations and outliers. An observation is *influential* if removing it from the data set dramatically changes our perception of the association. Typically influential observations are extreme in the explanatory variable. Outliers are observations that don't follow the overall pattern of the relationship. They may or may not be influential and they may or may not be extreme in either variable individually but are unusual in terms of the combination of values.

Are Dinner Plates Getting Larger?

EXPLORATION 10.1

1. Look at the two pictures in Figure 10.3. What do you think: Are the food portions the same size or is one larger than the other?

Courtesy of Ken Karp

FIGURE 10.3 Is there the same amount of food on each plate? Or is one portion larger than the other?

For many people, the portion on the right looks smaller, but in fact they are about the same size. (This is known as the Delboeuf illusion.) You have probably seen many articles and television reports about the growing obesity problem in America. Many reasons are given for this problem, ranging from fast food to lack of exercise. One reason that some have given is simply that the size of dinner plates has increased. Figure 10.3 illustrates that people may tend to put more food on larger dinner plates without even realizing they are doing so.

STEP 1: Ask a research question. An interesting research question is whether dinner plates are getting larger over time.

STEP 2: Design a study and collect data. To investigate the claim that dinner plates are getting larger, some researchers gathered data for American dinner plates being sold on ebay.com on March 30, 2010 (Van Ittersum and Wansink, 2011). They recorded the size and the year of manufacture for each distinct plate in a sample of 75 American-made dinner plates.

2. What is the explanatory variable? Is it categorical or quantitative?

3. What is the response variable? Is it categorical or quantitative?

4. In your own words, explain what it would mean for there to be an association between the explanatory and response variables in this study.

5. What are the observational units? How many are there?
6. Is this study an experiment or an observational study? Why?

This study is different than studies we've looked at before because both of the variables of interest are quantitative. For this reason, the graphical and numerical techniques we will use to summarize the data are different from those we've seen before.

STEP 3: Explore the data. The data in Table 10.1 represent a subset of the data values reported in the research paper.

TABLE 10.1 Data for size (diameter, in inches) and year of manufacture for 20 American-made dinner plates

Year	1950	1956	1957	1958	1963	1964	1969	1974	1975	1978
Size	10	10.75	10.125	10	10.625	10.75	10.625	10	10.5	10.125

Year	1980	1986	1990	1995	2004	2004	2007	2008	2008	2009
Size	10.375	10.75	10.375	11	10.75	10.125	11.5	11	11.125	11

Graphical summary of two quantitative variables: Scatterplots

7. Paste the **PlateSize** data set into the **Corr/Regression** applet. Which variable is on the *x*-(horizontal) axis? Which variable is on the *y*-(vertical) axis?

A *scatterplot* is a graph showing a dot for each observational unit, where the location of the dot indicates the values of the observational unit for both the explanatory and response variables. Typically, the explanatory variable is placed on the *x*-axis and the response variable is placed on the *y*-axis.

8. Create a rough sketch of the scatterplot from the applet. Be sure the axes are well-labeled. Show that you understand how a scatterplot is created by circling the dot on the scatterplot corresponding to a plate made in 1958 that is 10 inches in diameter.

When describing a scatterplot we look for three aspects of association: direction, form, and strength.

The *direction* of association between two quantitative variables is either positive or negative, depending on whether or not the response variable (size) increases as the explanatory variable (year) tends to increase (positive association) or decrease (negative association).

9. **Direction.** Is the association between year and plate size positive or negative? Interpret what this means in context.

The *form* of association between two quantitative variables is described by indicating whether a line would do a reasonable job summarizing the overall pattern in the data or if a curve would be better. It is important to note that, especially when the sample size is small, you don't want to let one or two points on the scatterplot change your interpretation of whether or not the form of association is linear. In general, assume that the form is linear unless there is compelling (strong) evidence in the scatterplot that the form is not linear.

10. **Form.** Does the association between year and size appear to be linear or is there strong evidence (over many observational units) suggesting the relationship is nonlinear?

In describing the *strength* of association revealed in a scatterplot, we see how closely the points follow the form: that is, how closely do the points follow a straight line or curve. If all of the points fall pretty close to this straight line or curve, we say the association is strong. Weak associations will show little pattern in the scatterplot, and moderate associations will be somewhere in the middle.

11. In your opinion, would you say that the association between plate size and year appears to be strong, moderate, or weak?

It is also important to consider any *unusual observations* that do not follow the overall pattern.

12. Are there any observational units (dots on the scatterplot, representing individual plates) that seem to fall outside of the overall pattern?

In this example, the largest plate diameter was 11.50 inches. Compared to other plate diameters in the sample, this is fairly large. But based on the scatterplot we see that the plate doesn't appear to be unusual. On the other hand, if the 11.50-inch plate had been manufactured in 1950, then the scatterplot would indicate that to be unusual.

Note: There are two kinds of unusual observations seen in scatterplots: influential observations and outliers. An observation is *influential* if removing it from the data set dramatically changes our perception of the association. Typically influential observations are extreme in the explanatory variable. *Outliers* are observations that don't follow the overall pattern of the relationship. They may or may not be influential and they may or may not be extreme in either variable individually but are unusual in terms of the combination of values.

> **KEY IDEA**
>
> Association between quantitative variables can be described with direction, form, and strength.
>
> - If above-average values of one variable tend to correspond to above-average values of the other variable, the **direction** is positive. If, however, above-average values of one variable are associated with below-average values of the other, the **direction** is negative.
> - The **form** of the association is whether the data follow a linear pattern or some more complicated pattern.
> - The **strength** of an association refers to how closely the data follow a particular pattern. When an association is strong, the value of one variable can be accurately predicted from the other.
> - Also look for, and investigate further, any **unusual observations** that do not fit the pattern of the rest.

Numerical summaries

Describing the direction, form, and strength of association based on a scatterplot, along with investigating unusual observations, is an important first step in summarizing the relationship between two quantitative variables. Another approach is to use a statistic. One of the statistics most commonly used for this purpose is the correlation coefficient.

The **correlation coefficient**, often denoted by the symbol **r**, is a single number that takes a value between -1 and 1, inclusive. Negative values of r indicate a negative association, whereas positive values of r indicate a positive association. The stronger the linear association is between the two variables, the closer the value of the correlation coefficient will be to either -1 or 1, whereas weaker linear associations will have correlation coefficient values closer to 0. Moderate linear associations will typically have correlation coefficients in the range of 0.3 to 0.7 or -0.3 to -0.7.

13. Will the value of the correlation coefficient for the year–plate size data be negative or positive? Why?

> **KEY IDEA**
>
> The correlation coefficient uses a rather complex formula (see the Calculation Details appendix for specifics) that is rarely computed by hand; instead, people almost always use a calculator or computer to calculate the value of the correlation coefficient. But you should be able to apply the above properties to interpret the correlation coefficient that is found.

14. Without using the applet, give an estimated range for the value of the correlation coefficient between plate size and year based on the scatterplot.

15. Now, check the **Correlation coefficient** box in the applet to reveal the actual value of the correlation coefficient. Report the value.

> **KEY IDEA**
>
> The correlation coefficient is only applicable for data which has a linear form; nonlinear data are not summarized well by the correlation coefficient. In fact, we could say that the correlation coefficient is a numerical summary of the strength and direction of a *linear* association between two quantitative variables.

Another point about correlation is that it is sensitive to influential observations. Influential observations are unusual observations which substantially impact the value of the correlation coefficient based on whether or not they are included in the data set.

16. In the **Add/remove observations** section of the applet, enter a year (*x*) of 1950 and plate size (*y*) of 11.5 and press **Add**. Note how this is an unusual observation on the scatterplot. How did the correlation change as a result?

We have now seen a graphical technique (scatterplot) and numerical summary (correlation coefficient) to summarize the relationship between two quantitative variables. Using techniques you will learn in the next section, we find the sample correlation coefficient between plate size and year to be significantly different than zero (p-value ≈ 0.01), meaning that there is strong evidence of a genuine association between year and plate size, though we need to be cautious about generalizing too far because this is only a random sample of plates for sale on a single day on eBay.

- -

SECTION 10.1   Summary

Examining the *association* between two quantitative variables involves looking at scatterplots.

- The **direction** of the association indicates whether large values of one variable tend to go with large values of the other (*positive* association) or with small values of the other (*negative* association).

- The **form** of association refers to whether the relationship between the variables can be summarized well with a straight line or some more complicated pattern.

- The **strength** of association entails how closely the points fall to a recognizable pattern such as a line.

- As always, **unusual observations** that do not fit the pattern of the rest of the observations are worth examining closely or have an undue impact on our perception of the association.

  - **Influential observations** are observations whose removal would dramatically impact the overall direction, form, or strength of the association. (Often you find them by looking for observations that are extreme in the *x*-direction.)

  - **Outliers** are unusual observations that do not follow the overall pattern of the association. They may or may not be influential.

A numerical measure of the linear association between two quantitative variables is the **correlation coefficient, *r*.**

- A correlation coefficient is between -1 and 1, inclusive.
- The closer the correlation coefficient to -1 or 1, the stronger the linear association between the variables.

- The closer the correlation coefficient to 0, the weaker the linear association between the variables.
- The correlation coefficient is not resistant to influential observations.

INFERENCE FOR THE CORRELATION COEFFICIENT: SIMULATION-BASED APPROACH

SECTION 10.2

INTRODUCTION

In the previous section we learned about how the correlation coefficient and scatterplots are used to explore the association between two quantitative variables. We will now learn how to test whether a sample correlation coefficient provides convincing evidence of an association between the two quantitative variables in the larger population or process.

Exercise Intensity and Mood Changes

Example 10.2

You have probably heard that exercise helps relieve stress. Exercising has been shown to decrease tension and elevate one's mood. However, is this change in mood related to the intensity of the exercise? Szabo (2003) investigated this question with a sample of female college students who jogged or ran on a treadmill for 20 minutes. Participants were allowed to go at any speed they desired as long as they didn't walk. Using heart rate monitors, researchers calculated their exercise intensity as a percentage of their maximal heart rate. (The subjects' maximal heart rates were estimated from their base heart rates. As a result, a couple of these percentages are over 100.)

Before exercising, the subjects also took a quick test about their mood. The test measured things like anger, confusion, and depression. This test was given again after exercising, and the researchers determined a numerical score for the change in mood of the subjects before and after exercising. Negative numbers indicate a decrease in measures of bad mood like anger, and so forth. Although the researchers found significant results in the participants' change of mood when comparing before and after exercise, we are interested to see whether there is a significant association between the *change of mood* and *exercise intensity*. Let's look at this study using the six-step statistical investigation method.

STEP 1: Ask a research question. Is there an association between how much the mood of a person changes during exercise and the intensity of the exercise?

STEP 2: Design a study and collect data. The study design was detailed above. What we haven't done yet, however, is to convert our research question into hypotheses. Writing our hypotheses out in words should look very familiar to the way we have done this in the past few chapters.

Null hypothesis: There is no association between exercise intensity and changes in mood in the population.

Alternative hypothesis: There is an association between exercise intensity and changes in mood in the population.

We are going to use the correlation coefficient to measure the (linear) association between these two variables. See FAQ 10.2.1 for further discussion.

FAQ 10.2.1   www.wiley.com/college/tintle

Where's the parameter? Why no confidence interval?

The researchers used 32 volunteer female college students as their subjects. Their results are shown in Table 10.2.

TABLE 10.2   Exercise intensity as a percentage of maximal heart rate and the change in mood test scores

Ex. intensity	41.8	56.1	56.8	59.1	59.5	60.9	61.6	62.6	64.9	65.6	66.4
Mood change	−12	−4	−5	−6	−24	1	−24	−3	−5	−12	−16

Ex. intensity	66.5	67.1	67.8	68.3	68.4	69.7	69.9	70.1	70.3	72	72.2
Mood change	−3	−8	−2	−24	−10	−12	−4	−12	−18	−13	−31

Ex. intensity	73.9	76.1	77	77.3	79.9	82.5	83.3	87	106	109.6
Mood change	−20	−26	−3	8	2	3	−11	−3	5	−13

STEP 3: Explore the data. A scatterplot of the change in mood and exercise intensity is shown in Figure 10.4.

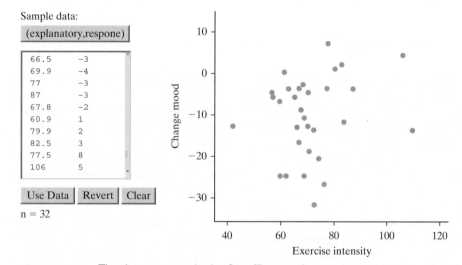

FIGURE 10.4   The data were put in the **Corr/Regression** applet and a scatterplot of change in mood and exercise intensity was produced.

> **THINK ABOUT IT**
>
> Do these data support the research conjecture?

The scatterplot shows a weak positive association between change in mood and intensity of exercise, with a sample correlation of $r = 0.187$.

Now suppose there is no association between these two variables in the population. Would it be *possible* to get a sample correlation coefficient as large as $r = 0.187$ just by random chance? The answer to this question, as always, is yes, it's possible. The real question, though, is whether it is *unlikely*. Answering this question will take more investigation.

One way to explore this question is to investigate how much sample-to-sample variability we can expect to see in the correlation coefficient when the two variables are not related; that is, if the change in mood numbers were essentially assigned at random to the exercise intensity numbers, how strong is the typical "by chance" association?

> **THINK ABOUT IT**
>
> Suggest a procedure for evaluating the strength of evidence against the null hypothesis.

STEP 4: Draw inferences. We will proceed just as before with our simulation-based approach, starting with the 3S strategy. 10.2.1

1. **Statistic:** In this case, we found the observed correlation coefficient between exercise intensity and mood change for our sample to be $r = 0.187$.

2. **Simulate:** We will assume there is no relationship between change in mood and exercise intensity in the population (this is our null hypothesis). If this is the case, it does not matter which change in mood value is paired up with which exercise intensity value. Therefore we will shuffle the response variable, change in mood, and find the correlation coefficient for our new shuffled data. We will repeat this random shuffling a large number of times to obtain a null distribution that models the behavior of the correlation coefficient under the null hypothesis.

   To better understand the simulation approach, consider the following copy of the original data table where we have removed the mood change values from the table. 10.2.2

TABLE 10.3	Data table of exercise intensity and mood change										
Ex. intensity	41.8	56.1	56.8	59.1	59.5	60.9	61.6	62.6	64.9	65.6	66.4
Mood change											
Ex. intensity	66.5	67.1	67.8	68.3	68.4	69.7	69.9	70.1	70.3	72	72.2
Mood change											
Ex. intensity	73.9	76.1	77	77.3	79.9	82.5	83.3	87	106	109.6	
Mood change											
Mood change	−12	−4	−5	−6	−24	1	−24	−3	−5	−12	−16
	−3	−8	−2	−24	−10	−12	−4	−12	−18	−13	−31
	−20	−26	−3	8	2	3	−11	−3	5	−13	

Imagine that the actual mood change scores were now randomly matched to the different exercise intensity values. You can envision this random matching process by imagining that the 32 different mood change scores were each written on a slip of paper, so you could shuffle all the mood change scores and randomly pair up each mood change score with an exercise intensity score. Thus, this simulation means that for this process there really is no underlying association between exercise intensity and mood change; any association observed in the sample is simply due to chance.

3. **Strength of evidence:** If the observed statistic (correlation coefficient of our sample, $r = 0.187$) is in the tail of the null distribution created by our simulation, then we say we have found evidence against the null hypothesis in favor of the alternative hypothesis.

To complete Steps 2 and 3 of our 3S strategy, we used the **Corr/Regression** applet to shuffle the mood change values 1,000 times and after each shuffle calculated the correlation coefficient. These 1,000 shuffled correlation coefficients are shown in a histogram in Figure 10.5. We counted that 328 of these 1,000, or 32.8%, were as large as or larger than our sample correlation coefficient of 0.187 or as small as or smaller than −0.187 (two-sided), giving us an approximate p-value of 0.328. Therefore, our sample correlation coefficient is not very unlikely to occur by chance alone when the null hypothesis is true. Hence these data do not provide strong evidence against the null hypothesis and do not support the alternative hypothesis that change in mood is associated with intensity of exercise in the population. 10.2.3

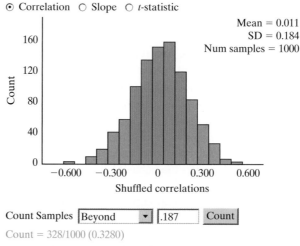

FIGURE 10.5   The null distribution of correlation coefficients for 1,000 shuffles of mood change values assuming no association between mood change and exercise intensity.

Here is a summary of the simulation model:

Null hypothesis	=	No association between *x* and *y* variables
One repetition	=	Re-randomizing the response outcomes to the explanatory variable outcomes
Statistic	=	Correlation coefficient

STEP 5: Formulate conclusions. We do not have strong evidence that there is a genuine association between change in mood and exercise intensity in the population. Hence, we cannot really talk about cause and effect. Even if we found a significant association, we would still not be able to draw a cause-and-effect conclusion because this was an observational study in which subjects chose for themselves the level of exercise intensity. Also, this study does not appear to have selected a random sample, so we should be cautious in generalizing these results to a larger population. At best, they apply to female college students. The study did report that they had significant results when comparing mood before and after exercise; however, the intensity of the exercise does not seem to significantly influence the amount of the change in mood for students like those in this study.

STEP 6: Look back and ahead. The researchers in this study now have some important decisions to make. The results of this analysis did not provide compelling evidence that exercise intensity and mood change were associated in the population. But is this an example of a missed opportunity to establish that such a hypothesis is true? Or, are the researchers incorrect in what they've hypothesized? Although we'll never know for sure from a single study, there are a number of possible improvements if the researchers do a follow-up study, including potentially:

a. Gathering a larger sample size in a follow-up study

b. Considering whether that sample should be randomly chosen from a population of interest

c. Randomly assigning subjects to different exercise intensity levels

d. Improving the way that "mood" and "mood change" were measured (e.g., using reliable and valid instruments)

e. Considering starting only with subjects who had a negative mood before exercising as those with positive moods before exercising may show little change afterwards

Draft Lottery

In 1970, the United States Selective Service conducted a lottery to decide which young men would be drafted into the armed forces (Fienberg, 1971). Each of the 366 birthdays in a year (including February 29) was assigned a draft number. Young men born on days assigned low draft numbers were drafted.

We will regard the 366 dates of the year as observational units. We will consider two variables recorded on each date: *draft number* assigned to the date and *sequential date* in the year (so January 31 is sequential date 31, February 1 is sequential date 32, and so on).

1. In a perfectly fair, random lottery, what should be the value of the correlation coefficient between *draft number* and *sequential date of birthday*?

Figure 10.6 displays a *scatterplot* of the assigned draft numbers and the sequential dates. There are 366 dots, one for each day of the (leap) year.

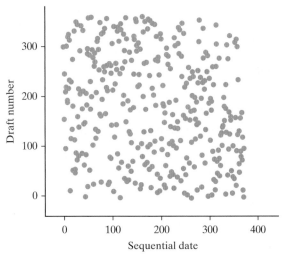

FIGURE 10.6 A scatterplot of the draft numbers and sequential dates.

2. Let's take a look at the scatterplot in Figure 10.6.
   a. Does the scatterplot reveal much of an association between draft number and sequential date?
   b. Based on the scatterplot, guess the value of the correlation coefficient.
   c. Does it appear that this was a fair, random lottery?

It's difficult to see much of a pattern or association in the scatterplot, so it seems reasonable to conclude that this was a fair, random lottery with a correlation coefficient near zero. But let's dig a little deeper:

3. The 1970 Draft Lottery data sheet (at the end of the exploration) shows the draft number assigned to each of the 366 birthdays.
   a. Find and report the draft number assigned to *your* birthday.
   b. Is your draft number in the bottom third (1–122), middle third (123–244), or top third (245–366)?

4. The second table at the end of the exploration has ordered the draft numbers within each month.
   a. Use this table to determine the *median* draft number for your birth month.
   b. Collaborate with your classmates to determine and report the median draft number for all 12 months.

Month	Jan	Feb	Mar	Apr	May	June	July	Aug	Sep	Oct	Nov	Dec
Median draft number												

c. Do you notice any pattern or trend in the median draft numbers over the course of the year? (*Hint:* If you do not see a trend, compare the six medians from January to June with the six medians from July to December.)

5. The correlation coefficient for the full data set is $r = -0.226$. What does this number reveal? Is it consistent with the scatterplot?

6. Let's think about how we would complete a test of significance for correlation.

   a. Suggest two possible explanations (hypotheses) which could have generated the value of the nonzero correlation coefficient.

   b. In your own words, how could we go about determining whether random chance is a plausible explanation for the observed correlation value between sequential date and draft number? Explain how the 3S strategy could be applied here, in particular identifying a simulation strategy you could conduct "by hand." *Note:* You do not need to actually carry out a simulation analysis.

      i. What is the statistic?

      ii. How would you simulate?

      iii. How would you evaluate the strength of evidence?

The null hypothesis to be tested is that the lottery was conducted with a fair, random process. The null hypothesis would therefore imply that there is *no* association between sequential date and draft number for this process. The alternative hypothesis is that this lottery was *not* conducted with a fair, random process, so there *is* an association between sequential date and draft number. See FAQ 10.2.1 for further discussion.

FAQ 10.2.1   www.wiley.com/college/tintle

Where's the parameter? Why no confidence interval?

How can we assess whether the observed correlation coefficient of $r = -0.226$ is far enough from zero to provide convincing evidence that the lottery process was not random? Like always, we ask how unlikely it would be for a fair, random lottery to produce a correlation value as far from zero as -0.226. Also like always, we answer that question by simulating a large number of fair random lotteries (a true null hypothesis), calculating the correlation coefficient for each one, and seeing how often we obtain a correlation coefficient as or more extreme (as far from zero) as -0.226.

7. Open the **Corr/Regression** applet. Copy the data from **DraftLottery** into the applet (remember to include the column titles). Check the **Correlation Coefficient** box and confirm that the correlation coefficient is -0.226.

   a. Check the **Show Shuffle Options** box and select the **Correlation** radio button to the right to keep track of that statistic. Then press **Shuffle Y-values** to simulate one fair, random lottery. Record the value of the correlation coefficient between the shuffled draft numbers and sequential date.

   b. Press **Shuffle Y-values** four more times to generate results of four more fair, random lotteries. Record the values of the shuffled correlation coefficients in a table like the following.

Repetition	1	2	3	4	5
Correlation coefficient					

c. Did any of your simulated statistics from fair, random lotteries produce a correlation coefficient as extreme (far from zero) as the observed -0.226?

d. Change the **Number of Shuffles** from 1 to 995 and press **Shuffle Y-values** to simulate 995 more fair, random lotteries. Look at the null distribution of these 1,000 correlation coefficients. Where is this distribution centered? Why does this make sense?

e. Next to the **Count Samples** box choose **Beyond** from the pull-down menu. Specify the observed correlation coefficient (-0.226) and press **Count**. What proportion, of the 1,000 simulated random lotteries produced a correlation coefficient as extreme (as far from zero in either direction) as -0.226? Report the approximate p-value.

f. Interpret this p-value: This is the probability of what, assuming what?

g. What conclusion would you draw from this p-value? Do you have strong evidence that the 1970 draft lottery was not conducted with a fair, random process? Explain the reasoning behind your conclusion.

Once they saw these results, statisticians were quick to point out that something fishy happened with the 1970 draft lottery. The irregularity can be attributed to improper mixing of the balls used in the lottery drawing process. (Balls with birthdays early in the year were placed in the bin first, and balls with birthdays late in the year were placed in the bin last. Without thorough mixing, balls with birthdays late in the year settled near the top of the bin and so tended to be selected earlier.) The mixing process was changed for the 1971 draft lottery (e.g., two bins, one for the draft numbers and one for the birthdays), for which the correlation coefficient turned out to be $r = 0.014$.

8. Use your simulation results to approximate the p-value for the 1971 draft lottery. Is there any reason to suspect that this 1971 draft lottery was not conducted with a fair, random process? Explain the reasoning behind your conclusion. Also explain why you don't need to paste in the data from the 1971 lottery first.

- -

SECTION 10.2 Summary

The 3S strategy can be used to assess whether a sample correlation coefficient is extreme enough to provide strong evidence that the variables are associated in the population.

- The null hypothesis is that there is no association between the two variables in the population.
- The statistic used to measure the (linear) association is the correlation coefficient.
- Shuffling the values of the response variable is used to produce simulated values of the statistic.
    - This shuffling simulates values of the statistic under the assumption of no underlying association between the two variables.
- As always, the p-value is calculated as the proportion of repetitions in which the simulated value of the statistic is at least as extreme as the observed value of the statistic.
    - Also, as always, a small p-value provides evidence against the null hypothesis in favor of the alternative hypothesis.
    - We can test for positive or negative associations (one-sided p-values) or for any association (two-sided p-value).

- -

1970 Draft Lottery Data

Date	Jan	Feb	Mar	Apr	May	Jun	Jul	Aug	Sep	Oct	Nov	Dec
1	305	86	108	32	330	249	93	111	225	359	19	129
2	159	144	29	271	298	228	350	45	161	125	34	328
3	251	297	267	83	40	301	115	261	49	244	348	157
4	215	210	275	81	276	20	279	145	232	202	266	165
5	101	214	293	269	364	28	188	54	82	24	310	56
6	224	347	139	253	155	110	327	114	6	87	76	10
7	306	91	122	147	35	85	50	168	8	234	51	12
8	199	181	213	312	321	366	13	48	184	283	97	105
9	194	338	317	219	197	335	277	106	263	342	80	43
10	325	216	323	218	65	206	284	21	71	220	282	41
11	329	150	136	14	37	134	248	324	158	237	46	39
12	221	68	300	346	133	272	15	142	242	72	66	314
13	318	152	259	124	295	69	42	307	175	138	126	163
14	238	4	354	231	178	356	331	198	1	294	127	26
15	17	89	169	273	130	180	322	102	113	171	131	320
16	121	212	166	148	55	274	120	44	207	254	107	96
17	235	189	33	260	112	73	98	154	255	288	143	304
18	140	292	332	90	278	341	190	141	246	5	146	128
19	58	25	200	336	75	104	227	311	177	241	203	240
20	280	302	239	345	183	360	187	344	63	192	185	135
21	186	363	334	62	250	60	27	291	204	243	156	70
22	337	290	265	316	326	247	153	339	160	117	9	53
23	118	57	256	252	319	109	172	116	119	201	182	162
24	59	236	258	2	31	358	23	36	195	196	230	95
25	52	179	343	351	361	137	67	286	149	176	132	84
26	92	365	170	340	357	22	303	245	18	7	309	173
27	355	205	268	74	296	64	289	352	233	264	47	78
28	77	299	223	262	308	222	88	167	257	94	281	123
29	349	285	362	191	226	353	270	61	151	229	99	16
30	164		217	208	103	209	287	333	315	38	174	3
31	211		30		313		193	11		79		100

The following table arranges the draft numbers in order for each month:

Rank	Jan	Feb	Mar	Apr	May	Jun	Jul	Aug	Sep	Oct	Nov	Dec
1	17	4	29	2	31	20	13	11	1	5	9	3
2	52	25	30	14	35	22	15	21	6	7	19	10
3	58	57	33	32	37	28	23	36	8	24	34	12
4	59	68	108	62	40	60	27	44	18	38	46	16
5	77	86	122	74	55	64	42	45	49	72	47	26
6	92	89	136	81	65	69	50	48	63	79	51	39
7	101	91	139	83	75	73	67	54	71	87	66	41
8	118	144	166	90	103	85	88	61	82	94	76	43
9	121	150	169	124	112	104	93	102	113	117	80	53
10	140	152	170	147	130	109	98	106	119	125	97	56
11	159	179	200	148	133	110	115	111	149	138	99	70
12	164	181	213	191	155	134	120	114	151	171	107	78
13	186	189	217	208	178	137	153	116	158	176	126	84
14	194	205	223	218	183	180	172	141	160	192	127	95
15	199	210	239	219	197	206	187	142	161	196	131	96
16	211	212	256	231	226	209	188	145	175	201	132	100
17	215	214	258	252	250	222	190	154	177	202	143	105
18	221	216	259	253	276	228	193	167	184	220	146	123
19	224	236	265	260	278	247	227	168	195	229	156	128
20	235	285	267	262	295	249	248	198	204	234	174	129
21	238	290	268	269	296	272	270	245	207	237	182	135
22	251	292	275	271	298	274	277	261	225	241	185	157
23	280	297	293	273	308	301	279	286	232	243	203	162
24	305	299	300	312	313	335	284	291	233	244	230	163
25	306	302	317	316	319	341	287	307	242	254	266	165
26	318	338	323	336	321	353	289	311	246	264	281	173
27	325	347	332	340	326	356	303	324	255	283	282	240
28	329	363	334	345	330	358	322	333	257	288	309	304
29	337	365	343	346	357	360	327	339	263	294	310	314
30	349		354	351	361	366	331	344	315	342	348	320
31	355		362		364		350	352		359		328

SECTION 10.3 ▶ **LEAST SQUARES REGRESSION**

In the last two sections we used graphical and numerical methods to describe the observed association between two quantitative variables and then looked at a simulation method for drawing inferences based on the correlation coefficient. If we decide the association is linear, it is helpful to develop a mathematical model of that association. This is especially helpful in allowing us to make predictions about the response variable from the explanatory variable. The most common way to do this is with a ***least squares regression line*** (often called the best fit line, or simply regression line), which is the line that gets as "close" as possible to all of the data points.

10.3 ─ **Are Dinner Plates Getting Larger (Revisited)?** ─────────

Example 10.3

10.3.1

In Exploration 10.1 we looked at a recent study investigating a potential association between the year of manufacture and dinner plate size, finding strong evidence of a positive association, meaning that, based on a random sample of plates for sale on eBay on a given day, plate sizes appear to be increasing over time. A scatterplot of the data is presented again in Figure 10.7.

   This scatterplot reveals a moderately strong positive association, as there does appear to be a trend of increasing plate sizes in more recent years. This observation is supported by the correlation coefficient ($r = 0.604$). The association also appears to be roughly linear, indicating that a line would do a reasonable job of summarizing the overall relationship. We have added such a line, specifically the least squares regression line, to the scatterplot in Figure 10.7.

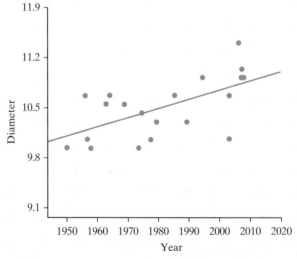

FIGURE 10.7   A scatterplot and least squares regression line for the size of American dinner plates and the year of manufacture.

As you may recall, lines can be summarized by equations which indicate the slope and y-intercept of the line. The line shown above has a slope of 0.0128 and a y-intercept of -14.80.

─── **NOTATION** ───────────────────────────────────

The equation of the best fit line is written as $\hat{y} = a + b(x)$, where:
- a is the ***y-intercept*** and b is the ***slope***
- x is a value of the explanatory variable
- $\hat{y}$ is the predicted value for the response variable

The least squares line for the dinner plate data turns out to be $\hat{y} = -14.8 + 0.0128x$ or better written as

$$\widehat{\text{diameter}} = -14.8 + 0.0128\,(\text{year}).$$

Such an equation allows us to predict the plate diameter in a particular year. If we substitute 2000 for the year, we predict a plate diameter of $-14.8 + 0.0128(2000) = 10.80$ inches.

10.3.2

THINK ABOUT IT

What do you predict for a plate diameter for a plate manufactured in the year 2001? How does this compare to our prediction for the year 2000?

The slope of this equation is $b = 0.0128$. This means that, according to our line, dinner plate diameters are predicted to increase by 0.0128 inches per year on average. Your prediction for 2001 should have been 10.8128, or roughly 0.0128 inches larger than your prediction for 2000. This is true no matter what two years you use, as long as they are one year apart. If you wanted to predict the change in average plate size associated with a 10-year difference in manufacturing dates, you could simply multiply the slope by 10.

KEY IDEA

The slope of a least squares regression line is interpreted as the predicted change in the average response variable for a one-unit change in the explanatory variable.

Note that the slope of the regression line for the dinner plate data is positive, as was the correlation coefficient. These two statistics will always have the same sign.

KEY IDEA

For a given data set, the signs (positive, negative, or zero) for the correlation coefficient and the slope of the regression line must be the same.

10.3.3

You can think of the y-intercept in a couple of different ways. Graphically, it is where the regression line crosses the y-axis. Because the x-value of the y-axis is 0, the y-intercept can also be thought of as the $\hat{y}$-value (or predicted response) when the x-value (or explanatory variable) equals 0. We had a y-intercept of -14.8 in the dinner plate equation. This tells us that, according to the line, the predicted size of American dinner plates in year 0 was -14.8 inches. Now this doesn't make much sense, does it? For one, we can't have a negative value for the size of dinner plates. Our equation might work reasonably well within the range of values of the explanatory variable with our given data but may fail miserably outside that range. In fact, our equation should only be used to predict the size of dinner plates from about 1950 to 2010. We don't know whether the same relationship between year and plate size holds outside this range, so we should not make predictions outside this range. Going way back to year 0, for example, gives us an answer that makes no sense at all. Never mind the fact that the U.S. didn't exist in year 0!

KEY IDEA

Predicting values for the response variable for values of the explanatory variable that are outside of the range of the original data is known as ***extrapolation***, and can give very misleading predictions.

10.3.4

We should also make sure the interpretation is meaningful in the study context. In many situations the intercept can have a meaningful interpretation, such as the start-up (time = 0) cost of a manufacturing process.

WHAT MAKES THIS LINE THE "BEST"?

We've talked about how the line above is the "best" line. But what makes it the best? Intuitively, we said that the best fitting line gets as close as possible to all of the points, but we can be more precise by better understanding the idea of a *residual*. The vertical distance from a point to the line is called a **residual**. So the residuals measure the difference between the predicted and observed values of the response variable (in this case, plate size) for each *x* value. Figure 10.8 shows the residuals for the plate example.

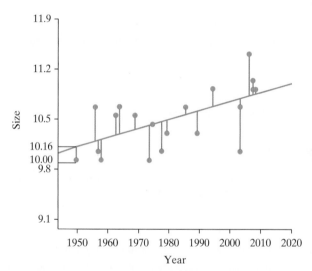

FIGURE 10.8: Residuals for best fit line of year vs. plate size.

Each observational unit (plate) has a residual which can be found by subtracting the predicted plate size from the observed (real) plate size (in other words finding the value of $y - \hat{y}$). For example, the plate manufactured in 1950 has a predicted plate size of 10.16 inches but is actually 10 inches, and so the residual is $10 - 10.16 = -0.16$ inches.

There are actually a number of ways to get "as close" to all of the points as possible; one way would be to add up all of the values of the residuals (making them positive first, so they didn't cancel out) and find the line that minimized the sum of the (absolute) residuals. In practice, however, finding such a line is very difficult. Instead, we will find the line that minimizes the sum of the squared residuals.

KEY IDEA

The least squares regression line minimizes the sum of the squared residuals.

Although the reasons for this change are due to calculus (and not something we really want you to worry about!), the implications aren't too different than if we were minimizing the sum of the absolute residuals. The only subtle difference is that because we are squaring, unusual observations (extreme in the *x*-direction) have more "pull" as the squared value of the residual is larger relative to more typical points. Thus, these kinds of points can be particularly influential—just like they were when we explored the correlation coefficient. See FAQ 10.3.1 for more.

 10.3.7

FAQ 10.3.1 www.wiley.com/college/tintle

Why least squares?

KEY IDEA

An observation or set of observations is considered *influential* if removing the observation from the data set substantially changes the values of the correlation coefficient and/or the least squares regression equation. Typically, observations that have extreme explanatory variable values (far below or far above $\bar{x}$) are potentially influential. They may not have large residuals, having pulled the line close to them.

One final statistic that is of interest in a linear regression is called the *coefficient of determination* (R^2). This statistic measures the percentage of total variation in the response variable that is explained by the linear relationship with the explanatory variable. The value is literally the square of the correlation coefficient. In this example, the correlation coefficient is 0.604, and so the coefficient of determination is $(0.604)^2 \approx 0.365$, meaning that 36.5% of the observed variation in plate sizes is explained by knowing the year of manufacture.

Another way to compute the coefficient of determination is as follows:

 10.3.8

$$R^2 = 100\% \times \frac{SSE(\bar{y}) - SSE(regression\ line)}{SSE(\bar{y})}$$

where SSE(regression line) is the sum of the squared residuals for the least squares regression line and $SSE(\bar{y})$ is the sum of squared residuals for the horizontal line at the average value of the response variable. We can think of $SSE(\bar{y})$ as a measure of the overall variability in the response, and we are seeing how much less variability there is about the regression line compared to this "no-association" line.

There is a third way to think about the coefficient of determination. If we look at the plate sizes alone, variability of the plate sizes, as measured by the standard deviation, is 0.430. (See Figure 10.9a.) We can also use the squared standard deviation or *variance* to reflect this, $0.430^2 \approx 0.185$. But if we look at the residuals, the "unexplained variability" is down to 0.343. (See Figure 10.9b.) That is, the standard deviation of the residuals is 0.343, meaning that that the variance of the residuals is $0.343^2 \approx 0.118$, a reduction of $0.185 - 0.118 = 0.067$. So we've explained about $0.067/0.185$, or 36%, of the original variability in the plate sizes.

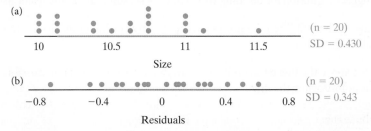

FIGURE 10.9 Variability in (a) plate sizes and in (b) residuals.

> ### KEY IDEA
>
> The coefficient of determination (R^2) is the percentage of total observed variation in the response variable that is accounted for by changes (variability) in the explanatory variable.

EXPLORATION 10.3 | Predicting Height from Footprints

Can a footprint taken at the scene of a crime help to predict the height of the criminal? In other words, is there an association between height and foot length? To investigate this question, a sample of 20 statistics students measured their height (in inches) and their foot length (in centimeters).

1. Let's think about this study.
   a. What are the observational units in this study?
   b. Identify the two variables recorded for each observational unit. Which is the explanatory variable, and which is the response? Also classify these variables as categorical or quantitative.

Explanatory:	Type:
Response:	Type:

   c. Is this an observational study or a randomized experiment?

The sample data for the 20 students appear in the **Corr/Regression** applet.

2. Open the applet and look at the scatterplot for the data already there. Describe the association between the variables as revealed in the scatterplot. (*Hint*: Remember to comment on direction, strength, and form of association as well as unusual observations.)

3. Would you say that a straight line could summarize the relationship between height and foot length reasonably well?

4. Check the **Show Movable Line** box to add a blue line to the scatterplot. If you place your mouse over one of the green squares at the ends of the line and drag, you can change the slope of the line. You can also use the mouse to move the green dot up and down vertically to change the intercept of the line.
   a. Move the line until you believe your line "best" summarizes the relationship between height and foot length for these data. Write down the resulting equation for your line (using traditional statistical notation).
   b. Why do you believe that your line is "best?"
   c. Did all students in your class obtain the same line/equation?
   d. How can we decide whether your line provides a better fit to the data than other students' lines? Suggest a criterion for deciding which line "best" summarizes the relationship.

One way to draw the best fit line is to minimize the distance of the points to the line (these distances are called *residuals*).

5. Would points above the line have a positive or negative residual, or is it impossible to tell? What about points below the line?

Above line:	Below line:

KEY IDEA

A *residual* is the difference between an observed response and the corresponding prediction made by the least squares regression line (*residual* = observed − predicted). Thus, negative residuals occur when points are below the best fit line and positive residuals occur when points are above the best fit line.

6. Check the **Show Residuals** box to visually represent these residuals for your line on the scatterplot. The applet also reports the sum of the values of the residuals (**SAE**). SAE stands for "sum of the absolute errors." The acronym indicates that we need to make residuals positive before we add them up and that sometimes people call residuals "errors."

    Record the SAE value for your line: _____

    What is the best (lowest) SAE in the class? _____

7. It turns out that a more common criterion for determining the "best" line is to instead look at the sum of the *squared* residuals (**SSE**). This approach is similar to simply adding up the residuals but is even more strict in not letting individual residuals get too large. Check the **Show Squared Residuals** box to visually represent the squared residual for each observation. Note that we can visually represent the squared residual as the area of a square where each side of the square has length equal to the residual.

    a. What is the SSE (sum of squared residuals) for your line?

       What is the best (lowest) SSE in the class?

    b. Now continue to adjust your line until you think you have minimized the sum of the squared residuals. Report your new equation and your new SSE value. What is the best SSE in the class?

KEY IDEA

The least squares regression line minimizes the sum of squared residuals.

8. Now check the **Show Regression Line** box to determine and display the equation for the line that actually does minimize (as can be shown using calculus) the sum of the squared residuals.

    a. Record the equation of the least squares regression line by indicating the appropriate slope and intercept of the line. Note that we've used variable names in the equation, not generic *x* and *y*. And put a caret ("hat") over the *y* variable name to emphasize that the line gives predicted values of the *y* (response) variable.

$$\widehat{\text{Height}} = \underline{\hspace{1cm}} + \underline{\hspace{1cm}} \text{(FootLength)}$$

    b. Did everyone in your class obtain the same equation?

NOTATION

The equation of the best fit line is written as $\hat{y} = a + b(x)$, where:

- *a* is the *y-intercept*
- *b* is the *slope*
- *x* is a value of the explanatory variable
- $\hat{y}$ is the predicted value for the response variable

    c. Is the slope positive or negative? Explain how the sign of the slope tells you about whether your data display a positive or a negative association.

> **KEY IDEA**
>
> For a given data set, the signs (positive or negative) for the correlation coefficient and the slope of the regression line must be the same.

9. Let's investigate what the slope means in the context of height and foot length.

   a. Use the least squares regression line to predict the height of someone whose foot length is 28 cm. (Simply plug in the value of 28 cm for foot length in the equation of the line.)

   b. Use the least squares regression line to predict the height of someone whose foot length is 29 cm.

   c. By how much do your predictions in (a) and (b) differ? Does this number look familiar? Explain.

> **KEY IDEA**
>
> The *slope* coefficient of a least squares regression model is interpreted as the predicted change in the response (*y*) variable for a one-unit change in the explanatory (*x*) variable.

   d. Interpret the slope in context:

   The slope of the regression line predicting height based on foot length is _____, meaning that for every additional _____ cm increase in foot length, the predicted height increases by _____ inches.

10. Let's investigate the meaning of the *y*-intercept in the context of height and foot length.

    a. Use the least squares regression line to predict the height of someone who has a foot length of 0 cm.

    b. Your answer to (a) should look familiar. What is this value?

> **KEY IDEA**
>
> The *y-intercept* of a regression line is interpreted as the predicted value of the response variable when the explanatory variable has a value of zero (though be wary of extrapolation (see next Key Idea) in interpreting the intercept or other values outside the original data range).

> **KEY IDEA**
>
> Predicting values for the response variable for values of the explanatory variable that are outside of the range of the original data is known as *extrapolation* and can give very misleading predictions.

    c. Explain how your prediction of the height of someone whose foot length is 0 cm is an example of extrapolation.

11. Earlier, we explored the notion of a residual as the distance of a point to a line.

    a. Using the equation for the best fit line that you reported in #8, find the residual for the person whose foot length is 32 centimeters and height is 74 inches. *Note:* Find this value by taking the actual height and subtracting the person's predicted height from the equation.

    b. Is this person's dot on the scatterplot above or below the line? How does the residual tell you this?

Residuals are helpful for identifying unusual observations. But not all observations of interest have large residuals.

12. Uncheck the **Show Movable Line** box to remove it from the display and check the **Move observations** box.

    a. Now click on one student's point in the scatterplot and drag the point up and down (changing the height, without changing the foot length, the original regression line will remain in grey). Does the regression line change much as you change this student's height?

    b. Repeat the previous question using a student with a very small x (foot size) value and then a point with an x value near the middle and then a point with a very large x value. Which of these seem(s) to have the most *influence* on the least squares regression line? Explain.

KEY IDEA

An observation or set of observations is considered *influential* if removing the observation from the data set substantially changes the values of the correlation coefficient and/or the least squares regression equation. Typically, observations that have extreme explanatory variable values (far below or far above $\bar{x}$) are potentially influential. They may not have large residuals, having pulled the line close to them.

Residuals also help us measure how accurate our predictions are from using the regression line. In particular, we can compare the "prediction errors" from the regression line to the prediction errors if we made no use of the explanatory variable.

13. Press the **Revert** button to reload the original data set. Recheck the **Show Movable Line** box to redisplay the blue line. Notice that this line is flat at the mean of the y (height) values.

    a. Check the **Show Squared Residuals** box (under the **Movable Line** information) to determine the SSE if we were to use the average height ($\bar{y}$) as the predicted value for every x (foot size). Record this value.

    b. What is the slope of this line?

    c. If the slope of the best fit line is zero, our data shows _____ (positive/ negative/no) association between the explanatory and response variables.

14. Now compare this to the SSE value from the regression line. Which is smaller? Why does that make sense?

COEFFICIENT OF DETERMINATION (R^2)

15. A quantity related to the correlation coefficient is called the coefficient of determination, or R-squared (R^2).

    a. To measure how much the regression line decreases the "unexplained variability" in the response variable, we can calculate the percentage reduction in SSE:

    $$R^2 = 100\% \, \frac{\text{SSE}(\bar{y}) - \text{SSE}(\text{regression line})}{\text{SSE}(\bar{y})}. \text{ Find } R^2 \text{ and report it.}$$

> **KEY IDEA**
>
> The *coefficient of determination* (R^2) is the percentage of total observed variation in the response variable (height) that is accounted for by changes (variability) in the explanatory variable (foot length).

  b. Complete the following statement: The coefficient of determination is _____ %; this means that _____ % of the variation in people's _____ is attributable to changes in their _____.

  If we think of $\hat{y} = \bar{y}$ as the "worst" line (no association with x), then we are seeing how much better the actual line is than this worst line. The best possible line would have zeros for all of the residuals and would have an R^2 of 100%.

  c. Find the value of the correlation coefficient using the applet and confirm that when you square the correlation coefficient you get the same number as the applet reports for the coefficient of determination.

For more on the coefficient of determination see Example 10.3.

SECTION 10.3   Summary

When the association between two quantitative variables has a linear form, a line can be used as a mathematical model for summarizing the relationship and for predicting values of the response variable from the explanatory variable.

- The **least squares regression line** selects the intercept and slope coefficients to minimize the sum of the squared vertical deviations between the observations (y values) and the line.
  - These vertical deviations between the observed y values and the line are called **residuals**.
  - A primary use of the least squares regression line is to make predictions for the response variable based on the explanatory variable.
    - Making predictions for values of the explanatory variable not included in the range of our data values is called **extrapolation** and is often unwise.
  - The **slope coefficient** is interpreted as the predicted change in the response variable associated with a one-unit change in the explanatory variable.
  - The **intercept coefficient** is interpreted as the predicted value of the response variable when the explanatory variable equals zero.
    - In many contexts the interpretation of the intercept is not sensible and/or may be extrapolation.
  - The square of the correlation coefficient (R^2) indicates the proportion of variability in the response variable that is explained by the least squares line with the explanatory variable.
    - This is sometimes called the **coefficient of determination**.
- The sign of the slope (positive, negative, or zero) matches the sign of the correlation coefficient (positive, negative, or zero).
- **Influential observations** affect the regression line substantially.
  - Influential observations typically have extreme values of the explanatory variable.
  - Outliers in a regression setting have large residuals.
  - Influential observations are typically not outliers because they pull the line toward themselves.

MORE ON LEAST SQUARES REGRESSION

SECTION 10.3: Part 2

INTRODUCTION

In the previous section you looked at the relationship between two quantitative variables measured on the same observational unit. Recall that if you decide the association between the explanatory and response variables is linear, then it is helpful to develop a mathematical model of that association. The model helps you make predictions about the response variable given a particular value of the explanatory variable. The **least squares regression line** is the most common model used to make these predictions. In this section you will build on what you learned in the previous three sections with emphasis on things you will need to know for the AP exam. In particular, you will learn more about residual plots, interpreting computer output of regression models, and a special property of least squares regression equations.

Halloween Candy Grab

10.3.2

Example 10.3.2

An AP Statistics teacher has a large bowl filled with candies (all the same size). As a Halloween treat, students may reach into the bowl once and take a handful of candies. But because there's no such thing as free candy, the teacher poses the question, "Is there a relationship between a student's hand span and the number of candies that he or she can grab in one handful?" and asks students how they would go about answering this question. One of the teacher's AP Statistics classes collected data to investigate whether a relationship exists between a person's hand span and the number of candies that they can grab in a single handful by doing the following.

The students in the class measured their hand spans by placing their dominant hand on a flat surface and spreading their fingers as far apart as they could comfortably go. They then had another student measure their hand span to the nearest tenth of a centimeter, as shown in Figure 10.3.1. Each student then reached into the bowl of candies and grabbed a handful of candies. For each student in the class, his or her hand span (cm) and the number of candies he or she grabbed in a single handful were recorded.

Courtesy of Todd Swanson

FIGURE 10.3.1 Measuring hand span.

THINK ABOUT IT

What are the two variables here? Which do you consider the explanatory variable and which the response variable? Are they quantitative or categorical?

EXAMPLE

It makes sense to consider a student's hand span as the explanatory variable, helping to explain why some students could grab more candies than other students. It also makes sense to think of the number of candies grabbed as the response variable, because you can try to predict this number from the length of the student's hand span. Both variables are quantitative.

The data in Table 10.3.1 are from a class of 13 AP Statistics students. They represent the hand span (cm) of each student and the number of candies each student could grab.

TABLE 10.3.1 Data for hand spans (cm) and number of candies grabbed for a class of 13 AP Statistics students												
Hand span (cm)	23.3	20	21.2	23.2	22.2	21.5	19.4	20.8	22.3	22.5	21.8	23.3	19.4
Number of candies	27	23	23	29	28	25	23	31	25	27	31	32	17

A scatterplot of the data with the least squares regression line for predicting the number of candies a student can grab from his or her hand span is given in Figure 10.3.2. Recall from the previous section that the least squares regression line is the line that makes the sum of the squared residuals as small as possible.

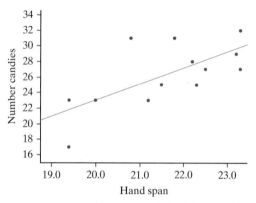

FIGURE 10.3.2   Scatterplot of students' hand spans and number of candies grabbed for 13 AP Statistics students.

CALCULATOR TIPS

You may use your calculator to construct a scatterplot and find the equation of the least squares regression line. For example,

- **TI 84:** Enter the data into two lists, for example, L1 and L2. Define a scatterplot in the statistics plot menu, Stat Plot → Type: Choose scatterplot → Xlist: L1 → Ylist: L2. To find the equation of the least squares regression line, STAT → CALC → LinReg (a + bx).
- **TI-Nspire:** Enter the data into two named lists in a List and Spreadsheets page. Open a Data and Statistics page, click on the horizontal axis and choose your x-variable from the drop-down menu, click on the vertical axis and choose your y-variable from the drop-down menu. To find the equation of the least squares regression line, from a Calculator page, Menu → Statistics → Stat Calculations → Linear Regression (a + bx).

Your calculator output will likely be similar to what is shown in Figure 10.3.3.

LinRegBx *hand_span, number_candies,* 1 Co▶

$$\begin{bmatrix} \text{``Title''} & \text{``Linear Regression (a+bx)''} \\ \text{``RegEqn''} & \text{``a+b x''} \\ \text{``a''} & -18.2933 \\ \text{``b''} & 2.06057 \\ \text{``}r^2\text{''} & 0.466153 \\ \text{``r''} & 0.682754 \\ \text{``Resid''} & \text{``( )''} \end{bmatrix}$$

FIGURE 10.3.3 Calculator output for linear regression.

EVALUATING THE LINEARITY OF THE ASSOCIATION

THINK ABOUT IT

Is a linear model appropriate for the data collected on the 13 AP Statistics students?

> **Definition**
>
> A *residual plot* is a scatterplot with the residuals on the vertical axis and the explanatory variable or the predicted response values on the horizontal axis.

From Figure 10.3.2, the association between the number of candies and hand span appears to be linear, but we could also examine a *residual plot*.

Recall that the residuals measure the difference between the observed and predicted values of the response variable. The residual plot may make it easier to examine departures from linearity or other ways in which the data aren't following the linear pattern. (Some nonlinear patterns that are difficult to see in the scatterplot may be more evident in the residual plot.) Figure 10.3.4 shows the two different horizontal axes (explanatory variable and predicted values) that can be used for a residual plot. Note that because number of candies had a positive association, the graphs are equivalent. If the association between the two variables is negative, the graph using the fitted values will be "flipped" compared to the graph using the explanatory variable.

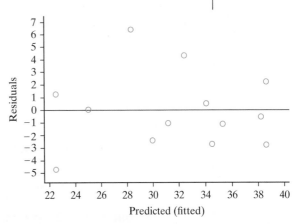

FIGURE 10.3.4 Plot of residuals vs. explanatory variable (hand span) on the left and plot of residuals vs. predicted (fitted) values on the right.

If a linear model is appropriate, what is "left over" after fitting the model (residuals) should be random, with no discernible pattern (e.g., a curved pattern in the dots that might suggest a different model for the data). From Figure 10.3.4 we can see that there is no apparent pattern in the residual plot; thus, a linear model is appropriate.

The scatterplot and corresponding residual plot in Figure 10.3.5 of median head circumference measured in centimeters vs. age of baby girls 3 to 36 months reveal a nonlinear pattern. Rather than showing no distinct pattern, the residual plot reveals a curved pattern, indicating that the original association would be better summarized by a curved model. In the next section you will learn about methods to transform one or both of the variables to make the association linear. If we obtain a linear association after transforming the data, we can then use all the tools for linear regression.

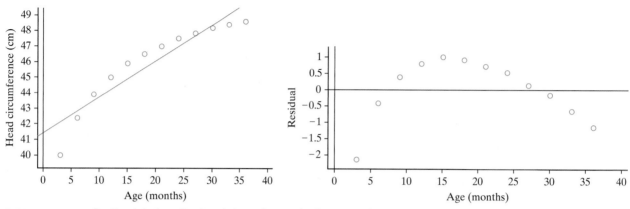

FIGURE 10.3.5   Scatterplot of median head circumference (cm) vs. age of baby girls 3 to 36 months with corresponding residual plot.

 10.3P2.1

> **AP TIP**
>
> When asked on the AP exam whether a linear model is appropriate, you should sketch a graph of the residuals (vs. the explanatory or predicted values) and comment on whether it reveals a pattern.

INTERPRETING COMPUTER OUTPUT

Instead of being given the actual data on each individual in your sample, you may be provided with the computer output from regression. Figure 10.3.6 shows an example of what the output could look like, with some of the key values for regression from the computer output labeled.

FIGURE 10.3.6   Computer output for linear regression annotated with some of the key values for regression.

> **THINK ABOUT IT**
>
> Use the computer output from Figure 10.3.6 to determine the equation of the least squares regression line for predicting the number of candies a student can grab based on his or her hand span. Identify all variables used in the equation.

From the computer output given in Figure 10.3.6, the equation of the least squares regression line (LSRL) for predicting number of candies from hand span is

$$\widehat{\text{Number of candies}} = -18.29 + 2.06(\text{hand span})$$

10.3P2.2

Note: Be sure to identify your predictor and response variable (in context, as shown above by writing the formula using the explanatory and response variable from the problem in place of x and $\hat{y}$) when writing the equation of the least squares regression line. Don't forget that you are predicting y from x, so your response variable must be written with a hat (^), or as *a predicted response variable*.

> **THINK ABOUT IT**
>
> Identify the slope of the least squares regression line and interpret the slope in context.

Recall that the slope is the predicted change of the response variable for a one-unit change in the explanatory variable:

$$\text{slope} = \frac{2.06}{1} = \frac{\text{change in predicted number of candies grabbed}}{\text{change in hand span (cm)}}$$

Thus, for each 1 centimeter increase in a student's hand span, the predicted number of candies that he or she can grab increases by an average of 2.06 candies. We could also say that our estimate of the number of candies grabbed increases, on average, by 2.06 with each 1 cm increase in hand span.

10.3P2.3

> **AP TIP**
>
> When interpreting the slope of the regression line, be sure to talk about the predicted change in the response variable (name response variable) for a one-unit (give units) increase in the explanatory variable (name explanatory variable).

In using a regression equation to make a prediction for the response variable, we are also often interested in a measure of how accurate that prediction is. In other words, how far do we think an observation typically falls from the regression line? This is summarized by the standard deviation of the residuals of the regression equation or the **regression standard error**, denoted by S in Figure 10.3.6.

> **THINK ABOUT IT**
>
> Note that $S = 3.19$ in Figure 10.3.6. How would you interpret this value in the context of this study?

Definition

- - - - - - - - - - - - -
The **regression standard error** (also known as the standard deviation of the residuals) measures how far the sample observations tend to fall from the regression line. It can be interpreted as a typical or average prediction error.
- - - - - - - - - - - - -

The value $S = 3.19$ candies estimates the standard deviation of the residuals and measures the variability in the residuals around the regression line (or typical distances of the observations from the regression line). In other words, for a given hand span, it is a measure of the variation in the number of candies students with that hand span can grab. Similarly, we can interpret it as the typical prediction error when using the least squares regression line to predict the number of candies a student can grab from his or her hand span. That is, a student with a hand span of 20 cm is predicted to grab 22.9 candies, but we realize that prediction could be off by up to about 2×3.19 or 6.38 candies, on average. So, we would be fairly surprised to find a student with a hand span of 20 cm grabbing fewer than 16 candies or more than 29 candies.

10.3P2.4

SPECIAL PROPERTY OF THE LEAST SQUARES REGRESSION LINE

Keep the following notation in mind:

$\bar{x}$ is the mean of the x (explanatory) values.

$\bar{y}$ is the mean of the y (response) values.

s_x is the sample standard deviation of the x values.

s_y is the sample standard deviation of the y values.

r is the correlation coefficient between the x and y values.

From our data for predicting the number of candies (y) from a student's hand span (x), the following values were calculated:

$\bar{x} = 21.61$ cm $s_x = 1.39$ cm

$\bar{y} = 26.23$ candies $s_y = 4.19$ candies

$r = 0.683$

We can see from the scatterplot of *number of candies* vs. *hand span* (Figure 10.3.7) that the least squares regression line passes through the mean of the hand spans and the mean of the number of candies $(\bar{x}, \bar{y})$.

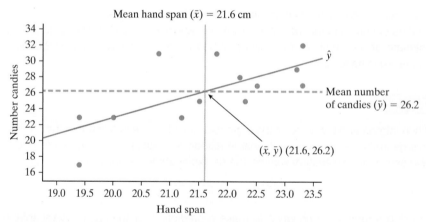

FIGURE 10.3.7   Scatterplot showing least squares regression line, $\bar{x}$ line, and $\bar{y}$ line.

10.3P2.5

> **KEY IDEA**
>
> In fact, *every* least squares regression line passes through the mean of the x values and the mean of the y values, that is, the point $(\bar{x}, \bar{y})$.

It turns out that if you know $\bar{x}$, $\bar{y}$, s_x, s_y, and r, you can actually calculate the slope and intercept of the line using only those summary statistics.

> **KEY IDEA**
>
> The least squares regression coefficients can also be computed from the following formulas:
>
> Intercept of line $= a = \bar{y} - b\bar{x}$
>
> Slope of line $= b = r\,(s_y/s_x)$

Let's see how these alternative shortcut formulas would work for the example on hand span and number of candies.

$$b = r \, (s_y/s_x)$$
$$= 0.683 \, (4.19/1.39)$$
$$= 2.06$$

$$a = \bar{y} - b\bar{x}$$
$$= 26.23 - 2.06 \, (21.61)$$
$$= -18.29$$

$$\hat{y} = -18.29 + 2.06 \, x \qquad \text{where } x = \text{hand span in centimeters and}$$
$$\hat{y} = \text{predicted number of candies}$$

10.3P2.6

But notice what happens when you use $\bar{x} + s_x$ as the value you want to predict at

$$\hat{y} = a + b(\bar{x} + s_x) = \bar{y} - b\bar{x} + b(\bar{x} + s_x) = \bar{y} + bs_x = \bar{y} + r \, (s_y/s_x) \, s_x = \bar{y} + rs_y$$

With a bit more work, one can also show that every least squares regression line will satisfy $b_1 = r \, (s_y/s_x)$. In other words, for an increase in one standard deviation in the explanatory variable (s_x), the least squares regression line predicts an increase of r standard deviations in the response variable (s_y).

In Figure 10.3.8, a vertical line one standard deviation above the mean of the hand spans ($\bar{x} + s_x$), and a horizontal line one standard deviation above the mean number of candies ($\bar{y} + s_y$), have been added to the above graph. You can see that this point is what would be predicted by the least squares regression line (an increase in one standard deviation in the *hand span* corresponds to a predicted increase of r standard deviations in *number of candies*), $29 \approx -18.29 + 2.06(21.61 + 1.39) = 26.23 + 0.683(4.19)$.

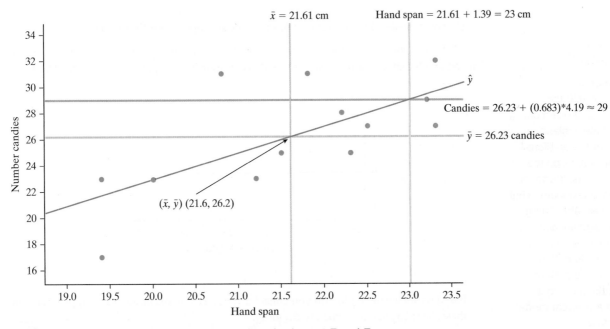

FIGURE 10.3.8 Scatterplot showing the predicted values at $\bar{x}$ and $\bar{x} + s_x$.

Human Body Proportions

EXPLORATION
10.3.2

In the movie *Pretty Woman*, starring Julia Roberts and Richard Gere, Roberts' character Vivian states, "Did you know that the distance from your wrist to your elbow is the same as the length of your foot?" A statistics class decided to test the validity of this statement. They measured the right forearm from the middle of the elbow to the bone that protrudes on the wrist and the length of the right foot (without shoes) to the nearest tenth of a centimeter for each of the 10 females in the class.

1. What are the observational units in this study?
2. What two variables are measured on each observational unit and what type of variables are they, categorical or quantitative?

3. Would you consider one variable an explanatory variable and the other a response variable? Explain.

A scatterplot of the data along with the least squares regression line and computer output from fitting the least squares regression line to the data are shown below.

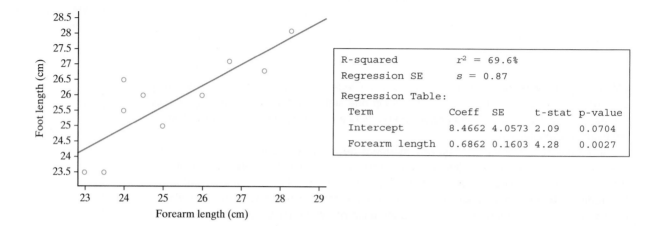

R-squared	r^2 = 69.6%			
Regression SE	s = 0.87			
Regression Table:				
Term	Coeff	SE	t-stat	p-value
Intercept	8.4662	4.0573	2.09	0.0704
Forearm length	0.6862	0.1603	4.28	0.0027

4. Do you consider the least squares model to be appropriate for these data?

Whereas the scatterplot helps you judge the fit of the equation to the data, a more detailed graph that may more clearly show departures from that pattern is a *residual plot*.

Definition

A *residual plot* is a scatterplot with the residuals on the vertical axis and the explanatory variable or the predicted response values on the horizontal axis. If a linear model is appropriate, what is "left over" after fitting the model (residuals) should be random, with no discernible pattern (e.g., a curved pattern in the dots that might suggest a different model for the data).

5. Based on the residual plot, do you consider the least squares model to be appropriate for these data? Explain how you are deciding.

AP TIP

When asked on the AP exam whether a linear model is appropriate, you should sketch a graph of the residuals (vs. the explanatory or predicted values) and comment on whether it reveals a pattern.

Computer output for a regression analysis will typically show the estimated values of the slope and intercept (the "coefficients" of the equation), as well as the coefficient of determination, R^2. Most output will also report the "regression standard error" or S for the regression model.

6. Use the computer output above to determine the equation of the least squares regression line. Identify all variables used in the equation.

Note: Be sure to identify your predictor and response variable (in context, by writing the formula using the explanatory and response variable from the problem in place of x and $\hat{y}$) when writing the equation of the least squares regression line. Don't forget that you are predicting *y* from *x*, so your response variable must be written with a hat (^) or as a *predicted response variable*.

> **Definition**
>
> The **regression standard error** (also known as the **standard deviation of the residuals**) measures how far the sample observations tend to fall from the regression line. It can be interpreted as a typical or average prediction error.

> **KEY IDEA**
>
> The least squares regression coefficients can also be computed from the following formulas:
>
> Intercept of line = $a = \bar{y} - b\bar{x}$
>
> Slope of line = $b = r(s_y/s_x)$

Here are the relevant summary statistics for the data on the 10 students:

$$\bar{x} = 25.26, \ s_x = 1.806, \ \bar{y} = 25.8, \ s_y = 1.485, \ r = 0.834$$

7. Use the summary statistics to determine the slope of the least squares regression line. [*Hint:* This should be similar to the one reported in the above "Regression Table" output.]

8. Interpret the slope of the least squares regression line in context.

> **AP TIP**
>
> When interpreting the slope of the regression line, be sure to talk about the predicted change in the response variable (name response variable) for a one-unit (give units) increase in the explanatory variable (name explanatory variable).

9. Use the summary statistics to determine the *y*-intercept of the least squares regression line. [*Hint:* This should be similar to the one reported in the above "Regression Table" output.]

10. Does the y-intercept you calculated in the previous question have a meaningful interpretation in the context of these data? If so, provide the interpretation in context. If not, explain why not.

11. Use your model to predict the foot length of a student whose forearm length measures 26.7 cm.

12. One of the students in the class has a foot length of 27.1 cm and forearm length of 26.7 cm. Calculate the residual for this student and determine whether the least squares regression line is over or under her predicted foot length.

13. What proportion of the variation in a student's foot length is explained by the linear relationship with forearm length?

14. What number in the computer output provided represents the regression standard error (standard deviation of the residuals)? Interpret this number in the context of the study.

A scatterplot of the data with the line $y = x$ (i.e., foot length = forearm length) is shown below.

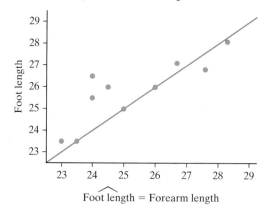

Foot length = Forearm length

15. What information does the scatterplot with the line $y = x$ provide that the scatterplot with the least squares regression line did not? What does this tell you in context?

SECTION 10.3: Part 2   Summary

In Section 10.3 you learned that when the association between two quantitative variables has a linear form, a line can be used as a mathematical model for summarizing the relationship and for predicting values of the response variable from the explanatory variable. In this section you built on that knowledge by examining residual plots and the information they can provide about the fit of a linear model.

- When fitting a linear model to data, a residual plot may make it easier to examine departures from linearity.
  - A **residual plot** is a scatterplot with the residuals on the vertical axis and the explanatory variable or the predicted response values on the horizontal axis.

You also learned how to read and interpret computer output of regression models and to use the output to write the equation of the least squares regression line, in addition to learning a formula for writing the equation of the least squares regression line given summary statistics.

- The least squares regression coefficients can also be computed from the following formulas:
  - Intercept of line = $a = \bar{y} - b\bar{x}$
  - Slope of line = $b = r\,(s_y/s_x)$

You were introduced to a new measure, the regression standard error or standard deviation of the residuals, for assessing how well the linear model fits the data.

- The **regression standard error** (also known as the standard deviation of the residuals) measures how far the sample observations tend to fall from the regression line. It can be interpreted as a typical or average prediction error.

SECTION 10.3: Part 3

TRANSFORMATIONS TO ACHIEVE LINEARITY

INTRODUCTION

In the previous sections you examined linear relationships between two quantitative variables measured on the same observational units. The least squares regression line was used to model the linear relationship and to predict values of the response variable for values of the explanatory variable. What if the relationship between the quantitative variables isn't linear? What do you do when your data look as if they follow some nonlinear type of model? When a straight line is not the best mathematical model for a relationship, you can often transform one or both variables to make the association linear. After transforming the data, we can use all the tools for linear regression.

> **Definition**
>
> A *transformation* is a mathematical function applied to a variable, re-expressing the variable on a different scale.

Linear transformations such as adding/subtracting a constant or multiplying/dividing by a constant, say, changing temperature measurements from Fahrenheit to Celsius, preserve a linear relationship and do not change the correlation between variables or the form of the association. Nonlinear transformations such as logarithmic, square root, and other power transformations change the correlation and the form of association between variables. In regression, a "transformation to achieve linearity" is a nonlinear transformation that results in a linear relationship between the explanatory and response variables. These transformations could transform the explanatory variable (x) only, transform the response (y) only, or transform both variables. There are many ways to transform variables to achieve linearity for a regression analysis. In this section, we will focus on the use of logarithmic transformations. A brief review of the properties of logarithms and how they are used to transform data is given in Table 10.3.2. More details on carrying out some of these transformations appear at the end of this section.

TABLE 10.3.2 A review of properties of logarithms

Review of Properties of Logarithms: For $M > 0$, $N > 0$, $b > 0$, and $b \neq 1$:

1. $\log_b MN = \log_b M + \log_b N$

2. $\log_b \left(\dfrac{M}{N} \right) = \log_b M - \log_b N$

3. $\log_b M^k = k \log_b M$, where k is any real number

Sometimes the nonlinear relationship between two variables is known from prior research (e.g., in chemistry, Boyle's Law says that the relationship between pressure and volume of a gas is a nonlinear relationship of a particular form). However, in other cases, trial and error is needed to select the transformation that establishes a linear relationship. After transforming one or both variables, we should produce a scatterplot of the transformed data to see whether the transformation achieved a linear association between the variables. We should confirm the linear relationship by also examining a residual plot of the transformed data as we learned in the previous section. Figure 10.3.9 suggests some log transformations we might try for curved data. (*Note:* Using the natural log or some other base has the same effect on the form of the association.)

When our original data in (x, y) are linear, our interpretation of the slope of the regression line is that an increase of one unit in the explanatory variable is associated with a change of b units in the predicted value of the response variable. When we use a log transformation to make the association linear, the interpretation is no longer as straightforward. For example, if we obtain a linear relationship by regressing $\ln y$ on x, our linear relationship is in $(x, \ln y)$, not (x, y). Thus, the interpretation of the slope of the regression line for the transformed model in this case is that for every one-unit increase in the explanatory variable, the predicted change of the natural log of the response variable is b. Also, if you use the regression model to make a prediction, you may need to transform the predictor variable first, or back-transform the response variable so your prediction is in the original scale.

Note that using logarithm with base e (the natural log, $\ln$) is also a common choice. Additional details on logarithms are provided at the end of this section.

Graph of Original Data (x, y)	Transformation to Achieve Linearity	Transformed Equation
	If your original data follow a *logarithmic* model in (x, y), e.g., $x = ab^y$, try plotting **(log x, y)** to achieve a linear association.	$\hat{y} = a + b \times \log x$
	If your original data follow an *exponential* model in (x, y), e.g., $y = ab^x$, try plotting **(x, log y)** to achieve a linear association.	$\log \hat{y} = a + bx$
	If your original data follow a *power model* in (x, y), e.g., $y = ax^b$, try plotting **(log x, log y)** to achieve a linear association.	$\log \hat{y} = a + b \times \log x$

FIGURE 10.3.9 Transformations to achieve linearity. (Note that the values of *a* and *b* in the right column are not necessarily the same as the values of *a* and *b* in the middle column.)

Animal Trotting Speeds

Example 10.3.3A

Heglund and Taylor (1988) describe a study in which they trained animals to use a treadmill to determine how speed, stride, and gait compare across different kinds of animals. One part of their study recorded the speeds at which animals trot, looking for a relationship with the size of an animal as measured by its body mass. The data, with body mass measured in kilograms and speed measured in meters per second, are given in Table 10.3.3. The scatterplot in Figure 10.3.10 displays *trot speed* vs. *body mass*.

Looking at the scatterplot, we can see that a linear model is clearly not an appropriate fit for the data. The corresponding residual plot after fitting a linear model shows a distinctly curved pattern. From the table we also see that the values of the explanatory variable, *body mass*, range almost three orders of magnitude (factor of $10^3 = 1,000$) while the response variable has a much smaller range. Replacing the explanatory variable *body mass* with the *logarithm (base 10 or base e) body mass* should help achieve a more linear association.

TABLE 10.3.3	Animal trotting speeds				
Animal	Body Mass	Trot Speed	Animal	Body Mass	Trot Speed
White mouse	0.029	0.19	Fat-tailed sheep	23	1.41
Ground squirrel	0.193	0.67	Dog #4	25	1.25
White rat	0.362	0.11	Wildebeest	98	1.89
Dog #1	0.96	0.84	Pony	110	1.64
Antelope #1	3.5	1.15	Waterbuck	114	1.92
Dog #2	3.89	1.39	Pony	140	1.69
Antelope #2	4.35	0.99	Zebu cattle	160	2.08
Dog #3	9.21	1.15	Pony	170	1.81
Gazelle	11.2	1.53	Donkey	170	1.8
African goat	20	1.53	Antelope #3	213	1.75

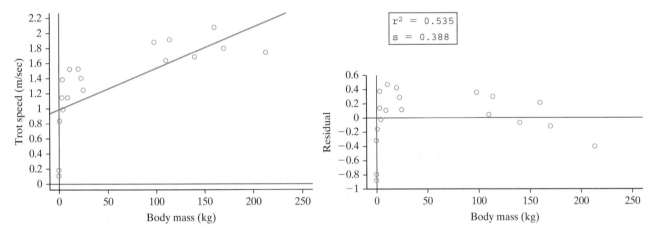

FIGURE 10.3.10   Trot speed (meters per second) vs. body mass (kg) for 20 animals.

A scatterplot and residual plot of the transformed data (ln(*body mass*), *trot speed*), along with computer output from fitting a least squares regression line to the transformed data, are shown in Figure 10.3.11

The transformation achieved a linear association and the residual plot shows no apparent pattern, so a linear model in (*ln body mass, trot speed*) is appropriate.

THINK ABOUT IT

How would you use the computer output above to determine the equation of the least squares regression line for predicting the trot speed of an animal from the natural log of its body mass? Also, what is the slope of the least squares regression line, and how would you interpret the slope in context?

From the computer output, the equation of the least squares regression line for predicting trot speed from the natural log of body mass is

$$\text{predicted } Trot\ Speed = 0.8209 + 0.2014\ \ln(body\ mass)$$

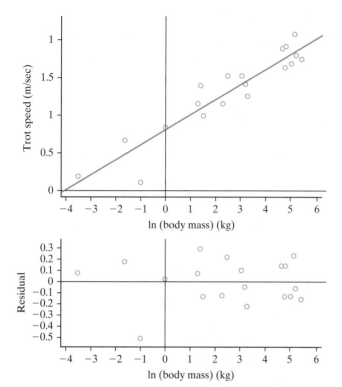

R-squared	r^2 = 88.2%
Regression SE	s = 0.20
Regression Table:	

Term	Coeff	SE	t-stat	p-value
Intercept	0.8209	0.0626	13.11	0.0000
ln body mass	0.2014	0.0174	11.58	0.0000

FIGURE 10.3.11 Scatterplot of transformed data, corresponding residual plot, and regression output for trot speed data.

Thus, we can interpret the slope in this equation (0.2014) as follows: For each one-unit (ln kg) increase in the natural log of an animal's body mass, the predicted increase in average trot speed is 0.2014 m/sec.

THINK ABOUT IT

What's the value of the coefficient of determination and what is its meaning in this context?

From the computer output we read the coefficient of determination to be r^2 = 88.2%. Thus, about 88.2% of the variability in animals' trot speeds can be explained by the linear relationship with natural log of body mass.

THINK ABOUT IT

How would you use the least squares equation to predict the trot speed of an animal with body mass of 10 kg? (Remember to consider which base was used on the log transformation.)

Substituting ln(10) for the explanatory variable value yields

$$\widehat{Trot\ Speed} = 0.8209 + 0.2014\ \ln(10)$$

$$\widehat{Trot\ Speed} = 1.285\ \text{m/sec}$$

Thus, the predicted trot speed for an animal with a body mass of 10 kg is 1.285 m/sec.

Predicting Head Circumference

Data from the National Center for Health Statistics (2000) for the median head circumference, measured in centimeters, for baby girls ages 3 to 36 months are given in Table 10.3.4.

TABLE 10.3.4 Age (in months) and head circumference for baby girls												
age (months)	3	6	9	12	15	18	21	24	27	30	33	36
head circumference (cm)	40	42.4	43.9	45	45.9	46.5	47	47.5	47.8	48.2	48.4	48.6

1. Create a scatterplot of head circumference vs. age and a residual plot. Does a linear model appear to be appropriate? How are you deciding?

2. Based on what you see in the graphs drawn for #1, what transformation would you suggest trying, to achieve a linear association? (*Hint:* See Figure 10.3.9.)

3. Perform the transformation and assess the appropriateness of a linear model. (*Hint:* Remember to consider both the scatterplot and the residual plot.) If you do not feel a linear model is appropriate, try a different transformation.

4. Once you have identified a suitable transformation, run the linear regression on the transformed data and write the equation of the least squares regression line in terms of the transformed variable(s). Don't forget to identify all variables used in the equation.

5. Identify the slope of the least squares regression line and give its meaning in this context. Keep in mind that the value of the slope that you are interpreting is for transformed data.

6. State the value of the coefficient of determination and give its interpretation in this context.

7. Use your regression equation to predict the head circumference of a 10-year-old girl.

8. A confidence interval for a prediction can be approximated by taking the prediction value ($\hat{y}$) plus/minus $2S$ (where S is the standard deviation of the residuals). Determine and interpret such an interval.

Brain and Body Weights

Example 10.3.3B

Can a land animal's body weight be used to predict its brain weight? Table 10.3.5 gives the body weight and brain weight for 27 species of land animals.

TABLE 10.3.5 Average brain and body weight for 27 species of land animals					
Animal	Body Weight (kg)	Brain Weight (g)	Animal	Body Weight (kg)	Brain Weight (g)
Mountain beaver	1.35	465	African elephant	6,654	5,712
Cow	465	423	Triceratops	9,400	70
Grey wolf	36.33	119.5	Rhesus monkey	6.8	179
Goat	27.66	115	Kangaroo	35	56
Guinea pig	1.04	5.5	Golden hamster	0.12	1
Dipliodocus	11,700	50	Mouse	0.023	0.4
Asian elephant	2,547	4,603	Rabbit	2.5	12.1
Donkey	187.1	419	Sheep	55.5	175
Horse	521	655	Jaguar	100	157
Potar monkey	10	115	Chimpanzee	52.16	440
Cat	3.3	25.6	Brachiosaurus	87,000	154.5
Giraffe	529	680	Mole	0.122	3
Gorilla	207	406	Pig	192	180
Human	62	1,320			

EXAMPLE

The following scatterplot displays *brain weight* vs. *body weight* for the 27 species of land animals.

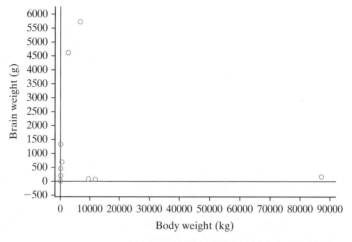

From the scatterplot, we can see that a linear model is not an appropriate fit for the data. We also note it is very difficult to judge the shape of the association with so many observations clumped in the lower left corner. From Table 10.3.5, we see that the values of the explanatory variable, *body weight*, and the response variable, *brain weight*, both range over more than four orders of magnitude. Replacing the explanatory variable *body weight* with the *logarithm (base 10 or base e) body weight* **and** the response variable *brain weight* with the *logarithm (base 10 or base e) brain weight* should help us better view the data.

A scatterplot and residual plot of the transformed data *(ln body weight, ln brain weight)* along with computer output from fitting a least squares regression line to the transformed data are shown in Figure 10.3.12.

10.3P3.1 ▶

10.3P3.2 ▶

| R-squared | r^2 = 49.8% | | | |
| Regression SE | s = 1.65 | | | |

Regression Table:

Term	Coeff	SE	t-stat	p-value
Intercept	2.9906	0.4705	6.36	0.0000
In body weight	0.4358	0.0875	4.98	0.0000

FIGURE 10.3.12 Natural log of body weight, natural log of brain weight, and model residuals.

THINK ABOUT IT

Use the computer output Figure 10.3.12 to determine the equation of the least squares regression line for predicting the natural log of brain weight from the natural log of body weight. Identify all variables used in the equation. Identify the slope of the least squares regression line, and interpret the slope in context. State the value of the coefficient of determination and give its meaning in this context.

From the computer output, the equation of the least squares regression line for predicting the natural log of brain weight from the natural log of body weight is

$$\widehat{\ln(\textit{brain weight})} = 2.9906 + 0.4358 \ln(\textit{body weight})$$

From the slope, we can see that as ln(body weight) increases by 1, the predicted (average) increase in natural log of brain weight is 0.4358 g.

From the computer output, $r^2 = 49.8\%$, so about 49.8% of the variability in the natural log of brain weight can be explained by its linear relationship with the natural log of body weight.

THINK ABOUT IT

Use your model to predict the brain weight of a land animal with a body weight of 100 kg.

In this case, we need to consider that both the explanatory variable and the response variable have been transformed (using the natural log):

$$\widehat{\ln(\textit{brain weight})} = 2.9906 + 0.4358 \ln(100)$$

$$\widehat{\ln(\textit{brain weight})} = 4.99753$$

$$\widehat{\textit{brain weight}} = e^{4.99753}$$

$$\widehat{\textit{brain weight}} = 148.05 \text{ g}$$

The predicted brain weight of a land animal with a body weight of 100 kg is about 148.05 g.

10.3P3.3

THINK ABOUT IT

Are you comfortable with the above model? What might you suggest next in analyzing these data?

After the transformation, the residual plot still shows some pattern (mostly negative residuals, then positive, then negative). This seems to arise from a few influential observations with the largest body weights. Looking back at the data set, we see these belong to the dinosaurs! We could consider re-analyzing these data without the dinosaurs (or any reptiles) to see if the linear association is more appropriate, again considering the possible need to transform one or both variables first. How do the results compare?

African Raptors

EXPLORATION
10.3.3B

A sample of data to predict body mass (in grams) from wing area (in square centimeters) of diurnal and nocturnal African raptors, such as falcons, owls, and hawks, was obtained (Mendelsohn, Kemp, Biggs, & Brown, 1989). The scatterplot in Figure 10.3.13 displays wing area (in square centimeters) and body mass (in grams) for 23 African raptors.

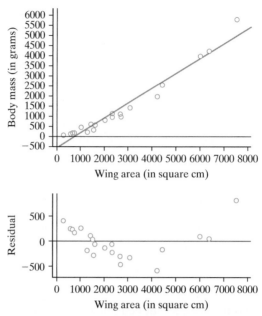

FIGURE 10.3.13   Plot of body mass vs. wing area and associated residual plot.

From the scatterplot, we can see that a linear model is not the most appropriate for the data. A transformation to straighten the data was achieved by plotting log body mass vs. log (wing area). A scatterplot and residual plot of the transformed data ($\log_{10}$ (wing area), $\log_{10}$ (body weight)) along with computer output from fitting a least squares regression line to the transformed data are provided in Figure 10.3.14.

FIGURE 10.3.14   Graphs of transformed wing area and body mass.

1. Use the computer output above to determine the equation of the least squares regression line for predicting the log of body mass from the log of wing area. Identify all variables used in the equation.

2. Identify the slope of the least squares regression line and give its meaning in this context.

3. Explain what the value $s = 0.11$ from the regression table means in this context.

4. Use your regression equation to predict the body mass of an African raptor with a wing area of 5,000 cm^2.

SECTION 10.3: Part 3 Summary

In this section you looked at using transformations when the relationship between two quantitative variables follows a curved pattern. Specifically, you looked at using logarithms to transform data to achieve a linear association. Deciding on which transformation to use is often a combination of what theory might suggest—for example, we might expect the relationship between height and weight to follow a power model because height is one-dimensional and weight is three-dimensional—and trial and error. We try a transformation and then examine the residual plot to see whether the transformation corrected the problem. A review of some key ideas when transforming data with logarithms is provided below.

Transforming data with logarithms

- A logarithmic model has the form $x = ab^y$, where a is a constant.

  If your original data are **logarithmic** in (x, y):
  - Take the logarithm of both sides of this equation.
    $$\log(x) = \log(a^y)$$
  - Using the properties of logarithms, we obtain
    $$\log(x) = y \log(a)$$
    Note: $\log(a)$ is a constant because a is a constant, giving us a linear equation in terms of $(\log(x), y)$.

  If the relationship between (x, y) is logarithmic, plotting $(\log(x), y)$ should produce a linear pattern.

- An exponential model has the form $y = ab^x$, where a and b are constants.

  If your original data follow an **exponential** model in (x, y):
  - Take the logarithm of both sides of this equation.
    $$\log(y) = \log(ab^x)$$
  - Using the properties of logarithms, we obtain
    $$\log(y) = \log(a) + \log(b^x)$$
    $$\log(y) = \log(a) + x \log(b)$$
    Note: $\log(a)$ and $\log(b)$ are constants because a and b are constants, giving us a linear equation in terms of $(x, \log(y))$.

  If the relationship between (x, y) is exponential, plotting $(x, \log(y))$ should produce a linear pattern.

- A power model has the form $y = ax^b$, where a and b are constants.

  If your original data follow a **power** model in (x, y):
  - Take the logarithm of both sides of this equation.
    $$\log(y) = \log(ax^b)$$
  - Using the properties of logarithms, we obtain
    $$\log(y) = \log(a) + \log(x^b)$$
    $$\log(y) = \log(a) + b \log(x)$$
    Note: $\log(a)$ is a constant because a is a constant, giving us a linear equation in terms of $(\log(x), \log(y))$.

  If the relationship between (x, y) is described by a power model, plotting $(\log(x), \log(y))$ should produce a linear pattern.

INFERENCE FOR THE REGRESSION SLOPE: SIMULATION-BASED APPROACH

In the previous section, we looked at how least squares linear regression can be used to describe a linear relationship between two quantitative variables. In that section, we mentioned that the sign on the slope of the regression equation and the sign on the correlation coefficient are always the same. For example, when there is a positive association in the data, both the correlation coefficient and the slope of the regression equation are positive. In Section 10.2, we saw how to use the sample correlation coefficient in a simulated-based test about a null hypothesis of no association. In this section, we will see how we can do the same type of inference but now with the population slope as the parameter of interest.

Example 10.4

EXAMPLE

Do Students Who Spend More Time in Non-Academic Activities Tend to Have Lower GPAs?

College students have lots of opportunities to be involved in different activities. Some also hold jobs or participate in athletics. Both of these can be very time consuming. Time just socializing with friends also takes up lots of time for some. Does time spent on these types of activities have a negative association with students' GPAs? Many researchers have conducted studies to answer this question. We will look at results from a study carried out by a couple of undergraduate students at the University of Minnesota (Ock, 2008). They surveyed 42 students (34 from a research methods class and 8 from a business management class). They asked questions about time spent per week on various nonacademic activities like work, watching TV, exercising, and socializing. They calculated the total time spent on all nonacademic activities and compared that with the students' GPAs. Those data, gleaned from a scatterplot in their paper, are presented in Figure 10.10, along with the least squares regression line.

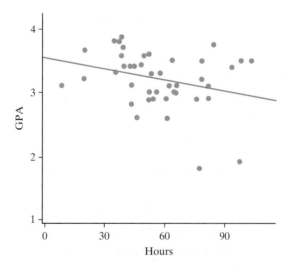

FIGURE 10.10 A scatterplot of students' GPAs and the total number of hours spent on nonacademic activities for 42 students.

THINK ABOUT IT

Describe the nature of the association between GPA and hours spent on nonacademic activities revealed by this scatterplot.

The correlation coefficient for the data in Figure 10.10 is $r = -0.290$ and the regression equation is

$$\widehat{GPA} = 3.60 - 0.0059(\text{nonacademic hours}).$$

As you can see, for the sample of 42 students both the correlation coefficient and the slope of the regression equation are negative.

THINK ABOUT IT

Interpret the slope and intercept of this regression line in the context of nonacademic hours and GPA.

The slope of -0.0059 indicates that the predicted GPA decreases by 0.0059 grade points for each additional hour spent on nonacademic activities per week. The intercept reveals that the predicted GPA for a student who spends absolutely no time on nonacademic activities is 3.60.

What can we infer about the larger population represented by this sample? Are we convinced that the slope in the population is negative, as we suspected in advance? Or is it plausible that the GPA values we observed are just arbitrarily paired up with the hours spent on nonacademic activities and that the association we observed in this sample arose just by chance? Our hypotheses are as follows.

Null hypothesis: There is no association between the number of hours students spend on nonacademic activities and student GPA in the population.

Alternative hypothesis: There is a negative association between the number of hours students spend on nonacademic activities and student GPA in the population.

In Section 10.2 we tested the statistical significance of an association between two quantitative variables using the correlation coefficient as our statistic. In this example we will use the slope of the sample regression equation as our statistic. We previously said that a regression line can be represented by the equation $\hat{y} = a + b(x)$ where a is the y-intercept and b is the slope. This is the form of the equation that represents a sample. For this reason, both the y-intercept (a) and slope (b) are statistics.

 10.4.1

We will now use the sample slope as the statistic in the test of no association. To do this we will use the **Corr/Regression** applet we used for correlation coefficients. We do this exactly the same way as was done with correlation except we select the slope radio button so that the slope is used as our statistic instead of the correlation coefficient.

In particular, we shuffle the values of the response variable in the data table, which is equivalent to "dealing" the response variable values out randomly to the values of the explanatory variable in the data table. We did 1,000 shuffles and the results are shown in Figure 10.11. (See FAQ 10.4.1 for more on the unique behavior of the 1,000 shuffled lines.) We look for the lower-tail p-value to coincide with our one-sided alternative hypothesis.

 10.4.2

FAQ 10.4.1 **www.wiley.com/college/tintle**

What is the point of averages?

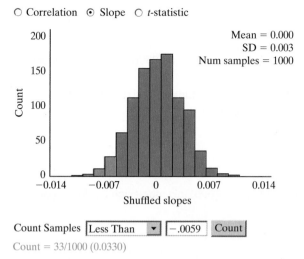

FIGURE 10.11   Assuming there was no genuine association between number of hours of nonacademic activities and GPA, we did 1,000 shuffles of the response variable and calculated the slope of the resulting regression equation each time.

Here is a summary of our simulation model:

Null hypothesis	=	No association between x and y variables
One repetition	=	Re-randomizing the response outcomes to the explanatory variable outcomes
Statistic	=	Slope coefficient

From our 1,000 shuffles we found 33 simulated slopes that were as small as or smaller than our observed sample slope of −0.0059. Thus our simulated p-value is 0.033, and we can conclude there is strong evidence of a negative association between the number of hours students spend on nonacademic activities and their GPA for this population. If we had used the correlation coefficient for our statistic instead of the slope, our results would have been exactly the same (unlike what we saw in Chapters 8 and 9 when we used the MAD statistic as an alternative to a chi-squared or ANOVA F-statistic). We will revisit this idea in the next section.

10.4.3

10.4.4

> **KEY IDEA**
>
> For a given data set, a test of association based on a slope is equivalent to a test of association based on a correlation coefficient.

We must ask, "To what population we can make this inference?" The researchers used a convenience sample of mostly research methods students. They also added a few business management students in order for the sample to more closely match the racial demographics of the undergraduates at the University of Minnesota. It would seem they did this because their population of interest was all undergraduates at the university. Do you think the sample collected is representative of all students at the university in terms of the association that was being studied? If we had a simple random sample of all students, then we could easily make this connection. A convenience sample, however, brings with it some concerns. When we are talking about student behavior, it is probably not safe to assume that a convenience sample will produce representative results. We should be very cautious as to exactly what population we can make this inference. Perhaps all social science students (the type that would take a research methods class) might be okay, but beyond that we would have a pretty weak argument.

Finally, we should note that because this study is observational, we cannot conclude that time spent on nonacademic activities *causes* a decrease in GPA.

Perceptions of Heaviness

EXPLORATION
10.4

Researchers believe a person's body is used as a perceptual ruler and people will judge the size of an object based on its relationship to parts of their body. Specifically, some researchers thought people with smaller hands will perceive objects to be bigger and hence heavier than those with larger hands. Linkenauger, Mohler, and Proffitt (2011) collected data on 46 participants, recording their hand width and estimated weight of bean bags. The results are shown in Table 10.4.

TABLE 10.4 Hand widths (in centimeters) and estimated weight of bean bags (in grams) for 46 participants

Hand width	Estimated weight	Hand width	Estimated weight	Hand width	Estimated weight	Hand width	Estimated weight
7.4	75.2	7.7	89.2	8.6	96.8	9.2	92.1
7.4	83.6	7.7	83.6	8.6	103.1	9.2	95.9
7.4	86.2	8.0	97.0	8.6	111.9	9.2	103.0
7.4	92.6	8.0	97.0	8.6	112.5	9.5	88.5
7.4	98.1	8.0	97.0	8.9	110.5	9.8	99.3
7.4	99.2	8.0	103.3	8.9	103.2	9.8	80.9
7.4	103.1	8.0	112.5	8.9	95.4	9.8	79.3
7.0	107.2	8.1	108.6	8.9	92.8	9.8	79.0
7.7	104.3	8.3	105.1	8.9	91.9	10.1	72.8
7.7	100.6	8.3	89.9	8.9	85.6	10.1	87.0
7.7	96.8	8.6	71.6	9.2	86.2		
7.7	96.4	8.6	93.0	9.2	89.1		

1. Write the null and alternative hypotheses for this study in words (use the term "association").

In Section 10.2 we used the **Corr/Regression** applet to perform a simulation-based test for a correlation coefficient. Doing the simulation-based test for the slope of the regression line is extremely similar. The only difference is that we use the slope as our statistic instead of the correlation coefficient. The applet has a radio button to select to switch from one statistic to the other.

2. Paste the data, **handwidth**, in the **Corr/Regression** applet and make a scatterplot. Describe the direction, form, and strength of the scatterplot.

3. Use the applet to determine the least squares regression line for predicting estimated weight based on hand width. What is the value of the slope of the regression line? What does this number imply in terms of hand width and estimated weight?

4. You should have found a negative association between hand width and estimated weight of the bean bag in the sample. The question, however, is if there were no association between hand width and the weight of an object in the population, how likely is it that we would get a slope as small (as far below zero) as we did. Let's apply the 3S strategy.

   a. **Statistic:** What is the value of the slope in the sample?

   b. **Simulate:** To simulate you can use the same general approach we used for correlation in Section 10.2. Explain how you would conduct the approach by hand. Assume you have 46 slips of paper with the sample hand widths written on them and 46 slips of paper with the perceived weight values written on them.

   c. **Strength of evidence:** Explain how you will calculate the strength of evidence in support of the conjecture that people with larger hands tend to perceive less weight in the bean bags.

5. Now let's complete a test of significance.

   a. Let's shuffle the response variable (estimated weight) and see what we get for sample slope values when we break the association between the data pairs. Use the applet to do this five times and write down the five simulated slopes you get. Are any of them as small as or smaller than the value of the actual sample slope?

   b. Now do at least 1,000 shuffles with the applet and find the p-value.

   c. Click on **Plot** in the **Shuffle Options** section of the applet. This will now display each of the 1,000 simulated regression lines (in blue). Describe the behavior of the 1,000 regression lines across the different shuffles (see FAQ 10.4.1 for some discussion about this).

   d. Explain what your p-value measures in the context of the study.

   e. Can we conclude that there is strong evidence of a genuine negative association between hand width and estimated weight of the object in the population?

FAQ 10.4.1   www.wiley.com/college/tintle

What is the point of averages?

---

6. As you did in Section 10.2, find the p-value corresponding to the correlation coefficient. How does this p-value compare with the p-value corresponding to the slope? (*Note:* You should have the p-value for the slope in #5(d).)

KEY IDEA

For a given data set, the test for slope is equivalent to the test for correlation coefficient.

---

7. The sample used here was not a random sample. The article just said that the researchers obtained data on 46 participants.

   a. Describe the population to which we could legitimately make our inference. Explain your reasoning.

   b. Can we conclude that having smaller hands causes a person to estimate the weight of the bean bag to be larger? Explain your answer.

SECTION 10.4   Summary

The 3S strategy can be used with the sample slope as the statistic of interest and applying the same simulation strategy we have used before.

- We can use the shuffling of the values of the response variable to produce simulated values of the statistic that could have occurred if there was no genuine association between the two variables.
  - As always, the p-value is calculated as the proportion of repetitions in which the simulated value of the statistic is at least as extreme as the observed value of the statistic, and a small p-value provides evidence against the null hypothesis.
- For a given data set, the test of significance for the slope is equivalent to the test of significance for the correlation coefficient.

INFERENCE FOR THE REGRESSION SLOPE: THEORY-BASED APPROACH

SECTION 10.5

INTRODUCTION

You may have noticed a very familiar looking pattern to the null distributions you generated of sample correlation coefficients in Section 10.2 and of sample slopes in Section 10.4. For example, two null distributions from Examples 10.2 and 10.4 are shown again in Figure 10.12.

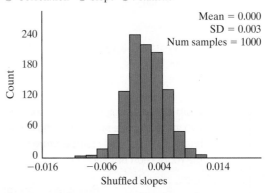

FIGURE 10.12   Null distributions for sample correlation (left) and sample slope (right) from previous examples.

The null distribution on the left in Figure 10.12 is of sample correlations from Example 10.2 (change in mood and exercise intensity), and the null distribution on the right is of sample slopes from Example 10.4 (GPA and hours spent on nonacademic activities). Both are centered around zero and fairly bell-shaped.

Although we won't precisely predict the correlation or slope null distributions we obtained through simulation, under certain conditions, the null distributions of a standardized version of these statistics are well modeled by *t*-distributions. Thus, theory-based inference can be conducted. This theory-based test has some additional differences from the simulation version which we will also explore.

Example 10.5

EXAMPLE

10.5A —Predicting Heart Rate from Body Temperature——————————

We will use data on the heart rates and body temperatures of healthy adults to see whether there is an association between body temperature and heart rate. The data set consists of body temperatures and heart rates from 65 females and 65 males.

Let's start by looking at a scatterplot (see Figure 10.13) of the heart rate (beats per minute) and body temperature (degrees Fahrenheit) for the 130 subjects.

> **THINK ABOUT IT**
>
> What does the scatterplot reveal about the relationship between heart rate and body temperature for this sample?

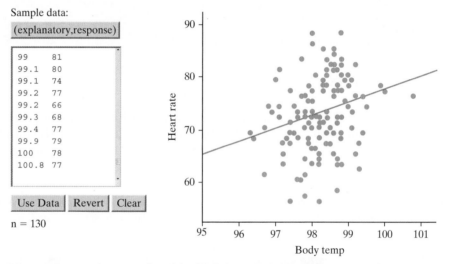

FIGURE 10.13 A scatterplot of the body temperature and heart rate of 130 individuals.

From the scatterplot it appears there is a fairly weak positive linear association between these two variables. We also found the correlation coefficient and regression equation for predicting heart rate from body temperature by using the applet. The correlation coefficient is 0.254 and the regression equation is

$$\text{Predicted heart rate} = -166.3 + 2.44 \,(\text{body temp}).$$

> **THINK ABOUT IT**
>
> Interpret the slope value from this equation.

From the regression equation, we can see that the slope is 2.44. This means that we predict heart rate to increase 2.44 beats per minute for every 1 degree rise in body temperature.

To evaluate whether this is convincing evidence that there is in fact a relationship between heart rate and body temperature in the population, we will first use a simulation-based approach. Our hypotheses are as follows:

Null hypothesis: There is no association between heart rate and body temperature in the population.

Alternative hypothesis: There is an association between heart rate and body temperature in the population.

The response variable values (heart rate) in the data set of 130 individuals were shuffled and redistributed to the body temperature values 10,000 times, and each time, a simulated value for the slope of the regression line was computed. A graph of those simulated slopes is shown in Figure 10.14. We see that our observed sample slope of 2.44 is very unlikely in the null distribution. Only 36 out of 10,000 shuffles yielded a slope that was as extreme as 2.44 (either greater than or equal to 2.44 or less than or equal to −2.44). Thus our p-value of 0.0036 gives us strong evidence of a relationship between heart rate and body temperature in the population.

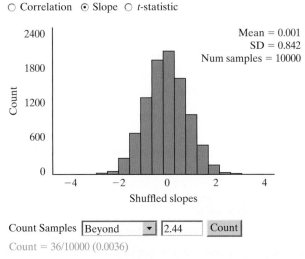

FIGURE 10.14 A null distribution for slope between heart rate and body temperature along with other output from the **Corr/Regression** applet.

As you can see from Figure 10.14, the null distribution has the nice, familiar bell shape. However, as has been the case before, we need a standardized version of the test statistic in order to obtain an accurate theory-based prediction of the null distribution.

FORMULAS
The theory-based approach computes a standardized statistic (t-statistic) using either of the following equations:

10.5.1

$$t = \frac{r}{\sqrt{\dfrac{1 - r^2}{n - 2}}} = \frac{b - 0}{SE(b)}.$$

More specifics are provided in the Calculation Details appendix, but notice that the t-statistic can be computed based on either the correlation coefficient or the slope, and it yields the same standardized value—further underscoring that tests for the correlation and for the slope are essentially identical.

Figure 10.15 shows the results of simulating when using the t-statistic.

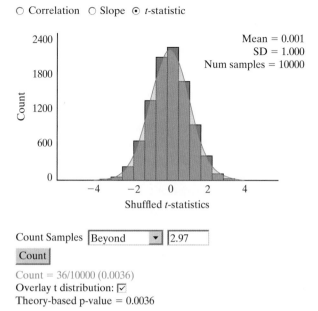

○ Correlation ○ Slope ⊙ t-statistic

Mean = 0.001
SD = 1.000
Num samples = 10000

Shuffled t-statistics

Count Samples [Beyond ▼] [2.97]

[Count]

Count = 36/10000 (0.0036)
Overlay t distribution: ☑
Theory-based p-value = 0.0036

FIGURE 10.15 Simulated standardized statistics with t-distribution overlaid.

VALIDITY CONDITIONS

10.5.2

As has been the case before, theory-based tests have **validity conditions** which are needed in order to obtain an accurate prediction of the simulated distribution.

> ### VALIDITY CONDITIONS
>
> **Validity conditions for a theory-based test for a regression slope**
> 1. The general pattern of the points in the scatterplot should follow a linear trend; the pattern should not show curved or other nonlinear patterns.
> 2. There should be approximately the same distribution of points above the regression line as below the regression line (symmetry about the regression line).
> 3. The variability of the points around the regression line should be similar regardless of the value of the explanatory variable; the variability (spread) of the points around the regression line should not differ as you slide along the x-axis (equal variance/ standard deviation).

To check the validity conditions for using the theory-based approach, we examine the scatterplot in more detail. First, the pattern of the points in the scatterplot doesn't look curved; a linear trend seems reasonable. Second, we note that the points above the regression line appear similar in spread and shape as the points below the regression line (like a mirror image to the pattern). Finally, the variability in heart rates is approximately the same for different body temperatures (e.g., we don't see that low body temperatures have low variability in heart rates and high body have high variability in heart rates or vice versa). When checking validity conditions, we use logic much like we do when testing hypotheses—we will assume the condition is true unless we see strong evidence that it is not.

You know by now that theory-based tests, when valid, predict the behavior of the null distribution (of the standardized statistic) you would have gotten from simulation if you had simulated. In this case, we know that the theory-based approach will accurately predict the shape of the null distribution because the validity conditions are met. This is confirmed by overlaying the theoretical t-distribution on our simulated slopes (Figure 10.15). But, it's actually a bit more complicated than that, as FAQ 10.5.1 and the following discussion point out.

FAQ 10.5.1   www.wiley.com/college/tintle

What are the gains from assuming linearity?

```
Regression Table: ☑

Term       Coeff    SE      t-stat  p-value
Intercept  −166.28  80.91   −2.06   0.0419
BodyTemp   2.44     0.82    2.97    0.0036
```

FIGURE 10.16   Formal regression table output for theory-based approach.

Figure 10.16 shows a more formal presentation of the output for a regression analysis illustrating some of the calculation details.

The last line of the regression output shows the theory-based p-value for our test. This p-value of 0.0036 is the same as our simulated p-value of 0.0036. The theory-based p-value will always be given as a two-sided p-value in the regression table (see Figure 10.16). In this case, we are conducting a two-sided test. If we had suspected beforehand that heart rates and body temperatures have a positive association, then our p-value would simply be half of the theory-based p-value of 0.0036, namely 0.0018.

Also note that the output reports the standardized statistic of $t = 2.97$ for the slope. This tells us that the observed sample slope (2.44) is almost 3 standard errors (0.82) above the hypothesized slope of zero. Note that the standard error here is telling us about random variation in the sample slopes. This value is smaller than what we saw in the simulation for the standard deviation of the simulated slopes (there SD of simulated statistics was 0.842; see Figure 10.14) because (as discussed in FAQ 10.5.1) the simulation is for a more general "no-association" hypothesis, whereas the theory-based p-value is for a more specific set of hypotheses about linearity (and makes slightly different assumptions about the random process).

FAQ 10.5.1   www.wiley.com/college/tintle

What are the gains from assuming linearity?

In particular we can now specify that we are testing for linearity:

Null hypothesis: There is no *linear* association between heart rate and body temperature in the population.

Alternative hypothesis: There is a *linear* association between heart rate and body temperature in the population.

This gives us the ability to state hypotheses using population parameters. We use the symbol β ("beta") to indicate the population slope and ρ ("rho") to indicate the population correlation. We can write the hypotheses as shown here:

 10.5.3

Null hypothesis: $\beta = 0$ (the population slope equals 0)

Alternative hypothesis: $\beta \neq 0$ (the population slope is not 0)

Or, equivalently:

Null hypothesis: $\rho = 0$ (the population correlation equals 0)

Alternative hypothesis: $\rho \neq 0$ (the population correlation is not 0)

CONFIDENCE INTERVAL

The theory-based confidence interval (Figure 10.17) for the slope tells us that we are 95% confident that a one degree increase in body temperature is associated with an average increase of 0.8137 to 4.0728 heart beats per minute in the population represented by this sample. Note

 10.5.4

that this can be approximated using the 2SD method by using the estimate of the standard deviation from the regression table (0.82), yielding 2.44 ± 1.64 = (0.80, 4.08).

95% Confidence interval for slope: ☑
(0.8138, 4.0727), df = 128

FIGURE 10.17   Confidence interval for regression slope.

Smoking and Drinking

EXAMPLE

The scatterplot in Figure 10.18 shows the relationship between number of alcoholic drinks consumed per week (*x*-axis) and number of cigarettes smoked per week (*y*-axis) for a random sample of students at a college.

Note: The scatterplot will only show one "dot" for people who have the same values of the explanatory/response variable. So, although we only see one "dot" on the point (0, 0), there are actually 524 students at that point!

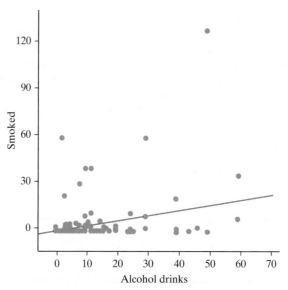

FIGURE 10.18   A scatterplot of alcoholic drinks and cigarettes smoked per week for a sample of college students.

> **THINK ABOUT IT**
>
> Do the data in the scatterplot appear to meet the validity conditions to conduct a theory-based test?

Examining the scatterplot of the *sample* data should help reveal any strong violations of the validity conditions described in Example 10.5A. Both conditions appear violated. In particular, the scatterplot in Figure 10.18 reveals that most dots lying below the regression line (along the *x*-axis) are much closer to the line on average than the values lying above the regression line. For example, at any value of number of drinks per week, there are many people who smoked zero cigarettes, a few with a small number of cigarettes smoked, and very few with large values for number of cigarettes smoked. In other words, the distribution of cigarettes smoked per week for each different value of alcoholic drinks per week is highly right skewed. The other condition is that there is similar variability of the dots around the regression line for different values of the explanatory variable (alcoholic drinks per week). The scatterplot suggests that there is evidence that this condition is also violated because the distributions of the number of cigarettes smoked seem to be more variable for larger values of alcoholic drinks per week than for smaller values.

Because these two conditions are violated, we should not apply theory-based inference procedures to these data. In Figure 10.19 we see both the theory-based prediction for the null distribution of the standardized slope coefficient and simulation results for 1,000 shuffles. Notice that the theory-based prediction of the null distribution is mound-shaped (a t-distribution) with a mean of zero, but the simulated null distribution for the standardized slope coefficient is highly right skewed. In this case, the theory-based prediction for the null distribution is not a good match to the actual null distribution, so p-values and confidence intervals from the theory-based approach could be quite misleading.

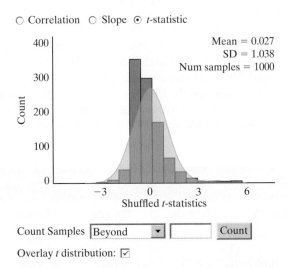

FIGURE 10.19   Theory-based and simulated null distribution for t-statistics by standardizing shuffled slope coefficients of alcohol drinks and cigarettes smoked per week.

When the validity conditions are not met for theory-based inference for a population slope, you can rely on the simulated-based approach. Another common strategy is to reexpress (*transform*) the data on a different scale, such as a logarithmic scale, in such a way that the conditions would be met. See Exercise 10.5.20 for an example.

CAUTION: OUTLIERS AND INFLUENTIAL OBSERVATIONS
Reconsidering Figure 10.18, we also note that there may be some influential points in this sample. Specifically, the person who says they smoke 130 cigarettes a week is also one of the largest alcohol consumers (50 drinks per week). If we remove this person from the data set, the correlation coefficient drops from 0.37 to 0.30, a noticeable decrease. This is the best way to check whether extreme observations unduly affect the analysis: Remove them from the data set and see how the relationship changes. It is a judgment call about how big of a change is large, but any point that substantially changes the correlation coefficient or regression slope is considered influential. Depending on the context, influential points should be considered for removal from the analysis in order to get a more robust estimate of the correlation coefficient and regression line but should only be done with proper justification.

> **KEY IDEA**
>
> Remove possible influential points and outliers and recompute the correlation coefficient and/or regression slope. If the statistic has changed a lot after removing the point, the point is considered influential and you may want to consider whether you have any justifications to keep that point out of the analysis (or report your conclusions both with and without that observation).

EXPLORATION 10.5 | Predicting Brain Density from Number of Facebook Friends

How often did you check your Facebook account today? How many Facebook friends do you have? Does everyone have the same number? Might the number of Facebook friends that a person has be associated in some way with the person's brain structure? Researchers used MRIs to examine areas of the brain that are involved with social interaction, memory, and emotional responses (Kanai, Bahrami, Roylance, and Rees, 2011). Their subjects were 40 university students in London. They examined five areas of the brain that have been previously linked to social perception and associative memory, and they compared each to the number of Facebook friends the subject reported. The results from each brain area were quite similar. We will look at one set of measurements focusing on the left MTG (middle temporal gyrus, which has been linked in other studies to face recognition). These results are shown in Table 10.5. Note that number of friends is given in units of 100 friends, so that 0.30 = 30 friends, 1.09 = 109 friends, etc.

TABLE 10.5 The number of Facebook friends (in 100s of friends) and the brain density (in arbitrary units) for 40 university students

Friends	Density	Friends	Density	Friends	Density	Friends	Density
0.30	−2.14	3.41	−0.72	5.08	−0.17	2.93	1.24
1.09	−1.09	3.97	−0.74	5.15	−0.09	3.09	0.93
0.39	−0.72	4.10	−0.85	5.01	−0.03	3.65	1.02
1.20	−0.53	4.39	−0.69	3.92	0.26	4.73	0.75
0.80	−0.43	4.60	−0.71	3.13	0.42	3.95	1.34
1.71	−0.26	5.07	−1.07	2.53	0.46	6.14	0.96
2.24	−0.34	5.08	−0.49	1.51	0.23	7.32	1.05
2.40	−1.51	5.83	−0.59	1.73	0.27	6.17	1.6
3.23	−1.45	6.34	−0.41	1.52	0.55	5.47	1.97
3.81	−1.48	5.63	0.21	2.71	1.09	5.70	2.08

The researchers wanted to explore whether there is a positive relationship between these two variables, and we will do the same. In particular, the researchers tried to predict brain density based on number of Facebook friends, asking: Does brain density tend to increase as a person's number of Facebook friends increases?

1. What are the null and alternative hypotheses for this study?
2. Paste the data (**Facebook**) in the **Corr/Regression** applet and make a scatterplot where brain density is the response variable and number of Facebook friends is the explanatory variable. (Note that the number of Facebook friends is reported in terms of hundreds of

friends.) Describe the direction, form, and strength of association between the variables as revealed in the scatterplot. Are there any unusual observations?

3. What is the slope of the regression equation for predicting brain density based on number of Facebook friends? Does this slope imply a positive or a negative association between these variables?

4. You should have found a positive slope between brain density and number of Facebook friends. The question, however, is if there were no association between brain density and number of Facebook friends, how likely is it that we would get a slope as far above zero as we did.

   a. In your own words, explain how you could use slips of paper to model the null hypothesis of no association between brain density and number of Facebook friends.

   b. Let's shuffle the response variable (brain density) to see what we get for the slope if we break the association between the data pairs. Use the applet to do this five times and write down the five simulated slopes you get. Are any of them as large as or larger than the actual value of the sample slope?

   c. Now do at least 1,000 shuffles with the applet and find your p-value.

   d. Interpret what your p-value measures in context of the study.

   e. Can we conclude that there is convincing evidence of a positive association between the density of the left MTG and the number of Facebook friends a person has in the population? Explain your reasoning.

5. What is the shape of the null distribution of shuffled slopes?

By now, you've seen many times that when the null distribution of statistics takes a familiar, mound-shaped curve, we can often use theory-based methods to predict the null distribution of related standardized statistics—as long as certain validity conditions are true. This is no different for regression (and correlation!).

The theory-based approach computes a standardized statistic (t-statistic) using one of the following equations:

$$t = \frac{r}{\sqrt{\dfrac{1 - r^2}{n - 2}}} = \frac{b - 0}{SE(b)}.$$

More information is provided in the Calculation Details appendix, but notice that the t-statistic can be computed based on either the correlation coefficient or the slope, and it yields the same value—further underscoring that tests for the correlation coefficient and for the slope are essentially identical.

6. Use the applet to find the correlation coefficient.

7. Use the correlation coefficient to find the t-statistic using the equation shown above.

There are three validity conditions for regression which are needed in order to use the theory-based approach to yield a p-value.

VALIDITY CONDITIONS

Validity conditions for a theory-based test for a regression slope

1. The general pattern of the points in the scatterplot should follow a linear trend; the pattern should not show curved or other nonlinear patterns.
2. There should be approximately the same distribution of points above the regression line as below the regression line (symmetry about the regression line).
3. The variability of the points around the regression line should be similar regardless of the value of the explanatory variable; the variability (spread) of the points around the regression line should not differ as you slide along the x-axis (equal variance/standard deviation).

8. Based on the scatterplot you used in #2, is Validity Condition 1 met? Namely, is the general pattern of the scatterplot linear?

9. Based on the scatterplot you used in #2, is Validity Condition 2 met? Namely, is the distribution of points above the regression line the same as below the line?

10. Based on the scatterplot you used in #2, is Validity Condition 3 met? Namely, is the variability of the points around the line similar regardless of the value of the explanatory variable?

11. Select the **t-statistic** radio button, then check the **Overlay t distribution** button. Does the t-distribution appear to do a good job of predicting the distribution of the simulated t-statistics? Why?

12. In the applet, click the box for **Regression Table**. This table provides the observed t-statistic for the data as well as the two-sided, theory-based test p-value. Use the theory-based approach to test whether there is convincing evidence of a linear association between the variables in the population. Report the standardized statistic and p-value. Summarize your conclusion.

When using the theory-based approach for regression you can write your hypotheses in terms of population parameters. The relevant population parameters are the population slope (indicated by the Greek letter β) and the population correlation (indicated by the Greek letter ρ). See FAQ 10.5.1 for more discussion about parameters.

FAQ 10.5.1   www.wiley.com/college/tintle

What are the gains from assuming linearity?

13. Write the null and alternative hypotheses in terms of the population slope.

14. Write the null and alternative hypotheses in terms of the population correlation coefficient.

15. Produce and interpret a 95% confidence interval for the population slope coefficient. (*Hint:* Make sure that your interpretation refers to how to interpret the slope coefficient in the population and remember that the units of the explanatory variable are 100s of Facebook friends.) To get the confidence interval, check the box below the regression table **for 95% Confidence interval for Slope**.

16. Imagine if we added someone to this data set whose brain density was −10 and had 5,000 Facebook friends. Uncheck **Show Shuffle Options** and enter this observation into the data set using **Add/remove observations** or typing this new row into the **Sample data** window. Conduct a two-sided test. *Caution:* Make sure you enter 5,000 Facebook friends in terms of the units used in this study; what would 5,000 Facebook friends be in terms of 100s of Facebook friends?

    a. Find the p-value using a simulation-based approach with shuffled t-statistics.

    b. Find the p-value using the theory-based approach.

    c. Why are the p-values from the two approaches not very similar?

17. Remember that the sample used here was not randomly selected, but rather a group of 40 volunteer university students.

    a. Describe a population in which you would be comfortable drawing inferences. Explain your reasoning.

    b. Can we conclude that acquiring more Facebook friends would lead to an increase in a person's brain density? Explain your answer.

    c. What about the opposite direction: Can we conclude that having a larger brain density causes a person to acquire more Facebook friends? Explain.

18. The researchers originally searched for positive associations between many areas of the brain and the number of Facebook friends for 125 subjects. They found significantly positive associations for a number of brain areas. The second part of the study is with the 40 subjects that we looked at in this exploration.

Why do you think this method of "look at a bunch of regions to see which are significant" is often criticized? (*Hint:* If you run lots of tests of significance using a 5% level of significance, how often will you reject the null hypothesis when you really shouldn't have?)

SECTION 10.5 Summary

A theory-based method can be used to conduct inference for the population slope coefficient or population correlation coefficient. We will consider the two methods identical.

- The test of significance and the confidence interval are based on the *t*-distribution.
- The validity conditions for the slope coefficient are that the general pattern of the points in the scatterplot should follow a linear trend, the response variable has approximately the same distribution of points above the regression line as below the regression line (symmetry about the line), and the variability of the points around the regression line should be similar regardless of the value of the explanatory variable (equal variance about the line).

CONFIDENCE INTERVAL AND SIGNIFICANCE TEST FOR THE SLOPE OF A REGRESSION LINE

SECTION 10.6

INTRODUCTION

We saw in Section 10.5 that when certain validity conditions have been met, we can use a theory-based model to conduct inference for the population slope coefficient. As you've seen before, the AP exam sometimes requires slightly different versions of the validity conditions from those we've seen in previous sections. Earlier in Section 10.5, the validity conditions we noted for a theory-based test for a regression slope were that the general pattern of the points in the scatterplot should follow a linear trend, there should be symmetry of points about the regression line, and the variability of the points about the regression line should be similar for different values of the explanatory variable. For the AP exam, you are expected to be a bit more specific, stating information about both the study design and also about the distribution of the residuals.

> **AP TIP**
>
> **Validity conditions for conducting a *t*-test for the slope of a regression line**
> - The relationship between the explanatory and response variables is linear.
>   - Verify that the scatterplot is linear and there is no pattern in the residual plot.
> - Individual observations are independent. The prediction errors (residuals) should be independent of one another.
>   - Verify that the data were obtained from a random sample or randomized experiment.
> - For any fixed x, the responses y follow a normal distribution with standard deviation σ (the responses y at each value of x vary normally about the mean at that value of x).
>   - Verify that the residuals are approximately normally distributed by examining a dotplot or histogram or normal probability plot of the residuals.
> - Nearly equal variation in the residuals for different values of the explanatory variable.
>   - Examine the residual plot. The variability in the residuals should be nearly the same for all values of the explanatory variable.

To perform a ***t-test for the slope of a regression line***, where the null hypothesis is $H_0: \beta = 0$, that is, the population slope is 0, the standardized statistic has the form

$$t = \frac{b - 0}{SE(b)}$$

where b denotes the sample slope, 0 is the hypothesized value of the population slope under the null, SE_b denotes the standard error of the sample slopes, and n is the sample size (the number of ordered pairs). You use $n - 1$ degrees of freedom to determine the p-value.

In Section 1.7 and elsewhere you learned the work you must show on the AP Statistics exam when a hypothesis test is called for. The format you learned is the same for all hypothesis tests.

1. State the hypotheses either in words or using appropriate symbols.
2. Name the test that will be used and state and verify the validity conditions for the test chosen.
3. Calculate the test statistic (standardized statistic) and corresponding p-value.
4. State your conclusion (with appropriate justification based on your p-value and stated significance level) in the context of the research question.

In Section 3.2, Part 2, and elsewhere you learned the work you must show on the AP Statistics exam when a confidence interval is called for. The format you learned is the same for all confidence intervals.

1. Identify the parameter you want to estimate and the theory-based model you will use.
2. Verify the validity conditions for the theory-based method you have chosen.
3. Construct the confidence interval, showing the values that you plug into the formula.
4. Interpret the confidence interval you obtained in the context of the problem.

Now we illustrate how to summarize the results from inference for the slope of a least squares regression line in AP Statistics style.

Instagram Followers

Example 10.6

EXAMPLE

Recent research has explored the relationship between the number of followers vs. the number following on social media sites. After reading an article on this research, a student in an AP Statistics class decided to conduct a study to determine whether there is a relationship between the number of followers a teen has on Instagram and the number of people he or she is following. To do this, the student randomly selected 50 students from her high school who had Instagram accounts and for each student recorded the number of people they were following and the number of followers they had, using the site's analytics features.

> **THINK ABOUT IT**
>
> What are the observational units? What are the variables? Are they categorical or quantitative? Which is the explanatory and which is the response variable?

Each student at this high school is an observational unit. The number of people a student is following on Instagram is the explanatory variable, and the number of followers is the response variable. Both variables are quantitative.

Computer output for the regression analysis predicting the number of *Instagram followers* from the number of people the student is *following on Instagram* is provided in Figure 10.20. Also included are a scatterplot with the least squares regression line drawn in, the residual plot, and a histogram of the residuals.

```
R-squared        r² = 87.2%
Regression SE    s = 126.60

Regression Table:

Term        Coeff   SE      t-stat  p-value
Intercept  -45.30  48.13   -0.94   0.3513
Following   1.21    0.07    18.11   0.0000
```

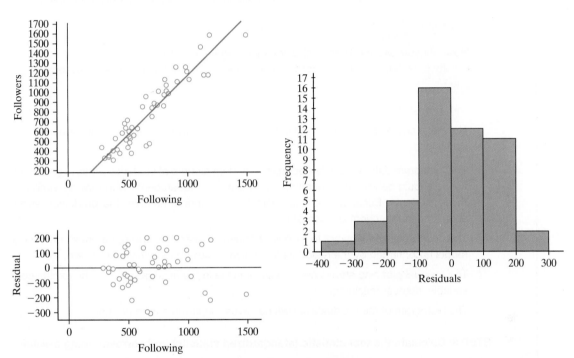

FIGURE 10.20 Computer output from least squares regression analysis predicting number of Instagram followers one has from the number of Instagram users one is following.

Using the computer output from Figure 10.20, we can determine the equation of the least squares regression line. Remember to identify the variables used in the equation:

$$\widehat{followers} = -45.30 + 1.21 \ following$$

The slope of 1.21 tells us that for each additional person someone follows on Instagram, the predicted (average) increase in the number of followers is 1.21.

THINK ABOUT IT

Do the data provide convincing evidence at a significance level of $\alpha = 0.01$ of a linear relationship between followers and the number being followed on Instagram?

Let's look at a solution according to the AP Statistics style.

STEP 1: State the hypotheses either in words or using appropriate symbols. Let β represent the population slope for predicting *followers* based on number *following* on Instagram. We want to decide whether we are convinced that a linear relationship exists between these two variables. Thus, the hypotheses can be stated in symbols as

$H_0: \beta = 0$

$H_a: \beta \neq 0$

or in words as

Null: There is no linear association between followers and the number of people followed on Instagram.

Alternative: There is a linear association between followers and the number of people followed on Instagram.

STEP 2: Name the test that will be used and state and verify the validity conditions for the test chosen.   We will use a t-test for the slope of a regression line because we are conducting a test on two quantitative variables measured on the same observational units.

> THINK ABOUT IT
>
> How will you use the graphical displays in Figure 10.20 to determine whether the validity conditions for a t-test for the slope of a regression line have been reasonably met?

Now let's check the validity conditions needed to perform a t-test for the slope of a regression line.

* The Instagram data were obtained from a random sample of students at this high school, so we should be able to generalize our results to other students who may be similar to these students. Because our data were from a random sample, the prediction errors should be independent of each other.
* The scatterplot of *followers* to *following* appears linear. The appropriateness of a linear model is confirmed by the residual plot, which shows no recognizable pattern.
* The residual plot also shows near-equal variance in the residuals across the explanatory variable, number following.
* The histogram of the residuals shows no severe departures from normality.

STEP 3: Calculate the test statistic (standardized statistic) and corresponding p-value.

> THINK ABOUT IT
>
> How will you use the computer output in Figure 10.20 to obtain the test statistic (standardized statistic) and the corresponding p-value?

From the computer output, we find $t = 18.11$, df = 48, p-value ≈ 0.

From Table B with conservative (rounding down) df = 40, we find the two-sided p-value is easily less than $0.0005 \times 2 = 0.0010$.

Typically, you are given computer output for inference for the slope of a regression line. If you are given the raw data instead, you may use your calculator to obtain your test statistic and corresponding p-value.

> CALCULATOR TIPS
>
> You can determine the test statistic and p-value using graphing calculators. For example:
> * **TI-84:** STAT → TESTS → LinREgT-Test
> * **TI-Nspire:** Statistics → Stat Tests → Linear Reg t Test

STEP 4: State your conclusion (with appropriate justification based on your p-value and stated significance level) in the context of the research question.   Our obtained p-value of approximately 0 is smaller than our significance level of 0.01. Therefore, we have very strong evidence that there is a linear relationship between the number of people being followed and the number of followers on Instagram in the population. Because a controlled, randomized experiment was the *not* conducted, we cannot attribute a cause-and-effect relationship between the number of people being followed and the number of followers on Instagram. The students were selected randomly from students at this high school, and thus we should be able to generalize these results to other high school students who may be similar to those in our study.

10.6.1

THINK ABOUT IT

How would you use the data from this study to construct and interpret a 99% confidence interval for the slope of the population regression line for predicting followers from the number followed on Instagram?

Again, we will present a solution in the AP style.

STEP 1: Identify the parameter you want to estimate and the theory-based model you will use. Let β represent the population slope for predicting followers from the number following on Instagram.

We will use a *t*-interval for slope to construct a 99% confidence interval for β, the slope of the population regression line.

STEP 2: Verify the validity conditions for the theory-based method you have chosen. The validity conditions needed to construct a *t*-interval for slope are the same as those needed to perform a *t*-test for slope. We checked these earlier on this data and they were OK.

STEP 3: Construct the confidence interval, showing the values that you plug into the formula.

$$b = 1.21$$
$$SE(b) = 0.07$$
$$n = 50$$
$$df = 50 - 2 = 48$$
$$t^*_{48} = 2.682$$

99%CI for β: $1.21 \pm 2.682(0.07)$

$(1.022, 1.398)$

CALCULATOR TIPS

You can determine the critical value for 48 degrees of freedom with 99% confidence for your calculator. For example:

- **TI-84:** Distr → invT (0.995, 48) → 2.682
- **TI-Nspire:** Statistics → Distributions → Inverse t → Area: 0.995, df: 48

Note: From Table B with conservative (rounding) df = 40, we find the t^* critical value for a 99% confidence interval is 2.704.

STEP 4: Interpret the confidence interval you obtained in the context of the problem. We can be 99% confident that the slope of the regression line to predict followers from the number following on Instagram for the population of students similar to those in our study is between 1.022 and 1.398 (assuming the sample is indeed representative of this entire population). A one-unit increase in the number of people a student follows on Instagram is associated with an average increase of 1.022 to 1.398 followers in the population represented by this sample.

THINK ABOUT IT

What aspect of the confidence interval reported above supports the decision made in the hypothesis test?

10.6.2

Based on our p-value of approximately 0 at an α level of 0.01, we had strong evidence to claim that there is a significant linear relationship between the number following and followers on Instagram. Because our entire 99% confidence interval is above zero, this supports our claim that a slope of zero (no linear relationship) is not a plausible value for the population slope.

EXPLORATION 10.6 | Human Body Proportions Revisited

Let's revisit Exploration 10.3.2 based on the remark in the movie *Pretty Woman*, starring Julia Roberts and Richard Gere, by Roberts' character Vivian: "Did you know that the distance from your wrist to your elbow is the same as the length of your foot?" A statistics class decided to test the validity of this statement. They measured the right forearm from the middle of the elbow to the bone that protrudes on the wrist and the length of the right foot (without shoes) to the nearest tenth of a centimeter for each of the 10 females in the class.

Computer output for the regression analysis for predicting the length of a student's foot from her forearm length is provided in Figure 10.21. Also included are a scatterplot with the least squares regression line drawn in, the residual plot, and a dotplot of the residuals.

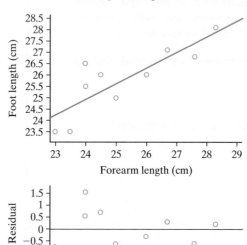

Term	Coeff	SE	t-stat	p-value
Intercept	8.4662	4.0573	2.09	0.0704
Forearm length	0.6862	0.1603	4.28	0.0027

R-squared $r^2 = 69.6\%$
Regression SE $s = 0.87$

FIGURE 10.21 Computer output from least squares regression analysis predicting foot length in cm from arm length in cm.

1. Do the data provide convincing evidence at a significance level of $\alpha = 0.05$ of a linear relationship between foot length and forearm length? Remember to model your solution according to the AP style.

   STEP 1: State the hypotheses either in words or using appropriate symbols.

   STEP 2: Name the test that will be used and state and verify the validity conditions for the test chosen.

   STEP 3: Report the test statistic (standardized statistic), degrees of freedom, and corresponding p-value.

STEP 4: State your conclusion (with appropriate justification based on your p-value and stated significance level) in the context of the research question.

Typically, on the AP exam you are given computer output for inference for the slope of a regression line (see output above). If you are given the raw data instead, you may use your calculator to obtain your test statistic and corresponding p-value.

CALCULATOR TIPS

You can determine the test statistic and p-value using graphing calculators. For example:

- **TI-84:** STAT → TESTS → LinREgT-Test
- **TI-Nspire:** Statistics → Stat Tests → Linear Reg t Test

---

2. Suppose you had been given only the slope (0.6862) and the standard error (0.1603). Explain how you could find the test statistic and p-value.

3. Use the data from this study to construct and interpret a 95% confidence interval for the slope of the population regression line for predicting foot length from forearm length. Remember to model your solution according to the AP style.

   STEP 1: Identify the parameter you want to estimate and the theory-based model you will use.

   STEP 2: Verify the validity conditions for the theory-based method you have chosen.

   You can use the table or the calculator to find the critical value needed in the confidence interval construction.

CALCULATOR TIPS

You can determine the critical value for 8 degrees of freedom with 95% confidence for your calculator. For example:

- **TI-84:** Distr → invT (0.975, 8) → answer
- **TI-Nspire:** Statistics → Distributions → Inverse t → Area: 0.975, df: 8

   STEP 3: Construct the confidence interval, showing the values that you substitute into the formula.

   STEP 4: Interpret the confidence interval you obtained in the context of the problem.

SECTION 10.6   Summary

In this section you investigated theory-based methods for tests of significance and confidence intervals for inference for the population slope coefficient. You saw that a t-distribution provides a good approximation for the distribution of the statistic b provided the general pattern of the points in the scatterplot follow a linear trend, there is symmetry of points about the regression line, and the variability of the points about the regression line is similar for different values of the explanatory variable. The theory-based test for a regression slope is referred to as a ***t-test for the slope of a regression line***. In addition to the test of significance, you examined a theory-based ***t-interval for the slope of a regression line*** for estimating the population slope coefficient.

As you've seen before, the AP exam sometimes requires slightly different versions of the validity conditions from those that we've seen in previous sections. For regression:

- The relationship between the explanatory and response variables is linear.
  - Verify that the scatterplot is linear and there is no pattern in the residual plot.
- Individual observations are independent. The prediction errors (residuals) should be independent of one another.
  - Verify that the data were obtained from a random sample or randomized experiment.
- For any fixed x, the responses y follow a normal distribution with standard deviation σ (the responses y at each value of x vary normally about the mean at that value of x).
  - Verify that the residuals are approximately normally distributed by examining a dot-plot or histogram or normal probability plot of the residuals.
- Nearly equal variation in the residuals for different values of the explanatory variable.
  - Examine the residual plot. The variability in the residuals should be nearly the same for all values of the explanatory variable.

CHAPTER 10   Summary

In this chapter we looked at relationships between two quantitative variables. We saw that scatterplots are used to explore the relationship between two quantitative variables. In creating a scatterplot, we put the explanatory variable on the horizontal axis and the response variable on the vertical axis. Which variable is which is sometimes straightforward (especially if you are doing an experiment) and sometimes not so straightforward.

We saw that the correlation coefficient is a measure of the strength and direction of a *linear* relationship between two quantitative variables.

A regression line has the form $\hat{y} = a + bx$ where a is the y-intercept, b is the slope, x is a value of the explanatory variable, and $\hat{y}$ is the predicted value for the response variable. You should always put the variables in context when writing out the equation and be able to give contextual interpretations of the slope and intercept (but watch for extrapolation). For a specific value of x, the corresponding $y - \hat{y}$ value is a residual and the least squares regression line is found by minimizing the sum of the squared residuals. If data do not fit a linear pattern they can sometimes be transformed using logarithms to make their pattern more linear. A regression line can then be used to model these transformed data.

The simulation-based technique that we learned in the previous chapters was adapted to work with looking for an association between two quantitative variables. We again used the 3S strategy:

1. **Statistic:** In this chapter our statistic was either the correlation coefficient or the regression slope.
2. **Simulate:** Shuffle the response variable, recompute the statistic, and repeat this process many times.
3. **Strength of evidence:** We find evidence against the null hypothesis if the original sample statistic is in the tail of the distribution used to model the null hypothesis.

Similar to previous chapters, we saw that the p-value is the probability of getting a value of the (standardized) statistic equal to or more extreme than the one from our original sample data when the null hypothesis is true. We also used the standard deviation from the null distribution and the 2SD rule to approximate a 95% confidence interval for the parameter.

The theory-based test for a regression slope was discussed and compared to the simulation-based test. We saw how the predicted null distribution was similar to all the others we have seen so far: symmetric, bell-shaped, and centered at zero. This allowed us (the computer) to formally standardize the statistic and use the t-distribution (with $n - 2$ degrees of freedom) to approximate the p-value and estimate the confidence interval.

CHAPTER 10
GLOSSARY

correlation coefficient   Statistic that measures direction and strength of a *linear* relationship between two quantitative variables.

coefficient of determination (R^2)   A statistic that measures the percentage of total variation in the response variable that is explained by the linear relationship with the explanatory variable. The value is literally the square of the correlation coefficient.

extrapolation   Predicting values for the response variable for values of the explanatory variable that are outside of the range of the original data.

form   When describing a scatterplot, the form is a summary of the overall pattern, usually described as linear or non-linear (exhibiting some curvature).

influential observations   An observation is considered influential if removing it from the data set dramatically changes the correlation coefficient or regression line; often have extreme x values.

least-squares regression line   The best fit line on a scatterplot; the line that gets as "close" as possible to all of the data points.

predictor   Another word for explanatory variable, often used in correlation/regression settings.

r   Symbol for correlation coefficient, where values range from −1 to 1 and are unitless; values close to −1 and 1 denote a strong linear relationship; values close to 0 denote a weak or no linear relationship.

regression standard error   (also known as the standard deviation of the residuals) A measure of how far the sample observations tend to fall from the regression line. It can be interpreted as a typical or average prediction error.

residuals   The vertical distances between a point and the least squares regression line.

residual plot   A scatterplot with the residuals on the vertical axis and the explanatory variable or the predicted response values on the horizontal axis.

scatterplot   A graphical summary of the relationship between two quantitative variables. Each dot on the scatterplot shows the values for both variables on that observational unit.

slope   Change in predicted response variable for each unit change in explanatory variable.

strength   When describing a scatterplot, the strength of association is a summary of how closely the dots follow the pattern (form). For example, if the form is linear, how close are the dots to the best fit line? Scatterplots demonstrating stronger association have the dots fairly close to the underlying pattern.

SSE   Sum squared error; the sum of all the squared residuals.

transform   Express data on a different scale, such as logarithmic, often used to meet validity conditions.

unusual observations   Any observations that do not fit in with the pattern of the rest of the observations.

validity conditions for regression theory-based test   General form of the scatterplot is linear, the data is symmetric about the regression line and the variability in the response variable across the x values is generally equal.

y-intercept   Graphically, the y-intercept is where the regression line crosses the y-axis. Because the x-value of the y-axis is 0, the y-intercept can also be thought of as the $\hat{y}$-value (or predicted response) when the x-value (or explanatory variable) equals 0.

β   Symbol for the population slope.

ρ   Symbol for the population correlation coefficient.

CHAPTER 10
EXERCISES

SECTION 10.1

10.1.1*   Suppose that a study measures how far each student sits from the front of the classroom and also records the student's final exam score. If better students tend to sit closer to the front, would the association between distance and exam score be positive, negative, or close to zero? Explain briefly.

10.1.2   Suppose that you record the daily high temperature and the daily amount of ice cream sold by an ice cream vendor at your favorite beach this summer, starting on Memorial Day weekend and ending on Labor Day weekend. Would you expect to find a positive or negative association between these variables? Explain briefly.

10.1.3*   Suppose that every student in this class scored 5 points lower on the second exam than on the first exam. Consider the correlation coefficient between *first exam score* and *second exam score*. What would the value of this correlation coefficient be? Explain briefly. [*Hint:* You might draw a scatterplot of hypothetical data that fit the description.]

10.1.4 Six statements about what you can learn from the correlation coefficient are listed below. Label each statement, choosing from A (can always tell), N (can never tell), or S (can sometimes tell). For each statement you label S for sometimes, explain briefly when you can tell and when you cannot.

a. Whether there is a relationship between *x* and *y*.

b. Whether the relationship between *x* and *y* is linear or curved

c. How closely the points fall near a line

d. Whether there are outliers or influential points

e. How steep the least squares line is

10.1.5* Fill in the blanks, choosing from: values of the response, values of the explanatory variable, observational units:

In a scatterplot, the points are _____; the *x*-axis represents _____; and the *y*-axis represents _____.

10.1.6 The data shown in the following scatterplot show a very nice relationship between the two variables. However, the correlation here is 0.03, very close to zero. Explain why we can have a nice relationship between two quantitative variables and yet have a correlation of 0.

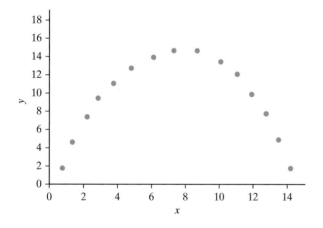

10.1.7* Which of the following is *not* a property of correlation, *r*?

A. $-1 \leq r \leq 1$

B. Correlation measures the strength of a linear relationship between two quantitative variables.

C. The sign on *r* tells the direction of the linear relationship between two quantitative variables.

D. If the correlation between two quantitative variables is zero, then there is no relationship between these two variables.

10.1.8 Which of the following statements is correct?

A. Changing the units of measurements of the explanatory or response variable does not change the value of the correlation.

B. A negative value for the correlation indicates that there is no relationship between the two variables.

C. The correlation has the same units (e.g., feet or minutes) as the explanatory variable.

D. Correlation between *y* and *x* has the same number but opposite sign as the correlation between *x* and *y*.

10.1.9* If two variables are negatively associated, then we know that:

A. Above-average values in one variable correspond to below-average values in the other variable.

B. Above-average values in one variable correspond to above-average values in the other variable.

C. Below-average values in one variable correspond to below-average values in the other variable.

D. Below-average values in one variable correspond either above-average or below-average values in the other variable.

10.1.10 For each of the following statements, say what, if anything, is wrong.

a. Because the correlation coefficient between test time and test score is −0.56, the correlation coefficient between *test score and test time* must be 0.56 (the positive value).

b. There is a strong positive correlation between a person's yard size and whether or not they have a dog.

c. For a sample of 50 students, the correlation coefficient between weight (kg) and height (inches) was found to be 0.78 kg/inches.

d. A correlation coefficient of $r = 0.84$ denotes just as strong a relationship as a correlation coefficient of $r = -0.84$.

House prices*

10.1.11 The data file **HousePrices** contains data on prices (\$) and sizes (in square feet) for a random sample of houses that sold in the year 2006 in Arroyo Grande, California. Enter the data into the **Corr/Regression** applet.

a. Identify the type of study: randomized experiment or observational study.

b. Identify the experimental/observational units in this study.

c. Identify the two variables of interest and whether each is categorical or quantitative. Which variable do you think makes more sense to use as the explanatory variable and which as the response variable?

d. Produce a scatterplot and comment on the association between the variables as revealed in the scatterplot. (Remember to comment on form, direction, strength, and unusual observations.)

e. Report the value of the correlation coefficient. Does the value of the correlation coefficient support your answer in part (d)? Explain how you are deciding.

Roller coasters

10.1.12 The data file **RollerCoasters** contains data (collected from www.rcdb.com) on the maximum speed (miles per hour) and the maximum height (feet) for each of a sample of roller coasters in the U.S. Enter the data into the **Corr/Regression** applet.

a. Identify the type of study: randomized experiment or observational study.

b. Identify the experimental/observational units in this study.

c. Identify the two variables of interest and whether each is categorical or quantitative. Which variable do you think makes more sense to use as the explanatory variable and which as the response variable?

d. Produce a scatterplot and comment on the association between the variables as revealed in the scatterplot. (Remember to comment on form, direction, strength, and unusual observations.)

e. Report the value of the correlation coefficient. Does the value of the correlation coefficient support your answer in part (d)? Explain how you are deciding.

Height and finger length*

10.1.13 An article titled "Giving the Finger to Dating Services" appeared in *Chance* magazine (2008) that investigated the association between length of index finger and height. This research was spurred by a report that online dating sites were asking members for the length of their index fingers. Perhaps this information could be used to verify whether the member was reporting his or her correct height on the profile? The data file **HeightAndFingerLength** contains data on the height (inches) and the length of index finger of dominant hand (cm) for students in a statistics class. Enter the data into the **Corr/Regression** applet.

a. Identify the type of study: randomized experiment or observational study.

b. Identify the experimental/observational units in this study.

c. Identify the two variables of interest and whether each is categorical or quantitative. Which variable do you think makes more sense to use as the explanatory variable and which as the response variable?

d. Produce a scatterplot and comment on the association between the variables as revealed in the scatterplot. (Remember to comment on form, direction, strength, and unusual observations.)

e. Report the value of the correlation coefficient. Does the value of the correlation coefficient support your answer in part (d)? Explain how you are deciding.

10.1.14 Refer to the previous exercise that investigated the association between length of index finger and height. The data file **HeightAndFingerLength** contains data on the height (inches) and the length of index finger of dominant hand (cm) for students in a statistics class.

a. Using appropriate technology (applet or statistical software) create a scatterplot of the data. On the scatterplot, locate the individual who reported a finger length of 5 cm and height of 70 inches. Does this individual appear to be an unusual observation? Explain you reasoning.

b. Next, report the correlation coefficient for these data.

c. Now, remove this individual (finger length of 5 cm and height of 70 inches). Recalculate the correlation coefficient for the data without this individual.

d. Did the correlation coefficient increase (move farther from zero) or decrease (move closer to zero) on the removal of the individual who reported a finger length of 5 cm and height of 70 inches? Explain why that makes sense.

10.1.15 Refer to the previous exercises that investigated the association between length of index finger and height. The data file **HeightAndFingerLength** contains data on the height (inches) and the length of index finger of dominant hand (cm) for students in a statistics class.

a. Once again, using appropriate technology (applet or statistical software) create a scatterplot of the data. On the scatterplot, locate the individual who reported a finger length of 10.16 cm and height of 78 inches. Does this individual appear to be an unusual observation? Explain you reasoning.

b. Next, report the correlation coefficient for these data.

c. Now, remove this individual (finger length of 10.16 cm and height of 78 inches). Recalculate the correlation coefficient for the data without this individual.

d. Did the correlation coefficient increase (move farther from zero) or decrease (move closer to zero) on the removal of the individual who reported a finger length of 10.16 cm and height of 78 inches? Explain why that makes sense.

Relationship between parents' and their children's heights

10.1.16 In 1885, Sir Francis Galton first used regression to explore the association between children's heights and (biological) parents' heights. The data file **MomandChildHeights** contains data for students in a statistics class on the following two variables: student's height (inches) and biological mother's height (inches). Enter the data into the **Corr/Regression** applet.

a. Identify the type of study: randomized experiment or observational study.

b. Identify the experimental/observational units in this study.

c. Identify the two variables of interest and whether each is categorical or quantitative. Which variable do you think makes more sense to use as the explanatory variable and which as the response variable?

d. Produce a scatterplot and comment on the association between the variables as revealed in the scatterplot. (Remember to comment on form, direction, strength, and unusual observations.)

e. Report the value of the correlation coefficient. Does the value of the correlation coefficient support your answer in part (d)? Explain how you are deciding.

10.1.17 Refer back to the previous exercise that explores the association between children's heights and (biological) mothers' heights. The data file **DadandChildHeights** contains data for students in a statistics class on the following two variables: student's height (inches) and biological father's height (inches). Enter the data into the **Corr/Regression** applet.

a. Identify the type of study: randomized experiment or observational study.

b. Identify the experimental/observational units in this study.

c. Identify the two variables of interest and whether each is categorical or quantitative. Which variable do you think makes more sense to use as the explanatory variable and which as the response variable?

d. Produce a scatterplot and comment on the association between the variables as revealed in the scatterplot. (Remember to comment on form, direction, strength, and unusual observations.)

e. Report the value of the correlation coefficient. Does the value of the correlation coefficient support your answer in part (d)? Explain how you are deciding.

10.1.18 Refer back to the previous two exercises that explore the association between children's heights and (biological) parents' heights. Recall that the data file **DadandChildHeights** contains data for students in a statistics class on the following two variables: student's height (inches) and biological father's height (inches), whereas the data file **MomandChildHeights** contains data for students in a statistics class on the following two variables: student's height (inches) and biological mother's height (inches).

a. Report the value of the correlation coefficient for children's and fathers' heights.

b. Report the value of the correlation coefficient for children's and mothers' heights.

c. In which case does there appear to be a stronger association between child's and parent's heights: with father's height or with mother's height? Explain your reasoning.

Scrabble names*

10.1.19 Have you ever played the game *Scrabble*®? It is a word building game where certain letters earn you more points than others when you use them in your word. Here is the table of letters and the corresponding Scrabble points:

A	B	C	D	E	F	G	H	I	J	K	L	M
1	3	3	2	1	4	2	4	1	8	5	1	3

N	O	P	Q	R	S	T	U	V	W	X	Y	Z
1	1	3	10	1	1	1	1	4	4	8	4	10

In a statistics class, students were asked to calculate the number of Scrabble points their names would earn. For example, the Scrabble score for the name Tom Sawyer would be $1 + 1 + 3 + 1 + 1 + 4 + 4 + 1 + 1 = 17$ points. The data file **ScrabbleNames** contains data on the following two variables: number of letters in a student's name and the corresponding Scrabble score. Enter the data into the **Corr/Regression** applet.

a. Identify the type of study: randomized experiment or observational study.

b. Identify the experimental/observational units in this study.

c. Identify the two variables of interest and whether each is categorical or quantitative. Which variable do you think makes more sense to use as the explanatory variable and which as the response variable?

d. Produce a scatterplot and comment on the association between the variables as revealed in the scatterplot. (Remember to comment on form, direction, strength, and unusual observations.)

e. Report the value of the correlation coefficient. Does the value of the correlation coefficient support your answer in part (d)? Explain how you are deciding.

10.1.20 Refer back to the previous exercise about exploring the relationship between the number of letters in a name and the corresponding Scrabble score. Recall that students were asked to calculate the number of Scrabble points their names would earn. Students were also asked to calculate the points per letter, that is, *ratio* = (Scrabble score)/(number of letters in name). The data file **ScrabbleRatio** contains Scrabble points for a student's name and the corresponding *ratio*.

a. Enter the data into the **Corr/Regression** applet. Produce a scatterplot and comment on the association between the variables as revealed in the scatterplot. (Remember to comment on form, direction, strength, and unusual observations.)

b. Report the value of the correlation coefficient. Does the value of the correlation coefficient support your answer in part (a)? Explain how you are deciding.

10.1.21 Refer back to the previous two exercises that explore the association between number of letters in a name and the corresponding Scrabble score. Recall that the data file **ScrabbleNames** contains data on number of letters in students' names and the corresponding Scrabble points, whereas the data file **ScrabbleRatio** contains Scrabble points for a student's name and the corresponding ratio of Scrabble points to number of letters.

a. In which case is the linear association stronger: between the number of letters in a student's name and the corresponding Scrabble points or between Scrabble points for a student's name and the corresponding ratio? How are you deciding?

b. With regard to your finding in part (a), explain why that makes sense.

TV and life expectancy

10.1.22 The data file **TVLife** provides information on life expectancy and number of televisions per thousand people in a sample of 22 countries, as reported by the *2006 World Almanac and Book of Facts*. Enter the data into the **Corr/Regression** applet.

a. Identify the type of study: randomized experiment or observational study.

b. Identify the experimental/observational units in this study. (*Hint:* "People" is not the answer.)

c. Produce a scatterplot using life expectancy as the response variable and number of TVs per 1,000 as the explanatory variable. Comment on the association between the variables as revealed in the scatterplot. (Remember to comment on form, direction, strength, and unusual observations.)

d. Report the value of the correlation coefficient. Does the value of the correlation coefficient support your answer in part (c)? Explain how you are deciding.

e. As you (should) have discovered in parts (c) and (d), the association between life expectancy and number of televisions per thousand people appears pretty strong. Based on this finding, is it okay to conclude that simply sending televisions to the countries with lower life expectancies would cause their inhabitants to live longer? Explain why or why not.

SECTION 10.2

10.2.1* An instructor wanted to investigate whether there was an association between height (inches) and hand span (cm). She collected data from 10 students and after analyzing the data found the p-value to be 0.022. For each of the following statements, indicate whether or not the statement is valid or invalid.

a. The p-value says that there is a 2.20% probability that there is no association between height and hand span.

b. The p-value says that there is a 2.20% probability that there is an association between height and hand span.

c. If there were no association between height and hand span, the probability of observing the association observed in the sample data of 10 students is 0.022.

d. If there were no association between height and hand span, the probability of observing the association observed in the sample data or an even stronger association in a sample of 10 students is 0.022.

e. If there were an association between height and hand span, the probability of observing the association observed in the sample data or an even stronger association in a sample of 10 students is 0.022.

10.2.2 A researcher wants to investigate whether there is a relationship between annual company profit ($) and median annual salary paid by the company ($). The researcher collects data on a random sample of companies and after analyzing the data finds the p-value to be 0.56. Which of the following is an appropriate conclusion based on this p-value?

A. There is no relationship between annual company profit ($) and median annual salary paid by the company ($).

B. There is a relationship between annual company profit ($) and median annual salary paid by the company ($), and the corresponding value of the correlation coefficient is $r = 0.56$.

C. There is not convincing evidence of a relationship between annual company profit ($) and median annual salary paid by the company ($).

D. There is a 56% chance that there is no relationship between annual company profit ($) and median annual salary paid by the company ($).

10.2.3* Two researchers want to investigate whether there is a relationship between annual company profit ($) and median annual salary paid by the company ($). Researcher Bart collects data on a random sample of 40 companies, and researcher Lisa collects data on a random sample of 140 companies. After analyzing their respective data sets, each finds a correlation coefficient of $r = 0.601$.

a. Who will have a smaller p-value?
   A. Bart
   B. Lisa
   C. Both will find the same p-value.
   D. More information is needed to answer this question.

b. Explain the reasoning for your choice in part (a).

Height and finger length

10.2.4 Recall from Exercise 10.1.13 that the data file **HeightAndFingerLength** contains data on the height (inches) and the length of the index finger of the dominant hand (cm) for students in a statistics class. State in words the appropriate null and alternative hypotheses to test whether there is an association between height and length of index finger.

10.2.5 Refer to the previous exercise about the association between height and length of index finger. Recall that the data file **HeightAnd FingerLength** contains data on the height (inches) and the length of the index finger of the dominant hand (cm) for students in a statistics class. Describe how one might use everyday items (for example, coins, dice, cards, etc.) to conduct a tactile simulation-based test of the hypotheses. Be sure to clearly describe how the p-value will be computed from the simulation.

10.2.6 Refer to the previous exercise about the association between height and the length of the index finger. Recall that the data file **HeightAnd FingerLength** contains data on the height (inches) and the length of the index finger of the dominant hand (cm) for students in a statistics class.

The correlation coefficient for the sample data is 0.474. A simulated null distribution is shown to test the null hypothesis of no association between height and length of index finger.

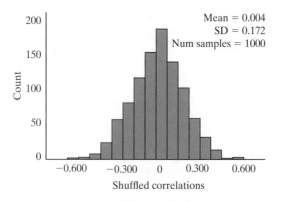

On the null distribution indicate the region that denotes the p-value, being sure to include any number that you are using to decide on the region. Also, make sure that you answer is consistent with the hypotheses chosen in part (a) of Exercise 10.2.4.

Used Honda Civics*

10.2.7 The data in the file **UsedHondaCivics** come from a sample of used Honda Civics listed for sale online in July 2006. The variables recorded in this data file are the car's age (calculated as 2006 minus year of manufacture) and price. Consider conducting a simulation analysis to test whether the sample data provide strong evidence of an association between a car's price and age in the population.

a. Identify the type of study: randomized experiment or observational study.

b. Identify the experimental/observational units in this study.

c. Identify the two variables of interest and whether each is categorical or quantitative. Which variable do you think makes more sense to use as the explanatory variable and which as the response variable?

d. State the appropriate *null* hypothesis *in words*.

e. State the relevant *alternative* hypothesis *in words*.

f. Enter the data into the **Corr/Regression** applet. Produce a scatterplot and comment on the association between the variables as revealed in the scatterplot. (Remember to comment on form, direction, strength, and unusual observations.)

g. Report the value of the correlation coefficient. Does the value of the correlation coefficient support your answer in part (f)? Explain how you are deciding.

h. Describe how one might use everyday items (for example, coins, dice, cards, etc.) to conduct a tactile simulation-based test of the hypotheses. Be sure to clearly describe how the p-value will be computed from the simulation.

10.2.8 Refer to the previous exercise about the association between the age and price of used Honda Civics. Consider conducting a test of significance to investigate whether the sample data provide strong evidence of an association between a car's price and age in the population of used Honda Civics. The data are in the file **UsedHondaCivics.**

a. Enter the data into the **Corr/Regression** applet and conduct a simulation-based test of significance using the correlation coefficient as the statistic. Report the approximate p-value.

b. Interpret the p-value reported in part (a).

c. Summarize your conclusion (significance, causation, generalizability) from this simulation analysis. Also describe the reasoning process by which your conclusion follows from your simulation results.

House prices

10.2.9 Recall from Exercise 10.1.11 that the data file **HousePrices** contains data on prices ($) and sizes (in square feet) for a random sample of houses that sold in the year 2006 in Arroyo Grande, California.

a. State in words the appropriate null and alternative hypotheses to test whether there is an association between prices and sizes of houses.

b. Describe how one might use everyday items (for example, coins, dice, cards, etc.) to conduct a tactile simulation-based test of the hypotheses. Be sure to clearly describe how the p-value will be computed from the simulation.

10.2.10 Refer to the previous exercise about the association between prices and sizes of houses. Recall that the data file **HousePrices** contains data on prices ($) and sizes (in square feet) for a random sample of houses that sold in the year 2006 in Arroyo Grande, California.

a. Enter the data into the **Corr/Regression** applet and conduct a simulation-based test of significance. Report the approximate p-value.

b. Interpret the p-value reported in part (a).

c. Summarize your conclusion (significance, causation, generalizability) from this simulation analysis. Also describe the reasoning process by which your conclusion follows from your simulation results.

Roller coasters*

10.2.11 Recall from Exercise 10.1.12 that the data file **Roller Coasters** contains data (collected from www.rcdb.com) on the maximum speed (miles per hour) and the maximum height (feet) for each of a sample of roller coasters in the U.S.

a. State in words the appropriate null and alternative hypotheses to test whether there is an association between maximum speed and maximum height of such roller coasters.

b. Describe how one might use everyday items (for example, coins, dice, cards, etc.) to conduct a tactile simulation-based test of the hypotheses. Be sure to clearly describe how the p-value will be computed from the simulation.

10.2.12 Refer to the previous exercise about the association between maximum speed and maximum height of roller coasters. Recall that the data file **Rollercoasters** contains data on the maximum speed (miles per hour) and the maximum height (feet) for each of a sample of roller coasters in the U.S.

a. Enter the data into the **Corr/Regression** applet and conduct a simulation-based test of significance. Report the approximate p-value.

b. Interpret the p-value reported in part (a).

c. Summarize your conclusion (significance, causation, generalizability) from this simulation analysis. Also describe the reasoning process by which your conclusion follows from your simulation results.

Relationship between parents' and their children's heights

10.2.13 Recall from Exercise 10.1.16 that the data file **MomandChildHeights** contains data for students in a statistics class on the following two variables: student's height (inches) and biological mother's height (inches).

a. State in words the appropriate null and alternative hypotheses to test whether there is an association between a person's height and their biological mother's height.

b. Describe how one might use everyday items (for example, coins, dice, cards, etc.) to conduct a tactile simulation-based test of the hypotheses. Be sure to clearly describe how the p-value will be computed from the simulation.

10.2.14 Refer to the previous exercise about the association between a person's height and their biological mother's height. Recall that the data file **MomandChildHeights** contains data for students in a statistics class on the following

two variables: student's height (inches) and biological mother's height (inches).

a. Enter the data into the **Corr/Regression** applet and conduct a simulation-based test of significance. Report the approximate p-value.

b. Interpret the p-value reported in part (a).

c. Summarize your conclusion (significance, causation, generalizability) from this simulation analysis. Also describe the reasoning process by which your conclusion follows from your simulation results.

10.2.15 Refer back to Exercise 10.1.17, which explores the association between children's heights and (biological) fathers' heights. The data file **DadandChildHeights** contains data for students in a statistics class on the following two variables: student's height (inches) and biological father's height (inches).

a. State in words the appropriate null and alternative hypotheses to test whether there is an association between a person's height and their biological father's height.

b. Describe how one might use everyday items (for example, coins, dice, cards, etc.) to conduct a tactile simulation-based test of the hypotheses. Be sure to clearly describe how the p-value will be computed from the simulation.

10.2.16 Refer to the previous exercise about the association between a person's height and their biological father's height. Recall that the data file **DadandChildHeights** contains data for students in a statistics class on the following two variables: student's height (inches) and biological father's height (inches).

a. Enter the data into the **Corr/Regression** applet and conduct a simulation-based test of significance. Report the approximate p-value.

b. Interpret the p-value reported in part (a).

c. Summarize your conclusion (significance, causation, generalizability) from this simulation analysis. Also describe the reasoning process by which your conclusion follows from your simulation results.

Scrabble names*

10.2.17 Recall from Exercise 10.1.19 that in a statistics class students were asked to calculate the number of Scrabble points their names would earn. For example, the Scrabble score for the name Tom Sawyer would be 17 points. The data file **ScrabbleNames** contains data on the following two variables: number of letters in a student's name and the corresponding Scrabble score.

a. State in words the appropriate null and alternative hypotheses to test whether there is an association between the number of letters in a person's name and the Scrabble points their name earns.

b. Describe how one might use everyday items (for example, coins, dice, cards, etc.) to conduct a tactile simulation-based test of the hypotheses. Be sure to clearly describe how the p-value will be computed from the simulation.

10.2.18 Refer back to the previous exercise about exploring the relationship between the number of letters in a name and the corresponding Scrabble score. Recall that the data file **ScrabbleNames** contains data on the following two variables: number of letters in a student's name and the corresponding Scrabble score.

a. Enter the data into the **Corr/Regression** applet and conduct a simulation-based test of significance. Report the approximate p-value.

b. Interpret the p-value reported in part (a).

c. Summarize your conclusion (significance, causation, generalizability) from this simulation analysis. Also describe the reasoning process by which your conclusion follows from your simulation results.

10.2.19 Refer back to Exercise 10.1.20 about exploring the relationship between the number of letters in a name and the corresponding Scrabble score. Students were also asked to calculate the points per letter, that is, *ratio* = (Scrabble score)/(number of letters in name). The data file **ScrabbleRatio** contains Scrabble points for a student's name and the corresponding *ratio*.

a. State in words the appropriate null and alternative hypotheses to test whether there is an association between the Scrabble points for a student's name and the corresponding *ratio*.

b. Describe how one might use everyday items (for example, coins, dice, cards, etc.) to conduct a tactile simulation-based test of the hypotheses. Be sure to clearly describe how the p-value will be computed from the simulation.

10.2.20 Refer back to the previous exercise. Recall that the data file **ScrabbleRatio** contains Scrabble points for a student's name and the corresponding ratio of Scrabble points to number of letters.

a. Enter the data into the **Corr/Regression** applet and conduct a simulation-based test of significance. Report the approximate p-value.

b. Interpret the p-value reported in part (a).

c. Summarize your conclusion (significance, causation, generalizability) from this simulation analysis. Also describe the reasoning process by which your conclusion follows from your simulation results.

TV and life expectancy

10.2.21 Recall from Exercise 10.1.22 that the data file **TVLife** provides information on life expectancy and number of televisions per thousand people in a sample of 22 countries, as reported by the *2006 World Almanac and Book of Facts*.

a. State in words the appropriate null and alternative hypotheses to test whether there is an association between the life expectancy and number of televisions per thousand people in such countries.

b. Describe how one might use everyday items (for example, coins, dice, cards, etc.) to conduct a tactile simulation-based test of the hypotheses. Be sure to clearly describe how the p-value will be computed from the simulation.

10.2.22 Refer back to the previous exercise. Recall that the data file **TVLife** provides information on life expectancy and number of televisions per thousand people in a sample of 22 countries, as reported by the *2006 World Almanac and Book of Facts*.

a. Enter the data into the **Corr/Regression** applet and conduct a simulation-based test of significance. Report the approximate p-value.

b. Interpret the p-value reported in part (a).

c. Summarize your conclusion (significance, causation, generalizability) from this simulation analysis. Also describe the reasoning process by which your conclusion follows from your simulation results.

FAQ

10.2.23 Read FAQ 10.2.1. Was there a parameter in the draft lottery example? Why or why not?

SECTION 10.3

10.3.1* Which of the following does the method of least squares minimize?

A. Sum of vertical distances between observations and the line

B. Sum of squared vertical distances between observations and the line

C. Sum of perpendicular distances between observations and the line

D. Sum of squared perpendicular distances between observations and the line

E. Sum of horizontal distances between observations and the line

F. Sum of squared horizontal distances between observations and the line

10.3.2 Explain what is wrong with the following statements about correlation and regression.

a. The correlation between the number of years of education and yearly income is 1.23.

b. The regression equation that describes the relationship between the age of a used Ford Mustang and its value is

$\hat{y} = -1,000x + 10,000$ where the explanatory variable is the age of the automobile (in years) and the response is its value (in dollars). The correlation describing this relationship is 0.83.

10.3.3* It can be shown that the *sum* of residuals from a least squares line always equals zero.

a. Does it follow from this result that the *mean* of the residuals from a least squares line always equals zero? Explain briefly.

b. Does it follow from this result that the *median* of the residuals from a least squares line always equals zero? Explain briefly.

10.3.4

a. Can a slope coefficient ever be negative?

b. Can a slope coefficient ever be greater than 1?

c. Can a slope coefficient ever equal zero?

10.3.5* Reconsider the previous exercise. For each of the descriptions presented that is indeed possible, produce a scatterplot of hypothetical data to show that the description is indeed possible.

10.3.6 Reconsider the previous two exercises. Answer the questions with regard to the *intercept* coefficient rather than the slope coefficient.

Legos*

10.3.7 A colleague went to the lego.com website in February 2014 and recorded the number of pieces and the sales price for 157 Lego products listed there. The data appear in the **Legos** data file.

a. Which variable do you think makes more sense to use as the explanatory variable and which as the response variable?

b. Enter the data into the **Corr/Regression** applet. Produce a scatterplot and comment on the association between the variables as revealed in the scatterplot. (Remember to comment on form, direction, strength, and unusual observations.)

c. Report the value of the correlation coefficient.

d. Calculate the value of r^2 and interpret what the value means in this context.

10.3.8 Reconsider the previous exercise and the **Legos** data file.

a. Determine the equation of the least squares line for predicting price from number of pieces. Report this equation using good statistical notation.

b. Interpret the value of the slope coefficient in this context.

c. Interpret the value of the intercept coefficient. Is this a context for which the value of the intercept provides relevant information? Explain.

10.3.9 Reconsider the previous two exercises and the **Legos** data file. The equation of the least squares line turns out to be $\widehat{price} = 4.86 + 0.105 \times pieces$, and the value of $r^2 = 0.949$. Identify which of the following interpretations are correct, which are incorrect, and which are correct but incomplete or poorly worded.

a. The Legos cost 10.50 cents per piece.

b. For each additional dollar in price, the predicted number of pieces in the set increases by about 10.50.

c. For each additional piece in the set, the predicted price increases by about 10.50 cents.

d. The price goes up 10.50 cents for each additional piece in the set.

e. The predicted price for a set with 0 pieces is $4.86.

f. The predicted price increases by $10.50 for each additional 100 pieces in the set.

10.3.10 Reconsider the previous three exercises and the **Legos** data file. The equation of the least squares line turns out to be $\widehat{price} = 4.86 + 0.105 \times pieces$, and the value of $r^2 = 0.949$. Identify which of the following interpretations are correct, which are incorrect, and which are correct but incomplete or poorly worded.

a. 10.50% of the variability in prices is explained by the least squares line with number of pieces.

b. 94.90% of the variability in prices is explained by the least squares line with number of pieces.

c. 94.90% of the prices fall on the least squares line based on number of pieces.

d. The least squares line correctly predicts the price for 94.90% of the Lego products.

10.3.11 Reconsider the previous four exercises and the **Legos** data file.

a. Determine the predicted price for a product with 500 pieces.

b. Determine the predicted price for a product with 1,500 pieces.

c. Determine the difference between the two predictions in parts (a) and (b). Also indicate how you could have determined this value directly from the equation of the least squares line.

d. Determine the predicted price for a product with 5,000 pieces.

e. Do you feel very confident with this prediction in part (e)? Explain why or why not.

10.3.12 Reconsider the previous five exercises and the **Legos** data file. The last product listed in the data file has 415 pieces and a price of $49.99.

a. Determine the predicted price for such a product.

b. Determine the residual value for this product.

c. Interpret what this residual value means.

d. Does the product fall above or below the least squares line in the graph? Explain how you can tell, based on its residual value.

10.3.13 Reconsider the previous six exercises and the **Legos** data file. This is very unrealistic, but suppose that one of the products were to be offered at a price of $0.

a. Would you expect this change to affect the least squares line very much? Explain.

b. For which one product would you expect this change to have the greatest impact on the least squares line? Explain how you choose this product.

c. Change the price to $0 for the product that you identified in part (b). Report the (new) equation of the least squares line and the (new) value of r^2. Have these values changed considerably?

Crickets

10.3.14 Consider the following two scatterplots based on data gathered in a study of 30 crickets, with temperature measured in degrees Fahrenheit and chirp frequency measured in chirps per minute.

a. If the goal is to predict temperature based on a cricket's chirps per minute, which is the appropriate scatterplot to examine—the one on the left or the one on the right? Explain briefly.

One of the following is the correct equation of the least squares line for predicting temperature from chirps per minute:

A. predicted temperature = 35.78 + 0.25 chirps per minute

B. predicted temperature = −131.23 + 3.81 chirps per minute

C. predicted temperature = 83.54 − 0.25 chirps per minute

b. Which is the correct equation? Circle your answer and explain briefly.

c. Use the correct equation to predict the temperature when the cricket is chirping at 100 chirps per minute.

d. Interpret the value of the slope coefficient, in this context, for whichever equation you think is the correct one.

Cat jumping*

10.3.15 Harris and Steudel (2002) studied factors that might be associated with the jumping performance of domestic cats. They studied 18 cats, using takeoff velocity (in centimeters per second) as the response variable. They used body mass (in grams), hind limb length (in centimeters), muscle mass (in grams), and percent body fat in addition to sex as potential explanatory variables. The data can be found in the **CatJumping** data file. A scatterplot of takeoff velocity vs. body mass is shown in the figure for Exercise 10.3.15.

a. Describe the association between these variables.

b. Use the **Corr/Regression** applet to determine the equation of the least squares line for predicting a cat's takeoff velocity from its mass.

c. Interpret the value of the slope coefficient in this context.

d. Interpret the value of the intercept coefficient. Is this a context in which the intercept coefficient is meaningful?

e. Determine the proportion of variability in takeoff velocity that is explained by the least squares line with mass.

EXERCISE 10.3.14

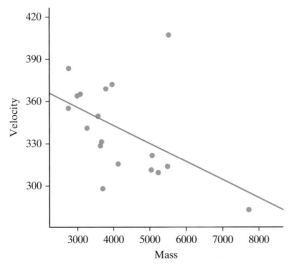

EXERCISE 10.3.15

10.3.16 Reconsider the previous exercise and the **CatJumping** data file.

a. Determine the predicted takeoff velocity for a cat with a mass of 5,000 grams (which is about 11 pounds).

b. Determine the predicted takeoff velocity for a cat with a mass of 10,000 grams. Also explain why it's not advisable to have much confidence in this prediction.

c. Determine the predicted takeoff velocity and the residual value for the cat with the largest mass. Also interpret what this residual value means.

10.3.17 Reconsider the previous two exercises. Answer the following based on the scatterplot presented above. Do not bother to perform any calculations.

a. Which cat has the *largest predicted* value for its takeoff velocity?

b. Which cat has the *smallest predicted* value for its takeoff velocity?

c. Which cat has the *largest residual* value?

d. Which cat has the *smallest residual* value?

10.3.18 Reconsider the previous three exercises and the **CatJumping** data file. Investigate the association between the response variable (takeoff velocity) and the other explanatory variables (hind limb length, muscle mass, percent body fat).

a. Select the explanatory variable that has the strongest association with the response. Describe this association.

b. Report the equation of the least squares line for predicting the cat's takeoff velocity using this explanatory variable.

c. Interpret the value of the slope coefficient.

d. Determine and interpret the value of r^2.

Honda Civic pricing

10.3.19 The data in the file **UsedHondaCivics** come from a sample of used Honda Civics listed for sale online in July

2006. The variables recorded are age (calculated as 2006 minus year of manufacture) and price.

a. Identify the observational units.

b. Produce a scatterplot of price vs. age. Describe the association revealed in the graph.

c. Determine the least squares line for predicting price from age and produce a scatterplot with the least squares line superimposed.

d. Report and interpret the value of the slope coefficient.

e. What percentage of the variability in car prices is explained by knowing the car's age?

Textbook prices*

10.3.20 Two Cal Poly freshmen gathered data on a random sample of textbooks from the campus bookstore in November of 2006. Two of the variables recorded were the price of the book and the number of pages that it contained. These data are in the file **TextbookPrices**.

a. Identify the explanatory and response variables in this study.

b. Determine the equation of the least squares line for predicting price from number of pages. Report the equation, being sure to use good statistical notation.

c. Use the least squares line to predict the price of a 500-page textbook. Then do the same for a 1,500-page textbook. Which prediction would you have more confidence in? Explain.

d. Interpret what the slope coefficient means in this context.

e. Determine the proportion of variability in textbook prices that is explained by knowing the number of pages in the book.

Day hikes

10.3.21 The book *Day Hikes in San Luis Obispo County* lists information about 72 hikes, including the distance of the hike (in miles), the elevation gain of the hike (in feet), and the time that the hike is expected to take (in minutes). Consider the scatterplot below, with least squares regression line superimposed:

a. Report the value of the slope coefficient for predicting time from distance.

b. Write a sentence interpreting the value of the slope coefficient for predicting time from distance.

c. Use the line to predict how long a 4-mile hike will take.

d. Would you feel more comfortable using the line predict the time for a 4-mile hike or for a 12-mile hike? Explain your choice.

e. The value of the correlation coefficient between time and distance is 0.916, and the value of $r^2 = 0.839$. Complete this sentence to interpret what this value means:

83.9% of _____ is explained by _____.

10.3.22 Reconsider the previous exercise. The following scatterplot displays hiking time vs. elevation gain, with the least squares line superimposed:

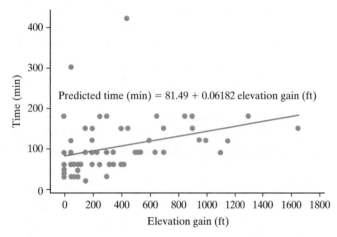

Predicted time (min) = 81.49 + 0.06182 elevation gain (ft)

a. Report the value of the slope coefficient for predicting time from elevation gain.

b. Write a sentence interpreting the value of the slope coefficient for predicting time from elevation gain.

c. Use the line to predict how long a hike with an 800-foot elevation gain will take.

d. Would you feel more comfortable using the line predict the time for a hike with an 800-foot elevation gain or a hike with a 2,800-foot elevation gain? Explain your choice.

e. The value of the correlation coefficient between time and distance is 0.344, and the value of $r^2 = 0.119$. Complete this sentence to interpret what this value means:

11.9% of _____ is explained by _____.

10.3.23 The slope b and intercept a of a least squares line can be calculated from the means and standard deviations of the two variables, along with the correlation coefficient, as follows: $b = r\dfrac{s_y}{s_x}$ and $a = \bar{y} - b\bar{x}$. These summary statistics for the day hikes described in the previous two exercises are:

	Mean	SD	Correlation with time
Distance	3.283	1.856	0.916
Elevation gain	333.2	355.5	0.344
Time	102.08	63.79	1.000

a. Use these statistics to determine the slope b and intercept a for predicting time from *distance*.

b. Use these statistics to determine the slope b and intercept a for predicting time from *elevation gain*.

c. Use the least squares line to predict the time needed for a hike with distance equal to the mean of the distances.

d. Use the least squares line to predict the time needed for a hike with elevation gain equal to the mean of the elevation gains.

e. What do you notice about your predictions in parts (c) and (d)?

Introductory statistics tests*

10.3.24 The following scatterplot represents scores on Test 2 and Test 3 in Introductory Statistics for a random sample of students.

a. In the accompanying scatterplot, there appears to be a positive relationship between scores on Test 2 and Test 3. Does this mean that a person who scores above the mean on Test 2 is expected to also score above the mean on Test 3? What about those who score below the mean on Test 2: Are they expected to score below the mean on Test 3?

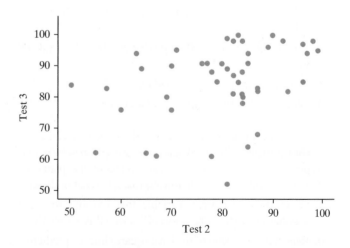

The regression equation for these data is $\hat{y} = 55.2 + 0.3708x$, where x is the score on Test 2 and $\hat{y}$ is the expected score on Test 3. The mean for Test 2 was 79.80 and the mean for Test 3 was 84.80.

b. If a student scores 79.80 on Test 2, what is their predicted score for Test 3? If that student then actually gets 90 on Test 3, what is the residual?

c. If someone scores 10 points *above* the mean on Test 2, how many points above the mean on Test 3 is their expected score?

d. If someone scores 10 points *below* the mean on Test 2, how many points below the mean on Test 3 is their expected score?

10.3.25 Reconsider the previous exercise.

a. Determine the predicted score on Test 3 for a student who scores 55 on Test 2.

b. Determine the predicted score on Test 3 for a student who scores 95 on Test 2.

c. Of the two students in parts (a) and (b), which student is predicted to achieve a *higher* score on Test 3 than he or she scored on Test 2? Which student is predicted to achieve a *lower* score on Test 3 than he or she scored on Test 2? (This phenomenon is known as the *regression effect*.)

FAQ

10.3.26 Read FAQ 10.3.1. In your own words explain why using the sum of the absolute deviations is problematic in some scatterplots and, in turn, why the sum of squared deviations is preferred.

SECTION 10.3: Part 2

10.3.27* A residual is calculated by using which of the following?

A. $\hat{y} - y$

B. $y - \hat{y}$

C. $\hat{y} - x$

D. $x - \hat{y}$

E. $x - \hat{x}$

10.3.28 You are given the following regression output where the height of a person, in inches, is being used to predict the amount of sleep per night, in hours. What is the equation of the least squares regression line?

Regression Table: ☑

Term	Coeff	SE	t-stat	p-value	
Intercept	9.4370	1.5403	6.13	0.0000	$r^2 = 1.9\%$
Height	−0.0354	0.0228	−1.55	0.1236	$s = 0.99$

A. $\hat{y} = 9.4370 + 1.5403x$

B. $\hat{y} = -0.0354 + 0.0228x$

C. $\hat{y} = 9.4370 + 0.99x$

D. $\hat{y} = 9.4370 - 0.0354x$

E. $\hat{y} = -0.0354 + 9.4370x$

F. $\hat{y} = 1.5403 + 0.0228x$

10.3.29* Using the previous question's regression output, what is the value of the correlation coefficient for sleep and height?

A. −0.1378

B. −0.1236

C. −0.99

D. −0.019

E. −0.0004

10.3.30 Using the regression output from Exercise 10.3.28, the $s = 0.99$ value represents the standard deviation of the:

A. y-values

B. x-values

C. slope

D. y-intercept

E. residuals

10.3.31* If you know the slope of a regression line for a data set is 2 and the mean of the x-values and y-values of the data set are $\bar{x} = 3$ and $\bar{y} = 16$, what is the value of the y-intercept of the regression line?

A. −3

B. 5.33

C. 10

D. 11

E. 21

10.3.32 College students were asked how many classes they failed to attend in the last three weeks as well as their current grade point average. We obtained the following regression equation from the resulting data: $\widehat{GPA} = 3.49 - 0.07$ (*number of skipped classes*). What does the slope of the regression line mean in context?

A. As the predicted GPA increases by 1, the number of classes skipped goes down by 0.07.

B. As the predicted GPA increases by 1, the number of classes skipped goes down 0.07 times.

C. For every additional class skipped, the GPA is predicted to go down 0.07 points.

D. For every class skipped, the GPA will go down by 0.07 times.

10.3.33* Suppose the mean and standard deviation of the x-values of a certain data set are $\bar{x} = 6$ and $s_x = 4$, respectively. Also suppose the mean and standard deviation of the y-values of the same data set are $\bar{y} = 5$ and $s_y = 4$, respectively. Which (possibly more than one) of the following could be the least squares regression line, where the x-variable is the explanatory variable and the y-variable is the response variable?

A. $\hat{y} = 17 - 2x$

B. $\hat{y} = -7 + 2x$

C. $\hat{y} = 0.4x$

D. $\hat{y} = 2.6 + 0.4x$

E. $\hat{y} = 2.6 - 0.4x$

10.3.34 We want to predict the height of someone given his or her foot length. So we randomly sampled 81 high school students from the *Census at School* database in 2017 that gave their heights and foot lengths in centimeters and had software calculate the following regression table:

```
Term        Coeff SE    t-stat p-value
Intercept   95.20 7.42  12.83  0.0000
Footlength  2.96  0.30  9.99   0.0000
```

a. Give the equation of the least squares regression line for predicting height given foot length.

b. Interpret the slope coefficient in your regression line in the context of height and foot length.

c. One student's height was 168 cm and foot length was 24 cm. What is the residual for this person?

10.3.35* Students in college statistics classes were asked, "If you could magically be any height you wanted, what height would you be?" They were also asked what their actual heights were. The regression equations below give the predicted magical heights (in inches) given the actual heights (in inches) for both males and females in the classes.

Females	Males
$\widehat{\text{magical height}} =$	$\widehat{\text{magical height}} =$
$30.89 + 0.5408 \,(\text{height})$	$36.38 + 0.5283 \,(\text{height})$

a. Does a 72 in. tall female tend to wish to be taller? Explain.

b. Does a 72 in. tall male tend to wish to be taller? Explain.

c. According to the equation, shorter females tend to wish to be taller and taller females tend to wish to be shorter. To the nearest inch, where does the change happen from tending to wish to be taller to wish to be shorter?

10.3.36* Recall the previous question about students' heights.

a. One of the females from the data set is 64 in. tall and she wished she could magically be 68 in. tall. What is the value of the residual for that data point?

b. One of the males from the data set is 72 in. tall and he wished he could magically be 74 in. tall. What is the value of the residual for that data point?

10.3.37 What would the value of the coefficient of determination be if the standard deviation of the residuals was 0? Explain.

10.3.38* Use the scatterplot below to answer the questions below.

a. Which labeled point or points have positive residuals?

b. Which labeled point or points have negative residuals?

c. Which labeled point has the largest residual?

d. Which labeled point has the residual closest to zero?

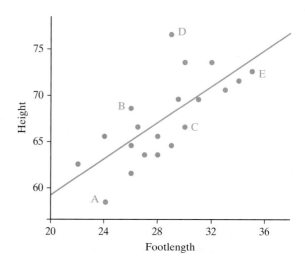

10.3.39 Suppose the mean and standard deviation of the x-values of a certain data set are $\bar{x} = 4$ and $s_x = 3$, respectively. Also suppose the mean and standard deviation of the y-values of the same data set are $\bar{y} = 8$ and $s_y = 6$, respectively. If the correlation between the x-variable and y-variable is 0.60, what is the equation of the least squares regression line, where the x-variable is the explanatory variable and the y-variable is the response variable?

10.3.40* Suppose the mean and standard deviation of the x-values of a certain data set are $\bar{x} = 7$ and $s_x = 5$, respectively. Also suppose the mean and standard deviation of the y-values of the same data set are $\bar{y} = 2$ and $s_y = 2$, respectively. If the correlation between the x-variable and y-variable is -0.80, what is the equation of the least squares regression line, where the x-variable is the explanatory variable and the y-variable is the response variable?

10.3.41 Researchers published in the journal *Nature* (Tatem et al., 2004) explored the winning times of the 100-meter dash at the Olympics for both men and women. Using the winning times in the 1900 to 2004 Olympics, they noted that women's times were decreasing faster than men's times. In the article, they state, "We show here that—if current trends continue—it is the winner of the event (the women's 100-meter dash) in the 2156 Olympics whose name will be etched in sporting history forever, because this may be the first occasion on which the race is won in a faster time than the men's event." They used two linear regression lines, one for men and one for women, to come up with their conclusion.

a. What, statistically, is quite troubling about the researchers' quoted claim?

b. The regression equation for the women's winning times is $\widehat{time} = 44.470 - 0.01688(year)$. Use this equation to find the year of the first Olympics where the winner is predicted to finish before she even starts! (Remember that the Summer Olympics are held in years that are multiples of 4; we assume the same will continue to hold true into the distant future.)

10.3.42* Research done at UCLA (Inagaki et al., 2016) investigated the relationship between physical warmth and social warmth. They measured physical warmth by taking the oral temperatures of 54 subjects (in degrees Celsius). To measure social warmth, they gave them a 12-item test that included questions like "I feel like being around other people." The subjects responded on a 5-point (1, not at all, to 5, very much so) scale for each item and the 12 responses were averaged, giving a "warmth score" for each subject. The regression output is shown below.

a. Use the regression output to determine the equation of the least squares regression line. Identify all variables used in the equation.

b. Is a linear model appropriate for these data? Explain.

c. What is the value of the slope of the least squares regression line, and what does it mean in the context of body temperature and average social warmth score?

d. What percentage of the variation in the warmth scores is explained by its linear relationship with body temperature?

e. Use the regression model to predict the social warmth score for someone with a body temperature of 37°C.

f. One of the subjects had a body temperature of 37°C and a social warmth score of 4.4. Calculate the residual for this subject and explain what it means.

g. Identify and interpret the standard deviation of the residuals.

10.3.43 A person who can identify or produce a musical tone correctly without any outside reference is said to have perfect pitch. This can be tested using a pitch identification test (PIT). Perfect pitch has also been associated with certain disabilities. Danish researchers (Dohn et al., 2012) tested to see whether PIT scores are associated with autism traits using the autism-spectrum quotient (AQ) with 34 adults. The regression output is shown on the next page.

a. Use the regression output to determine the equation of the least squares regression line. Identify all variables used in the equation.

b. Is a linear model appropriate for these data? Explain.

c. What is the value of the slope of the least squares regression line, and what does it mean in terms of the PIT and AQ scores?

d. What percentage of the variation in the AQ scores is explained by its linear relationship with the PIT score?

e. Use the regression model to predict the AQ score for someone with a PIT score of 62.

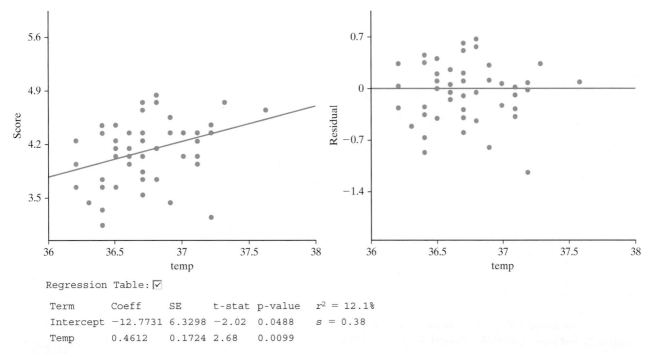

```
Regression Table: ☑

Term       Coeff     SE       t-stat  p-value    r² = 12.1%
Intercept  -12.7731  6.3298   -2.02   0.0488     s = 0.38
Temp        0.4612   0.1724    2.68   0.0099
```

EXERCISE 10.3.42

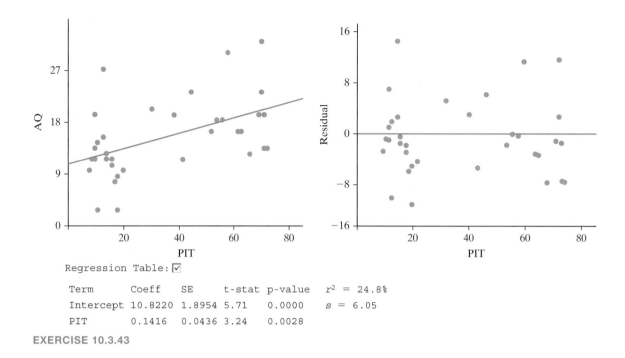

Regression Table: ☑

Term	Coeff	SE	t-stat	p-value	
Intercept	10.8220	1.8954	5.71	0.0000	$r^2 = 24.8\%$
PIT	0.1416	0.0436	3.24	0.0028	$s = 6.05$

EXERCISE 10.3.43

f. One of the subjects had a PIT score of 62 and an AQ score of 17. Calculate the residual for this subject and explain what it means.

g. Identify and interpret the standard deviation of the residuals.

10.3.44* Psychologists in many countries use children's human figure drawings (Draw-A-Person Intellectual Ability Test or DAPIQ) to assess intellectual ability. Basically, children are asked to draw full-body pictures of themselves, and the drawings are scored and normed based on the children's age. Researchers in New Zealand (Imuta et al., 2013) explored whether this type of test is correlated with the more standard intellectual test, the Wechsler Preschool and Primary Scale of Intelligence or WPPSI. They tested 100 four- and five-year-old children; the results appear in the regression output below.

a. Use the regression output to determine the equation of the least squares regression line. Identify all variables used in the equation.

Regression Table: ☑

Term	Coeff	SE	t-stat	p-value	
Intercept	79.3935	8.1033	9.80	0.0000	$r^2 = 9.0\%$
DAPIQ	0.2339	0.0753	3.10	0.0025	$s = 10.98$

EXERCISE 10.3.44

b. Is a linear model appropriate for these data? Explain.

c. What is the value of the slope of the least squares regression line, and what does it mean in terms of the DAPIQ and WPPSI scores?

d. What is the value of the coefficient of determination, and what does it mean in terms of the WPPSI and DAPIQ scores?

e. Use the regression model to predict the WPPSI score for someone with a DAPIQ score of 100.

f. One of the subjects had a DAPIQ score of 100 and a WPPSI score of 82. Calculate the residual for this subject and explain what it means.

g. Identify and interpret the standard deviation of the residuals.

h. Does the DAPIQ score seem to be a good predictor of the WPPSI score for these subjects?

10.3.45   It is said that if someone is more left-brained, they are more analytical and verbal, whereas a more right-brained person is more visual and intuitive. Student researchers used an online 30-second brain test that determines whether a person is left-brained or right-brained and gives percentages for each. The student researchers were curious whether these percentages change as a person ages. They gave 89 college students this test, recording their ages and their left-brain percentages, and the results are shown in the regression output below.

a. Use the regression output to determine the equation of the least squares regression line. Identify all variables used in the equation.

b. Is a linear model appropriate for these data? Explain.

c. What is the value of the slope of the least squares regression line, and what does it mean in terms of the age and left-brain percentage?

d. What is the value of the coefficient of determination, and what does it mean in terms of age and left-brain percentage?

e. Use the regression model to predict the left-brain percentage for someone who is 18 years old.

f. One of the 18-year-old subjects' test results gave him a left-brain percentage of 31%. Calculate the residual for this subject and explain what it means.

g. Identify and interpret the standard deviation of the residuals.

h. Does age appear to be a useful predictor of left-brain percentages for these subjects?

10.3.46*   Using *Census at School*, we randomly sampled 15 students from the database of high school students in 2017. The data in the chart below list those students' heights and the width of their outstretched arms from fingertip to fingertip; both are given in centimeters.

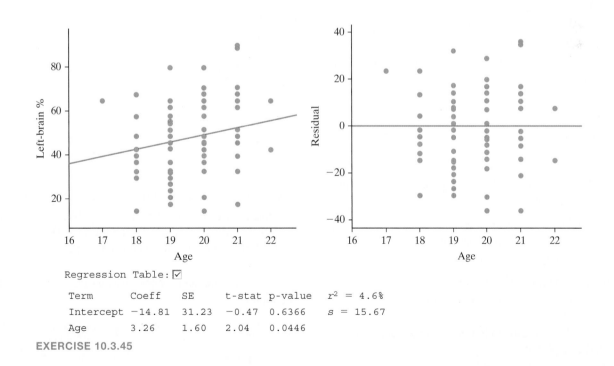

Regression Table: ☑

Term	Coeff	SE	t-stat	p-value	
Intercept	−14.81	31.23	−0.47	0.6366	$r^2 = 4.6\%$
Age	3.26	1.60	2.04	0.0446	$s = 15.67$

EXERCISE 10.3.45

Height	182	182	174	175	174	181	164	180	160	163	182	158	152	168	173
Arm span	180	182	191	192	182	187	159	180	165	157	180	162	155	173	171

EXERCISE 10.3.46

a. Use a calculator or software to find the least squares regression line that will predict arm span given height.

b. Is a linear model appropriate for these data? Explain.

c. What is the value of the slope of the least squares regression line, and what does it mean in terms of the arm span and height?

d. What is the value of the coefficient of determination, and what does it mean in terms of height and arm span?

e. The first subject in the table has a height of 182 cm and an arm span of 180 cm. Calculate the residual for this subject and explain what it means.

SECTION 10.3: Part 3

10.3.47* Which of the following is a nonlinear way to transform data when applied to all values of the response variable? (Choose all that apply.)

A. Multiplying by 3

B. Taking the square root

C. Finding the logarithm

D. Adding 7

E. Squaring

10.3.48 When you use a nonlinear transformation on data, you:

A. Can only transform the explanatory variable.

B. Can only transform the response variable.

C. Must transform both the explanatory and response variables.

D. Can transform either the explanatory or response variable, but not both.

E. Can transform the explanatory variable, the response variable, or both.

10.3.49* If your data follow an exponential model pattern in (x, y), then a plot of:

A. $(\log x, \log y)$ will give a linear pattern.

B. $(x, \log y)$ will give a linear pattern.

C. $(\log x, y)$ will give a linear pattern.

D. $(\ln x, y)$ will give a linear pattern.

E. None of the above will give a linear pattern.

10.3.50 If your data follow a power model pattern in (x, y), then a plot of:

A. $(\log x, \log y)$ will give a linear pattern.

B. $(x, \log y)$ will give a linear pattern.

C. $(\log x, y)$ will give a linear pattern.

D. $(\ln x, y)$ will give a linear pattern.

E. None of the above will give a linear pattern.

10.3.51* Suppose you have a linear regression model of the form $\hat{y} = 2.3 + 1.7\ln x$. What is the approximate value of $\hat{y}$ when $x = 3.4$?

A. 2.13

B. 3.20

C. 4.38

D. 4.90

E. 8.08

10.3.52 Suppose you have a linear regression model of the form $\ln \hat{y} = 0.3 + 1.2\ln x$. What is the approximate value of $\hat{y}$ when $x = 8.1$?

A. 2.81

B. 4.02

C. 10.02

D. 16.61

E. 22,471.43

10.3.53* Suppose you have a linear regression model of the form $\ln \hat{y} = 0.7 + 2.6x$. What is the approximate value of $\hat{y}$ when $x = 0.3$?

A. 0.99

B. 1.48

C. 2.69

D. 4.39

E. 30.20

10.3.54 The following table gives various values for the equation $y = 2^x$.

x	1	2	3	4	5
$y = 2^x$	2	4	8	16	32
$y = \log(2^x)$					

a. Complete the table by filling in the values for $y = \log(2^x)$.

b. Explain, by using your data from the table, why the function $y = \log(2^x)$ is a linear function in x. (Remember a function is linear if it has a constant slope.)

10.3.55* The following table gives various values for the equation $y = x^2$.

x	1	2	3	4	5
$y = x^2$	1	4	9	16	25
$\log(x)$					
$\log(x^2)$					

a. Complete the table by filling in the values for $\log(x)$ and $\log(x^2)$.

b. Explain, by using your data from the table, why the function $y = \log(x^2)$ is a linear function in $\log(x)$. (Remember a function is linear if it has a constant slope.)

10.3.56 A linear model is not a good fit for the data set in the following table.

x	1	2	3	4	5	6
y	24	28	33	39	49	60

a. Make scatterplots of x vs. $\ln y$, $\ln x$ vs. y, and $\ln x$ vs. $\ln y$. Which scatterplot looks the most linear?

b. Based on your answer to part (a), which type of model will best fit the original data set, exponential, power, or logarithmic?

c. Find the least squares regression line for the transformed data, including the appropriate logarithms in your equation.

d. Use your least squares regression line to determine the predicted value when $x = 5$. Is it close to the actual value when $x = 5$?

10.3.57* A linear model is not a good fit for the data set in the following table.

x	2	3	4	5	6	7
y	1	2	4	6	9	12

a. Make scatterplots of x vs. $\ln y$, $\ln x$ vs. y, and $\ln x$ vs. $\ln y$. Which scatterplot looks the most linear?

b. Based on your answer to part (a), which type of model will best fit the original data set, exponential, power, or logarithmic?

c. Find the least squares regression line for the transformed data, including the appropriate logarithms in your equation.

d. Use your least squares regression line to determine the predicted value when $x = 5$. Is it close to the actual value when $x = 5$?

10.3.58 One hundred dice were tossed onto a table. If a die landed with a 1 or a 2 showing, it was removed. The remaining dice were tossed on a table. Again, if a 1 or a 2 was showing, the die was removed. The number of dice remaining on the table after each toss is shown. Note that we are starting out with 100 dice and after each roll we should keep about 2/3 of them. This is the kind of situation that is modeled with exponential functions. The amount remaining should be about 2/3 times the previous amount. Repeated multiplication by 2/3 is just 2/3 raised to some exponent. So a theoretical model for our data should be: Dice Remaining $= 100(2/3)^{toss}$. Now let's see what the data tell us that model should be.

Toss	0	1	2	3	4	5	6	7	8	9	10	11
Dice Remaining	100	71	50	32	22	16	12	9	5	4	2	1

a. Assuming it is exponential, take the natural logarithm of the dice remaining and plot that (y) along with the number of tosses (x). Does the association in your graph look linear?

b. Find the least squares regression line for the transformed data.

c. From part (b), you should have a function of the form $\ln y = a + bx$. To "untransform" (or "back-transform") this equation so the logarithm goes away, we can do the following:

$$\ln y = a + bx$$
$$y = e^{a+bx}$$
$$y = e^a \times e^{bx}$$
$$y = e^a \times e^{bx}$$
$$y = e^a (e^b)^x$$

Follow the above procedure and "untransform" your answer to part (b) so that it is in exponential form. Remember that e^a and e^b are just numbers, so include these as decimal numbers in your final equation. Is your final equation close to the theoretical model Dice Remaining $= 100(2/3)^x$?

10.3.59* The following table gives the median weight for baby boys (in kilograms) given their age (in months) according to the Centers for Disease Control and Prevention.

age (months)	weight (kg)
3	6
6	7.9
9	9.3
12	10.3
15	11.1
18	11.7
21	12.2
24	12.6

We transformed the data by taking the log (base 10) of both the ages and the weights, and these results appear in the following graph along with the regression output.

```
Regression Table: ☑

Term       Coeff   SE      t-stat  p-value
Intercept  0.6162  0.0119  51.78   0.0000
Log(age)   0.3594  0.0109  32.95   0.0000

           r² = 99.5%
           s = 0.01
```

We transformed the data by taking the log (base 10) of both the age and the weight, and these results appear in the following graph along with the regression output.

```
Regression Table: ☑

Term       Coeff   SE      t-stat  p-value
Intercept  0.5639  0.0067  83.57   0.0000
Log(age)   0.3785  0.0062  61.20   0.0000

           r² = 99.8%
           s = 0.00
```

a. Give the equation of the least squares regression line, where the log of the age is the explanatory variable and the log of the weight is the response variable.

b. Using the regression equation, predict the median weight for a 12-month-old. How close is this to the actual median weight for a 12-month-old reported by the CDC?

c. Use the regression equation to predict the median weight for a 15-year-old. Convert the weight in kilograms to weight in pounds by multiplying it by 2.2. Does it seem reasonable to use this model to predict the median weight of a 15-year-old? Explain why or why not.

10.3.60 The following table gives the median weight for baby girls (in kilograms) given their age (in months) according to the Centers for Disease Control and Prevention.

age (months)	weight (kg)
3	5.5
6	7.2
9	8.5
12	9.5
15	10.3
18	11.0
21	11.5
24	12.0

a. Give the equation of the least squares regression line, where the log of the age is the explanatory variable and the log of the weight is the response variable.

b. Using the regression equation, predict the median weight for a 12-month-old. How close is this to the actual median weight for a 12-month-old?

c. Use the regression equation to predict the median weight for a 16-year-old. Convert the weight in kilograms to weight in pounds by multiplying it by 2.2. Does it seem reasonable to use this model to predict the weight of a 16-year-old? Explain why or why not.

10.3.61* A pendulum made with fishing line and a small metal weight was constructed. The length of the pendulum was changed and the number of periods per minute was counted for various lengths in inches. The length of one period (the time it takes to swing from one extreme to the other and then back) was calculated from the periods per minute and the results are shown in the following table and graph.

Length (in.)	Period (sec)
1	0.364
3	0.594
5	0.750
10	1.053
15	1.277
20	1.463
25	1.622

We transformed the data by squaring the period and the results are clearly more linear. These results appear in the following graph along with the regression output.

Regression Table: ☑

Term	Coeff	SE	t-stat	p-value
Intercept	0.0437	0.0119	3.67	0.0144
Length	0.1044	0.0008	123.49	0.0000

$$r^2 = 100.0\%$$
$$s = 0.02$$

a. Give the equation of the least squares regression line, where the length of the pendulum is the explanatory variable and the square of the period is the response variable.

b. Predict the period of a pendulum with length 12 in.

c. Find the length of a pendulum (in inches) that would swing at a (predicted) rate of one period per second (like one that would be needed for a clock).

10.3.62 The first graph below gives the percentage of the U.S. population that lives in rural areas, as defined by the Census Bureau, for 1900 through 2010, and the graph below that gives a residual plot for that data. (The Census numbers are based on the population as of April 1 of each year listed.)

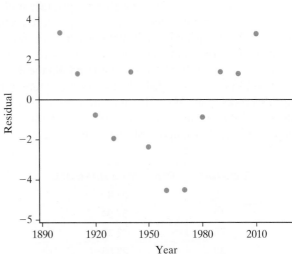

a. Based on the plots, explain why an exponential model might better describe the data than a linear model.

b. We transformed the data by taking the log (base 10) of the percent rural. Those data are shown in the graph below along with the regression output. Use these data to find the least squares regression line, where the explanatory variable is year and the response variable is log(*Percent Rural*).

c. What is the predicted percentage of the U.S. population that lived in rural areas in 2000?

d. Use this model to estimate the year when the U.S. population hit 50% rural, as predicted in the regression equation.

Regression Table: ☑

Term	Coeff	SE	t-stat	p-value
Intercept	10.4741	0.3538	29.61	0.0000
Year	−0.0046	0.0002	−25.28	0.0000

$$r^2 = 98.5\%$$
$$s = 0.02$$

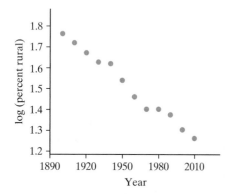

10.3.63* When a cup of hot water is set on a kitchen counter, the difference between the temperature of the hot water and the air temperature fits an exponential model. This exponential decay is known as Newton's law of cooling. We performed a similar activity with a temperature probe placed in a cup of hot water. After the temperature probe adjusted to the temperature of the hot water, it was removed and allowed to cool to room temperature. Every 10 sec, for the first 100 sec after the probe was removed from the water, the temperature was recorded. The room temperature during this process was 20°C. The time, in seconds, and the difference between the probe's temperature and the room temperature are shown in the following table and graph.

Time (sec)	Temperature above 20°C
0	51.41
10	37.34
20	29.32
30	23.83
40	19.76
50	16.29
60	13.36
70	11.65
80	9.95
90	8.58
100	7.42

We transformed the data by taking the log (base 10) of the temperature above 20°C, and these results appear in the following graph along with the regression output.

Regression Table: ☑

Term	Coeff	SE	t-stat	p-value
Intercept	1.6462	0.0183	89.87	0.0000
Time	−0.0081	0.0003	−26.30	0.0000

$$r^2 = 98.7\%$$
$$s = 0.03$$

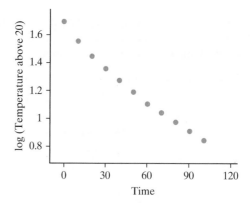

a. Give the equation of the least squares regression line, where time is the explanatory variable and the log (base 10) of the temperature above 20°C is the response variable.

b. Use the regression equation to predict the temperature of the probe after 60 sec. (Remember that the response variable was not the temperature of the probe, but how much higher it was than the temperature of the room.)

c. Assuming the cooling process will continue as it did for the first 100 sec (which it should according to Newton), how long will it take until the temperature of the probe is within 1°C of the temperature of the room?

10.3.64 Two hundred pennies were tossed. If the penny landed tail side up, it was removed from the group. The remaining pennies were tossed, and again the tails were removed from the group. This process was repeated until all the pennies were removed. The following table and graph give the number of coins remaining after each toss.

Tosses	Coins Remaining
0	200
1	95
2	48
3	23
4	10
5	5
6	4
7	3
8	1
9	0

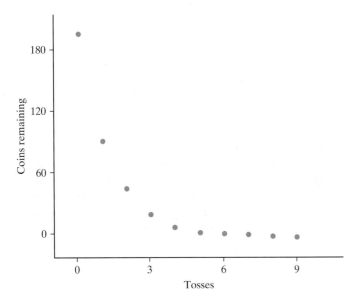

The last point, (9, 0), was eliminated (because we can't take the log of zero) and the log of the coins remaining was taken. The results appear in the following graph and regression output, where the number of tosses is the explanatory variable and the log (base 10) of the coins remaining is the response variable.

```
Regression Table: ☑

Term       Coeff    SE      t-stat  p-value
Intercept  2.2240   0.0654  34.03   0.0000
Tosses    -0.2755   0.0137 -20.07   0.0000

              r² = 98.3%
              s = 0.11
```

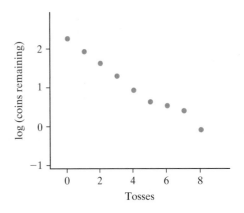

a. Give the equation of the least squares regression line, where the number of tosses is the explanatory variable and the log (base 10) of the coins remaining is the response variable.

b. Using the regression equation, predict the number of coins remaining after 3 tosses. How does that number compare to the actual result?

c. Theoretically, how many coins should remain after 3 tosses? (*Hint:* After each toss, we expect half the coins to remain.)

10.3.65* The following table shows the distance from the sun in astronomical units (the distance from the earth to the sun is 1 astronomical unit) and the time to orbit the sun (in earth years) of the eight planets in the solar system along with Pluto (which NASA scientists have proposed once again classifying as a planet). Treat orbit time as the response variable.

a. Determine whether an exponential or power model better fits the data.

b. Find the least squares regression equation for the appropriately transformed data.

c. Suppose someone discovers the planet Statooine (along with its two moons, Tooessdee and Ecksbar). Also suppose that Statooine has an average distance from the sun of 5.5 A.U. Use your regression equation to estimate the orbit time of Statooine.

Planet	Average distance from the sun (A.U.)	Orbit time (earth years)
Mercury	0.39	0.24
Venus	0.72	0.62
Earth	1.00	1.00
Mars	1.52	1.88
Jupiter	5.20	11.86
Saturn	9.59	29.46
Uranus	19.19	84.07
Neptune	30.06	164.82
Pluto	39.53	248.60

10.3.66 The Dow Jones Industrial Average (DJIA) is a stock market index, started in 1896, that reflects the value of the U.S. stock market as measured by 30 major public companies. The following table shows the DJIA at the end of every 10 years since its beginning. Treat DJIA as the response variable.

a. Determine whether an exponential or power model better fits the data.

b. Find the least squares regression equation for the appropriately transformed data. Would you say that the regression equation fits the data fairly well?

c. Use your regression equation to estimate the value of the DJIA in 2006. How well does the regression model work for 2006?

Year	DJIA
2016	19,762.60
2006	12,463.20
1996	6,448.30
1986	1,895.95
1976	1,004.65
1966	785.69
1956	499.47
1946	177.20
1936	179.90
1926	127.20
1916	95.00
1906	94.35
1896	40.45

SECTION 10.4

10.4.1* When testing the hypothesis that there is no association (null) vs. an association (alternative) you can use either the sample correlation coefficient or the sample slope as the statistic. How will the p-values compare when using both approaches on the same data set?

A. The result from using slope as our statistic is equivalent to using the correlation coefficient as our statistic in a test; therefore our p-values will be identical.

B. The result from using slope as our statistic is similar to using the correlation coefficient as our statistic in a test; therefore our p-values will be similar.

C. Because the slope and correlation coefficient measure two different things, our p-values will, most likely, not be similar.

D. There is no way to tell without running the tests.

Foot length and height

10.4.2 Suppose a sample of 10 people had their foot lengths (cm) and heights (inches) measured. The results, along with the regression line, are shown in the scatterplot below. The equation of the regression line, correlation coefficient, and r^2 are also shown.

Which one of the applet screenshots of null distributions for Exercise 10.4.2 (see the next page) displays the appropriate way to test whether there is a positive relationship between people's foot length and height?

10.4.3* Referring to the previous exercise, describe how you would construct a null distribution for this situation by hand using the slope of the regression line as your statistic. Assume you have 20 slips of paper.

10.4.4 Using foot length and height data, we shuffled the y-values 100 times and each time plotted the resulting regression line in the graph shown for Exercise 10.4.4. The regression line for the observed data is the one being pointed at with the dashed arrow. Based on the plot of these lines, what can you say about the p-value if we are testing to see whether there is a positive association between height and foot length? Explain.

Show Regression Line: ☑
  height^ = 37.48 + 1.10 × footlength
Show Residuals: ☐
Show Squared Residuals: ☐

Correlation coefficient: ☑ r = 0.700
R-squared: ☑ $r^2 = 48.9\%$

EXERCISE 10.4.2

(a)

Count = 88/1000 (0.0880)

(b)

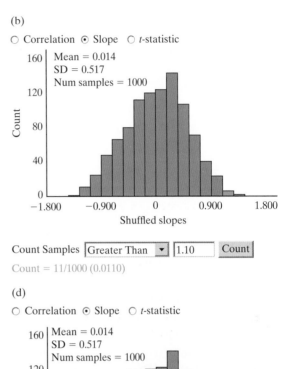

Count = 11/1000 (0.0110)

(c)

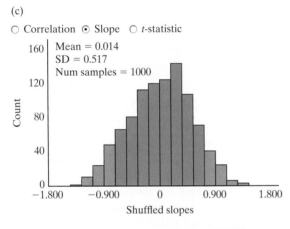

Count = 189/1000 (0.1890)

(d)

Count = 25/1000 (0.0250)

EXERCISE 10.4.2

EXERCISE 10.4.4

Height and leap*

10.4.5 Suppose you are testing to see if there is an association between a person's height and their vertical leap. You've collected data on this from 20 people. Describe how you would construct a null distribution for this situation by hand using the slope of the regression line as your statistic. Assume you have 20 slips of paper containing the 20 heights and 20 slips of paper containing the 20 vertical leap distances.

Textbook prices

10.4.6 A random sample of 15 textbooks in a campus bookstore was selected. Two of the variables recorded were the price of the book (in dollars) and the number of pages it contained. The data are displayed in the following scatterplot.

Summarize the form, direction and strength of association of the scatterplot for Exercise 10.4.6.

10.4.7 Refer to the data in the previous exercise.

a. State the null and alternative hypotheses for a test of possible association between pages and price.

b. The null distribution for Exercise 10.4.7 was created to test the hypotheses stated in the previous question using slope as the statistic.

i. Based on information shown in the null distribution, how many standard deviations is our observed statistic above the mean of the null distribution? (That is, what is the standardized statistic?)

ii. Based on your standardized statistic, do you have strong evidence of an association between number of pages and price of textbooks? Explain.

10.4.8 Reconsider the previous two exercises about textbook prices. The equation of the least squares regression line for predicting price from number of pages is $\widehat{price} = 14.11 + 0.13\,(pages)$.

a. Interpret what the slope coefficient means in the context of pages and price.

b. Interpret the intercept. Is this an example of extrapolation? Why or why not?

Sleep and maze performance*

10.4.9 Student researchers asked their subjects how much sleep they had the previous night (in hours) and then timed how long it took them (in seconds) to complete a paper and pencil maze. The results are shown in the scatterplot along with the regression line.

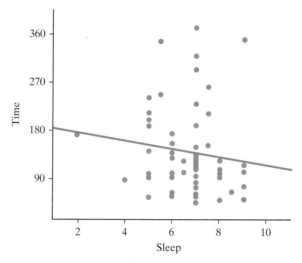

a. What is the explanatory variable?

b. What is the response variable?

c. The equation of the least squares regression line for predicting price from number of pages is $\widehat{time} = 190.33 - 7.76\,(sleep)$. The following null distribution was created to test the association between time to complete maze and amount of sleep using the slope as the statistic. The null and alternative hypotheses for this test can be written as: Null: No association between sleep and time in the population. Alt: Association between sleep and time in the population.

i. Based on information shown in the null distribution, how many standard deviations is our observed statistic away from the mean of the null distribution? (That is, what is the standardized statistic?)

ii. Based on your standardized statistic, do you have strong evidence of an association between the time it takes someone to complete the maze and how much sleep they got the night before? Explain.

10.4.10 Reconsider the previous exercise about the amount of sleep (in hours) obtained in the previous night and time to complete a paper and pencil maze (in seconds). The equation of the least squares regression line for predicting price from number of pages is $\widehat{time} = 190.33 - 7.76\,(sleep)$.

a. Interpret what the slope coefficient means in the context of sleep and time to complete the maze.

b. Interpret the intercept. Is this an example of extrapolation? Why or why not?

Weight loss and protein

10.4.11 In a study to see if there was an association between weight loss and the amount of a certain protein in a person's body fat, the researchers measured a number of different attributes in their 39 subjects at the beginning of the study. The article reported, "These subjects were clinically and ethnically heterogeneous." Two of the variables they measured were body mass index (BMI) and total cholesterol. The results are shown in the scatterplot along with the regression line.

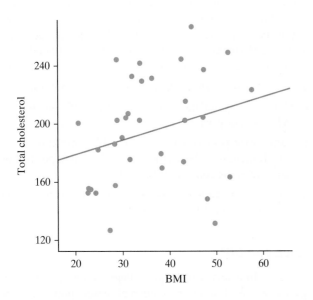

a. What are the observational units in the study?

b. The equation of the least squares regression line for predicting total cholesterol from BMI is $\widehat{cholesterol} = 162.56 + 0.9658\,(BMI)$. The following null distribution was created to test the association between people's total cholesterol number and their BMI using the slope as the statistic. The null and alternative hypotheses for this test can be written as: Null: No association between cholesterol and BMI in the population. Alt: Association between cholesterol and BMI in the population.

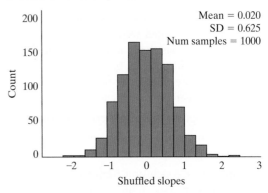

i. Based on information shown in the null distribution, how many standard deviations is our observed statistic below the mean of the null distribution? (That is, what is the standardized statistic?)

ii. Based on your standardized statistic, do you have strong evidence of an association between a people's total cholesterol and their BMI? Explain.

10.4.12 Reconsider the previous exercise about the cholesterol and BMI. The equation of the least squares regression line obtained was $\widehat{cholesterol} = 162.56 + 0.9658\,(BMI)$.

a. Interpret what the slope coefficient means in the context of cholesterol and BMI.

b. Interpret the intercept. Is this an example of extrapolation? Why or why not?

Honda Civic prices*

10.4.13 The data in the file **UsedHondaCivics** come from a sample of used Honda Civics listed for sale online in July 2006. The variables recorded are the car's age (calculated as 2006 minus year of manufacture) and price. Consider conducting a simulation analysis to test whether the sample data provide strong evidence of an association between a car's price and age in the population in terms of the population slope.

a. State the appropriate null and alternative hypotheses.

b. Conduct a simulation analysis with 1,000 repetitions. Describe how to find your p-value from your simulation results and report this p-value.

c. Summarize your conclusion from this simulation analysis. Also describe the reasoning process by which your conclusion follows from your simulation results.

10.4.14 Reconsider the previous exercise on prices of Honda Civics.

a. Find the regression equation that predicts the price of the car given its age.

b. Interpret the slope and intercept of the regression line.

Weight and haircut price

10.4.15 In a survey of statistics students at Hope College, two of the questions asked were their weight (in pounds) and the cost of their last haircut, including any hair treatments (in dollars). The data can be found in the file **Weight-Haircut**. Let's explore whether or not there is evidence of a strong association between weight and cost of haircuts.

a. State the appropriate null and alternative hypotheses.

b. Conduct a simulation analysis with 1,000 repetitions. What is your p-value?

c. Summarize your conclusion from this simulation analysis. If there is an association, describe if it is positive or negative in the context of the study.

d. Can you conclude a cause and effect between weight and cost of a haircut? Why or why not?

10.4.16 Reconsider the previous exercise on weight and haircut price.

a. Find the regression equation that predicts the haircut price based on weight.

b. Interpret the slope and intercept of the regression line.

Height and haircut price*

10.4.17 In a survey of statistics students at Hope College, two of the questions asked were their height (in inches) and the cost of their last haircut, including any hair treatments (in dollars). The data can be found in the file **HeightHaircut**. Let's explore whether or not there is evidence of a strong association between height and cost of haircuts.

a. State the appropriate null and alternative hypotheses.

b. Conduct a simulation analysis with 1,000 repetitions. What is your p-value?

c. Summarize your conclusion from this simulation analysis. If there is an association, describe if it is positive or negative in the context of the study.

d. Can you conclude a cause and effect between height and cost of a haircut? Why or why not?

10.4.18 Reconsider the previous exercise on height and haircut price.

a. Find the regression equation that predicts the haircut price based on height.

b. Interpret the slope and intercept of the regression line.

Age and BMI

10.4.19 Researchers in a clinical study collected information from their subjects at the beginning of the study. Two of the variables were body mass index (BMI) and age. We are interested in seeing if there is an association between BMI and age. The data from the study can be found in the file **AgeBMI**.

a. State the appropriate null and alternative hypotheses.

b. Conduct a simulation analysis with 1,000 repetitions. What is your p-value?

c. Summarize your conclusion from this simulation analysis. If there is an association, describe if it is positive or negative in the context of the study.

10.4.20 Reconsider the previous exercise on age and BMI. We are interested in seeing if there is an association between BMI and age. The data from the study can be found in the file **AgeBMI**.

a. Conduct a new simulation analysis with 1,000 repetitions using slope as the statistic. What is your p-value?

b. Using the same null distribution as in part (a), use correlation as the statistic. What is the p-value?

c. Are your two p-values exactly the same? (The two p-values should be the same; they may be just slightly different due to rounding of the statistics.)

Missing class and GPA*

10.4.21 In a survey of statistics students at Hope College, two of the questions asked were their current grade point average (GPA) and how many classes they failed to attend during the past three weeks at the college. The data can be found in the file **MissClassGPA**. Let's explore whether or not there is evidence of a strong association between these two variables.

a. State the appropriate null and alternative hypotheses.

b. Conduct a simulation analysis with 1,000 repetitions. What is your p-value?

c. Summarize your conclusion from this simulation analysis. If there is an association, describe if it is positive or negative in the context of the study.

d. Can you conclude a cause and effect between missing class and GPA? Why or why not?

Sleep and GPA

10.4.22 In a survey of Hope College students, two of the questions asked were their current grade point average (GPA) and how much sleep they got (in hours) on the previous school night. The data can be found in the file **SleepGPA**. Let's explore whether or not there is evidence of a strong association between these two variables.

a. What is the value of the correlation? Based on this number, does it appear there is a strong association between our two variables?

b. What is the value of the slope of the regression line? What does this number mean in terms of sleep and GPA?

c. State the appropriate null and alternative hypotheses.

d. Conduct a simulation analysis with 1,000 repetitions. What is your p-value?

e. Based on your p-value, is there evidence of a strong association between sleep and GPA for Hope College students?

f. There should be some conflict between your estimate of the strength of association in part (a) and your answer to part (e). Why did that occur with this data set?

Stroop effect*

10.4.23   You may have seen the test or puzzle where names of colors are written out in colors not denoted by the name. For example the word *green* might be written with red ink. The job of the person completing the test is to say the word and not the color. This interference in the reaction time of saying the words is called the Stroop effect. Student researchers at Hope College wanted to see if there was an association between age and the time it takes people to read a list of 20 of these colored words. Their results can be found in the data file **StroopAgeTime**. The age is given in years and the time to complete the task is given in seconds. Put the data in the **Corr/Regression** applet and complete the following.

a. Write out the null and alternative hypotheses for this study using a two-sided alternative.

b. What is the slope of the regression line? What does that number mean in the context of age and time to complete the task?

c. Conduct at least 1,000 shuffles of the data and find and report the resulting p-value.

d. Summarize your conclusion from this analysis.

10.4.24   Reconsider the previous exercise on the Stroop effect.

a. There was one point in the scatterplot that was a clear outlier. One of the researcher's great aunt, who was 87 years old, took 100.60 seconds to complete the task. This was almost three times as long as the next longest time. Remove that point from the data set and find a new p-value. Are your results significant?

b. After the great aunt's point is removed from the scatterplot, there now appears to be a couple of other points, representing an 8-year-old and a 10-year-old, that might be outliers. Perhaps an association between age and time won't be demonstrated when the subjects are too young. For this reason, delete all the points representing anyone 10 and under. There should be five of these. Find a new p-value. Are your results significant?

c. With the 87-year-old included, there is a significant association. When the result from the 87-year-old is deleted from the data, there is not a significant association. When results from everyone 10 and under are deleted from the study, there is a significant association. So, how would you answer the question, is there an association between

age and the time needed to complete this task of reading of color names? Explain.

FAQ

10.4.25   Read FAQ 10.4.1 and answer the following questions.

a. What is the name of the point $(\bar{x}, \bar{y})$?

b. Why does every shuffled regression line go through the point $(\bar{x}, \bar{y})$?

SECTION 10.5

10.5.1*   Which one of the following is a validity condition for theory-based tests for regression?

A. The variability of the points around the regression line should not differ as you slide along the x-axis.

B. There should be at least 10 successes and 10 failures in the data.

C. The variability of the explanatory variable should be the same as the variability of the response variable.

D. The scatterplot should show a positive association between the explanatory and response variables.

10.5.2   For a given data set, a test of association based on a slope is equivalent to a test of association based on a correlation coefficient. Being equivalent means which of the following is true?

A. The confidence intervals for the population correlation and population slope will be the same.

B. The observed correlation will be the same as the observed slope of the regression line.

C. The p-value will be the same whether you use correlation as the statistic or the slope of the regression line as the statistic.

D. All the above.

10.5.3*   The theory-based p-value given in the regression table in the **Corr/Regression** applet is:

A. A two-sided p-value

B. A one-sided p-value

C. Either a one-sided or two-sided p-value depending on how you count your samples (greater than, less than, or beyond) in the simulation part of the applet

D. A one-sided p-value when you're using correlation as the statistic but a two-sided p-value when you're using slope as the statistic

10.5.4   To explore the relationship between the runtime and profit made by movies, data were collected on a random sample of 15 movies released in the last four years. The p-value corresponding to the two-sided test for the slope turned out to be 0.06.

a. Based on the p-value, is it okay to conclude that "*there is evidence that there is no association between runtime and profit made by movies*"? How are you deciding?

b. Suppose that you were to create a 90% confidence interval for the population slope using the data from this study. Would this confidence interval contain 0? How are you deciding?

c. How, if at all, would the p-value change if you wanted to test whether there is a positive association between runtime and profit made by movies? Explain.

10.5.5* If there are influential points or outliers in your data, why is it a good idea to run the analysis with those points removed?

10.5.6 For the data in each of the following scatterplots, are the validity conditions met to run a theory-based test for regression? If the answer is no on any of them, explain why not.

a.

b.

c.

d.

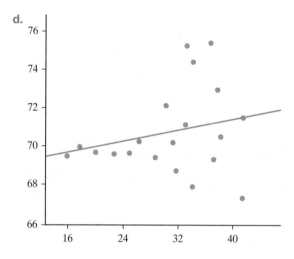

Sleep and maze completion*

10.5.7 A regression table is shown based on data used to test an association between the amount of sleep someone had the previous night (in hours) and the time needed to complete a paper and pencil maze (in seconds). Sleep is the explanatory variable and time needed to complete the maze is the response.

Term	Coeff	SE	t-stat	p-value
Intercept	198.33	51.75	3.85	0.0003
Sleep	−7.76	7.50	−1.03	0.3052

a. What is the regression equation where time to complete the maze is predicted from the amount of sleep?

b. If we were testing against the alternative hypothesis $\beta \neq 0$, what is the p-value?

c. If we were testing against the alternative hypothesis $\beta < 0$, what is the p-value?

BMI and glucose levels

10.5.8 In a study to see if there was an association between weight loss and the amount of a certain protein in a person's body fat, the researchers measured a number of different attributes in their 39 subjects at the beginning of the study. The article reported, "These subjects were clinically and ethnically heterogeneous." Two of the variables they measured were body mass index (BMI) and blood glucose levels and the results are in the file **BMIGlucose**. We are interested in seeing if there is an association between BMI and glucose levels.

a. Describe the population slope in the context of the study and assign a symbol to it.

b. State the appropriate null and alternative hypotheses in terms of the population slope using the symbol used in part (a).

c. Is a theory-based test appropriate? Why or why not?

d. Regardless of your answer to the previous question, use a theory-based approach to find the p-value to test the hypotheses stated in part (b). Report and interpret this p-value in the context of the study.

e. Summarize your conclusion based on the p-value reported in part (d).

f. If you were testing to determine whether there was a *positive* association between BMI and glucose levels, what is the theory-based p-value?

10.5.9 Reconsider the previous exercise on BMI and blood glucose levels.

a. Determine a 95% confidence interval for the population slope coefficient and interpret what this interval represents.

b. Based on your confidence interval, is there a positive association between BMI and blood glucose levels? Explain.

Height and weight*

10.5.10 At the beginning of the semester, students in a statistics class were asked to give their estimates of how much their professor weighed (in pounds) and his height (in inches). We want to see if students who give large estimates for height will they also give large estimates for weight. In other words, is there are positive association between these two variables. The data from the study can be found in the file **HeightWeight.** (The professor actually weighed about 160 pounds and was 72 inches tall.)

a. Describe the population slope in the context of the study and assign a symbol to it.

b. State the appropriate null and alternative hypotheses in terms of the population slope using the symbol used in part (a).

c. Is a theory-based test appropriate? Why or why not?

d. Regardless of your answer to the previous question, use a theory-based approach to find the p-value to test the hypotheses stated in part (b). Report and interpret this p-value in the context of the study.

Age and BMI

10.5.11 Researchers in a clinical study collected information from their subjects at the beginning of the study. Two of the variables were body mass index (BMI) and age. We are interested in seeing if there is an association between these two variables. The data from the study can be found in the file **AgeBMI.**

a. Describe the population slope in the context of the study and assign a symbol to it.

b. State the appropriate null and alternative hypotheses in terms of the population slope using the symbol used in part (a).

c. Is a theory-based test appropriate? Why or why not?

d. Use a theory-based approach to find the p-value.

e. Summarize your conclusion based on the p-value reported in part (d).

f. If you were testing to determine if there was a *positive* association between age and BMI, what is the theory-based p-value?

10.5.12 Reconsider the previous exercise on age and BMI.

a. Determine a 95% confidence interval for the population slope and interpret what this interval represents.

b. Based on your confidence interval, is there strong evidence for a positive association between age and BMI? Explain.

c. Based on a one-sided p-value, is there strong evidence for a positive association between age and BMI? Explain.

d. Your answers to parts (b) and (c) might contradict each other. Explain why that is.

Honda Civic prices*

10.5.13 The data in the file **UsedHondaCivics** come from a sample of used Honda Civics listed for sale online in July 2006. The variables recorded are the car's age (calculated as 2006 minus year of manufacture) and price. Consider conducting an analysis to test whether the sample data provide strong evidence of an association between a car's price and age in the population in terms of the population slope.

a. Describe the population slope in the context of the study and assign a symbol to it.

b. State the appropriate null and alternative hypotheses in terms of the population slope using the symbol used in part (a).

c. Is a theory-based test appropriate? Why or why not?

d. Use a theory-based approach to find a p-value to test the hypotheses stated in part (b).

e. Summarize your conclusion based on the p-value reported in part (d).

10.5.14 Reconsider the previous exercise on Used Honda Civics.

a. Determine a 95% confidence interval for the population slope coefficient and interpret what this interval represents.

b. Based on your confidence interval, is there a negative association between age and price for used Honda Civics? Explain.

Textbook prices

10.5.15 Two Cal Poly freshmen gathered data on a random sample of textbooks from the campus bookstore in November of 2006. Two of the variables recorded were the price of the book and the number of pages that it contained. These data are in the file **TextbookPrices**.

a. Describe the population slope in the context of the study and assign a symbol to it.

b. Suppose that you want to test whether there is a positive association between price and number of pages in the population of all textbooks for sale in the bookstore in November of 2006. State the appropriate null and alternative hypotheses in terms of the population slope using the symbol used in part (a).

c. Is a theory-based test appropriate? Why or why not?

d. Determine and report the value of the t-statistic and p-value for testing the hypotheses stated in part (b).

e. Do the sample data provide strong evidence that number of pages is a significant predictor of price? Explain how you can tell.

f. Determine and interpret a 95% confidence interval for the value of the population slope.

Height and BMI*

10.5.16 The data in the file **HeightBMI** was obtained from a survey of statistics students. The variables recorded are the student's heights (in inches) and their body mass index (BMI). Consider conducting an analysis to test whether the sample data provide strong evidence of an association between height and BMI using slope as the statistic. (Let height be the explanatory variable and BMI be the response.)

a. Describe the population slope in the context of the study and assign a symbol to it.

b. State the appropriate null and alternative hypotheses in terms of the population slope using the symbol used in part (a).

c. Is a theory-based test appropriate? Why or why not?

d. Use a theory-based approach to find a p-value.

e. Summarize your conclusion based on the p-value reported in part (d).

10.5.17 Reconsider the previous exercise on height and BMI.

a. Determine a 95% confidence interval for the population slope coefficient and interpret what this interval represents.

b. Based on your confidence interval, is there an association between height and BMI? Explain.

Gestation and life expectancy

10.5.18 The data in the file **GestationLifeExpectancy** gives the gestation period (in days) and the life expectancy (in years) for a sample of mammals. We will consider this sample to be representative of all mammals for these two variables. Consider conducting an analysis to test whether the sample data provide strong evidence of an association between gestation period and life expectancy.

a. What is the value of the slope of the regression line and what does it mean in terms of gestation period and life expectancy?

b. State the appropriate null and alternative hypotheses in terms of the population slope.

c. Use a theory-based approach to find a p-value. Do you have strong evidence of an association between the two variables?

d. Remember that a Type II error is not rejecting a false null hypothesis (or a missed opportunity). Do you think you made a Type II error for this exercise? Why or why not?

Sleep and height*

10.5.19 The data in the file **SleepHeight** was obtained from a survey of statistics students. The variables recorded are the student's heights (in inches) and the amount of sleep they typically get on a school night (in hours). Consider conducting an analysis to test whether the sample data provide strong evidence of a negative association between sleep and height.

a. Describe the population slope in the context of the study and assign a symbol to it.

b. State the appropriate null and alternative hypotheses in terms of the population slope using the symbol used in part (a).

c. Use a theory-based approach to find a p-value. Do you have strong evidence of a negative association between sleep and height?

d. There are a couple of errors in the data set. It appears as though two students reported their heights as 55 inches and they sleep 10 hours a night. Since all of the answers on the survey were identical for these two entries, it would appear they came from the same person. It is also obvious to the instructor that there was nobody in class as short as 55 inches, so we know the height is an error. Eliminate these two points (they are the last ones on the list) and find a new p-value. Do you now have strong evidence of a negative association?

GDP and infant mortality

10.5.20 The accompanying scatterplot gives data from a random sample of 27 countries where the response variable is infant mortality (deaths per 1,000 live births) and the explanatory variable is the gross domestic product (GDP) per capita (in thousands of dollars). The gross domestic product per capita is a representation of a country's standard of living.

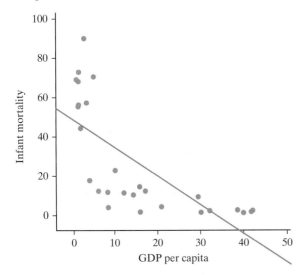

a. Describe the relationship between infant mortality and GDP per capita. Is this relationship linear?

b. The regression line is also included in the scatterplot. Will this regression line be a good prediction of infant mortality given GDP per capita? Why or why not?

Sometimes we can transform data that don't fit a linear pattern in such a way that they do fit a linear pattern. We calculated the logarithm of all the values of both the infant mortality and GDP per capita and plotted the results in the scatterplot below.

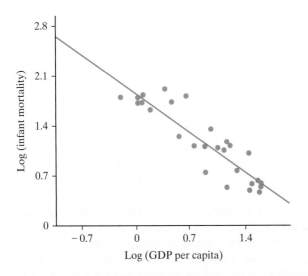

c. Describe the relationship between logarithm of infant mortality and logarithm of GDP per capita. Is this relationship linear?

d. The regression line is also included in the scatterplot. Will this regression line be a good prediction of the logarithm of infant mortality given the logarithm of GDP per capita? Why or why not?

FAQ

10.5.21 Read FAQ 10.5.1. Explain intuitively why conducting tests when you assume the relationship is linear is more powerful than if you have no linear assumption.

SECTION 10.6

10.6.1* Suppose we want to run a t-test for the slope of a regression line and our sample data set is in the following table. How many degrees of freedom will the t-distribution have that will be used for this test?

x	1	2	3	4	5	6	7	8	9	10	11	12	13	14	15
y	4	3	5	7	4	9	10	6	4	9	14	18	15	12	18

A. 2

B. 13

C. 15

D. 28

E. 30

10.6.2 When we complete a t-test for the slope of a regression line, which of the following is an appropriate way to write out the null hypothesis?

A. $H_0: \mu = 0$

B. $H_0: \pi = 0$

C. $H_0: \beta = 0$

D. $H_0: \bar{x} = 0$

E. $H_0: b = 0$

10.6.3* Which of the following is NOT one of the validity conditions for a t-test for the slope of a regression line?

A. We should have a large sample size, typically $n \geq 30$.

B. The scatterplot of the sample data should follow a linear pattern.

C. The residual plot should show near equal variance in the response variable for each value of the explanatory variable.

D. The histogram of the residuals should show no severe departure from normality.

E. All the above are validity conditions for a t-test for the slope of a regression line.

10.6.4 Suppose we are conducting a two-sided t-test for the slope of a regression line, where the null hypothesis is that there is no linear association between the explanatory and response variables and we get a p-value of 0.08. Based on this, what can you say about a 95% confidence interval for the slope of the regression line?

A. It will contain the p-value.

B. It will not contain the p-value.

C. It will contain 0.

D. It will not contain 0.

E. It will not contain b.

10.6.5* The following regression table output comes from a t-test for the slope of a regression line, where the number of classes missed in the past three weeks by 27 college students is the explanatory variable and their GPA is the response variable. What is the value of the missing t-statistic?

```
R-squared      r² = 32.3%
Regression SE  s = 0.29

Regression Table:

Term        Coeff    SE      t-stat  p-value
Intercept   3.7286   0.0649  57.44   0.0000
Miss Class  -0.1616  0.0468  ?       0.0020
```

A. -0.28

B. -0.56

C. -2.49

D. -3.45

E. -17.94

10.6.6 Using the regression table in the previous question, which of the following is the correct calculation for a 95% confidence interval for the slope of the regression line?

A. $-0.1616 \pm 1.96\,(0.0468)$

B. $-0.1616 \pm 1.96\left(\frac{0.0468}{\sqrt{27}}\right)$

C. $-0.1616 \pm 2.060\,(0.0468)$

D. $-0.1616 \pm 2.060\left(\frac{0.0468}{\sqrt{27}}\right)$

E. $-0.1616 \pm 2.052\,(0.0468)$

10.6.7* In the regression output from Exercise 10.6.5, which of the following is the correct interpretation of the -0.1616 in the table?

A. All the students' GPAs will decrease 0.1616 points for every additional class they miss.

B. The predicted number of missed classes will go down 0.1616 for each additional point in the GPA.

C. 16.16% of the variation in the GPAs can be explained by its linear association with the number of missed classes.

D. The predicted GPA goes down 0.1616 points for every additional missed class.

E. It is the average number of missed classes per student.

10.6.8 We sampled 40 high school students from the 2017 *Census at School* database and ran a regression analysis of their data, where the explanatory variable is their height in

centimeters and the response is the time, in seconds, on a computer-based reaction time test.

```
R-squared ☑          r² = 1.6%
Regression SE ☑      s = 0.22

Regression Table: ☑

Term         Coeff    SE      t-stat  p-value
Intercept    0.9772   0.6269  1.56    0.1273
Height cm   -0.0030   0.0037  -0.80   0.4307
```

a. What is the equation of the least squares regression line?

b. What is the p-value for a t-test for the slope of a regression line, where the null hypothesis is that there is no linear association between height and reaction time?

10.6.9 Recalling the previous question about looking for a relationship between height and reaction time, give and interpret a 90% confidence interval for the slope of the regression line, where the explanatory variable is student's height in centimeters and the response variable is the time, in seconds, on the computer-based reaction time test.

10.6.10* In a survey of college students, 42 females were asked what their height was and if they could magically be any height they wanted, what would it be. Both of these numbers were given in inches. We ran a regression analysis, where the actual height was the explanatory variable and the magical height was the response variable. The results are shown in the following table.

```
R-squared ☑          r² = 38.9%
Regression SE ☑      s = 2.05

Regression Table: ☑

Term         Coeff    SE      t-stat  p-value
Intercept    30.4647  7.1661  4.25    0.0001
Height       0.5486   0.1088  5.04    0.0000
```

a. What is the equation of the least squares regression line?

b. What is the p-value for a t-test for the slope of a regression line, where the null hypothesis is that there is no linear association between actual height and magical height?

10.6.11* Recalling the previous question about looking for a relationship between height and magical height, give and interpret a 99% confidence interval for the slope of the regression line, where the explanatory variable is the student's height in inches and the response variable is his or her magical height in inches.

10.6.12 Using *Census at School,* we randomly sampled 15 students from the database of high school students in 2017. The following data are those students' heights and the width of their outstretched arms from fingertip to fingertip; both are given in centimeters.

Height	182	182	174	175	174	181	164	180	160	163	182	158	152	168	173
Arm span	180	182	191	192	182	187	159	180	165	157	180	162	155	173	171

EXERCISE 10.6.12

a. Use a calculator or software to find the least squares regression line that will predict arm span given height.

b. Are the validity conditions met to complete a t-test for the slope of a regression line?

c. Write out the hypotheses to test to see if there is a linear association between height and arm span.

d. What is the p-value for your test and what is your conclusion?

10.6.13 Recall the previous question on height and arm span.

a. Compute a 95% confidence interval for the slope of the regression equation.

b. Explain what your confidence interval means in terms of height and arm span.

10.6.14* What number do we calculate to tell us whether there is a strong linear relationship between two variables, and what number do we calculate to tell us if there is strong evidence of a linear relationship between two variables? In each case, what sort of values of these numbers indicates increasing strength?

10.6.15 Research done at UCLA (Inagaki et al., 2016) investigated the relationship between physical warmth and social warmth. They measured physical warmth by taking the oral temperatures of the 54 subjects (in degrees Celsius). To measure social warmth, they gave them a 12-item test that included questions like "I feel like being around other people." The subjects responded on a 5-point scale (1 = not at all, to 5 = very much so), and the responses to the 12 items were averaged for each subject. The regression output is shown below.

a. Identify and interpret the standard error for the slope.

b. Check the validity conditions for a theory-based test for the slope of the regression line and discuss whether or not they are met here.

c. Assuming the 54 subjects can be considered a random sample from a larger population, is there strong evidence of a linear association between physical warmth and social warmth in the population? Carry out a complete test of significance.

$r^2 = 12.1\%$

$s = 0.38$

Regression Table: ☑

Term	Coeff	SE	t-stat	p-value
Intercept	−12.7731	6.3298	−2.02	0.0488
Temp	0.4612	0.1724	2.68	0.0099

EXERCISE 10.6.15

d. Approximate a 95% confidence interval for the slope of the population regression line and interpret its meaning.

e. Do the confidence interval and p-value lead you to the same conclusion about a linear association? Explain.

10.6.16* Does the amount of sleep influence performance on completing a puzzle? In particular, if you get less sleep, will it take you longer to complete a puzzle? Student researchers investigated this question by timing how long it took their 64 subjects to complete a paper and pencil maze (in seconds) and then asking them how long they slept the previous night (in hours). The regression output is shown below.

a. Identify and interpret the standard error for the slope.

b. Check the validity conditions for a theory-based test for the slope of the regression line and discuss whether or not they are met here.

c. If the validity conditions are met, carry out a theory-based test of significance to determine whether there is strong evidence of a negative linear association between time to complete the puzzle and the amount of sleep students got the previous night. If validity conditions aren't met, explain how the null hypothesis could be tested.

d. Suppose you determine there is significant evidence of a negative association. Does this imply that we can conclude that the amount of sleep influences performance when completing a puzzle? Explain.

e. How would you design the study differently so that you could make a causal conclusion?

10.6.17 A person who can identify or produce a musical tone correctly without any outside reference is said to have perfect pitch. This can be tested using a pitch identification test (PIT). Perfect pitch has also been associated with certain disabilities. Danish researchers (Dohn et al., 2012) tested to see whether PIT scores are associated with autism traits using the autism-spectrum quotient (AQ) with 34 adults. The regression output is shown on the next page.

a. Identify and interpret the standard error for the slope.

b. Check the validity conditions for a theory-based test for the slope of the regression line and discuss whether or not they are met here.

c. Is there strong evidence of a linear association between pitch identification test (PIT) score and autism-spectrum quotient (AQ) in the population represented by this sample? Carry out a complete test of significance.

d. Approximate a 95% confidence interval for the slope of the population regression line and interpret its meaning.

e. Do the confidence interval and p-value lead you to the same conclusion about a linear association? Explain.

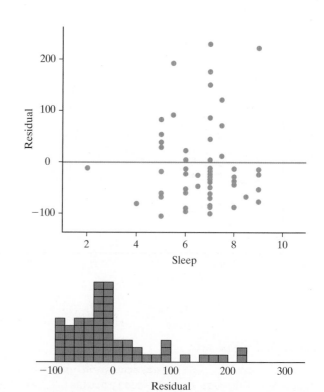

$r^2 = 1.7\%$

$s = 78.32$

Term	Coeff	SE	t-stat	p-value
Intercept	198.33	51.57	3.85	0.0003
Sleep	−7.76	7.50	−1.03	0.3052

EXERCISE 10.6.16

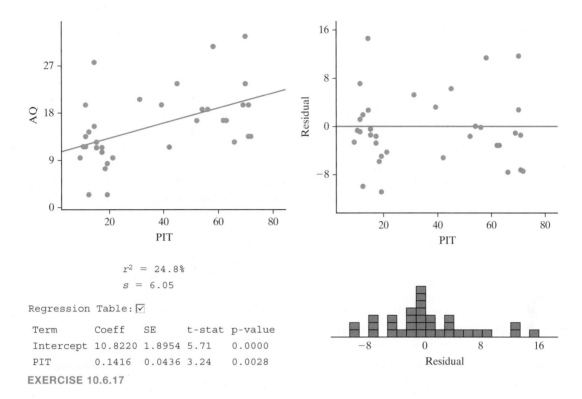

$r^2 = 24.8\%$

$s = 6.05$

Regression Table: ☑

Term	Coeff	SE	t-stat	p-value
Intercept	10.8220	1.8954	5.71	0.0000
PIT	0.1416	0.0436	3.24	0.0028

EXERCISE 10.6.17

10.6.18* Psychologists in many countries use children's human figure drawings (Draw-A-Person Intellectual Ability Test, or DAPIQ) to assess intellectual ability. Basically, children are asked to draw full-body pictures of themselves and they are scored and normed based on the age of the child.

Researchers in New Zealand (Imuta et al., 2013) explored whether this type of test is correlated with the more standard intellectual test, the Wechsler Preschool and Primary Scale of Intelligence or WPPSI. They tested 100 four- and five-year-old children. The regression output is shown below.

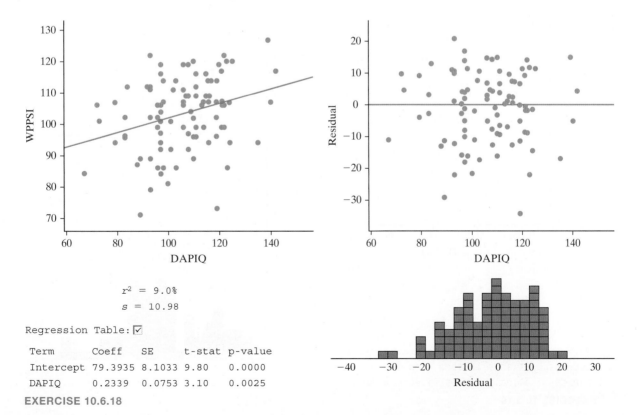

$r^2 = 9.0\%$

$s = 10.98$

Regression Table: ☑

Term	Coeff	SE	t-stat	p-value
Intercept	79.3935	8.1033	9.80	0.0000
DAPIQ	0.2339	0.0753	3.10	0.0025

EXERCISE 10.6.18

a. Identify and interpret the standard error for the slope.

b. Check the validity conditions for a theory-based test for the slope of the regression line and discuss whether or not they are met here.

c. Is there strong evidence of a linear association between Draw-A-Person Intellectual Ability Test (DAPIQ) score and Wechsler Preschool and Primary Scale of Intelligence (WPPSI)? Carry out a complete test of significance.

d. Approximate a 99% confidence interval for the slope of the population regression line and interpret its meaning.

e. Do the confidence interval and p-value lead you to the same conclusion about a linear association? Explain.

10.6.19 Refer to the previous question on drawing a person to determine intellectual ability. In addition to testing the children, they also tested 100 adults using the same Draw-A-Person Intellectual Ability Test or DAPIQ, but an intelligence test designed for adults, the Wechsler Abbreviated Scale of Intelligence (WASI), was used. The regression output is shown below.

a. Identify and interpret the standard error for the slope.

b. Check the validity conditions for a theory-based test for the slope of the regression line and discuss whether or not they are met here.

c. Is there strong evidence of a linear association between Draw-A-Person Intellectual Ability Test (DAPIQ) score and Wechsler Abbreviated Scale of Intelligence (WASI)

score in the population represented by this sample? Carry out a complete test of significance.

d. Approximate a 95% confidence interval for the slope of the population regression line and interpret its meaning.

e. Do the confidence interval and p-value lead you to the same conclusion about a linear association? Explain.

10.6.20* It is said that if someone is more left-brained, they are more analytical and verbal, whereas the more right-brained person is more visual and intuitive. Student researchers used an online 30-second brain test that determines whether a person is left-brained or right-brained and gives percentages for each. The student researchers were curious whether these percentages change as a person ages. They gave 89 college students this test, recording their ages and their left-brain percentages, and the results are shown in the regression output on the next page. Assume the conditions for regression inference are met.

a. Identify and interpret the standard error for the slope.

b. Check the validity conditions and explain how they are met or not for a theory-based test for the slope of the regression line.

c. Is there strong evidence of a linear association between age and the percentage of time a person is left-brained? Carry out a complete test of significance.

d. Approximate a 90% confidence interval for the slope of the population regression line and interpret its meaning.

$$r^2 = 1.0\%$$
$$s = 9.62$$

Regression Table: ☑

Term	Coeff	SE	t-stat	p-value
Intercept	91.3079	13.1902	6.92	0.0000
DAPIQ	0.1257	0.1255	1.00	0.3188

EXERCISE 10.6.19

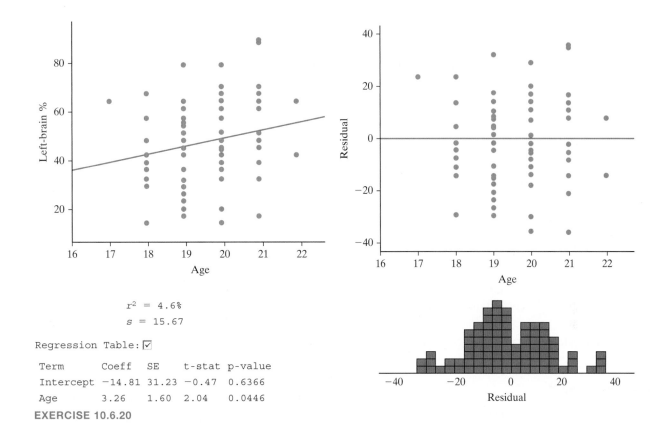

$r^2 = 4.6\%$

$s = 15.67$

Regression Table: ☑

Term	Coeff	SE	t-stat	p-value
Intercept	−14.81	31.23	−0.47	0.6366
Age	3.26	1.60	2.04	0.0446

EXERCISE 10.6.20

e. Does the confidence interval and p-value lead you to the same conclusion about a linear association? Explain.

END OF CHAPTER

10.CE.1*

a. Suppose that every student in your class scores 10 points *higher* on the final exam than on the midterm exam. What would the value of the correlation coefficient between the two exam scores equal? Explain. (*Hint:* Draw a scatterplot for some hypothetical data.)

b. Suppose that every student in your class scores 10 points *lower* on the final exam than on the midterm exam. What would the value of the correlation coefficient between the two exam scores equal? Explain. (*Hint:* Draw a scatterplot for some hypothetical data.)

c. Suppose that every student in your class scores *twice* as many points on the final exam than on the midterm exam. What would the value of the correlation coefficient between the two exam scores equal? Explain. (*Hint:* Draw a scatterplot for some hypothetical data.)

10.CE.2

a. When calculating a correlation coefficient between two quantitative variables, does it matter which is considered explanatory and which response?

b. When calculating a least squares line between two quantitative variables, does it matter which is considered explanatory and which response?

c. When calculating a residual value from a least squares line, does it matter whether you calculate the vertical, horizontal, or perpendicular distance to the line?

Teacher's age and distance to school*

10.CE.3 Is there an association between a teacher's age and how far he or she lives from school? For each of the following descriptions, draw a scatterplot of hypothetical data for a sample of 10 teachers that reveal what's described. (Be sure to label and put a reasonable scale on both axes.)

a. No association between age and distance

b. Strong, positive, linear association between age and distance

c. Moderate, positive, nonlinear association between age and distance

d. Moderate evidence that older teachers tend to live closer to school than younger teachers

e. Very little association between age and distance, except for a severe outlier

Major League Baseball

10.CE.4 Suppose that you record the following information about 15 Major League Baseball games played next Saturday:

A. Total number of runs scored in the game

B. Whether or not the home team wins the game

C. Time (in minutes) required to play the game

D. Attendance (number of people) at the game

E. Whether the game is played in the afternoon or evening

F. Temperature when the game begins

a. Identify all *pairs* of variables for which it does make sense to calculate the correlation coefficient between the variables.

b. Identify all *pairs* of variables for which it does *not* make sense to calculate the correlation coefficient between the variables.

Hint: There should be a total of 15 pairs of variables between your answers to parts (a) and (b).

Test-taking time*

10.CE.5 The data file **TestTimes** contains data on the time (in minutes) taken by 33 students to complete a multiple-choice exam and the students' scores (as a percentage out of 100) on the exam. Investigate whether the data provide evidence of an association between the time to take the test and the score achieved on the test.

a. Produce a scatterplot and describe the association between the variables.

b. Report the value of the correlation coefficient between these variables.

c. Conduct a simulation-based analysis of whether the correlation coefficient differs significantly from zero. Report the p-value along with a screen capture of the simulated null distribution of correlation values.

d. Conduct a *t*-test based on the correlation coefficient. Report the value of the test statistic and p-value.

e. Summarize your conclusion.

10.CE.6 Reconsider the previous exercise and the data in **TestTimes.**

a. Report the equation of the least squares line for reporting test score from time to take the test.

b. Interpret the value of the slope coefficient.

c. Interpret the value of the intercept coefficient. Does this make sense in this context?

d. Report and interpret the value of r^2.

10.CE.7 Reconsider the previous two exercises and the data in **TestTimes**.

a. Conduct a *t*-test of whether the slope coefficient differs significantly from zero. Report the value of the test statistic and p-value.

b. Produce a 95% confidence interval for the population slope coefficient.

c. Interpret this confidence interval.

d. Are the test result and confidence interval consistent with each other? Explain.

Planets

10.CE.8 The table below gives information on the eight planets in our solar system that were obtained from Wikipedia:

a. Describe the association between these variables as described in the graph on the scatterplot below. Comment on direction, strength, and form of the association.

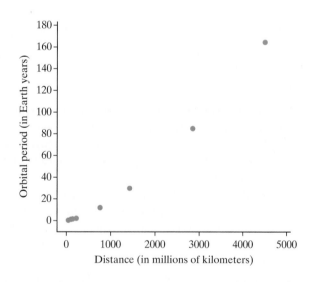

	Mercury	Venus	Earth	Mars	Jupiter	Saturn	Uranus	Neptune
Mean distance from sun (in million km)	57.90	108.20	149.60	227.90	778.40	1,426.70	2,871.00	4,498.30
Orbital period (in Earth years)	0.24	0.62	1.00	1.88	11.86	29.45	84.02	164.79

EXERCISE 10.CE.8

b. The correlation coefficient between these variables equals 0.988. Would you conclude that the relationship between these variables is linear? Explain.

10.CE.9 Reconsider the previous exercise. The accompanying graph displays the same data, with the least squares line superimposed:

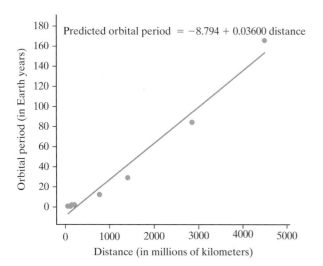

Predicted orbital period $= -8.794 + 0.03600$ distance

Would you feel comfortable using this line to make predictions? Explain.

Day hikes*

10.CE.10 Reconsider the data on day hikes in San Luis Obispo County from Exercises 10.3.21–10.3.23. The data on hiking time (in minutes) and distance (in miles) can be found in the data file **HikeDistances**.

a. Conduct a *t*-test to determine whether the data provide strong evidence of a positive association between hiking time and distance. Report the hypotheses, test statistic, and p-value. Summarize your conclusion.

b. Determine a 95% confidence interval for the population slope coefficient. Interpret this interval, including an interpretation of what slope means in this context.

10.CE.11 Repeat the previous exercise, replacing distance with elevation gain as the explanatory variable. The data on hiking time (in minutes) and elevation gain (in feet) can be found in the data file **HikeElevations**.

Walking straight

10.CE.12 While a high school student in Texas, Andrea Axtell conducted a project in which she investigated how well blindfolded students can walk in a straight line. She recruited 30 subjects by randomly selecting students at her school. She put the subjects on the center hash mark of a football field's goal line, blindfolded them, and asked them to walk in a straight line toward the opposite goal line. She then recorded the yard line at which the subject crossed the side-line, so larger values indicate that the subject walked farther before veering off course. The data, including the heights of the 30 subjects, appear in the file **WalkingStraight**.

Analyze the data to investigate whether taller people tend to walk farther before veering off course. Write a paragraph summarizing your findings. Include an appropriate graph and numerical summaries. Also conduct inference (p-values, confidence intervals) using both simulation- and theory-based methods. Summarize your conclusions.

Late to class*

10.CE.13 Does having a professor show up late for class influence students to be late for class? Or when professors are early, do students tend to show up early? In the spring of 2008, some statistics students randomly chose 31 different classes and recorded how many minutes a professor was early or late for class and the average number of minutes the students in the class were early or late. They wanted to see

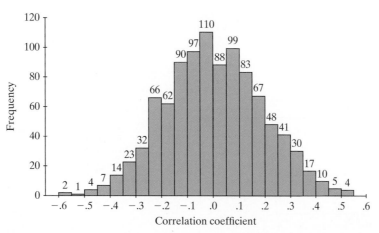

EXERCISE 10.CE.13

if there was a positive linear relationship between the professor's and the students' arrival times. We input these data into statistical software and found the correlation was 0.227. We then shuffled the data 1,000 times and found the corresponding 1,000 correlations. The simulated correlations are shown in the graph for Exercise 10.CE.13 on the previous page.

a. What is the null hypothesis in this study?

b. What is the alternative hypothesis in this study?

c. Which variable would it seem is the explanatory variable and which is the response?

d. Based on the histogram, what is the approximate p-value for this study?

e. What would be your complete conclusion for the one-sided study?

f. If this were a two-sided test, how would the alternative hypothesis change and what would be the new approximate p-value?

g. Even if you conclude that the association between these variables is statistically significant, can you legitimately conclude that the instructor's being late caused students to be late? Explain.

Least squares

10.CE.14 Consider a miniature data set:

x	0	1	2
y	1	0	2

Four copies of the scatterplot are shown below, each with a fitted line. Find the residuals for each line and the sum of squares. Match the sum of squared residuals to the plots, choosing from 3/2, 2, 2, and 9/4.

Line 1

Line 2

Line 3

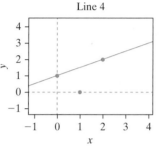

Line 4

Noise in New York*

On July 20, 2012, *The New York Times* ran an article about the noise level at 33 different locations in New York City. The scatterplots A–F below are all based on that study. Each shows noise level in decibels (dB) versus time of day (24-hour clock).

A. All locations

B. All restaurants

C. All stores

D. All other locations

E. Restaurants, evening

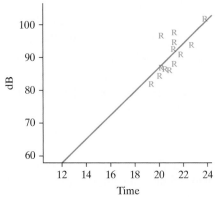

F. Other locations, including the gym

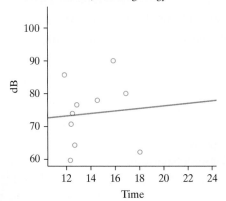

10.CE.15 Match each scatterplot with its correlation and regression slope, choosing from A–F:

	A	B	C	D	E	F
Correlations:	0.08	0.15	0.43	0.66	0.73	0.79
Slope:	0.38	1.31	2.29	1.83	3.62	1.64

10.CE.16 Match each scatterplot with its verbal description (a)–(c). You may need to use some descriptions more than once, and others may not be needed.

a. No big outliers, no influential points; strong linear relationship

b. No big outliers, no influential points; not convincing evidence of a linear relationship

c. No big outliers, but two influential points. Removing these points will decrease the correlation and increase the fitted slope.

10.CE.17 Fill in the blanks based on the patterns in the data.

a. For restaurants, the correlation between average noise level and time becomes _____ (stronger, weaker) if you exclude the two lunch-time measurements.

b. For stores, the noise level _____ (is, is not) related to time of day.

c. For the all other locations (Plot D), the suggestion of a possible relationship between noise level and time of day becomes _____ (stronger, weaker) if you exclude the gym measured at 6:30 PM.

d. On average, restaurants are _____ (more, less) noisy than stores.

e. On average, decibel levels measured later in the day tend to be _____ (higher, lower) than those measured earlier in the day.

f. Time of day _____ (is, is not) confounded with type of location.

g. For _____ (restaurants, stores, other locations) the fitted noise level increases by more than 10 decibels during the 3 hours from 7 PM to 10 PM.

h. If you go by the fitted line for all restaurants, the predicted decibel level at 5 PM is closest to _____ (round to the nearest 10 dB).

10.CE.18

a. Why is it not possible to conclude from the data that decibel levels increase as it gets later in the day?

b. How could the design of the study be improved in order to allow better conclusions about the effect of time of day on noise level?

10.CE.19

a. Refer to Plot A, the scatterplot for all locations in the survey. Note that between 12 noon and midnight (24) the fitted decibel level goes from about 75 to about 95. Use this fact to estimate the decibel level at the y-intercept. (For comparison, a measurement taken in the Evergreens Cemetery was 60 dB.)

b. What time of day does the y-intercept correspond to? Explain why the fitted decibel level for time 0 cannot possibly be right.

10.CE.20 Three histograms are shown here. Each shows simulated values of r obtained by breaking the association on one of the scatterplots (A)–(C) in (10.CE.15). Which histogram is for each plot? How can you tell?

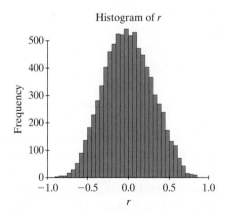

Coffee and height

10.CE.21 Suppose a friend of yours is telling you about a study reported in a popular magazine. The friend said that the study reported a correlation of zero between the amount of coffee a person drank as a child and his or her height as an adult. Your friend interprets this correlation to mean that the more coffee a child drinks, the shorter that person will be as an adult. In other words, drinking coffee stunts one's growth. Explain what is wrong with your friend's interpretation and explain what this type of correlation means.

U.S. states*

10.CE.22 This question is based on the 50 U.S. states. Each state is an observational unit, and the variables listed are measured separately for each of the 50 states. For each of the following pairs of variables, would you expect the correlation to be strong and positive, moderate and positive, weak or very weak, moderate and negative, or strong and negative.

a. 2012 popular vote for Romney and 2012 popular vote for Obama

b. Total 2012 popular vote for president and 2012 number of electoral votes

c. Number of McDonald's restaurants and number of attorneys

d. High school graduation rate and percentage of people over 25 with a four-year college degree

e. Year of statehood and number of years as a state

f. Year of statehood and longitude (east/west)

g. Longitude and latitude (north/south)

h. Latitude and average annual temperature

INVESTIGATION: ASSOCIATION BETWEEN HAND SPAN AND CANDY?

Is hand span a good predictor of how much candy you can grab? Using 45 college students as subjects, researchers set out to explore whether a linear relationship exists between hand span (cm) and the number of Tootsie Rolls® each subject could grab.

STEP 1: Ask a research question.

1. State the research question.

STEP 2: Design a study and collect data.

2. What are the observational/experimental units?

3. Is this a randomized experiment or an observational study? Explain how you know.

4. State the two variables measured on each unit.

5. Is there an explanatory/response relationship for these variables? Classify the variables in this study as categorical or quantitative.

6. State the null and alternative hypotheses to be investigated with this study.

STEP 3: Explore the data.

7. Use the data set **HandSpan** to calculate means, standard deviations, and the correlation coefficient.

8. Create a scatterplot of the data with hand span on the *x*-axis and number of Tootsie Rolls on the *y*-axis.

9. Does there appear to be an association between hand span and number of Tootsie Rolls? Describe the direction, form, and strength of the association: Is it positive, negative, weak, strong, linear?

10. Are there any unusual observations?

11. Find the least squares regression equation that predicts number of Tootsie Rolls based on hand span.

12. Interpret the slope of the least squares regression equation in terms of hand span and predicted number of Tootsie Rolls grabbed.

STEP 4: Draw inferences.

13. Use the appropriate applet to construct a simulated null distribution using the slope of the least squares regression line as the statistic. Mark the observed least squares slope on this graph.

    a. Paste a screenshot or draw your null distribution below with the observed slope marked and the approximate p-value shaded in.

    b. Is the observed statistic out in the tail of this null distribution or is it a fairly typical result?

    c. What is the p-value from your simulation? Based on this simulation analysis, would you conclude that the data provide *strong* evidence against the null hypothesis and conclude that there is a significant association between hand span and number of Tootsie Rolls grabbed? Explain your reasoning.

14. Are the validity conditions met to complete a theory-based *t*-test on these data? Explain. Whether the conditions are met or not, use a theory-based *t*-test to find a p-value. How does this p-value compare to the p-value your found using the randomization method?

15. Find a confidence interval for the slope that would describe the association between all hand spans and number of Tootsie Rolls grabbed. Is zero in this interval? Does this make sense based on the p-value from your test of significance?

STEP 5: Formulate conclusions.

16. Are you able to conclude that the association between hand span and number of Tootsie Rolls grabbed is causal? Explain.

17. What generalizations are you willing to make? Explain.

STEP 6: Look back and ahead.

18. Summarize the findings from the study. What worked well in this study design? What would you change? What are some follow-up research questions you would like to explore based on the findings from this study?

Research Article   www.wiley.com/college/tintle

- -

Music Problems   Read "Early Adolescent Music Preferences and Minor Deliquency by ter Bogt, Keijsers, Meeus, et al. (2013), 131(2), 1–10, in the *Journal of Pediatrics*.

- -

Probability and AP Exam Preparation

In the first three units you've seen how to complete tests of significance and calculate confidence intervals for several different types of data. You've also seen that the method of data collection used determines whether you can generalize to some population and whether you can make cause-and-effect conclusions.

UNIT 1–4 DATA STRUCTURES

UNIT 1: One Binary or One Quantitative Variable

UNIT 2: Comparing Two Groups

	EXPLANATORY	RESPONSE
Chapter 5	Binary	Binary
Chapter 6	Binary	Quantitative
Chapter 7	Binary	Quantitative (paired)

UNIT 3: Association Between Variables

	EXPLANATORY	RESPONSE
Chapter 8	Categorical	Categorical
Chapter 9	Categorical	Quantitative
Chapter 10	Quantitative	Quantitative

UNIT 4: Probability and AP Exam Preparation

At the root of these inferences is the principle of probability and how we can model chance outcomes. Because of this, Chapter 11 will give you a more in-depth look at probability. Although you have been using probability throughout your study of statistics—remember that p-values are probabilities—there is still more to explore with this topic. You will look at basic probability rules, see how discrete probability models can be used, and finally explore continuous probability distributions and see how these are related to sampling distributions you studied earlier.

The second part of this unit involves AP exam preparation. Although the previous chapters have covered the content of the exam (though perhaps in a different order) and given you exam tips, it is now time to focus on the exam itself in detail. Chapter 12 describes how the exam is laid out, gives ideas on what the people grading the exam are looking for, and provides you with additional tips to help you do your best. We also include two complete practice tests (one in the printed text and one online) so you can hone your skills and gain confidence.

Modeling Randomness

We have examined statistical studies throughout this book that have relied on randomness in the data collection process. Some of these studies have involved random sampling to select a representative sample from a population. Others have made use of random assignment for assigning subjects to treatment groups, with the goal of creating groups that are similar in all respects except for the explanatory variable being imposed. We have also used the randomness in the data collection process to draw inferences, particularly by approximating p-values and producing confidence intervals.

In this chapter we consider randomness more broadly and learn how to calculate probabilities involving random processes of various types. We will use simulation analyses to approximate probabilities, and where feasible, we will use mathematical analyses to calculate exact probabilities.

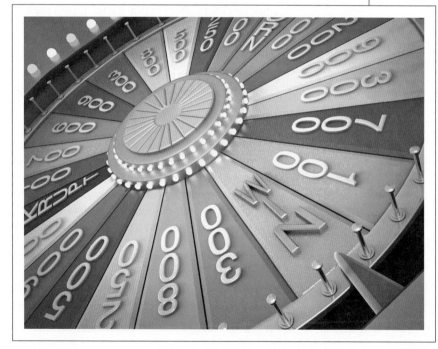

adventtr/E+/Getty Images

INTRODUCTION

Way back in Section P.3, you used simulation to investigate the probabilities that someone would pick the correct door and win a prize comparing two different strategies. Here, you will go further and see how you can not only use simulation to answer probability questions, but also use mathematical formulas and approaches to exactly calculate the long-run probability. In particular, in this section you will encounter basic ideas of randomness and probability. You will use simulation to approximate probabilities and will also use your own intuition about randomness to anticipate how probabilities change as a random process is modified. Then you will learn how to calculate exact probabilities for random processes where outcomes can reasonably be considered as equally likely.

Random Ice Cream Prices

Suppose that an ice cream shop offers a special promotion: The price of a small ice cream cone will be determined randomly by rolling a pair of fair, six-sided dice. The price, in cents, will be the larger number followed by the smaller number. (For example, if you roll a 2 and a 4, the price will be 42 cents.) You enter the shop with two quarters (50 cents). How likely is it that you'll be able to afford to buy the ice cream cone?

Example 11.1

> **THINK ABOUT IT**
>
> Do you think it's more likely than not that you'll be able to afford the cone, or less likely than not, or a 50-50 chance? Make a guess for the probability of being able to afford to buy the ice cream.

Throughout this book, you have investigated randomness and approximated probabilities by *simulating* the random process of interest. In most of the statistical studies you have examined, the random process has involved random sampling or random assignment. You will consider other kinds of random processes in this chapter. In the current example, the random process consists of rolling a pair of fair, six-sided dice.

> **THINK ABOUT IT**
>
> How could you use two dice to approximate the probability of being able to afford the ice cream cone with only 50 cents? Why would this method work?

You could approximate the probability of being able to afford the ice cream cone by

1. actually rolling the pair of dice a large number of times (say, 1,000 or more),
2. determining the price the ice cream cone would be for each roll,
3. counting how many rolls result in a price of 50 cents or less, and
4. dividing that count by the number of rolls.

The resulting proportion approximates the (true, long-run) probability that you'll be able to afford the ice cream cone, because that probability is the long-run proportion of times that you would be able to afford the cone if the random process were repeated over and over.

You could also use a computer to simulate this random process very quickly and efficiently, even for a very large number of repetitions (rolls) of the random process. To do this, you should ask the computer to simulate rolling a pair of fair, six-sided dice, and then get the computer to use the numbers rolled to calculate the price. The computer will repeat this a large number of times and will count how often the price is 50 cents or less. You can also examine graphs of the distribution of prices and calculate statistics such as the average (mean) price and the standard deviation of the prices.

11.1.1

> THINK ABOUT IT
>
> What's the smallest possible price? What's the largest? When we simulate this process a large number of times, what do you expect the distribution of prices to look like?

Figure 11.1 displays the distribution of ice cream prices for a simulation with 1,000,000 repetitions. This distribution has some unusual features, but they make sense in this context. Only one price less than 20 is possible (namely, 11 cents), and two prices in the twenties are possible (21 and 22 cents), and so on until six prices in the sixties are possible (61 through 66 cents). Prices with repeated numbers, such as 11 or 66 cents, occur about half as often those with different numbers, such as 32 or 61 cents.

FIGURE 11.1   Distribution of ice cream prices for 1,000,000 repetitions.

> THINK ABOUT IT
>
> Based on the histogram of the distribution of prices, make an educated guess on the mean price, the standard deviation of the prices, and the probability that you can afford the ice cream cone if you only have 50 cents.

It turns out that the average of these 1,000,000 simulated prices is 47.25 cents, and the standard deviation is 14.76 cents. For this simulation analysis, the computer counted that 444,991 of the 1,000,000 simulated prices are 50 cents or less, so the approximate probability that you can afford the ice cream cone is 0.444991, or about 44.5%.

Because the simulation used such a very large number of repetitions (namely, 1 million), this approximate probability (44.5%) is likely to be quite close to the exact, long-run probability. But can we find this exact, long-run probability? It turns out that in this case we can. As we'll see, a key to finding exact, long-run probabilities is to list all the possible outcomes.

11.1.2

> THINK ABOUT IT
>
> How many possible outcomes are there for the random process of rolling two six-sided dice? Is it reasonable to assume that these outcomes are equally likely?

Each die has 6 possible outcomes (1 through 6). And for each possible outcome on one die, the second one has 6 possible outcomes. Thus, when two six-sided dice are rolled, there are 6 × 6 = 36 possible outcomes: (1,1), (1,2), (1,3), ... (6,5), (6,6).

Figure 11.2 lists all possible outcomes. A term for the list of all possible outcomes of a random process is the *sample space*.

Definition

The *sample space* of a random process lists all possible outcomes. The probabilities of the outcomes in the sample space must add up to 1.

(1,1)	(1,2)	(1,3)	(1,4)	(1,5)	(1,6)
(2,1)	(2,2)	(2,3)	(2,4)	(2,5)	(2,6)
(3,1)	(3,2)	(3,3)	(3,4)	(3,5)	(3,6)
(4,1)	(4,2)	(4,3)	(4,4)	(4,5)	(4,6)
(5,1)	(5,2)	(5,3)	(5,4)	(5,5)	(5,6)
(6,1)	(6,2)	(6,3)	(6,4)	(6,5)	(6,6)

FIGURE 11.2 Sample space for rolling two six-sided dice.

11.1.3

Assuming that the dice are fair and rolled independently, it's reasonable to assume that the 36 possible outcomes are equally likely. Because the probabilities must sum to 1, each outcome has probability 1/36, which is about 0.0278.

In this case, we are interested in the outcomes that will allow us to pay for the ice cream. These outcomes, where neither a 5 nor a 6 is rolled, are indicated in bold in Figure 11.3 and we call this collection of outcomes the *event* of interest.

(1,1) 11¢	**(1,2) 21¢**	**(1,3) 31¢**	**(1,4) 41¢**	(1,5) 51¢	(1,6) 61¢
(2,1) 21¢	**(2,2) 22¢**	**(2,3) 32¢**	**(2,4) 42¢**	(2,5) 52¢	(2,6) 62¢
(3,1) 31¢	**(3,2) 32¢**	**(3,3) 33¢**	**(3,4) 43¢**	(3,5) 53¢	(3,6) 63¢
(4,1) 41¢	**(4,2) 42¢**	**(4,3) 43¢**	**(4,4) 44¢**	(4,5) 54¢	(4,6) 64¢
(5,1) 51¢	(5,2) 52¢	(5,3) 53¢	(5,4) 54¢	(5,5) 55¢	(5,6) 65¢
(6,1) 61¢	(6,2) 62¢	(6,3) 63¢	(6,4) 64¢	(6,5) 65¢	(6,6) 66¢

FIGURE 11.3 The 36 possible outcomes of rolling two dice, with the outcomes that result in a price of 50 cents or less in bold.

Definition

An *event* is a collection of outcomes from the sample space.

KEY IDEA

When the outcomes in a sample space are *equally likely*, the probability of an event is the number of outcomes in the event divided by the number of outcomes in the sample space.

11.1.4

We see that 16 of the 36 outcomes result in a price of 50 cents or less, so the (exact, theoretical) probability that you can afford the ice cream cone is 16/36, which is 4/9 ≈ 0.4444. This means that if we were to repeat this random die-rolling process for a very large number of rolls, the proportion of rolls for which the price would be 50 cents or less would be very close to 0.4444. So you would be able to afford the cone a little less than half the time in the long run. Recall that the approximate probability from simulation was 0.445, which is quite close to the exact, theoretical probability.

Now suppose that a friend offers to pay for your ice cream cone if the price (in cents) turns out to be an odd number.

THINK ABOUT IT

What's the probability that your friend would pay for your cone?

To find the probability that your friend would pay for your cone, you need to count how many outcomes in the sample space produce a price that is an odd number, and divide this by the number of outcomes in the sample space. From Figure 11.3, you can see that there are 21 outcomes where the price is an odd number. Thus, the probability that your friend will buy your ice cream cone is 21/36, which is 7/12 ≈ 0.5833. This means that if you and your friend go to this ice cream shop for a very large number of days (and if this promotion continues for a while), then your friend will buy your ice cream cone on about 58.33% of those days.

11.1.5

Now, let's consider how likely it is that you'll get an ice cream cone *either* a) because the price is 50 cents or less so you can afford it *or* b) because the price is odd and so your friend buys it for you.

11.1.6

THINK ABOUT IT

How would you calculate the probability that you'll get an ice cream cone in either (or both) of these two situations?

This time you need to count how many outcomes in the sample space achieve one *or* the other (or both) of these conditions. Figure 11.4 shows the 27 outcomes for which you achieve an ice cream cone in at least one of these two ways. The probability that you'll get an ice cream cone is therefore 27/36, which is ¾, or 0.75. If you could repeat this process for a very large number of times, you would obtain an ice cream cone 75% of the time in the long run.

(1,1) 11¢	**(1,2) 21¢**	**(1,3) 31¢**	**(1,4) 41¢**	**(1,5) 51¢**	**(1,6) 61¢**
(2,1) 21¢	**(2,2) 22¢**	**(2,3) 32¢**	**(2,4) 42¢**	(2,5) 52¢	(2,6) 62¢
(3,1) 31¢	**(3,2) 32¢**	**(3,3) 33¢**	**(3,4) 43¢**	**(3,5) 53¢**	**(3,6) 63¢**
(4,1) 41¢	**(4,2) 42¢**	**(4,3) 43¢**	**(4,4) 44¢**	(4,5) 54¢	(4,6) 64¢
(5,1) 51¢	(5,2) 52¢	**(5,3) 53¢**	(5,4) 54¢	**(5,5) 55¢**	**(5,6) 65¢**
(6,1) 61¢	(6,2) 62¢	**(6,3) 63¢**	(6,4) 64¢	**(6,5) 65¢**	(6,6) 66¢

FIGURE 11.4 The outcomes in the event that the price is an odd number or 50 cents or less are in bold (additional outcomes to those in Figure 11.3 are in italics).

Suppose things get a bit more complicated, and *three* (fair, six-sided) dice are rolled, and the price is still the largest value followed by the smallest value (in cents), ignoring the "middle" outcome?

THINK ABOUT IT

Would you expect the probability that you can afford the ice cream cone to be larger, smaller, or the same as when two dice were rolled? Why? How would you expect the mean and SD of the prices to compare to what they were before? Why?

Although you could write down the sample space of all the equally likely outcomes (there would be 6 × 6 × 6 = 216 of equally likely outcomes!) and then compute the exact probability, this is a case where simulation might be faster.

Figure 11.5 displays the distribution of prices for 1,000,000 simulated repetitions of three dice rolls.

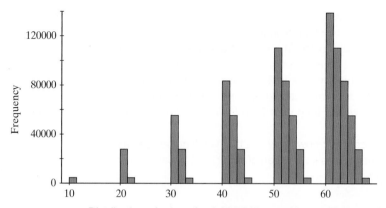

FIGURE 11.5 Distribution of prices for 1,000,000 repetitions with three dice.

The approximate probability that you can afford the ice cream cone is now 0.297054 because 297,054 out of 1 million times, the simulated ice cream cone price was less than 50 cents. Notice that this is considerably smaller than before. This makes sense because with three dice instead of two dice, it's more likely that at least one die will come up 5 or 6, which will result in a price higher than 50 cents. The mean of these 1,000,000 simulated prices is about 51.62 cents, which is larger than before. The standard deviation of these 1,000,000 simulated prices is about 11.86 cents, which is smaller than before, indicating less variability in the distribution of prices. This makes sense because with more dice, the rolls generally result in higher prices that are more consistent (less spread out) than before.

EXPLORATION 11.1 | Random Babies

Suppose that four mothers give birth to baby boys at the same hospital on the same evening. As a very, very sick joke (do not try this at home!), the hospital staff decides to return the babies to the mothers at random! You will investigate how likely it is (i.e., what is the probability) that *at least one* mother receives the correct baby. (This is a classic probability problem known as the *matching problem*. If you prefer to think of a different context, suppose that four college students bump into each other and drop their cell phones; then each student picks up one of the four cell phones at random.)

1. Make a guess for the probability that *at least one* mother receives the correct baby.

    You'll take two approaches to answering this question. You will start with an approximate analysis using simulation (as you have done throughout this book, usually for approximating p-values). Then you will proceed to a more mathematical, exact analysis.

2. Describe how you could use four index cards to simulate this random process and approximate the probability that at least one mother gets the right baby.

3. Use four index cards to conduct 5 repetitions of this random process. For each repetition, record the number of *matches*. (*Note:* A *match* occurs when a mother receives the correct baby.)

Repetition #	1	2	3	4	5
Number of matches					

4. Based on your (very small) simulation analysis with 5 repetitions, report the approximate probability that at least one mother receives the correct baby (that is, there is at least one match).

5. Suggest how to determine a more accurate approximation for this probability.

6. Now combine your simulation results with those of your classmates. Record the number and proportion of occurrences for each possible number of matches:

# of matches	0	1	2	3	4
Count Proportion					

7. Use these simulation results to approximate the probability that at least one mother gets the right baby (that is, there is at least one match).

Now we turn to technology in order to perform this simulation more quickly and efficiently.

8. Open the **Random Babies** applet. Press **Randomize**, and observe how many mothers get the right baby. Then repeat this four more times. Then enter 995 for the number of trials, in order to produce a total of 1,000 repetitions. Report the cumulative results in the table for the 1,000 repetitions:

# of matches	0	1	2	3	4
Count Proportion					

9. Based on the simulation with 1,000 repetitions, report the approximate probability that at least one mother gets the right baby.

10. Click on the bar in the applet graph corresponding to 0 matches. Describe what the resulting cumulative (over the number of trials) relative frequency plot reveals about how the approximate probability changes as the number of repetitions increases.

11. Use the radio button to return to the graph of the average number of matches vs. the number of trials. Report the average number of matches (per repetition of the random process) at the end of these 1,000 repetitions. Also describe what the graph of averages reveals about how the average number of matches changes as the number of repetitions increases.

An exact theoretical analysis of this random process would consider all of the possible ways to distribute the four babies to the four mothers.

12. How many possibilities are there for returning the four babies to their mothers?

The sample space of all possible ways to distribute four babies to their mothers is shown in Figure 11.6. (For example, outcome 1234 in the upper left corner means that mother 1 gets baby 1, mother 2 gets baby 2, mother 3 gets baby 3, and mother 4 gets baby 4—every baby ends up with the right mother!). Outcome 2134 (right below 1234) means that mothers 3 and 4 get the right babies, but the babies belonging to mothers 1 and 2 get switched. Note that there are 24 possible outcomes in the sample space.

> **Definition**
>
> The **sample space** of a random process lists all possible outcomes. The probabilities of the outcomes in the sample space must add up to 1.

```
1234   1243   1324   1342   1423   1432
2134   2143   2314   2341   2413   2431
3124   3142   3214   3241   3412   3421
4123   4132   4213   4231   4312   4321
```

FIGURE 11.6   Sample space of ways to return four babies to mothers.

> **Definition**
>
> An **event** is a collection of outcomes.

13. For each of these possibilities as shown in Figure 11.6, indicate how many mothers get the correct baby.

For example, we can think of the event "no matches" as consisting of the outcomes in the sample space where 0 mothers received the correct baby.

14. Using your answers to the previous question, how many outcomes are in the event "no matches"?

15. Count how many ways there are to get 0 matches, 1 match, and so on. Record these in the middle row of the table below.

# of matches	0	1	2	3	4
# possibilities					
Probability					

KEY IDEA

When the outcomes in a sample space are **equally likely**, the probability of an event is the number of outcomes in the event divided by the number of outcomes in the sample space.

16. Determine the (exact theoretical) probability of each event by dividing these counts by the total number of possible ways that babies can be returned to mothers. Record these probabilities in the last row of the table above.

17. Determine the exact probability of the event that *at least one* mother gets the correct baby (that is, there is at least one match).

18. Did the approximate probability from the simulation analysis (with 1,000 repetitions) come close to the exact probability? How could we adjust our simulation in order to get even closer?

19. Increase the number of repetitions in the simulation analysis to a total of 10,000. Report the approximate probability that at least one mother gets the right baby. Is this very close to the exact probability?

20. Write a sentence interpreting what the exact probability means in this context. Be sure to include a description of what "in the long run" means here.

21. What is the (exact) probability that exactly three mothers get the right baby? Explain what this value means and why that makes sense.

SECTION 11.1 Summary

This section has introduced you to probabilities involving ***random processes***. We have seen that probabilities involving random processes can be approximated with simulation or calculated exactly with a more mathematical analysis. Simulation analyses with a large number of repetitions can approximate probabilities quite accurately, because probability refers to the long-run proportion of times that the event would occur if the random process were repeated indefinitely.

A mathematical analysis of a random process can be based on its ***sample space***, which is a listing of all possible outcomes. In situations where the outcomes can be assumed to be equally likely, the probability of an ***event*** (collection of outcomes) can be calculated by counting the number of outcomes comprising the event and dividing by the number of outcomes in the sample space.

PROBABILITY RULES

INTRODUCTION

If you and a friend randomly select a movie from a list, how likely is it that neither you nor your friend has seen the movie yet? If you apply to two different colleges, how likely are you to be accepted by at least one of them? These kinds of questions can be answered by applying some basic probability rules that you will learn in this section.

In Section 11.1 you learned how to use simulation to approximate probabilities, and you saw how to calculate exact probabilities in situations where outcomes are equally likely.

In this section you are introduced to a somewhat more formal and mathematical examination of probability. You will learn mathematical rules that enable you to determine exact probabilities of some complicated situations. You will encounter and learn how to apply rules for calculating probabilities of one event *or* another event, and of one event *and* another event, as well as the probability an event does not occur.

Watching Films

In 2007, the American Film Institute created a list of the top 100 American films ever made (http://www.afi.com/100years/movies10.aspx). Two people, Allan and Beth, classified each film according to whether or not they had seen it at the time. The results are summarized in Table 11.1.

EXAMPLE   Example 11.2

TABLE 11.1 The number of films that Beth and Allan have seen (and not seen) from the list of the top 100 films

	Beth Yes	Beth No	Total
Allan Yes	42	6	48
Allan No	17	35	52
Total	59	41	100

Suppose that one of these 100 films is chosen "at random," which means each of the 100 films is equally likely to be chosen.

Remember, as we saw in Section 11.1, that an **event** is a set of outcomes and that the **sample space** is the set of all possible outcomes. In this case, the outcomes are the films chosen, so the set of all possible outcomes is the set of 100 films we are choosing from.

It is typical to use capital letters to represent events. So, let's let the letter A represent the event that Allan has seen the randomly selected film, and the letter B represent the event that Beth has seen the film. In other words, A consists of all the movies Allan has seen, and B consists of all the movies Beth has seen.

Because each of the 100 films is equally likely to be chosen, we can calculate the probability that Allan has seen the randomly selected film by counting how many films he has seen and then dividing that value by 100. So we can see from Table 11.1 the probability Allan has seen a randomly selected film is 0.48. Using mathematical symbols, we say that the probability Allan has seen a randomly selected film $= P(A) = \frac{48}{100}$, or 0.48. Similarly, the probability that Beth has seen the film is represented as $P(B) = \frac{59}{100}$, or 0.59. It is important to recognize that the probability of an event occurring will always be 0 (never could occur), 1 (guaranteed to occur), or something in between (might occur).

All probabilities are between 0 and 1, inclusive, so the probability of an event A is $0 \leq P(A) \leq 1$.

THINK ABOUT IT

What if we want to determine the probability that Allan has *not* seen the randomly selected film?

Definitions

The ***complement of an event*** A, denoted by A^C, is the event that A does not occur. The probability of a complement can be calculated as $P(A^C) = 1 - P(A)$. This is called the ***complement rule***.

From Table 11.1, we see that Allan has not seen 52 movies, so the probability he has not seen a randomly chosen movie from the list is $0.52 = 52/100$. But recall from the previous section that the probabilities for all possible outcomes of a random process must add up to 1. Because all films on the list were either seen by Allan or not seen by Allan, the probability that Allan has not seen the randomly selected film can also be calculated by subtracting the probability that Allan has seen the film from 1.

We will let A^C represent the event that Allan has not seen the film. This is referred to as the complement of A. Then the probability that Allan has not seen a film on the list can be calculated as

$$P(A^C) = 1 - P(A) = 1 - \frac{48}{100} = \frac{52}{100} = 0.52$$

THINK ABOUT IT

For a randomly selected film, what's the probability that both Allan and Beth have seen the film?

To determine the probability that both Allan and Beth have seen a randomly selected film, we can look at the table. In Table 11.2 we've circled the number 42, indicating that 42 out of 100 films have been seen by both Allan and Beth. Thus, the probability that a randomly chosen film has been seen by both Allan and Beth is 0.42.

KEY IDEA

When two events A and B both occur at the same time, we call this the ***intersection of the two events***. It is common to use the symbol $\cap$ to denote the intersection of A and B: $A \cap B$ is read as "A intersection B" or, more commonly, "A and B."

So the intersection of events *A and B* is the set of films that both Allan and Beth have seen. From Table 11.2 we can see that $P(A \text{ and } B) = P(A \cap B) = \frac{42}{100} = 0.42$.

TABLE 11.2   The number of films that Beth and Allan have seen (and not seen) from the list of the top 100 films, indicating which movies have been seen by both Beth and Allan

	Beth Yes	Beth No	Total
Allan Yes	42	6	48
Allan No	17	35	52
Total	59	41	100

For a randomly selected film, what's the probability that *either* Allan *or* Beth has seen the film?

Now let's determine the probability that either Allan *or* Beth has seen the randomly selected film.

KEY IDEA

When either event *A* and/or event *B* occurs, we call this the **union of the two events**. It is common to use the symbol ∪ to denote the union of *A* and *B*; *A* ∪ *B* is read as "*A* union *B*" or, more commonly, "*A* or *B*."

 11.2.1

You might think that the probability that Allan or Beth has seen a film, *P*(*A* or *B*), is equal to *P*(*A*) + *P*(*B*). We calculated these two probabilities to be *P*(*A*) = $\frac{48}{100}$ = 0.48, and *P*(*B*) = $\frac{59}{100}$ = 0.59. But 0.48 + 0.59 is 1.07—a number larger than 1—and that's impossible for a probability.

THINK ABOUT IT

What's wrong with using *P*(*A*) + *P*(*B*) to calculate the probability that Allan or Beth has seen the film? How should you do it correctly?

To answer this question, realize that the event *A* is composed of 48 films: the 42 films that Allan and Beth have both seen *and* the 6 films that Allan has seen but Beth has not. Similarly, the event *B* is composed of 59 films: the 42 films that they have both seen and the 17 films that Beth has seen but Allan has not.

So, if we simply add *P*(*A*) to *P*(*B*) in our attempt to calculate *P*(*A* or *B*), then the 42 movies that they both have seen are counted twice, once when we computed *P*(*A*) and again when we computed *P*(*B*). Instead, we want to count each movie only once. To do this, recognize that there are 42 movies they've both seen, 17 that only Beth has seen, and 6 that only Allan has seen. Thus, the correct answer is 42 + 17 + 6 = 65 movies they've both seen. The probability that either Allan or Beth (or both) have seen a randomly seleted movie is 0.65.

Alternatively, you can use the ***addition rule*** to compute this value. The addition rule adjusts the value of *P*(*A*) + *P*(*B*) to account for the fact that it "double counts" films that both Allan and Beth have seen. To see this, realize that *P*(*A*) + *P*(*B*) is 42/100 + 6/100 + 42/100 + 17/100. If we subtract 42/100 (the movies that have been seen by both Beth and Allan), we will get the correct value.

KEY IDEA

For two events *A* and *B*, the probability that either *A* or *B* (or both) occurs is given by *P*(*A* ∪ *B*) = *P*(*A*) + *P*(*B*) − *P*(*A* ∩ *B*). This is called the ***addition rule***. Thus, the addition rule says that to determine the probability of one event *or* another (or both) occurring, add the probabilities of the individual events and then subtract the probability of the *intersection* of the two events—those outcomes that are part of both events.

 11.2.2

In this case, using the addition rule, we find that the probability that either Beth or Allan has seen the movie is *P*(*A* ∪ *B*) = $\frac{48}{100}$ + $\frac{59}{100}$ − $\frac{42}{100}$ = $\frac{65}{100}$ = 0.65.

What is the complement of the event that Allan or Beth has seen the randomly selected film? How could you use the complement rule to calculate the probability that Allan or Beth has seen the film?

First, let's think about this in words. The complement of an event is that the event doesn't occur. So, what is the complement of the event that Allan or Beth has seen the movie? That neither one has seen the movie—Allan didn't see it and Beth didn't see it. In notation this means that $P((A \text{ or } B)^C) = P(A^C \text{ and } B^C)$.

We can see from Table 11.2 that there are 35 films that neither Allan nor Beth has seen, so the probability that neither Allan or Beth has seen the film is 0.35. To utilize this value to find the probability that either Allan or Beth has seen the movie, we use the complement rule introduced above. In other words, $P(\text{Allan or Beth}) = 1 - P(\text{not Allan and not Beth}) = 1 - 0.35 = 0.65$—the same value we obtained using the addition rule.

We used a 2 × 2 table of counts (Table 11.1) to reflect the sample space for the situation above. Another way to display a sample space in a way that can be used to find probabilities is with a Venn diagram. The 2 × 2 table of counts and corresponding Venn diagram are displayed in Figure 11.7.

Definitions

A **Venn diagram** uses partially overlapping circles, one circle for each event, to indicate the counts or probabilities of different combinations of events or their complements (e.g., A and B, A^C and B, A and B^C, and A^C and B^C).

	Beth Yes	Beth No	Total
Allan Yes	42	6	48
Allan No	17	35	52
Total	59	41	100

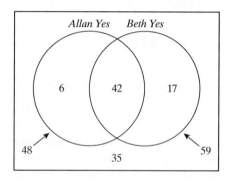

FIGURE 11.7   A sample space can be displayed in a 2 × 2 table (like that on the left) or in a Venn diagram (like that on the right).

Notice that the 42 movies that Allan and Beth have in common appear in the overlap (intersection) of the two circles representing Allan Yes and Beth Yes.

Probability tables contain probabilities rather than counts for the outcomes in the sample space.

Table 11.3 gives a probability table for these data. Note that the values inside a probability table must sum to 1.

Definition

A **probability table** contains probabilities, rather than counts, for all outcomes in the sample space.

TABLE 11.3 Probability table for randomly chosen movies			
	Beth Yes	Beth No	Total
Allan Yes	0.42	0.60	0.48
Allan No	0.17	0.35	0.52
Total	0.59	0.41	1.00

In what circumstance would it be valid to add the probabilities of two events to calculate the probability that one or the other event occurs? In other words, what would have to be true about events A and B in order for $P(A \text{ or } B) = P(A) + P(B)$?

11.2.3

If A and B have no outcomes in common (we call events that have no outcomes in common **mutually exclusive** or **disjoint**), then the probability of A or B occurring is the sum of their individual probabilities.

Consider two other people, Chad and Dori. Figure 11.8 illustrates the sample space of 100 films seen for both Chad and Dori.

	Dori Yes	Dori No	Total
Chad Yes	0	20	20
Chad No	40	40	80
Total	40	60	100

Definition

Two events A and B are **mutually exclusive (disjoint)** when it is impossible for both of them to occur simultaneously. In other words, $P(A \text{ and } B) = 0$. In this special case, $P(A \cup B) = P(A) + P(B)$.

FIGURE 11.8 A 2 × 2 table and Venn diagram displaying the sample space for films seen (and not seen) by Chad and Dori from the list of the top 100 films.

In this case, events C (Chad has seen the movie) and D (Dori has seen the movie) are mutually exclusive, because they have not seen any of the same movies! Chad has seen 20 films from the list and Dori has seen 40 films from the list, but none are the same. Because C and D are mutually exclusive, to find the probability that either Chad or Dori has seen the movie, you do the following: $P(C) + P(D) = 20/100 + 40/100 = 60/100 = 0.60$.

11.2.4

Random Ice Cream Prices (continued)

EXPLORATION 11.2

Recall from Example 11.1 that an ice cream shop offers a special promotion: The price of a small ice cream cone will be determined randomly by rolling a pair of fair, six-sided dice. The price, in cents, will be the larger number followed by the smaller number. (For example, if you roll a 2 and a 4, the price will be 42 cents.) You enter the shop with two quarters (50 cents). In addition, a friend offers to buy your ice cream cone if the price turns out to be an odd number.

Figure 11.2 back in Section 11.1 showed the sample space of 36 possible outcomes for the random process of rolling two six-sided dice.

1. Convert the sample space of 36 outcomes into a 2 × 2 table of counts by writing the appropriate counts into each box below.

	You can afford ice cream	You cannot afford ice cream	Total
Your friend buys ice cream for you			
Your friend does not buy ice cream for you			
Total			36

Let A represent the event that you can afford to buy the ice cream cone, and let B be the event that your friend buys the ice cream cone for you.

2. Report the probabilities of these events from the table:

$P(A) =$ $P(B) =$

KEY IDEA

All probabilities are between 0 and 1, inclusive, so the probability of an event A is $0 \leq P(A) \leq 1$.

The **complement of an event** A, denoted by A^C, is the event that A does not occur. The probability of a complement can be calculated as $P(A^C) = 1 - P(A)$. This is called the **complement rule**.

3. What is the probability that you *cannot* afford the ice cream cone?

4. Use the complement rule to determine the probability that your friend does not buy the ice cream for you. (*Hint*: Did you find $P(A^C)$ or $P(B^C)$?)

5. Find the probability that you can afford the ice cream cone *and* your friend buys the ice cream for you. Report this as both a fraction (with 36 in the denominator) and as a decimal.

KEY IDEA

When two events A and B both occur at the same time, we call this the **intersection of the two events**. It is common to use the symbol $\cap$ to denote the intersection of A and B; $A \cap B$ is read as "A intersection B" or, more commonly, "A and B."

6. Use the notation in the Key Idea box above to indicate the probability that you can afford the ice cream cone *and* your friend offers to buy it.

Now think about the event that the dice rolls result in you getting ice cream, either because you can afford it yourself *or* because your friend buys it for you (or both).

KEY IDEA

When either event A and/or event B occurs, we call this the **union of the two events**. It is common to use the symbol $\cup$ to denote the union of A and B; $A \cup B$ is read as "A union B" or, more commonly, "A or B."

7. Use the notation in the Key Idea box above to indicate the probability that you can afford the ice cream cone *or* your friend offers to buy it.

Now we will use three different ways to calculate the probability of the event that you can afford the ice cream cone or your friend offers to buy it.

8. Referring back to the table earlier in this exploration, which of the cells in the 2 × 2 table correspond to this event (that you end up with ice cream one way or the other)? Add the counts in these cells and divide by 36 (the total number of possible outcomes in the sample space).

9. Write a sentence interpreting what this probability means.

10. Would it have worked to simply find $P(A) + P(B)$ to determine the probability that either A or B occurs? Using numbers in your argument, explain why or why not.

11. By how much does $P(A) + P(B)$ exceed the actual probability that either A or B occurs? Express this difference as a fraction (with a denominator of 36) as well as a decimal. Does this number look familiar? Explain.

We've seen that $P(A) + P(B)$ is too large to be the probability of A or B. When we add $P(A)$ and $P(B)$, we are "counting" $P(A$ and $B)$ (the probability that your friend buys your cone and you can afford it) twice. Because this probability has been double counted, if we subtract this amount, we will arrive at the correct answer.

A **Venn diagram** uses partially overlapping circles, one circle for each event, to indicate the counts or probabilities of different combinations of events or their complements (e.g., A and B, A^c and B, A and B^c, and A^c and B^c).

KEY IDEA

For two events A and B, the probability that either A or B (or both) occurs is given by $P(A \cup B) = P(A) + P(B) - P(A \cap B)$. This is called the **addition rule**. Thus, the addition rule says that to determine the probability of one event *or* another (or both) occurring, add the probabilities of the individual events and then subtract the probability of the *intersection* of the two events—those outcomes that are part of both events.

12. Show how to use the addition rule to calculate the probability of the event (A or B). Confirm that this gives the same probability as we obtained earlier.

A **Venn diagram** uses partially overlapping circles to help visualize the probabilities associated with two different events.

13. In the Venn diagram below, enter the counts associated with each of the four disjoint (non-overlapping) regions in the picture. For example, the overlapping area in the middle represents A and B, the "moon-shaped" region on the left side represents the event A and B^c.

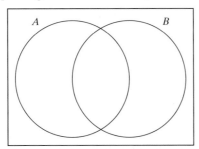

Sometimes Venn diagrams contain probabilities instead of counts. You can also use probabilities instead of counts in 2×2 tables of the sample space. When you do this, it is called a **probability table**.

14. In the table below, enter the probabilities associated with each event by dividing each count by the number of outcomes in the sample space.

	You can afford ice cream	You cannot afford ice cream	Total
Your friend buys ice cream for you			
Your friend does not buy ice cream for you			
Total			1.0

Definition

A **probability table** contains probabilities, rather than counts, for all outcomes in the sample space.

15. Under what circumstances would $P(A \text{ or } B) = P(A) + P(B)$? In other words, what would have to be true about you being able to afford the ice cream and your friend buying you the ice cream in order for $P(A \text{ or } B) = P(A) + P(B)$? (*Hint*: Think about what the Venn diagram would look like.)

A third way to calculate this same probability—that is, the probability that either you can afford to buy the ice cream yourself, or that your friend buys it for you, or both—uses the complement rule we saw earlier.

16. Describe (in words) the *complement* of the event that you can afford the ice cream or your friend buys it for you.

17. Which cell of the 2×2 table corresponds to the complement of the event that either you can afford to buy ice cream yourself or that your friend buys it for you? What is the probability this occurs?

18. Now, use the complement rule, and your answer to the previous question, to determine (yet again) the probability that you can afford the ice cream or your friend buys it for you. Confirm that your answer matches the ones that you have obtained above using different approaches.

Definition

Two events A and B are **mutually exclusive (disjoint)** when it is impossible for both of them to occur simultaneously. In other words, $P(A \text{ and } B) = 0$. In this special case, $P(A \cup B) = P(A) + P(B)$.

SECTION 11.2 Summary

In this section you continued your study of probability by learning several rules that are useful for calculating new probabilities based on known probabilities. Two of these rules are the **complement rule** and the **addition rule**, which proved useful for calculations involving random ice cream prices and film watching.

- The addition rule enables you to determine the probability that one or the other (or both) of two events occurs, provided that you know the probability of each event and the probability that both events occur. In fact, knowing any three of these probabilities allows you to determine the remaining one.

$$P(A \cup B) = P(A) + P(B) - P(A \cap B)$$

Remember to subtract the probability of the intersection (*A* and *B*) when applying the addition rule, unless the two events are mutually exclusive.

- When you speak of the probability of *A* or *B*, you include three disjoint events: *A* and *not B* ($A \cap B^C$), *B* and *not A* ($B \cap A^C$), and both *A* and *B* ($A \cap B$).

- In general, do not assume that "or" means that *only* one of the events occurs; it instead typically means one or the other or *both*.

- The probability that an event does not happen can be calculated as 1 minus the probability that it does happen. This is known as the **complement rule.**

  The complement rule enables you to find the probability of the complement (opposite) of any event, so it's always wise to be on the lookout for whether the probability of an event's complement may be easier to calculate than the event's probability itself. In such cases, you can first find the probability of the complement and then subtract this probability from 1 to calculate the probability of interest. (For example, we could have calculated the probability that neither had seen the film and subtracted from 1 to find the probability at least one person had seen the film.)

- All probabilities must be between 0 and 1, where 0 indicates the probability of an event that cannot possibly happen and 1 indicates the probability of an event that is guaranteed to happen.

- A **probability table** or a **Venn diagram** can be a useful device for organizing and calculating probabilities. A Venn diagram, like the one below, illustrates the probabilities or counts in each disjoint region.

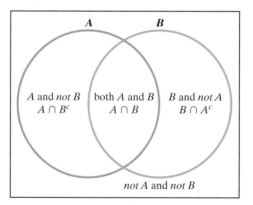

- Two events are said to be **mutually exclusive** when it is impossible for both of them to occur simultaneously. In other words, the intersection is empty.

- You do not necessarily need to use one of these rules when calculating probabilities. If you can perform the calculation with other methods, such as drawing a Venn diagram or constructing a probability table or table of counts, that's fine. Better yet, calculate the probability in a couple of different ways to verify your answer.

CONDITIONAL PROBABILITY AND INDEPENDENCE

INTRODUCTION

In the Preliminaries chapter, you investigated whether or not the method used to solicit participation in the organ donation program (neutral/opt-in/opt-out) had an effect on the participation rate. Suppose we wanted to find the probability that a randomly selected participant chooses to participate in the organ donation program. If we were provided with the information that the participant was given the opt-out method, does that give you additional information on his or her decision to participate? It would, because we saw that the type of organ donation was associated with the participation rates. When we update or change a prediction (probability) by using additional information, this is called a "conditional" probability. In this section you will learn mathematical rules that enable you to determine *conditional probabilities* of one event *given* another event has occurred. You will also examine the concept of *independence* as it applies to random events.

Watching Films Revisited

EXAMPLE Example 11.3

In Example 11.2, we looked at a breakdown of how many films Beth and Allan have seen from a list of the top 100 films ever made. Suppose again that one of these 100 films is chosen at random. Table 11.4 shows the counts of the 100 movies, illustrating who has seen which movies.

TABLE 11.4 The number of films that Beth and Allan have seen (and not seen) from the list of the top 100 films

	Beth Yes	Beth No	Total
Allan Yes	42	6	48
Allan No	17	35	52
Total	59	41	100

We can see from Table 11.4 that the probability Beth has seen the randomly selected film is 59/100. But now suppose you are told that Allan has seen the film that has been randomly chosen. Does this change the probability that Beth has seen it?

THINK ABOUT IT

Does the information that Allan has seen the film make it more or less likely (or just as likely) that Beth has seen it, compared to the original (unconditional) probability that Beth has seen the film? How likely is it?

Notice that there are 48 movies that Allan has seen. Because we're told that Allan has seen the movie, we now know that one of these 48 movies has been chosen. This means that the sample space has been reduced to those 48 movies. We also know that, of those 48 movies, Beth has seen 42 of them. Thus, the **conditional probability** that Beth has seen the film *given that* Allan has seen it is $\frac{42}{48} = 0.875$.

Using notation, we replace "given that" with the vertical line "|" so this conditional probability can be written as $P(B|A) = \frac{42}{48} = 0.875$. Notice that this is higher than 0.59, the original probability that Beth has seen the film. This is because Allan and Beth have a large number of movies that they've both seen, so knowing that Allan has seen the movie greatly improves the likelihood that Beth has also seen the movie.

Definition

The **conditional probability** of B given A is represented as $P(B|A)$ and is the probability that B occurs if we know that A has occurred.

THINK ABOUT IT

How could the conditional probability $P(B|A)$ have been calculated from $P(A$ and $B)$, $P(A)$, and $P(B)$? Which of these three values is not needed?

Think about the two values we used above, 48 (the number of movies Allan has seen) and 42 (the number of movies that Allan and Beth have both seen), and the fact that the total number of movies that Beth has seen (59) is not something we need to know in order to compute $P(B|A) = 42/48$. This suggests that perhaps $P(B)$ is what we do not need. In particular, note that

$$P(B|A) = \frac{42}{48} = \frac{42/100}{48/100} = \frac{P(A \cap B)}{P(A)}$$

In this approach, we are focusing on the *probabilities* instead of the *number* of films, and you'll notice that the denominators of the probabilities (in this case 100) cancel out.

11.3.1 ▶

KEY IDEA

The conditional probability of event B, given that event A has occurred, is calculated as $P(B|A) = \dfrac{P(A \cap B)}{P(A)}$.

Definitions

- - - - - - - - - - - - - - - -

Two events A and B are said to be ***independent*** if $P(B|A) = P(B)$. In other words, knowing that event A has occurred does not change the probability that event B will occur. If two events are not independent, they are said to be ***dependent***. In other words, knowing that event A has occurred does change the probability that event B will occur. Note that if events A and B are independent, then events *not A* and *not B* are also independent, as are A and *not B*, and so on.

- - - - - - - - - - - - - - - -

INDEPENDENCE

We call two events ***independent*** if the occurrence of one does not change the probability that the other event will happen.

THINK ABOUT IT

Are the events *Allan has seen the film* and *Beth has seen the film* independent?

No, the event that Allan has seen the film is not independent of the event that Beth has seen the film. Knowing that Allan had seen the film greatly impacted the probability that Beth had seen it. Before we knew that Allan had the seen the film, there was a 59% chance Beth had seen it, but this probability increased to 87.5% if we knew that Allan had seen it.

Because $P(B|A) \neq P(B)$, the events that Allan has seen the film and Beth has seen the film are not independent. Knowing that Allan has seen the film increased the probability that Beth has also seen it.

Now consider these hypothetical data concerning the number of these films seen by Chuck and by Donna:

	Donna Yes	Donna No	Total
Chuck Yes	15	10	25
Chuck No	45	30	75
Total	60	40	100

THINK ABOUT IT

Consider a randomly selected film. Does the knowledge that Chuck has seen the film change the probability that Donna has seen it?

To answer this question, you will need to compare Donna's (unconditional) probability of having seen the film with the conditional probability that she has seen it given we know that Chuck has seen the film.

$$P(D) = 60/100 = 0.60 \qquad P(D|C) = 15/25 = 0.60$$

Because these two probabilities are equal, the knowledge that Chuck has seen the film provides *no additional information regarding the chances that Donna has seen the film*. Another way to look at this is that the proportion of the films that Donna has seen is the same whether that proportion comes from all the films or that proportion comes from just films that Chuck has seen.

The events "Donna has seen the film" and "Chuck has seen the film" are independent because knowing Chuck has seen the film does not change the probability that Donna has also seen it. Donna has seen 60% of the films that Chuck has seen, and she has seen 60% of the films that Chuck has not seen, and she has seen 60% of the films overall.

MULTIPLICATION RULE

THINK ABOUT IT

How can we find the probability of two events both occurring if the events are not independent?

 11.3.2

We can rearrange the conditional probability formula, $P(B|A) = \frac{P(A \cap B)}{P(A)}$ to find a general formula for the probability of both A and B occurring, $P(A \cap B) = P(A) \times P(B|A)$, meaning the probability of both A and B occurring is the (unconditional) probability of A occurring times the (conditional) probability of B occurring, given that A has occurred.

If events A and B are independent, then this simplifies to $P(A \cap B) = P(A) \times P(B)$, as we saw earlier.

For example, if you are told that Ellen has seen 80% of the films that Donna has seen, you can express the value of 0.80 as a conditional probability: $P(E|D) = 0.80$. Remember that earlier we learned that Donna had seen 60% of the films ($P(D) = 0.6$). Using the general multiplication rule allows us to find the probability that a film has been watched by both Donna and Ellen. $P(D \text{ and } E) = P(E|D) \times P(D) = 0.8 \times 0.6 = 0.48$.

The multiplication rule for independent events also works for more than two events.

KEY IDEA

With a series of *independent* events, the probability that all of the events happen is the product of their individual probabilities. In symbols, if $A_1, A_2, ..., A_k$ are independent events, then $P(A_1 \text{ and } A_2 \text{ and } ... \text{ and } A_k) = P(A_1) \times P(A_2) \times ... \times P(A_k)$. This is an extension of the *multiplication rule for independent events*.

Definitions

The **general multiplication rule** allows you to calculate the probability that two events both occur (intersection), based on one of their probabilities and the conditional probability of the other event given the first: $P(A \cap B) = P(A) \times P(B|A) = P(B) \times P(A|B)$.

Note: If A and B are independent events, then this rule simplifies to the **multiplication rule for independent events:** $P(A \cap B) = P(A) \times P(B)$.

MUTUALLY EXCLUSIVE VS. INDEPENDENT

What if the films that Fred has seen (30% of the entire list) are mutually exclusive of the films that Donna has seen? Recall from the previous section that if two events are mutually exclusive, they do not have any outcomes in common. In this case, this means that Fred has not seen any of the films that Donna has seen, and Donna has not seen any of the films that Fred has seen. Using notation, this means that $P(D \text{ and } F) = 0$.

 11.3.3

THINK ABOUT IT

So if we pick a film and Donna has seen it, then what is the conditional probability Fred has seen it?

 11.3.4

To calculate $P(F|D)$, we would use $P(F \cap D)/P(D)$, but because the two events are mutually exclusive, $P(D \cap F) = 0$ (Donna and Fred haven't seen any of the same films), so $P(F|D) = 0$ (if Donna has seen the movie, there is no chance that Fred has also). This is clearly different from $P(F) = 0.30$.

THINK ABOUT IT

What if we tell you Donna has not seen it? Now what is the probability Fred has see it or what is $P(F|D^c)$?

First, what do you know about $F \cap D^c$? There are 40 films that Donna has not seen and Fred has seen 30 of those films, so $P(F \cap D^c) = 0.30$. $P(F|D^c) = P(F \cap D^c)/P(D^c) = 0.30/0.40 = 0.75$. In other words, Fred has seen 30 of the 40 films that Donna has not. Again, this is not equal to the unconditional probability.

Either one of these calculations illustrates that F and D are not independent events. In fact, this has to be the case when the events are mutually exclusive!

Careful, though—students often get these two ideas of mutually exclusive and independent confused and either think they are the same thing, or that one implies the other!

KEY IDEA

When two events are mutually exclusive, they are not independent.

TREE DIAGRAMS

When we have conditional probabilities, a ***tree diagram*** may be another useful way to organize the information.

Recall that Allan had seen 48% of the films and the probability that Beth has seen the film given Allan had seen it was 42/48. You can also find that the probability that Beth has seen the film if Allan hasn't is 17/52. (Why?)

Let's organize this information in a tree diagram. Each set of branches represents a single event, and thus the probabilities for each set of branches must sum to 1. The probability entered on each branch of the tree represents the likelihood of heading down each branch if we were "walking" down the tree (moving from left to right).

Let A be the event that Allan has seen the film and B be the event that Beth has seen the film. The first set of branches (Figure 11.9) show the probabilities of the two possible outcomes for Allan: either he has seen the film, $P(A)$, or he has not seen the film, $P(A^c)$. The two branches must sum to 1.

Definition

- - - - - - - - - - - - - - - - - - -

A ***tree diagram*** organizes conditional probabilities with a node representing an event and branches from the node representing the possible outcomes associated with the event. Typically, conditional probabilities are written on the branches of the tree.

- - - - - - - - - - - - - - - - - - - -

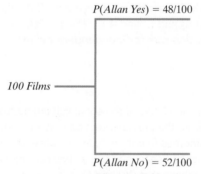

FIGURE 11.9   Tree diagram representing Allan's movie-watching probabilities.

The next set of branches shows the conditional probabilities. So from the top branch we then look at the probability that Beth has seen the film given that we know Allan has seen the film, $P(B|A)$, and the probability of the complement, that Beth has not seen the film given that we know Allan has seen it, $P(B^c|A)$. Notice that if there is a 42/48 chance that Beth has seen the film if Allan has, then there is a 6/48 chance that Beth hasn't seen the film if Allan has. If you multiply across the branches of the tree, you are applying the multiplication rule and will get the probabilities of the intersections. For example, the products along the upper set of branches give the probability Allan Yes and Beth Yes, $P(A \cap B)$, and the probability Allan Yes and Beth No, $P(A \cap B^c)$. Then from the bottom branch, we look at the probabilities that Beth has seen and not seen the film given that we know Allan has not seen it. The products along the lower set of branches give you $P(A^c \cap B)$ and $P(A^c \cap B^c)$.

THINK ABOUT IT

How would you use the tree diagram to find the probability that for a randomly selected film, neither Allan nor Beth has seen it?

The probability that neither Allan nor Beth has seen the film, ($P(A^c$ and $B^c)$), can be found by multiplying the values of the appropriate branches of the tree. *Allan No* and *Beth No* can be written as $P(A^c \cap B^c)$, which is the product of the probabilities P(*Allan No*) and P(*Beth No given Allan No*). The highlighted branches of the tree diagram in Figure 11.10 give this probability.

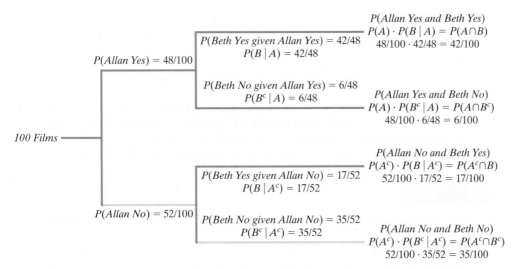

FIGURE 11.10 Tree diagram representing Allan and Beth's movie-watching probabilities.

Notice that the probability tree also allows us to find the unconditional probability of an event. The probability Allan has seen a movie will be the sum of the probability that Allan has seen it and Beth has not with the probability that both Beth and Allan have seen the movie.

 11.3.5

THINK ABOUT IT

Does $P(A \cap B) + P(A \cap B^c) = P(A)$? Why or why not?

Because the events $A \cap B$ and $A \cap B^c$ are mutually exclusive (no movie watched by Allan can be watched and not watched by Beth—that's impossible!), we can sum these probabilities. Intuitively, this just means that because 42 movies were seen by Allan and Beth $A \cap B$, and 6 movies were seen by Allan but not Beth $A \cap B^c$, the total seen by Allan is 48 movies. So $P(A) = 42/100 + 6/100 = 48/100$, as we saw earlier. Similarly, $P(B) = 42/100 + 17/100 = 59/100$.

College Admissions

EXPLORATION 11.3A

Suppose that you have applied to two colleges and believe that you have a 0.80 probability of being accepted by college A, a 0.40 probability of being accepted by college B, and a 0.35 probability of being accepted by both. You will investigate how the probability that you will be accepted by one of these colleges changes if you find out whether you have been accepted by the other.

1. Start by converting the given probabilities into a 2 × 2 table of counts to help make things more concrete. Let's assume that these probabilities held exactly for a hypothetical population of 1,000 applicants. Notice that the counts provided in the following table correspond to the given 0.80, 0.40, and 0.35 probabilities. Fill in the missing counts in the table.

	Accepted by B	Not accepted by B	Total
Accepted by A	350		800
Not accepted by A			
Total	400		1,000

Definition

The **conditional probability** of B given A is represented $P(B|A)$ and is the probability that B occurs if we know that A has occurred.

2. Among the 800 applicants who were accepted by college A, what proportion were also accepted by college B?

We will refer to the proportion from the previous question as the **conditional probability** of being accepted by college B, given that an applicant was accepted by college A.

3. How does the conditional probability of acceptance by college B, given acceptance by college A, compare to the (original, unconditional) probability of acceptance by college B? In other words, does learning that an applicant has been accepted by college A make it more or less likely (or just as likely) that the applicant will be accepted by college B?

KEY IDEA

The conditional probability of event B, given that event A has occurred, is calculated as $P(B|A) = \dfrac{P(A \cap B)}{P(A)}$.

4. Use the formula above to calculate $P(B|A)$. Verify that the answer agrees with what you found earlier.

5. Suppose that you learn that you have been accepted by *at least one* of these colleges. Determine the conditional probability that you have been accepted by *both* colleges. (*Hint*: You want to calculate $P((A \text{ and } B)|(A \text{ or } B))$. Use the definition of conditional probability, applied to these *compound* events.)

Definitions

Two events A and B are said to be **independent** if $P(B|A) = P(B)$. In other words, knowing that event A has occurred does not change the probability that event B will occur. If two events are not independent, they are said to be **dependent**. In other words, knowing that event A has occurred does change the probability that event B will occur. Note that if events A and B are independent, then events *not A* and *not B* are also independent, as are A and *not B*, and so on.

Independence

Now suppose that a friend has applied to colleges C and D, with acceptance probabilities of 0.80 and 0.50, respectively, and a 0.40 probability of acceptance to both.

6. Produce a 2 × 2 table of counts for a hypothetical population of 1,000 applicants who had these exact probabilities.

7. Calculate the conditional probability that your friend is accepted to college C if they hear that they have been accepted by college D. What is the probability they will be accepted by college D if they hear that they have been accepted by college C?

8. How do these conditional probabilities compare to the (unconditional) probabilities? Does learning about acceptance by one college change the probability of acceptance to the other?

9. Is acceptance by college C independent of acceptance by college D? Justify your answer.

10. Is acceptance by college A independent of acceptance by college B? Justify your answer.

On the AP Statistics exam, if you are asked to determine whether two events A and B are independent, to justify your response, you must show an appropriate calculation and comment on it. Several appropriate comparisons are given below:

- If $P(A|B) = P(A)$, then A and B are independent; otherwise, they are dependent.
- If $P(B|A) = P(B)$, then A and B are independent; otherwise, they are dependent.
- If $P(A \cap B) = P(A) \times P(B)$, then A and B are independent; otherwise, they are dependent.

Multiplication rule

Now suppose that you have applied to colleges G and H. You have a 0.70 probability of acceptance by G, and the conditional probability of acceptance by H given acceptance by G is 0.90. The general multiplication rule is found simply by rearranging the equation for conditional probability.

11. Use the general multiplication rule to determine the probability of acceptance by both G and H.

Definitions

The ***general multiplication rule*** allows you to calculate the probability that two events both occur (intersection), based on one of their probabilities and the conditional probability of the other event given the first: $P(A \cap B) = P(A) \times P(B|A) = P(B) \times P(A|B)$.

Note: If A and B are independent events, then this rule simplifies to the ***multiplication rule for independent events:*** $P(A \cap B) = P(A) \times P(B)$.

KEY IDEA

With a series of *independent* events, the probability that all the events happen is the product of their individual probabilities. In symbols, if $A_1, A_2, \ldots, A_k$ are independent events, then $P(A_1 \text{ and } A_2 \text{ and } \ldots \text{ and } A_k) = P(A_1) \times P(A_2) \times \cdots \times P(A_k)$. This is an extension of the ***multiplication rule for independent events***.

Now suppose that you have applied to four colleges, and your probabilities of acceptance are 0.70 for college I, 0.90 for college J, 0.60 for college K, and 0.20 for college L. Assume that the events of acceptance are independent among all these four colleges (I, J, K, and L).

12. Use the multiplication rule for independent events to determine the probability that you are accepted by *all* four colleges. Would you consider this to be a fairly likely event?

13. Determine the probability that you are *rejected* by all four colleges. Would you consider this to be a very unlikely event?

14. Use your answer from the previous question to calculate the probability that you are accepted by *at least one* of the four colleges. Would you consider this to be a very likely event?

15. Do you think it is reasonable to assume that your acceptances at the four colleges are independent events? Explain why or why not.

Mutually exclusive vs. independent

Assume that your probability of acceptance to college M is 0.30 and your probability of acceptance to college N is 0.40. Also assume that acceptance to college M is mutually exclusive of your acceptance to college N.

16. In your own words, explain what it means for acceptance to colleges M and N to be mutually exclusive of each other.

17. What is the probability that you are accepted to neither college M nor college N? (*Hint:* You may wish to use a probability table to help you answer this question.)

18. What is the probability that you are accepted to college M, given that you are accepted to college N?

19. What is the probability that you are accepted to college M, given that you are not accepted to college N?

20. Based on your answers to the previous two questions, is acceptance to college M independent of college N? Why or why not?

It turns out that this is an important general rule, and one that students often mix up.

> **KEY IDEA**
>
> When two events are mutually exclusive, they are not independent.

EXPLORATION 11.3B | Rare Disease Testing

Suppose that 1 in 1,000 people in the United States has a certain rare infectious disease. A diagnostic test is available for this disease, but the test is not perfect. When the person actually has the disease, the test gives a positive (correct) result 98% of the time. (This number is called the *sensitivity* of the test.) When the person does not actually have the disease, the test gives a negative (correct) result 95% of the time. (This number is called the *specificity* of the test.) A randomly selected person from the U.S. is selected and tested for this disease.

Let D be "Has the disease" and P be "Has a positive test."

> **Definition**
>
> A **tree diagram** organizes conditional probabilities with a node representing an event and branches from the node representing the possible outcomes associated with the event. Typically, conditional probabilities are written on the branches of the tree.

1. Write the sensitivity of the test as a conditional probability using D and P.
2. Write the specificity of the test as a conditional probability using D and P.
3. How would you use symbols to indicate that 1 in 1,000 people has the disease?

When we have conditional probabilities, like sensitivity and specificity, a **tree diagram** may be another useful way to organize this information.

4. Fill in the tree diagram below with the appropriate probabilities. (*Hint*: To find the probabilities on the right side, multiply across the branches of the tree. What rule that we saw in the previous exploration allows you to do this?)

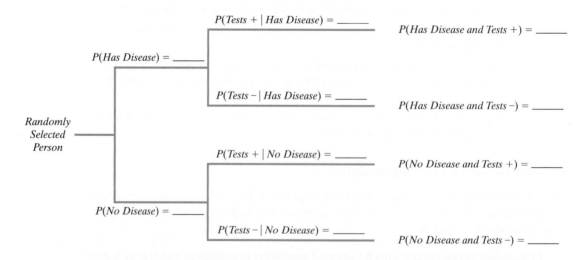

5. Suppose that a randomly selected person from the U.S. is tested for the disease. If the test is positive, what is the probability that the person has the disease? (*Hint*: Write this out as a conditional probability. What probability do you find in the numerator and what probability do you find in the denominator?)

6. Does the probability that you calculated above seem particularly low?

7. Explain why your calculated probability is so small even though the specificity and sensitivity of the diagnostic test are impressively large. (*Hint*: Follow the details of your calculation.)

The probability of 0.02 that a randomly selected person who tested positive for the disease actually has the disease may seem unusually low. Because this is a rare disease (only 1/1,000 people in the U.S. have the disease and 999/1,000 don't), even a low false-positive rate of 0.05 will result in a large number of false positives. If everyone in the population was tested, and if the population was over 300 million (e.g., population of the United States), that would result in over 15 million false positives! So, when we find a positive test result, by far most of them are false positives. So, do we not believe any test result? No, we ask for a second opinion!

SECTION 11.3 Summary

In this section you studied how to calculate conditional probabilities, which allow probabilities to be updated when additional information is known. A related idea that you studied is the concept of independence. For example, you found that whether Beth has seen a film is not independent of whether Allan has seen it, because learning that Allan has seen a film increases the probability that Beth has seen it (indicating they have similar movie tastes). Two events are ***independent*** when the probability of one event does not change once information about another event is provided.

Another probability rule that you studied is the multiplication rule, which enables you to find the probability that two events both occur (the intersection of two events) or even that multiple events all occur simultaneously.

Some useful definitions to remember and habits to develop from this section include:

- ***Conditional probability*** provides an update in the uncertainty regarding one event given information that another event has occurred. A conditional probability is calculated as the probability that both events occur divided by the probability of the event that has already occurred: $P(A|B) = P(A \cap B)/P(B)$.

- Two events are said to be ***independent*** if the conditional probability of one event occurring given the other event has already occurred is the same as the event's unconditional probability in the first place, e.g., $P(A|B) = P(A)$ or $P(B|A) = P(B)$ or $P(A \cap B) = P(A) \times P(B)$.

- The ***multiplication rule*** allows you to calculate the probability that two events both occur (intersection), based on one of their probabilities and the conditional probability of the other event given the first: $P(A \cap B) = P(A|B) \times P(B) = P(B|A) \times P(A)$.

- In the case of independent events, the multiplication rule states that the probability that both (or all) of the events occur is equal to the product of their individual probabilities: $P(A \cap B) = P(A) \times P(B)$.

  Note: This is different from being asked whether there is evidence that two categorical variables are associated (not independent). With two categorical variables, you should use a chi-square test of independence to determine whether any association observed in the sample data is plausibly a result of chance variation. With two quantitative variables, you should use regression to test the significance of the association between the two variables.

- You should also be able to discuss, *within a particular context*, whether or not you expect independence (e.g., should friends have similar movie tastes? does one person's diagnostic test result depend on another's?).

- Don't confuse the property of independence with the property of being mutually exclusive. These properties are very different. In fact, if two events (with nonzero probabilities) are mutually exclusive events, then they cannot be independent because $P(E|F) = 0$ when E and F are mutually exclusive.

- Many students are tempted to always multiply (unconditional) probabilities to calculate the probability that both events occur. Be careful to do this *only* when the events are independent or when one of the probabilities is a conditional one.
  - With real data, you will almost never find perfect (exact) independence, but you can determine whether the events are close to independent (the calculations almost agree).

SECTION 11.4 ▸ DISCRETE RANDOM VARIABLES

INTRODUCTION

This section continues your study of randomness and probability by introducing you to *random variables*. Random variables map observed outcomes from a random process (e.g., flipping a coin six times and getting HTHTHH) to a numerical value (e.g., summarizing the process by saying H = 4, you got four heads). In this section we will focus on random variables that take on a countable number of outcomes (*discrete random variables*) and their corresponding *probability distributions*. You will also investigate how ideas we have seen before, such as, the long-run average and standard deviation of a data distribution, apply to probability distributions as well.

A Game of Chance

Example 11.4

EXAMPLE

A carnival game consists of spinning a wheel that is divided into 12 equal sectors. Eight of the sectors are marked *no prize*, three are marked *Win $1*, and one is marked *Win $25*.

Definition

- - - - - - - - - - - - - - - -

A **random variable** assigns a number to each outcome in a sample space. A **discrete** random variable has a finite (or countably infinite) number of possible outcomes.

- - - - - - - - - - - - - - - -

↓

THINK ABOUT IT

If we charge someone $5.00 to play the game, are we likely to come out ahead in the long run? If yes, by how much? If not, how much should we charge?

   To decide how much to charge someone to play, we need to evaluate the possible outcomes and how likely they are to occur. The sample space is the 12 sectors, but we can assign each sector to a numerical value, the payout.

Random variables are usually denoted with a capital letter such as X and the values that the random variable can take on are denoted by the corresponding lowercase letter. The probability distribution of a random variable lists the possible values of the random variable and their corresponding probabilities. For example, the probability distribution for X indicates that $x_1, x_2, \ldots, x_n$, are the values the random variable can take, with corresponding probabilities of $P(X = x_1)$, $P(X = x_2)$, $\ldots$, $P(X = x_n)$. *Note:* We could also list these probabilities as $p(1)$, $p(2)$, ..., $p(n)$, or $p_1, p_2, \ldots, p_n$.

Definition

The **probability distribution** of a discrete random variable specifies the possible values and their corresponding probabilities.

THINK ABOUT IT

If we let X represent the possible payouts of a single play of this carnival game, what are the possible values for X? Is X a discrete random variable? What are the probabilities associated with each value of X? (Are you making any assumptions in assigning these probabilities?)

The *probability distribution of X*, the payout after a single spin of the wheel, is given in Table 11.5. Note that the probability for each payout corresponds to the number of (equally likely) sectors out of 12 on the wheel with that prize amount (8 of the 12 sectors correspond to winning \$0, 3 of the 12 correspond to winning \$1, and 1 of the 12 sectors corresponds to winning \$25).

TABLE 11.5 Probability distribution of payout after single spin of the wheel			
x (amount of payout)	\$0	\$1	\$25
p(x)	8/12	3/12	1/12

A probability histogram for the payout on a single spin of the wheel is given in Figure 11.11.

Definition

A **probability histogram** is a graphical display that is often used to describe the distribution of a discrete random variable. The horizontal axis gives the values that the random variable takes and the vertical axis corresponds to their corresponding probabilities.

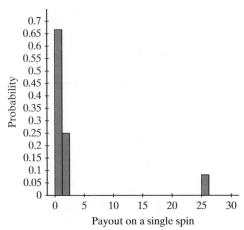

FIGURE 11.11 Probability histogram for the payout on a single spin of the wheel.

11.4.1

Throughout this text, we've seen value in summarizing data using both measures of center (e.g., the average; the median) and measures of variability (e.g., the standard deviation). Up to this point, we've typically talked about computing these values on data that were already collected (e.g., the average amount someone won after he or she played the carnival game 10 times). We saw with the Random Babies exploration that the more times you run a random process, the closer that average value approaches to one number. We will refer to that number, the long-run average value of a discrete random variable, as the **expected value** of the random variable.

Describe how we could use simulation to estimate the expected value of the payout on a single spin of the wheel. Do you think this expected value will be closer to 0 or closer to 20?

We could carry out this simulation a few different ways. One way would be to simulate the outcomes of the spinner and then determine the payout after each outcome. Another approach would be to simulate payouts directly from the probability distribution. In other words, we could generate a zero 67% of the time, a one 25% of the time, and a two 8.3% of the time.

Figure 11.12 shows the average payout after each number of spins. The payouts were $0, $1, $0, $25.... So after one spin, the average payout was 0. After two spins, the average payout was (0 + 1)/2 = $0.50, and so on for 10 spins. Notice how that running average takes a huge leap after we won the big prize on the fourth spin (($0 + $1 + $0 + $25)/4 = $6.50), but then begins to come back down after more spins.

FIGURE 11.12   The average payout after each set of spins vs. the number of spins.

Now look at the average payouts for the first 100 spins (on the left) and for the first 1,000 spins (on the right).

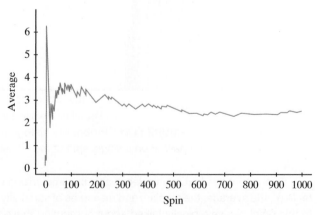

You should notice that initially the average can bounce around quite a bit, but eventually it starts to settle down and even approach a single value. This same pattern (more variability in the average value early and less after more spins) will happen regardless of the exact sequence of spins. So what is the average payout after 1,000 spins? In these 1,000 spins, we had 663 zeros, 252 ones, and 85 twenty-fives.

Explain why the reported frequencies for the payouts make sense? How do we use them to calculate the average payout in these 1,000 spins?

We expect the relative frequencies (663/1,000, 252/1,000, 85/1,000) to be fairly close to the theoretical probabilities (0.667, 0.25, 0.083) after 1,000 spins. To calculate the average payout across these 1,000 spins, we need to add up all the zeros (663 of them), the ones (252 of them), and the twenty-fives (85) of them.

$$\bar{x} = \frac{663(0) + 252(1) + 85(25)}{1,000} = 2.377$$

 11.4.2

Of course, if we kept playing, this value would change a bit. But based on the graph, we think we are close. In fact, there is a mathematical equation for an expected value that tells us what the long-run average value will be, without needing to do a simulation. To calculate the expected value for a discrete random variable, we simply sum the possible outcomes, weighting each by its probability of occurring.

The equation for the expected value of a discrete random variable looks a lot like the formula for $\bar{x}$ that we've seen before. But instead of weighting each outcome by how often it occurs (its relative frequency), we weight by the probabilities, which the relative frequencies will approach in the long run.

For the carnival game, the **mean** or **expected payout** is

$$\mu_x = \$0(8/12) + \$1(3/12) + \$25(1/12) = \$2.33$$

Note that the mean of a random variable does not have to be one of the possible values of the variable. A payout for a single play of this game would never be $2.33 because that is not one of the prize amounts. In fact, over 90% of the time (different spins), the payout will be less than $2.33. But also notice that the expected value is a lot closer to 0 and 1 than to 25, because an outcome of 25 is much less likely to occur.

Definitions

The **mean** or **expected value of a discrete random variable X** refers to the long-run average value of the random process if the process is repeated indefinitely under identical conditions. The mean of the random variable is a weighted average of the possible values the random variable can take, weighting each outcome x_i according to its probability, p_i. The symbol for the mean (also known as the expected value of X) is μ or $E(X)$.

$\mu_x = x_1 p_1 + x_2 p_2 + \cdots + x_n p_n$
$= \sum x_i p_i$

To go back to our initial questions: If we charge someone $5.00 to play the game, are we likely to come out ahead in the long run? If yes, how much will we make? If not, how much should we charge?

If the long-run average payout from playing this game is $2.33, and each time a person pays $5.00 to play, we are *expecting* to make a profit of $2.67 (= 5.00 − 2.33) every time someone plays. So, yes, we'll come out ahead in the long run! Some people will win the $25, but if enough people play, then we can be fairly sure we will come out ahead, on average. This is how casinos and carnivals stay in business. Most players only play a few games—and hope for a highly profitable payout like winning $25! But the carnival and the casino know that if enough people play, in the long run, they will come out ahead. Similarly, if players play long enough, they'll lose money. From the player's perspective the expected value represents a *loss* of $2.67 per game.

 11.4.3

VARIABILITY

As with distributions of sample data, in addition to measuring the average value, we are also often interested in how spread out (or variable) we can expect the values of the random variable to be. For our 1,000 spins, we can calculate the standard deviation as

$$s = \sqrt{\frac{(0 - 2.377)^2(663) + (1 - 2.05)^2(252) + (25 - 2.05)^2(85)}{999}} \approx 6.91$$

Similarly, for the random variable, we can focus on how far the possible outcomes are from the expected value of the random variable, e.g., (0 − 2.33), (1 − 2.33), (25 − 2.33), compute the squared deviations, but again, weight them not by the relative frequencies but by the theoretical probabilities. This weighted sum gives us the *variance* of the random variable. Taking the square root gives us the *standard deviation*.

Thus, the **variance** for this probability distribution with mean $2.33 is calculated as follows:

$$\sigma_X^2 = (0 - 2.33)^2\left(\frac{8}{12}\right) + (1 - 2.33)^2\left(\frac{3}{12}\right) + (25 - 2.33)^2\left(\frac{1}{12}\right) = 46.8889$$

The **standard deviation**, σ_x, is the square root of the variance:

$$\sigma_X = \sqrt{46.889} \approx \$6.85$$

For this game of chance, we can roughly say that the amount won on a single spin of the wheel will deviate, on average, from the expected amount won by $6.85. This gives you some insight as to the predictability of the game.

Notice that our theoretical mean and standard deviation are similar to our simulation results, but the equations tell us about this long-run behavior without the need to simulate first.

Definitions

The **variance of a discrete random variable** measures how far outcomes of the random variable tend to be from the expected value. The variance is defined as $Var(X) = \sigma_X^2 = E[(X - \mu)^2] = \sum_i (x_i - \mu)^2 p_i$. The **standard deviation** of a discrete random variable is the square root of the variance: $SD(X) = \sigma_x = \sqrt{Var(X)}$.

11.4.4

11.4.5

CALCULATOR TIPS

You can calculate the mean and standard deviation of a random variable using a graphing calculator. For example,

- **TI-84:** Put the values of the random variable in L1 and their corresponding probabilities (relative frequencies) in L2. In the Statistics Editor, choose 1-Var Stats. Change the frequency list from the default of 1 to L2 (your frequency list).
- **TI-Nspire:** Put the values of the random variable in a named list and their corresponding probabilities (relative frequencies) in a second named list. On a calculator page, choose 1-Variable Statistics. Change the frequency list from the default of 1 to the name of your frequency list.

EXPLORATION 11.4 | Traffic Lights

Suppose that Nicholas is a college senior with an 8 a.m. class he needs to attend regularly. But he is not a morning person and so leaves his apartment as late as possible to get to class on time. The time it takes to reach class depends on two traffic lights that he encounters on his drive. From past experience, he believes that the first light has a 0.7 probability of being green when he gets there and the second light has a 0.6 probability of being green when he gets there. He also believes that the colors of the two lights are independent.

1. Describe what the concept of independence means in this context.

2. Write out the sample space of possible outcomes with regard to the colors of the two lights that Nicholas encounters. (To keep things simple, assume that each light is either green or not green; because Nicholas is such a conscientious driver and always stops on yellow, we'll assume that getting a yellow light is the same as red.)

3. Determine the probability for each of these four possible outcomes. Confirm that the sum of all the probabilities in the sample space is 1.

Definitions

A **random variable** assigns a number to each outcome in a sample space. A **discrete** random variable has a finite (or countably infinite) number of possible outcomes.

Random variables are usually denoted with a capital letter such as X and the values that the random variable can take on are denoted by the corresponding lowercase letter. Let the random variable G represent the number of lights that are green on Nicholas's morning drive to school.

4. What are the possible values of G?

5. Determine the probabilities of these possible values. List them in the table below.

Possible value of G			
Probability			

6. What is the most likely outcome for the number of green lights that Nicholas encounters on his morning drive to school? How often will he encounter this number of green lights in the long run?

7. Make a guess for the *average* number of green lights that Nicholas will encounter on his morning drive if he makes this drive a very large number of times.

To investigate what would happen in the long run, Nicholas wrote a computer program to simulate a large number of morning drives. The program keeps track of how many green lights he encounters, as well as the average and standard deviation of the number of green lights. The results of simulating 100,000 morning drives are given in Figure 11.13.

FIGURE 11.13   Simulated numbers of green lights across 100,000 repetitions of Nicholas's drive to work.

8. Do these simulation results agree with your calculation of the probability distribution of G? Explain why or why not.

9. Calculate the average number of green lights in this sample of 100,000 simulated morning drives. (*Hint*: You need to add 100,000 numbers together, but you know how many of them are zero, how many are 1, and how many are 2. You can also tell your calculator the outcomes and the frequencies and have it find the mean.)

10. Do you think you would find the same average number of lights after 1,000,000 repetitions?

As we saw earlier in the course, the average will approach one number, the expected value of a random variable.

11. Use the definition for expected value shown in the margin to calculate the (theoretical) expected value $E(G)$ of the number of green lights that Nicholas encounters on his morning drive to school.

12. Is this expected value close to the average number of green lights in the simulated sample of 100,000 morning drives? Explain why it should be.

Sometimes you are interested in not only what happens on average in the long run, but also how variable the results are. Earlier in the course, we used the standard deviation to measure the variability of data around the mean.

Definition

The **probability distribution** of a discrete random variable specifies the possible values and their corresponding probabilities.

Definitions

The **mean** or **expected value of a discrete random variable X** refers to the long-run average value of the random process if it is repeated indefinitely under identical conditions. It is a weighted average of the possible values the random variable can take. The mean of a random variable weights each outcome x_i, according to its probability, p_i. The symbol for the mean (also known as the expected value of X) is μ or $E(X)$.

$$\mu_X = x_1 p_1 + x_2 p_2 + \cdots + x_n p_n$$
$$= \sum x_i p_i$$

13. Calculate the standard deviation of the 100,000 simulated outcomes, keeping in mind that you know how often each squared deviation occurs:

    Variance = $(11{,}961(0 - 1.299)^2 + 46{,}187(1 - 1.299)^2 + 41{,}852(2 - 1.299)^2)/99{,}999 =$

    SD =

    We will revisit the concept here for a random variable.

> **Definition**
>
> The **variance of a discrete random variable** is defined as Var(X) = $E[(X - \mu)^2]$, which in turn is defined as Var(X) = $\sigma_x^2 = \sum (x_i - \mu_x)^2 \, p_i$. The **standard deviation** of a discrete random variable is the square root of the variance: $\sigma_x = $ SD(X) $= \sqrt{\text{Var}(X)}$.

14. How should this formula generalize to talking about probabilities rather than relative frequencies?

15. Use the equation shown in the margin to calculate Var(G), the variance of the number of green lights that Nicholas encounters.

16. Use Var(G) to calculate the standard deviation of the number of green lights that Nicholas encounters.

17. Is this (theoretical) standard deviation very close to the standard deviation from the 100,000 simulated morning drives? Does the size of the standard deviation make sense? Explain.

> **CALCULATOR TIPS**
>
> You can calculate the mean and standard deviation of a random variable using a graphing calculator.
>
> - **TI-84:** Put the values of the random variable in L1 and their corresponding probabilities (relative frequencies) in L2. In the Statistics Editor, choose 1-Var Stats. Change the frequency list from the default of 1 to L2 (your frequency list).
> - **TI-Nspire:** Put the values of the random variable in a named list and their corresponding probabilities (relative frequencies) in a second named list. On a calculator page, choose 1-Variable Statistics. Change the frequency list from the default of 1 to the name of your frequency list.

Now let's make a change to our assumption that the colors of the two traffic lights are independent. Instead of assuming independence, let's suppose that the lights are synchronized so that when the first light is green, the second light is guaranteed to be green. And when the first light is red, the second light is guaranteed to be red. Continue to assume that the probability is 0.7 that the first light is green.

18. Determine the probability distribution of G, the number of green lights that Nicholas encounters, with this assumption that the lights are synchronized as described above.

Possible value		
Probability		

19. Before you do more calculations, do you predict that the *expected value* of the number of green lights will be greater than before, smaller than before, or the same as before? Explain your thinking.

20. Calculate $E(G)$. Also write a sentence interpreting this value.

21. Was your earlier prediction correct?

22. Before you do more calculations, do you predict that the *standard deviation* of the number of green lights will be greater than before, smaller than before, or the same as before? Explain your thinking.

23. Calculate Var(G) and SD(G). Also, write a sentence interpreting this standard deviation value.

24. Was your earlier prediction correct?

SECTION 11.4 Summary

This section has deepened your understanding of probability by giving you more experience working with *random variables*. You have learned that random variables assign a number to outcomes of a random process, such as the amount of money won on one spin of the wheel of a carnival game. Two important aspects of random variables are their *expected value* and *variance*.

The expected value reveals the long-term average value that would result from repeating the random process a large number of times. For example, you found that paying $5 for a spin of the carnival wheel results in an expected loss of about a $2.67 (–$2.67) per spin for the player. This means that if you play a large number of times, your average result across all the spins will be a loss of about $2.67.

Some useful definitions to remember and habits to develop from this topic include:

- A *random variable* assigns a number to each possible outcome of a random process.
- The *expected value* of a random variable is calculated by multiplying each possible value by its probability and then summing those products over all possible values of the random variable.
- The interpretation of expected value is that it reveals the long-term average value that would be achieved by the random variable if the random process were repeated a very large number of times.
- The *variance* of a random variable provides a measure of how variable (spread out) the results of the random variable are expected to be if the random process were repeated a very large number of times.
- The variance is calculated by finding the difference between each possible outcome value and the expected value of the random variable, squaring those differences, multiplying those squares by the corresponding probability for that value, and summing those products over all possible values.
- The *standard deviation* of a random variable is the square root of its variance.
- Expected values are often useful in making decisions where the goal is to maximize the expected gain (or minimize the expected loss) of a random process.

In the next section, you will expand your understanding of probability and random variables by investigating the effect of linear combinations (adding/subtracting a constant, multiplying/dividing by a constant) on the mean, variance, and shape of a random variable. You will also explore the rules for combining two or more independent random variables.

RANDOM VARIABLE RULES   SECTION 11.5

In Section 11.4 you examined the payout (the amount returned to the customer) for a single spin of a carnival wheel. You could also look at the distribution of the net amount (amount after deducting the cost to play the game) that a player wins on a single spin of the wheel or the expected winnings and corresponding variability in multiple spins of the wheel. In this section you will explore rules for linear transformations of a random variable (adding/subtracting a constant, multiplying/dividing by a constant) in addition to the rules for combining two or more independent random variables.

11.5 —A Game of Chance Revisited

Example 11.5

EXAMPLE

Earlier you explored a game of chance that costs $5 to play in which a wheel that was divided into 12 equal sectors is spun. Eight of the sectors are marked *no prize*, three are marked *win $1*, and one is marked *win $25*.

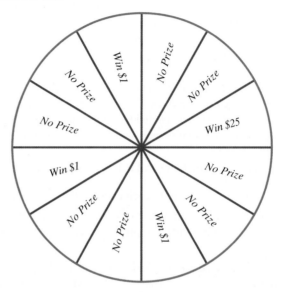

You saw that the probability distribution of X, the payout after a single spin of the wheel, was given by the following table:

x (amount of payout)	$0	$1	$25
p(x)	8/12	3/12	1/12

with the mean, variance, and standard deviation of X being $\mu_x = \$2.33$, $\sigma_X^2 = 48.89$, and $\sigma_x = \$6.85$, respectively.

THINK ABOUT IT

Suppose we want to define a new random variable Y as the net amount a player wins after paying $5 to play the game. What is the probability distribution, expected net amount won, and standard deviation of Y?

The new random variable, Y, can be expressed in terms of X (the payout) and $5 (the amount it costs to play the game):

$$Y = X - \$5$$

First, recognize that there are three possible values that Y can take: $-\$5$, $-\$4$, and $\$20$. This is easily seen by realizing that there are three possible values for X: $0, $1, and $25, and so the three possible values for Y are found by taking the values of X and subtracting $5. Similarly, the probability of the payouts of Y will be the same as those for X.

Thus, the probability distribution of Y is given in the following table:

y (net amount won)	−$5	−$4	$20
p(y)	8/12	3/12	1/12

A probability histogram for the net amount won on a single spin of the wheel is given in Figure 11.14.

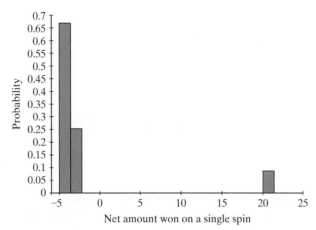

FIGURE 11.14   The probability distribution of the net amount won on a single spin (after deducting $5 to play).

Applying what you learned in the previous section, you see that the **mean** or **expected net amount won** in this game of chance is

$$\mu_Y = -\$5\left(\frac{8}{12}\right) - \$4\left(\frac{3}{12}\right) + \$20\left(\frac{1}{12}\right) = -\$2.67$$

In the long run, the expected net amount on a single play of this game is a loss of $2.67. So, the player will lose money, in the long run, if it costs $5 to play the game. Of course, this means that the owner of the game is coming out ahead!

Again, applying what you learned in the previous section, you can find the **variance** for the random variable Y as follows:

$$\sigma_Y^2 = \sum (y_i - \mu_Y)^2 p_i$$

$$= (-5 - (-2.67))^2\left(\frac{8}{12}\right) + (-4 - (-2.67))^2\left(\frac{3}{12}\right) + (20 - (-2.67))^2\left(\frac{1}{12}\right) = 46.889$$

The **standard deviation**, σ_Y, is the square root of the variance:

$$\sigma_Y = \sqrt{46.889} \approx \$6.85$$

For this game of chance, the net amount won on a single spin of the wheel will deviate on average from the expected amount won (a loss of $2.67) by $6.85.

THINK ABOUT IT

How do the expected value and the standard deviation of Y (net amount won on a single game) relate to the expected value and standard deviation of X (payout on a single game)? How does the shape of the two distributions compare?

Above, you found that the average loss on a single game is $-\$2.67$ by using the probability distribution for Y. But notice that $\mu_Y = \mu_X - \$5 = \$2.33 - \$5.00 = -\$2.67$. This is because the random variable Y is related to X by simply adding or subtracting a constant, that is, $Y = X - 5$.

In fact, any time you add or subtract a constant a to/from a random variable, you add or subtract a to/from the mean of the distribution of the random variable. So if $Y = a + X$, then $\mu_Y = \mu_{a+X} = a + \mu_X$.

You also saw that subtracting the amount to play the game, $5, had no effect on the variance and standard deviation of the net amount won. These values are 46.889 and $6.85 for the variance and standard deviation, respectively, for both X and Y.

> **THINK ABOUT IT**
>
> Why does this make sense?

Subtracting (or adding) a constant to the random variable shifts the distribution of the random variable but does not change the relative distances between values. Thus,

$$\sigma_Y^2 = \sigma_{a+X}^2 = \sigma_X^2$$

$$\sigma_Y = \sigma_{a+X} = \sigma_X$$

You can see from the graphs of the two distributions (Figure 11.15) that subtracting a constant does not change the spread of the distribution—it simply "slides" the distribution down $5. Thus, the variability in the distribution does not change. Also notice that the shape of the distribution does not change.

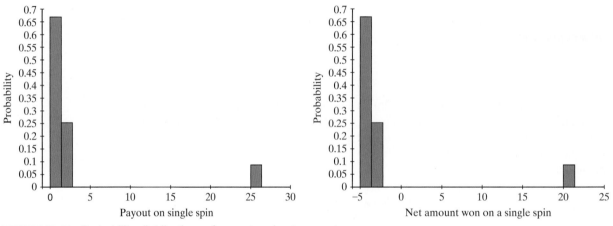

FIGURE 11.15 Probability distributions of payout and net amount won.

DOUBLING THE PRIZE MONEY

> **THINK ABOUT IT**
>
> Suppose the owner of this game decided to double the prize amounts for a single spin of the wheel. What effect would this have on the mean, standard deviation, and shape of the distribution of the random variable X, the payout (amount returned to the customer) after a single spin of the wheel?

You can define a new random variable D as the doubled prize amounts for a single spin of the wheel.

The probability distribution of D is shown in the following table:

d (payout with doubled prize values)	$0(2) = $0	$1(2) = $2	$25(2) = $50
p(d)	8/12	3/12	1/12

The mean or expected value of D (expected payout) is

$$\mu_D = \$0(8/12) + \$2(3/12) + \$50(1/12) = \$4.66$$

Notice that there is a close relationship between D and X, namely $D = 2X$, and that relationship carries over to the relationship between $E(X)$ and $E(D)$:

$$\mu_D = 2\mu_X = 2(2.33) = \$4.66$$

Once again, this fact is generally true: $\mu_D = \mu_{bX} = b\mu_X$.

A similar fact relates the standard deviations between two random variables with the relationship between the variances requiring you to square the constant: $\sigma_D^2 = \sigma_{bX}^2 = b^2\sigma_X^2$. Similarly, for SD,

$$\sigma_D = \sigma_{bX} = |b|\sigma_X$$

Thus, using the direct or shortcut approaches to calculate the variance of the random variable D yields

$$\sigma_D^2 = (0 - 4.66)^2(8/12) + (2 - 4.66)^2(3/12) + (50 - 4.66)^2(1/12) = 187.556$$

$$\sigma_D^2 = 2^2\sigma_X^2 = 2^2(46.889) = 187.556$$

Similarly, the standard deviation of D is

$$\sigma_D = \sqrt{187.556} \approx \$13.70$$

$$\sigma_D = |b|\sigma_X = 2(6.85) = \$13.70$$

You can combine the rules we've just learned that relate means, variances, and standard deviations for random variables into a single, comprehensive set of rules.

KEY IDEA

When we add (subtract) a constant a and/or multiply (divide) a random variable by a constant b, we call it a **linear transformation**. Thus, if random variable Y is related to X as $Y = a + bX$, then Y is a linear transformation of X and the following statements are true:

$$\mu_Y = \mu_{a+bX} = a + b\mu_X$$
$$\sigma_Y^2 = \sigma_{a+bX}^2 = b^2\,\sigma_X^2$$
$$\sigma_Y = \sigma_{a+bX} = |b|\,\sigma_X$$

Notably, although linear transformations can change the mean (shifting) and variability (stretching) of a random variable, linear transformations of a random variable do not change the general shape of the probability distribution.

WHAT IF YOU PLAYED TWICE?

Let's revisit our original scenario for the random variable X. Recall that the probability distribution of X, the payout after a single spin of the wheel, is given by

x (amount of payout)	$0	$1	$25
p(x)	8/12	3/12	1/12

with $\mu_X = \$2.33$, $\sigma_X^2 = 48.89$, and $\sigma_X = 6.85$.

What if you play twice? What will your combined payout be after playing two times? This is no longer doubling the payout but summing two different payouts together. Define a new random variable, T, to be the total payout after playing the game twice. We will consider the outcomes of the spins to be independent of each other, as you learned in Section 11.3. This means you can also consider the random variables (amount won on first spin and amount won on second spin) to be independent of each other as well.

THINK ABOUT IT

How will the distribution of the random variable T, the total payout on two spins of the wheel, compare to the distribution of the random variable D, the payout for a single spin of the wheel when the prize amounts are doubled?

For the random variable D, doubling the prize amounts had the same effect as multiplying by 2. Because each spin of the wheel is a chance event (there is no guarantee that the outcome of the first spin and the second spin will be the same), the random variable T is obtained by combining two independent random events, the outcomes of spin 1 and spin 2. We can label these two outcomes X_1 and X_2. Here are the probability distributions for the two spins:

11.5.1

x_1	$0	$1	$25	x_2	$0	$1	$25
$p(x_1)$	8/12	3/12	1/12	$p(x_2)$	8/12	3/12	1/12

The random variable T, the total payout on two spins of the wheel, consists of all of the combinations of $X_1 + X_2$ and their corresponding probabilities. How do you find $P(t)$? This is found by multiplying $P(x_1)$ and $P(x_2)$, because the two spins are independent of each other.

Spin 1 (x_1)	$p(x_1)$	Spin 2 (x_2)	$p(x_2)$	$t = x_1 + x_2$	$p(t)$
$0	8/12	$0	8/12	$t = 0	64/144
$0	8/12	$1	3/12	$t = 1	24/144
$0	8/12	$25	1/12	$t = 25	8/144
$1	3/12	$0	8/12	$t = 1	24/144
$1	3/12	$1	3/12	$t = 2	9/144
$1	3/12	$25	1/12	$t = 26	3/144
$25	1/12	$0	8/12	$t = 25	8/144
$25	1/12	$1	3/12	$t = 26	3/144
$25	1/12	$25	1/12	$t = 50	1/144

Combining outcomes that yield the same value of t, you find that the probability distribution of T can be written as in the table below.

t	$0	$1	$2	$25	$26	$50
$p(t)$	64/144	48/144	9/144	16/144	6/144	1/144

From this probability distribution, you can calculate the expected value and standard deviation of T:

$$\mu_T = 0(64/144) + 1(48/144) + 2(9/144) + 25(16/144) + 26(6/144) + 50(1/144)$$
$$\mu_T = \$4.66$$

You can see that the mean for the total payout of spin 1 and spin 2 is equal to the sum of the means of spin 1 plus spin 2:

$$\mu_T = \mu_{x_1} + \mu_{x_2} = 2.33 + 2.33 = \$4.66$$

11.5.2

What about the standard deviation? Calculating directly from the probability distribution, you find

$$\sigma_T^2 = (0 - 4.66)^2(64/144) + (1 - 4.66)^2(48/144) + (2 - 4.66)^2(9/144) + (25 - 4.66)^2(16/144)$$
$$+ (26 - 4.66)^2(6/144) + (50 - 4.66)^2(1/144)$$
$$\sigma_T^2 = 93.7777$$
$$\sigma_T = \sqrt{93.7777} \approx \$9.68$$

Notice that the standard deviation of T does not equal the sum of the standard deviations of spin 1 and spin 2:

$$\sigma_T \neq \sigma_{X_1} + \sigma_{X_2}$$
$$9.68 \neq 6.85 + 6.85$$

but the variance of T is equal to the sum of the variances of spin 1 and spin 2:

$$\sigma_T^2 = \sigma_{X_1}^2 + \sigma_{X_2}^2$$
$$93.78 = 46.89 + 46.89$$

 11.5.3

> ### KEY IDEA
>
> In general, when summing two or more random variables,
> - The expected value of the sum of the random variables is the sum of the expected values.
>   - For example, $E(X + Y) = E(X) + E(Y)$
> - If the random variables are independent, the variance of their sum is the sum of their variances.
>   - For example, $Var(X + Y) = Var(X) + Var(Y)$
> - The standard deviation of the sum of random variables is not necessarily equal to the sum of the standard deviations of the random variables, even if the random variables are independent.

DIFFERENCE IN PAYOUTS FOR TWO SPINS

Suppose we wanted to define a new random variable that represents the difference in the payout for two spins of the carnival wheel. Define the random variable L as $L = X_1 - X_2$, the difference in the payout amount for the first and second spin of the wheel.

> ### THINK ABOUT IT
>
> Do you think the mean of L will be equal to the difference of the means of spin 1 and spin 2? How about the variance?

The random variable L, the difference in the total payout on two spins of the wheel, consists of all of the combinations of $X_1 - X_2$ and their corresponding probabilities.

Spin 1 (x_1)	$p(x_1)$	Spin 2 (x_2)	$p(x_2)$	$l = x_1 - x_2$	$p(l)$
$0	8/12	$0	8/12	$l = \$0$	64/144
$0	8/12	$1	3/12	$l = -\$1$	24/144
$0	8/12	$25	1/12	$l = -\$25$	8/144
$1	3/12	$0	8/12	$l = \$1$	24/144
$1	3/12	$1	3/12	$l = \$0$	9/144
$1	3/12	$25	1/12	$l = -\$24$	3/144
$25	1/12	$0	8/12	$l = \$25$	8/144
$25	1/12	$1	3/12	$l = \$24$	3/144
$25	1/12	$25	1/12	$l = \$0$	1/144

$$\mu_L = 0(64/144) - 1(24/144) - 25(8/144) + 1(24/144) + 0(9/144) - 24(3/144)$$
$$+ 25(8/144) + 24(3/144) + 0(1/144)$$

$$\mu_L = \$0$$

You can see that the mean for the difference in payouts of spin 1 and spin 2 is equal to the difference of the means of spin 1 plus spin 2:

$$\mu_L = \mu_{X_1} - \mu_{X_2} = 2.33 - 2.33 = \$0$$

What about the variance? Calculating directly from the probability distribution yields

$$\sigma_T^2 = (0 - 0)^2(64/144) + (-1 - 0)^2(24/144) + (-25 - 0)^2(8/144) + (1 - 0)^2(24/144) + (0 - 0)^2(9/144)$$
$$+ (-24 - 0)^2(3/144) + (25 - 0)^2(8/144) + (24 - 0)^2(3/144) + (0 - 0)^2(1/144)$$

$$\sigma_L^2 = 93.7777$$

$$\sigma_L = \sqrt{93.7777} \approx \$9.68$$

Notice that the variance of L is equal to the **sum** of the variances of spin 1 and spin 2. This relation (the variance of the difference of two random variables equals the sum of the variations of the random variables) will always be true provided that the random variables are independent.

> ### KEY IDEA
>
> When combining random variables X and Y, $\mu_{X+Y} = \mu_X + \mu_Y$ and $\mu_{X-Y} = \mu_X - \mu_Y$. This is true regardless of whether X and Y are independent. If the random variables are independent, then it is also true that $\sigma_{X \pm Y}^2 = \sigma_X^2 + \sigma_Y^2$; however, that relationship is not true if X and Y are not independent.

EXPLORATION | Skee-Ball
11.5

In the game of Skee-Ball, a player rolls a small ball up a ramp, hoping to land the ball in the holes with the highest point values (see the diagram of point values below). The game of Skee-Ball has gained in popularity in recent years, with many cities running Skee-Ball leagues. There is even a Skee-Ball national championship!

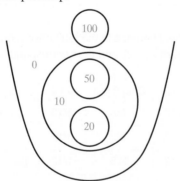

Todd and Jill, both experienced Skee-Ball players, are considering entering a partner Skee-Ball competition hosted by their local league.

Let T be the score associated with the ball landing in a particular region (0, 10, 20, 50, or 100) on a single roll when Todd plays the game. Based on his long history of playing this game, the probability distribution for Todd's score is

t (points)	0	10	20	50	100
p(t)	0.05	0.10	0.25	0.40	0.20

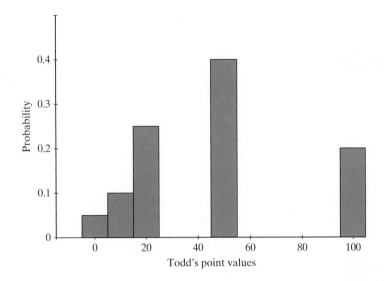

1. Determine the expected value of Todd's score from a single roll, $E(T)$.

2. Write a sentence interpreting what this expected value means in this context.

3. Determine the variance and standard deviation of Todd's score from a single roll. (i.e. What are $Var(T)$ and $SD(T)$?)

   What if Todd gets paid 1 penny per point each time he rolls? Let D be the dollars earned by Todd on a roll.

4. Make a probability distribution table for D showing the possible values of D and the probability of each value. (*Hint*: The outcome of D depends on the outcome of T, and you know the probability for each outcome of T.) Sketch the probability distribution.

5. What is the expected value of D? (i.e. What is $E(D)$?)

6. What is the numeric relationship between $E(D)$ and $E(T)$? Why does this relationship make sense?

7. Use the probability distribution for D to calculate the variance and standard deviation of D (Todd's earnings) from a single roll. (i.e. What are $Var(D)$ and $SD(D)$?)

8. What is the numeric relationship between $SD(T)$ and $SD(D)$? Why does this relationship make sense?

9. Now suppose Todd has to pay 25 cents each time he rolls the ball. Let the random variable R represent Todd's net profit from a single roll, where a net loss means that Todd's profit is negative (e.g., if he rolls a 10, his profit is $-\$0.15$). Determine the probability distribution of R. (*Hint*: Start by thinking about how many different values there will be for R. How does that number relate to the number of possible values of T? How will the probabilities for the different outcomes of T and R relate? Sketch a graph of the probability distribution of R.)

10. Determine the expected value of Todd's net profit from a single roll.

11. How does $E(R)$ compare to $E(D)$? Explain why this makes sense.

KEY IDEA

Subtracting (or adding) a constant a to the random variable subtracts (or adds) a from the expected value of the random variable. Thus,

$$\mu_Y = \mu_{a+X} = a + \mu_X$$

12. Use the probability distribution to calculate the variance and standard deviation of Todd's net profit from a single roll.

13. How does SD(R) compare to SD(D)? Explain why this makes sense.

> ### KEY IDEA
>
> Subtracting (or adding) a constant to the random variable shifts the distribution of the random variable but does not change the relative distances between values. Thus,
>
> $$\sigma_Y^2 = \sigma_{a+X}^2 = \sigma_X^2$$
> $$\sigma_Y = \sigma_{a+X} = \sigma_X$$

When we add (or subtract) a constant a and/or multiply (or divide) a random variable by a constant b, we call it a **_linear transformation_**. In fact, we can combine together the rules you just learned into one set.

> ### KEY IDEA
>
> If random variable Y is related to X as follows: $Y = a + bX$, then Y is a linear transformation of X and the following statements are true:
>
> $$\mu_Y = \mu_{a+bX} = a + b\mu_X$$
> $$\sigma_Y^2 = \sigma_{a+bX}^2 = b^2\sigma_X^2$$
> $$\sigma_Y = \sigma_{a+bX} = |b|\,\sigma_X$$
>
> Notably, although linear transformations can change the mean (shifting) and variability (stretching) of a random variable, linear transformations of a random variable do not change the general shape of the probability distribution.

14. Given that $R = T/100 - 0.25$, using the shortcut equations above, find Todd's average earnings from this game ($E(R)$). Does it match what you calculated from the probability distribution?

15. Using the shortcut equations above, find the standard deviation of Todd's average earnings from this game ($SD(R)$). Does it match what you calculated from the probability distribution?

Jill's Skee-Ball performance

Now let J be the score associated with the ball landing in a particular region on a single roll when Jill plays the game. The probability distribution for J is

j (point value)	0	10	20	50	100
p(j)	0.05	0.05	0.15	0.60	0.15

16. Produce graphs of Todd's and Jill's point-value probability distributions, using the same scales so they can be compared.

17. Summarize (in words, without doing calculations) how the probability distributions of Todd's points and Jill's points compare. Address who you think would have the larger average score in the long run, and who you think would have more variability in scores in the long run.

18. Determine the expected value and standard deviation of Jill's score on a single roll.

19. Who has the larger expected value: Todd or Jill? Who has the larger standard deviation? Were your earlier predictions correct?

Todd's and Jill's combined performance in a partner league

20. Now suppose that Todd's and Jill's points (from a single roll) are to be added. Let the random variable $C = T + J$ represent their combined (added) scores. Make a prediction of the expected value of C.

21. Do you think that the standard deviation of C will be larger, smaller, or the same as the standard deviations of T and J? Explain your thinking, without performing any calculations.

22. To find these values exactly, you first need to find the probability distribution for C. To do this, first list three possible values for C.

23. If you assume that Todd's roll is independent of Jill's roll, calculate the probability for each of the three possible values for C you provided in the previous question.

    To find the expected value and standard deviation for C, you could fill in the entire probability distribution for C. But this will be a fairly tedious process. We could use simulation to give us an idea of the behavior of C. Figure 11.16 shows the point values of 10,000 rolls by Todd added to the point values of 10,000 rolls by Jill.

FIGURE 11.16   Point totals summing Todd's and Jill's scores together for 10,000 rolls.

24. What is the least likely outcome (but possible) for the sum? Why? What is the largest possible sum? Roughly how often do they score a point total equaling this largest possible sum?

25. How do the mean and standard deviation of theses sums compare to your predictions in #20 and #21?

    Again, there are also shortcut formulas that tell us how certain types of combinations of random variables will behave without carrying out the simulation.

KEY IDEA

In general, when summing two or more random variables

- The expected value of the sum of the random variables is the sum of the expected values.
  - For example, $E(X + Y) = E(X) + E(Y)$
- If the random variables are independent, the variance of their sum is the sum of their variances.
  - For example, $\text{Var}(X + Y) = \text{Var}(X) + \text{Var}(Y)$
- The standard deviation of the sum of random variables is not necessarily equal to the sum of the standard deviations of the random variables, even if the random variables are independent.

26. Use the above rule for expected values to find the expected combined score. Is it similar to the simulation results?

27. Use the above rule for the variance of the combined score.

28. Take the square root of your previous answer to find the standard deviation of their combined score. Show that this is not equal to the sum of Todd and Jill's individual standard deviations. Is it similar to the simulation results?

The difference in Todd's and Jill's performance

Suppose instead of adding Todd's and Jill's scores together, you subtracted them (Todd – Jill). This would allow you to determine how often Todd scores higher than Jill in the long run.

29. Briefly describe how you could use simulation to explore the distribution of these differences.

30. Make predictions for the mean and the standard deviation of this distribution.

Figure 11.17 shows the differences in the scores (Todd – Jill) for 10,000 rolls.

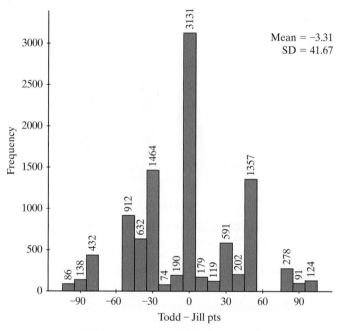

FIGURE 11.17   Differences in scores (Todd – Jill) for 10,000 rolls.

31. Which difference occurred the most frequently? Does this make sense? What is the largest possible difference? How likely is this outcome? Does that make sense?

32. How do the mean and standard deviation compare to your predictions? In particular, why does it make sense that the standard deviation of the differences is *larger* (in fact, similar to the standard deviation of the sums), rather than being the difference in the standard deviations?

KEY IDEA

When combining random variables X and Y, $\mu_{X+Y} = \mu_X + \mu_Y$ and $\mu_{X-Y} = \mu_X - \mu_Y$. This is true regardless of whether X and Y are independent. If the random variables are independent, then it is also true that $\sigma^2_{X \pm Y} = \sigma^2_X + \sigma^2_Y$; however, that relationship is not true if X and Y are not independent.

33. Use the rules shown above to determine the expected value and standard deviation of the *difference* between Todd's and Jill's scores ($S = T - J$). How does these values compare to the simulation results? How does $SD(T - J)$ compare to $SD(T + J)$?

34. Is $E(S)$ positive, negative, or zero? Interpret what this means about Todd's and Jill's scores in the long run.

Summing several random variables

A typical game of Skee-Ball consists of 9 rolls. Let's assume that the rolls are independent.

35. Determine the expected value and standard deviation of the sum of Todd's scores over 9 rolls. Also mention what assumption you need to make for one of these calculations.

Now suppose that Todd was given the option of: (A) adding his scores on 9 independent rolls, or (B) multiplying his score on one roll by 9.

36. Calculate and compare the expected values with option (A) and option (B). Which option (if either) would Todd prefer? Why?

37. Calculate and compare the standard deviations with option (A) and option (B). Which option (if either) would Todd prefer? Why?

SECTION 11.5 Summary

This section has expanded on your understanding of random variables. Some useful definitions to remember and habits to develop from this topic include:

- Adding/subtracting a constant a and multiplying/dividing the values of a distribution by a constant b are linear transformations.

  If $Y = a + bx$ is a linear transformation of the random variable X, then

  $$\mu_Y = \mu_{a+bX} = a + b\mu_X$$
  $$\sigma_Y^2 = \sigma_{a+bX}^2 = b^2\sigma_X^2$$
  $$\sigma_Y = \sigma_{a+bX} = |b|\,\sigma_X$$

  Linear transformations of a random variable do not change the shape of the distribution of the random variable.

- When combining random variables $X + Y$, $\mu_{X+Y} = \mu_X + \mu_Y$ and $\mu_{X-Y} = \mu_X - \mu_Y$ regardless of whether X and Y are independent.

  If the random variables are independent, then

  $$\sigma_{X \pm Y}^2 = \sigma_X^2 + \sigma_Y^2$$

- **Important note:** Because sample data are observations from random variables, these same rules hold true for sample data as well.

  Thus, if $y = a + bx$, then $\bar{y} = a + b\bar{x}$ and $s_y = |b|s_x$ where x is the original variable and y is the variable you are converting to.

  For example, if you know the sample mean in inches ($\bar{x}$) is 68 in., and you know that there are 2.54 cm in an inch, you can use these rules to find the sample mean in cm as $\bar{y} = 172.72$ cm. See Exercises 11.5.14 through 11.5.20 at the end of this chapter for examples.

BINOMIAL AND GEOMETRIC RANDOM VARIABLES

INTRODUCTION

In Section 1.1 you explored whether two dolphins, Doris and Buzz, could communicate abstract ideas. You learned that in one phase of the study Buzz pushed the correct button 15 times out of 16 attempts. You conducted a simulation to investigate how often Buzz would do that well, or even better, if he was just guessing and Doris could not communicate with him. In Section 1.2 you investigated how often a novice player would play "scissors" in the game rock-paper-scissors if he or she had no preference and was choosing randomly each time. For both the Buzz and Doris and rock-paper-scissors studies, we were dealing with repeated outcomes from the same random process. In both these studies, simulation allowed us to make inferences regarding whether our sample statistic (number of correct attempts by Buzz or proportion of times a novice player plays scissors in the game rock-paper-scissors) was unlikely to have occurred as a result of chance variation. We used the **3S strategy** to simulate *could have been* statistics under a specific chance model, and weighed our evidence (sample statistic) against the model to determine whether our observed statistic could plausibly have happened as a result of random chance. We estimated the p-value by finding the proportion of simulated statistics in the null distribution that are at least as extreme (in the direction of the alternative hypothesis) as the value of the statistic actually observed in our study. Recall that a p-value is the probability of obtaining a value of the statistic at least as extreme as the observed statistic, assuming that the null hypothesis (chance alone model) is true.

This type of problem, investigating the probability of a specific number of successes in a fixed number of trials of a random process, comes up often in statistics. In our previous examples, our goal in simulating the probability distribution of the chance process (null distribution) was to be able to do inference. Sometimes we know the value of the parameter, and our goal instead is simply to assess the chance of certain events (like a certain number of successes) occurring. In this section you will learn how to calculate such probabilities theoretically, confirming our simulation results, as well as how to modify the random process we are modeling. For example, we will also examine probabilities for a random process where our goal is to find the probability that our first success occurs on a specific trial.

The Binomial Distribution

Definition

Let the random variable X represent the number of successes in a random process with only two possible outcomes on each trial: success or failure. We will assume that there is a fixed number of trials, n, that are independent of each other and with the same probability of success π on each trial. X is a **binomial random variable** with parameters n and π.

In Section 1.1 we defined a **binary variable** as one with only two outcomes, where one of the outcomes could be defined as "success" and the other as "failure." In the Buzz and Doris study, success was defined as Buzz pushing the correct button, with probability of success $\pi = 0.50$ under the null hypothesis. In the rock-paper-scissors study, success was defined as a player choosing "scissors" and failure as "not choosing scissors," with probability of success $\pi = 1/3$ under the null hypothesis.

You can use simulations or mathematical models to find probabilities of events such as Buzz pushing the correct button 15 or more times. In this section you will use a **binomial distribution** to find the probability of a specific number of successes in a fixed number of trials of a random process with only two possible outcomes on each trial, designated as success or failure.

For example, suppose you wanted to know the probability that someone would play scissors exactly twice in six plays of the game rock/paper/scissors, assuming he or she is randomly choosing between the three gestures. You can define the random variable X as the number of times the player plays scissors in a game consisting of six plays ($n = 6$) in which the player is randomly choosing between three gestures ($\pi = 1/3$). The random variable X satisfies the conditions for a binomial random variable because:

- There is a fixed number of independent trials (in this case, six, which are independent because we assume that the player is randomly choosing).

- Each trial results in either success (*player played scissors gesture*) or failure (*player did not play scissors gesture*).
- Each trial has a constant probability of success ($\pi = 1/3$).

The Geometric Distribution

Sometimes, instead of looking for the probability of a specific number of successes occurring in a fixed number of trials, your interest might lie in finding the probability that the first success occurs on a specific trial. In those scenarios, you will use a *geometric distribution.* For example, suppose you wanted to know the probability that a player would choose "scissors" for the first time the fifth time he or she plays the game rock/paper/scissors. We'll continue to assume that the player is just randomly choosing among the three gestures. You can define the random variable Y as the number of trials it takes to obtain the first success (plays scissors). In this scenario, we do not have a fixed number of attempts (n), as we did for a binomial distribution. Instead, we are interested in the *trial on which the first success occurs*. The possible values of Y are 1, 2, 3, ….

A *geometric random variable* arises when we are interested in counting the number of trials it takes to get the first success in independent trials of the same random process with the same probability of success, π, on each trial.

Definition

Let the random variable Y represent the number of trials needed to obtain the first success in a random process with only two possible outcomes on each trial: success or failure. We assume that the trials are independent of each other with the same probability π of success on each trial. Y is a *geometric random variable* with parameter π.

Time to Leave the Nest?

11.6

Example 11.6

EXAMPLE

According to the U.S. Census Bureau's American Community Survey, in 2015, 34.1% of 18–34-year-olds lived in their parents' home. Suppose that you want to know the probability that, of five randomly selected U.S. 18–34-year-olds, exactly one of them lives in his or her parents' home.

We will define the random variable X as the number of 18–34-year-olds in a random sample of five U.S. residents in this age group who live in their parents' home.

THINK ABOUT IT

What are the possible values of X? Is X a binomial random variable?

The possible values of X are 0, 1, 2, 3, 4, and 5. Keep in mind that in order to be a *binomial random variable*, four characteristics must be true. Let's confirm that these are met for X.

1. **The data are binary.** There are only two outcomes, *living in parents' home* and *not living in parents' home*.

2. **Trials are independent.** What is a trial? A trial is randomly choosing someone from the population to be in our sample. Because we randomly sampled from U.S. 18–34-year-olds, whether or not one person in our sample lives at home does not impact whether someone else in our sample lives at home. Thus, the trials are independent.

3. **There is a fixed number of trials.** We decided to choose 5 individuals from the population. Thus, we have a fixed number of trials ($n = 5$) of the random process of selecting people from this age group.

4. **There is a constant probability of success.** We were given a probability of 0.341 that a person in this age group lives in his or her parents' home.

Caveat: Because we are sampling without replacement (i.e., after randomly choosing someone to be in our sample, we don't allow him or her to be randomly chosen again), the trials technically are not independent—the number of successes in the population will change if the first person selected is a success. However, because the population we are sampling from is so large and we are only choosing a few people from the population, the probability of choosing someone who lives in his or her parents' home stays nearly constant at 0.341, meaning that this is essentially a binomial random variable.

One convention that people use when taking random samples is that if the population size, N, is at least 10 times the sample size chosen, the distribution of the random variable counting the number of successes will be approximately binominal. In this case, because there were about 75.5 million 18–34-year-olds in the U.S. in 2015 and we only choose 5, using a binomial random variable is appropriate.

> ### KEY IDEA
>
> **10% Condition.** When sampling without replacement from a finite population, a binomial random variable can be used to model the number of successes in the sample, provided that the population is at least 10 times larger than the sample size. Using notation, we say that N should be greater than or equal to $10n$.

> ### THINK ABOUT IT
>
> So how do we use this binomial random variable to calculate the probability that 1 of the individuals in our sample of 5 U.S. young adults lives at home?

Using H to represent living at home and A to represent living away from home, one way to get exactly one 18–34-year-old who lives in his or her parents' home in our random sample of five 18–34-year-olds is for the first person to be living at home and the rest not: HAAAA.

To find the probability of H ∩ A ∩ A ∩ A ∩ A, we can multiply the probabilities together because the trials (randomly choosing people) are independent:

$$P(\text{HAAAA}) = (0.341)(0.659)(0.659)(0.659)(0.659) = (0.341)(0.659)^4 = 0.0643$$

But there are four other ways to get exactly one 18–34-year-old in our random sample of 5: the second, third, fourth, or fifth person we choose could be the one who lives at home.

$$P(\text{AHAAA}) = (0.659)(0.341)(0.659)(0.659)(0.659) = (0.341)(0.659)^4$$
$$P(\text{AAHAA}) = (0.659)(0.659)(0.341)(0.659)(0.659) = (0.341)(0.659)^4$$
$$P(\text{AAAHA}) = (0.659)(0.659)(0.659)(0.341)(0.659) = (0.341)(0.659)^4$$
$$P(\text{AAAAH}) = (0.659)(0.659)(0.659)(0.659)(0.341) = (0.341)(0.659)^4$$

In all, there are *five different* ways to obtain exactly one 18–34-year-old who lives with his or her parents in our sample of five 18–34-year-olds. Notice that any one arrangement of 1 H and 4 As has the same probability. Because these outcomes are mutually exclusive (e.g., if the second person is the one who lives at home, the fourth person can't be the one who lives at home), we can add their probabilities. Thus,

$$P(\text{HAAAA}) + P(\text{AHAAA}) + P(\text{AAHAA}) + P(\text{AAAHA}) + P(\text{AAAAH})$$
$$P(X = 1) = 5 \times (0.341)(0.659)^4 \approx 0.3216$$

In other words, there is about a 32% chance that exactly one of the five 18–34-year-olds in our random sample lives with his or her parents.

> ### THINK ABOUT IT
>
> What if we wanted to find the probability of obtaining exactly two 18–34-year-olds who live with their parents in our sample of five 18–34-year-olds? Do you think this number will be larger or smaller than the five ways of obtaining exactly one 18–34-year-old in a random sample of five who lives with his or her parents?

There are 10 different ways to have exactly 2 people in the sample who live at home in a random sample of five 18–34-year-olds. They are listed below.

| HHAAA | HAHAA | HAAHA | HAAAH | AHHAA |
| AHAHA | AHAAH | AAHHA | AAHAH | AAAHH |

The probability of any one of these 10 arrangements of 2 As and 3 Hs is $(0.341)^2 (0.659)^3$; thus,

$$P(X = 2) = 10 \, (0.341)^2 \, (0.659)^3 \approx 0.3328$$

There is about a 33% chance that exactly 2 of the 18–34-year-olds in our random sample live with their parents

You can imagine how tedious it could get to list the entire set of outcomes, particularly for larger sample sizes. Luckily, we have a mathematical formula for finding probabilities for binomial random variables.

KEY IDEA

If X is a **binomial random variable** with parameters n and π, then

$P(X = k) = \binom{n}{k} \pi^k (1 - \pi)^{n-k}$, where $\binom{n}{k} = \dfrac{n!}{k!(n-k)!}$ gives the number of arrangements of k successes in n trials, with $k = 0, 1, 2, \ldots, n$.

Note: $n!$ is "n factorial" and given by $n! = n(n-1)(n-2) \times \cdots \times 3 \times 2 \times 1$, and $0! = 1$. This discrete probability distribution is called the **binomial distribution** with parameters n and π. Shorthand notation for "X follows this binomial distribution" is $X \sim B(n, \pi)$.

CALCULATOR TIPS

You can determine the binomial probabilities using graphing calculators. For example:

- **TI-84:** DISTR → binompdf → enter *number of trials, probability of success, x-value*
- **TI-Nspire:** Menu → Probability → Distribution → Binomial Pdf

You can also use your calculator to find the number of arrangements of k successes in n trials:

- **TI-84:** MATH → PRB → n nCr k
- **TI-Nspire:** Menu → Probability → Combinations → nCr(n, k)

Let's use the formula for a binomial distribution to verify the probability we found above: that exactly 2 of 5 randomly selected 18–34-year-olds live with their parents.

X = number of 18–34-year-olds out of a random sample of 5 who live with their parents
$X \sim B(5, 0.341)$

$$P(X = 2) = \binom{5}{2}(0.341)^2(1 - 0.341)^3 = 10(0.341)^2 (1 - 0.341)^3 \approx 0.3328$$

where we note that $\binom{5}{2} = \dfrac{5!}{2!(5-2)!} = \dfrac{5!}{2!(3)!} = \dfrac{5 \times 4 \times 3 \times 2 \times 1}{2 \times 1 \times 3 \times 2 \times 1} = \dfrac{120}{12} = 10$. This confirms what we found above.

AP TIP

When solving a binomial distribution problem,

- Define your random variable (X = *number of 18–34-year-olds who live with their parents out of random sample of five 18–34-year-olds*).
- State the distribution you will use and the corresponding parameters: $X \sim B(n = 5, \pi = 0.341)$.
- State the probability that you are looking to find, and its value: $P(X = 2) \approx 0.3328$.
- Write your answer in the context of the problem (*There is about a 33% chance that exactly 2 of the 18–34-year-olds in our random sample live with their parents.*)

What if we wanted to know the probability that at least 2 of the 5 randomly sampled 18–34-year-olds live with their parents? How could you use what you learned above to find the probability that at least 2 of the 5 randomly sampled 18–34-year-olds live with their parents?

You can find this probability by adding the probability of exactly 2, plus exactly 3, plus exactly 4, plus exactly 5 of the 18–34-year-olds in our sample who live with their parents:

$$P(X \geq 2) = P(X = 2) + P(X = 3) + P(X = 4) + P(X = 5)$$

$$P(X \geq 2) = \binom{5}{2}(0.341)^2(1 - 0.341)^3 + \binom{5}{3}(0.341)^3(1 - 0.341)^2$$

$$+ \binom{5}{4}(0.341)^4(1 - 0.341) + \binom{5}{5}(0.341)^5 \approx 0.5542$$

There is about a 55.4% chance that at least 2 of the five 18–34-year-olds in our random sample live with their parents.

CALCULATOR TIPS

On your calculator, you can use the binomial cdf command to find a range of probabilities as was found in the example above:

- **TI-84:** DISTR → binomcdf → enter *number of trials, probability of success, X ≤ k*
- **TI-Nspire:** Menu → Probability → Distribution → Binomial Cdf

Note: This is an example where the complement might be a faster calculation:

$$P(X \geq 2) = 1 - P(X \leq 1) = 1 - \binom{5}{1}(0.341)^1(1 - 0.341)^4$$

$$- \binom{5}{0}(0.341)^0(1 - 0.341)^5 = 1 - 0.4458 = 0.5542$$

Just be careful to not include the event $X = 2$ in both the complement and the original event.

THINK ABOUT IT

On average, how many 18-34-year-olds in our sample will be living at home?

To this point we've focused on the probability that different numbers of people in the sample will be living at home. But what will happen, on average, in the long run? We've seen this question before. Because X is a random variable, you can use the formulas for the mean and standard deviation of a random variable that we developed in Section 11.4:

$$\mu_X = x_1 p_1 + x_2 p_2 + \cdots + x_k p_k$$
$$= \sum x_i p_i$$
$$\sigma_X^2 = \sum (x_i - \mu_x)^2 p_i$$

You can do this for all the different outcomes for a binomial random variable, but as n increases, you have lots and lots of values to calculate. It turns out there is a faster way!

If we asked you, "On average, how many times will you get heads when you flip a coin 100 times?" most students are quick to say, "50." Why? Since 100 times 0.50 is 50, the "average" number of times you get heads is 50. In general, n times π for a binomial distribution

---

Definition

If X is a binomial random variable with a **binomial distribution** with parameters n and π, then

$$E(X) = \mu_x = n\pi$$
$$\sigma_X = \sqrt{n\pi(1 - \pi)}$$

gives the average (or expected) value. A similar "shortcut" formula works for the standard deviation.

Let's use the formulas to find the expected number and standard deviation of 18–34-year-olds who live with their parents in a random sample of five 18–34-year-olds.

$$E(X) = 5(0.341) \approx 1.705$$
$$\sigma_X = \sqrt{5(0.341)(1 - 0.341)} \approx 1.06$$

In the long run, you would *expect* about 1.7 out of five randomly selected 18–34-year-olds to live with their parents with a standard deviation of about 1.06 people.

GEOMETRIC RANDOM VARIABLE

> **THINK ABOUT IT**
>
> Let's consider a different question. Suppose you want to sample 18–34-year-olds in the U.S. one at a time until you find the **first** 18–34-year-old who reports living with their parents. How many people do you expect to have to survey in order to find that **first** 18–34-year-old who reports living with his or her parents?

We'll answer this question shortly, but first let's define the random variable Y as the number of 18–34-year-olds you must survey in order to find the **first** 18–34-year-old surveyed who lives with his or her parents. It turns out that Y is a *geometric random variable* and has a *geometric distribution*.

Let's verify that what we said about Y being a *geometric random variable*.

1. **The data are binary.** There are only two outcomes, with success = *living in parents' home* and failure = *not living in parents' home*.

2. **Trials are independent.** Because we randomly sampled from U.S. 18–34-year-olds, the individual's living status responses (in parents' home or not) should be independent for different members of our sample.

3. **The variable of interest is the number of trials required to obtain the first success.** We will continue the random process of selecting people from this age group until we obtain (the first) one who lives with his or her parents.

4. **There is a constant probability of success.** We were given a probability of 0.341 that person in this age group lives in his or her parent's home.

We have verified that the random variable Y (the number of 18–34-year-olds we need to survey until we find the first who resides with his or her parents) follows a geometric distribution with probability of success $\pi = 0.341$ on each trial.

> **Definition**
>
> A *geometric random variable* has these four characteristics:
>
> 1. The data are binary.
> 2. Trials are independent.
> 3. The variable of interest is the number of trials required to obtain the first success.
> 4. The probability of success is constant for each trial.

 11.6.1

> **THINK ABOUT IT**
>
> What's the probability that the very first 18–34-year-old person you survey would be someone who lives with his or her parents?

Because we are interested in the probability that the very first 18–34-year-old person you survey would be someone who lives with his or her parents, this would mean that we are looking for the probability that $Y = 1$.

$$P(Y = 1) = P(\text{person lives at home}) = 0.341$$

There is a 34.1% chance that the very first 18–34-year-old person you survey would be someone who lives with his or her parents.

11.6.2

> **THINK ABOUT IT**
>
> Suppose you would like to know the probability that the **first** 18–34-year-old surveyed who lives with his or her parents is the fourth person randomly selected.

Because we are interested in the probability that the first success we encounter (18–34-year-old who lives with parents) occurs on the fourth person randomly surveyed, then it would mean that the first three people surveyed did not live with their parents but the fourth one did (Failure, Failure, Failure, Success). Again using the multiplication rule for independent events, this probability can be calculated as

$$P(Y = 4) = (1 - 0.341)^3 (0.341) \approx 0.0976$$

There is about a 9.76% chance that the first 18–34-year-old we find who lives with his or her parents will be the fourth person surveyed.

> **THINK ABOUT IT**
>
> Is it possible that the first success (*lives with parents*) happens before the fourth person you survey?

Yes, of course! As you saw before, there is a 34.1% chance that the very first 18–34-year-old person you survey would be someone who lives with his or her parents. And you can also verify that there is about a 22.5% chance that the second 18–34-year-old person you survey would be someone who lives with his or her parents. And, so on.

> **THINK ABOUT IT**
>
> What is the probability that the first success (finding a person in this age group who resides with his or her parents) does not occur until after the fourth person surveyed?

Now you want to find the probability that $Y > 4$, which can be calculated as follows:

$$
\begin{aligned}
P(Y > 4) &= 1 - P(Y \le 4) \\
&= 1 - [P(Y = 1) + P(Y = 2) + P(Y = 3) + P(Y = 4)] \\
&= 1 - [0.341 + (1 - 0.341)(0.341) + (1 - 0.341)^2 (0.341) + (1 - 0.341)^3 (0.341)] \approx 0.1886
\end{aligned}
$$

There is about a 18.86% chance that the first 18–34-year-old we find who lives with his or her parents will be found after the fourth person surveyed.

> **THINK ABOUT IT**
>
> Let's go back to the original question, "How many 18–34-year-olds would you expect to have to survey to find the first one who lives with his or her parents?"

11.6.3

> **KEY IDEA**
>
> If Y has a geometric distribution with probability of success π on each independent trial, then the probability that the first success occurs on the kth trial is
>
> $$P(Y = k) = (1 - \pi)^{k-1}\pi$$
>
> with expected value or mean $E(Y) = \mu_Y = 1/\pi$. This is called the ***geometric distribution*** and shorthand notation for saying Y follows a geometric distribution is $Y \sim G(\pi)$.

Applying the formula for the mean, you can see that $E(Y) = 1/0.341 \approx 2.9$. This can be interpreted to say that, in the long run, you would expect to have to survey about 2.9 U.S. 18–34-year-olds to find the first one who lives with his or her parents.

 11.6.4

CALCULATOR TIPS

To find geometric probabilities on your calculator:

- **TI-84:** DISTR → geometpdf → enter *probability of success, and trial for first success*
  - geometcdf → *enter probability of success, and k, first success occurs on ≤kth trial)*
- **TI-Nspire:** Menu → Probability → Distribution → Geometric Pdf (*first success occurs on kth trial*)
  - Menu → Probability → Distribution → Geometric Cdf (*first success occurs on lower bound, upper bound trial*)

GEOMETRIC OR BINOMIAL

You might have noticed that there are some similarities between binomial and geometric random variables, but they aren't the same. The similarities are that in both cases the random process consists of independent trials, where each trial results in either a success or a failure, with a constant probability of success.

The difference is that the binomial distribution counts how many successes occur in a fixed set of trials (e.g., we select 5 people and count how many live at home), whereas the geometric distribution keeps going until the first success occurs and thus counts the number of trials.

KEY IDEA

Although the geometric and binomial variables are similar and related (both focus on independent binary trials with success probability π), a binomial random variable fixes the number of trials ahead of time (n) and counts the number of successes in the n trials, whereas a geometric random variable keeps going (more and more trials) until the first success occurs.

Clueless Quiz

EXPLORATION

11.6

Suppose that a clueless student takes a multiple-choice quiz and guesses randomly among the options on every question. Suppose there are 5 questions, with 3 options to choose (guess) from on each question. The student must answer more than half of the questions correctly to pass.

1. Make a guess for the probability that the clueless student passes the quiz (by answering 3 or more of the 5 questions correctly).

Let the random variable X represent the number of questions that the clueless student answers correctly. Recall from the introduction that in order to be a binomial random variable, four characteristics must be met.

2. Confirm that X is a binomial random variable by justifying each of the following statements.

   a. Each trial results either in "success" or "failure." Identify:

   b. The likelihood of success is the same on each trial. Justify:

   c. The trials are independent of each other. Justify:

   d. There is a fixed number of trials. Identify:

3. What are the possible values of X?

4. What is the probability that the clueless student answers all 5 questions correctly $(X = 5)$? What is the justification for the mathematical operations you are using to find your answer?

5. What is the probability that the clueless student answers zero questions correctly $(X = 0)$?

6. Now determine the probability that the clueless student answers exactly 2 questions correctly. The answer to this question requires multiple steps of work. Let's do these one at a time.

   a. First, how many different ways could the student get questions correct/incorrect and get exactly 2 correct? Write down these different orderings (e.g., CICII, where C = Correct and I = Incorrect).

   b. Find the probability that the student gets exactly 1 of those orderings (e.g., CICII).

   c. Will the probabilities for the other orderings be the same or different? Why?

   d. What is the probability the clueless student answers exactly 2 questions correctly? (*Hint*: Since these outcomes are mutually exclusive, you can sum up their probabilities (using the addition rule).)

   $P(X = 2) =$

We can generalize this approach to finding probabilities from a ***binomial distribution***.

KEY IDEA

If X is a ***binomial random variable*** with parameters n and π, then

$P(X = k) = \binom{n}{k} \pi^k (1 - \pi)^{n-k}$, where $\binom{n}{k} = \dfrac{n!}{k!(n - k)!}$ gives the number of arrangements of k successes in n trials, with $k = 0, 1, 2, \ldots, n$.

Note: $n!$ is "n factorial" and given by $n! = n(n - 1)(n - 2) \times \cdots \times 3 \times 2 \times 1$, and $0! = 1$. This discrete probability distribution is called the ***binomial distribution*** with parameters n and π. Shorthand notation for "X follows this binomial distribution" is $X \sim B(n, \pi)$.

---

7. For the multiple-choice quiz taken by a clueless student (as described above), what are the values of n and π?

8. Using the equation above, determine the probabilities for the rest of the probability distribution $P(X = 1)$, $P(X = 3)$, and $P(X = 4)$ using the formula shown above.

9. Calculate the probability that a clueless student correctly answers 3 or more of the 5 questions.

10. Your answer to the previous question is the probability that the student passes the quiz by just guessing the answer on each question. Does this agree with what you predicted at the beginning of this exploration?

11. Without doing any calculations: Would you expect this probability of passing (getting at least half correct) to be larger, the same, or smaller, if the quiz consists of 15 questions rather than 5? Explain your reasoning.

CALCULATOR TIPS

You can use your calculator to find binomial probabilities:

- **TI-84:** DISTR → binompdf → enter *number of trials, probability of success, x-value*
- **TI-Nspire:** Menu → Probability → Distribution → Binomial Pdf

You can also use your calculator to find the number of arrangements of k successes in n trials:

- **TI-84:** MATH → PRB → n nCr k
- **TI-Nspire:** Menu → Probability → Combinations → nCr(n, k)

12. Use your calculator to determine the probability of passing the quiz if it consists of 15 questions rather than 5. (*Hint*: Let Y = number of questions answered correctly. Identify the probability distribution of Y, and express the probability of passing the quiz in terms of Y.) Is your intuition from the previous question supported?

AP TIP

When solving a binomial distribution problem,

- Define your random variable: X = *number of correctly guessed answers on quiz.*
- State the distribution you will use and the corresponding parameters: $X \sim B(n = 5, \pi = 0.3333)$.
- State the probability that you are looking to find, and its value: $P(X = 2) = 0.3292$.
- Write your answer in the context of the problem (*There is about a 32.9% chance that exactly 2 of the questions on the quiz are answered correctly.*)

---

13. Without doing any calculations: How would you expect the probability of passing the 15-question quiz to change if each question has 5 options rather than 3? Explain your reasoning.

14. Make this change (from 3 options per question to 5), and recalculate the probability of passing the 15-question quiz. How does this probability compare to the previous one?

Properties of binomial distributions

What if all the students taking this quiz are "clueless"? On average, how well will they do?

15. Predict what the average score on the "clueless" quiz (with 5 questions) will be. Why?

To find this value out exactly, we could do what we've done before:

$$\mu_X = x_1 p_1 + x_2 p_2 + \cdots + x_k p_k$$
$$= \sum x_i p_i$$

Or we could use the shortcut formula shown in the definition box in the margin. *Note:* The shortcut formula for the average value is simply found by multiplying the probability of success by the number of trials (e.g., if you want to know the average number of heads in 20 flips, you just multiply 20 by 50%, the probability of getting heads).

16. Find the mean number of questions answered correctly out of 5 questions if someone is just guessing.

17. Use the shortcut formula to find the standard deviation of the number of questions answered correctly on the quiz. Interpret this value.

> **Definition**
>
> If X has a **binomial distribution** with parameters n and π, then
> $$E(X) = \mu_X = n\pi$$
> $$\sigma_X = \sqrt{n\pi(1 - \pi)}$$

Geometric random variables

Now suppose that the teacher gives a very different kind of quiz: The teacher asks questions until the student answers a question correctly. As soon as the student answers a question correctly, no more questions are asked. Let the random variable Y represent the number of questions asked in order to obtain the first correct answer (in other words, Y is the total number of questions asked by the teacher). Assume that the student is still "clueless" and so is just guessing on each question, and that each question is multiple choice with 3 possible answers (only 1 of which is correct).

18. Explain why Y does *not* have a binomial distribution.

Recall from the introduction to this section that a geometric random variable must have certain characteristics.

19. Confirm that these characteristics are met for Y.

   a. Each trial has two outcomes. Identify:

   b. The trials are independent. Justify:

   c. The probability of success on each trial is the same. Justify:

   d. The random variable counts the number of trials to the first success. Justify:

20. What is the probability that the clueless student's first correct answer is the first question that he or she is asked?

21. What is the probability that the clueless student's first correct answer is the second question that he or she is asked?

22. What is the probability that the clueless student's first correct answer is the third question that he or she is asked?

You may be beginning to notice a pattern in how to find these probabilities. The general formula is shown in the box below.

> ### KEY IDEA
>
> If Y has a geometric distribution with probability of success π on each independent trial, then the probability that the first success occurs on the kth trial is
>
> $$P(Y = k) = (1 - \pi)^{k-1}\pi$$
>
> with expected value or mean $E(Y) = \mu_Y = 1/\pi$. This is called the **geometric distribution** and shorthand notation for saying Y follows a geometric distribution is $Y \sim G(\pi)$.

23. Use the formula to find the probability that the student's first correct answer occurs on the 12th question.

24. Calculate the expected value of the number of questions needed for the clueless student to obtain his or her first correct answer. Also write a sentence interpreting what this value means in this context.

25. How does the expected value change if each question has 5 possible answers to guess from instead of only 3? Why does this make sense?

In addition to using the formula, you can also use your calculator.

> ### CALCULATOR TIPS
>
> Your calculator may allow you to find geometric probabilities. For example:
>
> - **TI-84:** DISTR → geometpdf → enter *probability of success, and trial for first success*
>   - geometcdf → *enter probability of success, and k, first success occurs on ≤kth trial)*
> - **TI-Nspire:** Menu → Probability → Distribution → Geometric Pdf (*first success occurs on kth trial*)
>   - Menu → Probability → Distribution → Geometric Cdf (*first success occurs on lower bound, upper bound trial*)

Geometric or binomial

You might have noticed that there are some similarities between binomial and geometric random variables, but they aren't the same. The similarities are that in both cases the random process consists of independent trials, where each trial results in either a success or a failure, with a constant probability of success.

The difference is that the binomial distribution counts how many successes occur in a fixed set of trials (e.g., we take a 5-question quiz and count how many correct answers are obtained), whereas the geometric distribution keeps going until the first correct answer occurs and so counts the number of trials (questions).

> ### KEY IDEA
>
> Although the geometric and binomial variables are similar and related (both focus on independent binary trials with success probability π), a binomial random variable fixes the number of trials ahead of time (n) and counts the number of successes in the n trials, whereas a geometric random variable keeps going (more and more trials) until the first success occurs.

SECTION 11.6 Summary

In this section you investigated two particular types of discrete random variables that come up often in statistics, the binomial and geometric distributions. Some useful definitions to remember and habits to develop from this topic include:

- A binomial distribution can be used to model the counts of successes of a binomial variable X (with two outcomes: success or failure) for a fixed number of attempts, n, of a random process in which individual outcomes are independent with the same probability of success π on each trial.

- If X has a **binomial distribution** with parameters n and π, then

$$P(X = k) = \binom{n}{k}\pi^k(1 - \pi)^{n-k}$$

where $\binom{n}{k} = \dfrac{n!}{k!(n - k)!}$ gives the number of arrangements of k successes in n trials, with $k = 0, 1, 2, \ldots, n$, $n! = n(n - 1)(n - 2) \times \cdots \times 3 \times 2 \times 1$, and $0! = 1$.

- If X has a **binomial distribution** with parameters n and π, then

$$E(X) = \mu_X = n\pi$$
$$\sigma_X = \sqrt{n\pi(1 - \pi)}$$

- A **geometric distribution** can be used to model the number of trials (where there are two possible outcomes on each trial: success or failure) needed to obtain the first success, such that trials are independent of each other, with the same probability of success π on each trial.

- If Y has a geometric distribution with probability of success π on each independent trial, then the probability that the first success occurs on the kth trial is?

$$P(Y = k) = (1 - \pi)^{k-1}\pi$$

with expected value or mean

$$E(Y) = \mu_Y = 1/\pi$$

10% Condition: In Exploration 11.6, we looked at a student guessing randomly on every question. In this case, the outcomes (correct or incorrect) are independent from question to question. But in Example 11.6, we looked at the random sampling process from a finite population. Technically, these trials are no longer independent as you remove people from the population.

However, when sampling without replacement from a finite population, we can still model the trials as independent provided that the population size is at least 10 times larger than the sample size ($N \geq 10n$).

CONTINUOUS RANDOM VARIABLES AND NORMAL DISTRIBUTIONS

INTRODUCTION

Definition

A ***probability density function*** is a curve that describes the overall pattern or shape of a distribution of a continuous random variable, say, *X*. The area under a density curve within an interval of values along the horizontal axis gives the probability that a random variable *X* will be in that interval. The total area under the curve and above the horizontal axis over the entire range of values of the random variable *X* is equal to 1.

In the previous sections, we examined discrete random variables, ones that take on a countable number of outcomes. What if our variable of interest is a measurement variable, such as the amount of sleep a randomly selected student got the previous night? The random variable *sleep* can take on any value (to a specified number of decimal places) in an interval of values, so how can we possibly count or list all of the possible outcomes? We can't! A random variable that can take on all possible values in an interval of values is called a ***continuous random variable***. The probability distribution of a continuous random variable is described by a ***probability density function***, often referred to as a density curve. All density curves have the property that they are on or above the horizontal axis with an area of 1 (100% of observations) below the curve; however, their shapes can vary.

The Normal Distribution

We will focus our attention on one commonly encountered continuous distribution, the ***normal distribution***. You have encountered numerous bell-shaped distributions in examples and explorations, such as the null distributions used to approximate sampling distributions of the sample proportion (Section 1.6). In those instances, our goal was to assess how unlikely our sample results would have been as a result of chance variation alone. Our goal was inference about an unknown parameter. Sometimes we know the value of the parameter and our goal is to find the probability of seeing values in the distribution in a particular interval.

The normal distribution is a useful model for summarizing the behavior of many quantitative variables. Measurements, such as scores on standardized tests and heights, often have a bell-shaped distribution with most values near the mean and fewer observations farther away. For example, in Figure 11.18, we see that the normal distribution looks like a reasonable model for the distribution of hours of sleep. Using the normal model means that we can approximate how often certain kinds of data values (e.g., more than 10 hours of sleep) appear. Keep in mind that this model will not be a perfect match; for example, a normal distribution extends below zero, which, fortunately, is not possible for hours of sleep!

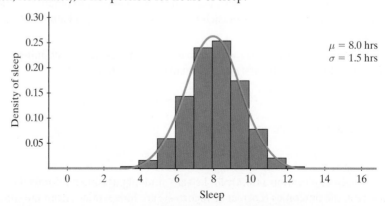

FIGURE 11.18 Histogram of number of hours of sleep for a population of students, with overlaid normal density curve.

As we saw earlier in the course, every normal distribution shares three distinguishing characteristics: all are symmetric, all have a single peak at their center, and all follow a bell-shaped curve. Two things, however, distinguish one normal distribution from another: its mean, μ, and its standard deviation, σ. In fact, those two parameters alone tell you everything you need. The peak of a normal curve occurs at its mean, and the curve is symmetric about the mean. The distance between the mean and the points where the curvature changes from concave down to concave up is equal to one standard deviation. Figure 11.19 illustrates this relationship.

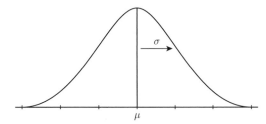

FIGURE 11.19 Normal distribution with mean μ and standard deviation σ.

Once we know our mean and standard deviation, we can use technology or a table (after first *standardizing* the observation) to calculate the probability of an observation in an interval by finding the area under the normal curve. Figure 11.20 illustrates a special property of the normal distribution: the **empirical rule** (also referred to as the **68-95-99.7% rule**). For data that follow an approximately normal distribution, about 68% of the data will fall within one standard deviation of the mean, about 95% will fall within two standard deviations of the mean, and almost all (about 99.7%) will fall within three standard deviations of the mean.

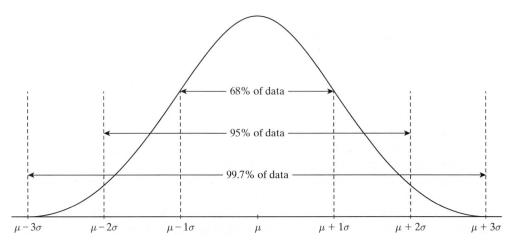

FIGURE 11.20 The empirical rule.

The distribution of the number of hours of sleep for the population of college students in Figure 11.18 is approximately normally distributed with mean $\mu = 8.0$ hours and standard deviation $\sigma = 1.5$ hours. Notice that most of the hours of sleep are between 6.5 hours and 9.5 hours (one standard deviation from the mean of 8.0 hours), and almost all of the observed values are within 3.5 hours and 12.5 hours (three standard deviations from the mean of 8.0 hours), which are consistent with the empirical rule.

11.7 ─ Heights of Adult Women ───────────────────────────

EXAMPLE

Example 11.7

According to data from the U.S. Department of Health and Human Services, the heights for women (ages 20 and over) in the United States are approximately normally distributed with a mean of 63.8 inches and a standard deviation of 2.8 inches.

In Figure 11.21, the values for the mean and one, two, and three standard deviations above and below the mean for the heights of women (ages 20 and over) in the United States are labeled.

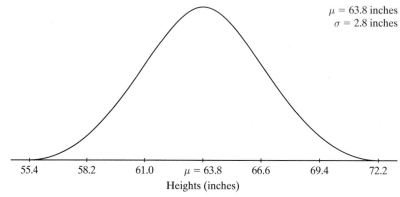

$\mu = 63.8$ inches
$\sigma = 2.8$ inches

55.4   58.2   61.0 $\mu = 63.8$ 66.6   69.4   72.2
Heights (inches)

FIGURE 11.21   Normal distribution of heights for U.S. women over the age of 20.

> **THINK ABOUT IT**
>
> Using the graph above, how could you approximate the percentage of adult U.S. women (ages 20 and over) that fall within different height ranges?

11.7.1

Definition

- - - - - - - - - - - - - - - -

If a random variable X has a normal distribution with mean μ and standard deviation σ, then the standardized variable $z = \frac{x - \mu}{\sigma}$ has the standard normal distribution with mean 0 and standard deviation 1. This is referred to as a **standard normal** random variable.

- - - - - - - - - - - - - - - -

According to the empirical rule, about 68% of women (ages 20 and over) in the U.S. will have heights between 61.0 inches and 66.6 inches, about 95% will have heights between 58.2 inches and 69.4 inches, and almost all (about 99.7%) will have heights between 55.4 inches and 72.2 inches.

What if we wanted to find the percentage of adult U.S. women with heights at least 68 inches, or the height of a woman at the 25th percentile (25% of women's heights are smaller)? In other words, how do we answer questions for heights that aren't exactly at 1, 2, or 3 standard deviations from the mean? Recall from Section 1.7 that a **standardized score**, also called a **z-score**, measures how far an observation is from the mean of the distribution, in terms of number of standard deviations. You saw in Section 11.5 that linear transformations of a random variable (adding/subtracting and multiplying/dividing by a constant) do not change the shape of a distribution. Therefore, if we standardize a random variable that is normally distributed, the standardized random variable is also normally distributed. This random variable follows a standard normal distribution, a normal distribution with mean 0 and standard deviation 1.

> **THINK ABOUT IT**
>
> What is the standard score for a woman (age 20 and over) from the U.S. with a height of 68 inches?

11.7.2

We have been assuming that the distribution of these heights is normally distributed, with mean 63.8 inches and standard deviation 2.8 inches. So, a height of 68 inches corresponds to a z-score equal to (68 − 63.8)/2.8 = 1.5. This gives us an idea that this observation is a little unusual, but not very surprising. We can use a normal probability table or calculator to convert this z-score to a probability. Figure 11.22 shows a sketch of the (standard) normal distribution on the scale of the data with the shaded area under the curve corresponding to the probability that a randomly selected woman from this age group will be at least 68 inches tall.

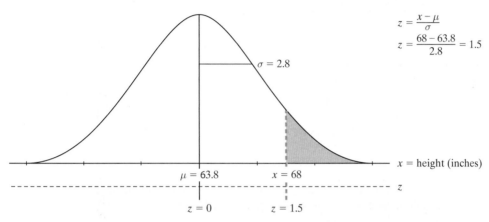

FIGURE 11.22 Normal distribution of heights for U.S. women over the age of 20 with standardized z-scores included.

The proportion of women in this age group with heights of at least 68 inches (the area under the standard normal distribution above a z-score of 1.5) can be found using your calculator or Table A on the AP Statistics formula sheet. Table A gives probabilities for z-scores less than a specified value (to the hundredths place). To find the probability for a z-score greater than a specified value, subtract the obtained proportion from 1. Figure 11.23 shows a snapshot of Table A. We can see that the probability of a z-score below $z = 1.50$ is 0.9332, and thus the probability of a z-score above 1.5 is 1 − 0.9332 = 0.0668. So we conclude that about 6.68% of women (ages 20 and over) in the U.S. have heights at or above 68 inches.

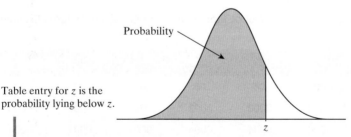

FIGURE 11.23 Snapshot of Table A from the AP Statistics formula sheet.

z	.00	.01	.02	.03	.04	.05	.06	.07	.08	.09
0.0	.5000	.5040	.5080	.5120	.5160	.5199	.5239	.5279	.5319	.5359
0.1	.5398	.5438	.5478	.5517	.5557	.5596	.5636	.5675	.5714	.5753
1.4	.9192	.9207	.9222	.9236	.9251	.9265	.9279	.9292	.9306	.9319
1.5	.9332	.9345	.9357	.9370	.9382	.9394	.9406	.9418	.9429	.9441

TABLE A (Continued)

> ### CALCULATOR TIPS
>
> You may use your calculator to obtain the area under a normal curve. For example,
>
> - **TI-84:** STAT → Distr → normalcdf(lower bound, upper bound, mean, std dev)
> - **TI-Nspire:** Statistics → Distributions → Normal Cdf (lower bound, upper bound, mean, std dev)
>
> *Note:* You can enter your information on either the scale of the data or as a standardized value (*z*-score).

> ### THINK ABOUT IT
>
> How would you use the standard normal distribution to find the height of a woman (age 20 and over) from the U.S. that would be at the 25th percentile (approximately 25% of the heights are smaller)?

If we know the mean and standard deviation of a distribution that is approximately normally distributed, we can find the values on the distribution that correspond to a given area under the normal density curve.

We want the value, *x,* so that 25% of women fall below that value. In Figure 11.24, we see that the *z*-score closest to 0.25 is $z = -0.67$.

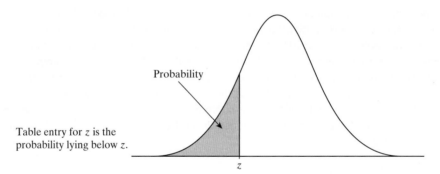

Table entry for *z* is the probability lying below *z*.

Probability

z

FIGURE 11.24 Snapshot of Table A from the AP Statistics formula sheet.

TABLE A	Standard normal probabilities									
z	.00	.01	.02	.03	.04	.05	.06	.07	.08	.09
−3.4	.0003	.0003	.0003	.0003	.0003	.0003	.0003	.0003	.0003	.0002
−3.3	.0005	.0005	.0005	.0004	.0004	.0004	.0004	.0004	.0004	.0003
....										
−0.9	.1841	.1814	.1788	.1762	.1736	.1711	.1685	.1660	.1635	.1611
−0.8	.2119	.2090	.2061	.2033	.2005	.1977	.1949	.1922	.1894	.1867
−0.7	.2420	.2389	.2358	.2327	.2296	.2266	.2236	.2206	.2177	.2148
−0.6	.2743	.2709	.2676	.2643	.2611	.2578	.2546	.2514	.2483	.2451
−0.5	.3085	.3050	.3015	.2981	.2946	.2912	.2877	.2843	.2810	.2776

Figure 11.25 depicts the normal distribution of heights for U.S. women over the age of 20 with the bottom 25% of heights shaded in. Substituting the standardized value of −0.67 found in the standard normal probabilities (Table A) into the *z*-score formula, we can solve for *x,* the height at the 25th percentile.

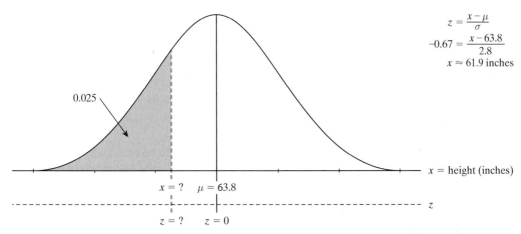

$$z = \frac{x - \mu}{\sigma}$$
$$-0.67 = \frac{x - 63.8}{2.8}$$
$$x \approx 61.9 \text{ inches}$$

FIGURE 11.25 Normal distribution of heights for U.S. women over the age of 20 with standardized z-scores included and bottom 25% of heights shaded.

So, we conclude that about 25% of women ages 20 and older in the U.S. have heights below 61.9 inches. (Use the shaded graph to check the reasonableness of your answer. For example, we know the height corresponding to the 25th percentile should be smaller than the mean of 63.8 inches.)

CALCULATOR TIPS

You may use your calculator to obtain a distribution value for a given area under the standard normal distribution.

- **TI-84:** STAT → Distr → invNorm(area, mean, std dev)
- **TI-Nspire:** Statistics → Distributions → Inverse Normal(area, mean, std dev)

Note: You can enter the mean and standard deviation on either the scale of the data or as a standardized value (z-score).

 11.7.5

THE DIFFERENCE IN TWO NORMAL RANDOM VARIABLES

According to data from the U.S. Department of Health and Human Services, the heights for men (ages 20 and over) in the United States are approximately normally distributed with a mean of 69.3 inches and a standard deviation of 3.0 inches. Recall that the heights for women (ages 20 and over) in the United States are also approximately normally distributed with a mean of 63.8 inches and a standard deviation of 2.8 inches. If you were to randomly select an adult woman and an adult man from this age group, what is the probability that the woman will be taller than the man?

THINK ABOUT IT

How does answering this question relate to what you learned about combining independent random variables in Section 11.4?

You would like to know the probability that a randomly selected woman is taller than a randomly selected man from this age group. If a randomly selected woman is taller than a randomly selected man, then the difference in their heights (woman – man) will be greater than 0.

You can define a new random variable D that is the difference in heights (woman − man), and use the random variable rules you learned in Section 11.5 to find the mean and standard deviation of D.

$$\mu_D = \mu_W - \mu_M = -5.5$$
$$\sigma_D^2 = \sigma_W^2 + \sigma_M^2 = (2.8)^2 + (3.0)^2 = 16.84$$
$$\sigma_D = \sqrt{\sigma_W^2 + \sigma_M^2} = \sqrt{16.84} \approx 4.10$$

We see that on average, for this age group, women tend to be about 5.5 inches shorter than men, with a standard deviation of 4.10. We need one more key property of normal distributions.

KEY IDEA

If two random variables follow normal distributions, then the sum or difference of those random variables will also follow a normal distribution.

Because the distributions of heights for both women and men in this age group are normally distributed, the key idea tells us that the distribution of their differences will also be normally distributed. Figure 11.26 displays the distribution for the random variable D. To calculate the probability that a randomly selected woman is taller than a randomly selected man from this age group, we need to find the probability that their difference (woman − man) is greater than zero ($D > 0$).

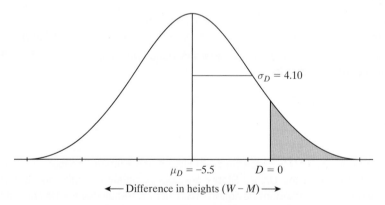

FIGURE 11.26 Distribution of differences in heights (D = woman − man).

Converting a difference in heights (woman − man) of 0 inches for a distribution with mean −5.5 inches and standard deviation 4.10 inches to a z-score, we obtain

$$z = \frac{0 - (-5.5)}{4.10} \approx 1.34$$

Using technology, we find the probability of obtaining a difference in heights (woman − man) greater than 0 is about 0.0901.

Alternatively, we could use Table A from the AP Statistics Formula Sheet as shown in Figure 11.27 below. We find that the probability of obtaining a z-score of at least 1.34 is $1 - 0.9099 = 0.0901$.

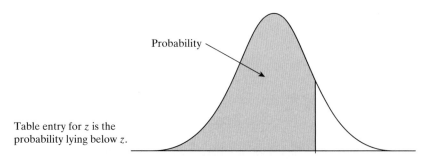

Table entry for z is the probability lying below z.

FIGURE 11.27 Snapshot of Table A from the AP Statistics formula sheet.

TABLE A	*(Continued)*								
z	.00	.01	.02	.03	.04	.05	.06	.07	.08	.09
0.0	.5000	.5040	.5080	.5120	.5160	.5199	.5239	.5279	.5319	.5359
0.1	.5398	.5438	.5478	.5517	.5557	.5596	.5636	.5675	.5714	.5753
1.2	.8849	.8869	.8888	.8907	.8925	.8944	.8962	.8980	.8997	.9015
1.3	.9032	.9049	.9066	.9082	.9099	.9115	.9131	.9147	.9162	.9177

So, we conclude that if we randomly select a woman and a man (both ages 20 and older), there is a 9% chance that the woman will be taller than the man.

 11.7.6

Birthweights

EXPLORATION

11.7A

Birthweights of babies born in the United States can be modeled by a normal distribution with mean 3,250 grams and standard deviation 550 grams.

1. Draw a well-labeled sketch of the normal distribution. (Include the horizontal axis label and include at least 5 values on the scale.)

2. According to the empirical rule (see the introduction for a reminder), 95% of babies will have birthweights between what two values?

3. Babies who weigh less than 2,500 grams are classified as "low birthweight." On your sketch from #1, shade the area corresponding to the proportion of all newborn babies who would be classified as having low birthweight. Then make an educated guess for the value of this proportion.

Recall from Section 1.7 that a ***standardized score***, also called a ***z-score***, measures how far an observation is from the mean of the distribution, in terms of number of standard deviations. You saw in Section 11.5 that linear transformations of a random variable (adding/subtracting and multiplying/dividing by a constant) do not change the shape of a distribution. Therefore, if we standardize a random variable that is normally distributed, the standardized random variable is also normally distributed. This random variable follows a standard normal distribution, a normal distribution with mean 0 and standard deviation 1.

4. Calculate the z-score corresponding to 2,500 grams. Also, interpret what this z-score reveals in this context.

Table A from the AP Statistics formula sheet provides the probability that an observation is less than a z-score. For example, in Figure 11.28 we see that the probability a randomly selected value is less than 1.50 is 0.9392.

> **Definition**
>
> If a random variable X has a normal distribution with mean μ and standard deviation σ, then the standardized variable $z = \frac{x - \mu}{\sigma}$ has the standard normal distribution with mean 0 and standard deviation 1. This is referred to as a ***standard normal*** random variable.

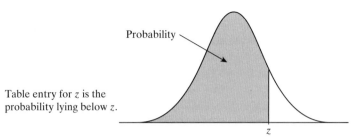

Table entry for z is the
probability lying below z.

FIGURE 11.28 Snapshot of Table A from the AP Statistics
formula sheet.

TABLE A	(Continued)									
z	.00	.01	.02	.03	.04	.05	.06	.07	.08	.09
0.0	.5000	.5040	.5080	.5120	.5160	.5199	.5239	.5279	.5319	.5359
0.1	.5398	.5438	.5478	.5517	.5557	.5596	.5636	.5675	.5714	.5753
....										
1.4	.9192	.9207	.9222	.9236	.9251	.9265	.9279	.9292	.9306	.9319
1.5	.9332	.9345	.9357	.9370	.9382	.9394	.9406	.9418	.9429	.9441

5. Now, using the z-score you obtained for a birthweight of 2,500 grams and Table A from the AP Statistics formula sheet, determine the proportion of all newborn babies who would be classified as having low birthweight. Is the proportion close to what you guessed earlier?

> **CALCULATOR TIPS**
>
> You may also use your calculator to obtain the area under a normal distribution. For example:
>
> - **TI-84:** STAT → Distr → normalcdf(lower bound, upper bound, mean, std dev)
> - **TI-Nspire:** Statistics → Distributions → Normal Cdf (lower bound, upper bound, mean, std dev)
>
> *Note:* You can enter your information on either the scale of the data or as a standardized value (z-score).

6. Use the normcdf command on a graphing calculator to confirm the probability that a baby weighs less than 2,500 at birth. (*Hint:* You will need to enter -9999 as the lower bound.)

7. Determine the proportion of babies who weigh more than 10 pounds (4,536 grams) at birth. (*Hint:* Start with a sketch that shades in the area of interest. Include a horizontal axis label and show at least 5 values on the horizontal scale. The sketch will help you confirm that your final calculated answer is reasonable.)

8. Describe two different ways that you could have used a normal probability table to answer the previous question. (*Hint:* One way uses a positive z-score and the other a negative z-score.)

9. Determine the proportion of newborn babies who weigh between 3,000 and 4,000 grams at birth. (*Hint:* Start with a sketch. Look at the sketch to decide what to do with the table values for the two relevant z-scores. Use technology to confirm your answer from the table.)

Inverting the question

What if the question was different and, instead of asking for a probability, asked for a value so that a certain probability is below that value? For example, in Figure 11.29, if you wanted to find the cutoff point for the lowest 25%, you can see that this corresponds to a z-score of -0.67. You would then take your score and convert it back to the units of interest using the same equation $\left(z = \frac{x - \mu}{\sigma} \right)$ that you've used before.

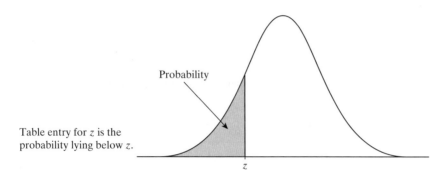

FIGURE 11.29 Snapshot from Table A of the AP Statistics formula sheet.

TABLE A	Standard normal probabilities									
z	.00	.01	.02	.03	.04	.05	.06	.07	.08	.09
−3.4	.0003	.0003	.0003	.0003	.0003	.0003	.0003	.0003	.0003	.0002
−3.3	.0005	.0005	.0005	.0004	.0004	.0004	.0004	.0004	.0004	.0003
....										
−0.9	.1841	.1814	.1788	.1762	.1736	.1711	.1685	.1660	.1635	.1611
−0.8	.2119	.2090	.2061	.2033	.2005	.1977	.1949	.1922	.1894	.1867
−0.7	.2420	.2389	.2358	.2327	.2296	.2266	.2236	.2206	.2177	.2148
−0.6	.2743	.2709	.2676	.2643	.2611	.2578	.2546	.2514	.2483	.2451
−0.5	.3085	.3050	.3015	.2981	.2946	.2912	.2877	.2843	.2810	.2776

10. How light would a baby have to weigh to be among the lightest 2.5% of all newborns? Draw a sketch to support your answer and explain how you must read a normal probability table differently to solve this question.

> **CALCULATOR TIPS**
>
> You may use your calculator to obtain a distribution value for a given area under the standard normal distribution. For example:
>
> - **TI-84:** STAT → Distr → invNorm(area, mean, std dev)
> - **TI-Nspire:** Statistics → Distributions → Inverse Normal(area, mean, std dev)
>
> *Note:* You can enter the mean and standard deviation on either the scale of the data or as a standardized value (z-score).

11. Use technology to confirm this calculation.

12. How much would a baby have to weigh to be among the heaviest 10% of all newborns?

Four runners from the *Run Girl Run!* running club plan to take part in an upcoming race that features both individual and team events. The team is planning to participate in a race in which each member of a four-person team runs a 5K race. Prizes are awarded for best individual time and to the team with the best overall time. The mean time and standard deviation, in minutes, for each of the runners in similar 5K races are given below. Running times for the individual runners are approximately normally distributed, and it is reasonable to assume that the individual times of the four runners are independent of each other.

	Mean (minutes)	Std Dev (minutes)
Jill	22.45	0.25
Karen	19.65	0.12
Ruth	20.47	0.17
Soma	22.58	0.28

1. Do you notice any relationship between a runner's mean time and standard deviation? For example, do faster runners tend to have more or less variability in their times than slower runners?

2. In last year's race, the individual award went to a runner who completed the race in 19.5 minutes. Is this time a realistic goal for any of the four runners on this team? Justify your answer. (*Hint*: Calculate z-scores.)

3. Determine the probability that Karen (the fastest runner on this team) will finish the race in 19.5 minutes or less.

4. The time for the team event is the sum of the individual times for the four runners. Determine the mean and standard deviation of the distribution of *team* times. (*Hint*: Recall rules about sums of random variables from earlier sections in this chapter.)

Earlier, when we learned about sums and differences of (independent) random variables, we focused on the mean and standard deviation, but not as much on the *distribution* of the sums (or differences). When the variables being combined are normal random variables, the result is another normal random variable.

KEY IDEA

If two random variables follow normal distributions, then the sum or difference of those random variables will also follow a normal distribution.

5. Given your answers above, draw a sketch of the distribution of team times. (Include the horizontal axis label and include at least 5 values on the scale.)

6. Last year the winning team time was 84.4 minutes. What is the probability that the *Run Girl Run!* Team will beat this time?

7. Who do you expect to finish the race first: Jill or Soma? Determine the probability that Jill finishes before Soma. (*Hint*: First determine the distribution of the difference between Jill's time and Soma's time.)

SECTION 11.7 Summary

In this section you focused on one particular type of continuous random variable that comes up quite often in statistics, the ***normal distribution***. Some useful definitions to remember and habits to develop from this topic include:

- A ***probability density function*** is a curve that describes the overall pattern or shape of a distribution of a continuous random variable.

- The shapes of density curves can vary, but all density curves have the property that they are on or above the horizontal axis with an area of 1 (100% of observations) below the curve.

- The area under a density curve within an interval of values along the horizontal axis gives the probability that a random variable X will be in that interval. The total area under the curve and above the horizontal axis over the entire range of values of the random variable X is equal to 1.
    - *Note:* Probabilities of individual outcomes for a continuous random variable must always be zero. So we are limited to finding probabilities for intervals of values.

- The ***empirical rule*** for a normal distribution, also referred to as the ***68-95-99.7% rule***, provides a quick estimate of the variability of data in a normal distribution with mean μ and standard deviation σ. For data that follow an approximately normal distribution, about 68% of the data will fall within one standard deviation of the mean, about 95% will fall within two standard deviations of the mean, and almost all (about 99.7%) will fall within three standard deviations of the mean.

- A normal distribution can be fully described by two parameters, its mean μ and standard deviation σ.

- If a random variable X has a normal distribution with mean μ and standard deviation σ, then the standardized variable $z = \frac{x - \mu}{\sigma}$ has the ***standard normal distribution*** with mean 0 and standard deviation 1.

- If we know the mean and standard deviation of a distribution that is approximately normally distributed, we can use the standard normal distribution to find the proportion of values in a particular interval in the distribution or the values that correspond to a given area under the normal density curve.

- The rules you learned in Section 11.5 involving linear transformations of a random variable (adding/subtracting and multiplying/dividing by a constant) and combining random variables also apply to normal distributions.

REVISITING THEORY-BASED APPROXIMATIONS OF SAMPLING DISTRIBUTIONS

SECTION 11.8

INTRODUCTION

Throughout this text, you have seen several "theory-based" models for sampling distributions. It turns out that most of these models can be derived using the same random variable rules you saw in Sections 11.5 and 11.7—rules like:

- If $Y = a + bX$, then $\mu_Y = a + b\,\mu_X$ and $\sigma_Y = |b|\sigma_X$.
- When combining random variables X and Y:
    - $\mu_{X+Y} = \mu_X + \mu_Y$ and $\mu_{X-Y} = \mu_X - \mu_Y$.
    - If X and Y are independent, then $\sigma^2_{X \pm Y} = \sigma^2_X + \sigma^2_Y$.
    - If X and Y are normally distributed, so will be any linear combination of X and Y.

One Proportion

In Section 1.6 you saw that a normal distribution can be used to model the observed proportion of successes. If you let X count the number of successes (e.g., how many times candy was chosen instead of a toy when given a choice in a sample of 283 kids), then you were really assuming that X was a binomial random variable with parameters n and π. More recently, you've learned that $\mu_X = n\pi$ and $\sigma_X = \sqrt{n\pi(1 - \pi)}$. As you saw earlier, when the number of expected successes $n\pi$ and failures $n(1 - \pi)$ are both at least 10, then X can be modeled with a normal distribution.

To obtain the formula for the mean and standard deviation of the sampling distribution of the sample proportion $\hat{p}$ (e.g., the proportion of kids in the sample who chose candy), you make use of the fact that $\hat{p} = $ count of successes/sample size $= X/n = (1/n)X$. Then

$$\mu_{\hat{p}} = (1/n)\mu_X = (1/n)n\pi = \pi \text{ and}$$

$$\sigma_{\hat{p}} = 1/n\sigma_X = 1/n\sqrt{n\pi(1 - \pi)} = \sqrt{\frac{n\pi(1 - \pi)}{n^2}} = \sqrt{\frac{\pi(1 - \pi)}{n}}$$

One Mean

In Section 2.2 we focused on the sample mean $\bar{x}$ rather than the sample proportion. But, because a sample mean is really just a linear transformation of independent random variables, we have

$$\mu_{\bar{X}} = E\left(\frac{X_1 + \cdots + X_n}{n}\right) = \frac{1}{n}(E(X_1) + \cdots + E(X_n)) = \frac{n\mu}{n} = \mu$$

$$\sigma_{\bar{X}} = \sqrt{V((X_1 + \cdots + X_n/n)} = \sqrt{1/n^2(V(X_1) + \cdots + V(X_n))} = \sqrt{n\sigma^2/n^2} = \sigma/\sqrt{n}$$

Furthermore, if each random variable has a normal distribution, then so will the sample mean. Due to the central limit theorem, you also know that the distribution of sample means will be approximately normal when the sample size is large.

Two Proportions

In Section 5.4 you examined a theory-based method for comparing two independent groups on a binary response. As you saw with a single proportion, a normal distribution provides a good approximation for the distribution of the statistic $\hat{p}_1 - \hat{p}_2$ if you have at least 10 responses of each kind (10 successes and 10 failures) in each group. Now, applying the rules of random variables, you can also show

$$\mu_{\hat{p}_1 - \hat{p}_2} = \pi_1 - \pi_2$$

$$\sigma^2_{\hat{p}_1 - \hat{p}_2} = \sigma^2_{\hat{p}_1} + \sigma^2_{\hat{p}_2} = \frac{\pi_1(1 - \pi_1)}{n_1} + \frac{\pi_2(1 - \pi_2)}{n_2}$$

$$\sigma_{\hat{p}_1 - \hat{p}_2} = \sqrt{\frac{\pi_1(1 - \pi_1)}{n_1} + \frac{\pi_2(1 - \pi_2)}{n_2}}$$

Two Means

In Section 6.3 you examined the sampling distribution of the difference in sample means. Again, applying the random variable rules yields means and standard deviations for this statistic:

$$\mu_{\bar{X}_1 - \bar{X}_2} = \mu_1 - \mu_2$$

$$\sigma^2_{\bar{X}_1 - \bar{X}_2} = \sigma^2_{\bar{X}_1} + \sigma^2_{\bar{X}_2} = \frac{\sigma_1^2}{n_1} + \frac{\sigma_2^2}{n_2}$$

$$\sigma_{\bar{X}_1 - \bar{X}_2} = \sqrt{\frac{\sigma_1^2}{n_1} + \frac{\sigma_2^2}{n_2}}$$

The distribution of the difference in sample means will be normal if both random variables follow a normal distribution or approximately normal if both sample sizes are large (e.g., above 20 or 30).

In this section, you will formally apply these approximations and compare the results to the simulated sampling distributions for the one sample case. *Note:* See the homework exercises for more practice, including the two sample cases.

Time to Leave the Nest Revisited

11.8A

EXAMPLE

Example 11.8A

In Example 11.6, you examined a study conducted by the U.S. Census Bureau on the percentage of 18–34-year-olds who reside in their parents' home. You saw the number who live at home in a random sample of 5 individuals can be modeled by a binomial distribution with $\pi = 0.341$ (probability living with parents) and $n = 5$.

> ### THINK ABOUT IT
>
> Suppose instead of a sample of size $n = 5$, we had surveyed 1,000 18–34-year-olds and wanted to know the probability that 375 (37.5%) or more reside in their parents' home?

The work to find binomial probabilities when the sample size is large becomes more tedious. To find the probability that the random variable $X =$ *number of 18–34-year-olds living with parents* is greater than or equal to 375, you (or a calculator) would need to find the probability that $X = 375$ or 376 or 377 or ... or 1,000 and then add all of these probabilities together. If the *normal approximation to the binomial* is used (see the introduction for details), you only need to find the z-score corresponding to $375/1{,}000 = 0.375$ for a distribution with mean $\mu = 0.341$ and standard deviation

$$= \sqrt{\frac{0.341(1 - 0.341)}{1{,}000}} \approx 0.015$$

Using the z-score formula gives

$$z = \frac{0.375 - 0.341}{\sqrt{\dfrac{0.341(1 - 0.341)}{1{,}000}}} \approx 2.27$$

p-value ≈ 0.0116

From Figure 11.30, you can conclude that the probability of obtaining 375 or more 18–34-year-olds who still live with their parents in our sample is about 0.0116.

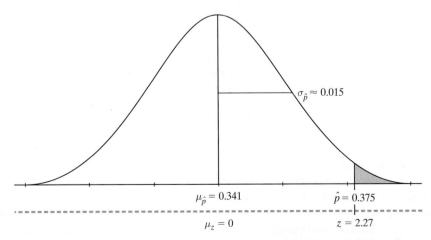

$\sigma_{\hat{p}} \approx 0.015$

$\mu_{\hat{p}} = 0.341$ $\hat{p} = 0.375$

$\mu_{z} = 0$ $z = 2.27$

FIGURE 11.30 Normal approximation to the binomial with $n = 1{,}000$ and probability of success $= 0.341$.

Using the **One Proportion** applet, you can see in Figure 11.31 that the exact binomial probability is 0.0131 (what we'd obtain if we added up all of the individual *X* values from the binomial distribution), simulated probability (also 0.0131), and normal approximation to the binomial (0.0117) are all very close in value, which we expect due to the large sample size (and sufficient number of repetitions in the simulation).

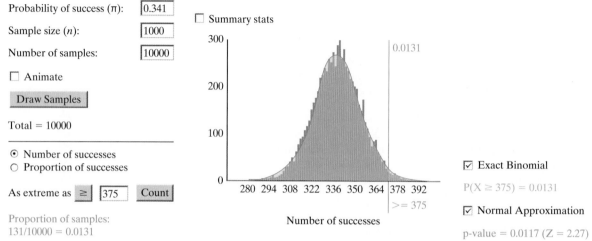

Probability of success (π): 0.341

Sample size (*n*): 1000

Number of samples: 10000

☐ Animate

Draw Samples

Total = 10000

⦿ Number of successes
○ Proportion of successes

As extreme as ≥ | 375 | Count

Proportion of samples:
131/10000 = 0.0131

☐ Summary stats

☑ Exact Binomial
P(X ≥ 375) = 0.0131

☑ Normal Approximation
p-value = 0.0117 (Z = 2.27)

FIGURE 11.31 One Proportion applet comparing simulated probabilities to those found using the normal aproximation and the exact binomial.

11.8.1

11.8B ──Intelligence Test

Example 11.8B

EXAMPLE

Results from the Wechsler Adult Intelligence Scale, a common IQ test, are approximately normally distributed with a mean of 100 and a standard deviation of 15. Suppose a class of 50 students had an average score above 104; would you be surprised?

> **THINK ABOUT IT**
>
> How would you go about calculating the probability of an average score of 104 or more? Do you need to make any assumptions?

The random variable of interest here is the sample mean IQ score. Because you are told that the population distribution is normally distributed, the sampling distribution of sample means will also be normally distributed (regardless of the sample size). The rules of random variables and central limit theorem tell you that the mean of the distribution of sample means will be 100 and the standard deviation will be $15/\sqrt{50} \approx 2.12$. Figure 11.32 shows the distribution of 1,000 sample means from the normal probability model with $\mu = 100$ and $\sigma = 15$, with this theory-based normal approximation overlaid.

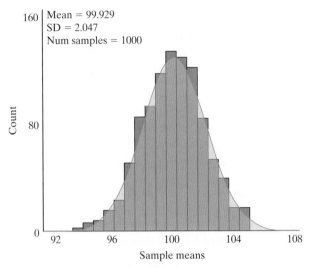

FIGURE 11.32   A sampling distribution of sample
means with a normal distribution approximation.

You can then determine the probability of finding a sample mean of 104 or more, in order to
answer the question originally posed. If you standardize, $z = (104 - 100)/2.12 = 1.89$. Using a
normal probability table or a graphing calculator, the area above $z = 1.89$ is 0.0297, which is quite
close to our simulated result of 0.0260 (with only 1,000 repetitions)—as shown in Figure 11.33.

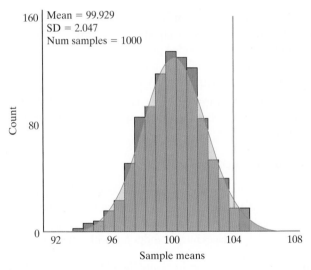

FIGURE 11.33   Estimating the probability of a sample
mean of 110 or larger.

So, it would be fairly unusual for a class of 50 students to average 104 or more *if they
were a randomly selected sample* from the population of takers of the Wechsler exam. By the
empirical rule, you would expect 95% of random samples of size 50 to have a sample mean
between 95.76 and 104.24.

EXPLORATION | Racquet Spinning
11.8A

When a tennis racquet is spun (see Exercise 1.1.1), is it equally likely to land with its label facing up as facing down? Or does the spinning process favor one outcome more than the other? A student investigated this question by spinning his tennis racquet 100 times. For each spin he recorded whether the racquet landed with the label up or down.

1. Let the random variable X be the number of "up" results that would result from spinning a tennis racquet 100 times, assuming that each spin is equally likely to land with the label up as down. Do the racquet spins follow the conditions for X to be a binomial random variable? Explain.

2. What is the expected value (mean) of X? Standard deviation?

   The student did the experiment 100 times and found that the label was facing up 46 times. If face up and face down are equally likely outcomes, the student is curious to find the probability of getting $P(X \leq 46)$. However, the student realizes this will be very tedious if he has to add all of the possible values of X less than or equal to 46.

3. Is it reasonable to think that the binomial random variable X can be well approximated by a normal distribution? Explain (see the introduction for details).

4. Use the normal approximation to the binomial distribution to approximate $P(X \leq 46)$.

5. This student may have been equally curious about $P(X \geq 54)$. [This is analogous to finding a two-sided p-value, where your alternative hypothesis just wants to know whether there is a difference but doesn't anticipate which label will be more common.] How does this value compare?

6. Use the **One Proportion** applet to simulate 10,000 repetitions of spinning a tennis racquet 100 times, assuming the outcomes are equally likely. Check the box for **Normal Approximation** and confirm that the two-sided probability matches what you obtained earlier.
   What is the estimated probability you obtain from simulation? Is this close to what you got from the normal approximation? Why?

7. Check the box for **Exact Binomial**. This is the exact probability of $P(X \leq 46) + P(X \geq 54)$ using the binomial distribution. How close is this to what you obtain using the normal approximation? Why?

Digging deeper: Beyond AP

This normal approximation to the binomial distribution is generally considered to be valid as long as $n\pi \geq 10$ and $n(1 - \pi) \geq 10$. Because this uses a continuous probability distribution (normal) to approximate a discrete one (binomial), the approximation can be improved by using what's called a ***continuity correction***, which replaces integer endpoints with endpoints ending in 0.5.

8. Use technology to determine $P(Y \leq 46.5)$ and then $P(Y \geq 53.5)$. Next sum these probabilities. Is the sum closer to the exact binomial p-value than the normal approximation you used earlier?

9. Now suppose that the racquet was spun 1,000 times rather than 100, and that it resulted in 460 spins landing up and 540 spins landing down. Use the normal approximation to the binomial distribution to approximate the probability of obtaining such an extreme result (in either direction) if the actual probability of landing up was 0.5. Be sure to draw a sketch of the normal distribution and indicate its mean and standard deviation.

EXPLORATION | Random Ice Cream Prices (continued)
11.8B

Recall from Example 11.1 that an ice cream shop owner is running a special promotion in which the price of a small ice cream cone is determined by rolling a pair of fair, six-sided dice. The price (in cents) is the larger number followed by the smaller number. Clearly, the owner would not be able to predict the price for an individual customer very accurately. But could the owner predict the average price across a larger number of customers fairly accurately?

Let the random variable X represent this price. We determined that the probability distribution of X is as shown in Figure 11.34.

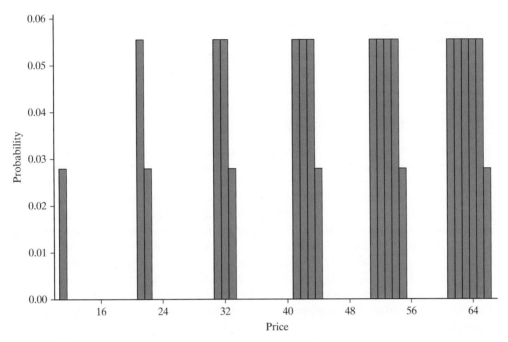

FIGURE 11.34 Graph of probability distribution of X, the price of an ice cream cone as determined by rolling two fair six-sided dice, where the price in cents is the larger number followed by the smaller.

Using the probability distribution, you can also determine that the expected price for each customer is $\mu = E(X) = 47.25$ cents, and the standard deviation is $\sigma = SD(X) \approx 14.7655$ cents.

Suppose that the owner is interested in the *average* price paid for a sample of 100 customers. (Let's denote this average price by $\bar{x}$.)

1. What is the average value of the sampling distribution of $\bar{x}$? What is the standard deviation?

2. What shape will the sampling distribution of $\bar{x}$ follow? Why? Does the shape in Figure 11.34 have an impact on the shape of the sampling distribution $\bar{x}$ in this example? (*Hint*: See the introduction, which talks about these ideas.)

3. Make a guess for the probability that the average price among 100 customers would be less than 45 cents.

4. Calculate the z-score for an average price of 45 cents. Make sure that your answer looks reasonable based on the sketch.

5. Use a table of normal probabilities or a graphing calculator to determine the probability that the average price for a sample of 100 customers would be less than 45 cents.

6. What is the probability that the *total* amount paid among 100 customers would be less than 45 *dollars*? Identify any probability rules that you are using.

7. Between what two values can the owner expect the *average* price to fall, with a probability of approximately 0.95?

8. Between what two values can the owner expect the *total* price to fall, with a probability of approximately 0.95?

9. If business is booming to the point that the owner gets 250 customers rather than 100, how will this change affect the sampling distribution of the sample mean price, $\bar{x}$? Justify your answer, without yet performing any calculations.

10. With 250 customers rather than 100, how would you expect the probability that the average price is less than 45 cents to change, if at all? Again justify your answer, without yet performing any calculations.

11. Now perform the calculations to determine the probability precisely. Be sure to include a well-labeled sketch.

12. Did this probability change as you had expected? Explain.

SECTION 11.8 Summary

There is a theoretical foundation to many of the approximations you have used in this text. The means and standard deviations of linear transformations of random variables (e.g., $\hat{p} = X/n$) and for combinations of random variables (e.g., $\bar{x}$) can be derived using the rules of random variables in Section 11.5. With categorical data, you can use a normal approximation to the binomial distribution to decide whether the shape of the distribution of sample proportions will be approximately normal. With quantitative data, you can use the result that the sum and difference of random variables that are normally distributed will also be normally distributed. This also gives us a guideline for when the difference in sample proportions will follow a normal distribution. The advantage of being able to apply the normal distribution is that you can use all the properties of the normal distribution, such as the empirical rule. Keep in mind that to predict the shape of the distribution, you need some validity conditions to be met:

- One proportion: at least 10 successes and at least 10 failures in the sample
- One mean: normally distributed population or large sample size
- Two proportions: at least 10 successes and at least 10 failures in each sample
- Two means: normally distributed populations or both sample sizes large

If you aren't sure whether your prediction of shape will be appropriate, you can usually run a simulation to assess the long-run behavior of the sampling distribution as well!

CHAPTER 11 Summary

In this chapter you learned how to calculate probabilities involving random processes of various types. You started by writing out a sample space, defining events, and calculating the probabilities of these events occurring. You then moved on to learn about rules that aid in probability calculations, namely the complement rule and the addition rule. You saw that probability tables and Venn diagrams can be useful for organizing and calculating probabilities.

In Section 11.3 you were introduced to the term independent. Two events are independent when knowing that one event has occurred does not change the probability of the other event occurring. Knowing that events are independent is required for most of the other probability concepts and calculations in subsequent sections of this chapter and for those that you studied earlier in this text. Properties of independent events were contrasted to properties of mutually exclusive events. Recall if two events (with nonzero probabilities) are mutually exclusive, then they cannot be independent.

In Sections 11.4–11.6 you were introduced to random variables and how to calculate their expected values and variances. You also explored linear transformations as well as properties of specific types of random variables, namely binomial and geometric. The binomial distribution is what you were modelling way back in Chapter 1 when you flipped coins to find out if it was unlikely Buzz would choose the correct button 15 out of 16 times.

We ended the chapter by looking at continuous probability distributions in Sections 11.7 and 11.8. In these sections you took another look at normal distributions and focused on some of their uses besides that of sampling distributions. However, many of the concepts you explored should have looked very similar to what you saw in earlier chapters when using normal distributions to find p-values.

CHAPTER 11
GLOSSARY

binomial distribution   A distribution used to model the counts of successes of a binomial variable X (with two outcomes: success or failure) for a fixed number of attempts, n, of a random process in which individual outcomes are independent with the same probability of success π on each trial.

complement of an event A   The event that A does not occur.

continuous random variable   A random variable that can take on all possible values on an interval.

event   A collection of outcomes from the sample space.

expected value of a random variable   The long-term average value that would be achieved by the random variable if the random process were repeated a very large number of times.

geometric distribution   A distribution used to model the number of trials (where there are two possible outcomes on each trial: success or failure) needed to obtain the first success, such that trials are independent of each other, with the same probability of success π on each trial.

independent events   When knowing that one event has occurred does not change the probability of the other event occurring.

intersection of two events   The set of outcomes that are in both events.

linear transformation   Adding (or subtracting) a constant and/or multiplying (or dividing) a random variable by a constant.

mutually exclusive (disjoint)   When it is impossible for two events to occur simultaneously.

probability density function   A curve that describes the overall pattern or shape of a distribution of a continuous random variable.

probability histogram   A graphical display that is often used to describe the distribution of a discrete random variable. The horizontal axis gives the values that the random variable takes, and the vertical axis corresponds to their corresponding probabilities.

probability table   A table that contains probabilities, rather than counts, for all outcomes in the sample space.

random variable   A variable in which a number is assigned to each outcome in a sample space.

sample space   A list of all possible outcomes of a random process.

standard normal distribution   A normal distribution with mean 0 and standard deviation 1.

tree diagram   A figure that organizes conditional probabilities with a node representing an event and branches from the node representing the possible outcomes associated with the event. Typically, conditional probabilities are written on the branches of the tree.

union of two events   The set of outcomes that are one event, the other, or both.

variance of a random variable   A measure of how variable (spread out) the results of the random variable are expected to be if the random process were repeated a very large number of times.

CHAPTER 11
EXERCISES

SECTION 11.1

11.1.1*   Suppose you are flipping two fair coins and you are interested in the probability of getting at least one head. Which of the following is the sample space for this experiment?

A. 3/4

B. $P(H \geq 1)$

C. HH, HT, TH, TT

D. HH, HT, TH

E. None of the above

11.1.2 We can use simulations to:

A. Get exact theoretical probabilities.

B. Approximate probabilities fairly precisely.

C. Get a very rough idea as to the value of a probability, but not at all precise.

D. Help us understand a situation, but not estimate probabilities.

E. Estimate things like p-values, but not estimate probabilities.

11.1.3* The probability of an event is:

A. The number of outcomes in the sample space divided by the number of outcomes in the event only if the outcomes in the event are equally likely.

B. The number of outcomes in the sample space divided by the number of outcomes in the event whether or not the outcomes in the event are equally likely.

C. The number of outcomes in the event divided by the number of outcomes in the sample space only if the outcomes in the sample space are equally likely.

D. The number of outcomes in the event divided by the number of outcomes in the sample space whether or not the outcomes in the sample space are equally likely.

E. The number of outcomes in the sample space only if the outcomes are equally likely.

11.1.4 Suppose you want to simulate the probability that a family of six children will have at least two boys. You assume the probability of having a boy or a girl is the same. (Both are 1/2.) To start the simulation, you could:

A. Flip six coins, letting heads represent a boy and tails represent a girl.

B. Create 10 cards, 5 of which have *boy* written on them and 5 have *girl* written on them. You then choose 6 of these 10 cards without replacement.

C. Roll six dice and let the numbers 1, 2, 3 represent a boy and 4, 5, 6 represent a girl.

D. Only A and B are appropriate

E. Only A and C are appropriate

F. Only B and C are appropriate

G. All three, A, B, and C, are appropriate

11.1.5* An event is:

A. A collection of outcomes in a sample space.

B. Another word for sample space.

C. The probability something will occur.

D. The number of outcomes.

E. How many times an outcome occurs.

11.1.6 Answer the following yes/no questions about simulation analyses.

a. Is it possible to conduct a simulation analysis by hand, without using a computer?

b. Are computers generally able to conduct simulation analyses more quickly and efficiently than non-computer simulations?

c. Do simulation analyses produce exact, rather than approximate, probabilities?

d. If two people conduct simulation analyses of the same random process, will they always obtain the same value for the approximate probability?

e. Does using more repetitions in a simulation analysis generally produce more accurate approximations for the exact probability than using fewer repetitions?

f. Does using more repetitions in a simulation analysis generally take longer than using fewer repetitions?

11.1.7* Suppose that three business executives drop their cell phones in an elevator and then pick them up at random. Describe how you could use index cards to conduct a simulation analysis to approximate the probability that none of them would pick up the correct phone. Include enough detail that someone else, with no knowledge of probability or statistics, could follow your directions to complete the simulation analysis and report the approximate probability.

11.1.8 Suppose that three business executives (call them Abby, Bernice, and Caitlin) drop their cell phones in an elevator and then pick them up at random.

a. Write out the sample space of all possible outcomes. (For example, let ACB mean that Abby gets her own phone, but Bernice and Caitlin's phones are swapped.)

b. List the outcomes that comprise the event that nobody gets the correct phone.

c. Report the probability that nobody gets the correct phone.

d. Write a sentence interpreting what this probability means.

11.1.9 Reconsider the previous question about three business executives dropping their cell phones in an elevator and then picking them up at random.

a. Report the probability that exactly one person picks up the correct phone.

b. Report the probability that exactly two people pick up the correct phone.

c. Report the probability that all three people pick up the correct phone.

d. Report the probability that at least one person picks up the correct phone.

11.1.10* Use the **Random Babies** applet to investigate what happens as the number of babies (and mothers) increases. Start with only 2 babies, and then proceed to 4, 6, and 8 babies. For each number, simulate 1,000 repetitions of returning the babies to their mothers at random. Report the approximate probability that *all* babies are returned to the right mother. Comment on how this probability changes as the number of mothers increases.

11.1.11* Repeat the previous question for the approximate probability that *at least one* baby is returned to the right mother.

11.1.12* Repeat the previous question for the *average* number of babies that are returned to the right mother.

11.1.13 Random ice cream prices: As in Example 11.1, consider rolling many (fair six-sided) dice, where price is still determined as the largest number followed by the smallest number (in cents). Answer the following without performing either a simulation or exact analysis.

a. How would you expect the probability that the price is 50 cents or less to change as the number of dice continues to increase? Explain your reasoning.

b. How would you expect the average price to change as the number of dice continues to increase? Explain your reasoning.

c. If you were allowed to choose the number of dice to be rolled, how many would you choose? Explain your answer.

11.1.14* Consecutive numbers:

a. Determine the (exact, theoretical) probability that rolling a pair of fair six-sided dice results in consecutive numbers, such as (1, 2) or (5, 4).

b. Suppose that the numbers 1–6 are written on six cards (one number per card), and you pick two cards at random. (Notice that, unlike with dice, it's impossible to get repeated numbers.) Write out the sample space of possible pairs of numbers that could be picked. Then determine the (exact, theoretical) probability of obtaining consecutive numbers.

c. With which scenario (dice or cards) is the probability of obtaining consecutive numbers higher? Explain why this makes sense.

11.1.15 Suppose that a family has three children, and each child is equally likely to be a boy or a girl.

a. Write out the sample space of 8 possible outcomes. (For example, use the notation $B_1G_2B_3$ to mean that the first child is a boy, second is a girl, and third is a boy.)

b. Which outcomes comprise the event that boys outnumber girls in the family?

c. Determine the probability that all three children are of the same sex.

11.1.16* Suppose that a family has four children, and each child is equally likely to be a boy or a girl.

a. Write out the sample space of 16 possible outcomes. (For example, use the notation $B_1G_2G_3B_4$ to mean that the first child is a boy, the next two are girls, and the last is a boy.)

b. Which outcomes comprise the event that boys (strictly) outnumber girls in the family?

c. Determine the probability that all four children are of the same sex.

d. Which is more likely: the family has 2 children of each sex or 3 of one sex and 1 of the other sex? Justify your answer with appropriate probability calculations.

11.1.17 A teacher was on a committee consisting of four male and two female teachers. Two members of the committee were chosen to do some extra work, and it turned out that both females were chosen. The teacher wondered how likely this result would have been if the selection (of two people to do the extra work) had been made at random (from among the six committee members).

a. Describe how you could use index cards to conduct a simulation analysis to approximate the probability that the teacher is interested in.

b. Would it work to simulate this random process by rolling a pair of six-sided dice and using the numbers rolled to represent the people selected? Explain why or why not.

11.1.18 Reconsider the previous question. Let's call the male members of the committee Abe, Bob, Carlos, and Dante. Let's call the female members Ellen and Fiona.

a. List the sample space of all possible pairs of people who could have been chosen. (Just use initials to represent the people. Notice that the order in which the two people are selected does not matter.)

b. Determine the probability that both women would be selected, if the selection had been made at random.

c. Write a sentence interpreting what this probability means, as if to someone who has never studied probability or statistics.

d. Report the probability that at least one woman would be selected, if the selection had been made at random.

11.1.19* Unfinished game: Suppose that Heather and Tom play a game that involves a series of coin flips. They agree that if 5 heads occur before 5 tails do, then Heather wins the game. But if 5 tails occur before 5 heads do, then Tom wins the game. The first five coin tosses result in: H_1, T_2, T_3, H_4, H_5. Unfortunately, the game is interrupted at that point and cannot be finished.

a. List the sample space of all possible outcomes for finishing the game, starting with the 6th flip, using notation similar to that of the coin-toss results above. (*Hint*: There are 10 outcomes.)

b. Identify which outcomes comprise the event that Heather wins, and which comprise the event that Tom wins.

c. Do you think it's reasonable to consider these 10 outcomes to be equally likely? Explain why or why not.

11.1.20* Reconsider the previous question.

a. Describe how you could use a simulation analysis to approximate the probability that Heather would win the game if it were finished.

b. Use the following results from simulating 1,000,000 repetitions of this process/game to approximate the probability that Heather would win the game if it were finished:

Winner	Heather	Tom
Number of repetitions	687,163	312,837

c. Use the following results from simulating 1,000,000 repetitions of this process/game to approximate the probability that the game would not end after two additional tosses:

Number of additional flips needed	2	3	4
Number of repetitions	249,373	374,341	376,286

11.1.21 Reconsider the previous two questions.

a. Suppose that the rules were changed so that the winner is the first to reach 10 heads or tails, rather than 5. (Continue to assume that the game is interrupted after 3 heads and 2 tails.) How would you expect this rule change to affect the probability that Heather will win the game: larger, smaller, or no change? Explain your reasoning.

b. Suppose that the rules were changed so that the winner is the first to reach 100 heads or tails, rather than 5 or 10. (Continue to assume that the game is interrupted after 3 heads and 2 tails.) Make an educated guess for the probability that Heather would win the game. Explain your reasoning.

SECTION 11.2

11.2.1* If two events, A and B, are mutually exclusive, then which of the following <u>must</u> be true? (There may be more than one correct answer.)

A. Events A and B will never occur at the same time.

B. $P(A \text{ or } B) = 1$.

C. $P(A^c) = 0$ and $P(B^c) = 0$.

D. $P(A \text{ and } B) = 0$.

E. Events A and B are complements of each other.

11.2.2 The intersection of events A and B is when:

A. $P(A \text{ and } B) = 1$.

B. $P(A \text{ and } B) = 0$.

C. Either A or B occurs.

D. Both A and B occur at the same time.

E. Either A or B occurs, but not both.

11.2.3* The complement of event A is when:

A. $P(A) = 0$.

B. $P(A) = 1$.

C. A does not occur.

D. A occurs.

E. A is very polite.

11.2.4 When does $P(A \text{ or } B) = P(A) + P(B)$?

A. Always.

B. Never.

C. When events A and B occur at the same time.

D. When events A and B are complements of each other.

E. When events A and B are mutually exclusive.

11.2.5* Which of the following Venn diagrams correctly represents the situation in which $P(A) = 0.20$, $P(B) = 0.30$, and $P(A \text{ and } B) = 0.10$?

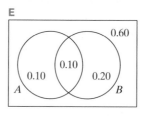

11.2.6 Which of the following Venn diagrams correctly represents the situation where $P(A) = 0.30$, $P(B) = 0.40$, and $P(A \text{ or } B) = 0.60$?

C

D

E
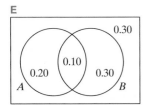

		Facebook		
		Yes	No	Total
Twitter	Yes	0.20	0.01	0.21
	No	0.48	0.31	0.79
	Total	0.68	0.32	1.00

a. What is the probability a randomly chosen American adult uses Facebook?

b. What is the probability a randomly chosen American adult uses Twitter?

c. What is the probability a randomly chosen American adult uses Facebook and Twitter?

d. What is the probability a randomly chosen American adult uses Facebook or Twitter?

11.2.7* Given that $P(A) = 0.4$, $P(B) = 0.5$, and $P(A \text{ and } B) = 0.2$, answer the following.

a. What is $P(A^c)$?

b. What is $P(B^c)$?

c. What is $P(A \text{ or } B)$?

d. Are events A and B mutually exclusive? Explain.

e. Draw a Venn diagram for events A and B and include the probabilities for each area.

11.2.8 Given that $P(A) = 0.7$, $P(B) = 0.2$, and $P(A \text{ and } B) = 0$, answer the following.

a. What is $P(A^c)$?

b. What is $P(B^c)$?

c. What is $P(A \text{ or } B)$?

d. Are events A and B mutually exclusive? Explain.

e. Draw a Venn diagram for events A and B and include the probabilities for each area.

11.2.9* Suppose you toss three fair coins.

a. What is the sample space? (*Hint*: TTH (or tails-tails-heads) is one of the outcomes in the sample space and there are a total of 8 outcomes.)

b. All 8 events you listed in part (a) are equally likely to occur if you are flipping fair coins.

   (i) What is the probability of tossing all heads in your three flips?

   (ii) What is the probability of tossing exactly one head in your three flips?

   (iii) What is the probability of tossing at least one head in your three flips?

   (iv) What is the probability of tossing no heads in your three flips?

11.2.10 As estimated by the Pew Research Center in 2016, the probabilities associated with a randomly chosen American adult using Facebook and Twitter are shown in the following two-way table.

11.2.11* As estimated by the Pew Research Center in 2016, the probabilities associated with a randomly chosen American adult using Facebook and Instagram are shown in the following two-way table.

		Facebook		
		Yes	No	Total
Instagram	Yes	0.27	0.01	0.28
	No	0.41	0.31	0.72
	Total	0.68	0.32	1.00

a. Use the numbers in the table to construct a Venn diagram for these probabilities.

b. What is the probability a randomly chosen American adult uses Instagram?

c. What is the probability a randomly chosen American adult uses Facebook and Instagram?

d. What is the probability a randomly chosen American adult uses Facebook or Instagram?

e. What is the probability a randomly chosen American adult uses neither Facebook nor Instagram?

11.2.12* In the previous question, are the events that a randomly chosen person uses Facebook and a randomly chosen person uses Instagram mutually exclusive? What would have to be true about Facebook and Instagram users for these two events to be mutually exclusive?

11.2.13 As estimated by the Pew Research in 2016, the probability a randomly chosen American adult uses Instagram is 0.28, the probability a randomly chosen American adult uses Twitter is 0.21, and the probability a randomly chosen American adult uses Instagram and Twitter is 0.14.

a. Using the Pew Research estimates, complete the following two-way table of probabilities.

		Twitter		
		Yes	No	Total
Instagram	Yes			
	No			
	Total			

b. What is the probability a randomly chosen American adult uses Twitter but not Instagram?

c. What is the probability a randomly chosen American adult uses Instagram but not Twitter?

d. What is the probability a randomly chosen American adult uses either Twitter or Instagram?

11.2.14 In the previous question, are the events that a randomly chosen person uses Twitter and a randomly chosen person uses Instagram complements of each other? What would have to be true about Twitter and Instagram users for these two events to be complements of each other?

11.2.15* Human blood types can be separated into four categories: A, B, AB, and O. The following partial distribution gives the approximate proportion in which these types occur in the U.S. population.

Blood Type	A	B	AB	O
Proportion	0.42	0.10	0.04	?

a. What proportion of the population has blood type O?

b. What is the probability that a randomly chosen person from the U.S. population has blood type A or O?

c. If A is the event that a randomly chosen person from the U.S. population has blood type A, what is $P(A^C)$?

11.2.16 In 2008 a college was shut down because of high rates of norovirus in the student population. The following table gives the numbers of male and female students who did and did not contract the virus at that time. We will let F and M represent the event that a randomly chosen student is female and male, respectively, and Y and N represent the event that a randomly chosen student contracted the norovirus or not, respectively.

		Female	Male	Total
Contracted Norovirus	Yes	212	124	336
	No	1,049	479	1,528
	Total	1,261	603	1,864

a. What is the value of $P(Y)$ and what does it mean in the context of this situation?

b. What is the value of $P(F)$ and what does it mean in the context of this situation?

c. What is the value of $P(F^c)$ and what does it mean in the context of this situation?

d. What is the value of $P(Y$ and $F)$ and what does it mean in the context of this situation?

e. What is the value of $P(Y$ or $F)$ and what does it mean in the context of this situation?

11.2.17 Use data from the table in the previous question about the norovirus to answer the following.

a. What is the value of $P((Y$ or $F)^c)$ and what does it mean in the context of this situation?

b. What is the value of $P(Y^c$ and $F^c)$ and what does it mean in the context of this situation?

11.2.18* The following two-way table categorizes the class standing at Hope College for males and females in the fall of 2016. Let S represent the event a student chosen is a sophomore and let F represent the event the student chosen is a female. Suppose a student is chosen at random from all Hope College students. Find the following probabilities.

CLASS	Male	Female	Total
Freshmen	297	440	737
Sophomore	332	457	789
Junior	264	445	709
Senior	325	545	870
Non-Degree	49	68	117
Total	1,267	1,955	3,222

a. $P(F)$

b. $P(S)$

c. $P(S \cap F)$

d. $P(S \cup F)$

e. Find $P(S^c \cap F^c)$ and describe what this probability is measuring (not what it does not measure).

f. Find $P(S \cup F^c)$ and describe what this probability is measuring (not what it does not measure).

11.2.19* Use the table in the previous question on the distribution of students to answer the following.

a. What proportion of all students are male?

b. What proportion of all students are both male and juniors?

c. What proportion of all students are male or juniors?

d. What proportion of just the male students are juniors?

e. What proportion of just the juniors are male?

11.2.20 To answer the following questions, we assume the probability that a family has a boy or a girl is the same (0.50) and that a family will have three children.

a. Write out the sample space by listing all 8 events.

b. What is the probability that the oldest two are girls and the youngest is a boy?

c. What is the probability that there are two girls and one boy in any order?

SECTION 11.3

11.3.1* In rolling a fair six-sided die twice, the event of getting a 2 on the first roll and the event of getting a 4 on the second roll are:

A. Independent.

B. Disjoint.

C. Neither independent nor disjoint.

D. Both independent and disjoint.

E. None of the above.

11.3.2 In rolling a fair six-sided die once, the event of getting a 2 and the first roll and the sum of 4 for both rolls are:

A. Independent.

B. Disjoint.

C. Neither independent nor disjoint.

D. Both independent and disjoint.

E. None of the above.

11.3.3* In rolling a fair six-sided die twice, the event of getting a 2 on the first roll and a sum of 12 for both the dice are:

A. Independent.

B. Disjoint.

C. Neither independent nor disjoint.

D. Both independent and disjoint.

E. None of the above.

11.3.4 For two events A and B, $P(A) = 0.80$, $P(B) = 0.20$, and $P(A \text{ and } B) = 0.16$. It follows that A and B are:

A. Independent but not disjoint.

B. Both disjoint and independent.

C. Neither disjoint nor independent.

D. Disjoint but not independent.

E. None of the above.

11.3.5* If two events, A and B, are independent, then which of the following must be true? (There may be more than one correct answer.)

A. Events A and B will never occur at the same time.

B. $P(A|B) = P(A)$

C. $P(A|B) = P(B)$

D. $P(B|A) = P(B)$

E. $P(B|A) = P(A)$

F. $P(A \text{ and } B) = 0$

G. $P(A \text{ and } B) = P(A) \times P(B)$

11.3.6 Suppose events A and B are independent, $P(A) \neq 0$ and $P(B) \neq 0$. Can events A and B also be mutually exclusive? Explain.

11.3.7* Given that $P(A) = 0.40$, $P(B) = 0.50$, and $P(A \text{ and } B) = 0.20$, answer the following.

a. What is $P(A|B)$?

b. What is $P(B|A)$?

c. What is $P(A \text{ or } B)$?

d. Are events A and B independent? Explain.

e. Draw a Venn diagram for events A and B and include the probabilities for each area.

11.3.8 Given that $P(A) = 0.80$, $P(B) = 0.50$, and $P(A \text{ and } B) = 0.40$, answer the following.

a. What is $P(A|B)$?

b. What is $P(B|A)$?

c. What is $P(A \text{ or } B)$?

d. Are events A and B independent? Explain.

e. Draw a Venn diagram for events A and B and include the probabilities for each area.

11.3.9* Suppose you toss 3 fair coins.

a. What is the sample space? (*Hint*: TTH (or tails-tails-heads) is one of the events in the sample space and there are a total of 8 events.)

b. All 8 events you listed in part (a) are equally likely to occur if you are flipping fair coins.

   (i) What is the probability of tossing at least one tail?

   (ii) What is the probability of tossing at least one tail given the first toss is heads?

   (iii) What is the probability the first toss is heads given you have at least one tail?

11.3.10* Suppose you toss 3 fair coins as described in Exercise 11.3.9. (If you haven't written out the sample space as described in Exercise 11.3.9, you should do that before answering the following.)

a. What is the probability of tossing all heads given at least one is heads?

b. What is the probability of tossing all heads given the first toss is a head?

c. What is the probability of tossing all heads given at least two are heads?

d. What is the probability of tossing all heads given the first two tosses are heads?

11.3.11 Assuming the probability that a family has a boy or a girl is the same (0.50), if a family has three children, what is the probability that:

a. The oldest two are girls and the youngest is a boy.

b. There are two girls and one boy in any order.

11.3.12* As estimated by the Pew Research Center in 2016, the probabilities associated with a randomly chosen American adult using Facebook and Twitter are shown in the following two-way table.

		Facebook		
		Yes	No	Total
Twitter	Yes	0.20	0.01	0.21
	No	0.48	0.31	0.79
	Total	0.68	0.32	1.00

a. What is the probability a randomly chosen American adult uses Facebook given he or she uses Twitter?

b. What is the probability a randomly chosen American adult uses Twitter given he or she uses Facebook?

11.3.13 As estimated by the Pew Research Center in 2016, the probabilities associated with a randomly chosen American adult using Facebook and Instagram are shown in the following two-way table.

		Facebook		
		Yes	No	Total
Instagram	Yes	0.27	0.01	0.28
	No	0.41	0.31	0.72
	Total	0.68	0.32	1.00

a. Use the numbers in the table to construct a Venn diagram for these probabilities.

b. What is the probability a randomly chosen American adult uses Facebook given he or she uses Instagram?

c. What is the probability a randomly chosen American adult uses Instagram given he or she uses Facebook?

d. What is the probability a randomly chosen American adult uses Facebook or Instagram?

11.3.14* As estimated by the Pew Research Center in 2016, the probability a randomly chosen American adult uses Instagram is 0.28, the probability a randomly chosen American adult uses Twitter is 0.21, and the probability a randomly chosen American adult uses Instagram given that he or she uses Twitter is 0.65.

a. Using the Pew Research estimates, complete the following two-way table of probabilities.

		Twitter		
		Yes	No	Total
Instagram	Yes			
	No			
	Total			

b. What is the probability a randomly chosen American adult uses Twitter given he or she uses Instagram?

c. What is the probability a randomly chosen American adult uses both Twitter and Instagram?

d. What is the probability a randomly chosen American adult uses neither Twitter nor Instagram?

11.3.15* In the previous exercise, are the events "a randomly chosen person uses Twitter" and "a randomly chosen person uses Instagram" independent? What would have to be true about Twitter and Instagram users for these two events to be independent?

11.3.16 In 2008 a college was shut down because of high rates of norovirus in the student population. The following table gives the numbers of male and female students who did and did not contract the virus at that time. We will let F and M represent the event that a randomly chosen student is female and male, respectively, and Y and N represent the event that a randomly chosen student contracted the norovirus or not, respectively.

		Female	Male	Total
Contracted Norovirus	Yes	212	124	336
	No	1,049	479	1,528
	Total	1,261	603	1,864

a. What is the value of $P(Y)$ and what does it mean in the context of this situation?

b. What is the value of $P(Y|F)$ and what does it mean in the context of this situation?

c. Are the events Y and F independent? Explain.

d. Did males and females contract the norovirus at the same rates?

e. If males and females contracted the norovirus at the same rates, would that mean the events Y and F have to be independent? Explain.

11.3.17 The following two-way table categorizes the class standing at Hope College for males and females in the fall of 2016. Let *So* represent the event a student chosen is a sophomore and let F represent the event the student chosen is a female. Suppose a student is chosen at random from all Hope students. Find the following probabilities.

CLASS	Male	Female	Total
Freshmen	297	440	737
Sophomore	332	457	789
Junior	264	445	709
Senior	325	545	870
Non-Degree	49	68	117
Total	1,267	1,955	3,222

a. $P(So)$

b. $P(F)$

c. $P(So|F)$

d. $P(F|So)$

e. Are the events So and F independent? Why or why not?

11.3.18* In a certain college statistics class, 61% of the students are female and 39% are male. Of the females, 40% are regular coffee drinkers. Of the males, 30% are regular coffee drinkers.

a. What percentage of all students are female and regular coffee drinkers?

b. What percentage of all students are male and regular coffee drinkers?

c. What percentage of all students are regular coffee drinkers?

11.3.19 It is estimated that 42% of all Americans have type A blood. Suppose two Americans are randomly selected (so the probability of one having type A blood is independent of the other). Find the probability of the following.

a. Both have type A blood.

b. Neither has type A blood.

c. Exactly one person has type A blood.

11.3.20* In the previous exercise we saw that 42% of all Americans have type A blood. Assume five Americans are chosen at random.

a. What is the probability that all of them have type A blood?

b. What is the probability that none of them has type A blood?

c. What is the probability that at least one of them has type A blood?

11.3.21 A string of cheap Christmas lights contains 10 lights. Each individual light has a 0.10 probability of failing during the Christmas season. Assume the lights fail independently of each other.

a. What is the probability that all the lights on the string fail during the Christmas season?

b. What is the probability that none of the lights on the string fail during the Christmas season?

c. What is the probability that at least one of the lights fails during the Christmas season?

11.3.22* According to the Kaiser Family Foundation, the proportions of the U.S. population who have various types of health insurance in 2015 are as shown in the table below.

a. Find the proportion of people who had health insurance.

b. What proportion of those who had health insurance had some type of public insurance?

Type of Insurance	Proportion
Private insurance	0.56
Public insurance Medicare/Medicaid/Other	0.35
No health insurance	0.09

11.3.23 According to a study done in the United Kingdom, a male's probability of death from lung cancer during his lifetime is 0.077. For someone that is a heavy smoker (at least 25 cigarettes a day), that probability goes up to 0.244. (For someone who has never smoked, that probability goes down to 0.002.) We will let C represent the event a male dies of cancer and S represent the event that a person is a heavy smoker.

a. Using probability notation, define the two probabilities (0.077 and 0.244) given above.

b. Are smoking and dying of lung cancer independent? Explain why or why not, based on the probabilities given.

11.3.24* Are metal bands used for tagging harmful to penguins? In *Nature*, researchers Saraux et al. reported the results of an investigation done to answer this question using a sample of 100 penguins near Antarctica. These penguins had already been tagged with RFID chips, and the researchers randomly assigned 50 of them to receive a metal band on their flippers in addition to the RFID chip. The other 50 penguins did not receive a metal band. The researchers then recorded which penguins were still living 4.5 years into the study. They found results similar to those shown in the table below.

	Banded	Unbanded	Total
Survived			48
Died			52
Total	50	50	100

a. Back in Chapter 6 we said that two variables were not associated when the two conditional proportions were the same. In this case, it means the proportion of banded penguins that survived needs to be the same as the proportion of unbanded penguins that survived. Fill in the table above under the assumption that there is no association between being banding and surviving.

b. Saying there is no association between banding and penguin survival is the same thing as saying banding and survival are independent. Explain why this is true.

SECTION 11.4

11.4.1 Which of the following is a valid probability distribution?

A

x	1	2	3
$P(x)$	0.30	0.20	0.30

B

x	1	2	3
P(x)	0.30	0.30	0.30

C

x	1	2	3
P(x)	0.30	0.40	0.30

D

x	1	2	3
P(x)	0.30	0.80	−0.10

E

x	1	2	3
P(x)	0.30	0.40	0.50

11.4.2* In the following probability distribution, what is $P(X > 2)$?

x	1	2	3	4
P(x)	0.40	0.10	0.30	0.20

A. 0.10

B. 0.30

C. 0.40

D. 0.50

E. 0.60

11.4.3* What is the mean outcome (expected value) in the probability distribution in the previous exercise?

A. 0.20

B. 0.25

C. 2.3

D. 2.5

E. 2.6

11.4.4* What is the standard deviation of the outcome in the probability distribution in Exercise 11.4.2?

A. 1.06

B. 1.19

C. 1.20

D. 1.41

E. 1.45

11.4.5 Which of the following probability distributions is correct, where X = the number of heads when 3 fair coins are flipped? (*Hint*: You may want to list the entire sample space to help you answer this.)

A

x	0	1	2	3
P(x)	1/4	1/4	1/4	1/4

B

x	0	1	2	3
P(x)	1/8	3/8	3/8	1/8

C

x	0	1	2	3
P(x)	1/6	1/3	1/3	1/6

D

x	0	1	2	3
P(x)	1/8	1/4	1/4	1/8

E

x	0	1	2	3
P(x)	1/2	1/2	1/2	1/2

11.4.6* Suppose a fair coin is tossed 3 times and we let X represent the number of coins that land heads up.

a. Create a probability distribution for X.

b. What does the event $X = 2$ mean in this context?

c. Report the value of $P(X = 2)$ and interpret what it means in this context.

d. Report the value of $P(X \leq 2)$ and interpret what it means in this context.

11.4.7 Suppose two fair 4-sided dice (yes, they do exist) with sides labeled 1, 2, 3, and 4 are tossed.

a. List the sample space of all possible outcomes. (*Hint*: A (1, 2) is different from a (2, 1), so there are 16 possible outcomes.)

b. Let X represent the sum of the outcomes rolled on the two dice. Create a probability distribution for X.

c. What does the event $X > 3$ mean?

d. Find the value of $P(X > 3)$ and describe what that means.

11.4.8* According to the U.S. Census Bureau, the following table gives the probability distribution that a randomly chosen *family* household in the U.S. in 2016 has X members. A family household is one in which two people or more in the household are related. (*Note*: The category of 7 is supposed to be 7 or more, but was changed for this exercise so that a mean and standard deviation can be calculated.)

x	2	3	4	5	6	7
P(x)	0.4390	0.2235	0.1936	0.0906	0.0341	0.0192

a. Calculate the value of $P(X = 4)$ and describe what it means.

b. Calculate the value of $P(X > 4)$ and describe what it means.

c. Calculate the value of $P(X \geq 4)$ and describe what it means.

11.4.9 According to the U.S. Census Bureau, the following table gives the probability distribution that a randomly chosen *nonfamily* household in the U.S. in 2016 has Y members. A nonfamily household is where people live alone or share a residence with unrelated individuals. (*Note:* The category of 7 is supposed to be 7 or more, but was changed so that a mean and standard deviation can be calculated. Also, because of rounding error, the sum of the probabilities is 0.9999.)

y	1	2	3	4	5	6	7
$P(y)$	0.8110	0.1536	0.0242	0.0081	0.0023	0.0003	0.0004

a. Calculate $P(Y = 3 \text{ or } 4)$ and describe what it means.

b. What is $P(Y \leq 3)$ and describe what it means.

c. What is $P(Y < 4)$ and describe what it means.

11.4.10* One way that large families often decide who will give each other Christmas presents is to do a drawing. All the names go in a hat and each person draws a name and that is the person to whom he or she gives a gift. The problem with this method is that there is a chance that one or more people will draw their own names. The following table gives the probabilities that X people in a family of 4 will draw their own names in this process.

x	0	1	2	3	4
$P(x)$	9/24	8/24	6/24	0	1/24

a. What is the probability that nobody will draw his or her own names?

b. What is the probability that at least one person will draw his or her name?

c. Explain why an outcome of exactly 3 matches is impossible.

11.4.11* Recall the probability distribution for family household size given in Exercise 11.4.8.

x	2	3	4	5	6	7
$P(x)$	0.4390	0.2235	0.1936	0.0906	0.0341	0.0192

a. What was the mean family household size in the U.S. in 2016?

b. What was the standard deviation for family household size in the U.S. in 2016?

11.4.12 Recall the probability distribution for nonfamily household size given in Exercise 11.4.9.

y	1	2	3	4	5	6	7
$P(y)$	0.8110	0.1536	0.0242	0.0081	0.0023	0.0003	0.0004

a. What was the mean nonfamily household size in the U.S. in 2016?

b. What was the standard deviation for nonfamily household size in the U.S. in 2016?

11.4.13* Recall the probability distribution for the number of people in a family of four who will draw their own name given in Exercise 11.4.10.

x	0	1	2	3	4
$P(x)$	9/24	8/24	6/24	0	1/24

a. What is the expected value for the number of people who will draw their own name?

b. What is the standard deviation for the number of people who will draw their own name?

11.4.14 Recall the scenario of drawing names to decide who would give a Christmas present in a family of four in Exercise 11.4.10. Suppose a family of three uses the same method.

a. Create a probability distribution for this scenario, where X is the number of people who will draw their own names.

b. What is the expected value for the number of people who will draw their own name?

c. What is the standard deviation for the number of people who will draw their own name?

d. How do the expected value and standard deviation for the family of three compare to those for the family of four?

11.4.15* The example in this section described a prize wheel divided into 12 equal-sized sectors where 8 are marked *no prize*, 3 are marked *win $1*, and 1 is marked *win $25*. We will call this wheel A. Suppose you had a similar wheel (which we'll call wheel B) that had 12 sectors: 2 of the sectors marked *no prize*, 1 marked *win $1*, and 9 marked *win $3*.

a. Find the expected payout for wheel B. How does it compare to the expected payout of wheel A?

b. Find the standard deviation for the payout for this wheel. How does it compare to the expected payout of wheel A?

c. If you were given a free spin on one of the wheels, which would you choose to spin and why?

11.4.16* Reconsider the prize wheels described in the example in this section and in the previous exercise. The average distance the outcomes are from the expected value for the wheel from the example (wheel A) can be computed as follows:

$$|0 - 2.33|(8/12) + |1 - 2.33|(3/12) + |25 - 2.33|$$
$$(1/12) = \$3.775$$

a. Find the average distance the outcomes for wheel B are from the expected value of the wheel.

b. We often think of standard deviation as approximately the average distance outcomes are away from their mean (or expected value). This tends to be a reasonable interpretation if a distribution is not highly skewed or has outliers. Compare the standard deviations and average distance from the mean for wheels A and B. Are the two standard deviations approximately the same as their respective average distances from the mean or not? Explain why or why not.

11.4.17 Suppose a litter of puppies has 3 males and 3 females. Suppose two puppies are chosen at random and we let X be the number of male puppies chosen.

a. Create a probability distribution for X.

b. What is the expected value for the number of male puppies? What does this expected value mean?

11.4.18* Suppose you are asked to play a game where you roll a single six-sided die. If it lands on a 6, you win $10. If it doesn't land on 6, you roll again. If it lands on a 6, the second time you win $6. For any other outcome, you lose. Let X be the amount of money you win.

a. Create a probability distribution for X.

b. What is the expected value for this distribution? What does this expected value mean?

c. How much money would you have to pay to play this game for it to be a fair game? (A fair game is when the expected value of winning is zero.)

11.4.19 The NPR show *Wait Wait… Don't Tell Me* gives its guests a three-question quiz in which they have three answer choices for each question. The questions are so obscure that the guest typically must just randomly guess at the answers. Let's suppose it is always true that a guest must randomly guess which of the three answers correctly.

a. Create a probability distribution where X is the number of questions (out of three) the guest answers correctly.

b. To win the game, someone must answer at least two out of three questions correctly. What is the probability someone wins if he or she is just guessing?

11.4.20* In 1938 Dr. Frank Benford, a physicist at General Electric, noticed that, given a list of numbers, more numbers started with the digit 1 than any other digit. He analyzed 20,222 sets of numbers including areas of rivers, baseball

statistics, numbers in magazine articles, and street addresses. He concluded that the probability of the numeral d appearing as the first digit was $\log(1 + 1/d)$ and this property is known as Benford's Law. The probabilities are shown in the table below.

a. According to Benford's Law, what is the probability that the leading digit of a randomly chosen number is 1 or 2?

b. According to Benford's Law, what is the probability that the leading digit of a randomly chosen number is more than 2?

c. What is the expected value of the leading digit of randomly chosen numbers according to Benford's Law?

d. What is the standard deviation of the leading digit of randomly chosen numbers according to Benford's Law?

SECTION 11.5

11.5.1* The following probability distribution represents the payout for a game. Suppose $2 is added to all the payouts. How would the mean and standard deviation change from those of the original distribution?

x = Payout	$0	$3	$5	$10
P(x)	15/25	6/25	3/25	1/25

A. They both would increase by $2.

B. The mean would increase by $2, but the standard deviation would stay the same.

C. The standard deviation would increase by $2, but the mean would stay the same.

D. They both would stay the same.

E. The mean would increase by $2, and the standard deviation would increase by the square of $2.

11.5.2* Suppose each payout was multiplied by 2 in the previous question. How would the mean and standard deviation change from those of the original distribution?

A. They both would be multiplied by 2.

B. The mean would be multiplied by 2, but the standard deviation would stay the same.

C. The standard deviation would be multiplied by 2, but the mean would stay the same.

D. They both would stay the same.

E. The mean would be multiplied by 2, and the standard deviation would be multiplied by the square of 2.

d	1	2	3	4	5	6	7	8	9
Probability the leading digit starts with d	0.301	0.176	0.125	0.097	0.079	0.067	0.058	0.051	0.046

EXERCISE 11.4.20

11.5.3 The following probability distribution represents payouts for spinning two different prize wheels, *X* and *Y*. Suppose a player gets to first spin wheel *X* and then wheel *Y*. What is the mean payout for the two spins combined?

x = Payout	$0	$3	$5
P(x)	1/2	1/4	1/4

y = Payout	$0	$3	$6
P(y)	2/3	1/6	1/6

A. $1.50

B. $3.00

C. $3.50

D. $6.00

E. $9.00

11.5.4 Recall the previous question about spinning both wheels. What is the standard deviation of the distribution of payouts when a player gets to spin both wheels? (*Hint*: The variances of the two distributions are 4.5 and 5.25.)

A. 2.206

B. 4.413

C. 4.875

D. 3.122

E. 9.75

11.5.5* When two distributions are subtracted to form a new distribution, the new distribution must have a standard deviation of zero when which of the following occur? (Choose all that apply.)

A. The difference in the two standard deviations from the original distributions is zero.

B. The difference in the two variances from the original distributions is zero.

C. One or the other original distributions has a standard deviation of zero, but not both.

D. Both original distributions have standard deviations of zero.

E. Never. A standard deviation of a distribution can never be zero.

11.5.6 The distribution of IQs is said to have a mean of 100 and a standard deviation of 15. Suppose a company was selling IQ+ pills so that those that took it would magically have their IQs transformed by the equation: New IQ = 1.05(Old IQ) + 10. If everyone took this pill (and it worked as advertised), what would be the mean and standard deviation of the distribution of new IQs?

A. Mean = 115, SD = 25.75

B. Mean = 105, SD = 25.75

C. Mean = 115, SD = 15.75

D. Mean = 105, SD = 15.75

E. Mean = 110, SD = 25

11.5.7* A regular six-sided die is a cube on which each side shows a different number of dots (1 to 6). The table shown below gives the probabilities of the sums of the dots on two regular six-sided dice when they are thrown.

Sum	2	3	4	5	6	7	8	9	10	11	12
P(Sum)	1/36	2/36	3/36	4/36	5/36	6/36	5/36	4/36	3/36	2/36	1/36

a. Find the mean of this distribution.

b. Find the standard deviation of this distribution.

c. Suppose we added one more dot on every face of both dice. What would be the mean and standard deviation of this new probability distribution?

d. Suppose we doubled the number of dots on every face of both dice. What would be the mean and standard deviation of this new probability distribution?

11.5.8 In the previous question we looked at the probability distribution of the sum of two dice. This time we focus on using probability rules to derive the properties of the sum of two dice.

a. Create a probability distribution for the numbers showing when you roll one fair six-sided die.

b. Find the mean and standard deviation for the distribution of number of dots showing when rolling one die.

c. Using the formulas for determining the mean and standard deviation for the sum of two random variables, find the mean and standard deviation for the sum of the numbers on two fair six-sided dice. How do these numbers compare to those from Exercise 11.5.7?

d. We can consider the sum of the two dice as *X* + *X*. What would 2*X* describe?

e. Find the mean and standard deviation of 2*X*. Does it have the same mean and standard deviation as *X* + *X*? If not, which standard deviation is larger and why does that make sense?

11.5.9* In a game we will call "gambling dice," you pay $1 to roll two dice. If you roll a sum of 5, 6, 7, or 8, you lose and don't get your dollar back (you are out $1). If you roll anything else, you are given $2 (you have gained $1). (*Hint*: Use the probability distribution shown in Exercise 11.5.7 to help you with these questions.)

a. When playing one game, what is the probability you will win?

b. When playing one game, what is the probability you will lose?

c. How much, on average, do you expect to win or lose per game, in the long run? In other words, what is the expected value of this game?

11.5.10 An American roulette wheel has numbers 1 through 36, where the even numbers are black and odd numbers are red. There are also numbers 0 and 00, which are green. The wheel is spun and a ball will randomly land on one of these 38 numbers. Suppose you plan always to bet $1 on red. If it lands on red, you will gain $1 (payout = $1). If it does not land on red, you will lose $1 (payout = −$1).

a. For one spin of the wheel, what is the expected payout for this game if you bet on red?

b. For one spin of the wheel, what is the standard deviation for the payout if you bet on red?

c. For two spins of the wheel, what is the expected payout if you always bet on red?

d. For two spins of the wheel, what is the standard deviation for the payout if you always bet on red?

11.5.11* An American roulette wheel has numbers 1 through 36, where the even numbers are black and odd numbers are red. There are also numbers 0 and 00, which are green. Suppose you plan always to bet $1 on the number 23 (your lucky number). If it lands on 23, you will gain $35. If it does not land on 23, you will lose $1.

a. For one spin of the wheel, what is the expected payout for this game if you bet on 23?

b. For one spin of the wheel, what is the standard deviation for the payout if you bet on 23?

c. For three spins of the wheel, what is the expected payout if you always bet on 23?

d. For three spins of the wheel, what is the standard deviation for the payout if you always bet on 23?

11.5.12 Recall Exercise 11.5.10 on betting on red on the roulette wheel.

a. Write out the probability distribution of the payout for betting $1 on red twice. (*Hint*: There should be three outcomes—you win twice, you win once, you lose twice.)

b. Find the mean of your probability distribution from part (a).

c. Find the standard deviation of your probability distribution from part (a).

11.5.13* Recall Exercise 11.5.11 on betting on the number 23 on the roulette wheel.

a. Write out the probability distribution for betting $1 on red twice. (*Hint*: There should be three outcomes—you win twice, you win once, you lose twice.)

b. Find the mean of your probability distribution from part (a).

c. Find the standard deviation of your probability distribution from part (a).

11.5.14 A Canadian study (Janssen et al., 2007) looked at the birthweights of babies of different ethnic groups. Their sample of newborns (born after 39 weeks) of European descent had a mean length of 50.5 cm with a standard deviation of 1.9 cm. What are these statistics in inches? (*Hint*: There are 2.54 cm in an inch.)

11.5.15 The Canadian study described in the previous exercise that looked at the birthweights of babies of different ethnic groups also had a sample of newborns of South Asian descent that had a mean length of 50.2 cm with a standard deviation of 1.7 cm. What are these statistics in inches? (*Hint*: There are 2.54 cm in an inch.)

11.5.16* A statistics instructor gave a 10-point quiz in which the mean was 7.72 with a standard deviation of 2.45. Suppose the instructor, being in a generous mood, adjusts all the scores by adding a point to each one. What are the values of the mean and standard deviation of the adjusted scores?

11.5.17 A statistics instructor gave a 10-point quiz in which the mean was 8.28 with a standard deviation of 1.58. Suppose the instructor, being a mean ogre, adjusts all the scores by dividing them all by 2 and then subtracting a point from each one. What are the values of the mean and standard deviation of the adjusted scores?

11.5.18 In the previous question the instructor divided all the scores by 2 and then subtracted 1 point from each. Suppose a second method is to first subtract 1 from the scores and then divide by 2.

a. How will the means of the two different methods compare?

b. How will the standard deviations of the two different methods compare?

11.5.19* A sample of 65 healthy males in a vaccine trial had a mean body temperature of 98.105° Fahrenheit with a standard deviation of 0.699° Fahrenheit. If all these temperatures were converted to degrees Celsius, what would be the mean and standard deviation of that new distribution? (*Hint*: To convert degrees Fahrenheit (F) to degrees Celsius (C), use the formula $C = \frac{5}{9}(F - 32)$.)

11.5.20 A sample of 65 healthy females in a vaccine trial had a mean body temperature of 98.394° Fahrenheit with a standard deviation of 0.743° Fahrenheit. If all these temperatures were converted to degrees Celsius, what would be the mean and standard deviation of that new distribution? (*Hint*: To convert degrees Fahrenheit (F) to degrees Celsius (C), use the formula $C = \frac{5}{9}(F - 32)$.)

SECTION 11.6

11.6.1* Suppose you are spinning a cash prize wheel in which you have a 25% chance of winning a prize. Most prizes are fairly small values like $1 or $5, but one spot on the wheel is worth $100. In which one of the following situations could you use a binomial model?

A. You spin the wheel 10 times and count the number of spins on which you win a prize.

B. You spin the wheel 10 times and total the value of your winnings.

C. You spin the wheel and count how many spins it takes you to win a prize.

D. You spin the wheel and count how many spins it takes you to win $20 or more.

11.6.2 Suppose you are spinning a cash prize wheel in which you have a 25% chance of winning a prize, as described in the previous question. Most prizes are fairly small values like $1 or $5, but one spot on the wheel is worth $100. In which one of the following situations could you use a geometric model?

A. You spin the wheel 10 times and count the number of spins on which you win a prize.

B. You spin the wheel 10 times and total the value of your winnings.

C. You spin the wheel and count how many spins it takes you to win a prize.

D. You spin the wheel and count how many spins it takes you to win a combined total of $20 or more.

11.6.3* Suppose people in your town are being surveyed about shopping habits. Which one of the following situations is best modeled by a binomial model?

A. You ask residents of your town, "Do you shop downtown at least once a month?" and count the number of people you have to ask until you get 50 to answer yes.

B. You ask a random sample of 50 residents in your town, "Do you shop downtown at least once a month?" and you record their answers.

C. You ask 25 random people who are walking around downtown and 25 random people who are coming out of a big-box store just outside of your town, "Do you shop downtown at least once a month?" and count the number who answered yes.

D. You ask a random sample of 50 residents, "Which stores would you like to see added in downtown?" and you record their answers.

11.6.4 What is the difference between a binomial model and a geometric model?

A. The geometric model doesn't have binary (success or failure) outcomes, whereas a binomial model does.

B. The geometric model doesn't have independent trials, whereas a binomial model does.

C. The geometric model doesn't have a fixed number of trials, whereas a binomial model does.

D. For a geometric model, the probability of success is not the same for each outcome, whereas for the binomial mode the probability of success is the same for each outcome.

11.6.5* Which of the two following scenarios would be better modeled with a binomial distribution? Explain your reasoning.

I. Your high school has 3,200 students consisting of 50% males and 50% females. Two students are randomly chosen. You want to determine the probabilities that 0, 1, or both of the students are female.

II. Your statistics class has 10 students consisting of 5 males and 5 females. Two students are randomly chosen. You want to determine the probabilities that 0, 1, or both of the students are female.

11.6.6 According to the Census Bureau, 33.4% of Americans 25 years old and older had a college degree (at least a bachelor's) in 2016.

a. If a random sample of 6 American 25 years old and older is taken, what is the probability that exactly 3 have a college degree?

b. If a random sample of 6 Americans is taken, what is the probability that fewer than 2 have a college degree?

c. If a random sample of 6 Americans is taken, what is the probability that at least 1 of them has a college degree?

d. If you take a random sample of 6 Americans on a certain street in a certain town, will the probabilities you calculated in the previous questions be the same as the probabilities for this group? Explain.

11.6.7* According to the U.S. Census Bureau, 74.8% of households in the U.S. had home Internet access in 2012.

a. Suppose 10 households in the U.S. are randomly chosen; what is the probability that all of them have home Internet access?

b. Suppose 10 households in the U.S. are randomly chosen; what is the probability that exactly 7 of them have home Internet access?

c. Suppose 10 households in the U.S. are randomly chosen; what is the probability that 7 or more of them have home Internet access?

d. Suppose 10 households in one neighborhood in the U.S. are randomly chosen and we want to find the probability that 7 or more of them have home Internet access. Is that probability the same as you determined in the previous question? Explain.

11.6.8 Calvin is taking a 10-question true/false test and determining which answer to choose for each question by flipping a fair coin. He picks true if he gets heads and false if he gets tails.

a. What's the probability Calvin gets all 10 questions correct?

b. What's the probability Calvin gets all 10 questions incorrect?

c. How do your answers to (a) and (b) compare? Why?

d. For Calvin to pass, he needs to get at least 6 correct. What is the probability he will pass the test?

11.6.9* In 1941, Joe DiMaggio got at least one hit in 56 consecutive games, still the record for the longest hitting streak in Major League Baseball. Let's try to estimate the probability of someone like DiMaggio achieving the success he did. That year, he had a batting average of 0.357. We will assume that for each at bat, the probability he would get a hit stays constant at 0.357. He had slightly fewer than four at bats per game. To simplify things, we will assume he bats exactly 4 times per game.

a. We first need to find the probability he would get at least one hit in a game.

(i) What is the probability he does not get a hit at one at bat?

(ii) What is the probability he does not get any hits (with four at bats) in a single game?

(iii) What is the probability he gets at least one hit in a single game?

b. Now what is the probability he gets at least one hit in 56 consecutive games?

c. In 1941, the regular baseball season consisted of 154 games. Is the probability you found in part (b) a good estimate for the probability he would have gotten at least one hit in 56 consecutive games sometime during the season, or should that estimate be larger or smaller?

11.6.10 About 51% of babies born in the United States are boys. Let's assume that the probability of a birth resulting in a boy is 0.51 for all U.S. births. Suppose a couple decides they want to have four children.

a. Develop a probability distribution in which X is the number of boys among these four children.

b. Develop a probability distribution in which X is the number of girls among these four children.

11.6.11 What are the mean and standard deviation for the two probability distributions for the number of boys and the number of girls in families of four from the previous question?

11.6.12* Airlines will often overbook their flights (selling more tickets than they have seats) because not all customers show up for some flights. The proportion that doesn't show up varies greatly, depending on the time of day and the airport. For this exercise, let's suppose any given customer has a 5% chance of not showing up and an airline has sold 44 tickets for a 42-seat plane.

a. What is the probability that there won't be enough seats for the customers who show up?

b. What is the probability that there will be enough seats for the customers who show up?

c. On average, how many customers will show up?

11.6.13 About 10% of the population is left-handed. Let's suppose this is exactly true and you are randomly choosing people from the population until you get a left-hander.

a. What is the probability you won't get a left-hander until your fifth pick?

b. What is the probability it will take five picks or less until you get a left-hander?

c. What is the smallest number of picks you need so that the probability of getting a left-hander is greater than 0.5?

11.6.14* In 2018, Tim Hortons® restaurants conducted a game called Roll up the Rim to Win® where you could roll up the rim of one of their medium-sized or larger beverage paper cups (to reveal something underneath) and possibly win a prize. About 1/6 of the cups were winners. The prizes mostly consisted of a free coffee or donut.

a. If you buy 3 beverages sold in these cups, what is the probability that you will have exactly one winner?

b. If you buy 3 beverages sold in these cups, what is the probability that you will have at least one winner?

c. Suppose you plan to keep buying beverages until you get a winner. What is the probability that you will have to buy 3 beverages until you get a winner?

d. Suppose you plan to keep buying beverages until you get a winner. What is the probability that you will have to buy 3 or fewer beverages until you get a winner?

11.6.15 In 2014, Jack in the Box® restaurants conducted a game called the Munchie Peel Instant Win Game® where you could peel a sticker off one of their meal boxes and possibly win a prize. They claimed that customers had a 1 in 4 chance of winning some sort of prize in this contest.

a. If you buy 4 meals that have these stickers, what is the probability that you will have exactly one winner?

b. If you buy 4 meals that have these stickers, what is the probability that you will have at least one winner?

c. Suppose you plan to keep buying meals until you get a winner. What is the probability that you will have to buy 4 meals until you get a winner?

d. Suppose you plan to keep buying meals until you get a winner. What is the probability that you will have to buy 4 or fewer meals until you get a winner?

e. A friend buys 4 meal boxes and does not get a winner. Should she be upset?

11.6.16 In the previous question about the Munchie Peel Instant Win Game®:

a. What is the expected number of winning stickers for those that buy 4 meals?

b. What is the standard deviation for the number of winning stickers for those who buy 4 meals?

c. What is the expected number of meals one would have to buy in order to get exactly one winning sticker?

11.6.17* Some marathons are so popular that they use lotteries to determine who can run in them. In the 2016 New York City Marathon, about 23% of those who registered to enter through the lottery were accepted. Let's assume this percentage stays the same in future years.

a. Suppose you plan to enter the lottery for the next 5 years. What is your probability of gaining entry into the marathon exactly once?

b. Suppose you plan to enter the lottery for the next 5 years. What is your probability of gaining entry into the marathon at least once?

c. Suppose you plan to enter the lottery until you gain entry and then won't apply again. What is the probability that it takes 5 years until you get in?

d. Suppose you plan to enter the lottery until you gain entry and then won't apply again. What is the probability that it takes 5 years or less until you get in?

11.6.18* In the previous question about getting into the New York City Marathon:

a. What is the mean number of times people get accepted if they enter the lottery for 5 years?

b. What is the mean number of times someone would have to enter the lottery to get accepted exactly once?

11.6.19* Recall Exercise 11.6.17 about getting into the New York City Marathon. You plan to enter until you get in and then won't apply again. What is the smallest number of times you would have to enter so that the probability of getting in once is above 0.50?

11.6.20 An American roulette wheel has numbers 1 through 36, where the even numbers are black and odd numbers are red. There are also numbers 0 and 00, which are green. The wheel is spun and a ball will randomly land on one of these 38 numbers.

a. What is the probability the ball will land on a red number?

b. Suppose you bet on red 4 times; what is the probability you will win exactly once? At least once?

c. Suppose you plan on betting on red until you win. What is the probability that it will take you 4 tries or fewer before you win?

11.6.21 Reconsider the roulette wheel description in the previous exercise. If you bet $1 on red and the ball lands on a red number, you will get your $1 back plus another $1. If the ball does not land on a red number, you will lose your dollar. If you kept betting like this, how much do you expect to win or lose per game in the long run?

11.6.22* Suppose two parents have blood genotypes such that the probability that any of their children have blood type A is 0.75.

a. If they have 5 children:

   (i) What is the probability that all have blood type A?

   (ii) What is the probability that least one has blood type A?

b. Suppose they are planning on having many children.

   (i) What is the probability that they will need to have 4 children to get one with blood type A?

   (ii) What is the probability that it will take fewer than 4 children until they get one with blood type A?

SECTION 11.7

11.7.1* Heights of a certain population are normally distributed with a mean of 68 inches and a standard deviation of 2.5 inches. What is the standardized statistic (z-score) for a person with a height of 66 inches?

A. -2

B. -0.8

C. 0.8

D. 2

E. 2.5

11.7.2 Suppose heights from a certain population are normally distributed and you determine that the standardized statistic for someone's height from that population is 1.56. What does that number mean?

A. That person's height is 1.56 inches above the mean height of the population.

B. That person's height is 1.56 times larger than the mean height of the population.

C. That person's standard deviation is 1.56 units higher than the standard deviation of the population.

D. That person's height is 1.56 standard deviations above mean height of the population.

E. That person's height is within 1.56 inches of the mean height of the population.

11.7.3* Heights of a certain population are normally distributed with a mean of 68 inches and a standard deviation of 2.5 inches. We can say that about 95% of all heights in the population are:

A. Greater than 70.5 inches.

B. Greater than 73 inches.

C. Between 65.5 inches and 70.5 inches.

D. Between 63 inches and 73 inches.

E. Below 63 inches or greater than 73 inches.

11.7.4* Suppose heights of a certain population are normally distributed with a mean of 68 inches and a standard deviation of 2.5 inches. What is the 80th percentile of this distribution?

A. 70 inches

B. 70.1 inches

C. 70.2 inches

D. 70.3 inches

E. 70.4 inches

11.7.5 Heights of a certain population are normally distributed with a mean of 68 inches and a standard deviation of 2.5 inches. The middle 50% of all the heights lie approximately between what two numbers?

A. 66.3 inches and 69.7 inches

B. 65.5 inches and 70.5 inches

C. 67.1 inches and 70.1 inches

D. 68.0 inches and 75.0 inches

E. 63 inches and 73 inches

11.7.6* Which is NOT true about probability density functions?

A. The total area under the curve of a probability density function and above the horizontal axis is 1.

B. Using a probability density function to compute the probability of a single value occurring (such as the probability that someone's weight is exactly 164 pounds) will result in zero.

C. Normal distributions are examples of probability density functions.

D. Probability density functions may extend indefinitely to negative or positive infinity.

E. All probability density functions are bell-shaped.

11.7.7 If adult male gerbil weights are normally distributed with a mean of 95 grams and a standard deviation of 10 grams, *using the empirical rule*, what proportion of adult male gerbils weigh:

a. Between 75 and 115 grams?

b. More than 115 grams?

c. Less than 75 grams?

11.7.8* If adult female guinea pigs weights are normally distributed with a mean of 800 grams and a standard deviation of 100 grams, *using the empirical rule*, what proportion of adult female guinea pigs weigh:

a. Between 700 and 900 grams?

b. Between 600 and 1,000 grams?

c. Between 800 and 1,000 grams?

d. Between 700 and 1,000 grams?

11.7.9 Results from the Wechsler Adult Intelligence Scale, a common IQ test, are approximately normally distributed with a mean of 100 and a standard deviation of 15.

a. Scores on the test that are 130 and above are said to be very superior. What proportion of the population will get very superior scores?

b. Scores that are 120 to 129 are said to be superior. What proportion of the population will get superior scores?

c. Above what score would you need to be in the top 10% of test takers?

11.7.10* Results from the Wechsler Adult Intelligence Scale, a common IQ test, are approximately normally distributed with a mean of 100 and a standard deviation of 15.

a. There are various IQs for which people classify someone as a genius. Some consider a genius a person that has an IQ of 145 or more. If someone is randomly chosen from the population, what is the probability that his or her score will be 145 or more?

b. Mensa is a high-IQ society. To gain membership, someone must have an IQ in the top 2% of the population. What IQs are in the top 2% of the population?

c. Would all members of Mensa be considered geniuses by the rule given in part (a)?

11.7.11 Birthweights of full-term newborns in the United States are approximately normally distributed with a mean of about 3,500 grams and a standard deviation of about 450 grams. We will assume this is exactly true.

a. Low birthweight is usually defined to be a newborn weight of less than 2,500 grams. What proportion of the births in the United States result in low birthweights?

b. What birthweights are in the bottom 5%?

11.7.12* Birthweights of full-term newborns in the United States are approximately normally distributed with a mean of about 3,500 grams and a standard deviation of about 450 grams. We will assume this is exactly true.

a. What is the probability that a randomly chosen newborn has a birthweight more than 4,536 grams (which is about 10 pounds)?

b. To be in the top 1% of birthweights, how heavy must a newborn be?

11.7.13 The SAT® and ACT® are two common standardized tests that high school students take as part of college applications. In 2016 the mean composite SAT score was 1,020 with a standard deviation of 194. For the ACT the mean composite score was 21.0 with a standard deviation of 5.4. We will assume both scores are normally distributed. If you score an 1100 on the SAT and a 24 on the ACT, which score would you consider the better of the two and why?

11.7.14* The SAT® is a common standardized test that high school students take as part of college entrance. In 2016 the mean composite SAT score was 1020 with a standard deviation of 194. These scores are approximately normally distributed.

a. If you scored 1200, what is your percentile? (That is, what percent of scores fall below your score?)

b. To be in the top 5% (95th percentile), what score do you have to achieve?

11.7.15 The ACT® is a common standardized test that high school students take as part of college entrance. In 2016 the mean composite ACT score was 21.0 with a standard deviation of 5.4. These scores are approximately normally distributed.

a. If you scored 30, what is your percentile? (That is, what percentage of scores fall below your score?)

b. To be in the top 10%, what score do you have to achieve?

11.7.16* Heights of males in the United States are approximately normally distributed with a mean of 69.3 inches and a standard deviation of 3.0 inches. Heights of females in the United States are approximately normally distributed with a mean of 63.8 inches and a standard deviation of 2.8 inches.

a. What is the standardized statistic (z-score) for a male who is 72 inches tall?

b. What female height has the same standardized statistic of a male who is 72 inches tall?

11.7.17 Heights of females in the United States are approximately normally distributed with a mean of 63.8 inches and a standard deviation of 2.8 inches.

a. What is the probability that a randomly chosen female in the United States has a height equal to 67 inches?

b. What is the probability that a randomly chosen female in the United States has a height greater than 67 inches?

c. If 5 females are randomly chosen, what is the probability that exactly 3 of them will have heights greater than 67 inches?

d. If 5 females are randomly chosen, what is the probability that at least 3 of them will have heights greater than 67 inches?

11.7.18* Heights of males in the United States are approximately normally distributed with a mean of 69.3 inches and a standard deviation of 3.0 inches.

a. What is the probability that a randomly chosen male in the United States has a height greater than 72 inches?

b. If 4 males are randomly chosen, what is the probability that exactly 3 of them will have heights greater than 72 inches?

c. If 4 males are randomly chosen, what is the probability that at least 3 of them will have heights greater than 72 inches?

11.7.19 The heights of females in the United States are approximately normally distributed with a mean of 63.8 inches and a standard deviation of 2.8 inches and the heights of males are approximately normally distributed with a mean of 69.3 inches and a standard deviation of 3.0 inches.

a. If we were to randomly choose 1 U.S. male and randomly choose 1 U.S. female, define S to be the sum of their two heights. What are the mean and the standard deviation of S?

b. What are the mean and standard deviation of the sum of the heights of 2 randomly chosen males and 2 randomly chosen females in the U.S.?

c. What are the mean and standard deviation of the sum of the heights of 3 randomly chosen males and 2 randomly chosen females in the U.S.?

11.7.20* In a bone density test, one of the results is given as a z-score. This is simply the number of standard deviations above or below the average bone density of someone of the same sex and age as the patient. For a certain age and sex, the bone density scores are thought to be normally distributed in the population. One of the authors had a bone density test and received a z-score of −0.3.

a. What percentage of the population (in this case, 56-year-old males) has bone density smaller than that of the author?

b. In what percentile does this score place the author?

SECTION 11.8

11.8.1* One estimate says that 46% of all Americans citizens have a valid passport. Suppose this is true exactly. Also suppose we wanted to randomly sample 100 Americans and find the proportion in our sample who had a valid passport. What is the standard deviation of the sampling distribution of *sample proportions* of 100 Americans who have a valid passport?

A. $\sqrt{100(0.46)(0.54)}$

B. $\sqrt{(0.46)(0.54)/100}$

C. $\sqrt{(0.46)(0.54)/100}$

D. $0.46(0.54)/\sqrt{100}$

E. $100\sqrt{(0.46)(0.54)}$

11.8.2 Reconsider the previous question where we assumed the proportion of all American citizens who have a valid passport is 0.46. Suppose again that a random sample of 100 Americans is to be taken and the proportion who have a valid passport determined. What is the standard deviation of the sampling distribution of *number* of 100 Americans who have a valid passport?

A. $\sqrt{100(0.46)(0.54)}$

B. $\sqrt{(0.46)(0.54)/100}$

C. $\sqrt{(0.46)(0.54)/100}$

D. $0.46(0.54)/\sqrt{100}$

E. $100\sqrt{(0.46)(0.54)}$

11.8.3* Reconsider the previous question where we assumed the proportion of all American citizens who have a valid passport is 0.46. Suppose again that a random sample of 100 Americans is to be taken and the proportion who have a valid passport determined. What is the mean of the sampling distribution of *sample proportions* of 100 Americans who have a valid passport?

A. $\hat{p}$

B. 0.46

C. $\sqrt{0.46/100}$

D. $(0.46)(1 - 0.54)$

E. 46

11.8.4 When a normal distribution is used to calculate probabilities about the distribution of a sample proportion, it gives:

A. Exact results.

B. Exact results for large sample sizes and approximate results for small sample sizes.

C. Approximate results that tend to get better with larger sample sizes.

D. Approximate results that tend to get worse with larger sample sizes.

E. The normal distribution cannot be used to give either exact or approximate binomial probabilities.

11.8.5* Suppose a population consists of 10% left-handers. Which is more unlikely, getting more than 12% left-handers in a random sample of 100 people from this population or getting more than 12% left-handers in a random sample of 500 people from this population?

A. More than 12% from the sample of 100 is more unlikely.

B. More than 12% from the sample of 500 is more unlikely.

C. They are both equally likely.

D. It cannot be determined without actually calculating the two probabilities.

E. None of the above.

11.8.6 In 2014, the U.S. Census Bureau estimated that 13% of U.S. residents were foreign-born. Suppose this is exactly true. If a random sample of 500 Americans was taken in 2014, use the normal approximation to the binomial distribution to estimate the probability that the sample would have had 14% or more who are foreign-born.

11.8.7* In 2014, the U.S. Census Bureau estimated that 13% of U.S. residents were foreign-born. Suppose this is exactly true. If a random sample of 500 Americans was taken in 2014, use the normal approximation to the binomial distribution to determine the probability that the sample would have had 11% or fewer who are foreign-born.

11.8.8* According to the Pew Research Center, in 2015, 58% of all American adults had Facebook accounts. Suppose this is true now. If a random sample of 100 Americans is to be taken, use the normal approximation to the binomial distribution to determine the probability that at least 60% of the sample will have a Facebook account.

11.8.9 According to the Pew Research Center, in 2015, 58% of all American adults had Facebook accounts. Suppose this is true now. If a random sample of 100 Americans is to be taken, use the normal approximation to the binomial distribution to determine the probability that at most 50% of the sample will have a Facebook account.

11.8.10* According to the Pew Research Center, in 2015, 19% of all American adults had Twitter accounts. Suppose this is true now.

a. If a random sample of 500 Americans is taken, use the normal approximation to the binomial distribution to determine the probability that between 17% and 21% of the sample has a Twitter account.

b. Do you think the percentage of all American adults with a Twitter account is now larger than 19% or smaller than 19%? How will this impact the probability you calculated in (a)?

11.8.11 According to the Pew Research Center, in 2015, 19% of all American adults had Twitter accounts. Suppose this is true now.

a. If a random sample of 500 Americans is taken, use the normal approximation to the binomial distribution to determine the probability that between 19% and 22% of the sample has a Twitter account.

b. How does your answer to Exercise 11.8.11 compare to your answer to 11.8.10(a)? Explain why this makes sense.

11.8.12* About 20% of the world's population lives in China. Suppose this is exactly true.

a. If a random sample of 1,000 people in the world is chosen, use the normal approximation to the binomial distribution to determine the probability that between 190 and 210 people in the sample live in China.

b. If a random sample of 1,000 people in the world is chosen, use the normal approximation to the binomial distribution to determine the probability that between 180 and 215 people in the sample live in China.

c. How do your answers to (a) and (b) compare? Why?

11.8.13 Results from the Wechsler Adult Intelligence Scale, a common IQ test, are approximately normally distributed with a mean of 100 and a standard deviation of 15.

a. If a person is randomly chosen from the population, what is the probability that his or her score is 110 or more?

b. If 10 people are randomly chosen from the population, what is the probability that the mean of their 10 scores is 110 or more?

11.8.14* Birthweights of full-term newborns in the United States are approximately normally distributed with a mean of about 3,500 grams and a standard deviation of about 450 grams. We will assume this is exactly true.

a. What is the probability that a randomly chosen newborn has a birthweight more than 4,000 grams?

b. What is the probability that 5 randomly chosen newborn have a mean birthweight more than 4,000 grams?

11.8.15 According to the Census Bureau, 33.4% of Americans 25 years old and older had a college degree in 2016.

a. Use the **One Proportion** applet to do a simulation (with at least 10,000 repetitions) to estimate the probability that in a random sample of 500 Americans, at most 150 have a college degree.

b. From a random sample of 500 Americans, determine the probability that at most 150 have a college degree. (Use the **Exact Binomial** feature on the **One Proportion** applet to find this answer.)

c. From a random sample of 500 Americans, what is the probability that at most 150 have a college degree? (Use the **Normal Approximation** to the binomial distribution to find this answer on the applet.)

11.8.16* An elevator near the office of one of the authors contains a sign that says its maximum capacity is 4,000 pounds or 26 people. It makes one wonder (well, at least it made one author wonder!), what is the probability that a random sample of 26 people would weigh over 4,000 pounds?

a. The average weight of females in the U.S. (in 2010) was about 166 pounds with a standard deviation of about 60 pounds. What is the probability that 26 (randomly chosen) females get on the elevator and their combined weight exceeds 4,000 pounds? (*Hint*: You can solve this problem in terms of the average weight exceeding 4,000/26 as well.)

b. The average weight of males in the U.S. (in 2010) was about 196 pounds with a standard deviation of about 74 pounds. What is the probability that 26 (randomly chosen) males get on the elevator and their combined weight exceeds 4,000 pounds?

11.8.17 A 19-foot Scout fishing boat contains a U.S. Coast Guard label for maximum capacity. It states that the maximum capacity is 6 persons or 1,000 pounds (not including gear).

a. The average weight of males in the U.S. (in 2010) was about 196 pounds with a standard deviation of about 74 pounds. What is the probability that 6 (randomly chosen) males get on the boat and their combined weight exceeds 1,000 pounds? (*Hint*: You can solve this problem in terms of the average weight exceeding 1,000/6 as well.)

b. Your answer to the previous question should have been above 0.50. What is the largest number of (randomly chosen) males that you can put on the boat so the probability of their combined weight exceeding 1,000 pounds is less than 0.50?

11.8.18* Heights of females in the United States are approximately normally distributed with a mean of 63.8 inches and a standard deviation of 2.8 inches.

a. What is the probability that a randomly chosen female in the United States has a height greater than 67 inches?

b. If 5 females are randomly chosen, what is the probability that their mean height is greater than 67 inches?

11.8.19 Heights of males in the United States are approximately normally distributed with a mean of 69.3 inches and a standard deviation of 3.0 inches.

a. What is the probability that a randomly chosen male in the United States has a height greater than 72 inches?

b. If 4 males are randomly chosen, what is the probability that their mean height is greater than 72 inches?

11.8.20 Suppose that a basketball player named Jose makes 60% of his free throws, and Kayla makes 70% of her free throws. Each player attempts 100 free throws at the end of practice one day. Regard these as independent random samples for each player. They plan to calculate the difference in their sample proportions of successfully made free throws, $\hat{p}_{Kayla} - \hat{p}_{Jose}$.

a. Explain what the event $(\hat{p}_{Kayla} - \hat{p}_{Jose} > 0)$ means in this context.

b. Is it reasonable to approximate the sampling distribution of $(\hat{p}_{Kayla} - \hat{p}_{Jose})$ with a normal distribution? Explain why or why not.

c. Determine the mean and standard deviation of $(\hat{p}_{Kayla} - \hat{p}_{Jose})$.

d. Calculate the z-score corresponding to $(\hat{p}_{Kayla} - \hat{p}_{Jose} = 0)$.

e. Use the z-score to approximate the probability that $(\hat{p}_{Kayla} - \hat{p}_{Jose} > 0)$.

11.8.21 Reconsider the previous question. Describe how the probability that $(\hat{p}_{Kayla} - \hat{p}_{Jose} > 0)$ would change if:

a. The sample sizes were larger.

b. Kayla's probability of successfully making a free throw was larger.

11.8.22 Suppose that Karen and John get together to grade their students' exams. The time required for Karen to grade a question on a student's exam is normally distributed with mean 90 seconds and standard deviation 20 seconds. The time required for John to grade a question on a student's exam follows a normal distribution with mean 120 seconds and standard deviation 30 seconds. Suppose that each person grades a random sample of 10 questions on their students' exams.

a. Explain what the event $(\bar{x}_{Karen} - \bar{x}_{John} > 0)$ means in this context.

b. Is it reasonable to approximate the sampling distribution of $(\bar{x}_{Karen} - \bar{x}_{John})$ with a normal distribution? Explain why or why not.

c. Determine the mean and standard deviation of the sampling distribution of $(\bar{x}_{Karen} - \bar{x}_{John})$.

d. Calculate the z-score corresponding to $(\bar{x}_{Karen} - \bar{x}_{John} = 0)$.

e. Use the z-score to approximate the probability that $(\bar{x}_{Karen} - \bar{x}_{John} > 0)$.

11.8.23 Reconsider the previous question, but with different sample sizes. Determine the probability that Karen grades a random sample of 5 exams in less total time than it takes John to grade a random sample of 4 exams. First express this event in terms of $(\bar{x}_{Karen} - \bar{x}_{John})$, keeping in mind the different sample sizes for the two graders.

END OF CHAPTER

11.CE.1* Suppose that a U.S. adult is selected at random. What do you expect for the probability that the adult is a male?

A. Close to zero

B. Close to one-fourth

C. Close to one-half

D. Close to three-fourths

E. Close to 1

11.CE.2 Suppose that a U.S. adult is selected at random. What do you expect for the probability that the adult is a member of Congress?

A. Close to zero

B. Close to one-fourth

C. Close to one-half

D. Close to three-fourths

E. Close to 1

11.CE.3* Suppose that a U.S. adult is selected at random. What do you expect for the conditional probability that the adult is a member of Congress, given that he is male?

A. Close to zero

B. Close to one-fourth

C. Close to one-half

D. Close to three-fourths

E. Close to 1

11.CE.4 Suppose that a U.S. adult is selected at random. What do you expect for the conditional probability that the adult is a male, given that he or she is a member of Congress?

A. Close to zero

B. Close to one-fourth

C. Close to one-half

D. Close to three-fourths

E. Close to 1

11.CE.5* A classic probability problem is called the collector's problem. For example, suppose that cereal boxes contain one prize each, with a total of 4 prizes to be collected. Also suppose that each box of cereal is equally likely to contain any one of the 4 prizes, and the particular prize appearing in one box has no bearing on the prize that appears in another box. You purchase one cereal box at a time, see which prize is in it, and continue buying one box at a time until you have the complete set of 4 prizes. Describe (in detail) how you could (in principle, not necessarily practically) use four index cards to conduct a simulation analysis to approximate the probability that you would need to buy at least 10 boxes to find a complete set of prizes.

11.CE.6 Suppose that a couple has four children. Assume that all 16 outcomes in the sample space are equally likely.

a. List the sample space of all possible outcomes for the sexes of these four children. (For example, three of the possible outcomes are $B_1B_2B_3B_4$, $B_1G_2B_3G_4$, and $B_1B_2G_3G_4$, where B_i means that the ith child is a boy and G_i means that the ith child is a girl.)

b. Determine the probability that all four children are of the same sex.

c. Which is more likely—that the couple will have 2 children of each sex or a 3–1 breakdown? Justify your answer.

11.CE.7* Suppose that you encounter two traffic lights on your drive to school. From past experience, you judge that the probability is 0.45 that the first light will be red when you get to it, 0.35 that the second light will be red, and 0.25 that *both* lights will be red.

a. Determine the probability that *at least one* light will be red. Show how to answer this with a probability table, with a Venn diagram, and with a probability rule.

b. Describe (in words) the *complement* of the event that at least one light will be red. Also report the probability of this event (the complement of the event that at least one light is red).

11.CE.8 The 2012 *U.S. Pet Ownership and Demographics Sourcebook* reported that 36.5% of American households have a pet dog and 30.4% have a pet cat.

a. Does it follow from this information that 36.5% + 30.4% = 66.9% of American households have a pet dog *or* a pet cat? Explain your answer, referring to at least one probability rule.

b. Based on the given percentages, what is the *smallest* possible value for the percentage of American households that have a pet dog *or* a pet cat?

c. Describe (in words) the (very unrealistic) circumstance in which this (your answer to part (b)) would occur.

11.CE.9* Suppose that 28% of adults in a certain community have received a speeding ticket, that 42% have received a parking ticket, and that 17% have received both a speeding ticket and a parking ticket. Suppose that an adult from this community is randomly selected.

a. Determine the probability that the person has received at least one ticket of either type.

b. Determine the probability that the person has received no tickets of either type.

c. Determine the conditional probability that the person has received a speeding ticket, given that he or she has received a parking ticket.

d. Are the events that the person has received a speeding ticket and that the person has received a parking ticket *independent*? Justify your answer, based on the given probabilities.

e. Are the events that the person has received a speeding ticket and that the person has received a parking ticket *mutually exclusive*? Justify your answer, based on the given probabilities.

f. Determine the conditional probability that the person has received both types of tickets, given that he or she has received at least one type of ticket.

11.CE.10 Suppose that there's a 20% chance of rain on Saturday. The probabilities for Sunday depend on what happens on Saturday. If it rains on Saturday, then there's an 80% chance of rain on Sunday and if it doesn't rain on Saturday, there's a 10% chance of rain on Sunday.

a. Express these three percentages as probabilities, using appropriate notation.

b. Create a probability tree to represent these probabilities.

c. Determine the probability that it rains on both Saturday and Sunday.

d. Determine the probability that it rains on Sunday.

e. Determine the conditional probability that it rained on Saturday, given that it rained on Sunday.

(1) (2) (3) (4) (5) (6) (7) (8) (9) (10) (11) (12)

Preparing for the AP Statistics Exam: Pulling It All Together

In this chapter we will review the four broad conceptual themes that make up the AP Statistics curriculum. Our focus will be on how and when to use the tools that you have learned on the AP Statistics exam. Pay close attention to the AP Tips. If you need additional review, go back and revisit the sections in the text where you were first introduced to these concepts.

The curriculum for the AP Statistics exam has these four basic themes:

I. Exploring Data: Describing patterns and departures from patterns (20%–30%)

II. Sampling and Experimentation: Planning and conduction of a study (10%–15%)

III. Anticipating Patterns: Exploring random phenomena using probability and simulation (20%–30%)

IV. Statistical Inference: Estimating population parameters and testing hypotheses (30%–40%)

The percentage indicates the approximate percentage of exam questions on that topic.

Details of the exam—content, coverage, and timing

In the appendices of this book is a full-length exam modeled after the Advanced Placement Statistics Exam. There is also another exam available online at the book companion site. The AP Statistics exam has two parts: A multiple-choice section and a Free Response section with 90 minutes allotted for each. Section I (Multiple Choice) consists of 40 multiple-choice questions with five possible

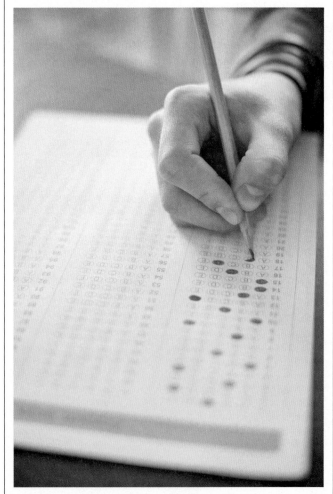

mediaphotos/iStock/Getty Images

answers for each question. There is no penalty for guessing on the AP Statistics exam: both an incorrect answer and an answer left blank receive no credit. Because there is no penalty for guessing, you should answer every question before the end of the 90 minutes allotted for this section.

Section II (Free Response) consists of six free response questions and is allotted a separate 90-minute time block (you will be given a short break between Sections I and II). Section II is broken down into two parts—Part A consists of five free response questions, which should take you approximately 65 minutes. Part B is the Investigative Task Question, which should take you approximately 25 minutes. You will have to pace yourself through Parts A and B of Section II. The Investigative Task Question typically has several parts and, as the name suggests, it may ask you to expand what you have learned in statistics to answer a question that goes a bit beyond the curriculum.

The grading for the two sections is combined as follows:

- Section I (Multiple Choice) comprises 50% of the total score. Each correct answer in this section is awarded 1.25 points for a possible total of 50 points.
- Section II (Free Response) comprises 50% of the total score. Each free response question is assigned a score from 0 to 4.
  - Part A counts for 75% of the Section II Free Response score. The attained score (0-4) for each of the first five free response questions is multiplied by 1.875 to obtain the total score for Part A.
  - Part B counts for 25% of the Section II Free Response score. The attained score (0-4) for question number 6, the Investigative Task, is multiplied by 3.125 to obtain the total score for Part B.

After completing Chapter 12, you may want to set aside a 3-hour block of time to take one of the practice exams. This will help you gain insight into pacing for the actual AP exam in addition to specific topics in the curriculum for which additional review would be beneficial.

EXPLORING DATA

SECTION 12.1

The first of the four broad conceptual themes that make up the AP Statistics curriculum is **Exploring Data: Describing patterns and departures from patterns.** Questions on this theme make up 20%–30% of exam questions. This means that typically there will be several multiple-choice and at least one free response question that focus on this topic. This major concept is further broken down into five subtopics labeled A through E.

Exploring Data: Subtopics A, B, and C

Subtopics A, B, and C are related and so we review them first:

A. **Constructing and interpreting graphical displays of univariate data (dotplot, stemplot, histogram, cumulative frequency plot)**
   1. Center and spread
   2. Clusters and gaps
   3. Outliers and other unusual features
   4. Shape

> **B. Summarizing distributions of univariate data**
>
> 1. Measuring center: median and mean
> 2. Measuring spread: range, interquartile range, standard deviation
> 3. Measuring position: quartiles, percentiles, standardized scores (z-scores)
> 4. Using boxplots
> 5. The effects of changing units on summary measures

> **C. Comparing distributions of univariate data (dotplots, back-to-back stemplots, parallel boxplots)**
>
> 1. Comparing center and spread: within-group. Between-group variation
> 2. Comparing clusters and gaps
> 3. Comparing outliers and unusual features
> 4. Comparing shapes

When given a set of data to analyze,

- Determine the observational units and the variable(s) of interest (don't forget measurement units!). This will make it possible for you to meaningfully describe and analyze the data in the context of the study.

- Determine whether the data are categorical or quantitative, and whether you have a single variable or more than one variable. If you have more than one set of observations, ask yourself, "Are the observations independent? Or are the observations paired or matched in some way?" This will determine the appropriate graphical displays and summary statistics to use to analyze the data.

If the problem involves a *single quantitative variable*, you could be asked to construct a graph of the data (e.g., dotplot, stemplot, histogram, or boxplot). If you are not told which graph to use, then you may prefer to use dotplots or stemplots for smaller data sets and boxplots or histograms for larger data sets. Alternatively, you could be asked to interpret a graph of the data. If so, focus your comments on the key elements of the graph, talking about shape, center, and variability and stating your comments in the context of the study, including how the graphs relate to the research question(s). You should also consider and possibly explain any unusual observations (outliers).

AP TIP

When describing a graphical display for a single quantitative variable, note the shape, center, variability, and any unusual features such as gaps, outliers, bimodality, etc. Always describe the distribution of your data in context. From your description, the reader should know the observational units and the variable or variables of interest and their corresponding measurement units.

- If you are asked to compare two groups on a quantitative variable, be sure to appropriate use comparative words such as "more," "less," or "about the same" when comparing the centers and variability of the groups. Be sure it is clear what is being compared to what. If numerical summaries are provided or asked for, you should consider using the mean and/or median as the measure of center and the standard deviation and/or IQR as the measure of variability.

When comparing two distributions, make sure to compare the variable of interest in context, with appropriate units. Consider, for example, data from scores on a test broken down by sex. One common mistake would be for students to say, "The females' shape is symmetric" rather than more precisely and correctly saying, "The distribution of scores for female students is symmetric." Another common mistake is to talk about the "data" or the "graph" instead of the variable of interest.

When asked to compare one or more groups for a quantitative response variable, make sure to use comparative words such as "more," "less," or "about the same" when comparing the centers and variability of the groups and to include what you are comparing to. Simply listing the characteristics of each group rather than comparing them will result in lower scores on the free response questions.

- Parallel boxplots can be useful for comparing potential differences in the quantitative variable between two or more groups such as differences in center (median), variability (IQR and range), and outliers.

When describing the shape of a distribution displayed by a boxplot, you may wish to indicate whether the data are symmetric or skewed, but because you do not know whether there are any peaks in the data, you cannot precisely describe the distribution as bell-shaped or approximately normal. Recall that in a boxplot the data set is split into quarters by the median and the quartiles, with each section containing roughly 1/4th of the data values. If the minimum is much closer to the first quartile than the maximum is to the third quartile (or vice versa), this shows a high density of the data values in that in the lower end of the data and lower density of the data values in the upper end of the data, indicating skewness. If the data values are more densely clustered for the lower values, the distribution is skewed to the right, and if they are more densely clustered toward the higher data values, then the distribution is skewed to the left.

- If you are given summary statistics for your data (e.g., mean, median, standard deviation, IQR, range), consider which summary statistics would be most appropriate to describe the center and variability of the data. If the distribution has extreme skewness or outliers, resistant measures such as the median and IQR are more appropriate.

Exploring Data: Subtopic D

What if you are asked to explore the relationship between **two quantitative variables measured on the same observational units**? Subtopic D focuses on bivariate quantitative data.

D. **Exploring bivariate data**
1. Analyzing patterns in scatterplots
2. Correlation and linearity
3. Least squares regression line
4. Residual plots, outliers, and influential points
5. Transformations to achieve linearity: logarithmic and power transformations

AP TIP

When asked to describe a scatterplot of two quantitative variables, be sure to describe the form (linear or curved), direction (positive or negative), and strength (how closely the dots follow the overall pattern), all in the context of the data with appropriate measurement units.

- When you have two quantitative variables, you can describe the strength of association using either the correlation coefficient, r, or the coefficient of determination, r^2. You should know how to interpret each of these in the context of a particular study.
- When using r^2, be sure to focus on the variation in the *response variable* (identify) explained by the linear association with the *explanatory variable* (identify).

AP TIP

Recall that even though two variables may have a strong association, this does not necessarily mean that one variable caused the other. We can only determine a cause-and-effect relationship from a controlled, randomized experiment.

If we decide the relationship between two quantitative variables is linear, the **least squares regression line** (the line that makes the sum of the squared residuals as small as possible) is a mathematical model that helps us make predictions about the **response variable** (*y*-variable) from the **explanatory variable** (*x*-variable). The least squares regression line is given by

$$\hat{y} = a + bx \quad \text{or} \quad \hat{y} = b_0 + b_1 x$$

where the "hat" (^) on the y indicates that it is a predicted value.

AP TIP

You may be asked to write the equation of the least squares regression line and identify any variables. Be sure to identify your predictor and response variable (in context) and not just with the variables x and $\hat{y}$ when writing the equation of the least squares regression line. Don't forget that you are predicting y from x, so the left-hand side of the equation must be written in terms of y with a hat (^) or as predicted (response variable).

When given bivariate data with the goal of predicting values for the response variable (y) for values of the explanatory variable (x), you might be asked to:

- Identify the slope of the least squares regression line and give its meaning in the context of the research question.

AP TIP

When describing the slope of the least squares regression line, be sure to talk about the change (increase or decrease) in the predicted response variable for each unit increase in the explanatory variable. A common student error is to describe the change in the response variable (y) rather than the change in the **predicted** response variable ($\hat{y}$).

● Assess whether a linear model is appropriate for the data.

● Make or interpret a prediction for the response variable (y) for a given value of the explanatory variable (x).

● Write the equation of a least squares regression line and/or interpret summary statistics from computer output similar to the output shown in Figure 12.1.

FIGURE 12.1 Sample regression output.

● Some important pieces of information that you might be asked about based on the output include:
  ● Stating and interpreting the coefficient of determination (R-Sq).
  ● Stating and interpreting the correlation coefficient (r), find the square root of R-Sq with the sign of r ($+$ or $-$) the same as the slope.
  ● State and interpret S, the standard deviation of the residuals.
  ● Interpreting the p-value for a test of significance.
  ● Calculating a confidence interval for the slope of the population.

There may be values on the computer output such as R-sq(adj) that are not part of the AP Statistics curriculum—just ignore them.

If the scatterplot of the data does not follow a linear trend, then linear regression on the variables is not appropriate.

> **AP TIP**
>
> On the exam, one or both of the variables may have already been transformed to linearize the data. You may be asked to use this model to make predictions. For example, if the transformed data are in terms of $(x, \log y)$, make sure to give your answer in terms of the response variable y and not $\log y$. In other words, reverse-transform to the original units when stating the predicted response.

Exploring Data: Subtopic E

What if you are asked to explore **one categorical variable** or the relationship between **two categorical variables measured on the same observational units**? Subtopic E focuses on categorical data.

> E. **Exploring categorical data**
>   1. Frequency tables and bar charts
>   2. Marginal and joint frequencies for two-way tables
>   3. Conditional relative frequencies and association
>   4. Comparing distributions using bar charts

If the problem involves a *single categorical variable*, there are several things you could be asked to do. These include constructing and/or interpreting a graph of the data (bar chart).

> **AP TIP**
>
> Do not confuse a bar chart with a histogram. In a bar chart, categories of the variable are separated by a gap. In a histogram, a gap appears between bars only when there are no data values in that particular interval.

- If you are asked to compare data from *two categorical variables*, the data may be organized graphically (side-by-side bar charts or segmented bar charts) and/or in a two-way table.

> **AP TIP**
>
> If asked to produce a graphical display to examine the relationship between two categorical variables, constructing a separate bar chart for each variable is not appropriate, as it does not reveal anything about the relationship between the two variables. Side-by-side bar charts or a segmented bar chart allows the reader to examine the relationship (if there is one) between the two variables.

- You may be asked whether there is an association between the two variables. A segmented bar graph displays the association between two categorical variables by showing the **conditional proportions** of success and failure across the explanatory variable groups. If the variables have no association, then the breakdown of segments is identical across all the bars.

SAMPLING AND EXPERIMENTATION SECTION 12.2

The second of the four broad conceptual themes that makes up the AP Statistics curriculum is **Sampling and Experimentation: Planning and conducting a study.** Questions on this theme constitute 10%–15% of the exam. This means you can expect several multiple-choice and at least part of one free response question to focus on this topic. This major concept is further delineated into four subtopics labeled A through D, which we will review in this section.

Sampling and Experimentation: Subtopics A, B, C, and D

A. **Overview of types of studies**
  1. Observational study
  2. Experiment
  3. Sample survey
  4. Census

It is important to know the definitions of experiments, observational studies, surveys, and a census.

1. **Observational Study**—Observing a group that is already intact; no treatment is actively imposed or manipulated by the researchers. You can look at associations between variables but cannot assign a causal relationship. In observational studies, you need to be able to talk about confounding variables. A confounding variable is a variable whose effect on the response variable cannot be separated out from the explanatory variable's effect.

2. **Experiment**—A well-designed experiment includes random assignment to two or more treatments, and replication. If a significant relationship exists, cause-and-effect conclusions can be drawn between the explanatory and response variables. For more detail, see part C.

AP TIP

If you are asked to determine whether a study is an experiment or an observational study, determine whether there is active imposition of treatment(s) to the experimental units. For example, in a study investigating whether vitamin C reduces the risk of the common cold, an advantage of randomly assigning participants to take vitamin C or a placebo over a 2-week period is that it potentially allows a cause-effect conclusion. An observational study asking people whether they took vitamin C in the last two weeks and whether they had cold symptoms may find an association between the variables, but that association may be better explained by a confounding variable (e.g., people who exercise better, get more sleep, and eat better may be at decreased risk of colds for those reasons, and also be more likely to take vitamin C regularly).

3. **Surveys**—Typically, questions are posed to people, often a subset of a larger population of interest.

4. **Census**—Measurements are taken on the entire population.

B. **Planning and conducting surveys**
   1. Characteristics of a well-designed and well-conducted survey
   2. Populations, samples, and random selection
   3. Sources of bias in sampling surveys
   4. Sampling methods, including simple random sampling, stratified random sampling, and cluster sampling

- Be able to design different types of sampling plans and to discuss the relative advantages and disadvantage of different approaches.
- Do not confuse sampling bias with random sampling error. A sampling method is biased if, in repeated sampling, the statistic tends to systematically overrepresent or underrepresent segments of the population. Random sampling error is a natural result of sampling variability. With random sampling error, we can measure how close an estimate based on a random sample is likely to fall from the population parameter. Confidence intervals and p-values can account for random sampling error, but not bias.

AP TIP

You should be able to quickly identify common sources of sampling bias, e.g., voluntary response bias and incomplete sampling frames. Also, be on the lookout for non-sampling errors, such as questions worded in a slanted manner.

AP TIP

If asked to describe the bias in a sampling method, discuss why a sample found using that method is likely to not be representative of the population with respect to the variable of interest, and make a conjecture about the direction of the bias—whether the resulting sample statistics will likely overestimate or underestimate the parameter of interest. Recall the Sampling Words activity in Chapter 2 in which you were asked to use your judgment to select a sample of 10 words from the Gettysburg Address. Students tended to pick words with more letters, resulting in a systematic overestimate of the population mean word length.

C. **Planning and conducting experiments**
   1. Characteristics of a well-designed and well-conducted experiment
   2. Treatments, control groups, experimental units, random assignments, and replication
   3. Sources of bias and confounding, including placebo effect and blinding
   4. Completely randomized design
   5. Randomized block design, including matched pairs design

- When asked to design an experiment, it is assumed that the experiment you design will control for as much anticipated variability as possible in the design of the experiment. This may include some form of blocking.
- Also make sure to include enough detail in the description of the study design that it could be easily replicated (e.g., number of experimental units, random assignment, and response variable to be measured).

AP TIP

If asked to explain why random assignment is necessary in an experiment, you should explain that it produces treatment groups that are as similar as possible before the treatment is applied so that any systematic differences in the response variable after the treatment has been applied can be attributed to the effects of the treatments.

AP TIP

If you are asked whether an experiment has been done in a double-blind manner, you need to explain that neither (1) the subject nor (2) those administering the treatments/evaluating the response know which treatment a subject received.

AP TIP

When asked whether it is possible to draw a cause-and-effect conclusion about a study, remember that this is only possible if the study was a controlled, randomized experiment (and even then you need a small p-value to rule out random chance).

Note that the term "control" is used in different ways. For example, a "control group" is typically defined as a group in an experiment that receives no treatment or a placebo treatment. In an experiment, it's important to have a second comparison group (which may be a second treatment group or a control group) so that any other changes occurring during the time of the experiment will occur for all treatment groups, again isolating the treatment variable as the only change between the groups. When designing a study, we also attempt to "control" other variables, such as keeping the temperature or level of lighting constant throughout the study.

D. **Generalizability of results and types of conclusions that can be drawn from observational studies, experiments, and surveys**

Keep in mind that there are two main uses of randomness in study design:

- Randomly selecting "units" from a larger population to use in the study. The purpose of random sampling is to allow us to generalize results from our study back to the larger population.
- Randomizing subjects to treatment groups. Random assignment allows us to draw a causal connection between our explanatory variable and response variable if an association exists.

You need to be able to describe an implementation of each type of randomness and the different goals of each. Random sampling (or not) has to do with how the individuals are selected for the study in the first place. Random assignment (or not) has to do with how any subgroups are created. Both how we select subjects/units for a study and what we do with them once selected will affect the scope of the conclusions that we can make. Figure 12.2 illustrates the scope of inference based on how the units were selected and whether they were randomly assigned to a treatment group.

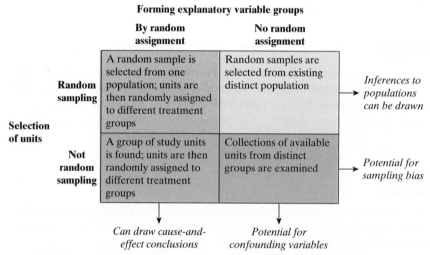

FIGURE 12.2 Study design factors and their impact on scope of conclusions (adapted from Ramsey and Schafer, *The Statistical Sleuth*).

The following table compares two additional steps that are sometimes taken in designing a study that control for more variability in random sampling or random assignment, respectively.

	Sampling	Experimentation
How do we control for anticipated variability?	Stratified Random Sampling	Blocking
How do you choose strata (sampling) or blocks (experiment)?	Classify the population into subgroups or strata with observational units within each stratum as similar as possible in ways that may be related to what you are measuring, and observational units in different strata are different in ways that may be related to the response variable.	Blocking is the experimental design equivalent of stratified random sampling. A block is a group of experimental units that are similar in some way that is expected to differ on the response we are measuring. Experimental units within each block should be as similar as possible in ways that may be related to the response variable, and experimental unit across different blocks should be different in ways that may be related to the response variable.

(continued)

Advantage?	An advantage of stratified sampling over simple random sampling is that the representativeness of the samples may be improved in terms of reduced sampling error. It also assures that you will get adequate representation from each subgroup.	Blocking helps to control for anticipated variability before we begin our experiment. We block on a variable because we anticipate that it may be related to our response variable.
Implementation	The population is broken down into non-overlapping strata and a simple random sample is taken from each stratum.	Once blocks are determined, we randomly assign experimental units to treatments within each block. We then run parallel experiments within each block.

AP TIP

When asked to choose between two or more sampling methods or experimental designs, students to you must identify both a positive statistical aspect of the chosen method and a negative statistical aspect of the method(s) not chosen. For example, the administration of a university would like to survey 100 students regarding a proposed initiative. Ten percent of the students are graduate students, and it is anticipated that undergraduate and graduate students might differ in their response to the proposed initiative. In a simple random sample of 100 students from this university, it is possible that graduate students may be underrepresented or not represented at all in the survey. On the other hand, taking a stratified random sample and stratifying on graduate vs. undergraduate student status will guarantee representation of both graduate and undergraduate students, and should reduce sample-to-sample variation in the results.

ANTICIPATING PATTERNS — SECTION 12.3

The third of the four broad conceptual themes that makes up the AP Statistics curriculum is **Anticipating Patterns: Exploring random phenomena using probability and simulation.** Questions on this theme constitute 20%–30% of the exam. This means you can expect several multiple-choice and at least one free response question to focus on this topic. This major concept is further delineated into four subtopics labeled A through D, which we will review in this section.

A. Probability
1. Interpreting probability, including long-run relative frequency interpretation
2. "Law of Large Numbers" concept
3. Addition rule, multiplication rule, conditional probability, and independence
4. Discrete random variables and their probability distributions, including binomial and geometric
5. Simulation of random behavior and probability distributions
6. Mean (expected value) and standard deviation of a random variable, and linear transformation of a random variable

Many probability problems can be solved using a formula, so you should familiarize yourself with the formulas involving probability on the AP^{TM} formula sheet.

Some General Probability Rules on the AP Formula Sheet

$$P(A \cup B) = P(A) + P(B) - P(A \cap B)$$

$$P(A|B) = \frac{P(A \cap B)}{P(B)}$$

$$E(X) = \mu_x = \sum x_i p_i$$

$$\text{Var}(X) = \sigma_x^2 = \sum (x_i - \mu_x)^2 p_i$$

The key will be in deciding which formula to use when. Watch for key words like "and," "or," "at least," "given," "average." Also consider whether there is an assumption of independence of events. The word "or" in a probability problem is not used in the same way that it is in conversational English. In conversational English, it typically refers to an *exclusive or*—you are doing A or B but not both. In probability, it is used as an *inclusive or*—you are doing A or B or both. The probability of A *or* B will generally be larger than either of the individual probabilities. The probability of A *and* B will generally be smaller than either of the individual probabilities.

> **AP TIP**
>
> Some strategies that you may employ when asked to solve a problem that involves calculating a probability are to look for an appropriate formula on the AP™ formula sheet, sketch a Venn diagram, and/or construct a two-way table of counts or a probability table. You might consider using multiple methods to confirm your answer. Always, always, always show calculation details and how you arrived at your final answer.

If a probability looks as if it will take a while to calculate, consider the complement of the event and whether that its probability might be easier to determine. You should also practice using proper random variable notation.

In addition to the general probability rules given above, you should also ask yourself whether one of the special probability distributions you studied such as the binomial, geometric, or normal distribution is appropriate to use to solve the problem. Often, the probability distribution will be named and you will be given parameters, but you should also be able to decide whether a "binomial process" has been described. You will be able to use either the formulas on the formula sheet or your calculator to perform these calculations. (Shortcuts for calculating the means and standard deviations are especially helpful.)

> **AP TIP**
>
> Try to avoid "explaining" your answer by only providing calculator output. If you do want to illustrate the work you did on your calculator, be sure to report the functions and inputs used. Finish with an interpretation of the calculated probability in English.

Be especially on the lookout between conditional and unconditional probabilities.

> **Recall:** If you know that some event (e.g., B) has (or has not) occurred, the sample space that you are interested in shrinks to that event (e.g., B). The **conditional probability** is then the probability of everything in the intersection of the two events (can A also occur?) divided by the probability of the sample space of the given event.
>
> $$P(A|B) = \frac{P(A \cap B)}{P(B)}$$

Independence means that knowledge of the outcome of one event does not affect the probability of another event occurring or not. If two events are independent, the conditional probability of an event is the same as the unconditional probability of the event. If you are asked to determine whether two events A and B are independent, you need to calculate both the conditional and unconditional probability of the event and compare them.

Recall: Events A and B are *independent* if $P(A|B) = P(A)$, or $P(B|A) = P(B)$, or $P(A \cap B) = P(A) \times P(B)$.

B. **Combining independent random variables**
   1. Notion of independence versus dependence
   2. Mean and standard deviation for sums and differences of independent random variables

---

Two random variables are independent if the probability distribution of one random variable does not change depending on the outcome of the other random variable. For example, the random variables could be the outcomes of two separate rolls of a die. Common questions on the exam for this topic will require you to give the distribution and/or the expected value and standard deviation of the sum or the difference of two random variables, or a linear combination. These formulas are not provided on the Formulas page.

Recall: When combining two independent random variables, remember that their standard deviations do **not** add but their variances do. Also keep in mind that if two random variables follow a normal distribution, so do their sum and their difference. This convenient property does not apply to many other distributions (e.g., the sum of two binomial random variables does not follow a binomial distribution).

C. **The normal distribution**
   1. Properties of the normal distribution
   2. Using tables of the normal distribution
   3. The normal distribution as a model for measurements

In a problem from this topic, you will often be told that the data are assumed to follow a normal distribution, but you should also think about the variable being measured to decide whether this makes sense in context.

AP TIP

You need two numbers to describe a normal distribution, its mean and standard deviation. Remember always to report the values you are using, even if you use your calculator to carry out the calculation. Always start a normal probability calculation by sketching a normal curve, labeling the horizontal axis, and labeling the mean, the mean ± 1 SD, and mean ± 2 SDs.

Standardized scores measure the position of a data value from the mean of the distribution in terms of standard deviation units. The sign (positive or negative) tells you whether the value is above or below the mean, and the absolute value of the standardized score tells you how far from the mean (in the tails of the distribution) your value is. If you know the mean and the standard deviation of a distribution, you can convert any value in the distribution to a standardized or z-score regardless of the shape of the distribution. However, if you want to use the z-score to find a probability, then the shape of the distribution should be approximately normal.

Also keep in mind that a normal distribution can often be used to approximate tail probabilities from the binomial distribution, provided that the number of expected successes $n\pi$ and the number of expected failures $n(1 - \pi)$ are both at least 10.

D. Sampling Distributions

1. Sampling distribution of a sample proportion
2. Sampling distribution of a sample mean
3. Central limit theorem (CLT)
4. Sampling distribution of a difference between two independent sample proportions
5. Sampling distribution of a difference between two independent sample means
6. Simulation of sampling distributions
7. t-distributions
8. Chi-square distribution

You have seen lots of sampling distributions in this course, even though we did not always use that term. Basically, any time you are talking about the distribution of a *statistic* (as a random variable, across repeated samples from the same population), you are referring to a sampling distribution. You also saw lots of similarities in how these sampling distributions behave. In particular, the distributions of sample proportions, sample means, differences in sample proportions, and differences in sample means are often well modeled by normal distributions— as long as the sample size is large enough. How you check whether the sample size is large enough looks a little different in each case (see the Recall box), and the formulas we use to predict the mean and standard deviation of these distributions also change. These formulas aren't given on the Formula Sheet directly but can be gleaned from the Inferential Statistics formulas.

Recall:

- With quantitative data, the distributions of sample means will be approximately normally distributed for sample sizes of at least 30 regardless of the shape of the population, with larger sample sizes needed for more skewed populations.

- With categorical data, the skewness of the population is captured by how far the population proportion is from 0.50. So we don't just look at the sample size, we look at the sample size relative to that probability (e.g., $n\pi$ and $n(1 - \pi)$).

You should always start by asking yourself whether the variable you are working with is a quantitative or a categorical variable.

AP TIP

If you are asked to describe the distribution of a sample statistic, be sure to address center, variability (show the values that you plug in to the appropriate formula to calculate the standard deviation of the statistic), and shape (justify your choice of shape; for example, the sampling distribution of the sample mean is approximately normally distributed because the sample size is greater than 30, thus, the CLT applies).

STATISTICAL INFERENCE

The last of the four broad conceptual themes that makes up the AP Statistics curriculum is **Statistical Inference: Estimating population parameters and testing hypotheses.** Questions on this theme constitute 30%–40% of the exam. This means you can expect several multiple-choice and at least one or two free response questions to focus on this topic. This major concept is further delineated into two subtopics labeled A and B, which we will review in this section.

> A. **Estimation (point estimators and confidence intervals)**
>   1. Estimating population parameters and margins of error
>   2. Properties of point estimators, including unbiasedness and variability
>   3. Logic of confidence intervals, meaning of confidence level and confidence intervals, and properties of confidence intervals
>   4. Large sample confidence interval for a proportion
>   5. Large sample confidence interval for a difference between two proportions
>   6. Confidence interval for a mean
>   7. Confidence interval for a difference between two means (unpaired and paired)
>   8. Confidence interval for the slope of a least squares regression line

- You learned that when a confidence interval is called for, you must show the following work to receive full credit on the AP Statistics exam.

  1. Identify the parameter you want to estimate and the theory-based method you will use.

  2. Verify the validity conditions for the theory-based method you have chosen.

  3. Construct the confidence interval, showing the values that you substitute into the formula.

  4. Interpret the confidence interval you obtained in the context of the problem.

Know the difference between interpreting a confidence **interval** and the corresponding confidence **level**. A confidence interval gives a range of plausible values for the specific population parameter that we want to estimate. The confidence level provides information about how much confidence we have in the **method** used to produce the confidence interval. The confidence level gives the long-run proportion of intervals constructed using this method that would succeed in capturing the population parameter within their endpoints. Keep in mind that the interval changes from sample to sample.

> **AP TIP**
>
> Be careful of common student mistakes when interpreting a confidence level. A statement such as "There is a 95% probability that the population proportion is contained in the confidence interval 0.2 to 0.6" is incorrect. The parameter is either in the reported interval or it is not. The uncertainty is in the sample statistic we use to estimate the population parameter, because we know that a different sample would likely yield a different estimate as a result of sample-to-sample variability. There is no uncertainty associated with the parameter; it is a fixed value, so we do not make probability statements about the parameter.

- Every confidence interval in this course is of the form:
  Confidence interval: *statistic* $\pm$ *(critical value)* $\times$ *(standard deviation of statistic)*

> **AP TIP**
>
> You may be asked a question about the margin of error, standard error, or critical value for a particular confidence level, so be certain that you know the names of the different components that make up the confidence interval formula.

If asked, you can often use either a table or your calculator to determine the critical values. Make sure it is clear how you have done so. It is recommended always to show the values substituted into the formula, even if you use your calculator to find the interval directly.

Determine whether the data are categorical or quantitative and whether you have a single variable or more than one variable. If you have more than one set of observations, ask yourself, "Are the observations independent? Or are the observations paired or matched in some way?" This will determine the appropriate theory-based method to use. See the tables below for a summary of each method.

B. Tests of significance

1. Logic of significance testing, null and alternative hypotheses; p-values; one- and two-sided tests; concepts of Type I and Type II errors; concept of power
2. Large sample test for a proportion
3. Large sample test for a difference between two proportions
4. Test for a mean
5. Test for a difference between two means (unpaired and paired)
6. Chi-square test for goodness of fit, homogeneity of proportions, and independence (one- and two-way tables)
7. Test for the slope of a least squares regression line

You learned that when a hypothesis test is called for, you must show the following work to receive full credit on the AP Statistics exam:

1. State the hypotheses either in words or using appropriate symbols.
2. Name the test that will be used, and state and verify the validity conditions for the test chosen.
3. Calculate the test statistic (standardized statistic) and corresponding p-value.
4. State your conclusion (with appropriate justification based on your p-value and significance level) in the context of the research question.

You can often use either a table or your calculator to determine the p-value, but be sure it is clear how you have done so. It is recommended always to show the values substituted into the formula and report the value of the test statistic (and any degrees of freedom), even if you use your calculator to find the p-value directly.

AP TIP

A question requiring a hypothesis test will not typically be phrased as obviously as something like, "Conduct a hypothesis test." Instead, key phrases to watch for that signal the need to conduct a hypothesis test are statements such as, *"Does this provide convincing evidence that…?"* and *"Is there a statistically significant difference…?"* This is in contrast to a question asking for a confidence interval, a question that may use the terms *"Provide a range of plausible values for…"* or *"Find an interval estimate…."*

When a hypothesis test is called for, how might you determine the appropriate test to use?

- First ask yourself whether your data are quantitative or categorical.
- Next ask yourself if you have one variable with one sample or two samples (independent or paired) or two variables (e.g., using one to predict the other).

The tables below outline the thought process you might use to determine the appropriate theory-based test or confidence interval.

Quantitative Response

One Sample	Two Independent Samples
If there is only one set of observations or the observations are paired (e.g., matched pairs), do a one-sample t-test of the mean or the mean difference (you may need to calculate the differences yourself).	If the two groups are independent (e.g., independent random samples or randomized experiment), do a two-sample t-test of the difference in means.
Example: Is the mean haircut price larger than $20 in this population?	Example: Is there evidence of a difference in the means of the two populations?
Example: Is the wide angle significantly better than the narrow angle (both measured for each runner)?	

One-Sample t-test for Population Mean	Two-Sample t-test for Difference in Population Means
$H_0 : \mu_1 = \mu_0$ (claim) $H_a : \mu \neq, >, < \mu_0$ (claim)	$H_0 : \mu_1 = \mu_2$ $H_a : \mu_1 \neq, >, < \mu_2$
Define μ in context as a population mean. If it is a mean difference, specify the direction of subtraction. $$t = \frac{\bar{x} - \mu_0}{s/\sqrt{n}}$$ $$df = n - 1$$	Define the two groups or use letters that clearly represent the data. $$t = \frac{\bar{x}_1 - \bar{x}_2 - 0}{\sqrt{\frac{s_1^2}{n_1} + \frac{s_2^2}{n_2}}}$$ df is from the calculator or a conservative estimate (the smaller of $n_1 - 1$ or $n_2 - 1$).

One-Sample t-interval for Population Mean	Two-Sample t-interval for Difference in Population Means
CI for μ: $\bar{x} \pm t^*_{df=n-1} \times (s/\sqrt{n})$	CI for $\mu_1 - \mu_2$: $(\bar{x}_1 - \bar{x}_2) \pm t^*_{df} \times \sqrt{\frac{s_1^2}{n_1} + \frac{s_2^2}{n_2}}$

Validity Conditions	Validity Conditions

• Data are from a random sample from the population of interest or from a matched-pairs randomized experiment.
 • Population distribution is approximately normally distributed, or sample size is large enough for the central limit theorem to apply (e.g., $n \geq 30$).
   • For smaller samples where the population shape is unknown, graph the sample data and comment on whether it is reasonable to assume that the sample data came from a population that is fairly symmetric (see Section 2.2, Part 2). Occasionally, you may also have other reasons to suspect that the population distribution is normal (e.g., historical evidence).
	• Data are from two independent random samples from the populations of interest, or from two groups in a randomized experiment.
	 • Both population distributions are approximately normally distributed, or the sample sizes for both groups are large enough for the central limit theorem to apply (e.g., n_1 and $n_2 \geq 30$).
	   • For smaller samples where the population shapes are unknown, graph the sample data and comment on whether it is reasonable to assume that the sample data from each group came from populations that are fairly symmetric (see Section 2.2, Part 2). Occasionally, you may also have other reasons to suspect that the population distributions are close to normally distributed (e.g., historical evidence).

Graphical Displays to Describe Data:	Graphical Displays to Compare Data:
• dotplot • boxplot • histogram • stemplot	• stacked boxplots (same scale) • dotplots (same scale) • histogram (same scale) • back-to-back stemplots

Two Quantitative Variables

Are you using one quantitative variable to predict another?

Linear Regression t-test for Slope

$$H_0 : \beta = 0$$

$$H_a : \beta \neq, >, < 0$$

$$t = \frac{b - 0}{SE_b}$$

$$df = n - 2$$

Linear Regression t-interval for slope

CI for β: $b \pm t^*_{df=n-2} \times SE_b$

Validity Conditions:

- The relationship between the explanatory and response variables is linear.
  - Verify that the scatterplot is linear and there is no pattern in the residual plot.
- Individual observations are independent. The prediction errors (residuals) should be independent of one another.
  - Verify that the data were obtained from a random sample or randomized experiment.
- For any fixed x, the responses y follow a normal distribution with standard deviation σ (the responses y at each value of x vary normally about the mean at that value of x).
  - Verify that the residuals are approximately normally distributed by examining a dotplot or histogram or normal probability plot of the residuals.
- Nearly equal variation in the residuals for different values of the explanatory variable.
  - Examine the residual plot. The variability in the residuals should be nearly the same for all values of the explanatory variable.

Graphical Displays:

- Scatterplot with least squares regression line
- Residual plot (residuals vs. explanatory variable)
  - Should not be a pattern (if curved, try a transformation).
  - Should be near constant variance in the residuals across the explanatory variable.
- Histogram/dotplot of residuals
  - Residuals should be approximately normally distributed.

Categorical Response

1-Sample (binary)	1-Sample (more than 2 categories)
Example: Do we have statistical evidence that the stated (claimed) proportion or long-run probability has changed?	Example: Is there statistical evidence that the stated distribution of the variable has changed from some stated or claimed distribution? (Refer to the fair die example.)
1-Proportion z-test for Population Proportion	**Chi-square χ^2 Goodness-of-Fit Test**
$$H_0 : \pi = \pi_0 \ (claim)$$ $$H_a : \pi \neq, >, < \pi_0 \ (claim)$$ Define π in context as a population proportion. $$z = \frac{\hat{p} - \pi_0}{\sqrt{\pi_0(1 - \pi_0)/n}}$$	H_0: The distribution of proportions in the population for [...] is as stated. H_a: At least one of the stated population proportions is different. $$\chi^2 = \sum \frac{(observed - expected)^2}{expected}$$ $df = k - 1$, where k is the number of categories of the variable.
1-Proportion z-interval for Population Proportion	
CI for π: $\hat{p} \pm z^* \times \sqrt{\hat{p}(1 - \hat{p})/n}$	

(continued)

Validity Conditions:	**Validity Conditions:**
• Data are from a random sample from the population or process of interest • Verify that $n\pi \geq 10$ and $n(1 - \pi) \geq 10$ by substituting the appropriate values into the formula. In a hypothesis test, you will use the hypothesized value of π to perform this check. In a confidence interval, use $\hat{p}$.	• Data (single categorical variable) are a random sample from the population or process of interest. • All **expected** cell counts are at least 5. If not, consider combining categories that make sense to combine.
Graphical Displays: • bar chart • pie graph	**Graphical Displays:** • side-by-side bar chart to compare observed with expected • segmented bar graph

Two Categorical Variables

Two Independent Samples	**Two-Way Tables**
Comparing a binary response variable across groups Example: Is there a statistically significant difference in the proportion of successes for the two populations?	Two categorical variables

2-Proportion *z*-test for Difference in Population Proportions	**Were Separate Random Samples Taken for One of the Category Variables?**

Two Independent Samples

2-Proportion *z*-test for Difference in Population Proportions

$$H_0 : \pi_1 = \pi_2$$
$$H_a : \pi_1 \neq, >, < \pi_2$$

Define the two groups or use letters that clearly represent the data.

$$z = \frac{\hat{p}_1 - \hat{p}_2}{\sqrt{\hat{p}(1 - \hat{p})(1/n_1 + 1/n_2)}}$$

$\hat{p} = $ (total # of successes)/$(n_1 + n_2)$

Two-Way Tables

Were Separate Random Samples Taken for One of the Category Variables?

Chi-square χ^2 Test of Homogeneity (Equal Proportions)

Example: A random sample of 57 males and a separate random sample of 58 females were taken. Each person was asked for his or her opinion about…

	Agree	Neutral	Disagree
Male	13	34	10
Female	36	13	9

H_0: The distribution of proportions for each opinion category is the same for each gender.

H_a: At least one of the stated proportions is different.

$$X^2 = \sum \frac{(observed - expected)^2}{expected}$$

$$df = (rows - 1)(columns - 1)$$

Was One Random Sample Taken and the Individuals Classified According to Two Categorical Variables?

Chi-square χ^2 Test of Independence

Example: A random sample of 100 students is taken and their hair color and eye color recorded.

H_0: There is no association between hair color and eye color.

H_a: There is an association between hair color and eye color.

$$X^2 = \sum \frac{(observed - expected)^2}{expected}$$

$$df = (num\ rows - 1)(num\ columns - 1)$$

(continued)

2-Proportion z-interval for Difference in Population Proportions CI for $\pi_1 - \pi_2$: $$\hat{p}_1 - \hat{p}_2 \pm z^* \times \sqrt{\frac{\hat{p}_1(1-\hat{p}_1)}{n_1} + \frac{\hat{p}_2(1-\hat{p}_2)}{n_2}}$$	
Validity Conditions: • Data are from two independent random samples from the populations of interest, or from two groups in a randomized experiment. • The distribution of the difference in sample proportions will be bell-shaped (approximately normal) if the counts of successes and failures in each sample or group $[n_1\hat{p}_1, n_1(1-\hat{p}_1), n_2\hat{p}_2, n_2(1-\hat{p}_2)]$ are all at least 10.	**Validity Conditions:** • Randomness in the data collection • Test of Independence: Data are from a random sample from the population of interest. • Test of Homogeneity: Data are from independent random samples or randomized experiment. • All expected cell counts are at least 5.
Graphical Displays: (use proportions or percentages) • side-by-side bar chart • segmented bar graph	**Graphical Displays:** (use proportions or percentages) • side-by-side bar chart • segmented bar graph

---

AP TIP

There are two main conditions to check in every theory-based procedure.

1. One is the **manner in which the data were collected**. Having obtained the data from random sampling or having used random assignment in the study allows us to conduct the test and generate a p-value or to generate a confidence interval.

2. A second validity condition for a theory-based approach is that the **model chosen is a good prediction** for the null distribution. For the theory-based approaches, this often requires sufficient sample size(s).

The method used to collect the data will also impact the scope of conclusions:

• Determining to what long-run process or population the results of our study can be generalized (What did you sample from?)

• Determining whether or not we can attribute a cause-and-effect relationship (Was there random assignment?)

Recall: The conclusion for a hypothesis test should include the criteria you used to make your decision (compare the p-value to the stated significance-level) and should be in the context of your research hypothesis (H_a), including any measurement units.

Recall: The conclusion for a confidence interval should include the confidence level and the range of plausible values for the population parameter in the context of the research study, including any measurement units.

You should know the relationship between a two-sided hypothesis test with significance level α and the corresponding $(1 - \alpha)\%$ confidence level.

AP TIP

If you fail to reject the null hypothesis in a test of significance, the value in the null is still a plausible value for the population parameter and should be contained in the corresponding confidence interval. Likewise, if you reject the null hypothesis, the value in the null is not a plausible value for the population parameter and should not be contained in the corresponding confidence interval.

- *Note:* This is a guideline and there are situations where this is not exactly true, e.g., one-sided p-values rather than two-sided p-values; using different standard errors between the confidence interval and the test statistic.

CHAPTER 12 Summary

In this chapter you reviewed the four broad conceptual themes that make up the AP Statistics curriculum.

- **Exploring Data: Describing patterns and departures from patterns.** Questions on this theme make up 20%–30% of the exam so you can expect several multiple-choice and at least one free response question on this topic.

- **Sampling and Experimentation: Planning and conducting a study.** Questions on this theme make up 10%–15% of the exam so you can expect several multiple-choice and at least part of one free response question on this topic.

- **Anticipating Patterns: Exploring random phenomena using probability and simulation.** Questions on this theme make up 20%–30% of the exam so you can expect several multiple-choice and at least one free response question on this topic.

- **Statistical Inference: Estimating population parameters and testing hypotheses.** Questions on this theme make up 30%–40% of the exam so you can expect several multiple-choice and at least one or two free response questions on this topic.

In addition to seeing how the exam is laid out, you were given ideas on what the graders look for and were provided with additional tips to help you do your best. Now it is important for you to practice. To help you with this, we include two complete practice exams (one included in the text and the other online at the Book Companion Site) so you can hone your skills and gain confidence.

STATISTICS SECTION I

Time: 1 hour and 30 minutes | **Number of questions: 40** | **Percent of total grade: 50**

DIRECTIONS: Solve each of the following problems, using the available space for scratch work. Decide which is the best of the choices given and fill in the corresponding box on the answer sheet. Do not spend too much time on any one problem.

---

1. A sample of 100 patients at a local hospital was selected, and the length of stay (LOS, measured in days) of each patient was recorded. The boxplot below displays the distribution of these hospital stays.

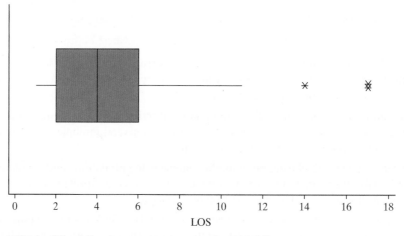

LOS

Which of the following statements <u>must</u> be <u>FALSE</u>?

   a. The distribution of length of stay is right-skewed.

   b. Half of the patients had stays lasting 4 days or less.

   c. About 25% of the patients had stays lasting 2 days or less.

   d. The mean length of stay is greater than 4 days.

   e. The 75th percentile is 11 days.

2. A sample of 25 students at Central High School were surveyed about their opinions of the school cafeteria selections. Each student gave a rating from 0 (terrible) to 100 (outstanding). The stemplot below displays the survey results.

3	2 4
4	0 3 4 7 8 9 9 9
5	0 1 1 2 3 4 5
6	1 2 5 6 6 8
7	
8	0 2

Key: 3|2 = 32

Using the 1.5 × IQR rule for determining outliers in a data set, which of the following statements is correct?

   a. The minimum rating of 32 is the only outlier.

   b. The maximum rating of 82 is the only outlier.

   c. The minimum rating of 32 and the maximum rating of 82 are outliers.

d. The two highest ratings of 80 ad 82 are outliers.

e. None of the ratings in this data set would be considered outliers.

3. A biologist is interested in predicting the brain weight of a certain species of bird from its body weight. A least squares regression line was determined from data collected on a random sample of 28 birds of this species. The equation of the least squares regression line is

$$\hat{y} = 3.79 + 0.08x$$

where $\hat{y}$ is the predicted brain weight (in grams) and x is the body weight (in grams) of the bird. Which of the following gives the best interpretation of the slope of the regression line?

a There is an increase of 0.08 grams in the predicted brain weight of this species of bird for every increase of 1 gram in body weight.

b. There is an increase of 0.08 grams in the predicted body weight of this species of bird for every increase of 1 gram in brain weight.

c. There is an increase of 3.79 grams in the predicted brain weight of this species of bird for every increase of 1 gram in body weight.

d. There is an increase of 3.79 grams in the predicted body weight of this species of bird for every increase of 1 gram in brain weight.

e. Approximately 8% of the variability in brain weight is predicted by its linear relationship with body weight.

4. In a study of fertilizers, researchers randomly selected 25 corn farms that use Brand A fertilizer and 25 corn farms that use Brand B fertilizer. Each corn farm that used Brand A was matched with a corn farm of similar acreage and soil type that used Brand B. The difference in the number of bushels of corn produced in one growing season was determined for each pair. What type of analysis would be used to determine whether there is a significant difference in the mean number of bushels of corn produced in one growing season for the two brands of fertilizer?

a. One sample z-test

b. Two-sample z-test

c. Two sample t-test

d. One-sample t-test (Matched Pairs)

e. Chi-square test

5. An increasing number of people in the U.S. own cell phones. A June 2010 Pew Research Center survey claimed that 82% of all U.S. adults own a cell phone. To conduct a simulation to estimate the number of U.S. adults that are expected to own a cell phone in a sample of size 10, you could assign the digits 00 to 81 as owning a cell phone and the digits 82 to 99 as not owning a cell phone. Use the random digits below to conduct one trial of this simulation. Start at the leftmost digit and move across the row.

59826 88804 04634 71197 19352 73089 84898 45785

In this trial of the simulation, the number of adults who own a cell phone out of 10 is:

a. 5

b. 6

c. 7

d. 8

e. 13

6. In a recent survey, a large class of college students was asked, "What is the fastest that you have ever driven a car?" The distribution of their responses (in miles per hour) had a mean of 77.1 and a standard deviation of 4.2. Which of the following best describes the meaning of the standard deviation?

a. About 4.2% of the students reported speeds within 1 mph of 77.1.

b. Students reported speeds that typically differed from 77.1 by about 4.2 mph.

c. About 50% of the speeds were in the interval 77.1 ± 4.2.

d. Speeds more than 4.2 mph away from 77.1 are considered outliers.

e. The fastest reported speed was 4.2 mph above 77.1.

7. Head circumferences of adult males are normally distributed with a mean of 57.5 cm and a standard deviation of 1.5 cm. A company sells hats labeled "one size fits most" that can be comfortably worn by anyone with a head circumference between 54.5 cm and 59 cm. What proportion of adult males have head circumferences that are too large to comfortably wear these hats?

a. 0.02   b. 0.16

c. 0.32   d. 0.82

e. 0.84

8. The table below classifies the students at a large suburban high school in the Midwest by their class standing (freshman, sophomore, junior, or senior) and their primary method of transportation for getting to school.

	Freshman	Sophomore	Junior	Senior	Total
Parent Drop Off	110	96	182	103	491
Drive Self	15	55	248	305	623
Ride Bus	403	361	106	52	922
Driven by Friend	152	203	166	189	710
Total	680	715	702	649	2,746

Which of the following statements is <u>true</u>?

a. Of the four class standings, Freshmen have the highest proportion of students with parent drop off as their primary method of transportation.

b. Of the four class standings, Seniors have the highest proportion of students who are driven by a friend as their primary method of transportation.

c. For each class standing, more than half of the students ride the bus as their primary method of transportation.

d. The proportion of Juniors is higher among students who primarily ride the bus than among students who primarily ride with a friend.

e. More than half of the students at this school primarily drive themselves to school.

9. One student made a purchase from each of three different online retailers, A, B, and C. She paid for next-day shipping on each purchase. The probabilities of next-day orders arriving on time for each retailer are 0.99, 0.97, and 0.96, respectively. If purchases from different retailers arrive on time independently of one another, what is the probability that <u>none</u> of the student's three purchases arrive the next day?

a. Less than 0.01   b. 0.078

c. 0.080   d. 0.922

e. Greater than 0.99

10. There is no cure for the common cold, but many cold remedies claim to make you feel better faster. A consumer watch group decides to compare the effectiveness of Vitamin C to the effectiveness of Echinacea in lessening the duration of the common cold. Sixty participants have volunteered to be infected with the cold virus for this study. In addition to the Vitamin C and Echinacea treatments, which will be administered in capsules that are identical in appearance, one of the researchers suggests that they add a group that receives no treatment but receives an identical-looking capsule with an inactive ingredient. If they decide <u>not</u> to add a group that receives no treatment, then:

a. This study will not be an experiment because there will not be a control group.

b. Even if there is a difference in recovery time between the Vitamin C and Echinacea groups, we will not know whether the recovery times tended to be shorter than if no treatment were given.

c. The experimental design will not be taking into consideration the natural variability in the duration of the common cold from person to person.

d. This study will be biased in favor of finding that the cold remedies are effective at reducing the length of the common cold in comparison to the length of an untreated common cold.

e. It will not be possible to conduct this study as a double-blind experiment.

11. Shown below are selected summary statistics and a histogram for a sample of eruptions of the Old Faithful geyser in Yellowstone National Park from several consecutive days. The data are durations of the eruptions in minutes.

Variable	N	Mean	Median	IQR
Duration (min)	54	3.350	4.108	2.641

In this set of observed eruptions of Old Faithful, how should the duration of a typical eruption be described?

a. A typical eruption lasted 2.641 minutes.

b. A typical eruption lasted 3.350 minutes.

c. A typical eruption lasted 4.108 minutes.

d. A typical eruption duration could be described using either the mean or the median because the distribution is fairly symmetric.

e. It is not appropriate to use a single measure of center to describe a typical eruption time for this data set.

12. Independent random samples of 100 east-side residents and 120 west-side residents of a large city were asked whether they will vote for candidate Jones in an upcoming election. Of the 100 east-side residents, 70 said they planned to vote for Jones. Of the 120 west-side residents, 72 said they planned to vote for Jones. In the calculation of a 90% confidence interval for the difference in the proportion of east-side and the proportion of west-side residents that will vote for candidate Jones, which of the following is the margin of error?

a. $1.28\sqrt{\dfrac{(0.7)(0.3)}{100} + \dfrac{(0.6)(0.4)}{120}}$

b. $1.645\sqrt{\dfrac{(0.7)(0.3)}{100} + \dfrac{(0.6)(0.4)}{120}}$

c. $1.96\sqrt{\dfrac{(0.7)(0.3)}{100} + \dfrac{(0.6)(0.4)}{120}}$

d. $1.645\sqrt{\left(\dfrac{142}{220}\right)\left(\dfrac{78}{220}\right)\left(\dfrac{1}{100}+\dfrac{1}{120}\right)}$

e. $1.96\sqrt{\left(\dfrac{142}{220}\right)\left(\dfrac{78}{220}\right)\left(\dfrac{1}{100}+\dfrac{1}{120}\right)}$

13. A researcher wants to know the percentage of villages in a certain African country that have access to a clean drinking water source less than 1/4 mile from the center of the village. The country is divided into 12 districts and each district has many villages in it, as indicated in the table below. The researcher selects a random sample of 10% of the villages from each district.

District	A	B	C	D	E	F	G	H	I	J	K	L
Number of Villages	50	40	30	80	50	30	80	90	20	20	40	70
Number Selected	5	4	3	8	5	3	8	9	2	2	4	7

Which of the following terms best describes this sampling method?

a. Simple random sampling

b. Stratified random sampling

c. Cluster sampling

d. Matched-pairs sampling

e. Voluntary response sampling

14. Suppose Nathan is a newborn baby boy whose weight has a z-score of 0.25. Which of the following gives the best interpretation of this z-score?

a. About 25% of newborn baby boys weigh less than Nathan.

b. About 25% of newborn baby boys weigh more than Nathan.

c. Nathan's weight is 0.25 pounds above average.

d. Nathan's weight is 0.25 standard deviations above average.

e. Nathan's weight is 0.25 standard deviations below average.

15. The distribution of the number of cars sold per month over the past year is displayed below for two different salespeople who work at the same car dealership.

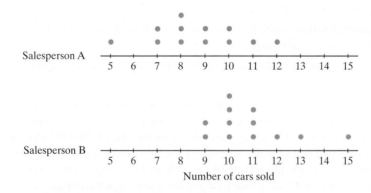

Number of cars sold

Which of the following statements is <u>true</u>?

a. The median number of cars sold by salesperson A is greater than the median number of cars sold by salesperson B.

b. The range in number of cars sold by salesperson A is smaller than the range in number of cars sold by salesperson B.

c. The mean number of cars sold by salesperson A is smaller than the mean number of cars sold by salesperson B.

d. The interquartile range of number of cars sold by salesperson A is twice the interquartile range of number of cars sold by salesperson B.

e. For both salespeople, the distribution of number of cars sold is approximately symmetric.

16. The rising popularity of energy drinks reflects a successful campaign to convince consumers, particularly teenagers, that energy drinks provide a mental and physical edge. For her AP Statistics project, Neela wants to test this claim. She plans to recruit 20 students to take part in the study. Students in the treatment group will be given a 6-ounce bottle of the energy drink *Red Bull* to drink, while students in the control group will not be given anything to drink. Both groups will complete an online test that measures their reaction time, in seconds.

    Neela is concerned that the variability in individual students' reaction times might make it difficult to discern whether or not the energy drink actually improves reaction time. Which of the following designs should lead to the greatest improvement in the study design?

    a. Randomly assign 10 students to the *Red Bull* group and the remaining 10 students to the control group. Have each student complete the reaction time test and compare the difference in mean times for the two groups.

    b. Randomly assign 10 students to the *Red Bull* group and the remaining 10 students to the control group, but give the control group 6 ounces of water. Have each student complete the reaction time test and compare the difference in mean reaction times for the two groups.

    c. Block by gender. In each block, randomly assign half of the students to the *Red Bull* group and half to the control group. Have each student complete the reaction time test and compare the difference in mean reaction times for the two groups.

    d. Block by whether or not the student is an athlete. In each block, randomly assign half of the students to the *Red Bull* group and half to the control group. Compare the difference in mean reaction times for the two groups.

    e. Have all students complete the reaction time test twice over a two-day period, once after drinking *Red Bull* and once without being given anything to drink. Randomly assign 10 students to do the reaction test after drinking the *Red Bull* first and the other 10 students to complete it without the drink first. Compare the mean difference in reaction time scores to zero.

17. Based on a random sample of 100 students at a large university, a 95% confidence interval for the mean monthly amount spent on coffee by all students at this university is ($34.42, $46.12). Which of the following statements is true?

    a. Approximately 95% of the students at this university spend between $34.42 and $46.12 every month on coffee.

    b. In approximately 95% of all months, the mean amount that students at this university spend on coffee will be between $34.42 and $46.12.

    c. Approximately 95% of all random samples of 100 students from this university will result in a 95% confidence interval that contains the population mean monthly amount spent on coffee by students at this university.

    d. Approximately 95% of all random samples of 100 students from this university will result in a 95% confidence interval that contains the sample mean monthly amount spent on coffee by students at this university.

    e. Approximately 95% of all random samples of 100 students from this university will result in a sample mean monthly amount spent on coffee between $34.42 and $46.12.

18. To estimate the proportion of the general public that believes global climate change is a man-made phenomenon, a radio host asked her listeners to call in and give their opinions.

Of the seven listeners who called in, one said "Yes" while the remaining six callers said "No" to the question whether climate change was man-made. Which of the following is NOT a concern regarding this study?

a. There was no random selection of respondents

b. Not everyone listening to the show chose to call in

c. The value of $n\hat{p}$ is too small for a large sample confidence interval

d. The show airs during the daytime and most listeners are retired from their jobs

e. There was no random assignment to be a "listener" or not

19. Scholars agree that the book *Rhetoric A* was written by the Greek philosopher Aristotle, but there is some suspicion that the book *Rhetoric to Alexander* was not written by Aristotle. To test their theory they selected a random sample of 100 sentences from each of these two books and classified these sentences as ending with a noun, ending with a verb, or ending with some other part of speech. The data are shown in the table below.

	Noun	Verb	Other	Total
Rhetoric A	28	32	40	100
Rhetoric to Alexander	27	52	21	100
Total	55	84	61	200

If the distribution of speech parts that end a sentence were the same in the two books, which of the following expressions is equal to the expected number of sentences in *Rhetoric to Alexander* that end with a verb?

a. $\dfrac{(84)(100)}{200}$

b. $\dfrac{(55)(100)}{200}$

c. $\dfrac{(52)(84)}{100}$

d. $\dfrac{(52)(100)}{200}$

e. $\dfrac{(52)(84)}{200}$

20. A data set contains measurements taken on a response variable y and five different explanatory variables, x_1, x_2, x_3, x_4, and x_5. Five different simple linear regression models were fit to determine whether any of the five explanatory variables has a linear relationship with the response variable y. The residual plots from each regression line are shown below. Which of the following residual plots gives the strongest evidence that its least squares regression line is an appropriate model for the relationship between the given explanatory variable and the response variable y?

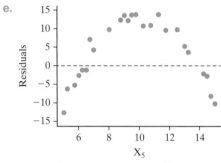

21. The annual salary of a registered nurse working in the U.S. follows an approximately normal distribution with a mean of \$66,000 and a standard deviation of \$11,000. Let $\bar{x}$ denote the average annual salary for a random sample of 10 registered nurses working in the U.S. Which of the following statements is correct?

   a. The sampling distribution of $\bar{x}$ will not necessarily be approximately normally distributed because of the small sample size.

   b. The sampling distribution of $\bar{x}$ will not necessarily be approximately normally distributed because of the large population standard deviation.

   c. The sampling distribution of $\bar{x}$ will be approximately normally distributed because the sample size is large enough.

   d. The sampling distribution of $\bar{x}$ will be approximately normally distributed because the size of the population of interest is quite large.

   e. The sampling distribution of $\bar{x}$ will be approximately normally distributed because the sample is selected from a population that is approximately normally distributed.

22. An online clothing store claims that 1 in 4 site visitors eventually make a purchase. A random sample of 60 site visitors is selected, and it is determined that 9 of those selected made a purchase. Do the data provide convincing statistical evidence, at the 5% significance level, that the population proportion of all site visitors who make a purchase is less than the company's claim of 1 in 4?

   a. Yes, because the p-value is greater than 0.05.

   b. No, because the p-value is less than 0.05.

   c. Yes, because the p-value is less than 0.05.

   d. No, because the p-value is greater than 0.05.

   e. There is not enough information to make a decision.

23. In which of the following scenarios would it be most appropriate to analyze the collected data using a paired t-test?

   a. At the end of the semester, Andrea's class has a mean of 82% on the final exam and Jessica's class has a mean of 79%. Is the difference in means statistically significant?

   b. In 2000, a prosecuting attorney's conviction rate (number of convictions as a percentage of total number of prosecutions undertaken) was 54%. By 2015, his conviction rate has increased to 62%. Is this change in conviction rates statistically significant?

c. In every football game, the referee flips a coin at the beginning of the game to determine who first receives the ball. The National Collegiate Athletic Association (NCAA) commissions a study where one referee flips a coin 10 times from his dominant hand and another referee flips a coin 10 times from his non-dominant hand. Both referees then record the number of heads flipped. Is the number of heads flipped by the dominant hand significantly different from the number of heads flipped by the non-dominant hand?

d. A golf instructor is interested in which brand of driver gets the most distance. For 6 weeks he asks each of his clients on the driving range to take one swing with each of two drivers and records the difference in the distance each ball travels. Which driver the client uses first is determined randomly. Is the mean difference in travel distance for the two brands statistically significant?

e. Automobile accidents occurring from distracted driving seem to have increased in the last 10 years. In 2004, the Department of Motor Vehicles reported that motorists had an average of 2.6 accidents on their current driving record. A survey was conducted in 2014 in which motorists reported an average of 3.1 accidents on their current driving record. Is the change in mean number of accidents statistically significant?

24. Suppose the correlation coefficient between two quantitative variables is $r = 0.23$. What will the new correlation coefficient equal if 14 is added to all values of the x variable, every value of the y variable is doubled, and the two variables are interchanged?

a. -0.74 b. -0.23

c. 0.23 d. 0.37

e. 0.74

25. A simple random sample of 90 female grocery shoppers and a simple random sample of 70 male grocery shoppers were selected to investigate the usage of reusable shopping bags. It was found that 35 of the female shoppers and 16 of the male shoppers brought reusable shopping bags. Researchers want to determine whether there is a difference in the population proportions of all male and female grocery shoppers who bring their own reusable bags. A two-proportion z-test where $H_0: p_F = p_M$ and $H_a: p_F \neq p_M$ yields a p-value of 0.03. Which of the following is the best interpretation of this p-value?

a. There is a 3% chance of obtaining a sample result like this or more extreme.

b. Assuming there is no difference in the proportion of male and female grocery shoppers who bring their own reusable bags, there is a 3% chance of obtaining a sample result like this or more extreme.

c. There is a 3% chance that more females than males will bring their own reusable bags.

d. Assuming there is no difference in the proportion of male and female grocery shoppers who bring their own reusable bags, there is a 3% chance of obtaining a difference in the sample proportions.

e. Assuming there is a difference in the proportion of male and female grocery shoppers who bring their own reusable bags, there is a 3% chance of obtaining a sample result like this or more extreme.

Questions 26–27 refer to the following scenario.

Anthony and Brett each have a snow-shoveling business in their respective neighborhoods. Based on previous winters, the average number of driveways that Anthony shovels in a day is 2.0 with a standard deviation of 0.7. For Brett, the average number of driveways shoveled in a day is 2.2 with a standard deviation of 0.4.

26. Assuming that the number of driveways shoveled by Anthony's and Brett's businesses are independent of each other, what are the mean and standard deviation for the combined number of driveways the two businesses will shovel each day?

a. Mean: 2.1, Standard Deviation: 0.81

b. Mean: 2.1, Standard Deviation: 1.05

c. Mean: 4.2, Standard Deviation: 0.81

d. Mean: 4.2, Standard Deviation: 1.05

e. Mean: 4.2, Standard Deviation: 1.10

27. If Anthony charges $15 per driveway and also received a $5 allowance from his parents each day, what are the mean and standard deviation of the amount of money Anthony will receive each day in the winter?

a. Mean: $30, Standard Deviation: $10.50

b. Mean: $35, Standard Deviation: $10.50

c. Mean: $30, Standard Deviation: $15.50

d. Mean: $35, Standard Deviation: $15.50

e. Mean: $35, Standard Deviation: $18.50

28. The three graphs below are approximate sampling distributions for sample proportions from a population with $p = 0.50$. All three graphs were created by selecting 1,000 samples from this population, but each graph was based on samples of a different sample size n.

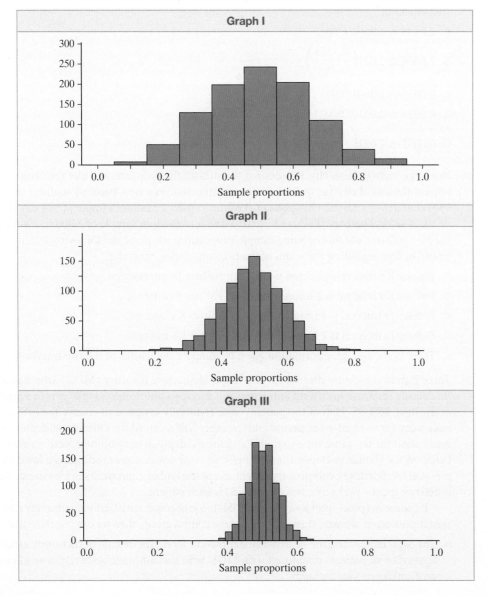

Which graph was based on samples with the largest sample size?

a. Graph I

b. Graph II

c. Graph III

d. The sample size does not affect the sampling distribution.

e. The sample sizes cannot be compared based on these graphs.

29. Hiking in the Smoky Mountains can be challenging, so trails are rated based on their difficulty. One method of rating trails is based on their total distance, in miles, and elevation gain, in feet. A rating of less than 5 is considered easy, between 5-10 moderate, and anything over 10 strenuous. Forty-two trails were rated, and a regression analysis was conducted using only elevation gain to predict difficulty rating. Some of the results are shown in the output below.

Parameter	Estimate	Standard Error
Intercept	2.0436	0.4505
Slope	0.0051	0.0002

Use this information to construct a 95% t-confidence interval for the slope of the regression equation.

a. $2.0436 \pm 1.96(0.4505)$

b. $2.0436 \pm 2.021\left(\dfrac{0.4505}{\sqrt{42}}\right)$

c. $0.0051 \pm 1.96(0.0002)$

d. $0.0051 \pm 2.021(0.0002)$

e. $0.0051 \pm 2.021\left(\dfrac{0.0002}{\sqrt{42}}\right)$

30. In a large metropolitan city, it is desired to estimate the proportion of city residents who oppose the use of city tax dollars for the construction of a new baseball stadium with a 95% confidence interval. One pollster (Pollster J) used a random sample of 500 city residents. A second pollster (Pollster K) used a different random sample of 2,000 residents. If the two pollsters obtain the same sample proportion, which of the following statements would be true regarding the width of the two confidence intervals?

a. Pollster K's interval is 4 times wider than Pollster J's interval.

b. Pollster K's interval is 2 times wider than Pollster J's interval.

c. Pollster J's interval is 4 times wider than Pollster K's interval.

d. Pollster J's interval is 2 times wider than Pollster K's interval.

e. There is not enough information given to compare the widths of the two intervals.

31. Three hundred patients diagnosed with major depressive disorder (MDD) who had an inadequate response to current antidepressant therapy volunteered to take part in a study of the drug MSI-95. Half of the patients were randomly assigned to receive the MSI-195 once a day for an eight-week period and the other half received the current antidepressant medication for the same time period. Participants' depressive symptoms were measured based on the Hamilton Depression Rating Scale (with lower scores indicating a lower depression level) before beginning treatment and at the end of eight weeks of treatment. The difference (post—pre) score was calculated for each patient.

If the mean (post—pre) score for the MSI-195 group was statistically significantly lower (less depressed on average) than the mean of the control group, then we can conclude that:

a. The MSI-195 caused the decrease in depression level. The results of this study can be applied to all patients diagnosed with MDD who had an inadequate response to current antidepressant therapy.

b. The MSI-195 is associated with a decrease in depression level, but no cause-effect relationship can be attributed since this was an observational study. The results of this study can be applied to all patients diagnosed with MDD who had an inadequate response to current anti-depressant therapy.

c. The MSI-195 caused the decrease in depression level. The results of this study can be applied to the patients who took part in the study and to other patients diagnosed with MDD who are similar to the patients in our study.

d. The MSI-195 is associated with a decrease in depression level, but no cause-effect relationship can be attributed since this was an observational study. The results of this study can be applied to the patients who took part in the study and to other patients diagnosed with MDD who are similar to the patients in our study.

e. The MSI-195 is associated with a decrease in depression level, but no cause-effect relationship can be attributed since this was an observational study. The results of this study cannot be applied to any group because they did not conduct an experiment.

32. A recent *Consumer Reports* article examined whether top-loading and front-loading washing machines differed in their mean cost. They sampled several different models of top-loading and front-loading machines from several different brands. Which of the following gives the null and alternative hypotheses tested by *Consumer Reports*?

a. $H_0: \mu_{Top} = \mu_{Front}$ and $H_a: \mu_{Top} < \mu_{Front}$

b. $H_0: \mu_{Top} = \mu_{Front}$ and $H_a: \mu_{Top} \neq \mu_{Front}$

c. $H_0: \mu_{Top} \neq \mu_{Front}$ and $H_a: \mu_{Top} = \mu_{Front}$

d. $H_0: \bar{x}_{Top} = \bar{x}_{Front}$ and $H_a: \bar{x}_{Top} < \bar{x}_{Front}$

e. $H_0: \bar{x}_{Top} = \bar{x}_{Front}$ and $H_a: \bar{x}_{Top} \neq \bar{x}_{Front}$

33. The weights of ripened peaches grown in the southeastern United States follow an approximately normal distribution with a mean of 6.2 ounces and a standard deviation of 0.8 ounces. Determine the interquartile range (IQR) of the weights of these peaches.

a. Because a normal distribution is continuous, the IQR cannot be calculated.

b. 0.5

c. 1.1

d. 1.6

e. 4.8

34. A consumer group is investigating Apple's claim that the latest iPad has a 10-hour battery life. After running a random sample of 15 of the latest iPads under identical conditions, the group finds a 99% confidence interval for the mean battery life of this iPad model to be (8.45, 10.05) hours. Assuming battery life of this iPad is approximately normally distributed, does this confidence interval provide evidence, at the 1% significance level, that this iPad model does <u>not</u> have an average battery life of 10 hours?

a. No, because the 99% confidence interval contains 10 hours.

b. Yes, because 10 is near the upper endpoint of the confidence interval and the majority of the plausible values for the mean battery life of this iPad are less than 10 hours.

c. Yes, because if a 95% confidence interval for the true mean battery life were constructed it most likely would not contain 10 hours.

d. The sample size is not large enough to make a conclusion about the mean battery life of an iPad.

e. It is not appropriate to use a confidence interval to test a claim about a population value.

35. According to the National Center for Education Statistics, 57% of the students enrolled in American colleges and universities are female. Also, 59% of college students are expected to graduate within 6 years of enrolling and 62% of females enrolled are expected to graduate

within 6 years. If one college student is randomly selected from all college students in the U.S., what is the probability that the selected student will be a female and will graduate within 6 years?

a. 0.3534

b. 0.3658

c. 0.5900

d. 0.6200

e. 1.0508

36. At professional football tryouts, speed is measured by the time to run 40 yards (with lower times indicating a better performance) and strength is measured by the number of times (reps) a player can bench press 225 pounds (with more reps indicating a better performance). In 2014, the z-score for the fastest 40-yard dash time was -1.45. Given that the mean number of reps by the players trying out was 25.90 with a standard deviation of 5.28 reps, how many reps does a player need to achieve an equally impressive strength performance that is equally impressive to the fastest player?

a. Speed and strength performances cannot be compared.

b. 18

c. 26

d. 31

e. 34

37. From data collected on a random sample of 11 car repairs at Paul's garage, the mean cost of replacing a front windshield is $215 and the standard deviation is $52.45. A dotplot of the 11 repair costs is roughly symmetrical and has no outliers. Which of the following gives a 95% confidence interval for the population mean cost of replacing a front windshield at Paul's garage?

a. $215 \pm 1.812\left(\dfrac{52.45}{\sqrt{11}}\right)$

b. $215 \pm 1.96\left(\dfrac{52.45}{\sqrt{11}}\right)$

c. $215 \pm 2.228\left(\dfrac{52.45}{\sqrt{10}}\right)$

d. $215 \pm 2.228\left(\dfrac{52.45}{\sqrt{11}}\right)$

e. The results cannot be trusted; the sample is too small.

38. The mean wait time in the drive-thru at a local fast food restaurant is 60 seconds. There is concern that the mean wait time has increased. A random sample of four cars is selected and the mean wait time is calculated. For this study, $H_0: \mu = 60$ seconds and $H_a: \mu > 60$ seconds where μ is the true mean wait time. Which of the following gives all the values of t that would lead to a rejection of H_0 at the 10% level of significance?

a. $|t| \geq 1.282$

b. $t \geq 1.638$

c. $t \geq 1.645$

d. $t \geq 2.353$

e. $t \geq 1.533$

39. A quality control manager wants to estimate the mean breaking strength of all ½-inch 3-strand nylon ropes made by his company. The manager will randomly select a sample of these ropes and subject each rope to a stress test. Assume that the breaking strength of these ropes have a standard deviation of 10 pounds. Which of the following should be used to find the minimum sample size (n) needed to estimate the true mean breaking strength to within 4 pounds of the true value with a 98% level of confidence?

a. $\left(\dfrac{1.96(10)}{4}\right)^2$

b. $\left(\dfrac{1.96(10)}{2}\right)^2$

c. $\dfrac{2.33(10)}{4}$

d. $\left(\dfrac{2.33(10)}{4}\right)^2$

e. $\left(\dfrac{2.33(10)}{2}\right)^2$

40. A random sample of 20 county roads was selected, and the mileage between two points was measured using the actual road distance and also using a computer program (called "as a crow flies") that measures the linear distance between the two points. A regression analysis was conducted to determine whether there was a linear relationship between the road distance and linear distance, both measured in miles, using linear distance as the explanatory variable. The results of the analysis are shown below.

R (correlation coefficient) = 0.92   R-sq = 0.85

Parameter	Estimate	Std. Err.	DF	T-Stat	P-value
Intercept	1.750957	2.0333604	18	0.86111493	0.4005
Slope	1.1533815	0.1152422	18	10.008325	<0.0001

Assuming that the conditions for inference are met, is there a statistically significant linear relationship between road distance and linear distance?

a. Yes, because the correlation coefficient is close to 1.

b. Yes, because $r^2 = 0.85$.

c. Yes, because the p-value for the slope is less than 0.05.

d. No, because the p-value for the intercept is greater than 0.05.

e. No, because the p-value for the slope is less than 0.05.

STATISTICS SECTION II: PART A

Questions 1-5 | Spend about 65 minutes on this part of the exam. |
Percent of Section II grade: 75

DIRECTIONS: Show all your work. Indicate clearly the methods you use, because you will be scored on the correctness of your methods as well as on the accuracy and completeness of your results and explanations.

1. Students in an AP Statistics class participated in an online memory game. All the students first played the game at Level 1 (the lowest difficulty level), and then played the game again at Level 4 (a higher level of difficulty). The graphs below display the distribution of student scores for the two difficulty levels—Level 1 and Level 4.

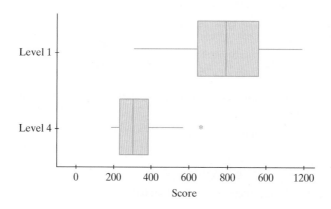

   a. Use the graphical display above to compare the distribution of student scores for the two difficulty levels (Level 1 and Level 4) of the memory game.

   The difference in scores (Level 4–Level 1) on the memory game was calculated for each student. The graph below displays the distribution of the differences.

   b. What added information does the graph above of the difference in scores (Level 4–Level 1) give you about students' scores on the two different levels of the game that was not apparent in the first graphical display?

2. The National Park Service is interested in determining whether placing predator cages over the loggerhead turtle nests on Cape Lookout National Seashore will keep raccoons from stealing eggs from the nests. Due to budget constraints, funding for the predator cages will only be approved if the Park Service can provide convincing evidence that the predator cages increase the number of turtles that successfully hatch.

The Park Service plans to collect data from the loggerhead turtle nests at Cape Lookout one season, 35 of which will have a predator cage placed over them and 35 of which will not. A test of significance will be conducted at a significance level of $\alpha = 0.05$ for the following hypotheses:

$$H_0: \mu_C = \mu_{NC}$$
$$H_a: \mu_C > \mu_{NC},$$

where μ_C is the mean number of eggs that would successfully hatch per nest for all loggerhead turtle nests on Cape Lookout *with* a cage and μ_{NC} is the mean number of eggs that would successfully hatch per nest for all nests on Cape Lookout with *no* cage.

a. Describe what a Type I error would be in the context of the study, and also describe a consequence of making this type of error.

b. Each season, the Park Service moves approximately half the turtle nests at Cape Lookout very soon after they are laid because they are placed in locations that are vulnerable to extreme high tides. The Park Service decides to collect data for their study by randomly selecting 35 of the nests that were moved and placing a cage over them and comparing the hatching rate to the rate for 35 randomly selected nests that were neither moved nor caged. This resulted in a p-value of 0.0003 for the hypotheses stated above. If it was reasonable to conduct a test of significance for the hypotheses stated above using the data collected, what would the p-value of 0.0003 lead you to conclude?

c. Describe the primary flaw in the study described in part (b), and explain why it is a concern.

3. A smartphone manufacturer is concerned about the proportion of defectives produced at a certain plant that produces many smartphones every day. Historically, approximately 15% of phones produced at this plant have been defective. As part of their quality assurance testing, four smartphones are selected at random from a day's production.

a. Let X represent the number of defective phones in the sample of four phones. Complete the table below for the probability distribution of X, assuming the historic defective rate holds.

x	0	1	2	3	4
P(x)	0.522	0.368			0.001

b. What is the expected number of defective phones in this sample?

c. What is the conditional probability that all four phones were defective, given that at least two defectives were found in the sample?

d. Suppose that each day the phones are produced independently of all other days' phones. If a sample of size 4 is taken every weekday (five total samples), what is the probability that there are no defective phones found in any of the five samples taken?

4. The National Sleep Foundation conducts an annual survey to track sleep related behaviors of U.S. adults. In their most recent survey, a random sample of 1,018 adults answered the question "About how much actual sleep would you estimate you typically get on work nights or weeknights?" The two-way table below summarizes the responses by whether they were less than, equal to, or more than the recommended 7 to 9 hours of sleep and by the age group of the respondent.

| Age Group | Typical Weeknight Sleep Time | | | |
	Less Than 7 Hours	Recommended 7 to 9 Hours	More Than 9 Hours	Total
18–34	44	78	109	231
35–54	144	200	218	562
55 or older	47	77	101	225
Total	235	355	428	1,018

At the $\alpha = 0.05$ significance level, do the data provide convincing statistical evidence that there is an association between age group and typical weeknight sleep time for adults in the United States?

5. In 2006, professional tennis introduced a challenge system in which a player can challenge decisions on whether a tennis ball was correctly called 'in' or 'out' by an official. A video replay then determines whether or not the call was correct ("upheld") or incorrect ("reversed"). A player wants to determine whether "in" calls or "out" calls are more likely to be reversed. The table below shows the 2015 Women's Singles challenges based on whether the tennis ball was called "out" or "in" and whether the official's call was reversed or upheld.

Outcome of Player Challenge	Official Called Ball Out	Official Called Ball In
Official's call reversed	61	11
Official's call upheld	111	120

a. Calculate the proportion of all challenges in which the official's call was reversed.

b. Use these data as a representative sample of all player challenges in professional tennis to find a 95% confidence interval for the difference in the proportion of reversed calls when the official calls the ball "out" and when the official calls the ball "in" (out–in). Be sure to also provide an interpretation of this confidence interval. You may assume that all conditions for inference were met.

c. Does the confidence interval from (b) provide convincing statistical evidence that there is a difference in the proportion of reversed challenges between when the official calls the ball "out" and when the official calls the ball "in"? Justify your answer.

d. Would your answer to (c) change if the confidence interval in (b) were a 90% confidence interval rather than a 95% confidence interval? Explain how you are arriving at your answer.

STATISTICS SECTION II: PART B

Question 6 | **Spend about 25 minutes on this part of the exam.** |
Percent of Section II grade: 25

DIRECTIONS: Show all your work. Indicate clearly the methods you use, because you will be scored on the correctness of your methods as well as on the accuracy and completeness of your results and explanations.

6. In a large manufacturing company every item produced is inspected for defects and will go through a repair process if the defects are serious. Management wanted to investigate whether items produced on Mondays are more likely to require repair than items produced on the midweek day Wednesday. A random sample of 9 weeks from the past 5 years was selected, and the number of items that required repair for the 9 weeks are shown in the table below.

Week	Number of items requiring repair on Monday	Number of items requiring repair on Wednesday	Difference (Monday– Wednesday)	More Repairs on Monday?
A	17	18	−1	NO
B	14	17	−3	NO
C	19	12	7	YES
D	21	17	4	YES
E	18	13	5	YES
F	19	10	9	YES
G	24	4	20	YES
H	25	17	8	YES
I	22	16	6	YES

A boxplot of the differences in number of items that required repairing on Monday and Wednesday for the 9 sampled weeks is shown below.

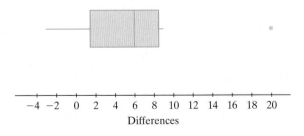

a. Management wanted to test these hypotheses:

$$H_0: \mu_{\text{difference}} = 0$$
$$H_a: \mu_{\text{difference}} > 0$$

where $\mu_{\text{difference}}$ is the mean of the differences in the number of produced items that required repair on Monday and on Wednesday for all weeks in the past 5 years.

Explain why performing a matched-pairs *t*-test may not be appropriate for this sample of differences.

A different possible set of hypotheses for this investigation could be:

$$H_0: p = 0.5$$
$$H_a: p > 0.5$$

where *p* is the proportion of all weeks in which Monday produces more items that require repair than Wednesday.

Suppose we decide to test these hypotheses using the statistic *X*, the number of weeks of the 9 sampled weeks in which more items required repair on Monday than Wednesday.

b. Assuming the null hypothesis (that Mondays and Wednesdays are equally likely to have the most items which require repair) is true, what is the probability distribution for the statistic *X*?

c. Calculate the p-value and use this p-value to provide the conclusion of the test for a significance level of $\alpha = 0.05$.

A different possible set of hypotheses for this investigation is:

H_0: The distributions of the numbers of items that require repair for Mondays and Wednesday are the same.

H_a: The distribution of the numbers of items that require repair for Mondays is shifted to the right of the distribution of the number of items that require repair on Wednesdays.

To test these hypotheses using the *signed rank test*, we first order the absolute values of the differences and then determine the ranks of the 9 values (1 = smallest, 9 = largest). Then we return the original positive or negative sign. The statistic is the sum of the positive ranks.

d. Calculate the statistic for the signed rank test by completing the signed rank of the difference column in the table below and then adding up the positive ranks.

Week	Monday	Wednesday	Difference	More Repairing on Monday	Signed Rank of |Difference|
A	17	18	−1	NO	−1
B	14	17	−3	NO	−2
C	19	12	7	YES	6
D	21	17	4	YES	3
E	18	13	5	YES	
F	19	10	9	YES	
G	24	4	20	YES	
H	25	17	8	YES	
I	22	16	6	YES	

Sum of Positive Ranks = _____

Under the assumption of the null hypothesis, that the distributions of the numbers of items requiring repair for Mondays and Wednesday are the same, a simulation with 10,000 repetitions was performed and the signed rank statistic was calculated for each repetition. The histogram below shows the distribution of the simulated signed rank statistics.

e. Based on the value of the signed rank test statistic calculated in part (e) and the distribution of the 10,000 simulated signed rank test statistics above, what should be the conclusion for the manufacturing company in comparing the number of items requiring repair on Mondays and Wednesdays?

Calculation Details

*Appendix A (Calculations Details) can be found on the Student Companion Site for *Introduction to Statistical Investigations, AP® Edition* located at <u>wiley.com/go/highschool</u>. The Calculations Details appendix is a single location for notation and equations used to compute descriptive statistics, confidence intervals, test statistics, and more.

Stratified and Cluster Samples

*Appendix B (Stratified and Cluster Samples) can be found on the Student Companion Site for *Introduction to Statistical Investigations, AP® Edition* located at wiley.com/go/highschool. The Stratified and Cluster Samples appendix is a single location to read more about Stratified and Cluster Samples, and complements Section 2.1 Part 3 of the textbook.

Formulas

(I) Descriptive Statistics

$$\bar{x} = \frac{\sum x_i}{n}$$

$$s_x = \sqrt{\frac{1}{n-1}\sum(x_i - \bar{x})^2}$$

$$s_p = \sqrt{\frac{(n_1 - 1)s_1^2 + (n_2 - 1)s_2^2}{(n_1 - 1) + (n_2 - 1)}}$$

$$\hat{y} = b_0 + b_1 x$$

$$b_1 = \frac{\sum(x_i - \bar{x})(y_i - \bar{y})}{\sum(x_i - \bar{x})^2}$$

$$b_0 = \bar{y} - b_1\bar{x}$$

$$r = \frac{1}{n-1}\sum\left(\frac{x_i - \bar{x}}{s_x}\right)\left(\frac{y_i - \bar{y}}{s_y}\right)$$

$$b_1 = r\frac{s_y}{s_x}$$

$$s_{b_1} = \frac{\sqrt{\dfrac{\sum(y_i - \hat{y}_i)^2}{n-2}}}{\sqrt{\sum(x_i - \bar{x})^2}}$$

(II) Probability

$$P(A \cup B) = P(A) + P(B) - P(A \cap B)$$

$$P(A|B) = \frac{P(A \cap B)}{P(B)}$$

$$E(X) = \mu_x = \sum x_i p_i$$

$$\text{Var}(X) = \sigma_x^2 = \sum(x_i - \mu_x)^2 p_i$$

If X has a binomial distribution with parameters n and p, then

$$P(X = k) = \binom{n}{k}p^k(1 - p)^{n-k}$$

$$\mu_x = np$$

$$\sigma_x = \sqrt{np(1-p)}$$

$$\mu_{\hat{p}} = p$$

$$\sigma_{\hat{p}} = \sqrt{\frac{p(1-p)}{n}}$$

If $\bar{x}$ is the mean of a random sample of size n from an infinite population with mean μ and standard deviation σ, then

$$\mu_{\bar{x}} = \mu$$

$$\sigma_{\bar{x}} = \frac{\sigma}{\sqrt{n}}$$

(III) Inferential Statistics

Standardized test statistic: $\dfrac{\text{statistic} - \text{parameter}}{\text{standard deviation of statistic}}$

Confidence interval: statistic $\pm$ (critical value) $\bullet$ (standard deviation of statistic)

Single-Sample

Statistic	Standard Deviation of Statistic
Sample Mean	$\dfrac{\sigma}{\sqrt{n}}$
Sample Proportion	$\sqrt{\dfrac{p(1-p)}{n}}$

Two-Sample

Statistic	Standard Deviation of Statistic
Difference of sample means	$\sqrt{\dfrac{\sigma_1^2}{n_1} + \dfrac{\sigma_2^2}{n_2}}$ Special case when $\sigma_1 = \sigma_2$ $\sigma\sqrt{\dfrac{1}{n_1} + \dfrac{1}{n_2}}$
Difference of sample proportions	$\sqrt{\dfrac{p_1(1-p_1)}{n_1} + \dfrac{p_2(1-p_2)}{n_2}}$ Special case when $p_1 = p_2$ $\sqrt{p(1-p)}\sqrt{\dfrac{1}{n_1} + \dfrac{1}{n_2}}$

Chi-square test statistic $= \displaystyle\sum \frac{(\text{observed} - \text{expected})^2}{\text{expected}}$

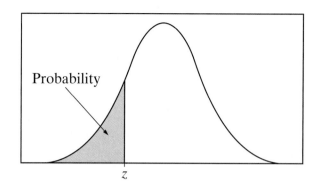

Table entry for z is the
probability lying below z.

TABLE A   Standard normal probabilities

z	.00	.01	.02	.03	.04	.05	.06	.07	.08	.09
−3.4	.0003	.0003	.0003	.0003	.0003	.0003	.0003	.0003	.0003	.0002
−3.3	.0005	.0005	.0005	.0004	.0004	.0004	.0004	.0004	.0004	.0003
−3.2	.0007	.0007	.0006	.0006	.0006	.0006	.0006	.0005	.0005	.0005
−3.1	.0010	.0009	.0009	.0009	.0008	.0008	.0008	.0008	.0007	.0007
−3.0	.0013	.0013	.0013	.0012	.0012	.0011	.0011	.0011	.0010	.0010
−2.9	.0019	.0018	.0018	.0017	.0016	.0016	.0015	.0015	.0014	.0014
−2.8	.0026	.0025	.0024	.0023	.0023	.0022	.0021	.0021	.0020	.0019
−2.7	.0035	.0034	.0033	.0032	.0031	.0030	.0029	.0028	.0027	.0026
−2.6	.0047	.0045	.0044	.0043	.0041	.0040	.0039	.0038	.0037	.0036
−2.5	.0062	.0060	.0059	.0057	.0055	.0054	.0052	.0051	.0049	.0048
−2.4	.0082	.0080	.0078	.0075	.0073	.0071	.0069	.0068	.0066	.0064
−2.3	.0107	.0104	.0102	.0099	.0096	.0094	.0091	.0089	.0087	.0084
−2.2	.0139	.0136	.0132	.0129	.0125	.0122	.0119	.0116	.0113	.0110
−2.1	.0179	.0174	.0170	.0166	.0162	.0158	.0154	.0150	.0146	.0143
−2.0	.0228	.0222	.0217	.0212	.0207	.0202	.0197	.0192	.0188	.0183
−1.9	.0287	.0281	.0274	.0268	.0262	.0256	.0250	.0244	.0239	.0233
−1.8	.0359	.0351	.0344	.0336	.0329	.0322	.0314	.0307	.0301	.0294
−1.7	.0446	.0436	.0427	.0418	.0409	.0401	.0392	.0384	.0375	.0367
−1.6	.0548	.0537	.0526	.0516	.0505	.0495	.0485	.0475	.0465	.0455
−1.5	.0668	.0655	.0643	.0630	.0618	.0606	.0594	.0582	.0571	.0559
−1.4	.0808	.0793	.0778	.0764	.0749	.0735	.0721	.0708	.0694	.0681
−1.3	.0968	.0951	.0934	.0918	.0901	.0885	.0869	.0853	.0838	.0823
−1.2	.1151	.1131	.1112	.1093	.1075	.1056	.1038	.1020	.1003	.0985
−1.1	.1357	.1335	.1314	.1292	.1271	.1251	.1230	.1210	.1190	.1170
−1.0	.1587	.1562	.1539	.1515	.1492	.1469	.1446	.1423	.1401	.1379
−0.9	.1841	.1814	.1788	.1762	.1736	.1711	.1685	.1660	.1635	.1611
−0.8	.2119	.2090	.2061	.2033	.2005	.1977	.1949	.1922	.1894	.1867
−0.7	.2420	.2389	.2358	.2327	.2296	.2266	.2236	.2206	.2177	.2148
−0.6	.2743	.2709	.2676	.2643	.2611	.2578	.2546	.2514	.2483	.2451
−0.5	.3085	.3050	.3015	.2981	.2946	.2912	.2877	.2843	.2810	.2776
−0.4	.3446	.3409	.3372	.3336	.3300	.3264	.3228	.3192	.3156	.3121
−0.3	.3821	.3783	.3745	.3707	.3669	.3632	.3594	.3557	.3520	.3483
−0.2	.4207	.4168	.4129	.4090	.4052	.4013	.3974	.3936	.3897	.3859
−0.1	.4602	.4562	.4522	.4483	.4443	.4404	.4364	.4325	.4286	.4247
−0.0	.5000	.4960	.4920	.4880	.4840	.4801	.4761	.4721	.4681	.4641

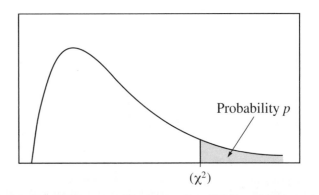

Table entry for p is the point (χ^2) with probability p lying above it.

Probability p

(χ^2)

TABLE C χ^2 critical values

df	.25	.20	.15	.10	.05	.025	.02	.01	.005	.0025	.001	.0005
1	1.32	1.64	2.07	2.71	3.84	5.02	5.41	6.63	7.88	9.14	10.83	12.12
2	2.77	3.22	3.79	4.61	5.99	7.38	7.82	9.21	10.60	11.98	13.82	15.20
3	4.11	4.64	5.32	6.25	7.81	9.35	9.84	11.34	12.84	14.32	16.27	17.73
4	5.39	5.99	6.74	7.78	9.49	11.14	11.67	13.28	14.86	16.42	18.47	20.00
5	6.63	7.29	8.12	9.24	11.07	12.83	13.39	15.09	16.75	18.39	20.51	22.11
6	7.84	8.56	9.45	10.64	12.59	14.45	15.03	16.81	18.55	20.25	22.46	24.10
7	9.04	9.80	10.75	12.02	14.07	16.01	16.62	18.48	20.28	22.04	24.32	26.02
8	10.22	11.03	12.03	13.36	15.51	17.53	18.17	20.09	21.95	23.77	26.12	27.87
9	11.39	12.24	13.29	14.68	16.92	19.02	19.68	21.67	23.59	25.46	27.88	29.67
10	12.55	13.44	14.53	15.99	18.31	20.48	21.16	23.21	25.19	27.11	29.59	31.42
11	13.70	14.63	15.77	17.28	19.68	21.92	22.62	24.72	26.76	28.73	31.26	33.14
12	14.85	15.81	16.99	18.55	21.03	23.34	24.05	26.22	28.30	30.32	32.91	34.82
13	15.98	16.98	18.20	19.81	22.36	24.74	25.47	27.69	29.82	31.88	34.53	36.48
14	17.12	18.15	19.41	21.06	23.68	26.12	26.87	29.14	31.32	33.43	36.12	38.11
15	18.25	19.31	20.60	22.31	25.00	27.49	28.26	30.58	32.80	34.95	37.70	39.72
16	19.37	20.47	21.79	23.54	26.30	28.85	29.63	32.00	34.27	36.46	39.25	41.31
17	20.49	21.61	22.98	24.77	27.59	30.19	31.00	33.41	35.72	37.95	40.79	42.88
18	21.60	22.76	24.16	25.99	28.87	31.53	32.35	34.81	37.16	39.42	42.31	44.43
19	22.72	23.90	25.33	27.20	30.14	32.85	33.69	36.19	38.58	40.88	43.82	45.97
20	23.83	25.04	26.50	28.41	31.41	34.17	35.02	37.57	40.00	42.34	45.31	47.50
21	24.93	26.17	27.66	29.62	32.67	35.48	36.34	38.93	41.40	43.78	46.80	49.01
22	26.04	27.30	28.82	30.81	33.92	36.78	37.66	40.29	42.80	45.20	48.27	50.51
23	27.14	28.43	29.98	32.01	35.17	38.08	38.97	41.64	44.18	46.62	49.73	52.00
24	28.24	29.55	31.13	33.20	36.42	39.36	40.27	42.98	45.56	48.03	51.18	53.48
25	29.34	30.68	32.28	34.38	37.65	40.65	41.57	44.31	46.93	49.44	52.62	54.95
26	30.43	31.79	33.43	35.56	38.89	41.92	42.86	45.64	48.29	50.83	54.05	56.41
27	31.53	32.91	34.57	36.74	40.11	43.19	44.14	46.96	49.64	52.22	55.48	57.86
28	32.62	34.03	35.71	37.92	41.34	44.46	45.42	48.28	50.99	53.59	56.89	59.30
29	33.71	35.14	36.85	39.09	42.56	45.72	46.69	49.59	52.34	54.97	58.30	60.73
30	34.80	36.25	37.99	40.26	43.77	46.98	47.96	50.89	53.67	56.33	59.70	62.16
40	45.62	47.27	49.24	51.81	55.76	59.34	60.44	63.69	66.77	69.70	73.40	76.09
50	56.33	58.16	60.35	63.17	67.50	71.42	72.61	76.15	79.49	82.66	86.66	89.56
60	66.98	68.97	71.34	74.40	79.08	83.30	84.58	88.38	91.95	95.34	99.61	102.7
80	88.13	90.41	93.11	96.58	101.9	106.6	108.1	112.3	116.3	120.1	124.8	128.3
100	109.1	111.7	114.7	118.5	124.3	129.6	131.1	135.8	140.2	144.3	149.4	153.2

Section P.1

P.1.1

a. Observational units: 47 students; Variables: (1) How much each student spent ($); (2) what the student was told (rebate or bonus)

b. Observational units: Typical American consumers; Variable: (1) How much each consumer spent ($)

c. Observational units: College students; Variables: (1) GPA of each student, (2) Whether or not each student pulls all-nighters (yes/no)

d. Observational units: College students; Variables: (1) Alcohol consumption of each student (e.g., typical drinks per week), (2) Residence situation of each student (on-campus, off-campus with parents, off-campus without parents)

e. Observational units: Cats; Variables: (1) How far the cat can jump (inches); (2) How long the cat is (inches)

P.1.3

a. Variables: (1) How much each student spent ($, quantitative), (2) what the student was told (rebate or bonus, categorical-binary)

b. Variable: (1) How much each consumer spent ($, quantitative)

c. Variables: (1) GPA of each student (quantitative), (2) Whether or not each student pulls all-nighters (yes/no, categorical-binary)

d. Variables: (1) Alcohol consumption of each student (e.g., typical drinks per week, quantitative), (2) Residence situation of each student (on-campus, off-campus with parents, off-campus without parents, categorical–not binary)

e. Variables: (1) How far the cat can jump (inches, quantitative), (2) How long the cat is (inches, quantitative)

P.1.5

Answers will vary.

P.1.7

a. Violin students

b. How much time spent practicing

c. Which of the three groups (international soloist, good violinists, teachers) the student was in

P.1.9

a. Quantitative variable

b. Research question

c. Categorical variable

d. Categorical variable

e. Research question

P.1.11

a. Do novice skydivers tend to have higher levels of self-reported anxiety prior to a skydive than experienced skydivers?

b. i. The 24 skydivers ii. From a parachute center in Northern England iii. Novice or expert skydiver (Categorical) and anxiety score (quantitative)

c. i. 43 among novice skydivers and 27 among experienced skydivers, ii. There are 11 first time skydivers and 13 experienced skydivers.

d. Self-reported anxiety levels are substantially higher among novice skydivers.

e. That these 24 skydivers have similar anxiety levels to most skydivers. In other words, that these 24 'represent' (look like) most skydivers.

f. If older people tend to have lower anxiety levels, this could explain the difference. In a future study, researchers could make sure the ages of the novice and experienced skydivers are similar.

P.1.13

Answers will vary.

P.1.15

Answers will vary.

P.1.17

Answers will vary.

Section P.2

P.2.1

a. We would expect Sandy to have the larger mean because temperatures in San Diego tend to be warmer than in New York

b. We would expect Nellie to have a larger standard deviation because the high temperatures in New York City should vary more throughout the year (high temperatures may not get above 30 in the winter but may exceed 100 in the summer), whereas in San Diego there is much less variation in daily temperatures, almost all values falling rather close to the overall average high temperature.

P.2.3

Quiz B has the smallest standard deviation (zero) because all the quiz scores are the same.

Quiz D has the next smallest standard deviation because most of the scores are equal to the mean, with only four students deviating from the mean by 2 points.

Quiz C has the second largest standard deviation because four students differ from the mean by 2 points as with Quiz D, but four other students also deviate by one point, so there is less consistency in the scores than in Quiz D.

Quiz A has the largest standard deviation. All quiz scores deviate by 5 points (as much as possible) from the mean score.

P.2.5

a. Replacement $3/43 \approx 0.07$; Regular $8/48 \approx 0.167$

b. Replacement $5/48 \approx 0.104$; Regular $11/43 \approx 0.256$

c. The replacement referees tended to have longer games (about 195 minutes on average compared to 185 minutes).

d. The replacement referees also tended to have more variability in the game lengths.

e. Neither distribution of game durations is symmetric, because both have a few games that took a very long time compared to the others. The games with replacement referees tended to take a bit longer than those with regular referees, roughly 10 minutes longer on average. Games with replacement referees also displayed more variability in game durations, as compared to the slightly greater consistency in game durations for regular referees. The two distributions show considerable overlap: Both types of referees saw most games take between roughly 180 and 210 minutes (3–3.5 hours).

P.2.7

a. The distribution of predicted high temperatures in San Luis Obispo County on July 8, 2012 shows a bimodal (two clustered) distribution, with many predictions between 63 and 73 degrees, but with another cluster of predictions between 85 and 96 degrees. The center of the overall distribution is between 70 to 75.

b. The bimodal distribution is likely due to widely varying geography in San Luis Obispo County, including locations nearer to the ocean (cooler) and farther away from the ocean (warmer)

P.2.9

a. US, CA, SLO-County, World (highest to lowest average high temperature)

b. World, CA, US, SLO-County (most to least variability)

c. Anchorage or Juneau, Alaska

d. Northern and southern hemisphere cities

Section P.3

P.3.1

About 60% of all new businesses (in the long run) close or change owners within the first three years.

P.3.3

B, C and E cannot be probabilities, because probabilities must be numbers between 0 and 1 or percentages between 0% and 100%.

P.3.5

a. If these two teams play each other many, many times under identical conditions, Team A will win 2/3 of the games in the long run.

b. No, this is a long-run proportion, not the proportion for every set of 3 games.

c. No, although we expect the proportion to tend to be closer to 2/3, this is still not a guarantee.

d. We expect the proportion of games that Team A wins to be close to 2/3, but with so many different possibilities that are also close to two-thirds (such as 18, 19, 21, 22 wins), there could still be a low probability that A wins exactly 2/3 of the 30 games.

P.3.7

a. Let heads represent a boy and tails a girl. Flip the coin four times and record the number of boys (heads) in those four children (tosses). Repeat this a large number of times (say 1,000) and look at what proportion of those 1,000 repetitions resulted in 2 boys and 2 girls.

b. In a very large number of couples with four children, roughly 37.5% of the couples will have 2 boys and 2 girls (assuming each birth is equally likely to be a boy or a girl).

c. $100 - 37.5\% = 62.5\%$

d. Having exactly two of each gender is pretty specific. Even though a specific 3-1 or 4-0 split is less likely than a 2-2 split, there are more ways to obtain a result other than a 2-2 split.

CHAPTER 1

Section 1.1

1.1.1

a. The true proportion of times the racquet lands face up

b. Parameter

c. 50%

d. 48 out of 100 does not constitute strong evidence that the spinning process is not fair, because if the spinning process was fair (50% chance of racquet landing face up), getting 48 out of 100 spins landing face up is a typical result.

e. Plausible that the spinning process is fair

1.1.2

a. 24 out of 100 does constitute strong evidence that the spinning process is not fair, because if the spinning process was fair (50% chance of racquet landing face up), getting 24 out of 100 spins landing face up is an atypical result.

b. Statistically significant evidence that spinning is not fair

1.1.3

A (100, 1,000)

1.1.4

C

1.1.8

a. Parameter

b. Statistic

c. The correct matches are shown below:

Column A	Column B
Coin flip	Author plays a game of *Minesweeper*
Heads	Author wins a game
Tails	Author loses a game
Chance of Heads	Long-run proportion of games that the author wins
One repetition	One set of 20 *Minesweeper* games played by author

1.1.9

a. 100 dots

b. Each dot represents the number of times out of 20 attempts the author wins a game of *Minesweeper* when the probability that the author wins is 50%.

c. 10, because that is what will happen on average if the author plays 20 games and wins 50% of her games

d. No, we are not convinced that the author's long-run proportion of winning at *Minesweeper* is above 50% because 12 is a fairly typical outcome for the number of wins out of 20 games when the long-run proportion of winning is 50%. Stated another way, 50% is a plausible value for the

long-run proportion of games that the author wins *Minesweeper* based on the author getting 12 wins in 20 games.

e. No, 50% is just a plausible (reasonable) explanation for the data. Other explanations are possible (e.g., the author's long-run proportion of wins could be 55%).

f. Yes, it means that there were special circumstances when the author played these 20 games and so these 20 games may not be a good representation of the author's long-run proportion of wins in *Minesweeper*.

1.1.11

a. Statistic

b. Parameter

c. Yes, it is possible to get 17 out of 20 first serves in if Mark was just as likely to make his first serve as to miss it.

d. Getting 17 out of 20 first serves in if Mark was just as likely to make the serve as to miss it is like flipping a coin 20 times and getting heads 17 times. This is fairly unlikely, so 17 out of 20 first serves in is not a very plausible outcome if Mark is just as likely to make his first serve as to miss it.

1.1.15

a. The long-run proportion of times that Zwerg chooses the correct object

b. Zwerg is just guessing or Zwerg is choosing the correct object because she understands the cue.

c. 37 out of 48 attempts seems fairly unlikely to happen by chance, since 24 out of 48 is what we would expect to happen in the long run.

d. 50%

1.1.16

a. 37 times out of 48 attempts

b. Applet input: probability of success is 0.5, sample size is 48, number of samples is 1,000

c. Yes, it appears as if the chance model is wrong, as it is highly unlikely to obtain a value as large as 37 when there is a 50% chance of picking the correct object.

d. We have strong evidence that Zwerg can correctly follow this type of direction more than 50% of the time.

e. The results are statistically significant because we have strong evidence that the chance model is incorrect.

1.1.17

a. Zwerg is just guessing or Zwerg is picking up on the experimenter cue to make a choice.

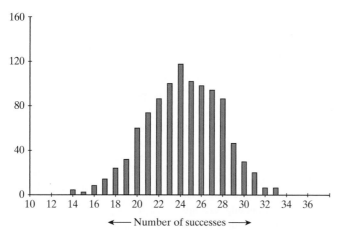

SOLUTIONS 1.1.16b

b. 26 out of 48 seems like the kind of thing that could happen just by chance since 24 out of 48 is what we would expect on average in the long run.

c. 50%

1.1.18

a. 26 times out of 48 attempts

b. Applet input: probability of success is 0.5, sample size is 48, number of samples is 1,000. This distribution is centered at 24.

c. We cannot conclude the chance model is wrong since a value as large or larger than 26 is fairly likely.

d. We do not have strong evidence that Zwerg can correctly follow this type of direction more than 50% of the time.

e. The chance model (Zwerg guessing) is a plausible explanation for the observed data (26 out of 48), since the observed outcome was likely to occur under the chance model.

f. Less convincing evidence that Zwerg can correctly follow this type of direction more than 50% of the time. We could have anticipated this since 26 out of 48 is closer to 24 out of 48 than is 37 out of 48.

g. This does not prove that Zwerg is just guessing. Guessing is just one plausible explanation for Zwerg's performance in this experiment. We cannot rule out guessing as an explanation for Zwerg getting 26 out of 48 correct.

1.1.23

a. 0.50

b. 20

c. 1,000 (or some large number)

d. 12 out 20 is a fairly likely value because it occurred frequently in the simulated data.

1.1.24

a. 0.50

b. 100

c. 1,000 (or some large number)

d. 60 out of 100 is somewhat unlikely because it occurred somewhat infrequently in the simulated data.

e. The sample size was different (20 serves vs. 100 serves).

1.1.25

B

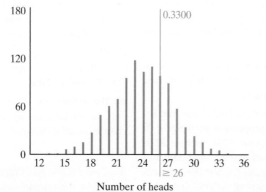

SOLUTIONS 1.1.18b

Section 1.2

1.2.1

D

1.2.3

A

1.2.5

A

1.2.7

C

1.2.9

a. .0.25

b. 25 (since $0.25 \times 100 = 25$)

1.2.11

$\hat{p}$ is the value of the observed statistic, while the p-value is the probability that the observed statistic or more extreme occurs if the null hypothesis is true; p-value is a measure of strength of the evidence.

1.2.13

a. Null: The long-run proportion of times Hope will go to the correct object is 0.50, Alt: The long-run proportion of times that Hope will go to the correct object is more than 0.50

b. H_0: $\pi = 0.50$, H_a: $\pi > 0.50$

c. 0.23 (23 dots are 0.60 or larger)

d. No, the approximate p-value is 0.23, which provides little to no evidence that Hope understands pointing.

e. 0.70

f. i.

1.2.14 Researcher A has stronger evidence against the null hypothesis since his p-value is smaller.

1.2.15

a. Roll a die 20 times, and keep track of how many times 'one' is rolled. Repeat this many times.

b. Using a set of five black cards and one red card, shuffle the cards and choose a card. Note the color of the card and return it to the deck. Shuffle and choose a card 20 times keeping track of how many times the red card is selected. Repeat this many times.

c. Roll 30 times, then repeat.

d. Shuffle and choose a card 30 times, then repeat.

e. Roll a die 20 times, and keep track of how many times a 'one, two, three, or four' is rolled. Repeat this many times.

f. Using a set of one black card and two red cards, shuffle the cards and choose a card. Shuffle and choose a card 20 times keeping track of how many times the red card is selected. Repeat this many times.

1.2.18

a. Obs units: each of the 40 monkeys. variable: correct choice or not (categorical)

b. The long-run proportion of times that a monkey will make the correct choice, π

c. 30/40 = 0.75. Statistic. we use the symbol $\hat{p}$ to denote this quantity.

d. Null hypothesis: The long-run proportion of times that rhesus monkeys make the correct choice when observing the researcher jerk their head is 50% (just guessing). Alt hypothesis: The long-run proportion of times that rhesus monkeys make the correct choice is more than 50%

$$H_0: \pi = 0.50, H_a: \pi > 0.50$$

e. Flip a coin 40 times and record the number of heads. Repeat this process 999 more times, yielding a set of 1,000 values of the number of heads received in 40 coin tosses. Compute the p-value as the proportion of times 30 or larger was obtained by chance in the 1,000 sets of 40 coin tosses. If the p-value is small (indicating 30 or larger rarely occurs by chance), then this is convincing evidence that rhesus monkeys can interpret human gestures better than by random chance.

f. The approximate p-value from the applet (using $\pi = 0.50$, $n = 40$, number of samples = 1,000) is 0.001 (probability of 30 or greater). This small p-value means that 30 out of 40 is strong evidence that the rhesus monkeys are not guessing, which may lead us to believe that rhesus monkeys may be able to understand a head jerk to indicate which box to choose.

1.2.19

a. Obs units: each of the 40 monkeys. Variable: correct choice or not (categorical)

b. The long-run proportion of times that a monkey will make the correct choice, π

c. 31/40 = 0.775. Statistic. We use the symbol $\hat{p}$ to denote this quantity.

d. Null hypothesis: The long-run proportion of times that rhesus monkeys make the correct choice when the researcher looks towards the correct box is 50% (just guessing). Alt hypothesis: The long-run proportion of times that rhesus monkeys make the correct choice is more than 50%

$$H_0: \pi = 0.50, H_a: \pi > 0.50$$

e. Flip a coin 40 times and record the number of heads. Repeat this process 999 more times, yielding a set of 1,000 values of the number of heads received in 40 coin tosses. Compute the p-value as the proportion of times 31 or larger was obtained by chance in the 1,000 sets of 40 coin tosses. If the p-value is small (indicating 31 or larger rarely occurs by chance), then this is convincing evidence that rhesus monkeys can interpret human gestures better than by random chance.

f. The approximate p-value from the applet (using $\pi = 0.50$, $n = 40$, number of samples = 1,000) is 0.001 (probability of 31 or greater). This small p-value means that 31 out of 40 is strong evidence that the rhesus monkeys are not guessing, which may lead us to believe that rhesus monkeys can interpret gestures to indicate which box to choose.

1.2.20

The p-value is approximately 0.25. We don't have strong evidence that the author's long-run proportion of wins in *Minesweeper* is greater than 50%. The null hypothesis (long-run proportion of wins is 50%) is a plausible explanation for her winning 12 out of 20 games.

1.2.22

a. The long-run proportion of times a spun penny lands heads

b. The p-value = 0.16. There is little-to-no evidence that a spun penny lands heads less than 50% of the time.

c. Null would be the same, Alternative would be > 0.50. To calculate the p-value, find the probability that 29 or larger (58% or larger) occurred.

1.2.24

A simulation analysis using a null hypothesis probability of 0.75 yields a p-value of 0.10, meaning that the set of 20 free throws by your friend (and making 12/20 of them) provides little-to-no evidence that your friend's long-run proportion of free throws made is worse than the NBA average.

1.2.25

A simulation analysis using a null hypothesis probability of 0.75 yields a p-value of 0.02, meaning that the set of 40 free throws by your friend (and making 24/20 of them) provides strong evidence that your friend's long-run proportion of free throws made is worse than the NBA average.

Section 1.3

1.3.1

C

1.3.3

A, because the standard deviation is smaller

1.3.5

a. FALSE, b. TRUE, c. FALSE, d. FALSE

1.3.7

a. –3.47 (100 out of 400; 25%), –3.80 (20 out of 120; 16.7%), –4.17 (65 out of 300; 21.7%)

b. 65 out of 300 is the strongest evidence, 100 out of 400 is the least strong evidence

1.3.8

a. Friend D because they played more games

b. Friend D because this is more evidence against the null hypothesis

c. Friend D because this is more evidence against the null hypothesis

d. Friend D because a smaller standard deviation leads to a larger standardized statistic

1.3.9

Friend G because the value of their statistic (30 out of 40) is larger than Friend F (15 out of 40) and thus will be farther in the tail of the distribution.

1.3.11

Simulation yields a standard deviation of the null distribution of 0.125, and a standardized statistic of approximately $(0.9375 - 0.50)/0.125 = 3.5$, which provides very strong evidence that the long-run proportion of Buzz pushing the correct button is higher than 50%.

1.3.12

Simulation yields a standard deviation of the null distribution of approximately 0.094, and a standardized statistic of approximately 0.76, which provides little to no evidence that the long-run proportion of times Buzz pushes the correct button is higher than 50%.

1.3.15

a. Null: The long-run proportion of all couples that have the male say "I love you" first is 50%. Alt: The long-run proportion is more than 50%.

b. $z = (0.70 - 0.50)/0.079 = 2.53$.

c. The observed proportion of couples where the males says "I love you" first is 2.53 standard deviations above the null hypothesized parameter value of 0.50.

d. We have strong evidence that the proportion of couples for which the male says "I love you" first is more than 50%.

1.3.17

a. The long-run proportion of times the lady correctly identifies which was poured first, π

b. Null: $\pi = 0.50$, Alt: $\pi > 0.50$

c. $8/8 = 1 = \hat{p}$

d. 0.50, because that is the value of the parameter if the null hypothesis is true. The standard deviation will be positive because the standard deviation must be at least 0, and is only equal to zero if there is no variability in the values (there will be variability in the simulated statistics).

e. $z = (1 - 0.50)/0.177 = 2.82$.

f. The observed proportion of times the lady correctly identified which was poured first is 2.82 standard deviations above the null hypothesized parameter value of 0.50.

g. We have strong evidence that the long-run proportion of times that the lady makes the correct identification is greater than 50%.

1.3.20

a. The long-run proportion of times that 10-month olds choose the helper toy, π

b. Null: $\pi = 0.05$, Alt: $\pi > 0.50$

c. $14/16 = 0.875 = \hat{p}$

d. $z = (0.875 - 0.50)/0.125 = 3$.

e. The observed proportion of times the 10-month-old babies chose the helper toy is 3 standard deviations above the null hypothesized parameter value of 0.50.

f. We have strong evidence that the long-run proportion of times that 10-month- old babies choose the helper toy is greater than 50%.

1.3.21

a. Yes, the p-value will be small because the standardized statistic is large

b. A p-value of approximately 0.002. The p-value is the probability observing 14/16 or larger assuming the null hypothesis is true.

c. We have strong evidence that the long-run proportion of times that 10-month-old babies choose the helper toy is greater than 50%.

d. Yes, because both the p-value and the standardized statistic are measuring the strength of evidence (how far out in the tail the observed value is), and so should lead to the same conclusion.

Section 1.4

1.4.1

D

1.4.2

A

1.4.3

D

1.4.7

a. Stronger. The statistic (18/20 = 90%) is much farther away from the null hypothesized value (50%) than before (12/20 = 60%).

b. Stronger., The statistic is the same (60%) but the sample size is much larger (100 vs. 20).

c. No, 12/30 = 40% is less than the null hypothesis value of 50%: thus this is not evidence that the long-run proportion of wins in *Minesweeper* is more than 50%

1.4.13

a. Sample size

b. Stronger

1.4.14

a. Distance

b. Weaker

1.4.15

a. Double it. The alternative would now be two-sided.

b. Weaker

1.4.18

a. The long run proportion of times that Krieger chooses the correct object, π.

b. 50%

c. Null: The long-run proportion of times that Krieger chooses the correct object is 50%; Alt: The long-run proportion of times that Krieger chooses the correct object is more than 50%.

1.4.19

a. 6 out of 10 for a proportion of 0.60

b. Mean = 0.50, SD = 0.16

c. The p-value (The probability of obtaining 0.60 or larger when the true chance Krieger chooses the correct object is 0.05) is approximately 0.38

d. We do not have strong evidence that Krieger will choose the correct object more than 50% of the time. It is plausible that Krieger will choose the correct object 50% of the time.

e. Stronger

1.4.20

a. Values of the long-run proportion less than 0.50

b. Increase, a two-sided p-value will be approximately twice as big as the corresponding one-sided p-value.

c. The two-sided p-value will approximately double to 0.75.

d. Stronger

1.4.21

a. Decrease, larger sample size.

b. The p-value decreased to 0.244, yes it did behave as predicted.

c. Stronger

1.4.22

a. The long-run proportion of times Krieger makes the correct choice when the experimenter leans towards the object, π.

b. 50%

c. Null: The long run proportion of times Krieger makes the correct choice when the experimenter leans towards the object is 50%; Alt: The long-run proportion of times Krieger makes the correct choice when the experimenter leans towards the object is more than 50%.

d. Decrease, 9 out of 10 is farther out in the tail of the null distribution than 6 out of 10

1.4.23

a. 9 out 10 (0.90)

b. Mean = 0.50, SD = 0.16

c. 0.01

d. Approximately 0.80

1.4.24

a. $z = (0.90 - 0.50)/0.16 = 2.5$

b. Using both the p-value and the standardized statistic, we have strong evidence that the long-run proportion of times that Krieger makes the correct choice is more than 50%.

c. Yes, the p-value got smaller (evidence got stronger).

1.4.25

a.

Analysis method	Sample size n	Null value π_0	Value of $\hat{p}$
A: 1.4.8 – 1.4.12	938,223	0.50	0.516276
B: 1.4.25	82	0.50	1.00

b. Analysis Method A provides strong evidence, but Method B is overwhelming.

1.4.27

a. one-sided

b. 6 out of 8 seems fairly likely to occur by chance; thus it is plausible that bees are just as likely to sting a target that has already been stung as they are to sting a target that is pristine.

c. p-value = 0.1094 + 0.0313 + 0.0039 = 0.1446. We have little to no evidence that bees are more likely to sting a target that has already been stung compared to a pristine target.

1.4.30

D = Sample size is $n = 25$, alternative hypothesis is right-sided: $\pi > \frac{1}{2}$.

A = Sample size is $n = 225$, alternative hypothesis is right-sided: $\pi > \frac{1}{2}$.

C = Sample size is $n = 25$, alternative hypothesis is left-sided: $\pi < \frac{1}{2}$.

B = Sample size is $n = 225$, alternative hypothesis is left-sided: $\pi < \frac{1}{2}$.

E = Sample size is $n = 25$, alternative hypothesis is two-sided: $\pi \neq \frac{1}{2}$.

F = Sample size is $n = 225$, alternative hypothesis is two-sided: $\pi \neq \frac{1}{2}$.

1.4.31

a. Increasing: B,C

b. Decreasing: A,D

c. Up-down: E,F

1.4.32

a. 100%

b. 50%

c. 0%

1.4.33

a. Smaller, decreasing, A,D

b. Larger, increasing, B,C

c. Up-down, E,F

d.

Alternative hypothesis	Strongest evidence	Shape of curve
$\pi > 0.05$	$\hat{p} = 1$	Decreasing
$\pi < 0.05$	$\hat{p} = 0$	Increasing
$\pi \neq 0.05$	$\hat{p} = 0$ or $\hat{p} = 1$	Up-down

1.4.34

a. Lower

b. Larger

c. Always lies above

d. Less steep

1.4.35

	Increasing	Decreasing	Up-Down
Steeper	B	A	F
Flatter	C	D	E

Section 1.5

1.5.1

C

1.5.3

60. Smaller standard deviations occur when the sample size is larger, for the same value of the proportion, π.

1.5.5

The value of the standardized statistic, z.

1.5.7

The standardized statistic; a measurement of how many standard deviations from the mean the observed statistic is on the null distribution

1.5.9

a. Null: The long-run proportion of times that a penny lands heads when spun is 0.02

Alt: The long-run proportion of times that a penny lands heads when spun is >0.02

b. The simulation based p-value of 0.077, because the validity conditions are not met. There are not at least 10 times where the penny landed heads and at least 10 times where the penny landed tails in the sample.

c. No, we do not have strong evidence that a penny will land heads more than 20% of the time in the long run, since the p-value is only 0.077.

1.5.11

a. 0.152; this is very close to the hypothesized parameter value of 0.15

b. No, the validity conditions are not met. There are not at least 10 successes and 10 failures in the data (only 8 and 2)

1.5.12

a. 0.15; this is the hypothesized parameter value of 0.15

b. 0.019; $\sqrt{\pi(1-\pi)/n} = \sqrt{0.15(1-0.15)/361} = 0.019$

c. Yes

d. Because the validity conditions are met for this data set (larger sample size)

1.5.15

a. Null: The long-run proportion of times that the male says "I love you" first is 50%.

Alt: The long-run proportion of times that the male says "I love you" first is more than 50%.

b. 0.0057

c. We have very strong evidence that the long-run proportion of times that the male says "I love you" first is more than 50%

d. $z = 2.53$. That the proportion of males that say "I love you first" is 2.53 standard deviations above the mean of the null distribution.

e. $0.0057 \times 2 = 0.0114$

1.5.17

a. Null: The long-run proportion of times that a player starts with scissors is 33%

Alt: The long-run proportion of times that a player starts with scissors is different than 33%

Null: $\pi = 33\%$

Alt: $\pi \neq 33\%$

b. p-value = 0

c. We have very strong evidence that the long-run proportion of times that a player starts with scissors is different than 33%.

1.5.18

a. Null: The long-run proportion of times that a player starts with rock is 33%.

Alt: The long-run proportion of times that a player starts with rock is different than 33%.

Null: $\pi = 33\%$

Alt: $\pi \neq 33$

b. p-value = 0

c. We have very strong evidence that the long-run proportion of times that a player starts with rock is different than 33%.

1.5.20

a. Null: The long-run proportion of times that the most competent-looking candidate wins is 50%.

Alt: The long-run proportion of times that the most competent-looking candidate wins is more 50%.

b. $n = 279$, $\hat{p} = 67.7\%$

c. 0

d. We have very strong evidence that the most competent-looking candidate wins more than 50% of the time.

1.5.23

a. The long-run proportion of times a six is rolled

b. Null: The long-run proportion of times a six is rolled is 16.7%.

Alt: The long-run proportion of times a six is rolled is more than 16.7%.

c. 0.1497

d. We have little-to-no evidence that the long-run proportion of times a six is rolled is more than 16.7%.

1.5.24

a. The long-run proportion of times a one is rolled.

b. Null: The long-run proportion of times a one is rolled is 16.7%.

Alt: The long-run proportion of times a one is rolled is less than 16.7%.

c. 0.0866

d. We have moderate evidence that the long-run proportion of times a one is rolled is less than 16.7%.

Section 1.6

1.6.1

B, C, D

1.6.3

E

1.6.5

A sampling distribution is a distribution of a sample proportion from all possible samples of a certain size from the same population or long-run process where a simulated null distribution is a distribution of a sample proportion from many samples of the same size using a hypothesized value for the population parameter.

1.6.7

a. 0.50, 0.112, approximately normal

b. 0.50, 0.079, approximately normal

1.6.9

Getting a sample proportion of 0.70 in your friend's larger sample of 40 would be more surprising. With larger samples, the sample proportion is more unlikely to vary greatly from the population proportion of 0.60. This can be seen in the smaller SD in its sampling distribution.

1.6.11

a. Answer will vary a little, but should be about 0.113.

b. 0.113.

1.6.13

a. 0.80.

b. 0.02.

c. Yes, because both $n\pi = 320$ and $n(1 - \pi) = 80$ are greater than 10.

1.6.15

a. 0.50 if she is just guessing and more than 0.50 if she can do better than guessing.

b. $H_0: \pi = 0.50$ $H_a: \pi > 0.50$.

c. 0.144.

d. 2.89.

e. Answers will vary, but should be about 2.89.

f. Because the standardized statistic is greater than 2, we have strong evidence that Joy Milne will correctly identify the shirt more than 50% of the time in the long run.

g. No, because the $n\pi = 12(.5)$ is not at least 10.

h. Using a simulation-based test, you should get a p-value of about 0.0010. We have strong evidence against the null, just as we did in part (f).

1.6.17

a. The mean should be around 0.466, the standard deviation should be around 0.223.

b. Answers will vary.

c. Answers will vary but should be similar to the mean and standard deviation calculated in part (a).

d. The expected mean is 0.466, theoretical standard deviation is .1577. Simulation results should match.

1.6.19

a. The distribution of sample proportions from samples of $n = 50$ will be centered at the long-run process probability of type O-negative blood of 0.07 (because the sample proportion is an unbiased estimator of the long-run process proportion). The standard deviation of the sample proportions is $\sqrt{0.07(0.93)/50} \approx 0.036$. The expected number of people in the sample (0.07*50 = 3.5) is less than 10, so the distribution is not approximately normal. Because it is bounded on the left by 0 (you can't have fewer than 0 people in your sample with O-negative blood), the distribution is skewed to the right.

b. The distribution of sample proportions from samples of $n = 500$ will be centered at the long-run process probability of type O-negative blood of 0.07 (because the sample proportion is an unbiased estimator of the long-run process proportion). The standard deviation of the sample proportions is $\sqrt{0.07(0.93)/500} \approx 0.011$. The expected number of people in the sample is (0.07*500 = 35). Because the expected number of

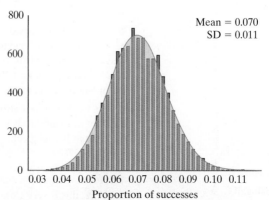

SOLUTIONS 1.6.19b

successes and failures (0.93*500 = 465) are both at least 10, the distribution of sample proportions is approximately normal.

Section 1.7

1.7.1

B

1.7.2

C

1.7.3

D

1.7.4

B

1.7.5

Technically yes, because $n\pi = 40(0.75) = 30$ and $n(1 - \pi) = 40(0.25) = 10$ are both at least 10, and as long as the sample of free throws is representative of her long-run free-throw percentage.

1.7.12

a. H_0: The proportion of statistics students picking a number greater than 5 is 0.50 in the long run ($\pi = 0.50$). H_a: The proportion of students picking a number greater than 5 is different from 0.50 in the long run ($\pi \neq 0.50$).

b. One-proportion z-test.

c. The validity conditions are met because both $n\pi = 101(0.50) = 50.5$ and $n(1 - \pi) = 101(0.50) = 50.5$ are at least 10. We don't know how the statistics students in the sample were chosen so we cannot generalize our results beyond this group of students.

d. $z = (62/101 - 0.5)/\text{sqrt}(0.5(0.5)/101) \approx 2.29$.

e. With a small p-value of 0.022 (e.g., smaller than 0.05), we have strong evidence that the proportion of statistics students (like those in this sample) who would pick a number greater than 5 in the long run, when asked to randomly pick a number between 1 and 10, is different from 0.50. Because our statistic was larger than 0.50, we can also conclude that there is strong evidence that more than half of all students (like those in this sample) will "randomly" pick a number greater than 5.

1.7.14

a. H_0: Mercury will pick the container with a larger number of bananas 50% of the time in the long run ($\pi = 1/2$). H_a: Mercury will pick the container with a larger number of bananas more than 50% of the time in the long run ($\pi > 1/2$).

b. One-proportion z-test.

c. The validity conditions are met (barely) because both $n\pi = 20(1/2) = 10$ and $n(1 - \pi) = 20(1/2) = 10$ are at least 10. As long as we can consider these 20 trials to be representative of Mercury's long-run ability, we can generalize the results to his long-run probability of success.

d. $z = (16/20 - 0.5)/\text{sqrt}(0.5(0.5)/20) \approx 2.68$.

e. With a p-value of 0.0036, which is less than an alpha-level of 0.05, we have strong evidence that Mercury will pick the container with a larger number of bananas more than 50% of the time in the long run. [With the small sample size, we could compute a binomial p-value (see Chapter 11), P(X ≥ 16 when $n = 20$ and $\pi = 0.50$) = 0.0059. This is almost twice as large as the p-value from the one-proportion z-test but is still strong evidence against the null hypothesis.]

1.7.15

a. H_0: Panzee will pick the container with a larger number of bananas 50% of the time in the long run ($\pi = 1/2$). H_a: Panzee will pick the container with a larger number of bananas more than 50% of the time in the long run ($\pi > 1/2$).

b. One-proportion z-test.

c. The validity conditions are met (barely) since both $n\pi = 20(1/2) = 10$ and $n(1 - \pi) = 20(1/2) = 10$ are at least 10. As long as we can consider these 20 trials to be representative of Panzee's long-run ability, we can generalize the results to his long-run probability of success.

d. $z = (11/20 - 0.5)/\text{sqrt}(0.5(0.5)/20) \approx 0.447$.

e. With a p-value of 0.3274, which is greater than an α-level of 0.05, we do not have strong evidence that Panzee will pick the container with a larger number of bananas more than 50% of the time in the long run.

1.7.18

a. H_0: The probability that a sniffer will correctly match the odor of the two identical twins is 0.25 ($\pi = 1/4$). H_a: The probability that a sniffer will correctly match the odor of the two identical twins is greater than 0.25 ($\pi > 1/4$).

b. One-proportion z-test.

c. The validity conditions are met because both $n\pi = 113(1/4) = 28.25$ and $n(1 - \pi) = 113(3/4) = 84.75$ are at least 10 and as long as the 4 pads were presented to the sniffers in a random order.

d. $z = (42/113 - 0.25)/\text{sqrt}(0.25(0.75)/113) \approx 2.99$.

e. With a small p-value of 0.0014, which is less than an α-level of 0.05, we have strong evidence that a sniffer has a greater than 25% chance of correctly matching the odor of the two identical twins in the long run. This provides some evidence that there is a genetic component to body odor.

1.7.19

a. H_0: The probability that a sniffer will correctly match the odor of the two non-identical twins is 0.25 ($\pi = 1/4$). H_a: The probability that a sniffer will correctly match the odor of the two non-identical twins is greater than 0.25 ($\pi > 1/4$).

b. One-proportion z-test.

c. The validity conditions are met because both $n\pi = 113(1/4) = 28.25$ and $n(1 - \pi) = 113(3/4) = 84.75$ are at least 10 10 and as long as the 4 pads were presented to the sniffers in a random order.

d. $z = (35/113 - 0.25)/\text{sqrt}(0.25(0.75)/113) \approx 1.47$.

e. With a p-value of 0.0708, we do not have strong evidence (p-value > α-level of 0.05) that a sniffer has a greater than 25% chance of correctly matching the odor of the two non-identical twins in the long run. This, combined with the previous study, provides some evidence that there is a genetic component to body odor.

End of chapter exercises

1.CE.1

Null

1.CE.3

a. Null: The probability the statistics professor wins is 0.02, Alternative: The probability the statistics professor wins is larger than 0.02.

b. Start with 5 playing cards—one red and four black. Shuffle the cards. Randomly choose one card, record if it is red or not, and then place the card back in the deck. Shuffle and randomly choose cards until 12 cards have been selected. Record the number of red cards selected out of the 12 selections. Repeat this entire process 999 more times to generate a distribution of counts of red cards. If 7 out of 12 red cards chosen rarely happened in the 1,000 simulations, then this would be convincing evidence that 7 out of 12 was unlikely to have occurred by chance.

SOLUTIONS 1.CE.3c

c. The observed data (7 wins out of 12 attempts) provide convincing evidence that the statistics professor's probability of winning in one week was larger than would be expected if the 5 competitors were equally likely to win because 7 out of 12 rarely happens by chance, when everyone is equally likely to win; in particular the p-value is 0.005.

d. The p-value is the probability of observing 7 or more successes out of 12 attempts when each attempt has a 20% chance of being correct.

e. The theory-based approach is not appropriate here because the resulting simulated distribution of statistics is not normal. This is because the sample size is not large enough. In particular, there are only 7 successes and 5 failures, instead of at least 10 of each.

1.CE.5

a. Even though 34.6% (the percent of players suspended for PED use who were from the US) is less than the percent of all baseball players born in the US (57.3%), it's possible that this could have happened by chance (just like it's possible to flip a coin and get heads 8 times out of 8); the question is how likely this (34.6%) would happen just by chance. If it is quite unlikely then we say that the result is statistically significant, meaning that there is something about US baseball players which make them less likely to be suspended for PED use.

b. The likelihood of having only 34.6% of 595 suspended baseball players be from the US when the proportion of all baseball players who are from the US is 57.3% is extremely unlikely; in other words, 34.6% is (statistically) significantly less than 57.3%.

c. $z = -11.19$. This tells us that the observed proportion (34.6%) is 11.19 SDs less than the mean of the null distribution, confirming that we have extremely strong evidence that the null hypothesized value of the parameter is incorrect.

1.CE.6

a. Even though 61.8% (the percent of players suspended for PED use who were from Latin America) is more than the percent of all baseball players born in Latin America (34.6%), it's possible that this could have happened by chance (just like it's possible to flip a coin and get heads 8 times out of 8); the question is how likely is it that this (61.8%) would happen just by chance. If it is quite unlikely then we say that the result is statistically significant, meaning that there is something about Latin American baseball players which make them more likely to be suspended for PED use.

b. The likelihood of having 61.8% of 595 suspended baseball players be from Latin America when the proportion of all baseball players who are from the US is 34.6% is extremely unlikely; in other words, 61.8% is (statistically) significantly more than 34.6%.

c. $z = 13.95$. This tells us that the observed proportion (61.8%) is more than 13.95 SDs less than the mean of the null distribution, confirming that we have extremely strong evidence that the null hypothesized value of the parameter is incorrect.

1.CE.9

Not necessarily. A larger sample size yields a smaller p-value if the value of the statistic is the same; there is no guarantee the value of the statistic (proportion of heads) will be the same in Jose and Roberto's separate samples

1.CE.10

A is the only correct answer.

1.CE.13

a. The long-run proportion of times that Rick makes a free throw underhanded

b. a) Null: The long-run proportion of times that Rick makes a free throw underhanded is 90%.

Alt: The long-run proportion of times that Rick makes a free throw underhanded is more than 90%.

Null: $\pi = 90\%$

Alt: $\pi > 90\%$

1.CE.14

a. The long-run proportion of times that Lorena makes a 10-foot putt

b. a) Null: The long-run proportion of times that Lorena makes a 10-foot putt is 60%.

Alt: The long-run proportion of times that Lorena makes a 10-foot putt is more than 60%.

Null: $\pi = 60\%$

Alt: $\pi > 60\%$

1.CE.17

a. We don't have strong evidence that the probability a spun tennis racquet lands with the label up is different from 0.05.

b. If the probability that a spun tennis racquet lands with the label is actually 0.05, then it is quite likely to get 46 spins out of 100 with the label up; thus, a reasonable (plausible) explanation for the author's data (46 out 100) is that the tennis racquet is fair (0.05 chance of label landing up).

1.CE.18

Null hypothesis probability = 0.05

Statistic = 0.46

p-value = 0.484

CHAPTER 2

Section 2.1

2.1.1

A

2.1.3

B

2.1.5

A. FALSE

B. FALSE

C. FALSE

2.1.7

B

2.1.9

While some of these could be argued the other way, all of them could likely not be representative. If you have food that finches like and other birds don't, you would overestimate the proportion of finches. You could have food that finches don't like and you would rarely see more than one eating at a time. The proportion of male birds could be species-dependent and depending on the type of food you have could affect the type of species and hence affect the proportion of male birds that come to your feeder. This proportion could then be different than the proportion of males in your area as well as those that typically visit feeders.

2.1.18

a. The population is all the likely voters in the city.

b. Since it is a random sample, I would think the proportion that favor the incumbent in the sample is similar to that for the population.

2.1.19

a. The proportion of all city voters that plan to vote for the incumbent.

b. The proportion of those in the sample that plan to vote for the incumbent (0.65).

2.1.20

a. The variable is who they plan to vote for or whether or not they plan to vote for the incumbent.

b. Categorical.

c. Proportion.

d. Bar graph.

2.1.21

a. Null: 50% of the all the city voters plan to vote for the incumbent. Alternative: A majority of all the city voters plan to vote for the incumbent.

b. The proportion of all city voters that plan to vote for the incumbent (0.65).

2.1.22

a. p-value = 0.

b. We have strong evidence that a majority of all the city voters plan to vote for the incumbent.

c. We can infer these results to all likely city voters since it came from a random sample.

d. Using theory-based methods is appropriate and we also obtain a p-value of 0.

2.1.23

a. How long people spend reading or learning about local politics.

b. Quantitative.

c. Mean or Median.

d. Dotplot.

2.1.24

Voter	Time spent reading/learning about local politics	Voting for incumbent?
#1	0	Yes
#2	0	Yes
#3	60	No
…	…	…

2.1.25

The study was done using a random sample. It could have been done by obtaining a list of all the voters in the city and then assigning every voter a number. Then have a random number generator give 267 random numbers. The voter's names that match the numbers chosen will be the random sample.

2.1.34

a. The population is all the sharks at the zoo.

b. The proportion should be similar to the population since it came from a random sample.

2.1.35

a. The parameter is the proportion of sharks in the zoo that have the disease.

b. The statistic is the proportion of sharks in the sample (0.20) that have the disease.

2.1.36

a. The variable measured is whether or not they have the disease.

b. Categorical.

c. Proportion.

d. Bar graph.

2.1.37

a. Null: The proportion of sharks at the zoo that have the disease is 0.25. Alternative: The proportion of sharks at the zoo that have the disease is less than 0.25.

b. 3/15 = 0.20.

2.1.38

a. p-value = 0.46.

b. We do not have any evidence that the proportion of sharks in the zoo that have the disease is less than 0.25.

c. The sharks at the zoo.

d. A theory-based approach using the normal distribution is not reasonable to use since there were only 3 sharks with the disease. We need at least 10.

2.1.39

a. The shark's blood oxygen content.

b. Quantitative.

c. Mean or median.

d. Dotplot.

2.1.40

Shark	Has disease?	Blood oxygen content
#1	Yes	1.2%
#2	No	5.6%
#3	No	6.2%
…		…

2.1.41

The study was done using a random sample. It could have been done by obtaining a list of all the sharks at the zoo and assigning each a number. Then have a random number generator give 15 random numbers. The sharks that match the numbers chosen will be the random sample.

2.1.44

A. All the customers of the store.

B. The 100 people asked to fill out the survey.

C. The proportion of all customers that visit the store because of the sale on coats.

d. The proportion of the sample that said they visited the store because of the sale on coats (0.40).

2.1.45

It may not be representative since it was not a random sample.

Section 2.1: Part 2

2.1.50

E

2.1.52

B

2.1.54

41, 28, 44, 5, 6

2.1.56

You would first assign each of the voters a random number between 1 and 2237. Then use a computer to randomly pick 100 numbers from 1 to 2237. If any numbers are picked more than once, have the computer pick more random numbers until the 100 chosen are unique. Finally, match your 100 unique randomly chosen numbers to the numbers assigned the voters and that will be the sample.

Section 2.1: Part 3

2.1.57

B

2.1.59

A

2.1.61

A

2.1.63

a. Answers could vary, but a logical variable to use in stratification is grade level.

b. The stratified sample has an advantage over a simple random sample because you are guaranteed you won't have too many or too few from one grade level in your sample. Parents of students at different grade levels could have very different views of the district's website. Parents of high school students will probably be looking for very different things on the website than parents of elementary students.

2.1.66

Ag-Food-Envro 96, Arch-ED 44, Eng 144, LA 79, Bus 70, Sci-Math 67.

2.1.68

Randomly pick (say) 50 one-square-mile sections in the Manistee National Forest. In the 50 sections chosen, determine the proportion of trees that are sugar maples. Combine this into an estimate of the overall proportion.

2.1.70

In a simple random sample, the number in your sample of those giving $500 or more will probably be quite small. Because these people give more money than those in other groups, their opinion about some issue may be particularly valuable, so you might want

to make sure their opinion is at least proportionally represented.

2.1.72

No this is not a truly random sample, but is a convenience sample. The sample will not include students who live off campus and don't eat lunch on campus. These tend to be the older students, so it will probably have too few juniors and seniors (who may feel differently on the issue). Some students don't tend to eat lunch and they will be underrepresented. Also, many students may ignore someone sitting at a table asking people to fill out a survey (and they may feel differently on the issue).

Section 2.2

2.2.1

a. Since the distribution is skewed to the left, the mean will be to the left of the median; hence, 65.86°F is the mean and 67.50°F is the median.

b. Mean: Larger, Median: Larger, Standard Deviation: Smaller.

2.2.6

a. The mean and median would increase by 5 points; the standard deviation would stay the same since the entire distribution would move up but the variability stays the same.

b. The mean would increase since 5 would be added to the total of the scores. The median would stay the same since the high score remains the high score. The standard deviation would increase since there would be more variability with the larger number.

c. The mean would increase since 5 would be added to the total of the scores. We can't really say for certain how or if the median or standard deviation would change. It depends on the original distribution of scores. For example if adding the 5 points to the lowest score could still keep it the lowest score or it could change it to the highest score.

2.2.8

B

2.2.10

a. The distribution is skewed to the right.

b. Since the distribution is skewed to the right we should expect the mean to be higher than the median.

c. The median is $35 and the mean is $45.68. The mean is higher, as expected.

d. If a $150 haircut is changed to $300 we should expect the median to stay the same (since $150 or $300 is just another larger value), but the mean should increase (since the total of all haircut costs will increase). When the change is made, we can see the median does stay the same and the mean increases to $48.68.

2.2.16

a. The SPF value for students at a certain school.

b. μ = mean SPF of sunscreens used by all students at this school.

c. $H_0: \mu = 15$ versus $H_a: \mu > 15$.

d. $n = 48, \bar{x} = 3.01, s = 17.19$.

e. No, it just came from students in her class.

f. They probably don't differ much from the students as a whole on this issue.

g. It may not be representative for students at a Midwestern college where it is very cloudy.

2.2.17

a. You would have to fabricate a large data set to represent the population of SPF numbers for all students at the school with the variability similar to that of the sample data and a mean of 30. From that data you would take a sample of 48 and find its mean. Repeat this at least 1000 times to develop a null distribution. To determine the p-value, determine the proportion of simulated statistics that are at more than 35.29.

b.

Simulation		Real study
One repetition	=	A sample of 48 students
Null model	=	Population mean is 30
Statistic	=	Average SPF number in the sample

2.2.18

a. Yes, since the sample size is larger than 20.

b. The standardized statistic: $t = 8.18$ and the p-value = 0 (applet output is shown above).

c. If the mean SPF for all students at the school is 30, the probability we would get a sample mean as large or larger than 35.29 from a random sample of 30 is 0.

d. We have strong evidence that the average SPF used by students at the school is more than 30.

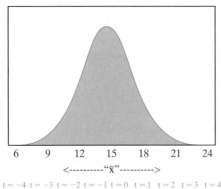

test statistic t = 8.18

p-value 0.0000

Reverse

confidence level 95 %

(30.299, 40.281)

SOLUTION 2.2.18b

2.2.22

a. The distribution is fairly symmetric.

b. The mean and the median will be about the same since the distribution of temperatures is fairly symmetric.

c. The mean is 98.105 and the median is 98.100. Yes, they are very close.

d. The actual standard deviation is 0.699.

2.2.23

a. Null: The average body temperature for males is 98.6 degrees ($\mu = 98.6$), Alt: The average body temperature for males is not 98.6 ($\mu \neq 98$).

b. The standardized statistic is -5.71 and the p-value is 0.

c. Since the p-value is less than 0.05 we have strong evidence that the average male body temperature is not 98.6 degrees.

d. Any generalization should be done with caution, but we can probably generalize it to healthy male adults similar to those that were in the study.

2.2.24

a. Null hypothesis: The average body temperature for females is 98.6 degrees ($\mu = 98.6$) Alt hypothesis: the average body temperature for females is not 98.6 degrees ($\mu \neq 98.6$).

b. Hard to tell, there is a lot of variability in the data.

c. The standardized statistic is -2.24 and the p-value $= 0.0289$.

d. Since the p-value is less than 0.05 we have strong evidence that the average body temperature for females is different than 98.6 degrees.

Section 2.2: Part 2

2.2.28

C

2.2.30

D

2.2.32

a. Mean = 10, SD = 0.8

b. Mean = 10, SD = 0.4

2.2.34

The sample size has to increase by a factor of 4.

2.2.36

a. Mean = 3.53 kg, SD = 0.123 kg

b. Mean = 3.53 kg, SD = 0.087 kg

c. See graph; we predict a normal distribution because the sample size is larger than 30 and the population is not severely skewed.

d. Somewhat surprising because 3.70 kg is out in the tail of the distribution.

2.2.38

Distribution A is from the samples of size 30 and B from size 10. The larger sample size will have a distribution with a smaller SD.

2.2.41

a. Skewed left because most students will have GPAs between 3 and 4, no students will have GPAs above 4, and fewer and fewer students will have GPAs smaller than 3

b. (i) Answers will vary, but we expect it to be 3.288.

(ii) Answers will vary, but we expect it to be 0.174.

(iii) The distribution is slightly skewed to the left.

c. Answers will vary, but we expect the mean to be 3.288 and the SD to be 0.087. The distribution is fairly symmetric or perhaps slightly skewed to the left.

2.2.42

a. Answers will vary, but we expect a mean of 0.776 (the population proportion, which is also the mean of the zeros and ones in the population).

b. 0.093

c. It is the same as b, 0.093.

d. It might appear slightly skewed to the left.

e. Answers will vary, but we expect a mean of 0.776; 0.0417; it is the same as previously, 0.0417; it should appear fairly symmetric.

f. If we think of these as proportions, then the sample size needs to be about 45 so that $n(1 - \pi)$ is at least 10. If we think of these as 0s and 1s and means, we need a sample size of at least 30.

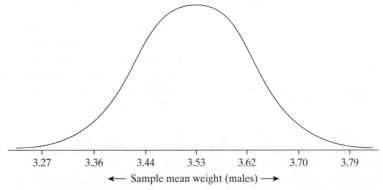

← Sample mean weight (males) →

SOLUTION 2.2.36c

2.2.45

a. We expect a mean of 8.001 hours, a SD of 0.475 hours, and a distribution that is fairly normal looking because the population is normal.

b. Answers will vary, but they should be close to expected.

2.2.47

a. We expect a mean of 7.996 hours, a SD of 1.487 hours, and a distribution that is fairly normal looking because the population is symmetric.

b. Answers will vary, but they should be close to expected.

c. Because the population mean was about 8 hours in all three cases, we expect the sampling distribution to center at 8 hours each time. When the population standard deviation is larger (pop 3), we have more variability in the sampling distribution. When the population distribution is symmetric, the sampling distribution will be approximately normal. This was not quite true with pop 2, when the population was skewed to begin with and the sample size was still small (10 < 30).

Section 2.2: Part 3

2.2.48

A has 5 degrees of freedom and B has 100. A t-distribution with more degrees of freedom will be taller in the middle and shorter in the tails.

2.2.50

You will get a larger p-value. A t-distribution is heavier in the tails, meaning there is a greater area beyond a given standardized statistic than in a normal distribution. (A sample size of 20 is small enough to see a bit of a difference.)

2.2.52

C

2.2.54

C (a bit larger than the z-probability)

2.2.56

A, C, F

2.2.58

The t-statistic is $(38.8-36)/(0.9/\text{sqrt}(15)) \approx 12.05$, which indicates that in the sampling distribution of means of samples of size 15, the observed sample mean 38.8 is 12.05 standard errors above the mean of the distribution, 36 (the hypothesized population mean).

2.2.60

Let μ represent the mean weight of all such bags in Michigan. Note: 1 lb = 16 oz, so a 5 lb bag should weigh 80 oz. H_0: $\mu = 80$ oz, H_a: $\mu > 80$ oz. We will use a one-sample t-test. The validity conditions are met because the sample distribution was roughly normal, so we assume the population distribution of weights to be roughly normal. We are also told to assume the sample is representative of the population of interest. $t = (90.3 - 80)/(5.0/\text{sqrt}(10)) \approx 6.51$, df = 9, p-value = $P(T_9 > 6.51) < 0.0001$. With a p-value less than 0.0001, we have very strong evidence that "5 lb" bags of Michigan apples weigh more than 5 lb (or 80 oz), on average.

2.2.62

Let μ represent the long-run mean waiting time at this Wendy's. H_0: $\mu = 134$ s, H_a: $\mu \neq 134$ s. We will use a one-sample t-test. Below is a dotplot of the same data.

Summary statistics: $\bar{x} = 93.96$ s, $s = 46.66$ s

We are told the drive-through times are representative of all drive-through times at this Wendy's restaurant. The data show some skewness to the right but we have a fairly large sample size (27). We will cautiously proceed with the one-sample t-test.

$t = (93.96 - 134)/(46.66/\text{sqrt}(27)) \approx -4.46$. With df = 26, $2 \times P(T_{26} < -4.46) \approx 0.00014$.

With a p-value < 0.001, we have very strong evidence that the population mean drive-through times of Holland's Wendy's are different from (lower than) the national average of 134 s.

2.2.64

Let μ represent the long-run average score subjects find in this process. H_0: $\mu = 0$, H_a: $\mu \neq 0$. We will use a one-sample t-test. The validity conditions are met because we have a fairly large sample size (27) and symmetric sample data. We would like more information about how these subjects were selected to know what population we can generalize to, but the experimenters did use randomness in the ordering of the pictures.

$t = (6.3 - 0)/\text{sqrt}(12.45/\text{sqrt}(27)) \approx 2.63$, p-value = $2P(T_{26} > 2.63) \approx 0.0142$. With a p-value of 0.0142 (<0.05), we have strong evidence that people tend not to pick their own face, but on average pick a face that is better looking than their own.

2.2.66

Let μ represent the long-run average score subjects find in this process. H_0: $\mu = 0$, H_a: $\mu \neq 0$. We will use a one-sample t-test. The validity conditions are met because we have a fairly large sample size (24) and the data are reported as being fairly symmetric. $t = (10.09-0)/(19/\text{sqrt}(24)) \approx 2.60$, p-value = $2P(t_{23} > 2.60) \approx 0.0160$. With a p-value of 0.0160 < 0.05, we have strong evidence that people tend not to pick their friend's face, but on average pick a face that is better looking than their friend's.

Section 2.3

2.3.1

a. 5%

b. Larger, because each test itself has a 5% chance, so if we do multiple tests, the overall chance of at least one error will be larger than 5%. This is like saying the chance of getting at least one head when flipping a coin 10 times is larger than 50%.

2.3.3

a. Fail to reject

b. Fail to reject

c. Reject

d. Fail to reject

2.3.5

a. Reject, since the p-value is less than 0.01, it must be less than 0.10

b. Reject

c. Not enough information

d. Reject

2.3.6

a. p-values less than or equal to 0.05

b. p-values larger than 0.05

SOLUTION 2.2.62

2.3.8

a. 0.001

b. Type II error rate will decrease

2.3.10

a. We find strong evidence that Buzz is not guessing, but he is guessing

b. We do not have evidence that Buzz is not guessing (guessing is plausible), when Buzz is actually not guessing

2.3.11

A Type I error is possible here, which means that we conclude there is strong evidence Buzz is not guessing, when in fact Buzz is guessing.

2.3.14

Because this would increase the Type II error rate, meaning we'd frequently conclude "not enough evidence to reject the null hypothesis" when the null hypothesis is false, leading to many "missed opportunities"

2.3.17

a. The proportion of all students at the school who state they would likely read an alternative campus newspaper

b. Null: The proportion of all students at the school who state they would likely read an alternative campus newspaper is 10%, Alt: The proportion of all students at the school who state they would likely read an alternative campus newspaper is more than 10%

c. We find strong evidence the proportion is more than 10%, when it is not. The consequence is that readership of the newspaper may be lower than anticipated.

d. We don't have evidence the proportion of student readers is more than 10%, when it actually is more than 10%. You won't start the newspaper even though you would have enough readership.

2.3.19

a. We have strong evidence the subject is not telling the truth.

b. It's plausible the subject is telling the truth (we can't rule out the fact that they are telling the truth).

c. We have strong evidence the subject is not telling the truth, when in fact they are telling the truth.

d. We don't have strong evidence the subject is not telling the truth (it's plausible they are telling the truth), when in fact they are lying.

2.3.21

a. We have strong evidence the new treatment is better, when it actually isn't.

b. We don't have evidence the new treatment is better, when it actually is.

2.3.23

a. We have strong evidence that at least two of the proportions of organ donors between the three default options are different between the groups, but the proportions actually are not different.

b. We don't have evidence that at least two of the three default options are different, when they actually are.

2.3.25

a. We have strong evidence that trick or treaters prefer candy over toys, when actually there is no preference (long-run probability of choosing candy is 50%).

b. We don't have strong evidence that trick or treaters prefer candy over toys, when actually trick or treaters do prefer candy over toys.

c. No.

d. Type II error is possible.

End of chapter exercises

2.CE.1

a. No, all games during a certain period were selected, instead of randomly choosing some.

b. Number of runs is likely more representative of the population (all games) since attendance fluctuates dramatically during the year due to weather, opponent, and timing of the games during the season.

2.CE.3

a. No, the instructor did not list all games in the 2010 season and randomly choose some.

b. Null hypothesis: 75% of all major league baseball games have a "big bang" ($\pi = 0.75$), Alt hypothesis: Less than 75% of all games have a "big bang" ($\pi < 0.75$)

c. $\hat{p} = \dfrac{21}{45} = 0.467$.

d. Using applet with 0.75 = probability of success, $n = 45$, and number of samples = 1000, calculate probability of 0.467 or less. The p-value is approximately 0.

e. The data provide strong evidence that the true proportion of all major league baseball games with a big bang is less than 75%, since it's extremely unlikely that in a sample of 45 games only 21 would have a big bang if the true proportion of all games with a big bang was 75%.

2.CE.5

a. The observational units are the 600 brides in the sample. The variable is whether or not they kept their own name.

b. The population is the U.S. brides in 2001 to 2005. The sample is the 600 brides with wedding announcements in the NY Times.

c. The proportion of all US brides that keep their own names

d. Yes, concerned because people with wedding articles in NY Times are likely to be different than "typical" US adults. Probably reasonable to generalize to other brides who could/would have their wedding announcement in the NY Times.

2.CE.6

a. p-value = 0.0451. Strong enough evidence at 0.05 significance level since $0.0451 < 0.05$

b. Strong enough evidence at 0.10 significance level since $0.0451 < 0.10$

c. Not enough evidence at 0.01 significance level since $0.0451 > 0.01$

2.CE.9

a. The sample size is large, but it would be good to know that the data was not strongly skewed to feel better about running a theory-based test on the data.

b. Null: The average adult body temperature is 98.6 degrees, Alt: The average adult body temperature is not 98.6 degrees, p-value is 0.0000, we have strong evidence that average body temperature is different than 98.6

c. t-statistic of 6.32 means our sample mean is more than 6 standard deviations from 98.6

d. Yes, the t-statistic is very different than 0 (in particular > 3) which means there is very strong evidence against the null hypothesis.

2.CE.10

a. Type I

b. The p-value is > 0.05

c. Change significance level, increase sample size

## CHAPTER 3

Section 3.1

3.1.1
B

3.1.3
A

3.1.5
D

3.1.7
B

3.1.9
A

3.1.11
A

3.1.13
a. B
b. B

3.1.15 0.01

3.1.17 The confidence interval is estimating the *proportion of all American adults* that thought math was the most valuable subject they studied in school.

3.1.19
a. (0.48, 0.56)
b. (0.46, 0.59)

3.1.21 p-values will differ for each students' simulation, one possible example follows.

Null	p-value	Null	p-value
Proportion = 0.45	0.001	Proportion = 0.53	0.640
Proportion = 0.46	0.006	Proportion = 0.54	0.316
Proportion = 0.47	0.010	Proportion = 0.55	0.130
Proportion = 0.48	0.053	Proportion = 0.56	0.058
Proportion = 0.49	0.140	Proportion = 0.57	0.014
Proportion = 0.50	0.342	Proportion = 0.58	0.007
Proportion = 0.51	0.667	Proportion = 0.59	0.001
Proportion = 0.52	1.000	Proportion = 0.60	0.000

The 95% confidence interval is (0.48, 0.56).

3.1.24
a. The symbol π represents the proportion of all American adults that think same-sex marriages should be legal and have the same rights as traditional marriages.

b. The p-value is about 0.028.

c. No, 0.50 does not appear to be a plausible value for π. Since we have a small p-value, we have evidence against $\pi = 0.50$, so 0.50 is NOT a plausible value.

d. A 95% confidence interval for π is 0.505 to 0.555.

e. We are 95% confident that the value for π (the proportion of all American adults that think same-sex marriages should be legal and have the same rights as traditional marriages) is between 0.505 and 0.555.

3.1.25
A 99% confidence interval is (0.495, 0.561) (answers will vary due to simulation).

Section 3.2

3.2.1
B

3.2.3
B

3.2.5
D

3.2.7
0.38 ± 0.11

3.2.9
a. We need to know the sample size.
b. As the sample size gets larger, the variability will be smaller and hence the confidence intervals will be narrower. Therefore the confidence interval based on the sample size of 250 will be widest and the one based on the sample size of 4000 will be the narrowest.

c. For a sample size of 250, we got a standard deviation of 0.025 and a confidence interval of 0.182 ± 0.05. For a sample size of 1,000, we got a standard deviation of 0.012 and a conf idence interval of 0.182 ± 0.024. For a sample size of 4,000, we got a standard deviation of 0.006 and a confidence interval of 0.182 ± 0.012.

d. The midpoints of the intervals are all the same.

e. As the sample size increases, the widths of the intervals decrease.

f. Four times as much.

g. Yes

3.2.11
a. $0.60 \pm 2(0.070)$, or (0.46, 0.74)
b. No, since values less than 0.50 are contained in the confidence interval of plausible values.

3.2.12
a. $0.719 \pm 2(0.090)$, or (0.539, 0.899) (0.4642, 0.7358)
b. Yes, since values contained in the confidence interval of plausible values are all greater than 0.50. (0.2642, 0.5358)

3.2.15
a. 95% (0.5503, 0.7831)
b. 99% (0.5137, 0.8197)
c. The p-value for the test is less than 0.01.

3.2.16
$0.667 \pm 2(0.063) = 0.667 \pm 0.126$, (0.541, 0.793). Similar because validity conditions are met.

3.2.18
a. H_0: $\pi = 0.33$; H_a: $\pi > 0.33$; p-value = 0.4515, which offers weak evidence against the null so we can say that it is plausible that the long-run probability of correctly identifying the cup with Pepsi is 0.33.

b. $0.344 \pm 2(0.058)$, or (0.228, 0.460)

c. Yes. Since our p-value was larger than 0.05 the value under the null was found to be plausible; thus it would be contained in an approximate 95% confidence interval of plausible values.

3.2.19

a. (0.2274, 0.4602)

b. 0.1164

3.2.22

(0.4267, 0.6071)

3.2.23

(0.1036, 0.2528)

Section 3.2: Part 2

3.2.33

C

3.2.35

D

3.2.37

A, C, E

3.2.39

1.282

3.2.41

1,068 for 95% and 1,844 for 99%.

3.2.43

a. The parameter is the proportion of all American youth aged 8–18 who personally have a cell phone and the theory-based method we will use to estimate it is a one-proportion z-interval.

b. The method is valid since we have a random (therefore representative) sample, and $n\hat{p} = 2{,}002(0.66) = 1{,}321$ and $n(1 - \hat{p}) = 2{,}002(0.34) = 681$ are both at least 10.

c. $0.66 \pm 1.96\sqrt{0.66(0.34)/2{,}002} = 0.66 \pm 0.021 = (0.639, 0.681)$.

d. We are 95% confident that the proportion of all American youth aged 8–18 that personally have a cell phone is between 0.639 and 0.681.

e. No, because 0.70 is not contained in the confidence interval.

3.2.44

c. $0.66 \pm 1.645\sqrt{0.66(0.34)/2{,}002} = 0.66 \pm 0.017 = (0.643, 0.677)$.

d. We are 90% confident that the proportion of all American youth aged 8–18 who personally have a cell phone is between 0.643 and 0.677. The width of the 90% interval is narrower and the midpoint is the same as the 95% interval.

3.2.45

8,621

3.2.49

a. The parameter is the proportion of all American high-school-aged students who agree with the statement, "Issues like climate change can be solved if action is taken now" and the theory-based method we will use to estimate it is a one-proportion z-interval.

b. The method is valid since we have a random (therefore representative) sample, and $n\hat{p} = 602(0.76) = 458$ and $n(1 - \hat{p}) = 602(0.24) = 144$ are both at least 10.

c. $0.76 \pm 1.96\sqrt{0.76(0.24)/602} = 0.76 \pm 0.034 = (0.726, 0.794)$.

d. We are 95% confident that the proportion of all American high-school-aged students who agree with the statement, "Issues like climate change can be solved if action is taken now" is between 0.726 and 0.794.

e. Yes, the confidence interval is entirely above 0.50.

3.2.50

c. $0.76 \pm 1.645\sqrt{0.76(0.24)/602} = 0.76 \pm 0.029 = (0.731, 0.789)$.

d. We are 90% confident that the proportion of all American high-school-aged students that agree with the statement, "Issues like climate change can be solved if action is taken now" is between 0.731 and 0.789. The width of the 90% confidence interval is narrower and the center is the same as the 95% interval.

3.2.51

a. 779

b. You would need a smaller sample size for 90% confidence. It makes intuitive sense that a smaller sample would yield less confidence if you kept the margin of error the same. In the formula, you would have a smaller number (1.645) in the numerator for 90% confidence than that (1.96) for 95% confidence.

c. It would not change. Population size is not a factor in this.

Section 3.3

3.3.1

False

3.3.3

False

3.3.6

a. Male rattlesnakes, all male rattlesnakes, 21 male rattlesnakes

b. Sample size is greater than 20 and data are not strongly skewed.

c. Average age of all male rattlesnakes at this single site

d. False, the parameter is fixed and is either in the interval or not.

3.3.8

a. Students

b. Hours/week studying statistics outside of class, quantitative

c. (7.1114, 9.2886)

d. Yes, sample size is greater than 20 and the data were not strongly skewed.

We are 95% confident that the average hours/week all statistics students will spend studying is between 7.11 and 9.29.

3.3.11

a. Students

b. Number of U.S. states visited, quantitative

c. Probably, since statistics students wouldn't be different on the number of states visited compared to all students at the school.

d. $H_0: \mu = 16$, $H_a: \mu \neq 16$

e. The midpoint of the interval is 9.48. $9.48 \pm 2(7.13/\sqrt{50}) = 9.48 \pm 2.02 = (7.46, 11.50)$

3.3.12

a. (7.4537, 11.5063)

b. Yes, 16 is not in the confidence interval.

c. Yes, sample size was greater than 20, and the data were not strongly skewed.

3.3.13

a. (7.8844, 11.0756)

b. 2SD method is a rough approximation for a 95% confidence interval. It will not work for other levels of confidence.

3.3.14

a. Invalid

b. Valid

c. Invalid

d. Valid

e. Invalid

f. Invalid

3.3.19

a. Students

b. Number of Facebook friends, quantitative

c. The sample size is greater than 20 and the data are not strongly skewed.

d. (453.605, 624.795). We are 95% confident that the population average number of Facebook friends for students at this school is between 453.605 and 624.795.

3.3.20

a. Invalid

b. Valid

c. Invalid

3.3.22

a. Albacore tunas

b. Mercury level in parts per million, quantitative

c. The sample size is greater than 20 and the data are not strongly skewed.

d. (0.3155, 0.4005). We are 95% confident that the population average ppm of mercury in Albacore tunas is between 0.3155 and 0.4005.

3.3.23

a. The sample size is greater than 20 and the data are not strongly skewed.

b. (0.3241, 0.3839). We are 95% confident that the population average ppm of mercury in Yellowfin tunas is between 0.3241 and 0.3839.

3.3.25

a. The sample standard deviation is very large compared to the mean.

b. The sample size is greater than 20 and the data are not strongly skewed.

c. (1.8977, 2.1063). We are 95% confident that the population average number of close friends of U.S. adults is between.

d. No, because 2 is in the interval.

Section 3.3: Part 2

3.3.28

D

3.3.30

C

3.3.32

A, F, H

3.3.34

1.711, larger

3.3.36

2.670 (using Table B, can use df = 50 and find $t^* = 2.68$)

3.3.38

Yes, with a smaller sample size like 16, the data have to be fairly symmetric and these data are fairly symmetric.

3.3.41

a. Let μ represent the average reaction time for all student athletes at the school. We will use a one-sample t-interval to estimate this.

b. Even with a bit of skewness in the data, we have a large data set with a sample size of 42, so we should be able to use a theory-based t-interval. The sample is a random sample so it should be representative of the population.

c. $0.297 \pm 2.020 \left(\frac{0.041}{\sqrt{42}} \right) = 0.297 \pm 0.013 = (0.284, 0.310)$

d. We are 95% confident that the average reaction time for all student athletes at the school is between 0.284 and 0.310 seconds.

3.3.42

c. $0.297 \pm 1.683 \left(\frac{0.041}{\sqrt{42}} \right) = 0.297 \pm 0.011 = (0.286, 0.308)$.

d. We are 90% confident that the average reaction time for all student athletes at the school is between 0.286 and 0.308 seconds. The midpoints of the 95% and 90% intervals are the same, but the 90% interval is narrower.

3.3.45

a. The average estimate for the number of beans in a bag for students at the school. We will use a one-sample t-interval to estimate this.

b. Even with a bit of skewness in the data, we have a large data set with 40 so we should be able to use a theory-based t-interval. The 40 students are representative of all students at the researcher's school so we can generalize our results.

c. $962.9 \pm 2.023 \left(\frac{351.7}{\sqrt{40}} \right) = 962.9 \pm 112.5 = (850.4, 1,075.4)$

d. We are 95% confident that the average estimate for the number of beans in the bag for all the students at the school is between 850.4 and 1075.4.

e. Yes, we have strong evidence that students cannot accurately estimate the number of beans in the bag, on average, because our confidence interval is completely

below the actual number of beans in the bag (1,470).

3.3.46

c. $962.9 \pm 2.798 \left(\frac{351.7}{\sqrt{40}} \right) = 962.9 \pm 150.6 = (812.3, 1,113.5)$.

d. We are 99% confident that the average estimate for the number of beans in the bag for all the students at the school is between 812.3 and 1,113.5.

e. Yes, we have very strong evidence that students cannot accurately estimate the number of beans in the bag, on average, because our confidence interval is completely below the actual number of beans in the bag (1,470). The midpoints of the 95% and 99% intervals are the same, but the 99% interval is wider.

Section 3.4

3.4.1

a. $\hat{p}$ is the sample proportion (statistic) and π is the population proportion (parameter)

b. $\hat{p}$

c. Standard deviation of $\hat{p}$ (or the standard error)

d. Margin of error

3.4.3

The sample size, the level of confidence, and the value of $\hat{p}$. The value of $\hat{p}$ is hardest to control.

3.4.5

a. 90%: (0.0993, 0.1327); 95%: (0.0962, 0.1358); 99%: (0.0899, 0.1421)

b. Midpoints are all the same.

c. 90% is narrowest, 99% is widest; as confidence level increases width of interval increases

d. No, because all of the intervals include 10%.

e. Yes, because there are at least 10 people who said "yes" (116) and at least 10 who said "no" (884).

3.4.6

a. Narrower

b. Wider

3.4.8

E

3.4.10

Decreases, slowly

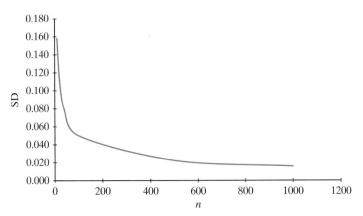

SOLUTION 3.4.13b

3.4.13

a.

N	SD of $\hat{p}$
10	0.158
20	0.112
40	0.079
100	0.050
500	0.022
1,000	0.016

b. See graph above.

c. Decreases

d. Less

3.4.14

a. Rodgers. The benefit of the additional 25 flips decreases as the sample size increases.

b. They will go down similar amounts because both Rodgers and Hammerstein are doubling the number of flips they are doing.

3.4.23

A

3.4.24

D

3.4.25

Decrease

3.4.26

Increase

3.4.27

a. Remain same

b. Increase

3.4.28

Increase

3.4.29

Decrease

3.4.30

95%

3.4.31

99%

3.4.33

B

Section 3.5

3.5.1

a. If one coffee bar opens earlier than the other, the lines may be different at the bars when they first open (if one opens before the first class starts it may have a longer line than one that opens after the first class starts).

b. A more representative sample of students might be observed at different times of the day and on different days of the week.

3.5.3 The question is awkwardly phrased. "Does it seem possible or impossible…it never happened?" The latter part ('impossible it never happened') involves a double negative.

3.5.4 This question is more clearly phrased; they got rid of the double negative.

3.5.5

a. See graph below.

b. Substantially fewer individuals reported that it was "possible it didn't happen" in 1994 as compared to 1992.

c. For 1992: (0.6305, 0.6895); for 1994: (0.8922, 0.9278)

d. The confidence intervals are quite different; they do not overlap.

c. Wording of the question can dramatically impact survey results.

3.5.7

Probably the question which did not give two options will yield a higher percentage of affirmative responses.

3.5.9

Affordable Care Act since Obamacare links the program to the president, which may prove more divisive than the program itself.

3.5.11

Whether the respondent supports social/welfare programs may differ by race.

3.5.12

Self-reporting of sexually transmitted diseases might differ based on the sex of interviewer and the sex of subject.

3.5.13

If the clothing worn by the interviewer suggests that the interviewer is wealthy, the respondent may be less likely to report support of increased taxes of the wealthy.

3.5.14

If the interviewer is smoking, respondents may be less likely to report antismoking opinions.

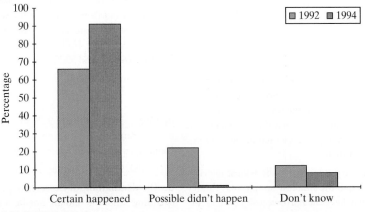

SOLUTION 3.5.5a

3.5.17

a. Maybe overstate, since students may tend to think they are getting more sleep than they are.

b. Maybe overstate, since students may tend to think they are volunteering more than they are.

c. Maybe overstate, since students may tend to think they are attending church more often than they actually are.

d. Maybe overstate, since students may tend to think they are studying more than they actually are.

e. Maybe overstate, since students may tend to think they are wearing a seat belt more often than they actually do.

3.5.23

a. (0.4242, 0.4274)

b. Yes, significantly less than 50%. The difference may be only modestly practically important since it's not that much lower than 50%.

c. This sample was taken in such a way that we should have major concerns about the ability to infer that the 350,847 participating in the survey are representative of all U.S. citizens. Only those who happened upon the site had the opportunity to answer.

End of chapter exercises

3.CE.1

a. 0.115 to 0.229

b. We can be 95% confident that between 11.5% and 22.9% of all water specimens from aircraft carrying domestic and international passengers will test positive for the presence of bacteria, thus failing to meet federal safety standards.

3.CE.3

C

3.CE.4

B

3.CE.6

a. It is unlikely that our sample proportion will be the same as the population proportion, but if the sample was taken randomly, we can be fairly sure that it is close and that closeness can be represented through an interval estimate.

b. Country B will have the widest interval since it had the smallest sample size. Country C will have the narrowest since it had the largest sample size.

c. The interval for country B will contain 0.20.

d. The p-value for this test for country B will be large (above 0.05) since the interval contained 0.20. The p-value for this test on the other two countries will be small (less than 0.05) since their intervals did not contain 0.20 and so 0.20 is not plausible.

3.CE.7

a. A: $z = 8.16$, B: -1.44, C: 3.95

b. Researcher A has strongest evidence. Researcher B has least evidence.

3.CE.10

a. 0.121 to 0.159.

b. Values between 0.121 and 0.159 should not be rejected at the 0.01 significance level since they are plausible values for the population proportion.

3.CE.13

99.99% confidence intervals will often be extremely wide and uninformative.

3.CE.14

The difference in width between an interval based on a sample of 1000 Americans vs. 1,000,000 Americans may not be that practically different, but the sample of 1,000,000 Americans will cost substantially more to obtain.

3.CE.15

70% is not a very high confidence level and researchers often want to be more confident in their conclusion than just 70% confident.

3.CE.16

a. Increase

b. Decrease

3.CE.19

a. Statistics, because they are based on samples.

b. (0.2863, 0.3057). We are 95% confident that the proportion of Americans who reported that the state of the U.S. economy would affect their Halloween spending is between 28.63% and 30.57%.

c. The sample standard deviation

3.CE.20

a. (55.67, 56.95). We are 95% sure that the average amount Americans will spend on Halloween is between $55.67 and $56.95.

b. (55.25, 57.37). The interval is wider.

c. The distribution of expected Halloween spending amounts should not be strongly skewed.

3.CE.23

a. The distribution of difference in ages is fairly symmetric and centered slightly above zero, indicating a typical difference of approximately 1 to 2 years in male and female ages (males slightly older), though the overall distribution ranged from −7 to 18, with a slight tail to the right indicating a handful of marriages where the male is more than 10 years older than the female.

b. Yes, data are not strongly skewed and sample size is more than 20.

c. (0.5944, 3.2456)

d. We are 99% confident that the true difference in male and female ages of soon to be married couples in Cumberland County is between 0.59 and 3.25 years.

e. Yes, 0 is not in the interval.

f. Soon to be married couples in Cumberland County

3.CE.24

a. 27 out 100 (0.27)

b. Yes, because there are at least 10 couples where the wife is older than the husband (27) and at least 10 couples where the husband is at least as old as the wife (73).

c. (0.197, 0.343); We are 90% confident that the population proportion of married couples for whom the wife is older than the husband is between 0.197 and 0.343.

d. Yes, 50% is not in the interval, and the entire interval is below 50%.

3.CE.25

a. Invalid

b. Invalid

c. Invalid

d. Valid

3.CE.27

a. The random sample, because the 4.5% of women who returned the questionnaire are likely quite different from the 95.5% of women who didn't.

b. (0.3938, 0.4862)

c. We are 95% confident that the proportion of all American women who believe that they give more emotional support than they receive is between 39.38% and 48.62%.

d. The Hite survey would have a smaller margin of error because the sample size is larger.

CHAPTER 4

Section 4.1

4.1.1

a. B

b. A

c. A

d. Categorical

e. Quantitative

4.1.2

B

4.1.3

In short, students who pull all-nighters are more likely to make other poor lifestyle choices (e.g., poor diet, lack of exercise, etc.) and those lifestyle choices may have a negative impact on GPA. (The diagram is shown below.)

4.1.5

a. 2,622 adults in the survey

b. Explanatory: generation (categorical); Response: whether someone believes marriage is obsolete (categorical)

c. Yes, the proportions are different between the groups, suggesting the different generations tend to view marriage differently.

4.1.7

A confounding variable may explain this relationship: wealth of the country (e.g., GDP). In particular, wealthier countries have better health care and longer life expectancy and also can afford to buy more televisions.

4.1.8

a. C

b. B

c. Quantitative

d. D

e. Quantitative

4.1.10

a. B

b. C

c. Yes, the proportions are quite different.

4.1.12

a. Explanatory: whether or not eat breakfast; Response: whether able to maintain weight loss

b. Whether or not getting enough sleep (The diagram is shown below.)

4.1.14

a. Pregnant women

b. Whether or not smoke, categorical

c. Weight of baby at birth. quantitative

d. People of lower socioeconomic status are more likely to smoke and also more likely to have a poorer diet (and other factors) that may lead to lower-weight babies.

4.1.16

Since 46% of people who are overweight have overweight friends, compared to only 30% of people who are not overweight, there is an association; the proportions are different.

4.1.18

a. Income level, categorical

b. Happiness level, categorical

c. The proportions are different between the groups, showing evidence of association.

d. Can't conclude cause and effect. A potential confounding variable is intelligence.

4.1.20

a. Explanatory: political party (categorical); Response: whether or not believe that humans evolved (categorical)

b. Yes, the proportions are different.

4.1.22

a. Whether or not attend religious service weekly, categorical

b. Blood pressure, quantitative

c. Overall health/diet could be associated with church attendance and blood pressure.

4.1.24

a. Political party, categorical

b. Whether or not someone thinks that states should ignore federal gun laws, categorical

c. Yes, the proportions are different between the different political parties.

4.1.26

a. Countries

b. Explanatory: chocolate consumption; Response: number of Nobel prizes

c Wealth of nation.

Section 4.2

4.2.1

A

4.2.3

A

4.2.5

Random sampling

4.2.7

Random assignment

4.2.9

Random assignment

SOLUTION 4.1.3

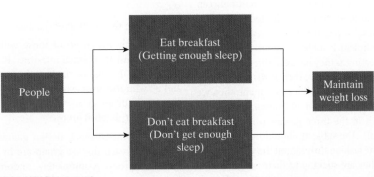

SOLUTION 4.1.12

4.2.11

Yes, a study can have both random sampling and random assignment. In this case researchers can generalize to the population and infer cause and effect.

4.2.13

No, not always. On average random assignment balances variables between two groups, so there is a tendency for balance, but confounding variables won't be exactly balanced every time due to the randomness in the assignment.

4.2.15

a. Yes, cause and effect; type of video changed quiz score

b. No cause and effect

c. No cause and effect

4.2.17

a. Observational studies

b. No

c. Babies

4.2.18

To conduct a randomized experiment you would have to randomly assign some mothers to smoke and others not to. This would be unethical, especially if we feared potential negative health outcomes for the baby.

4.2.20

a. Observational

b. No

c. Children

d. Whether or not classical music was played when in womb or when an infant

e. Intelligence test score

4.2.22

a. This is an experiment because of the random assignment to receive a friend request from either a male or female student.

b. Students who received friend requests on Facebook

c. Sex of person giving friend request (categorical; explanatory); whether or not friend request was accepted (categorical, response)

d. No, all students from one class, so can't generalize to all students at the college or elsewhere

e. Yes, individuals were randomly assigned to receive the friend request from a male or female. The advantage of having done the

random assignment is that we may be able to conclude causation.

f. Yes, because of the random assignment

4.2.24

a. This is an experiment because researchers determined who would be in which pose.

b. Participants (42 of them)

c. Type of pose to be held (categorical; explanatory); whether or not took bet (categorical; response)

d. No random sampling—participants were volunteers; yes, random assignment—researchers randomly assigned who would be in which pose.

e. Yes, because the random assignment suggests cause and effect is possible.

Section 4.3

4.3.1

B

4.3.3

E

4.3.5

A control

4.3.7

Double-blindness

4.3.9

a. No. Because this is an observational study, cause and effect cannot be concluded so we cannot conclude that the naming of a hurricane will affect the number of deaths.

b. Yes, because this was a randomized experiment with significant results, we can determine cause and effect.

Section 4.4

4.4.1

C

4.4.3

Because dieting might be different between males and females, we will block on a person's sex. We might also want to add a control group in which subjects are just told to continue eating as they have done in the past. All the subjects will have their BMIs determined at the beginning of the experiment; then we will randomly assign 50 women and 40 men to each of the three groups (diet 1, diet 2, control). The subjects should be supervised in some fashion throughout the year to make sure they are sticking to their assigned diet. After the year is over, their BMIs will again

be determined and the changes in BMI will be compared across the three groups. Strict guidelines should be set up in advance so all the subjects are treated and interacted with in the same manner, as well as how their BMIs are determined.

4.4.5

a. Experiment, because the subjects were randomly assigned to groups.

b. Double-blind is when the subjects (the physicians) and the researchers who are directly involved with the subjects or making decisions about the subjects do not know which treatment group the subjects are in. If subjects know they have been given a treatment, it might alter their behavior. If the researcher knows, it could bias the results when he or she has to make a diagnosis about the subject.

c. A placebo is an object that is made to look like a drug but does not contain any active drug. Placebo-controlled is when a placebo is used so the subjects do not know if they are in the treatment (drug) group or the control (placebo) group.

d. These 14,641 physicians were probably randomly assigned to one of 16 groups: (beta-car, vit E, vit C, multivit), (beta-car placebo, vit E, vit C, multivit), (beta-car, vit E placebo, vit C, multivit), (beta-car, vit E, vit C placebo, multivit), (beta-car, vit E, vit C, multivit placebo), (beta-car placebo, vit E placebo, vit C, multivit), (beta-car placebo, vit E, vit C placebo, multivit), (beta-car placebo, vit E, vit C, multivit placebo), (beta-car, vit E placebo, vit C placebo, multivit), (beta-car, vit E placebo, vit C, multivit placebo), (beta-car, vit E, vit C placebo, multivit placebo), (beta-car placebo, vit E placebo, vit C placebo, multivit), (beta-car placebo, vit E placebo, vit C, multivit placebo), (beta-car placebo, vit E, vit C placebo, multivit placebo), (beta-car, vit E placebo, vit C placebo, multivit placebo), (beta-car placebo, vit E placebo, vit C placebo, multivit placebo).

4.4.7

a. Block on the location of the disease.

b. Randomly assign 60 of those with the disease in just their small intestine, 40 with those with the disease in just their colon, and 50 with the disease in both areas to the treatment (drug) group and the others to the control (placebo) group.

c. A randomized block design guarantees that half of each disease group are in each treatment group. A completely randomized design may not do this exactly.

End of chapter exercises

4.CE.1

A

4.CE.3

a. Type of visit

b. Heart rate, blood pressure, anxiety levels, etc.

c. Randomized experiment because patients were randomly assigned to one of the three types of experimental groups

d. To potentially draw a cause-and-effect conclusion

e. No, they were hopefully controlled for by the random assignment, eliminating them as potential confounding variables.

4.CE.5

a. Explanatory: price of pill (categorical); Response: whether or not experienced a reduction in pain? Yes or no (categorical)

b. Randomized means subjects were randomly assigned which price group they were in.

c. Double-blind means neither the participant nor the researchers interacting with the participants knew which group the participants were in.

d. The results are statistically significant, meaning that there is evidence of a potential cause-and-effect relationship between the price of the pill and perceived reduction in symptoms. Because there is not random sampling this result should be generalized, with caution, only to individuals with similar characteristics of the volunteers.

4.CE.7

a. Explanatory: whether male or female,; Response: whether or not satisfied with attractiveness

b. Observational study. There is no random assignment of the explanatory variable (a person's sex).

c. Random sampling, to generalize to all U.S. adults, but not random assignment because you can't randomly assign people to be male or female.

4.CE.9

a. Experiment because visitors to Google were assigned to see one ad or the other

b. Explanatory: name of book on ad, ; Response: Did person click through? Yes or no

c. Yes, assuming Google visitors were randomly assigned which ad to see

4.CE.11

a. Explanatory: whether teenager is from the US or UK (categorical); Response: number of Harry Potter books read (quantitative)

b. Random sampling because you want to generalize to US and UK teenage populations; random assignment makes less sense because you would have to randomly assign teenagers to live in the US or UK.

4.CE.13

Randomly assign student essays to be graded by a professor with a blue or red pen, and then keep track of the scores given on the essays.

4.CE.15

Randomized experiment is not really feasible because you would have to randomly assign some people to go to church regularly and others not.

CHAPTER 5

Section 5.1

5.1.1

a. Tables 1 and 4 have the same pair of conditional proportions, namely, 0.50 of A's are Yes and 0.50 of B's are Yes in both tables.

b. The difference in conditional proportions is largest in Table 3, where 0.667 of A's are Yes and 0.333 of B's are Yes.

c. The difference in conditional proportions is smallest in Tables 1, 2, and 4, where the difference equals zero because the proportion of A's that are Yes equals the proportion of B's that are Yes.

5.1.3 See table below.

5.1.5

a. The observational units are the college students.

b. The response variable is whether or not the student is wearing clothing that displays the college name or logo on a particular day. Categorical.

c. Yes, random sampling can be used. Obtain a numbered list of the students at each college, and use software to randomly select the number that you want for the sample size.

d. No, random assignment cannot be used. You cannot randomly assign students to attend one college or the other.

e. A 2×2 table suitable for summarizing the data is shown below.

5.1.7

a. More rattlesnakes were caught at Site G than at Site B, so looking at conditional proportions (rather than counts) takes this into account.

b. The explanatory variable is site, so we calculate the conditional proportions of males/females at each site.

c. The proportion of rattlesnakes that are female are $11/21 \approx 0.524$ at Site B and $12/33 \approx 0.364$ at Site G. Reasoning informally, these proportions appear to be different enough to provide evidence of an association between site and sex of rattlesnakes.

5.1.12

a. Observational study because researchers did not assign respondents to attend church in differing amounts

b. Explanatory: level of church attendance; response: smoke (yes/no)

c. See table below.

d. Because the percentages are different, this is evidence of an association between regularity of church attendance and smoking.

e. No, because this is an observational study.

		Male	Female	Total
Played sports in high school	Yes	83	117	200
	No	67	93	160
	Total	150	210	360

SOLUTION 5.1.3

	ESU	MSU	Total
Wearing school name/logo			
Not wearing school name/logo			
Total			

SOLUTION 5.1.5e

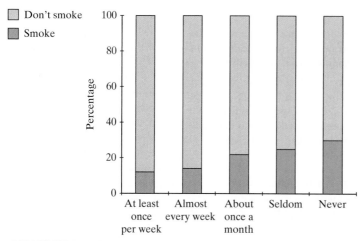

SOLUTION 5.1.12c

5.1.13

a. 0.30/0.12 = 2.5. People who never attend church are 2.5 times as likely as those who attend church weekly to be smokers.

b. Seldom vs. at least once: 2.08; about once a month vs. at least once: 1.83; almost every week vs. at least once: 1.17

5.1.16

a. Experiment

b. Explanatory: receive AZT yes/no
Response: baby born with HIV yes/no

c.

	AZT	No AZT	Total
HIV positive	13	40	53
HIV negative	151	120	271
Total	164	160	324

d. 0.079 (AZT) vs. 0.250 (no AZT)

e. 3.16

f.

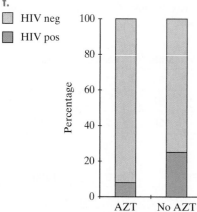

g. Due to the difference in conditional proportions there appears to be an association between taking AZT and a reduction in the

chance that the child of an HIV-positive woman will be HIV positive.

5.1.19

a.

	Male	Female	Total
Coffee	5	6	11
No coffee	5	10	15
Total	10	16	26

b. Males: 0.50; females: 0.375

c.

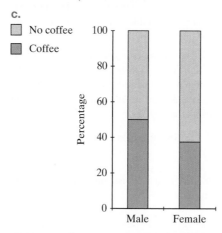

d. Because the proportion of coffee drinking men is different than coffee drinking women this is some evidence of an association between sex of respondent and coffee drinking.

5.1.20

a.

	Males	Females	Total
R	6	8	14
L	4	5	9
Total	10	13	23

b. Proportion of people choosing R: males 0.60, females 0.62

c.

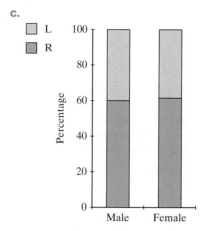

d. The proportions of men and women choosing R are quite similar, suggesting little association between sex of respondent and letter choice.

5.1.21

a.

	Coffee	No coffee	Total
R	9	5	14
L	2	7	9
Total	11	12	23

b. Proportion of people who chose R: coffee 0.82, no coffee 0.42

c.

d. There is an association between letter choice and coffee drinking because the proportions are quite different.

5.1.24

a. Male acceptance rate: 533/1198 = 0.445; female acceptance rate: 113/449 = 0.252. Males have a higher acceptance rate overall.

b. Males: 511/825 = 0.619; females: 89/108 = 0.824. Females have a higher acceptance rate.

c. Males: 22/373 = 0.059; females: 24/341 = 0.070. Females have a higher acceptance rate.

d. Yes, even though the overall proportion of males accepted is higher, females have a higher acceptance rate within each group.

e. Program F is highly competitive, but Program A is not. However, the majority of female applicants received applied to Program F, while the majority of males applied to Program A. Thus, the overall proportion of males accepted was higher.

Section 5.2

5.2.1

a. C

b. D

c. B, D

d. C

e. C, D

f. 30 in each pile, representing 30 medium claims and 30 small claims (explanatory variable)

g. Difference in conditional proportions or relative risk

h. Find how often the observed statistic value or more extreme occurred in the simulation (both tails since two-sided).

5.2.2

a. 0, because if the null hypothesis is true there is no difference in the two group proportions

b. See graph below.

c. There is a 0.184 chance of getting a difference in proportions of 0.20 (the value of the statistic) or larger, or −0.20 or smaller, if the probability a claim is judged to be an overpayment is the same for small and medium claims.

d. There is little to no evidence against the null hypothesis.

e. (0.20 − 0)/0.125 = 1.6. The statistic is approximately 1.6 standard deviations from the mean of the null distribution.

f. They give similar indications about evidence—there is not much evidence against the null hypothesis. *Note:* The standardized statistic (1.6) is near the "cutoff" of moderate evidence, but this modest difference isn't a problem: Neither gives "strong" evidence.

g. 0.20 ± 0.125 × 2 = (−0.05, 0.45).

h. We are 95% confident that the true difference in proportions of overpaid claims between the two groups is between −5% and 45%.

i. Yes, 0 is in the interval, meaning that it's plausible that there is no difference in the proportions.

j. We have little to no evidence that the proportion of overpaid claims is different between the two groups. We're 95% confident that the true difference in the proportion of overpaid claims is between −5% and 45%. This is a random sample, and so this conclusion can be generalized to other Medicare/Medicaid claims at the company being audited; however, this is not a randomized experiment and so cause-and-effect conclusions cannot be drawn.

5.2.3

a. C

b. D

c. 24% − 16% = 8% or 0.24/0.16 = 1.5

d. Sample size in each group

e. Large sample sizes in each group

f. Small sample sizes in each group

5.2.7

a. C

b. C

c. A

d. B

e. Categorical

f. Categorical

g. A, D

h. The difference happened by chance because no difference in survival rate between CC and CPR techniques or there is an actual difference in the survival rate from the two different techniques.

5.2.8

a. A

b. B

c. 3,031

d. Two different colors, 389 of one color and 2,642 of the other color

e. Two piles, 1,500 in one pile, 1,531 in the other pile, because that's how many people receive the two techniques in the actual study

f. The difference in the proportion of one of the colors of cards between the two groups subtracting the group with 1,531 from the group with 1,500 (or use ratio of proportions)

g. Find the proportion of times that the actual difference in the study (0.024) or larger occurred in the simulated statistics.

h. C

5.2.9

a. p-value is approximately 0.025. We obtained statistics 0.024 or larger in 2.5% of simulations.

b. We have strong evidence against the null hypothesis.

c. 0.024/0.012 = 2. The observed statistic is 2 SDs from the mean of the null distribution.

d. Yes, both suggest strong evidence against the null hypothesis.

e. 0.024 ± 2*0.012 = (0,0.048). We are 95% confident that the difference in survival rates when comparing CC to CPR is between 0 and 4.8% better with CC.

f. Yes, more or less. Zero is (barely) in the interval and the p-value rejects zero. Note that the test is one-sided and the interval is two-sided, so the strength of evidence will change a bit depending on which approach you take.

SOLUTION 5.2.2b

g. We have strong evidence that the true difference in survival percentages is greater for CC than for traditional CPR (p = 0.025; 95% CI: 0, 0.048). Because this is a randomized experiment, this suggests that the use of CC is causing the survival rate to increase. There is no information provided as to how the sample was gathered, but it was likely not a random sample of calls for help but instead all calls during certain time periods in one or more cities. Thus, this result may not generalize to other locations with different types of people who may respond differently to different types of CPR.

5.2.10

a. 0.042

b. 0.024

c. The Hallstrom et al. study had a larger difference in proportions.

d. The one-sided p-value is 0.10. This is the probability of obtaining 0.042 or larger in the simulated data assuming the null to be true.

e. We have little to no evidence against the null hypothesis.

f. The Hallstrom et al. study provides less evidence than the meta-analysis.

g. The sample size is smaller.

h. The 95% CI for the Hallstrom study is approximately −0.016 to 0.099. The Hallstrom study has a wider interval than the meta-analysis (0, 0.042) because the sample size is larger. The Hallstrom study CI is centered on 0.042, while the meta-analysis CI is centered on 0.024. CIs are centered on the statistic.

5.2.15

a. $3/20 - 18/22 = -0.668$

b. There is an actual difference in the likelihood of taking the double or nothing bet based on pose or this result occurred merely by chance.

5.2.16

a. The parameter is the difference in probabilities of selecting the high-risk option between those who held a low-power pose and those who held a high-power pose. This parameter can be denoted as $\pi_{low} - \pi_{high}$.

b. The null hypothesis is that the probability of selecting the high-risk option is the same, regardless of whether the person holds a high-power pose or a low-power pose. The alternative hypothesis is that the probability of selecting the low-risk option is lower for a person who holds a low-power pose than for a person who holds a high-power pose.

c. $H_0: \pi_{low} = \pi_{high}$, $H_a: \pi_{low} < \pi_{high}$

d. Use 21 red cards to represent the people who chose the risky (double-or-nothing) option, and use 21 black cards to represent the people who chose the safe option. Shuffle the 42 cards thoroughly. Deal out 20 cards to represent the people assigned to the low-power pose, with the remaining 22 cards then representing the people assigned to the high-power pose. Count how many red cards (representing the high-risk choice) are in each group. Calculate the proportion of red cards in each group and subtract those proportions, taking the low-power pose group's proportion minus the high-power pose group's proportion. Repeat this process a large number of times, say 1,000. The p-value will be approximated by the proportion of repetitions in which this difference is $3/20 - 18/22 \approx -0.668$ or smaller.

5.2.17

a. The approximate p-value is 0.000, which means that a difference in group proportions who choose the risky option of −0.668 or smaller would almost never occur by random assignment alone if there were really no difference in the probabilities of selecting the risky option between the two groups.

b. The very small p-value indicates that the experimental data provide extremely strong evidence that people who hold a high-power pose are more likely to choose the risky, double-or-nothing option than people who hold a low-power pose.

c. $-0.668/0.157 = -4.25$. The observed statistic is 4.25 SDs below the mean of the null distribution.

d. Yes, both give very strong evidence against the null hypothesis.

e. $-0.668 \pm 2 \times 0.157 = (-0.982, -0.354)$. We are 95% confident that the group in the low-power pose takes double or nothing between 0.354 and 0.982 less often than the group in the high-power pose.

f. Yes, 0 is not in the interval.

g. We have very strong evidence that the pose yields different proportions of people taking the bet (p < 0.001). We are 95% confident that the difference in actual probability

of choosing the risky option is between 0.360 and 0.976 lower for people who hold a low-power pose than for people who hold a high-power pose. Because this was a randomized experiment, we conclude that the high-power pose causes an increased probability of selecting the risky option. We are not told how the participants were chosen, so it's not clear how broadly we can reasonably generalize this conclusion to other people beyond those involved in this experiment.

5.2.18

a. 5.46 (or 0.183)

b. Null: The relative risk is 1. Alt: The relative risk is greater than 1,

c. The p-value is <0.001, meaning that the chances of getting a relative risk as or more extreme than the one observed (5.46) is <0.001

d. The conclusions are the same because the data are not changing, just our way of summarizing the data.

5.2.22

a. See table below.

b. $195/526 - 271/973 = 0.092$

c. The proportion of people who know that participating in the Census is required by law is the same for those with a college degree as for those without. The observed difference is due to chance alone. Or there is actually a difference in the two proportions in the population.

d. Observational study; the researchers have not assigned the values of either variable to the observational units.

5.2.23

a. Null: There is no association between education level and knowledge that the Census is required by law. Alt: There is an association between education level and knowledge that the Census is required by law.

b. Null: $\pi_{College} = \pi_{NoCollege}$, $\pi_{College}$ = proportion of people with college degree in population of all U.S. adults who know participating in the Census is required by law; Alt: $\pi_{College} \neq \pi_{NoCollege}$

		College degree	No college degree	Total
Knows Census required by law	Yes	195	271	466
	No	331	702	1,033
Total		526	973	1,499

SOLUTION 5.2.22a

c. Use 466 red cards to represent the people who know Census is required and 1,033 black cards to represent the people who don't. Shuffle the 1,499 cards thoroughly. Deal out 526 cards to represent the college group, with the remaining 973 cards representing the no-college group. Count how many red cards are in each group. Calculate the proportion of red cards in each group and subtract those proportions, taking the college degree proportion minus the no-college degree proportion. Repeat this process a large number of times, say 1,000. The p-value will be approximated by the proportion of repetitions in which this difference is −0.092 or smaller or 0.092 or larger.

5.2.24

a. The p-value is approximately 0, meaning that we did not observe any simulated differences in proportions larger than 0.092 or smaller than −0.092,

b. We have very strong evidence against the null hypothesis.

c. $0.092/0.025 = 3.68$. The observed statistic is 3.68 standard deviations from the mean of the simulated null distribution.

d. Yes, both give very strong evidence against the null hypothesis.

e. $0.092 \pm 0.05 = (0.042, 0.142)$. We are 95% confident that the difference in the proportions of people who know the Census is required by law when comparing people with a college degree and people without is between 0.042 and 0.142.

f. Yes, 0 is not in the interval.

g. We have very strong evidence of an association between education level and knowledge that the Census is required, with between 4.2% and 14.2% more people with a college education knowing the Census is required when compared to people without a college education. This result generalizes to the population of all U.S. adults but does not suggest a cause-and-effect relationship between having a college degree and knowledge of the Census law.

5.2.26

a. A

b. B

5.2.29

a. Experiment, because some households were assigned to receive incentive and others not

b.

		Incentive yes	Incentive no	Total
Participated?	Yes	286	245	531
	No	82	122	204
Total		368	367	735

c. $286/368 - 245/367 = 0.11$

d. There is no effect of the incentive, and the difference we saw was due to random chance or there is an effect of the incentive.

5.2.30

a. Null: There is no association between whether or not the household received the incentive and participation. Alt: There is an association between whether or not the household received the incentive and participation.

b. Null: $\pi_{\text{incentive}} = \pi_{\text{no-incentive}}$, Alt: $\pi_{\text{incentive}} > \pi_{\text{no-incentive}}$, where π is the long-run proportion of households that will participate

c. Use 531 red cards to represent the households that participated and 204 black cards to represent the households that didn't. Shuffle the 735 cards thoroughly. Deal out 368 cards to represent the households receiving the incentive and 367 to represent the households that didn't. Count how many red cards are in each group. Calculate the proportion of participators in each group and subtract those proportions. Repeat this process a large number of times, say 1,000. The p-value will be approximated by the proportion of repetitions in which this difference is 0.11 or larger.

5.2.31

a. 0, none of the simulated statistics were 0.11 or larger.

b. We have very strong evidence against the null hypothesis.

c. $0.11/0.033 = 3.33$, the observed statistic is 3.33 standard deviations from the mean of the null distribution.

d. Yes, both give very strong evidence against the null hypothesis.

e. $0.11 \pm 2*0.033 = (0.044, 0.176)$. We are 95% confident that the proportion of homes that will participate when given a financial incentive is between 4.4% and 17.6% higher than when no incentive is given.

f. Yes, 0 is not in the interval.

g. We have very strong evidence that the proportion of participating households is higher when a financial incentive is used than when no incentive is used (4.4%, 17.6% more households participate). This is a cause-and-effect relationship that generalizes to all households in the nation.

Section 5.3

5.3.1

A.

5.3.2 Notice that the parameter here subtracts in the opposite order, so a 95% CI would turn out to be:

B. Negative of above: $(-0.0467, -0.0015)$

5.3.3

A. A larger confidence level will increase the length of the confidence interval.

5.3.4 The midpoint for the 99% confidence interval will be the same as the midpoint for the 95% confidence interval. The midpoint of the 95% confidence interval is $(0.0015 + 0.0467)/2 = 0.0241$. Therefore, we know that the 2005–2006 sample proportion with hearing loss was 0.0241 larger than the 1988–1994 sample proportion.

5.3.5 We cannot find the width exactly without knowing the sample sizes involved.

5.3.7

a. The parameters of interest are the population proportion of all American households that would respond to the survey when offered a monetary incentive ($\pi_{\text{incentive}}$) and the population proportion of all American households that would respond to the survey when not offered a monetary incentive (π_{non}).

b. The null hypothesis is that the population proportion of all American households that would respond to the survey is the same whether offered a monetary incentive or not. The alternative hypothesis is that the population proportion of all American households that would respond to the survey is greater when offered a monetary incentive than when not offered a monetary incentive.

Scenario: [Two proportions ▼]

☐ Paste data

	Group 1		Group 2
n:	368	n:	367
Count:	286	Count:	245
sample p̂:	0.7772	sample p̂:	0.6676

[Calculate]

[Reset]

Sample data

Theory-based inference

☑ Test of significance

$H_0: \pi_1 - \pi_2 = $ [0]

$H_a: \pi_1 - \pi_2 \geq $ [0]

[Calculate]

Mean = 0.00
SD = 0.033

<---------- $\hat{p}_1 - \hat{p}_2$ ---------->

z = −4   z = −2   z = 0   z = 2   z = 4

Standardized statistic [z = 3.32]

p-value [0.0005]

☑ Confidence level

confidence level [95] % [Calculate CI]

(0.0453, 0.1739)

SOLUTION 5.3.7f

c. $H_0: \pi_{incentive} = \pi_{none}$, $H_a: \pi_{incentive} > \pi_{none}$

d. All four values in the two-way table (286, 245, 82, and 122) are larger than 10, so the theory-based approach should be valid.

e. The standardized statistic is $z = 3.32$. The theory-based one-sided p-value is 0.0005. The 95% confidence interval is (0.0453, 0.1739).

f. See output shown for Solution 5.3.7f.

g. The p-value says that if there were really no difference in the population proportions who would respond to the survey between those offered a monetary incentive and those not offered such an incentive, then there's only a 0.0005 probability of obtaining sample proportions as far apart, in the direction of favoring the incentive group, as was observed in this study (namely, a difference of 0.1096).

h. We are 95% confident that the proportion who will respond to a telephone survey is between 4.5% and 17.4% higher after receiving an incentive.

i. The p-value is small enough to indicate that the sample data provide very strong evidence that offering a monetary incentive does help to increase the response proportion to the survey. This is a randomized experiment, so we can conclude that the monetary incentive caused the higher response proportion. Furthermore, the households were randomly selected, so we can generalize this conclusion to all households in the U.S. The confidence interval reveals that the magnitude of the increase in response proportion is between 4.5 and 17.4 percentage points higher when the household is offered a monetary incentive than when no such incentive is offered.

5.3.11

a. These data arise from sampling from two processes.

b. Let π_A represent the long-run proportion of times Author A wins and π_B the long-run proportion of times Author B wins.

c. The null hypothesis would be that the authors have the same probability of winning.

The alternative hypothesis is that Author B has a different probability of winning than Author A.

d. $H_0: \pi_A = \pi_B$, $H_a: \pi_A \neq \pi_B$

e. Using the **Two Proportions** applet, we find a p-value of approximately 0.071. (See the applet output for Solution 5.3.11e.)

f. It would be okay to use a theory-based approach here because all four cell counts (25, 74, 192, 370) are larger than 10.

g. Using the **Theory-Based Inference** applet, we find a standardized statistic of $z = -1.74$, a p-value of 0.0814, and a confidence interval of (−0.1063, 0.0033).

h. The p-value tells us that approximately 8.14% of random samples from processes with the same probability of success would yield a difference in sample proportions as small as −0.051 or smaller or as large as 0.051 or larger by chance alone (assuming the null hypothesis is true).

i. While we have moderate evidence against the null hypothesis, at the 5% significance level there is not enough evidence to reject the null hypothesis.

j. A 95% confidence interval for the difference in their winning probabilities ($\pi_A - \pi_B$) is (−0.1063, 0.0033), indicating that A's win probability could be as much as 0.1063 smaller than B's or as much as 0.0033 higher than B's. This analysis depends on assuming

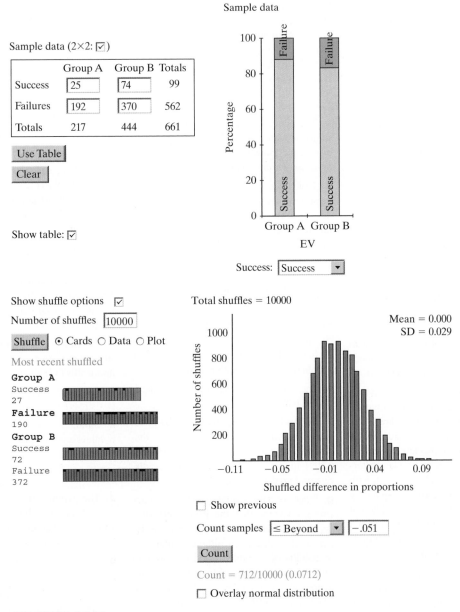

Sample data

Sample data (2×2: ☑)	Group A	Group B	Totals
Success	25	74	99
Failures	192	370	562
Totals	217	444	661

Use Table

Clear

Show table: ☑

Success: Success ▼

Show shuffle options ☑

Number of shuffles 10000

Shuffle ● Cards ○ Data ○ Plot

Most recent shuffled

Group A
Success 27
Failure 190
Group B
Success 72
Failure 372

Total shuffles = 10000

Mean = 0.000
SD = 0.029

☐ Show previous

Count samples ≤ Beyond ▼ −.051

Count

Count = 712/10000 (0.0712)

☐ Overlay normal distribution

SOLUTION 5.3.11e

that the sample of games is essentially a random sample for each player.

k. Zero is inside the 95% confidence interval, meaning that it's plausible there is no difference in the proportions.

l. The data provide moderate evidence (but not strong) that the performance of Author B is different than that of Author A ($p = 0.0814$; 95% CI: -0.1063 to 0.0033). These results cannot be generalized to the typical performances of Authors A and B, unless the games in the sample are representative of their typical performance. There is no potential for a cause-and-effect conclusion because this is not a randomized experiment.

5.3.13

a. The parameters are the long-term probabilities of men that have localized prostate cancer dying of the disease if they have surgery (call this proportion π_s) and if they are just observed (call this proportion π_o).

b. Null: The probability for men with localized prostate cancer and who have surgery dying of the disease is equal to the probability for men with localized prostate cancer and are just observed dying of the disease. Alternative: The probability for men with localized prostate cancer and who have surgery dying of the disease is less than the probability for men with localized

prostate cancer and are just observed dying of the disease.

c. $H_0: \pi_s = \pi_o$, $H_a: \pi_s < \pi_o$

d. We can use the theory-based approach to test the hypotheses because at least 10 men died and 10 men survived in each group.

e. Our p-value is 0.0794 and the standardized statistic is -1.41.

f. We can be 99% confident that the probability of dying of prostate cancer for those that get surgery is between -0.0757 lower and 0.0221 higher than those that are just observed for 10 years.

g. Since our p-value is large, we don't have strong evidence that the probability for men with localized prostate cancer and who have surgery dying of the disease is less than the probability for men with localized prostate cancer and who are just observed dying of the disease (99% CI: −0.0757, 0.0221). If we did have significance, we could determine causation since it was an experiment. The ability to generalize this conclusion to a broader population is suspect since this study is not based on a random sample.

5.3.17 No, it is not valid to use a theory-based approach here because there are cells in the table with only 3 and 4. They all should be at least 10.

5.3.19

a. The parameters are the proportion of all U.S. adults with some college or less that knew responding to the Census is required by law (π_{SC}) and the proportion of all U.S. adults with a college degree or more that knew responding to the Census is required by law (π_{CD}).

b. Null: The proportion of all U.S. adults with some college or less that knew responding to the Census is required by law is the same as the proportion of all U.S. adults with a college degree or more that knew responding to the Census is required by law. Alternative: The proportion of all U.S. adults with some college or less that knew responding to the Census is required by law is different than the proportion of all U.S. adults with a college degree or more that knew responding to the Census is required by law.

c. $H_0: \pi_{SC} = \pi_{CD}$, $H_a: \pi_{SC} \neq \pi_{CD}$

d. Theory-based methods are valid since we have at least 10 people that knew and 10 people that didn't know responding to the Census is required by law for both groups.

e. The p-value is 0.0002 and the standardized statistic is −3.68.

f. We can be 95% confident that the proportion of U.S. adults with a college degree or more that knew that responding to the Census is required by law is 0.0422−0.1422 higher than for those with some college or less.

g. We have strong evidence that the proportion of all U.S. adults with some college or less that knew responding to the Census is required by law is different than the proportion of all U.S. adults with a college degree or more that knew responding to the Census is required by law (0.0422 to 0.1422 higher among those with a college degree).

We can generalize this to the population of all U.S. adults since it was a random sample of all U.S. adults, but this does not provide cause and effect between education level and Census knowledge because it is not a randomized experiment.

5.3.21

a. The parameters are the probabilities of someone with cardiac disease dying of that disease for those with depression (π_D) and for those without depression (π_N).

b. Null: The probability of a depressed person with cardiac disease dying of that disease is the same as the probability of a nondepressed person with cardiac disease dying of that disease. Alternate: The probability of a depressed person with cardiac disease dying of that disease is different than the probability of a nondepressed person with cardiac disease dying of that disease.

c. $H_0: \pi_D = \pi_N$, $H_a: \pi_D \neq \pi_N$

d. Theory-based methods are valid since we have at least 10 people that died and 10 people that didn't in both groups.

e. The p-value is 0.0263 and the standardized statistic is 2.22.

f. We can be 95% confident that the probability of dying for those with cardiac disease and depression is between 0.0039 and 0.2091 higher than those with cardiac disease and no depression.

g. Since we have a small p-value, we have strong evidence that the probability of a depressed person with cardiac disease dying of that disease is different than the probability of a nondepressed person with cardiac disease dying of that disease, with depressed individuals' risk of death between 0.0039 and 0.2091 higher. Since it is an observational study we can't conclude depression caused the deaths. We can probably generalize this to people similar to those that were in the study.

5.3.23

a. This is an experiment since the physicians were randomly assigned to treatment groups.

b. The explanatory variable is taking aspirin or placebo. The response variable is

whether they suffered a heart attack or not. Both of these are categorical.

c. Double blind means neither the tester nor the subject knows which treatment is being received. This helps control for any bias that could develop affecting the behavior of either the tester or the subject.

d. See table below.

e. −0.0077

f. Null: The probability of a heart attack for those taking aspirin is the same as for those taking the placebo. Alternative: The probability of a heart attack for those taking aspirin is different than that for those taking the placebo.

g. We get a p-value of 0.

h. Since our p-value is very small, we have very strong evidence that the probability of a heart attack for those taking aspirin is different (and less) than that for those taking the placebo.

i. We can use a theory-based approach since there are more than 10 deaths and nondeaths in each group.

j. The p-value is 0 and the standardized statistic is 5.00.

k. Simulation-based and theory-based p-values are the same.

5.3.24

a. The parameters are the probability of a heart attack for those taking aspirin (π_A) and the probability of a heart attack for those not taking aspirin (π_P).

b. $H_0: \pi_A = \pi_P$, $H_a: \pi_A \neq \pi_P$

c. We can use a theory-based approach since there are more than 10 deaths and nondeaths in each group.

d. We can be 99% confident that the probability of having a heart attack is between 0.0037 and 0.0117 higher for those not taking aspirin compared to those that do take aspirin.

e. We get a p-value of 0.

f. There is very strong evidence of a difference in the probability of heart attacks between aspirin takers and non–aspirin takers since our p-value is so small.

		Placebo	Aspirin	Total
Heart attack?	Yes	189	104	293
	No	10,845	10,933	21,778
Total		11,034	11,037	22,071

SOLUTION 5.3.23d

g. We have strong evidence that the probability of having a heart attack is higher for those not taking aspirin compared to those that do (between 0.0037 and 0.0117 higher). We can conclude aspirin is causing this difference since this was a randomized experiment. We can probably infer these results to middle-aged to older men similar to those in the study.

h. Relatively speaking, the 99% confidence interval is narrow because we had such large sample sizes.

i. It all depends on your perspective if you think this is a very large difference or not. If you just look at the difference in sample proportions, it doesn't look that much different. However, if you looked at relative risk the difference in probabilities is quite large. If you think you are likely to have a heart attack, no matter what you look at, this difference might seem huge.

5.3.25

a. Rounding your final answer to two decimal places, you should get 5.00, the same standardized statistic as that in the applet.

b. Rounding your final answer to four decimal places, you should get 0.0037 to 0.0117, the same confidence interval as that in the applet.

5.3.26

a. The relative risk is 1.82.

b. Since our p-value was very small, we should not expect 1 to be contained in the confidence interval.

Section 5.4

5.4.1
C

5.4.3
B

5.4.5
D

5.4.7
E

5.4.9

a. False, as sample sizes increase, the standard error of the statistic decreases.

b. False; for a confidence interval $\hat{p}_1$ and $\hat{p}_2$ are used in the calculation and for a test the pooled $\hat{p}$ is used.

c. True

d. True

5.4.11

a. One proportion

b. Two proportions

5.4.13

a. The standard error of the statistic is $\sqrt{0.30625(1 - 0.30625) \times \left(\frac{1}{500} + \frac{1}{300}\right)}$ ≈ 0.0337, which is the standard deviation of the sampling distribution.

b. The standardized statistic is $z = (0.25 - 0.40)$ $/ \sqrt{0.30625(1 - 0.30625) \times \left(\frac{1}{500} + \frac{1}{300}\right)}$ $\approx -0.15/0.0337 \approx -4.456$, which means the observed difference in proportions is 4.456 standard deviations below the mean (0) of the sampling distribution.

5.4.15

a. We want to estimate the difference in the proportion of all students in Florida and New York who think winter is their favorite season. $\pi_F - \pi_{NY}$

b. The conditions for our two-sample z-interval are met as we have more than 10 students from each state who said winter is their favorite season and more than 10 from each state who said winter is not their favorite season.

c. $(0.3184 - 0.1659) \pm 1.96$ $\sqrt{\frac{0.3184(1 - 0.3184)}{468} + \frac{0.1659(1 - 0.1659)}{458}}$ $= 0.1525 \pm 0.0542 = (0.0983, 0.2067)$

d. We are 95% confident that the proportion of all students in Florida who think winter is their favorite season is between 0.0983 to 0.2067 higher than the proportion of all students in New York who think winter is their favorite season.

5.4.17

a. We want to estimate the difference in the proportion of all American adults who were married in 2014 to those who were married in 1974. $\pi_{2014} - \pi_{1974}$.

b. The conditions for our two-sample z-interval are met because we have more than 10 people from each year who said they were married and more than 10 from each year who said they were not.

c. $(0.456 - 0.778) \pm 2.576$ $\sqrt{\frac{0.456(1 - 0.456)}{2,538} + \frac{0.778(1 - 0.778)}{1,484}}$ $= -0.322 \pm 0.038 = (-0.360, -0.284)$

d. We are 99% confident that the proportion of all U.S. adults who were married in 2014 is between 0.284 and 0.360 smaller than the proportion of all U.S. adults who were married in 1974.

5.4.19

a. $H_0: \pi_{NB} = \pi_B$, $H_a: \pi_{NB} > \pi_B$

b. The two-proportion z-test we will use is valid because we have more than 10 penguins in each group that lived and more than 10 in each group that died.

c. $z = \dfrac{0.62 - 0.32}{\sqrt{0.47(1 - 0.47)\left(\frac{1}{50} + \frac{1}{50}\right)}} = 3.01$ and the p-value is 0.0013.

d. Based on a p-value of 0.0013, we have very strong evidence the proportion of unbanded penguins that survive is greater than the proportion of banded penguins that survive. Because this was a randomized experiment, we have strong evidence that banding causes more deaths. Nothing is said about the representativeness of the sample, so it is hard to generalize.

End of chapter exercises

5.CE.1

a. Yes, the sample sizes in the two groups can be different. While this makes it unreasonable to compare the number of successes in each group, computing the conditional proportions between the two groups allows for meaningful comparisons to be made.

b. Yes, small sample sizes alone are not enough to prevent comparisons being made. The challenge, of course, will be that you will need to have a very large difference in the groups to be convinced. Consider a sample size of 5 in each group, where all the observations in Group A are successes and all in Group B are failures. This is fairly compelling evidence of a difference in the groups (p = 0.008).

5.CE.2

a. Not small at all. There won't be convincing evidence of a difference in the groups

b. Very small because the difference in group proportions will be 1.

5.CE.3
For the first research question, the response variable (number of Harry Potter books) is quantitative, not categorical, so comparing proportions (as we are doing in this chapter) doesn't make sense. Similar to the first research question, the response variable for the second research question is also quantitative (milk production).

		Minority	Nonminority	Total
First base	Yes	20	10	30
	No	7	23	30
Total		27	33	60

SOLUTION 5.CE.5c

5.CE.5

a. Observational study

b. Explanatory variable: minority group; response: type of coach

c. See table for Solution 5.CE.5c

d. p-value is 0.001.

e. We have strong evidence that minority coaches are more likely to be first base coaches than nonminorities.

f. No, cause-and-effect conclusions are not possible. This is an observational study, not a randomized experiment.

5.CE.10

a. Random sampling only; random assignment of sex of respondent not possible

b.

c. Null: The proportion of men who are satisfied with their attractiveness is the same as the proportion of women. Alt: The proportions are different.

d. The sample size in each group

5.CE.11

a. $z = 1.66$, $p = 0.0978$

b. $z = 3.7$, $p = 0.0002$

c. As sample size increases and the difference in proportions remains the same, the strength of evidence against the null hypothesis increases.

5.CE.16 The proportion of males who consider life to be exciting in the sample is 52.8%; for women the proportion is only 48.6%, as shown in the accompanying bar chart.

This difference (4.2%) is not statistically significant (p = 0.13; 95% CI on difference: −1.3%, 9.8%), meaning that we don't have evidence of a difference in the proportion of men and women who think that life is exciting.

5.CE.17 The proportion of males who consider life too dull in the sample is 5.9%; for women the proportion is 4.6% as shown in the following segmented bar chart.

This difference (1.3%) is not statistically significant (p = 0.30; 95% CI on difference: −1.2%, 3.8%), meaning that we don't have evidence of a difference in the proportion of men and women who think that life is dull.

## CHAPTER 6

Section 6.1

6.1.1

B

6.1.3

B

6.1.5

IQR

6.1.7

B

6.1.9

a. All five numbers will increase by 5; the IQR will not change because it is a measure of variability—the difference in the 3rd and 1st quartiles will not change.

b. The maximum will change; there will be little to no impact on the other four values in the five-number summary or on the IQR.

c. The minimum will change; there will be little to no impact on the other four values in the five-number summary or on the IQR.

6.1.11

a. 25th value is 7 and 26th value is 8, so median is 7.5.

b. Lower quartile is 6; upper quartile is 12.

c. Larger since the data are right-skewed.

6.1.12

Mean: smaller, median: same, SD: smaller, IQR: same

6.1.15 The shape of the female study hours distribution is right skewed, while the distribution for males is more symmetric. In particular, no males report more than 20 hours of studying per week, while a number of females report more than 20 (as many as 45 hours) of studying per week. Thus, the spread of the female distribution is quite a bit larger than for males. Finally, the center of the female study hour distribution is closer to 15–20 hours per week, compared to only approximately 10 hours per week for males.

6.1.16

a. Males: 10, females: 15. Females tend to study more than males.

b. Males: 11, females: 14. The variability in study hours per week is larger for females.

c. See boxplots for 6.1.16c.

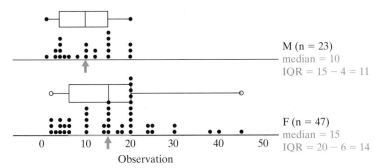

M (n = 23)
median = 10
IQR = 15 − 4 = 11

F (n = 47)
median = 15
IQR = 20 − 6 = 14

SOLUTION 6.1.16c

6.1.18

a. Min = −0.50, first quartile = 0.50, median = 1.25, third quartile = 2, Max = 4

b. 2 − 0.50 = 1.50

c. No change to IQR; change to standard deviation

6.1.21

a. 85 seconds is Wendy's, 173 seconds is Hot 'n Now.

b. The IQR for Hot 'n now is 116.5 seconds, for Wendy's it is 75 seconds.

c. For both restaurants the mean will be larger than the median since the data is right skewed.

6.1.22

a. Hot 'n Now mean is 203 seconds, Wendy's is 93.7 seconds.

b. SD of Hot 'n Now is 89.6 seconds, for Wendy's it is 46.7 seconds.

6.1.24

a. Right

b. Mean larger

c. No because the distributions look fairly similar.

6.1.27

a. Explanatory: shelf level, response: sugar content

b. The distributions suggest less sugar content on high shelves (an association).

c. Mean, low: 11.925; mean, high: 9.625—supports an association since they are different.

d. Median, low: 13; median, high: 9—supports an association since they are different.

e. The medians are farther apart than the means are.

Section 6.1: Part 2

6.1.33

A

6.1.35

D

6.1.37

A, D, E

6.1.39

D

6.1.41

a. You can see that not all the male heights are greater than all the female heights. For example, you can see that the tallest female is about 74″ and the shortest male is about 65″.

b. You can see that all the corresponding numbers in the five-number summary are greater for the males because the male graph is to the right of the female graph along any horizontal line.

c. The approximate difference between the median male and median female heights can be found by the length (in units from the horizontal axis) of the horizontal line segment between the two graphs that goes through 50% on the vertical axis.

d. The approximate difference in the percentiles for a female height that is 70″ and a male height that is 70″ can be found by the length (in units from the vertical axis) of the vertical line segment between the two graphs that goes through the 70″ on the horizontal axis.

6.1.43

a. min = 3, Q1 = 10, med = 30, Q3 = 75, max = 250.

```
0    1 1 1 2 3 4
0    5 5 6 7 7
1    0 0 0 0 2 3 4 4 4
1    6 8
2    0 1
2    6
Key: 1|6 = 16
```

SOLUTION 6.1.50a

b. Skewed right. The max is much farther away from the median than the min is and the third quartile is much farther away from the median than the first quartile is.

6.1.44 Yes, 200 and 250 are outliers.

6.1.46

a. The min, median, and quartiles are larger for Victor than for either Victoria or the unnamed hurricane, while the maximum is the same for all three.

b. Since larger numbers mean greater perceived risk, and four of the numbers in the five-number summary are larger for Victor than for either Victoria or the unnamed hurricane, yes, it appears there is preliminary evidence that the male name is a greater perceived threat.

6.1.48

a. 20 min for the bus and 10 min for the car. The bus median is larger, telling us that the bus times tend to be longer.

b. The IQR for those that rode a bus is 20 min and the IQR for those that took a car is 12 min. The bus being larger tells us that the variability of the bus times is larger than that of the car times.

c. We see that in 32 of the 44 times the number has a last digit of 0 or 5 (like 25 or 30). This makes sense because when people estimate their time for something, they tend to round a bit and many are rounding to the nearest 5 minutes.

6.1.50

b. Median = 10 cups, quartiles are 4.5 and 14 cups, and the IQR is 9.5, which means the middle half of the data set has a spread (range) of 9.5 cups.

c. No.

e. The data are just a bit skewed to the right (mostly because of the 26 cups). Both graphs illustrate the skewness to the larger cups. The shape makes sense in that it is easy to imagine that a few people would drink a lot of coffee.

SOLUTION 6.1.50d

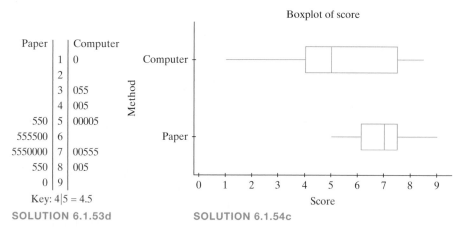

Paper		Computer
	1	0
	2	
	3	055
	4	005
550	5	00005
555500	6	
5550000	7	00555
550	8	005
0	9	

Key: 4|5 = 4.5

SOLUTION 6.1.53d

Boxplot of score

SOLUTION 6.1.54c

6.1.53

a. Experiment

b. Method of taking notes (categorical)

c. Quiz score (quantitative)

d. The distribution of scores is fairly symmetric for the paper group and a bit skewed to the left for the computer group. There is some clustering in the computer group, with several students in the 3–5 range and several in the 7–8.5 range. We do not see the same gap in the paper group. The paper group tended to have higher scores. The paper group is centered around 7 points and the computer group is centered around 5 points (out of 10).

e. The paper group tended to have higher scores. There are seven scores below 5 in the computer group and none in the paper group. This does give initial evidence in the direction of the students' conjecture.

6.1.54

a. Paper: Median = 7, Q1 = 6.25, Q3 = 7.5, IQR = 1.25, Computer Median = 5, Q1 = 4, Q3 = 7.5, IQR = 3.5. The paper group has the higher median, Q1, and max quiz score, and these do provide preliminary evidence in favor of the students' research conjecture.

b. No.

d. Both distributions are fairly symmetric, with the paper group tending to have higher scores. The paper group is centered around 7 and the computer group is centered around 5. Fifty percent of the computer group scores below the lowest score in the paper group.

6.1.56

a. Females

b. Females

c. The median and the upper quartile are the same for the males and hence the lines are indistinguishable.

d. The high value for the males and the high value for the females are clearly more than 1.5 times the IQR (width of the box) above the upper quartile (right edge of the box). The second highest for each are close and may be considered outliers.

Section 6.2

6.2.1

A, B, C, and D are all appropriate.

6.2.2

A

6.2.3

B, C

6.2.5

a. Observational study; there is no randomization of treatment.

b. Each student

c. Explanatory: sex (categorical); response: study hours (quantitative)

d. B

e. E

6.2.11

a. Observational study; no randomization of sex.

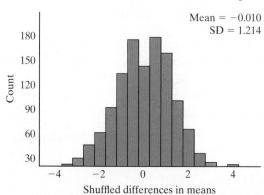

Mean = −0.010
SD = 1.214

SOLUTION 6.2.11h

b. Statistics students

c. Explanatory: sex, (categorical); response: number of flip flops, (quantitative).

d. B

e. A

f. B, C

g. C

h. See histogram below.

6.2.12

a. 3.68/1.214 = 3.03.

b. We have very strong evidence against the null hypothesis.

6.2.13

a. The probability of obtaining a difference in the average number of flip-flops for men and women of 3.68 or larger or −3.68 or smaller by chance (if the null is true) is approximately 0.001.

b. We have very strong evidence against the null hypothesis.

6.2.14

a. $3.68 \pm 2 \times 1.214 = 3.68 \pm 2.43 = (1.25, 6.11)$

b. We are 95% confident that females own between 1.25 and 6.11 more flip-flops on average than males in the population.

c. Yes, the confidence interval does not include 0.

6.2.15

a. See histogram 6.2.15a.

b. 5/2.348 = 2.13

6.2.20

a. The observational units are the obituaries, the explanatory variable is whether or not they had children, and the response variable is the age of death.

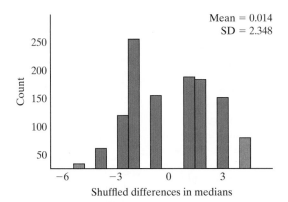

Mean = 0.014
SD = 2.348

SOLUTION 6.2.15a

b. Observational study because the researcher did not assign variable values to the observational units.

c.

	Sample size	Sample mean	Sample SD
Had children	70	78.43	14.36
No children	20	63.9	25.81

d. $78.43 - 63.9 = 14.53$

e. There is a difference in the population mean lifespans of the two groups. There isn't a difference in the population mean lifespans, and the observed difference happened by chance.

6.2.21

a. The population average lifespan of men with children (μ_{Had}); the population average lifespan of men without children (μ_{None}).

b. Null: The population average lifespan of men with children is the same as without. Alt: The population average lifespan of men with children is longer than without.

c. Null: $\mu_{\text{Had}} = \mu_{\text{None}}$; Alt: $\mu_{\text{Had}} > \mu_{\text{None}}$

d. Write out all 90 lifespans on 90 separate slips of paper. Shuffle the papers and deal into two stacks (70 and 20, respectively). Find the difference in the averages of the two stacks. Repeat many times and count what proportion of the time values greater than 14.53 occur in the simulated data.

6.2.22

a. The p-value is approximately 0, meaning that we never got values of 14.529 or larger in the simulation.

b. We have very strong evidence against the null hypothesis.

c. $14.529/4.987 = 2.91$; the observed difference in the average lifespan of men with children and men without children is 2.91 standard deviations above the hypothesized difference of 0.

d. $14.529 \pm 9.974 = (4.56, 24.503)$. We are 95% confident that the men with children lived on average between 4.56 and 24.503 years longer than those without children.

e. Yes, 0 is not in the interval.

f. We have strong evidence that the average life span of men with children is longer than those without; between 4.56 and 24.503 years longer on average. This is not a cause-and-effect conclusion (necessarily) but can be generalized to men with obituaries in the *San Luis Obispo Tribune* in 2012.

6.2.23

a. The p-value is approximately 0.009, meaning that we rarely got values of 16.5 or larger in the simulation.

b. We have very strong evidence against the null hypothesis (that the medians are the same in the two groups).

c. $16.5/6 = 2.75$; the observed difference in the median lifespan of men with children and men without children is 2.75 standard deviations above the hypothesized difference of 0.

d. $16.5 \pm 2 \times 6.5 = (3.5, 29.5)$. We are 95% confident that the difference in population medians is between 3.5 and 29.5.

e. Yes, 0 is not in the interval.

f. We have very strong evidence of a difference in the medians; in fact, men with children have a median lifespan between 3.5 and 29.5 years longer than men without children. While not necessarily a cause-and-effect relationship, the result can be generalized to men with obituaries in the *San Luis Obispo Tribune* in 2012.

6.2.26

a. Yes, the SD for carbon is higher.

b. Any value between 0 and infinity

c. $6.25/4.89 = 1.28$

d. Write the 56 commute times on 56 slips of paper. Shuffle and deal into two piles of 26 and 30 each. Compute the SD of each pile and then compute the ratio of the two SDs (SD of pile of 26 over SD of pile of 30). Repeat many times and see how often a ratio of 1.28 or larger is obtained in the simulations.

e. 1, since having the SDs be equal is what happens if the null hypothesis is true

f. See histogram 6.2.26f.

g. B

h. D

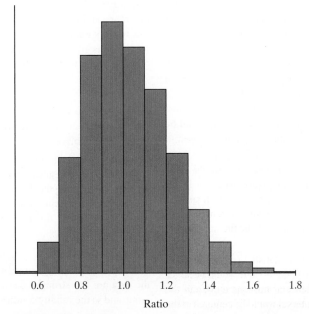

SOLUTION 6.2.26f

Section 6.3

6.3.1

a. The difference in the population mean number of hours spent online daily, in particular how many more hours are spent by females then males

b. (i) No change. (ii) No change. (iii) Will change in sign (negative to positive or vice versa). (iv) No change. (v) Will change in sign. (vi) No change. (vii) Will change in sign. (viii) Both will change in sign. (ix) No change.

c. Yes, the exact same conclusion will be reached about strength of evidence against the null hypothesis. The CI will be different because it is estimating a different parameter but will mean the same thing in terms of whether males or females are, on average, spending more hours online each day.

6.3.4
Null: The population average VDAS score for early birds is the same as the population average VDAS score for night owls. Alt: The population averages are different for the two groups. Since the sample sizes in each group are over 20 and the data within each group are not strongly skewed, a theory-based approach is appropriate here. The p-value for this test is <0.0001, with a t-statistic of -5.06, meaning that we have very strong evidence that the population averages are different. In particular, the early bird group has between 0.5298 and 1.2102 lower VDAS scores on average (95% confidence) than the night owl group. We cannot infer cause and effect from this study because students were not randomly assigned to a sleep group. Furthermore, we cannot generalize to a broader population because this is not a random sample—more information about the characteristics of the students in the sample is needed to infer more broadly.

6.3.5
The test statistic (t) would have been even farther from 0, the p-value would be even smaller (stronger evidence against null), and the confidence interval would be centered on the same value but narrower.

6.3.6
The test statistic (t) would have been closer to 0, the p-value would be larger (weaker evidence against the null), and the confidence interval would be centered at a different value but would be the same width.

6.3.7
The test statistic (t) would have been closer to 0, the p-value would be larger (weaker evidence against the null), and the confidence interval would be centered at the same value but would be wider.

6.3.8
Null: The population average fear score is the same for early birds as it is for night owls. Alt: The population average fear scores are different in the two groups. Since the sample sizes are both over 20 and the data within each group are not strongly skewed, a theory-based approach is appropriate here. The p-value for this test is 0.1722, with a t-statistic of -1.37, meaning that we have little to no evidence that the population averages are different. A 95% confidence interval indicates that the early bird group average fear scores are between 0.6594 lower and 0.1194 higher than the night owl group. If the result was statistically significant, we could not infer cause and effect from this study because students were not randomly assigned to a sleep group. Furthermore, we cannot generalize to a broader population because this is not a random sample—more information about the characteristics of the students in the sample is needed to infer more broadly.

6.3.10
Null: The long-run average MRT score for men is the same as for women. Alt: The long-run average MRT scores are different between the two groups. The validity conditions are met because the sample sizes are over 20 in each group and there is not strong skewness. The p-value (<0.0001; $t = 5.57$) means that there is very strong evidence that the long-run averages are different. A 95% confidence interval indicates that men have an average MRT score between 2.92 and 6.16 higher than women. This does not suggest cause and effect because it is not a randomized experiment, and the results should be generalized to other men and women with caution because this was not a random sample and little information is given about the characteristics of the men and women in the study.

6.3.12

a. To see if the price of the pill was associated with its perceived effectiveness (measured via pain tolerance)

b. Null: The average maximum tolerance when taking the regular-price pill is the same as when taking the discount-price pill. Alt: The average maximum tolerance for the regular-price pill is different than for the discount-price pill.

c. Two-sample t-test

d. At least 20 people are in each group, and the data are not strongly skewed in either group and so the validity conditions are met.

e. p-value = 0.51, $t = -0.66$.

f. The probability of getting a t-statistic of -0.66 or smaller or 0.66 or larger by chance if the null hypothesis is true is quite likely (51% of the time).

g. $(-12.39, 6.19)$

h. We have little to no evidence of a difference in the average maximum tolerance between the regular-price and discount-price pill (95% CI: $-12.39, 6.19$; $p = 0.51$). This study gives the potential for cause-and-effect conclusion due to the use of random assignment but not the ability to generalize to a larger population without some caution since a random sample was not used to obtain the study's participants.

6.3.14

a. Null: The average spatial score for men is the same as for women. Alt: The average spatial score for men is different than for women.

b. The sample sizes are at least 20 in both groups, and the data are not strongly skewed within either group.

c. p-value = 0.0007. The probability of obtaining a t-statistic of 3.57 or larger or -3.57 or smaller is 0.0007 if the null hypothesis is true.

d. 95% CI: (1.055, 3.745). Men have an average spatial score between 1.055 and 3.74 higher than women.

e. We have strong evidence that the average spatial score is significantly higher for men (95% confident between 1.055 and 3.745 higher) than for women. This is not necessarily a cause-and-effect conclusion, nor can the result be confidently generalized to a broader population since the sample was not obtained randomly from a larger population.

f. Null: The average verbal score for men is the same as for women. Alt: The average verbal score for men is different than for women. The sample sizes are at least 20 in both groups and the data are not strongly skewed within either group, so the theory-based test on these data is valid. p-Value <0.0001. The probability of obtaining a t-statistic of 5.07 or larger or -5.07 or smaller is less than 0.0001 if the null hypothesis is true.

d. 95% CI: $(-5.86, -2.54)$. Men have average verbal scores between 2.54 and 5.86 lower than women.

e. We have strong evidence that the average verbal score is significantly higher for women (95% confident between 2.54 and 5.86 higher) than for men. This is not necessarily a cause-and-effect conclusion, nor can the result be confidently generalized to a broader population since the sample was not obtained randomly from a larger population.

6.3.15

a. The difference in the average spatial test scores between men who breathe through their left nostril as compared to their right nostril

b. Null: The average spatial score for men who breathe through their left nostril is the same as for men who breathe through their right nostril. Alt: The average spatial scores are different for the two groups.

c. Two-sample t-test

d. Since the sample size is less than 20 in both groups, the data should be distributed symmetrically in both groups, and it is.

e. p-value is 0.035 ($t = -2.30$).

f. We have strong evidence that the average spatial score for men is different based on whether or not they breathe through their left or right nostril (0.2 to 4.8 higher on average for those breathing through the right nostril). This suggests a cause-and-effect relationship between spatial score and nostril due to the random assignment; however, this result should be generalized with caution since the sample was not obtained randomly.

g. p-value will get smaller.

h. No change

i. p-value would get smaller.

6.3.16

a. We don't have enough evidence of a difference at the 1% significance level since 0.0162 is not less than 0.01.

b. There would be enough evidence since $0.0162 < 0.05$.

c. (ii) and (iii) are both true; (i) and (iv) are both false.

6.3.19 The samples in each group are above 20 (40 in each group) and the data are not strongly skewed, so a two-sample t-test is appropriate here. Null: The population average time in the bathroom for men is the same for women. Alt: The population average time in the bathroom is different. $t = 1.68, p = 0.097$. We have moderate evidence that the population average restroom times are different between the two sexes.

6.3.20 We are 95% confident that the average time in the bathroom is 5 seconds less to 58.7 seconds longer for women than

men. The interval does include 0, which is consistent with the test of significance in the previous question.

6.3.22

a. Randomized experiment because randomness was used to determine whether or not the waitress gave her name

b. Explanatory: gave name yes/no, response: amount of tip

c. Null: The average tip amount when the waitress gives her name is the same as when she doesn't give her name. Alt: The average tip amount is larger when she gives her name. (in symbols) Null: $\mu_{Name} = \mu_{NoName}$ Alt: $\mu_{Name} > \mu_{NoName}$.

d. $n_{Name} = 20, \bar{x}_{Name} = \$5.44, s_{Name} = \$1.75, n_{NoName} = 20, \bar{x}_{NoName} = \$3.49, s_{NoName} = \$1.13.$

e. Yes, sample size is 20 in both groups, without strong skewness.

f. $t = 4.19, p = 0.0002$

g. We have strong evidence that the average tip amount is higher when she states her name. This means the waitress will probably start stating her name every time to boost tip amounts on average.

6.3.23

a. 95% CI: 1.00 to 2.90.

b. We are 95% confident that tip amounts are between $1 and $2.90 larger on average when she states her name.

c. Yes, 0 is not in the interval.

d. We have very strong evidence that the waitress receives larger tip amounts, on average, when she states her name (between $1.00 and $2.90 more). This is a cause-and-effect relationship due to the random assignment, but the waitress should be cautious in generalizing since this was only with the 40 customers she had on a particular Sunday morning for brunch.

6.3.24

a. Midpoint same, wider interval

b. (0.81, 3.09), as predicted.

6.3.25

a. t-Statistic farther from 0, p-value smaller, and narrower confidence interval

b. $t = 5.92, p < 0.0001$, 95% CI: (1.29, 2.61), as predicted.

6.3.26

a. t-Statistic closer to 0, p-value larger, and wider confidence interval

b. $t = 3.08, p = 0.0019$, and 95% CI: (0.67–3.23), as predicted.

Section 6.4

6.4.1

A

6.4.3

D

6.4.5

A

6.4.7 Although the samples are independent, the sample size for the males is too small and the distribution of flip-flop counts is too skewed. Therefore, the conditions are not met.

6.4.9

a. $\sqrt{2.7^2/40 + 3.1^2/50} \approx 0.6119$.

b. With df = 39 and 99% confidence, $t^* = 2.708; 2.708 \times 0.6119 = 1.6570$.

c. $(34.2 - 26.2) \pm 1.6570 = (6.343, 9.657)$. We are 99% confident that the difference in means in the populations is between 6.343 and 9.657.

6.4.11

a. With df = 23 and 95% confidence, $t^* = 2.069; (69.97 - 85.71) \pm 2.069 \sqrt{24.24^2/24 + 38.78^2/24} = -15.74 \pm 2.069(9.3351) = (-35.05, 3.57)$, or $(-34.6320, 3.1484)$, using technology with more precise df (38.59). We can be 95% confident that the average creativity score for the biology majors will be between 34.6 lower to 3.15 points higher than the theater majors.

b. No, the interval includes 0 so it is plausible that there is no difference in the average creativity score for biology majors and theater majors (assuming these are representative samples).

c. We did not have significant results nor was this a randomized experiment, so we can't determine causation from this study.

6.4.14

a. Let μ_P represent the long-run mean score on this quiz using paper and pencil to take notes and μ_c the long-run mean taking notes on the computer: $H_0: \mu_P = \mu_C; H_a: \mu_P > \mu_C$.

b. We will use a two-sample t-test and the validity conditions are met because we have two independent groups with data sets that are fairly symmetric and the sample sizes are moderate.

c. $t = \dfrac{6.92 - 5.50}{\sqrt{1.07^2/20 + 2.04^2/20}} = 2.77$, p-value ≈ 0.005 (df = 28.7).

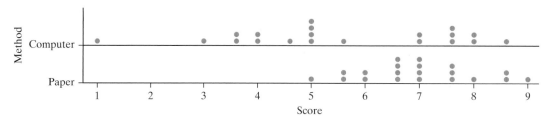

SOLUTION 6.4.14b

d. Based on a p-value of 0.005 < 0.05, we have strong evidence that students tend to memorize better using handwritten notes than taking notes on the computer. Because it was a randomized experiment, we can establish causation. Generalization is a bit harder because it wasn't a random sample, but it probably was fairly representative of Hope College students.

6.4.15

a. With df = 19, $t^* = 2.093$; $(6.92 - 5.50) \pm 2.093 \sqrt{1.07^2/20 + 2.04^2/20} = 1.42 \pm 2.093(0.5141) = (0.342, 2.498)$, or $(0.3720, 2.4780)$ using technology (with df ≈ 28.7, $t^* = 2.046$).

b. We can be 95% confident that, on average, people score between 0.343 and 2.497 points higher on the quiz if they take notes by pen and paper versus on the computer.

c. Yes, the interval is completely positive, indicating there is convincing evidence of a difference in population means.

6.4.18

a. Let μ_M represent the long-run mean number of words memorized when listening to music and μ_{NM} the long-run mean when not listening to music. $H_0: \mu_M = \mu_{NM}$; $H_a: \mu_M < \mu_{NM}$.

b. We will use a two-sample t-test. The validity conditions are met because we have two independent groups and the two data sets are fairly symmetric.

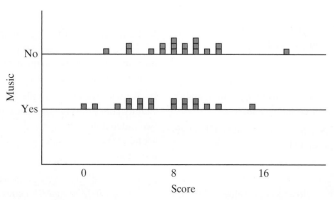

SOLUTION 6.4.18b

c. $t = \dfrac{7 - 8.611}{\sqrt{3.926^2/18 + 3.616^2/18}} = -1.28$, p-value = 0.1045 (df ≈ 34).

d. Based on a p-value of 0.1045 < 0.05, we do not have strong evidence that listening to music tends to hinder people's abilities to memorize words. Therefore, we conclude that in a population represented by these participants, there is no evidence that listening to music causes individuals to be less able to memorize words.

6.4.19

a. With df = 17, $t^* = 1.740$; $(7 - 8.611) \pm 1.740 \sqrt{3.926^2/18 + 3.616^2/18} = -1.61 \pm 1.740(1.258) = (-3.80, 0.58)$, or $(-3.74, 0.52)$ using technology (df ≈ 34).

b. We can be 90% confident that, on average, people will remember between 3.80 fewer to 0.58 more words, if they are listening to music than when they are not.

c. No, the interval contains 0 so it is plausible that the two population means are the same.

6.4.21

a. Let μ_M represent the long-run mean evaluation rating by those given the name Christopher (the male name) and μ_F the long-run mean for Christina (the female name). $H_0: \mu_M = \mu_F$; $H_a: \mu_M \neq \mu_F$.

b. We will use a two-sample t-test and the validity conditions are met because we have two independent groups with large sample sizes (both n's ≥ 30), though we would still like to see graphs of the sample distribution.

c. $t = \dfrac{2.94 - 2.34}{\sqrt{1.54^2/71 + 1.21^2/71}} = 2.58$, p-value = 0.0109 (df ≈ 132).

d. Based on a p-value of 0.011 < 0.05, we have strong evidence that the average rating of whether they would evacuate for the hurricane with the female name is different from that for a hurricane with a male name.

6.4.22

a. With df = 70, $t^* = 1.994$; $(2.94 - 2.34) \pm 1.994 \sqrt{1.54^2/71 + 1.21^2/71} = (0.1365, 1.0635)$, or using technology, $(0.140, 1.060)$ (df ≈ 132).

b. Because the confidence interval does not include 0, we do have significant results. Because the interval lies entirely above zero and our direction of subtraction was (female – male), the Christina-named hurricane was rated significantly higher; this means, on average, that people are more likely to think they would stay put and not evacuate for a hurricane named Christina than for a hurricane named Christopher.

End of chapter exercises

6.CE.1

a. The difference in the population mean of number of Harry Potter books read by girls vs. boys, in particular how many more books are read by girls compared to boys

b. (i) No change. (ii) No change. (iii) Will change in sign (negative to positive or vice versa). (iv) No change. (v) Will change in sign. (vi) No change. (vii) Will change in sign. (viii) Both will change in sign. (ix) No change.

c. Yes, the exact same conclusion will be reached about strength of evidence against the null hypothesis. The CI will be different because it is estimating a different parameter but will mean the same thing in terms of whether boys or girls are, on average, reading more Harry Potter books.

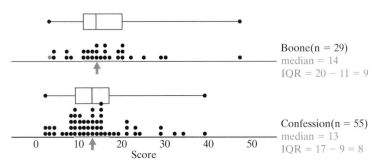

SOLUTION 6.CE.8b

Boone(n = 29)
median = 14
IQR = 20 − 11 = 9

Confession(n = 55)
median = 13
IQR = 17 − 9 = 8

6.CE.3

a. Each game is an observational unit. The variables are explanatory (categorical: regular vs. replacement) and response (duration, quantitative).

b. Neither

c. The dotplots suggest that games with replacements tended to be longer.

d. Null: The long-run average game duration is the same for replacement referees and regular referees. Alt: The long-run average game durations are different.

e. p-value = 0.009

f. The probability of obtaining a difference of 8.035 or larger (or −8.035 or smaller) in the sample means if there is no difference in the long-run average durations only occurs about 0.9% of the time.

g. 8.035 ± 2 × 3.05, (1.94, 14.14)

h. We are 95% confident that games with replacement referees take between 1.94 and 14.14 minutes longer on average than games with regular referees.

i. We have strong evidence of a difference in the long-run average length of games officiated by replacement referees, with such games taking between 1.94 and 14.14 minutes longer on average than games officiated by regular referees. This is not a cause-and-effect relationship, nor can this result, necessarily, be generalized to a broader set of NFL games.

6.CE.8

a. Confession: Min = 2, Q1 = 9, median = 13, Q3 = 17, Max = 39, Boone: Min = 3, Q1 = 11, median = 14, Q3 = 20, Max = 47

b. See boxplot below.

c. Based on the five-number summaries and boxplots, there does not appear to be much of a difference in the sentence lengths between the two books.

6.CE.9

a. Null: The average sentence length in Confession is the same as in Boone. Alt: The average sentence lengths are longer in Confession.

b. Boone: mean = 15.931, SD = 9.075, Confession: mean =13.982, SD = 8.027.

c. The average sentence lengths are longer in the sample from Boone, so there will not be evidence they are longer in Confession!

6.CE.11

a. Null hypothesis: Average SAT score improvement with coaching is the same as without coaching. Alt hypothesis: Average SAT score improvement with coaching is more than without coaching. $t = 4.28$, $p < 0.0001$. We have strong evidence that SAT scores improve more with coaching than without coaching.

b. 99% CI: (0.72, 2.88). Average SAT improvement scores are between 0.72 and 2.88 higher in the coaching group than the without-coaching group.

c. Yes, the CI does not include 0.

d. Yes, the p-value is very small.

e. No, the CI only indicates a small (0.72 to 2.88) improvement on average

f. Just because something is statistically significant it doesn't mean that it is, necessarily, practically important.

<hr/>

CHAPTER 7

Section 7.1

7.1.1

a. False

b. True

c. True

d. True

7.1.3

a. Paired

b. Not paired

c. Paired

7.1.5

a. Appropriate

b. Not appropriate

7.1.7

When using repeated measures, the same observational units are measured twice. When using matching similar (but not the same) observational units are each measured once.

7.1.9

D

7.1.11

a. Have 15 people play with Brand A and 15 people play with Brand B. Compare the average distances between the two groups.

b. Have each player play with each ball, with the order determined randomly; find the difference in distance hit for each player.

c. Part (b) is better because it uses pairing. It is better because some players will tend to hit the ball farther than others and the paired design accounts for that.

7.1.13

a. Experiment, paired

b. Experiment, not paired

c. Observational study, not paired

7.1.17

a. Randomly assign people to sit or exercise first. Have each person do the memorization activity while doing each activity. Find the difference in performances for each person.

b. Yes, because random assignment is used to determine which activity people did first.

7.1.18

a. Randomly assign each of the 20 people to two groups of 10, with one group exercising and the other sitting. Compare average performance between the two groups.

b. Paired with repeated measures, because there is probably quite a bit of person-to-person variability in memorization ability.

7.1.19

a. Have each person play the game once to get a baseline memorization score. Pair up people who have similar scores. Randomly assign one member of each pair to exercise and the other to sit. Find difference in scores within each pair of people.

b. Less variation within pairs when using the paired with repeated measures design, so that one is more appropriate.

7.1.23

a. Randomly assign people to first use caffeine supplement or not. Have each person run the 5K twice: once with supplement and once without. Find the difference in performances for each person.

b. Yes, because random assignment is used to determine which activity people did when.

7.1.24

a. Randomly assign each of the 30 people to two groups of 15, with one group getting caffeine supplement and the other group not. Compare average performance between the two groups.

b. Paired with repeated measures, because there is probably quite a bit of person-to-person variability in running ability.

7.1.25

a. Have each person run the 5K once to get a baseline time. Pair up people who have similar times. Randomly assign one member of each pair to run the 5K having taken the supplement and the other member not. Find difference in scores within each pair of people.

b. Less variation within pairs when using the paired with repeated measures design, so that one is more appropriate.

Section 7.2

7.2.1

B

7.2.3

A

7.2.5

a. 1

b. 3

c. 4

d. 5

7.2.7

a. Null: There is no association between a person's sex and body flexibility. Alt: There is an association between a person's sex and body flexibility such that females are more flexible than males.

b. Explanatory: sex, response: flexibility

c. Independent groups

7.2.9

Differences, since that is what is actually being tested.

7.2.11

The standard deviation of the differences is quite a bit smaller than the standard deviation of the response variable (weight) within each group (Fresh/Soph).

7.2.14

a. Music (yes/no; categorical)

b. Number of words memorized (quantitative)

c. 2.3

d. Yes, 2.3 is in the tail of the distribution.

e. $2.3/0.974 = 2.36$

f. Yes, the standardized statistic is more than 2.

7.2.15

a. $2.3 \pm 2 \times 0.974 = 2.3 \pm 1.948$, (0.352, 4.248)

b. Yes, because the confidence interval does not include 0.

7.2.16

a. -2.3

b. $\mu_d < 0$

c. No change

d. $(-4.248, -0.352)$

7.2.20

a. Explanatory: exercise or sit down, response: number of words memorized

b. Null: The long-run average difference in words memorized is 0. Alt: The long-run average difference in words memorized is not 0.

c. -0.07 is the average difference in number of words memorized between exercising and sitting down.

d. p-value is approximately 0.78.

e. We do not have strong evidence that exercising while trying to memorize words helps or hinders the process.

7.2.24

a. Explanatory: dominant vs. nondominant hand, response: reaction time

b. Null: The long-run average difference in reaction times between hands (dominant − nondominant) is 0. Alt: The long-run average difference is less than 0.

c. Yes, the average difference is -0.026 and most people's average differences are less than 0.

d. -0.026, the observed average difference in reaction times

e. p-value $= 0.009$

f. Yes, there is strong evidence that reaction times are slower when people use their non-dominant hand.

7.2.25

a. $-0.026/0.011 = -2.36$

b. Yes, the standardized statistic is less than 2.

7.2.26

a. $-0.026 \pm 0.022 = (-0.048, -0.004)$

b. We are 95% confident that the long-run average difference in reaction times is between 0.004 and 0.048 seconds faster with the dominant hand.

c. Yes, 0 is not in the interval.

Section 7.3

7.3.2

a. The average difference in husband and wife marriage ages in Cumberland County; μ_d

b. Null: The average difference in husband and wife marriage ages in Cumberland County is 0. Alt: The average difference in husband and wife marriage ages in Cumberland County (male − female) is greater than 0 (Husbands tend to be older than their wives).

c. Null: $\mu_d = 0$, Alt: $\mu_d > 0$

d. The validity conditions are met since there are 24 pairs, and distribution of paired differences in ages is not strongly skewed as shown in the dotplot for Solution 7.3.2d.

e. $t = 1.91$, p-value $= 0.0344$

f. We will obtain differences as extreme as the one we actually observed (>1.875) approximately 3.44% of the time (shuffling ages within pairs) when the null hypothesis is true. We have strong evidence for a one-sided test that the average difference in ages is greater than 0 (husbands tend to be older than their wives)

g. $(-0.157, 3.91)$. We are 95% confident that, on average, males are between 0.157 less and 3.91 years older than females when they get married.

h. With a one-sided p-value of 0.0344 we have strong evidence that, on average, husbands are older than their wives. We are also

Mean = 1.875
SD = 4.812

Differences

SOLUTION 7.3.2d

95% confident that males are between 0.157 less and 3.91 years older than females when they get married. (Since we were using a one-sided p-value we can have an instance like this where we get a small p-value and a confidence interval that contains zero.) This is not a randomized experiment so no cause-and-effect conclusion is possible. Furthermore, the sample may only be representative of Cumberland County, PA, and should not be generalized further.

7.3.6

a. Each infant is paired with itself.

b. Whether the helper or hinderer is being watched

c. Time looking at the approach

d. Null: The average time looking at the approach with the helper is the same as with the hinderer. Alt: The average time looking at the approach with the helper is longer than the same with the hinderer.

e. You need the data for each infant and it is not provided.

7.3.7

a. The long-run average difference in times looking at the helper and the hinderer condition (μ_d)

b. Null: $\mu_d = 0$ and Alt: $\mu_d > 0$

c. Because the sample size is less than 20, the distribution of differences should be fairly symmetric—and it is (stated as such in the problem).

d. $t = 2.60$, p-value $= 0.01$

e. The probability of obtaining an average difference in the sample of 1.14 seconds or larger, if the average difference in the population is 0, is 1%.

f. The long-run average difference in looking times is between 0.21 and 2.07 seconds longer when infants are looking at the hinderer as opposed to the helper.

g. We have strong evidence that the average difference in looking times is larger than 0 (infants, on average, look at the hinderer toy between 0.21 and 2.07 seconds longer than the helper toy). This suggests

a cause-and-effect relationship between condition and looking time because random assignment was used, but the result should be generalized to other infants with caution because this was not a random sample.

7.3.8

a. Smaller

b. Larger

c. Same

d. Smaller

7.3.9

a. Smaller

b. Larger

c. Larger

d. Same

7.3.10

a. Smaller

b. Larger

c. Same

d. Smaller

7.3.14

a. Overestimate, the sample average is greater than 0.

b. Because each person has two measurements of their kcal burning and we want to know whether the average difference is different than 0.

c. Null: The long-run average difference in estimated and actual calories burned is 0. Alt: The long-run average difference in estimated and actual calories burned is not 0.

d. With a reasonably large sample size of 80, we just need to assume that the population distribution of the differences is not strongly skewed.

e. $t = 2.93$, p-value $= 0.0044$

f. (41.4, 216.6) We are 95% confident that men such as those in this study tend to overestimate their EE by 41.4 to 216.6 kcal on average.

g. Confidence interval does not include 0 and p-value is less than 0.05.

h. We have very strong evidence that the average difference in estimated and actual kcal burned is different than 0, with men tending to overestimate calories burned by between 41.4 and 216.6 kcal on average. This is not a cause-and-effect relationship because no random assignment was used, and this result should be generalized with caution because these men are not necessarily representative of all men with regard to their ability to estimate calories burned.

7.3.15

a. $t = \dfrac{\bar{x}_d - 0}{s_d/\sqrt{n}} = \dfrac{129}{393.5/\sqrt{80}} = 2.93$

b. $\bar{x}_d \pm multiplier \times \dfrac{s_d}{\sqrt{n}}$. If we assume a multiplier of 2, we have $129 \pm 2(393.5/\sqrt{80}) = (41.0, 217.0)$. Or with $80 - 1 = 79$ degrees of freedom, the actual t-multiplier is 1.990 and $129 \pm 1.990(393.5/\sqrt{80}) = (41.45, 216.5)$.

7.3.16

a. $t = 2.27$, p-value $= 0.0257$

b. (16.05, 241.95)

c. The p-value is larger now, and the t-statistic smaller now (with wrong analysis). The confidence interval is centered at the same value but is now wider.

d. This suggests pairing was effective at reducing variability and improving strength of evidence against the null hypothesis.

7.3.17

a. Larger

b. Smaller

c. Same

d. Larger

7.3.18

a. Larger

b. Smaller

c. Smaller

d. Same

7.3.19

a. Smaller

b. Larger

c. Same

d. Smaller

7.3.22

a. $H_0: \mu_{new} = 0$ versus $H_a: \mu_{new} > 0$

b. p-value = 0.1172; no change in p-value from changing the order of subtraction

c. $(-7.78, 29.54)$. The signs of both endpoints of the interval will change due to changing the order of subtraction.

7.3.24

a. The long-run average difference in RMET scores between oxytocin and placebo (μ_d)

b. Null: $\mu_d = 0$ Alt: $\mu_d > 0$ (people tend to score higher on the RMET with oxytocin)

c. The sample size is more than 20 and the score differences are not strongly skewed.

d. $t = 2.18$, p-value = 0.0188

e. The probability of obtaining a difference of 3 or larger if the long-run average difference is 0 is 1.88%.

f. (0.1846, 5.8154)

g. We have strong evidence that the long-run average difference is greater than 0 (scoring between 0.18 and 5.82 higher on the RMET test, on average, after oxytocin). This result suggests a cause-and-effect relationship between oxytocin and perfromance on the RMET, but the result should be generalized with caution because little is known about how representative the volunteers in the sample are of any populations of interest.

7.3.25

a. $t = \dfrac{\bar{x}_d - 0}{s_d/\sqrt{n}} = \dfrac{3}{7.54/\sqrt{30}} = 2.18$

b. $\bar{x}_d \pm multiplier \times \dfrac{s_d}{\sqrt{n}}$. If we assume a multiplier of 2, we have $3 \pm 2(7.54/\sqrt{30}) = (0.25, 5.75)$

With 29 df, the t-multiplier is 2.045, so we have $3 \pm 2.045 (7.54/\sqrt{30}) = (0.18, 5.82)$

Section 7.4

7.4.1

D

7.4.3

A

7.4.5

C

7.4.7

a. $t = \dfrac{2.2}{4.9/\sqrt{34}} = 2.618$ (df = 33)

b. 0.0066

7.4.9

a. 2.069 (df = 23)

b. $2.069 (0.7/\sqrt{24}) = 0.2956$

c. (1.4044, 1.9956)

7.4.10

a. 2.807.

b. $2.807 (0.7/\sqrt{24}) = 0.4011$.

c. (1.2989, 2.1011). The 99% interval is centered on the same number, but is wider.

7.4.13

a. The parameter we want to estimate is the population mean difference in the number of objects people can remember when shown pictures of the objects in color compared to black and white. We will use a one-sample t-interval for paired data.

b. The test should be valid because we have a large sample size ($n \geq 30$), but it would also be good to look at a graph of the differences to make sure we don't have extreme skewness or outliers.

c. For 95% confidence and df = 49, $t^* = 2.010$. $0.180 \pm 2.010 (1.574/\sqrt{50}) = (-0.2674, 0.6274)$.

d. We are 95% confident that the population mean difference in the number of objects people can remember when shown pictures of objects in color is between 0.2674 less than to 0.6274 more than that of black and white pictures.

e. No, because 0 is contained in the interval.

7.4.16

a. Let μ represent the mean difference in the number of words memorized with lyrics and without lyrics; $H_0: \mu = 0$; $H_a: \mu > 0$.

b. A one-sample t-test for paired data should work well because we have a large data set (31) and our sample distribution looks as if it could easily have come from a symmetric population distribution.

c. $t = \dfrac{0.667}{1.661/\sqrt{31}} = 2.27$ (df = 30), p-value = 0.0153.

d. Based on a p-value of 0.0153, we have strong evidence (based on a significance level of 0.05) that listening to music with lyrics will decrease a person's average number of words memorized compared to a person's average number of words memorized while listening to music without lyrics.

7.4.18

a. Let μ represent the mean difference in rating (male – female name); $H_0: \mu = 0$; $H_a: \mu > 0$.

b. A one-sample t-test for paired data should work well because we have a very large data set (346).

c. $t = \dfrac{0.226}{0.925/\sqrt{346}} = 4.54$ (df = 345), p-value ≈ 0.0000.

d. Based on a p-value of ≈ 0.0000, we have very strong evidence (based on a significance level of 0.05) that hurricanes with male names are rated as more intense, on average, than those with female names.

7.4.19

a. For 95% confidence and df = 345, $t^* = 1.967$. $0.226 \pm 1.967 (0.925/\sqrt{346}) = (0.1282, 0.3238)$.

b. Because the interval is completely positive (and we did male – female), we have strong evidence that hurricanes with male names are rated as more intense, on average, than those with female names.

SOLUTION 7.4.16b

End of chapter

7.CE.1

a. A

b. D

c. C

d. B

7.CE.3

a. Incorrect because the hypotheses are about statistics instead of parameters.

b. Incorrect, the value in the null hypothesis (e.g., 40) should match the value in the alternative hypothesis.

c. Correct

7.CE.5

a. Have children, separately, use both smoke detectors, record the time needed to leave the house both times (randomly decide which detector to use first).

b. Some children (e.g., older) will be able to leave much faster than others (e.g., younger).

c. The first time, children may learn what they need to do and be faster the second time around, regardless of which smoke detector is used.

7.CE.7

a. The husbands' ages in the sample are not connected to the wives' ages in the sample.

b. Collect both husband and wife ages from each marriage license.

c. Because there is likely quite a bit of variation in ages at marriage but less variation in difference in husband and wife ages

7.CE.9

a. Null: Average pretest flexibility is the same for males and females. Alt: Average pretest flexibility is different for males and

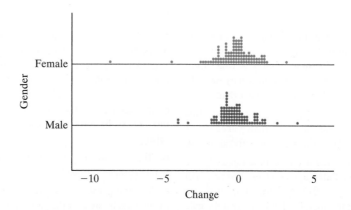

Summary statistics:

	n	Mean	SD
female	98	-0.36	1.33
male	81	-0.59	1.25
pooled	179	-0.46	1.30

SOLUTION 7.CE.9e

females. Sample sizes are 98 (F) and 81 (M), without strong skewness in either pretest distribution, meaning that a two-sample t test is valid. $t = 3.73$, p-value $= 0.0003$. We have very strong evidence of a difference in the average flexibility of males and females (females are between 0.748 and 2.43 inches more flexible than males; 95% CI).

b. Matched pairs test to evaluate whether there is a significant change in flexibility; this is different than an independent samples t-test to compare male and female flexibility.

c. Null: Average difference in flexibility pre vs. post is 0. Alt: Average difference is less than 0 (pre minus post).

The distribution of flexibility change scores is not strongly skewed (see graph for Solution 7.CE.9c) and there are more than 20 (actually 179) scores, so a one-sample t-test (paired t-test) is appropriate. We have

very strong evidence ($t = -4.76$, p-value < 0.0001) that the average difference (pre minus post) is less than 0. A 95% confidence interval finds an average increase in flexibility between 0.27 and 0.65 inches. This result generalizes to all students taking the class around this time but does not demonstrate cause and effect because random assignment was not used.

d. Explanatory: sex, response: change score. Use a two-sample t-test.

e. First, create the difference scores for each person, then use **Multiple Means** applet to look at distribution of change scores for males and females. (See graph for Solution 7.CE.9e.)

The sample sizes are above 20 in each group, but there is one potential outlier for females. Using a simulation-based approach yields a p-value of 0.21 (two-sided), compared to a two-sample t-test (theory-based) that yields a p-value of 0.24 ($t = 1.18$), so the outlier isn't making much of an impact. Null: The average change in flexibility is the same for men and women. Alt: The average change is different for men and women. Conclusion: We do not have evidence of a difference in the average change in flexibility for men and women. A 95% confidence interval finds that men, on average, change in flexibility between 0.15 less and 0.61 more than women over the course of the semester. This result can generalize to all students taking the course around that time but does not suggest cause and effect between sex and change in flexibility because sex was not randomly assigned to the participants.

Mean = 0.462
SD = 1.299

SOLUTION 7.CE.9c

7.CE.11

a. Null: The average difference in the percentage of times chimps open the gate is 0 (percentage of times open gate when food platform width is wide minus narrow). Alt: The average difference is greater than 0.

b. The fact that the data are paired. This may yield a p-value larger than you could get if you analyzed the data (correctly) as paired.

c. The p-value from a simulation using the **Matched Pairs** applet gives a very small p-value (< 0.001). We have strong evidence that chimps are more likely to open the gate in the collaborative condition than the solo condition.

7.CE.15

a. Each cat had negative interactions recorded before and after exposure to catnip.

b. Null: There is no association between exposure to catnip and negative interactions. Alt: There is an association between exposure to catnip and negative interactions (more negative interactions after catnip).

c. p-value = 0.004. The probability of obtaining a mean difference in the number of negative interactions of -1 or less is 0.004.

d. We have strong evidence against the null hypothesis. In other words, we would concude there is an association between exposure to catnip and an increase in the number of negative interaction (on average, more negative interactioins after exposure to catnip).

7.CE.16

a. Although there are only 15 pairs (cats) in the study, the distribution of their negative interaction scores is not strongly skewed.

b. $t = -3.24$, p-value = 0.003

c. We have strong evidence against the null hypothesis, in favor of the alternative of more negative interaction scores, on average, with the catnip.

7.CE.17

a. $-1.0 \pm 2 \times 0.396 = -1.0 \pm 0.792$, $(-1.79, -0.21)$. We are 95% confident that, on average, cats have between 0.21 and 1.79 more negative interactions after catnip than before.

b. $(-1.66, -0.34)$. We are 95% confident that, on average, cats have between 0.34 and 1.66 more negative interactions after catnip than before.

7.CE.18

a. Null: The average number of negative interactions before catnip is the same as after. Alt: The average number of negative interactions before catnip is less than after. $t = -1.34$, p-value = 0.096. We have moderate evidence that the number of negative interactions before catnip is less than after catnip.

b. The p-value has gotten quite a bit larger (0.003 compared to 0.096).

c. Yes, the p-value is much smaller, indicating that, because of the pairing, the study yields a statistically significant result, compared to the same study without pairing, which would not have yielded a statistically significant result.

CHAPTER 8

Section 8.1

8.1.1

A, B, E

8.1.3

C

8.1.5

$$\frac{|0.25-0.30| + |0.25-0.35| + |0.30-0.35|}{3}$$

$$= \frac{0.05 + 0.10 + 0.05}{3} = \frac{0.20}{3} = 0.067$$

8.1.7

If you don't take absolute values there are two potential problems, automatic zeros and ambiguity.

1. Automatic zeros. Recall Example 8.1: Coming to a stop. The differences were: $\hat{p}_S - \hat{p}_L = -0.047$, $\hat{p}_F - \hat{p}_S = -0.082$, and $\hat{p}_L - \hat{p}_F = 0.12$. If you add these with-

out taking absolute values first, you get zero. This is not a coincidence but an algebraic fact. Check that $(\hat{p}_S - \hat{p}_L) + (\hat{p}_F - \hat{p}_S) + (\hat{p}_L - \hat{p}_F) = 0$.

2. Ambiguity. If you take absolute values, order doesn't matter: $|\hat{p}_S - \hat{p}_L| = |\hat{p}_L - \hat{p}_S|$. If you don't take absolute values, order does matter. There's a difference between $(\hat{p}_S - \hat{p}_L) + (\hat{p}_F - \hat{p}_S) + (\hat{p}_L - \hat{p}_F) = 0$ and $(\hat{p}_L - \hat{p}_S) + (\hat{p}_F - \hat{p}_S) + (\hat{p}_L - \hat{p}_F) = 2(\hat{p}_L - \hat{p}_S)$.

8.1.9

a. Random sampling. Random assignment is not possible—you can't use random numbers to tell a person which party to belong to. Random sampling is both possible and important to avoid sampling bias. (Even if you can't get access to voter registration lists, you can take a random sample of individuals and ask their party affiliation.)

b. You would need to know the sample sizes—the number of Democrats, Republicans, and Independents in the sample.

8.1.11

a. Males: 0.50, Females: 0.60

b. 0.10

c. In this case the MAD statistic is just the absolute value of the observed statistic in this example. This will only be the case when both variables have two categories.

d. See the graphs for Solution 8.1.11d.

The distribution of the MAD statistic looks like the distribution of the difference in proportions, except all of the negative values have been made positive so it's right skewed and always positive, instead of bell-shaped and centered at 0.

e. Because the MAD statistic uses an absolute value

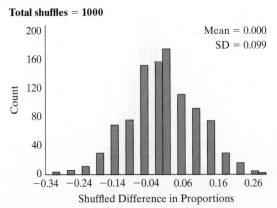

Total shuffles = 1000

Mean = 0.000
SD = 0.099

SOLUTION 8.1.11d

SOLUTION 8.1.11d

8.1.15

a. Control group: (i) little or no baldness (331 + 221)/771 = 71.50%, (ii) some or much baldness 100% − 71.50% = 28.50%

b. Those with heart disease: (i) little or no baldness (251 + 165)/663 = 62.75%; (ii) some or much baldness 100% − 62.75% = 37.25%

c. At this stage, there does seem to be an association between baldness and heart disease. Among those with heart disease, (higher levels of) baldness is more common (37%) than among those without heart disease (29%).

d. In words, the null hypothesis is that there is no association between baldness and heart disease. More specifically, the probability of heart disease does not differ among individuals with "none," "little," "some," or "much" baldness. The alternative is that at least one of the four probabilities is different. In symbols, H_0: $\pi_{none} = \pi_{little} = \pi_{some} = \pi_{much}$, where π is denotes the probability heart disease.

e. The value of the MAD is 0.099, with a null distribution that is unimodal and skewed to the right. The simulated p-value based on 10,000 repetitions is 0.003. The value of the chi-square statistic is 14.51, with a null distribution that is highly skewed to the right. The p-value, based on 10,000 repetitions, is 0.0033. Both tests give very strong evidence against the null hypothesis, which should be rejected. The conclusion is that there is in fact an association between degree of baldness and presence of heart disease. Degree of baldness could not be randomly assigned, so inference about cause and effect is not supported. The subjects were a sample chosen from the 22,000 doctors in the Physicians Health Study. If the sample was chosen by random sampling, then the results of the study generalize to all the physicians in the population.

8.1.17

a. See table below.

b. Comedian (categorical)

c. Type of joke (categorical)

d. Null: There is no association between comedian and whether or not the joke is political. Alternative: There is an association

e. Leno: 315/1, 313 = 0.24, Letterman: 136/648 = 0.21, Stewart: 83/252 = 0.329,

f. MAD = 0.08

g. It is very small (0.08 is in the far right tail of the null distribution).

h. We have very strong evidence of an association between comedian and political nature of jokes used.

8.1.20

a. 18−34: 68/232 = 0.293, 35−54: 128/332 = 0.386, 55+: 173/338 = 0.512

b. Yes, the proportions are different between the groups. Older individuals are more likely to approve of the practice than younger individuals.

c. Null: There is no association between age and whether or not someone approves of stop and frisk. Alt: There is an association between age and whether or not someone approves of stop and frisk.

d. 0.146

e. p-value < 0.001

f. We have strong evidence of an association between age and whether or not someone approves of stop and frisk.

8.1.21

Null: There is no difference between 18- to 34-year-olds and 55+ in their likelihood of saying "approve" about the police practice. Alt: There is a difference (proportions are different). The p-value is <0.001. We have very strong evidence of a difference in the approval rates of the stop and frisk practice when comparing 18- to 34-year-olds and 55+.

8.1.23

a. White: 3,801/4,223 = 0.900, Black: 611/664 = 0.920, Hispanic: 614/682 = 0.900

b. Not much of an association—the proportions are quite close together.

c. Null: There is no association between race and owning a cell phone (the population proportions are the same in each population). Alt: There is an association between race and owning a cell phone (at least one of the population proportions is different).

d. MAD = 0.013

e. p-value = 0.37

f. We don't have strong evidence of an association between race and whether or not someone owns a cellphone in the population.

8.1.24

Null: The population proportion of Whites that own a cell phone is the same as for Blacks. Alt: The population proportions of cell phone owners are different for Whites and Blacks. The p-value is 0.35. We don't have evidence of a difference in the proportion of Blacks and Whites that own a cell phone *Note:* We used Whites, but using Hispanics is also fine as the White and Hispanic proportions are the same in this sample.

8.1.25

a. White: 2,238/4,223 = 0.592, Black: 372/664 = 0.609, Hispanic: 382/682 = 0.622

b. Not much of an association—the proportions are quite close together.

c. Null: There is no association between race and owning a smartphone (the population proportions are the same in each group). Alt: There is an association between race and owning a smartphone (at least one of the population proportions is different).

	Leno	Letterman	Stewart
Political joke	315	136	83
Nonpolitical joke	998	512	169
Total	1313	648	252

SOLUTION 8.1.17a

		White	Black	Hispanic	Total
Own a smartphone?	**Yes**	2,238	372	382	2,992
	No	1,563	239	232	2,034
	Total	3,801	611	614	5,026

SOLUTION 8.1.26a

d. MAD = 0.020,

e. p-value ≈ 0.40

f. We don't have strong evidence of an association between race and whether or not someone owns a smartphone in the population of U.S. adults.

8.1.26

a. Smartphone ownership among cell phone owners: see Table 8.1.26a below.

b. White: 2,238/3,801 = 0.589, Black: 372/611 = 0.609, Hispanic: 382/614 = 0.622

8.1.28

a. Null: The population proportion of cars that stop when leading is the same as when following. Alt: The population proportions are different. The max-min statistic is 0.905 − 0.776 = 0.129. The p-value from simulation is approximately 0.089. We have moderate evidence that the probability that cars come to a complete stop when leading is different than when following.

b. The null distributions are both right skewed and always positive, but the null distribution of the MAD statistic is less variable (SD = 0.026) than the null distribution of the max-min statistic (SD = 0.039).

c. The strength of evidence is similar between the two approaches.

Section 8.2

8.2.1

a. The statistic can never be negative. The statistic is a sum of terms of the form $n_i(\hat{p} - \hat{p}_i)^2$, all divided by $\hat{p}(1 - \hat{p})$. All of the individual terms are nonnegative, and the overall divisor is positive.

b. The chi-square can be zero only if all the individual conditional probabilities $\hat{p}_i$ are equal to each other (and thus equal to $\hat{p}$).

c. (B) The distribution is skewed toward high values, with a long right tail. [More detail: For degrees of freedom greater than 2, the curve starts at (0,0), increases steadily to a unique peak, and then decreases steadily toward the x-axis. For degrees of freedom of 1 or 2, the curve has a vertical asymptote at x = 0, and decreases steadily for x > 0.]

d. The long right tail comes from the fact that there is a "wall" at zero. The statistic can take on any positive value but can never be negative. [More detail: In the formula for chi-square, the values of the n_i and $\hat{p}$ are fixed by the marginal totals; only the values of the squared terms $(\hat{p}_i - \hat{p})^2$ vary as you rerandomize. For some randomizations, just by chance, one of these terms will be unusually large.]

8.2.6

a. Null: There is no association between generation and marriage views. Alt: There is an association.

b. All cell counts are larger than 10.

c. Chi-square = 22.26, p-value = 0.0001

d. We have very strong evidence of an association between generation and marriage views.

e. Cause and effect is not possible here because this is not a randomized experiment; generalizing these findings to all adult Americans is possible because a random sample was used.

f. Mill − GenX (−0.0444, 0.0662), Mill–Boom (0.0401, 0.1407)*, Mill − 65 (0.0422, 0.1938)*, GenX–Boom (0.0341, 0.1248)*, GenX–65 (0.0345, 0.1797)*, Boom–65 = (−0.0412, 0.0965). The confidence intervals show that younger generations tend to more often report that marriage is obsolete. Millenials and GenX are both significantly more likely than Boomers and 65+ to report marriage being obsolete.

8.2.11

a. Each person in the study

b. The population proportion of men with heart disease in each baldness group (π)

c. Null: There is no association between baldness and heart disease. Alt: There is an association between baldness and heart disease.

d. Null: $\pi_{None} = \pi_{Little} = \pi_{Some} = \pi_{Much}$. Alt: At least one population proportion is different than the others.

e. Chi-square = 14.51, p-value = 0.0023. We have strong evidence of an association between heart disease and baldness, but this is not evidence of cause and effect because it

is an observational study. Furthermore, the results should be generalized with caution because the sample was not obtained by taking a random sample.

8.2.12

a. None: 0.431, little: 0.427, some: 0.513, much: 0.598

b. Two largest: much vs. none and much vs. little; smallest: none vs. little

c. Much vs. none: (−0.277, −0.056)*, much vs. little (−0.285, −0.056)*, none vs. little: (−0.06, 0.07),

d. Yes, there are least 10 with heart disease and 10 without heart disease in each group.

8.2.17

a. Observational study, individuals were not assigned values of either variable

b. Each participant in the survey (1883)

c. Explanatory: political leaning, response: favor tax? Both are categorical.

d. The population proportion that favor tax on unhealthy food/soda within each political group (π)

e. Null: $\pi_{Rep} = \pi_{Demo} = \pi_{Indep}$. Alt: At least one of the population proportions is different.

f. Null: There is no association between political leaning and whether or not someone favors a tax on food/soda. Alt: There is an association.

g. There are at least 10 individuals in each cell of the table.

h. Chi-square = 56.41, p-value < 0.001

i. The likelihood of getting a chi-square statistic of 56.41 or larger if the null hypothesis is true is < 0.0001.

j. We have very strong evidence of an association between political party and opinion on the tax. This does not, however, suggest a cause-and-effect relationship between political leaning and the tax (not randomly assigned to political leaning), but the result does generalize to all U.S. adults (random sampling).

k. Rep vs. Dem (−0.26, −0.16)*, Rep vs. Ind (−0.14, −0.04)*, Dem vs. Ind (0.07, 0.17)*. All groups are significantly different from each other with Democrats most in favor, followed by Independents, and Republicans showing the lowest support for the tax.

8.2.19

a. Observational study. Students were not randomly assigned outcomes for either variable.

b. Each of the 50 students

Relapse?		Desipramine HCl	Lithium carbonate	Placebo	Total
	Yes	10	18	20	48
	No	14	6	4	24
	Total	24	24	24	72

SOLUTION 8.2.21a

c. Explanatory: sex (male/female), response: eat breakfast frequency. Both are categorical.

d. Null: There is no association between a person's sex and breakfast eating frequency. Alt: There is an association.

e. Some of the cell counts are less than 10.

f. Get 50 cards: 26 blue, 11 red, 10 green, and 3 black. Shuffle and deal into two stacks of 37 and 13, respectively. Compute the chi-square statistic. Repeat many times. The p-value is the proportion of times the observed chi-square statistic or larger occurred in the simulations.

g. Chi-square = 1.4, p-value = 0.79

h. We obtain a chi-square value of 1.4 or larger approximately 79% of random shuffles when the null hypothesis is true.

i. We have little to no evidence of an association between sex and whether or not someone eats breakfast. This result should be generalized with caution (not random sampling), and if statistical significance was established, a cause-and-effect conclusion would not be possible (not random assignment).

8.2.21

a. See the table for Solution 8.2.21a.

b. Experiment. Subjects were assigned to the three drug groups.

c. Each of the 72 individuals in the study

d. Explanatory: type of medicine, response: did patient relapse again? Both variables are categorical.

e. Null: There is no association between type of medicine and relapse. Alt: There is an association.

f. Two of the cell counts are less than 10.

g. Get 72 playing cars: 48 black, 24 red. Shuffle and deal into three stacks of 24 each. Compute the chi-square statistic and repeat.

h. Chi-square = 10.50, p-value = 0.0052

i. The chances of getting a chi-square statistic of 10.50 or larger if the null hypothesis is true is 0.0052.

j. We have strong evidence of an association between treatment group and chance of relapse. This is a cause-and-effect conclusion because random assignment was used. The results cannot be generalized easily, as little is known about the participants.

8.2.23

a. Experiment. People are randomly assigned to a group.

b. Null: There is no association between treatment group and race. Alt: There is an association.

c. Some of the cell counts are less than 10.

d. Chi-square = 3.97, p-value = 0.46

e. Shows that random assignment "worked" in the sense that it kept the two treatment groups roughly the same in terms of race distribution (this is what the p-value tells you).

Section 8.3

8.3.1

B

8.3.3

D

8.3.5

B

8.3.7

B

8.3.9

	Female	Male	Total
Allergies? No	24.7	27.3	52
Allergies? Yes	13.3	14.7	28
Total	38	42	80

8.3.10

1.606

8.3.13

a. The explanatory variable is the time of day (morning, afternoon, evening) and it is categorical.

b. The response variable is whether or not the student was on his or her phone and it is categorical.

c. See the table for Solution 8.3.13c.

d. See the table for Solution 8.3.13d.

	Morning	Afternoon	Evening	Total
On Phone	44	48	45	137
Not on Phone	177	184	70	431
Total	221	232	115	568

SOLUTION 8.3.13c

	Morning	Afternoon	Evening	Total
On Phone	53.3	56.0	27.7	137
Not on Phone	167.7	176.0	87.3	431
Total	221	232	115	568

SOLUTION 8.3.13d

e. Chi-square test of homogeneity (we have three separate samples). The validity conditions are met because all the expected counts are greater than 5.

f. H₀: The population proportion of students on their phones while walking across campus is the same in the morning, afternoon, and evening. Hₐ: There is a different population proportion of students on their phones while walking across campus in at least one of the time periods (morning, afternoon, and evening).

g. $\chi^2 = 17.79$ (df = 2) and the p-value = 0.0001.

h. We have very strong evidence that there is a different population proportion of students on their phones while walking across campus in at least one of the time periods (morning, afternoon, and evening). We have more students than expected on their phones during the evening and fewer than expected in the morning and afternoon.

8.3.14

We could combine the morning and afternoon data and change this to a two-proportion test with hypotheses: H₀: $\pi_{evening} = \pi_{day}$ and H₀: $\pi_{evening} > \pi_{day}$. (We are using the two-proportion z-test rather than the chi-square test because the alternative hypothesis is one-sided.) Using the proportions $\hat{p}_{evening} = 45/115 = 0.3913$, $\hat{p}_{day} = 92/453 = 0.2031$, we get a one-sided p-value of <0.0001, so we have very strong evidence that in the long run a larger proportion of students

will be on their phones in the evening than during the day. A 95% confidence interval tells us that the evening population proportion of students on their phones is between 0.0916 to 0.2848 higher than the population proportion of students on their phones during the day.

8.3.16

a. See the table for Solution 8.3.16a.

b. Chi-square test of homogeneity (random assignment). The validity conditions are met because all the expected counts are greater than 5.

c. H₀: The probability of answering yes is the same across the interview modes. Hₐ: The probability of answering yes about exercising differs based on the interview mode.

d. $\chi^2 = 19.25$ (df = 3) and the p-value = 0.0002.

e. We have very strong evidence that the probability of answering yes to the exercising question differs depending on how the question is asked. Respondents in this study were less likely to say yes when it was a voice and more likely to say yes when it was a text (especially when it was an automated text).

8.3.17

a. See the table for Solution 8.3.17a.

b. See the table for Solution 8.3.17b.

c. Chi-square test of homogeneity (randomized experiment). The validity conditions are met because all the expected counts are greater than 5.

d. H₀: The probability of rounding an answer is the same across the interview modes. Hₐ: The probability of rounding an answer differs based on the interview mode.

e. $\chi^2 = 8.21$ (df = 3) and the p-value = 0.0419.

f. We have strong evidence that there is an association between the interview mode and whether people would round their answer to the question of how many movies they have seen in the past year. In this study, respondents were less likely to round when it was a text and more likely to round when it was a voice (especially when it was a human voice).

8.3.19

a. See the table for Solution 8.3.19a.

b. Chi-square test of homogeneity (treating as randomized experiment to the sign color). The validity conditions are met because all the expected counts are greater than 5.

c. H₀: The proportion of people who would obey the signs is the same for all conditions. Hₐ: The proportion of people who would obey the signs is not the same for all conditions.

d. $\chi^2 = 7.022$ (df = 2) and the p-value = 0.0299.

e. We have very strong evidence that the proportion of people that would obey the signs is not the same for all conditions. In this study, participants were more likely to obey the sign when it was red than expected and less likely for the other two conditions.

	Human Text	Automated Text	Human Voice	Automated Voice	Total
Yes	30.2	30.0	30.5	30.3	121
No	127.8	127.0	129.5	128.7	513
Total	158	157	160	159	634

SOLUTION 8.3.16a

	Human Text	Automated Text	Human Voice	Automated Voice	Total
Yes	27	19	39	29	114
No	131	138	121	130	520
Total	158	157	160	159	634

SOLUTION 8.3.17a

	Human Text	Automated Text	Human Voice	Automated Voice	Total
Yes	28.4	28.2	28.8	28.6	114
No	129.6	128.8	131.2	130.4	520
Total	158	157	160	159	634

SOLUTION 8.3.17b

	No sign	Yellow	Red	Total
Left (obeyed the sign)	17.31	17	16.69	51
Right (did not obey the sign)	37.69	37	36.31	111
Total	55	54	53	162

SOLUTION 8.3.19a

Section 8.4

8.4.1

C, D (keep in mind that the AP exam wants you to use the *expected* counts).

8.4.3

D

8.4.5

B

8.4.7

C

8.4.9

For a chi-square goodness-of-fit test, the data need to be a single categorical variable (usually with more than two outcomes). For a chi-square independence test, the data need to be made up of two categorical variables.

8.4.11

a. 1

b. 3.143

8.4.13

a. Each is 25.

b. The chi-square goodness-of-fit test is valid because the expected counts are all greater than 5.

c. H_0: Each season is equally likely to be a favorite ($\pi_1 = 1/4, \ldots, \pi_4 = 1/4$). H_a: Each season is not equally likely to be a favorite (at least one π differs from 1/4).

d. $\chi^2 = 20.72$ (df = 3) and the p-value = 0.0001.

e. With a p-value much smaller than 0.05, we have strong evidence that each season is not equally likely to be a favorite (or that the distribution of favorite seasons in the population is not equally distributed).

8.4.14

a. Each is 95/12 = 7.9167.

b. The chi-square goodness-of-fit test is valid because the expected counts are all greater than 5.

c. H_0: Each month is equally likely ($\pi_1 = 1/12, \ldots, \pi_{12} = 1/12$). H_a: Each month is not equally likely (at least one π differs from 1/12).

d. $\chi^2 = 7.189$ (df = 11) and the p-value = 0.784.

e. With a p-value much larger than 0.05, we do not have strong evidence that each month is not equally likely to occur (in other words, the distribution of birth months in the population is not equally distributed).

8.4.16

a. Each is 50/5 = 10.

b. The chi-square goodness-of-fit test is valid because the expected counts are all greater than 5.

c. H_0: Each value is equally likely to occur ($\pi_1 = 0.20, \ldots \pi_5 = 0.20$). H_a: Each value is not equally likely to occur (at least one π differs from 1/5).

d. $\chi^2 = 2$ (df = 4) and the p-value = 0.7358.

e. With a p-value much greater than 0.05, we don't have strong evidence that each value is not equally likely to occur (in other words, we don't have evidence that the phone is not picking random numbers).

f. A large p-value is not strong evidence for the null, so we do not have strong evidence that it is truly random; we would just say we don't have strong evidence against the process being random.

g. We could combine some categories. For example, we could test to see if values 1, 2, and 3 are distributed significantly different from 60% of the time, and values 4 and 5 distributed significantly different from 40% of the time.

8.4.19

a. See the table for Solution 8.4.19a.

b. The chi-square goodness-of-fit test is valid because the expected counts are all greater than 5.

c. H_0: The leading digits in the textbook are distributed according to Benford's Law ($\pi_1 = 0.301, \ldots, \pi_9 = 0.046$). H_a: The leading digits in the textbook are not distributed according to Benford's Law.

d. $\chi^2 = 11.849$ (df = 8) and the p-value = 0.1581.

e. With a p-value greater than 0.05, we don't have strong evidence that the leading digits in the textbook are not distributed according to Benford's Law.

8.4.21

a. H_0: The plants producing pea colors and shapes as described in the table are distributed in a 9:3:3:1 ratio. H_a: The plants producing pea colors and shapes as described in the table are not distributed in a 9:3:3:1 ratio.

b. Chi-square goodness-of-fit test.

c. All our expected counts should be at least 5 and our smallest is about 35.

d. $\chi^2 = 0.47$, df = 3, p-value = 0.9254.

e. With a p-value of 0.9254 > 0.05, we do not have strong evidence that the plants producing pea colors and shapes as described in the table are not distributed in a 9:3:3:1 ratio.

8.4.22

a. H_0: The plants producing pea colors and shapes as described in the table are distributed in a 1:2:2:4 ratio. H_a: The plants producing pea colors and shapes as described in the table are not distributed in a 1:2:2:4 ratio.

b. Chi-square goodness-of-fit test.

c. All our expected counts should be at least 5 and our smallest is about 33.

d. $\chi^2 = 1.517$, df = 3, p-value = 0.6784.

e. With a p-value of 0.6784 > 0.05, we do not have strong evidence that the plants producing pea colors and shapes as described in the table are not distributed in a 1:2:2:4 ratio.

8.4.23

a. H_0: The purple-flowered plants and the white-flowered plants are distributed in a 3:1 ratio. H_a: The purple-flowered plants and the white-flowered plants are not distributed in a 3:1 ratio.

Leading digit	1	2	3	4	5	6	7	8	9
Expected frequency	39.732	23.232	16.5	12.804	10.428	8.844	7.656	6.732	6.072

SOLUTION 8.4.19a

Count = 479/10000 (0.0479)

SOLUTION 8.4.30c

Count = 2370/10000 (0.2370)

SOLUTION 8.4.30e

Count = 8010/10000 (0.8010)

SOLUTION 8.4.30g

b. Chi-square goodness-of-fit test.

c. All our expected counts should be at least 5 and our smallest is about 232.

d. $\chi^2 = 0.391$, df = 1, p-value = 0.5319.

e. With a p-value of $0.5319 > 0.05$, we do not have strong evidence that the purple-flowered plants and the white-flowered plants are not distributed in a 3:1 ratio.

8.4.26

a. H_0: Heart attacks are distributed evenly across the days of the week for employed people. H_a: Heart attacks are not distributed evenly across the days of the week for employed people.

b. Chi-square goodness-of-fit test.

c. All our expected counts should be at least 5 and our smallest is about 126.

d. $\chi^2 = 18.254$, df = 6, p-value = 0.0056.

e. With a p-value of $0.0056 < 0.05$, we have strong evidence that heart attacks are not distributed evenly across the days of the week for employed people.

f. Looking at the observed counts, we see a larger number of heart attacks on Monday than the other days of the week, with the lowest on Sunday. It makes sense that Monday will be different for those who have weekends/days of rest on Saturday and Sunday than the rest of the week.

8.4.27

a. H_0: Heart attacks are distributed evenly across the days of the week for people who are not employed. H_a: Heart attacks are not distributed evenly across the days of the week for people who are not employed.

b. Chi-square goodness-of-fit test.

c. All our expected counts should be at least 5 and our smallest is about 170.

d. $\chi^2 = 2.227$, df = 6, p-value = 0.8977.

e. With a p-value of $0.8977 > 0.05$, we do not have strong evidence that heart attacks are not distributed evenly across the days of the week for people that are not employed.

f. We no longer see evidence of a "Monday effect" for individuals who do not have the work day/weekend day distinction.

8.4.30

a. H_0: $\pi_M = \pi_T = \pi_W = \pi_R = \pi_F = 1/5$; H_a: Not all the values of π_i are the same (at least one π differs from 1/5).

b. 4

c. Any chi-square statistic from 9.41 to 9.60 gives the same p-value of about 0.0479, which appears to be as close to 0.05 as we can get. Therefore a rejection region is any chi-square at or above 9.41 and the probability of a Type I error is about 0.0479. See the graph for Solution 8.4.30c.

d. They appear to be coming from the distribution in the alternative.

e. There are 2,370 out of 10,000 simulated statistics in the rejection region. See the graph for Solution 8.4.30e.

f. If the null hypothesis is false and in fact the true proportion of calling in sick is 0.26 on Monday and Friday and 0.16 on the rest of the days, the probability that a sample of size 50 would give significant results (a p-value less than 0.05) is about 0.2370.

g. The power is larger because the distribution in the alternative has proportions farther away from that under the null. The power of this test is now about 0.8010 or, if the null hypothesis is false and in fact the true proportion

of calling in sick is 0.32 on Monday and Friday and 0.12 on the rest of the days, the probability a sample of size 50 would give significant results (a p-value less than 0.05) is about 0.8010. See the graph for Solution 8.4.30g.

h. Using the MAD statistic, our rejection region is a MAD statistic equal to or greater than 3.61 (this gave us a p-value of 0.0436). The power of this test is about 0.2215, a little bit smaller than if we would use the chi-square statistic.

i. Using the Max-Min statistic, our rejection region is a Max-Min statistic equal to or greater than 0.25 (this gave us a p-value of 0.0338). The power of this test is about 0.1917, a little bit smaller than if we would use the chi-square statistic. Both the MAD and the Max-Min statistics give distributions that have gaps and are not as continuous as a chi-square distribution would be. Therefore, we could not get as close to 0.05 to determine a cut-off value. For example, using the Max-Min, our cut-off value of 0.25 only gave a p-value of 0.0338. With this smaller p-value (more difficult to reject the null), we would expect the power of the test to decrease because this also relies on rejecting the null.

End of chapter

8.CE.1

a. Sex and coffee consumption; both variables are categorical (sex = 2 categories, coffee consumption = 3 categories).

b. It could involve random sampling (give the survey to a random sample) but not random assignment unless you told people how much coffee they have to drink.

c. No, the data are not cross-tabulated (e.g., number of men, every day).

8.CE.2

a. The following answer gives the closest possible counts (with whole numbers) to having no association.

	Men	Women	Total
Every day	12	10	22
Sometimes	12	10	22
Almost never	14	10	26
Total	38	32	70

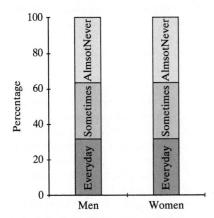

b. Answers will vary, below is one example. Here we see no men in the "almost never" category (but lots of women) and no women in the "every day" category (and lots of men).

	Men	Women	Total
Every day	22	0	22
Sometimes	16	6	22
Almost never	0	26	26
Total	38	32	70

8.CE.3

a.

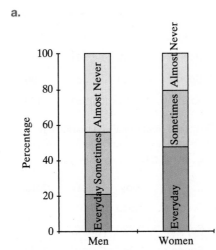

The graph reveals a strong association between sex and coffee consumption. For example, a higher proportion of "almost never" responses came from men but a higher proportion of "every day" responses came from women.

b. See the graph for Solution 8.CE.3b. Approximate p-value = 0.02.

c. Because 0.02 < 0.05, we have strong evidence of an association between sex and coffee.

d. Although we have strong evidence of an association (e.g., with women coffee more often than men), this result cannot generalize because a random sample wasn't taken, nor does this suggest a cause-and-effect relationship because random assignment was not used.

8.CE.4

No, two counts are less than 10. Chi-square statistic is 8.18. The theory-based p-value is 0.0168, compared to 0.02 by simulation. We have strong evidence of an association between coffee consumption and sex.

8.CE.5

a. None

b. Smaller

c. Stronger

8.CE.9

a. Explanatory: educational degree received, response: generally trust people

b. Less than HS: 0.138, HS: 0.272, JC: 0.308, Bach: 0.494, Grad: 0.634. See the graph for Solution 8.CE.9b.

The proportions and the segmented bar graph both indicate that as educational level increases people are generally more trusting.

c. Null: There is no association between educational degree and trusting others. Alt: There is an association between educational degree and trusting others.

d. MAD = 0.243

Mean = 2.108
SD = 2.099

Count samples [Greater Than ▾] [8.18] [Count]

Count = 20/1000 (0.0200)

☐ Overlay Chi-square distribution

SOLUTION 8.CE.3b

Sample Data

SOLUTION 8.CE.9b

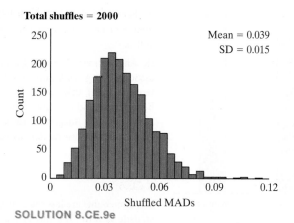

Total shuffles = 2000

Mean = 0.039
SD = 0.015

SOLUTION 8.CE.9e

e. The approximate p-value is 0. See the graph for Solution 8.CE.9e.

f. The probability of obtaining a MAD statistic of 0.243 or larger if the null hypothesis is true is approximately 0.

g. Yes

h. We have strong evidence of an association between educational degree attained and trust.

8.CE.10

Chi-square = 138.26, p-value < 0.0001. We have strong evidence of an association between educational degree attained and trust. Individuals with less than a HS education are significantly less trusting than individuals with more education (95% CIs: 0.076 to 0.191 less than HS, 0.064 to 0.275 less than JC, 0.278 to 0.444 less than Bach, 0.406 to 0.585 less than Grad). HS is significantly less than Bach (0.151 to 0.293 less) and Grad (0.279 to 0.446 less), JC is significantly less than Bach (0.073 to 0.300 less) and Grad (0.205 to 0.448 less), and Bach is significantly less than Grad (0.041 to 0.239). The only pair of groups that was not significantly different was HS and JC (−0.136 to 0.065).

8.CE.11

Chi-square = 156.67, p-value < 0.0001. We have strong evidence of an association between educational level attained and trust level, with trust increasing with educational level. There is little difference between this analysis and the one with the two-category response variable in the previous exercises.

8.CE.13

To answer these questions, it helps to have the row and column totals:

	Boy	Girl	Total
Grades	117	130	247
Popular	50	91	141
Sports	60	30	90
Total	227	251	478

To get the conditional and marginal proportions, divide a cell entry by the corresponding column total:

	Boy	Girl	Total
Grades	0.515	0.518	0.517
Popular	0.220	0.363	0.295
Sports	0.264	0.120	0.188
Total	1.000	1.000	1.000

a. 117/227 = 0.515 of boys think getting good grades is most important.

b. 130/251 = 0.518 of girls think getting good grades is most important.

c. 50/227 = 0.220 of boys think being popular is most important.

d. 91/251 = 0.363 of girls think being popular is most important.

e. 60/227 = 0.264 of boys think excelling in sports is most important.

f. 30/251 = 0.120 of girls think excelling in sports is most important.

g. Overall, 247/478 = 0.517 of boys and girls think getting good grades is most important.

h. Overall, 141/478 = 0.295 of boys and girls think being popular is most important.

i. Overall, 90/478 = 0.188 of boys and girls think excelling in sports is most important.

j. On balance, it looks like boys and girls do have differing goals. Boys and girls seem to be the same in terms of the proportion who think getting good grades is most important, but a higher proportion of girls think being popular is most important and a higher proportion of boys think excelling in sports is more important.

8.CE.14

The null hypothesis is that the conditional probabilities of students choosing each goal are the same for boys and girls. The alternative is that, for at least one goal, the two conditional probabilities in a pair are different. The value of the chi-square statistic is 21.46 with a theory-based p-value of 0.0000. (A simulation-based p-value was 0.0002 based on 10,000 repetitions.) There is very, very strong evidence that the null hypothesis should be rejected.

A 95% confidence interval for the difference in the population proportion of boys and girls that think grades are most important is −0.092 to 0.087; thus, because zero is in this interval, we find there is not strong evidence that the population proportion choosing good grades is different for boys and girls. A 95% confidence interval for the difference in the population proportion of boys and girls that think being popular is most important is −0.223 to 0.062; thus we find there is strong evidence that the population proportion that think being popular is lower among boys than girls. A 95% confidence interval for the difference in the population proportion of boys and girls that think sports is most important is 0.075 to 0.215; thus we find there is strong evidence that the population proportion of boys that think sports is most important is higher than girls.

Inference about cause and effect is not supported because the values of the explanatory variable (boy and girl) could not be randomly assigned. Generalization to a larger population is not justified on the basis of sampling, because it was not random. However, it is reasonable to think that the results here are typical of other U.S. students in grades 4–6.

8.CE.18

a. The observational units are the 47 Harvard undergraduates.

b. The (categorical) explanatory variable is whether the student received a bonus or a rebate.

c. The (categorical) response variable is whether the student spent or saved the money.

d. Abstractly, the null hypothesis is that there is no association between the explanatory and response variables. More concretely, in the context of the study, the null hypothesis is that the conditional probability of saving the money does not depend on whether it was called a rebate or a bonus. The alternative hypothesis is that the conditional probabilities differ.

8.CE.19

a. The number in the upper left cell is 9. The difference in conditional probabilities is $9/25 - 16/22 = -0.3673$. Both statistics lead to the same two-sided p-value of 0.012.

b. For 2×2 tables, the MAD and chi-square statistics are equivalent. They both lead to the same simulated p-value. For this data set, the MAD is 0.367 and the chi-square statistic is 6.34. Based on 10,000 repetitions, both statistics lead to a p-value of about 0.02. (The theory-based p-value is 0.012.)

c. The two p-values are quite close and lead to the same conclusion. Mathematically, it can be proved that for 2×2 tables of counts you always get the same p-value from a given set of shuffles, regardless of whether you use the count in the upper left cell, the difference in conditional proportions, the MAD, or the chi-square statistic.

CHAPTER 10

Section 10.1

10.1.1

The association will be negative: Larger distances go with lower exam scores and vice-versa.

10.1.3

The correlation coefficient will be exactly 1, because there is a perfect linear relationship with positive slope: Exam2 = Exam1 – 5.

10.1.5

In a scatterplot, the points are *observational units*, the x-axis represents the values of the *explanatory variable*, and the y-axis represents the values of the *response variable*.

10.1.7

D. There may be some nonlinear relationship.

10.1.9

A

10.1.11

a. Observational study

b. The 20 houses

c. The explanatory variable is square footage and the response is the price. Both of these are quantitative.

d. There is a fairly strong positive linear association beween square footage and price with no unusual observations. See the scatterplot below.

e. The correlation coefficient is 0.780 and this backs up the description given in part (d) as it is a number fairly close to 1.

10.1.13

a. Observational

b. The 34 people in the study

c. The explanatory variable is finger length and the response is height. Both of these are quantitative.

d. There is a moderate positive linear association beween finger length and height with no unusual observations. See the scatterplot below.

e. The correlation coefficient is 0.474 and this backs up the description given in part (d) as it is just a little bit below 0.5.

10.1.14

a. The point (5, 70) is circled in the scatterplot for Solution 10.1.14a. It is a bit unusual as it has the shortest finger length, but it is around the average height.

b. $r = 0.474$

c. $r = 0.566$

d. The correlation coefficient increased. This makes sense because the point removed did not nicely fall into the positive linear pattern of the data, so removing it would make the data better fit that overall pattern.

10.1.15

a. The point (10.16, 78) is circled in the scatterplot for Solution 10.1.15a. It is a bit unusual as it represents the longest finger and the greatest height.

b. $r = 0.474$

c. $r = 0.353$

d. The correlation coefficient decreased. This makes sense because the point removed very nicely fell into the positive linear pattern of the data (and was extreme on the x-axis), so removing it would make our measure of the overall association weaker.

SOLUTION 10.1.11d   SOLUTION 10.1.13d

SOLUTION 10.1.14a

SOLUTION 10.1.15a

SOLUTION 10.1.19d

SOLUTION 10.1.20a

10.1.19

a. Observational

b. The 16 students

c. The explanatory variable is name length and response is Scrabble score. Both of these are quantitative.

d. There is a moderate positive association beween name length and Scrabble score. There are a couple of scores that have fairly few letters but give high Scrabble scores. See scatterplot for Solution 10.1.19d.

e. The correlation coefficient is 0.476 and this backs up the description given in part (d) as it is around 0.5.

10.1.20

a. There is a fairly strong positive linear (perhaps a bit concave downward) association between the two variables. See scatterplot for Solution 10.1.20a.

b. The correlation coefficient is 0.782. This supports the answer in part (a) as it is fairly close to 1.

10.1.21

a. The linear association is stronger between the Scrabble points and the ratio as the correlation is closer to 1.

b. This makes sense because the Scrabble ratio will take into account the score of each letter, whereas the name length doesn't. These individual letter scores can be quite high or low so they have a great impact on the total word score.

Section 10.2

10.2.1

a. *Invalid*: The p-value is computed *assuming* there is no association. It does not tell the chance of no association.

b. *Invalid*, for the same reason as in (a) above.

c. *Invalid*, but close: See the answer to part (d) below.

d. *Valid*: If there were no association between height and hand span, the p-value (0.022) is the probability of observing the association observed in the sample data or an even stronger association in a sample of 10 students.

e. *Invalid*, for the same reason as in part (a) above.

10.2.3

a. B

b. With Lisa's larger sample we have more information and thus the strength of evidence is stronger.

10.2.7

a. Observational

b. The 90 Honda Civics

c. The explanatory variable is age and the response is price. They are both quantitative.

d. There is no association between age and price of used Honda Civics.

e. There is an association between age and price of used Honda Civics.

f. There is a fairly strong negative association between age and price of the cars. Not much unusual except perhaps the oldest and cheapest car. See scatterplot for Solution 10.2.7f.

g. The correlation of −0.820 backs up the answer to part (f) because it is close to −1.

h. Put the 90 ages on 90 index cards and the 90 prices on 90 other index cards. Shuffle the price index cards and randomly match them up with the 90 age cards. From this data set, compute the correlation coefficient. That simulated correlation coefficient will be one dot in the null distribution. Repeat this many, many times to create a null distribution. Find the proportion of simulated correlation coefficients that are −0.820 or below along with the simulated correlation coefficients that are 0.820 or above. This proportion will be the estimated p-value.

10.2.8

a. The p-value is about 0.

b. If there is no association between age and price of used Honda Civics, the probability we would get a sample correlation coefficient at least as extreme as −0.820 is about 0.

c. We have extremely strong evidence (small p-value) that there is an associa-tion between a car's price and its age in the population of all used Honda Civics adver-tised online. Because our sample correlation coefficient is negative, we can add that the association is negative in the population. Because this was an observational study, we are not drawing any causal conclusions. The data are a sample of used Honda Civics listed for sale online in July 2006 so we probably can't generalize to more recent populations.

10.2.11

a. Null: There is no association between maximum speed and maximum height of roller coasters. Alternative: There is an asso-ciation between maximum speed and maxi-mum height of roller coasters.

b. Put the 129 heights on 129 index cards and the 129 speeds on 129 other index cards. Shuffle the speed index cards and randomly match them up with the 129 height cards. From this data set, compute the correlation coefficient. That simulated correlation coef-ficient will be one dot in the null distribu-tion. Repeat this many, many times to create a null distribution. Find the proportion of simulated correlation coefficients that are at least as extreme as the observed correlation coefficient from the sample data.

10.2.12

a. The p-value is about 0.

b. If there is no association between maxi-mum height and maximum speed for roller coasters, the probability we would get a sample correlation coefficient at least as ex-treme as 0.895 is about 0.

c. We have extremely strong evidence (small p-value) that there is an association between maximum height and maximum speed for roller coasters around the world. Because our sample correlation coefficient is positive, we can go further and say the as-sociation is also positive in the population.

10.2.17

a. Null: There is no association between length of names and their Scrabble word score. Alternative: There is an association between length of names and their Scrabble word scores.

b. Put the 16 name lengths on 16 index cards and the 16 word scores on 16 other in-dex cards. Shuffle the word score cards and randomly match them up with the 16 name length cards. From this data set, compute the correlation coefficient. That simulated correlation coefficient will be one dot in the null distribution. Repeat this many, many times to create a null distribution. Find the proportion of simulated correlation coef-ficients that are at least as extreme as the observed correlation from the sample data.

10.2.18

a. The p-value is about 0.06.

b. If there is no association between name lengths and their scores, the probability we would get a sample correlation coefficient at least as extreme as 0.476 is about 0.06.

c. We do not have strong evidence (p-value > 0.05) that there is an association between name length and its Scrabble word score, but we do have moderate evidence (p-value < 0.10) of such an association and it is positive. We may cautiously generalize these results to statistics students like those in the study but we are not drawing a cause-and-effect con-clusion from this observational study.

10.2.19

a. Null: There is no association between Scrabble points per letter of names and their Scrabble score. Alternative: There is an asso-ciation between Scrabble points per letter of names and their Scrabble score.

b. Put the 16 points per name on 16 index cards and the 16 name scores on 16 other in-dex cards. Shuffle the name score cards and randomly match them up with the 16 points per name cards. From this data set, compute the correlation coefficient. That simulated cor-relation coefficient will be one dot in the null distribution. Repeat this many, many times to create a null distribution. Find the proportion of simulated correlation coefficients that are at least as extreme as the observed correlation coefficient from the sample data.

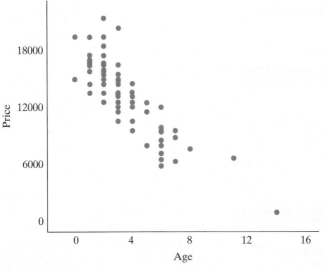

SOLUTION 10.2.7f

10.2.20

a. The p-value is about 0.0006.

b. If there is no association between name lengths and their scores, the probability we would get a sample correlation coefficient at least as extreme as 0.782 is about 0.0006.

c. We have strong evidence (p-value < 0.001) that there is an association between Scrabble points per letter of names and their Scrabble score and that that relationship is positive. We might cautiously generalize these results to statistics students like those in this study but we are not drawing any cause-and-effect conclusions from this observational study.

Section 10.3

10.3.1

B

10.3.3

a. Yes, the mean of the residuals is calculated as the sum of the residuals divided by the number of residuals. If the sum is zero, then zero divided by a positive number is also zero.

b. No, suppose that the least squares regression line does not go through any of the points on the scatterplot. Then none of the residuals would be zero, and if the 50th percentile fell on a residual it would necessarily be either negative or positive.

10.3.5

a. See applet output for Solution 10.3.5a and for an example of a negative slope coefficient.

b. See applet output for Solution 10.3.5b and for an example of a slope coefficient greater than 1.

c. See applet output for Solution 10.3.5c and for an example of a slope coefficient of zero.

10.3.7

a. Explanatory: number of pieces, response: price

b. The scatterplot for Solution 10.3.7b shows a strong positive linear association with no unusual observations.

c. $r = 0.974$

d. $r^2 = 0.949$. This means that 94.9% of the variation in price is explained by the linear association with number of pieces.

10.3.8

a. $\widehat{predicted\ price} = 4.86 + 0.105 \times pieces$

b. For each additional Lego piece, the estimate price increases 0.105 cents.

c. If there are no pieces in the Lego set, the predicted price is $4.86. Taken literally and in isolation, this interpretation is not meaningful, because no one would order zero pieces. (The large intercept suggests a substantial "fixed cost" to place an order regardless of the number of pieces.)

Sample data:

Use Data | Revert | Clear

n = 6

Show movable line: ☐

SOLUTION 10.3.5a

Sample data:

(explanatory,respone)

X	y
1	2
2	4
3	6
1	8
2	10
3	12

Use Data | Revert | Clear

n = 6

Show movable line: ☐

SOLUTION 10.3.5b

Sample data:

(explanatory,respone)

X	y
1	5
2	5
3	5
1	10
2	10
3	10

Use Data | Revert | Clear

n = 6

Show movable line: ☐

SOLUTION 10.3.5c

10.3.9

a. Correct but incomplete

b. Incorrect

c. Correct

d. Correct but incomplete

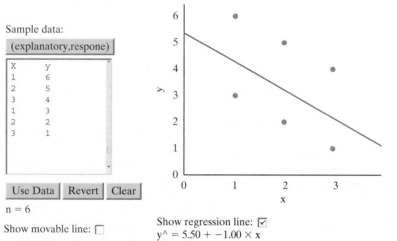

Show regression line: ☑
$y^\wedge = 5.50 + -1.00 \times x$

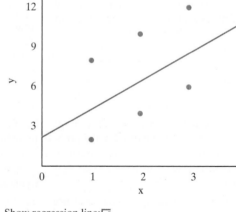

Show regression line: ☑
$y^\wedge = 3.00 + 2.00 \times x$

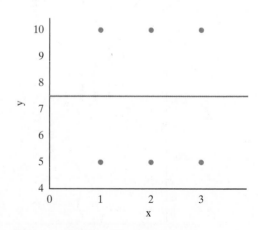

Show regression line: ☑
$y^\wedge = 7.50 + 00 \times x$

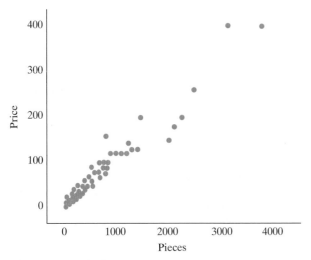

SOLUTION 10.3.7b

e. Correct

f. Correct

10.3.10

a. Incorrect

b. Correct

c. Incorrect

d. Incorrect

10.3.11

a. $57.36

b. $162.36

c. $105; [1,500 is 1,000 more pieces than 500 and 1,000 times the slope (0.105) gives $105].

d. $529.86

e. The data range from 34 pieces to 3,803 pieces. However, 5,000 pieces is beyond the range of the data and it is not clear that the linear relationship will hold beyond the range of the data, so there is not a lot of confidence in the predicted price for a 5,000-piece set.

10.3.12

a. $48.435

b. 49.99−48.44 = 1.55

c. The observed price is $1.55 above the predicted price for the set

d. Above, the residual is positive

10.3.13

a. It depends on which Lego set is offered for $0. If it is a Lego set that already doesn't cost very much, then no, the least squares line would not be impacted very much. If it is a Lego set that originally was very expensive, then yes, it would affect the least squares regression line.

b. Either of the sets that are $399.99. Choose the one with 3,803 pieces as this is the farthest away from the range of values for pieces.

c. Predicted price = 15.03 + 0.0756 (pieces), $r^2 = 0.636$; yes, they have changed quite a bit.

10.3.15

a. Moderately strong negative linear association

b. Predicted takeoff velocity = 394.47 − 0.0122 (bodymass)

c. For each additional gram of body mass the cat's predicted takeoff velocity decreases 0.0122 cm/sec.

d. For a cat whose body mass is zero the takeoff velocity is 394.47 cm/sec; this doesn't make sense in the context of the study because a cat wouldn't have a body mass of zero.

e. 24.6% of the variability seen in takeoff velocity is explained by the linear association with the body mass of the cat.

10.3.16

a. 333.47 cm/sec

b. 272.47 cm/sec. A 10,000-gram cat is beyond the range of the data and the linear relationship may not hold outside of this range.

c. A 7930-gram cat has observed takeoff velocity of 286.3 predicted takeoff velocity of 297.72, residual is −11.4. The predicted takeoff velocity is 11.4 cm/sec lower than the predicted takeoff velocity.

10.3.17

a. The cat with body mass 2,660 grams

b. The cat with body mass 7,930 grams

c. The cat with body mass 5,600 grams

d. The cat with body mass 3,550 grams

10.3.18

a. Percent body fat has the strongest association with takeoff velocity. It is a strong negative linear relationship.

b. Predicted takeoff velocity = 397.65 − 1.95 (bodyfat)

c. For each 1 percentage point increase in body fat the predicted takeoff velocity decreases 1.95 cm/sec.

d. $r^2 = 0.424$; 42.4% of the variability in takeoff velocities can be explained by the linear relationship with percent body fat.

10.3.20

a. The explanatory variable is the number of pages in the textbook. The response variable is the price of the textbook.

b. The equation of the least squares line is: predicted price = −3.42 + 0.1473 pages.

c. The predicted price of a 500-page textbook is: −3.42 + 0.1473 × 500 ≈ 70.23 dollars. The predicted price of a 1,500-page textbook is: −3.42 + 0.1473 × 1,500 ≈ 217.53 dollars. The first prediction is more believable, because 500 pages is within the range of the sample data, but no textbooks in the sample had close to 1,500 pages

d. The slope coefficient of 0.1473 means that for each additional page in a textbook the predicted price increases by about 0.1473 dollars, which is almost 15 cents.

e. The proportion of variability in textbook prices that is explained by knowing the number of pages is the square of the correlation coefficient, which is $r^2 = 0.677$, or 67.7%.

10.3.24

a. The answer to both questions is yes. The least squares line always goes through the "point of averages." If the fitted slope is positive, then values of x above the mean correspond to fitted values for y above the mean, and vice-versa.

b. If someone scores 79.8 on Test 2, the predicted score for Test 3 is 84.8. If they actually get 90 on Test 3, the residual is 90 − 84.8 = 5.2.

c. If someone scores 10 points *above* the mean on Test 2, the expected score on Test 3 is (0.3708)(10) = 3.708 points above the mean.

d. If someone scores 10 points *below* the mean on Test 2, the expected score on Test 3 is also 3.708 points below the mean.

10.3.25

a. 75.594, or 76

b. 90.426, or 90

c. The student who scored 55 on Test 2 is predicted to achieve a higher score on Test 3; the student who scored 95 on Test 2 is predicted to achieve a lower score on Test 3.

Section 10.3: Part 2

10.3.27

B

10.3.29

A

10.3.31

C

10.3.33

D. Because the slope $b = r (4/4) = r$, the slope has to be a number between -1 and 1, inclusive. So this means A and B are not correct. The point $(\bar{x}, \bar{y}) = (6, 5)$ must be on the line, so this means C and E are not correct. For example, in E, $5 \neq 2.6 - 0.4(6)$, but in D, $5 = 2.6 + 0.4(6)$.

10.3.35

a. No, because the predicted magical height for a 72 in. tall female is shorter at 69.8 in.

b. Yes, because the predicted magical height for a 72 in. tall male is taller at 74.4 in.

c. 67.27 in. You can get this by trial and error or by using the regression equation and have the magical height and the actual height be the same (x) and solve for $x = 30.89/(1 - 0.5408)$.

10.3.36

a. 2.50 in.

b. -0.42 in.

10.3.38

a. B, D

b. A, C, E

c. D

d. E

10.3.40

$b = -0.80(2/5) = -0.32$; $a = 2 - (-0.32)(7) = 4.24$. Therefore, $\hat{y} = 4.24 - 0.32x$.

10.3.42

a. $\widehat{social} = -12.7731 + 0.4612(temp)$, where $social$ is the predicted social warmth score and $temp$ is the body temperature in degrees Celsius.

b. Yes, because the residual plot (residuals vs. temp) shows no pattern.

c. The slope is 0.4612, which implies that as body temperature increases by 1°C, the

predicted social warmth scores increase by 0.4612 points.

d. 12.1%

e. $-12.7731 + 0.4612(37) = 4.2913$ points (on the 5-point scale).

f. The residual is $4.40 - 4.29 = 0.11$, which shows the actual social warmth score for this individual is 0.11 points higher than that predicted by the regression line.

g. The standard deviation of the residuals is 0.38 points. This is approximately the average distance by which the actual social warmth scores are away from their predicted values when using the least squares regression line to predict social warmth from physical warmth.

10.3.44

a. $\widehat{WPPSI} = 79.3935 + 0.2339(DAPIQ)$, where $\widehat{WPPSI}$ is the predicted Wechsler Preschool and Primary Scale of Intelligence score and $DAPIQ$ is the Draw-A-Person Intellectual Ability Test score.

b. Yes, because the residual plot (residuals vs. DAPIQ) shows no pattern.

c. The slope is 0.2339, which means as the Draw-A-Person Intellectual Ability Test score increases by 1 point, the predicted Wechsler Preschool and Primary Scale of Intelligence scores increase by 0.2339 points, on average.

d. The coefficient of determination is 9.0%, which is the percentage of the variation in the WPPSI scores that is explained by its linear relationship to the DAPIQ score.

e. $79.3935 + 0.2339(100) = 102.7835$ points.

f. The residual is $82 - 102.78 = -20.78$, which shows the WPPSI score for this individual is 20.78 points lower than that predicted by the regression line.

g. The standard deviation of the residuals is 10.98 points. This is approximately the average distance by which the actual WPPSI scores are away from their predicted values when using the least squares regression line to predict WPPSI score from DAPIQ.

h. The R^2 value is rather low and the s value is rather large, indicating that there is still a lot of variation in the WPPSI scores not accounted for by this model. We would only be able to predict the WPPSI scores to within about $2 \times 11 = 22$ points.

10.3.46

a. $\widehat{Armspan} = -3.04 + 1.04(Height)$.

b. Yes, because the residuals show no pattern.

c. The slope is 1.04, meaning that as height increases by 1 cm, arm span increases by 1.04 cm.

d. R^2 is 68.5%, meaning that 68.5% of the variation in arm span can be explained by its linear relationship with height.

e. $180 - 186.24 = -6.24$ in.. This individual's actual height is 6.24 in. below his or her predicted height.

Section 10.3: Part 3

10.3.47

B, C, E

10.3.49

B

10.3.51

C

10.3.53

D

10.3.55

a. See table below.

log (x)	0	0.301	0.477	0.602	0.699
log (x^2)	0	0.602	0.954	1.204	1.398

b. It is a linear function because there is a constant slope of 2. For example, $(0.954 - 0.602)/(0.477 - 0.301) = 2$. For every increase in 1 for log(x), the y-value (log x^2) increases by 2.

10.3.57

a. The three graphs are shown below and ln x vs. ln y is clearly the one that best fits a linear model.

b. power

c. ln $y = -1.44 + 2.02$ ln x.

d. ln $y = -1.44 + 2.02$ ln $5 = 1.811$, $e^{1.811} = 612$. Our prediction of 6.12 is very close to the actual value of 6.

x vs. ln y

ln *x* vs. *y*

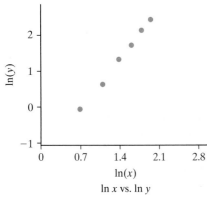

ln *x* vs. ln *y*

10.3.59

a. $\log(\widehat{weight}) = 0.6162 + 0.3594(\log(age))$.

b. $\log(\widehat{weight}) = 1.0041$, $10^{1.0041} = 10.1$ kg. The predicted weight is slightly less than the reported median weight of 10.3 kg.

c. $\log(\widehat{weight}) = 0.6162 + 0.3594(\log(15 \times 12)) = 1.4267$, $10^{1.4267} = 26.71$ kg $= 58.8$ lb. The predicted weight for a 15-year-old is not

accurate because it is far too low. This model for growth does not continue until a child is 15 years old, and extrapolating (making predictions for ages far outside the observed ages) can lead to very inaccurate predictions.

10.3.61

a. $\widehat{period}^2 = 0.0437 + 0.1044(length)$.

b. $\widehat{period}^2 = 1.2965$, $\widehat{period} = 1.138$ sec.

c. $1^2 = 0.0437 + 0.1044(length)$, $length = 9.16$ in.

10.3.63

a. $\log(\widehat{temp\ above}\ 20) = 1.6462 - 0.0081(time)$.

b. $\log(\widehat{temp\ above}\ 20) = 1.160210^{1.1602} = 14.46$. The temperature of the probe is predicted to be another 20 degrees higher $= 34.46°C$.

c. $\log(1) = 1.6462 - 0.0081(time)$, $time = (\log(1) - 1.6462/(-0.0081) = 203.23$ sec.

10.3.65

a. A power model better fits the data because the relationship is more linear (in fact, the correlation for the $\log(distance)$ vs. log $(time)$ is 1). See graphs in Solution 10.3.65a below.

b. predicted $\log(time) = 0 + 1.50(\log (distance))$. *Note:* This *corresponds* nicely to Kepler's Third Law: $revolution^2 \propto distance^3$ or $revolution \propto distance^{3/2}$ or $\log(revolution) \propto 1.5 \log(distance)$.

c. predicted $\log(time) = 0 + 1.50(\log (5.5)) = 1.1105$, $10^{1.1105} = 12.90$ earth years.

Section 10.4

10.4.1

A

10.4.3

Write the heights on 10 different slips of paper and foot lengths on 10 different slips of paper. Lay the 10 slips of paper with the heights written on them in a line on a flat surface. Shuffle the 10 slips of paper with the foot lengths on them and deal one out to each of the 10 slips of paper with the heights on them. Calculate the least squares regression equation for these 10 pairs of data and record the slope. Repeat this procedure 1,000 times to get 1,000 simulated slopes which make up the null distribution.

10.4.5

Lay the 20 slips of paper with the heights written on them in a line on a flat surface. Shuffle the 20 slips of paper with the vertical leap distances on them and deal one out to each of the 20 slips of paper with the heights on them. Calculate the least squares regression equation for these 20 pairs of data and record the slope. Repeat this procedure 1,000 times to get 1,000 simulated slopes which make up the null distribution.

10.4.9

a. Hours of sleep the previous night

b. Seconds needed to complete a paper and pencil maze

SOLUTION 10.3.65a

c. i) 1, ii) no, strong evidence is found when the observed statistic is 2 or more SDs away from the mean under the null, 7.76 is only 1 SD away.

10.4.10

a. For each additional hour of sleep per night the predicted number of seconds needed to complete the maze decreases by 7.76.

b. 19.33 is the predicted amount of time for someone who didn't sleep the previous night. This is extrapolation because no one in the sample pulled an all-nighter.

10.4.13

a. H_0: No association between year of manufacture and price and H_a: There is an association between year of manufacture and price.

b. Count the number of simulated slopes that are at least as extreme as the observed slope and divide by 1,000. The p-value is 0.

c. With a p-value of 0 we have very strong evidence against the null and in favor of the alternative that the slope describing the association between the number of years before 2006 a Honda Civic was manufactured and the sale price is different from zero. Based on our simulation, which assumed there was no association between number of years before 2006 a Honda Civic was manufactured and its sale price, not once did we find a simulated slope that was as steep as the one from the original data.

10.4.14

a. Predicted price = $18,785.31 − 1,397.47 (age)

b. Slope: For every additional year of age the price drops $1,397.47. Intercept: A car from 2006 (current model year) has a predicted price of $18,785.31.

10.4.17

a. Null: There is no association between height and haircut price in the population of students. Alt: There is an association between height and haircut price in the population of students.

b. p-value = 0.007

c. With a p-value of 0.007 we have very strong evidence against the null and in favor of the alternative that the slope describing the association between height and amount of last haircut is different from zero. It appears to be a negative association (taller people tend to spend less on haircuts).

d. No, this is an observational study and there are many potential confounding variables (like whether the person is male or female) that may explain the variability in haircut costs.

10.4.18

a. Predicted haircut price = 160.66 − 1.92 (height)

b. Slope: For every additional inch taller someone is, their predicted haircut price drops $1.92. Intercept: For someone who is 0 inches tall, the predicted price of their last haircut is $160.66 (although this is extrapolation).

10.4.21

a. H_0: There is no association between missing class and GPA in the population of students and H_a: There is an association between missing class and GPA in the population of students.

b. p-value = 0

c. With a p-value of 0 we have very strong evidence against the null and in favor of the alternative that the slope describing the association between number of classes skipped in the past three weeks and GPA is different from zero. There is a negative association; that is, people taking more classes tend to have lower GPAs.

d. No, this is an observational study and there are many potential confounding variables that may explain the variability in GPA.

10.4.23

a. H_0: There is no association between age and the time it takes to read a list of 20 color words. H_a: There is an association between age and the time it takes to read a list of 20 color words.

b. $b = 0.2383$. For each additional year it is predicted to take 0.2383 sec longer to read the 20 color words.

c. p-value = 0.003

d. A p-value of 0.003 provides very strong evidence against the null and in favor of there being an association between age and the time in seconds it takes for someone to read 20 color words. The association is positive; older people tend to take longer to read the 20 color words.

10.4.24

a. p-value = 0.188. Results are no longer significant.

b. p-value = 0. Yes, it is a significant result.

c. For ages 18–80, there is very strong evidence of an association between age and time to read 20 color words. As one moves beyond the range of the data, the linear model may not be the best model to describe the data and predictions using the linear model beyond the 18–80 age range may not be good predictions.

Section 10.5

10.5.1

A

10.5.3

A

10.5.5

To see whether or not you get a different conclusion

10.5.7

a. Predicted time in seconds = 198.33 − 7.76 (hours sleep)

b. 0.3052

c. 0.1526

10.5.10

a. In the population, β is the average amount the guessed weight changes when the guessed height increases by 1 inch.

b. H_0: $\beta = 0$, H_a: $\beta \neq 0$

c. Yes, the three validity conditions (linear trend, similar distributions, and equal spread around the line) are all reasonably well met for this data set.

d. p-value = 0.0159 provides strong evidence against the null and in support of there being an association between the guessed height and guessed weight for the professor.

10.5.13

a. In the population of all Honda Civics, the slope tells how much the price changes on average for each year older the car is; β is the symbol for the population slope.

b. H_0: $\beta = 0$, H_a: $\beta \neq 0$

c. Yes, the three validity conditions (linear trend, similar distributions, and equal spread around the line) are all reasonably well met for this dataset.

d. p-value = 0

e. With a p-value of 0 we have very strong evidence against the null and in favor of the alternative that the population slope describing the association between the number of years before 2006 a Honda Civic was manufactured and the sale price is different from zero.

10.5.14

a. (−1,603.93, −1,191.02). We are 95% confident that in the population of all Honda Civics for each additional year in age of a Honda Civic, the average sale price decreases between $1,191.02 and $1,603.93.

b. Yes, the entire interval is negative indicating a negative association (so as one variable increases (age of car) the other tends to decrease (sale price)).

10.5.16

a. In the population, slope tells us how much BMI changes on average for each additional inch in height; β is the symbol for the population slope.

b. $H_0: \beta = 0$, $H_a: \beta \neq 0$

c. Yes, the three validity conditions (linear trend, similar distributions, and equal spread around the line) are all reasonably well met for this dataset.

d. p-value = 0.0417

e. The p-value provides strong evidence against the null and in support of there being an association between BMI and height.

10.5.17

a. (−0.3033, −0.0060). We are 95% confident that, in the population, for each additional inch in height the average BMI decreases by between 0.0060 and 0.3003.

b. Yes, zero is not in the confidence interval and thus is not a plausible value for the population slope.

10.5.19

a. In the population the slope, β, is how much height in inches changes on average for each additional hour of sleep.

b. $H_0: \beta = 0$, $H_a: \beta < 0$

c. p-value = 0.0328 provides us with strong evidence against the null and in support of there being a negative association between amount of sleep per night in hours and height in inches.

d. The new p-value = 0.3622. Now we do not have strong evidence of a negative association between hours slept and height in inches.

Section 10.6

10.6.1

B

10.6.3

A

10.6.5

D

10.6.7

D

10.6.10

a. $\widehat{mag.ht.} = 30.4647 + 0.5486(act.ht.)$

b. 0.0000 (with t-ratio 5.04).

10.6.11 $0.5486 \pm 2.704(0.1088) = (0.2544, 0.8428)$. This means that we are 99% confident that the slope of the regression line in the population is between 0.2544 and 0.8428.

10.6.14 The strength of a linear relationship is measured by the correlation coefficient or by the coefficient of determination (r^2). The closer the correlation coefficient is to ± 1, the stronger the relationship. Strong evidence of a relationship is measured by the p-value when you are testing the slope of a regression line. The smaller it is, the stronger the evidence.

10.6.16

a. The standard error for the slope is 7.50. This is a measure of how much we would expect the slopes of the sample regression lines predicting the time to complete a maze given the number of hours of sleep the previous night to vary from sample to sample if we repeatedly sampled from a population with no association.

b. Although the scatterplot looks reasonably linear and the residual plot does not show a strong pattern or change in variation across the sleep values, the validity conditions are not met in the data because the histogram of the residuals is not roughly normal (though we might be OK with the moderate sample size).

c. If we let β represent the slope of the population regression line between times to complete the puzzle and amount of sleep, then we can write out our hypotheses as $H_0: \beta = 0$ (no association) and $H_0: \beta < 0$ (negative association). Even though the validity conditions for a theory-based test are not met, we could still do a simulation-based test on the data. This could involve reshuffling which times are matched to which sleep amounts to see whether a slope as small or smaller than −7.76 occurs often by chance alone.

d. Even if we found a small p-value, we could not draw a cause-and-effect conclusion from this observational study (the student researchers asked about the amount of sleep; they did not influence how much sleep the subjects got the night before). It's

also unclear whether these 64 subjects can be considered a random sample.

10.6.18

a. The standard error for the slope is 0.0753. This is a measure of how much we would expect the slopes of the sample regression lines predicting the WPPSI score given the DAPIQ to vary from sample to sample if we repeatedly sampled from a population with no association.

b. The validity conditions are met in the data because the scatterplot is linear with no pattern in the residual plot, the histogram of the residuals is roughly normal, and the variance of the residuals is about the same for all the values of the explanatory variable. We are not given much information about how the 100 children were selected for this study but we can assume the observations are independent.

c. If we let β represent the slope of the population regression line between the DAPIQ and WPPSI scores, then we can write out our hypotheses as $H_0: \beta = 0$ (no association) and $H_0: \beta \neq 0$ (is an association). Given that we considered the validity conditions met, then with a t-value of 3.10 (df = 98) and p-value of $0.0025 < 0.05$, there is strong evidence of a linear association between the WPPSI score and DAPIQ in the population of four- and five-year-old children represented by this sample.

d. The df = 100 − 2 = 98. Using Table B and df = 80, we get $t^* = 2.639$ for 99% confidence and a confidence interval of $0.2339 \pm 2.639(0.0753) = (0.0352, 0.4326)$. Using the calculator to find the critical t for 98 df, we get $t^* = 2.627$ and a confidence interval of $0.2339 \pm 2.627(0.0753) = (0.0361, 0.4317)$. We are 99% confident that a one-point increase in the DAPIQ is associated with an expected increase of 0.036 to 0.432 points in the WPSI scale in the population of four- and five-year-old children represented by this sample.

e. Both the small p-value (less than 0.01) and a 99% confidence interval that does not include 0 lead us to the same conclusion of very strong evidence of a linear association between the WPPSI score and DAPIQ. *Note:* Even though the association is *statistically significant*, it is not a very *strong* association, as measured by the coefficient of determination.

10.6.20

a. The standard error for the slope is 1.60. This is a measure of how much we would expect the slopes of the sample regression lines predicting the percentage of time someone is left-brained given his or her age to vary from sample to sample if we repeatedly sampled from a population with no association.

b. The validity conditions are met in the data because the scatterplot is linear with no pattern in the residual plot, the histogram of the residuals is roughly normal, and the variance of the residuals is about the same for all the values of the explanatory variable.

c. If we let β represent the slope of the population regression line between left-brain percentage and age, then we can write out our hypotheses as $H_0: \beta = 0$ (no association) and $H_0: \beta \neq 0$ (is an association). With the validity conditions met and a t-statistic of 2.04 (df = 87) and a p-value of $0.0446 < 0.05$, there is (just) strong evidence of a linear association between left-brain percentage and age in the population represented by these 89 college students.

d. The df = $89 - 2 = 87$. Using Table B and df = 80 with 90% confidence, we get $t^* = 1.664$ and a confidence interval of $3.26 \pm 1.664(1.60) = (0.5976, 5.9224)$. Using the calculator to find the critical t for 87 df of 90% confidence, we get $t^* = 1.663$ and the confidence interval of $3.26 \pm 1.663(1.60) = (0.5992, 5.9208)$. We are 90% confident that each one-year increase in age is associated with an expected 0.60 to 5.92 percentage point increase in left-brain percentage for the population represented by these college students.

e. Both the small p-value (less than 0.10) and a 90% confidence interval that does not include 0 lead us to the same conclusion. *Note:* Even though the association is *statistically significant*, it is not a very *strong* association, as measured by the coefficient of determination.

End of chapter

10.CE.1

a. $r = 1$. As midterm scores increase so do final exam scores and every final exam score is the same amount higher than the midterm score.

b. $r = 1$. As midterm scores increase so do final exam scores and every final exam score is the same amount lower than the midterm score.

c. $r = 1$. As midterm scores increase so do final exam scores and every final exam score is the same factor higher than the midterm score.

10.CE.3

Answers will vary. The scatterplots shown for Solutions 10.CE.3a–e give examples of correct answers where age is in years and distance is in miles from school.

a. See dotplot 10.CE.3a.

b. See dotplot 10.CE.3b.

c. See dotplot 10.CE.3c.

d. See dotplot 10.CE.3d.

e. See dotplot 10.CE.3e.

SOLUTION 10.CE.3a

SOLUTION 10.CE.3b

SOLUTION 10.CE.3c

SOLUTION 10.CE.3d

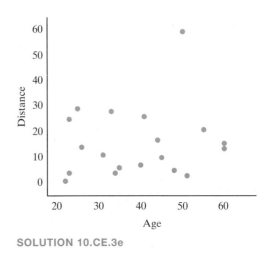

SOLUTION 10.CE.3e

10.CE.5

a. As seen in the scatterplot for Solution 10.CE.5a there is a weak negative linear association between the time to take the test and the score on the test.

b. $r = -0.035$

c. p-value = 0.8420. See screenshot of null distribution for Solution 10.CE.5c.

d. $t = -0.19$, p-value = 0.8481

e. Both simulation-based and theory-based tests of significance offer weak evidence against the null and so it is plausible that there is no association between time to take a test and score on the test.

10.CE.6

a. Predicted score = $73.74 - 0.0604$ (time)

b. For each additional minute needed to take the test, the predicted test score drops 0.0604 points.

c. If you take 0 min to take the exam, your predicted score is 73.74. This doesn't make sense in the context of the problem.

d. $r^2 = 0.001$ so 0.1% of the variation in test scores can be explained by the linear association with time to take the test.

10.CE.7

a. $t = -0.19$, p-value = 0.8481

b. $(-0.6978, 0.5771)$

c. We are 95% confident that, in the population, for each additional minute taken on the test the average score decreases by as much as 0.6978 points or increases by as much as 0.5771 points.

d. This is consistent with the test result because 0 is a plausible value for the population slope coefficient and we found weak evidence against the null of no association between time to take test and score on test.

10.CE.10

a. $H_0: \beta = 0$, $H_a: \beta \neq 0$, $t = 19.05$, p-value $= 0$. We have very strong evidence against the null and in support of an association between distance in miles of a hike and time in minutes the hike takes, specifically the more miles in a hike, the longer it will take on average.

SOLUTION 10.CE.5a

SOLUTION 10.CE.5c

b. (28.18, 34.77). We are 95% confident that on average each additional mile in a hike increases the time it takes to make the hike by between 28.18 and 34.77 minutes.

10.CE.11

a. H_0: $\beta = 0$, H_a: $\beta \neq 0$, $t = 3.07$, p-value = 0.003. We have very strong evidence against the null and in support of an association between elevation gain in feet of a hike and time in minutes the hike takes, specifically the higher the elevation gain of a hike, the longer it will take on average.

b. (0.0217, 0.1020). We are 95% confident that in the long run each additional foot gain in elevation in a hike increases the time it takes to make the hike by between 0.0217 and 0.102 minutes on average.

10.CE.13

a. H_0: $\rho = 0$

b. H_a: $\rho > 0$

c. Professor's arrival time in minutes early (or late) is the explanatory variables and students' average arrival time in minutes early (or late) is the response variable.

d. $0.107 <$ p-value < 0.155

e. We have little evidence against the null and in support of the alternative that there is a positive correlation between the time a professor arrives for class and the average time the students arrive for class.

f. H_a: $\rho \neq 0$ and $0.190 <$ p-value < 0.304

g. No, this is an observational study and there are many possible confounding variables present so cause-and-effect conclusions can't be made.

10.CE.15

Corr/Slope A B C D E F

Scatterplot F C D A E B

10.CE.16

a. A and E

b. C, D, and F

c. B

10.CE.17

a. For restaurants, the correlation between average noise level and time becomes *weaker* if you exclude the two lunchtime measurements.

b. For stores, the noise level *is not* related to time of day.

c. For the "other" locations, the suggestion of a possible relationship between noise level and time of day becomes *stronger* if you exclude the gym measured at 6:30 PM.

d. On average, restaurants are *more* noisy than stores.

e. On average, decibel levels measured later in the day tend to be *higher* than those measured earlier in the day.

f. Time of day *is* confounded with type of location.

g. For *restaurants* the fitted noise level increases by more than 10 dB during the three hours from 7 to 10 PM.

h. If you go by the fitted line for all restaurants, the predicted decibel level at 4 PM is closest to 90 dB to the nearest 10.

10.CE.18

a. The obstacle to reaching a conclusion about the effect of time is that location and time of day are confounded. For example, most restaurants were observed late in the day and were loud. Most stores were observed early in the day and were not loud. There is no way—based on this badly planned data set—to disentangle the effects of location from effects of time of day.

b. A better design would measure noise levels at different times for each location.

10.CE.19

a. At the y-intercept the decibel level is about 55dB. (Between 12 and midnight the fitted level goes up 20, so from 12 back to zero the fitted level goes down 20, from 75 to 55.)

b. The fitted level of 55 cannot be correct, because 0 corresponds to midnight (24), for which the fitted level is 95dB.

10.CE.20

The first histogram is for Plot A, all locations. The second is for Plot B, restaurants. The third is for Plot C, stores. All histograms are centered at 0 (the null hypothesis of no association), but the histograms differ in the size of their variability. The first (black) histogram is least spread out, with almost all outcomes between −0.50 and 0.50. The last histogram is the most spread out, with the smallest percentage of outcomes between −0.5 and 0.5. The size of variability is negatively correlated with sample size: The larger the sample, the smaller the variability. Thus

the first histogram is for the largest of the three samples, and the last histogram is for the smallest of the three.

10.CE.22

a. Correlation should be *strong and positive*: For states with large populations, both vote totals will be large. For states with small populations, both vote totals will be small.

b. Correlation will be *positive and very strong*. A state's electoral vote total is roughly proportional to its population, so states with large populations will have large numbers of electoral votes, and vice-versa. (In more detail, the number of electoral votes is equal to its number of senators plus number of representatives. Each state has two senators and its number of representatives is proportional to its population, so (electoral vote) $\approx 2 + k \times$ (population size), where k is a positive constant.

c. Correlation will be *strong and positive*, because both numbers are related to population size. States with larger populations will have more attorneys and more McDonald's restaurants. States with smaller populations will have fewer of both.

d. Correlation will be *strong and positive* because, as a rule, graduation from high school is a requirement for applying to college. States with high rates of graduation from high school will tend to have higher percentages of college graduates.

e. Correlation will be *strong and negative*. In fact the correlation will equal −1 because there is a perfect linear relationship with slope −1: (year of statehood) + (years as a state) = (current year).

f. Correlations will be *positive and moderate*. The U.S. was settled from east to west, which means that as a rule the year of statehood is earlier (lower) for eastern states and later (higher) for western states. Longitude also increases as you go from east to west in the U.S. Thus both quantitative variables tend to increase together as you go from east to west.

g. Correlation will be *near zero*, because there is no systematic relationship between a state's north-south location and its east-west location.

h. Correlation will be *negative and moderate*. As a rule, southern states (lower latitudes) tend to have warmer (larger) average annual temperatures, whereas northern states (higher latitudes) tend to have colder (lower) annual temperatures.

CHAPTER 11

Section 11.1

11.1.1

C

11.1.3

C

11.1.5

A

11.1.7

Number the index cards 1, 2, and 3 (they each represent a phone). Shuffle them and place them on the table in spots labeled 1, 2, and 3. If all the numbers on the cards fail to match all the numbered spots on the table, call that a success; anything else call a failure. Repeat this 1,000 times. The number of successes divided by 1,000 is an estimate for the probability none of them would get their own phones.

11.1.10

With 2 babies the probability is 0.5 that they both are returned to the correct mothers. As the number of babies increases, the probability they all are returned to the correct mothers goes down. For 4 mothers the probability is 0.0417. For 6 mothers the probability is 0.0014. For 8 mothers the probability is 0.0007.

11.1.11

With 2 babies the probability is 0.5 that at least one is returned to the correct mother. For 4, 6, and 8 babies, the probabilities that at least one is returned to the correct mother are all very similar, around 0.63.

11.1.12

The average number of babies returned to the correct mother is always 1.

11.1.14

a. $1/6(1/6)(2) + 1/6(2/6)(4) = 10/36$.

b. $(1, 2) (1, 3) (1, 4) (1, 5) (1, 6) (2, 1) (2, 3) (2, 4) (2, 5) (2, 6) (3, 1) (3, 2) (3, 4) (3, 5) (3, 6) (4, 1) (4, 2) (4, 3) (4, 5) (4, 6) (5, 1) (5, 2) (5, 3) (5, 4) (5, 6) (6, 1) (6, 2) (6, 3) (6, 4) (6, 5)$ P(consecutive) = 10/30.

c. The cards. This makes sense because while the numerator is the same, six pairs were eliminated from the denominator when we switched to the cards; therefore, that probability increased in value.

11.1.16

a. $B_1B_2B_3B_4, G_1B_2B_3B_4, B_1G_2B_3B_4, B_1B_2G_3B_4, B_1B_2B_3G_4, G_1G_2B_3B_4, G_1B_2G_3B_4, G_1B_2B_3G_4, B_1G_2G_3B_4, B_1G_2B_3G_4, B_1B_2G_3G_4, G_1G_2G_3B_4, G_1G_2B_3G_4, G_1B_2G_3G_4, B_1G_2G_3G_4, G_1G_2G_3G_4$.

b. $B_1B_2B_3B_4, G_1B_2B_3B_4, B_1G_2B_3B_4, B_1B_2G_3B_4, B_1B_2B_3G_4$.

c. $2/16 = 1/8$.

d. A 3 to 1 breakdown is more likely because this probability is 8/16, whereas that for two boys and two girls is 6/16.

11.1.19

a. H_6H_7; $H_6T_7H_8$; $T_6H_7H_8$; $T_6T_7H_8H_9$; $T_6H_7T_8H_9$; $H_6T_7T_8H_9$; $T_6T_7T_8$; $H_6T_7T_8T_9$; $T_6H_7T_8T_9$; $T_6T_7H_8T_9$.

b. Heather wins on the first 6 listed in part (a) and Tom wins on the last 4 listed.

c. No, as they are different length sequences, the probabilities won't all be the same.

11.1.20

a. Flip four coins and count the number of heads. Repeat this until you have done it 1,000 times. Count how many times 2 or more heads occurred. Divide that number by 1,000 and that is an estimate for the probability that Heather would win.

b. 0.687163.

c. 0.750627.

Section 11.2

11.2.1

A and D

11.2.3

C

11.2.5

E

11.2.7

a. 0.6.

b. 0.5.

c. 0.7.

d. No, because $P(A \text{ and } B) \neq 0$.

e.

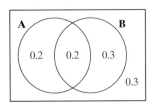

11.2.9

a. HHH, HHT, HTH, THH, TTH, THT, HTT, TTT.

b. (i) 1/8.

(ii) 3/8.

(iii) 7/8.

(iv) 1/8.

11.2.11

a.

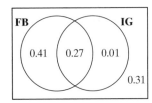

b. 0.28.

c. 0.27.

d. 0.69.

e. 0.31.

11.2.12

The events are not mutually exclusive. To be mutually exclusive, there would need to be no one who uses both Facebook and Instagram.

11.2.15

a. $1 - (0.42 + 0.10 + 0.04) = 0.44$.

b. $0.42 + 0.44 = 0.86$.

c. $1 - 0.42 = 0.58$.

11.2.18

a. $1,955/3,222 \approx 0.6068$.

b. $789/3,222 \approx 0.2449$.

c. $457/3,222 \approx 0.1418$.

d. $(1,955 + 332)/3,222 = 2,287/3,222 \approx 0.7098$.

e. Because it is measuring those who are not female and not sophomores, it is measuring those males who are freshmen, juniors, seniors, or non-degree, which is $935/3,222 \approx 0.2902$.

f. Because it is measuring those who are neither female nor sophomores, it is measuring those males who are freshmen, juniors, seniors, or non-degree, which is

935/3,222 ≈ 0.2902, the same as in the previous question.

11.2.19

a. 1,267/3,222 ≈ 0.3932.

b. 264/3,222 ≈ 0.0819.

c. (1,267 + 445)/3,222 = 1,712/3,222 ≈ 0.5313.

d. 264/1,267 ≈ 0.2084.

e. 264/709 ≈ 0.3724.

Section 11.3

11.3.1

A

11.3.3

B

11.3.5

B, D, G

11.3.7

a. 0.2/0.5 = 0.4.

b. 0.2/0.4 = 0.5.

c. 0.4 + 0.5 − 0.2 = 0.7.

d. Yes, because $P(A \text{ and } B) = P(A)P(B) = 0.2$.

e. See below.

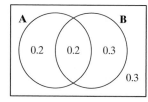

11.3.9

a. TTT, TTH, THT, HTT, HHT, HTH, THH, HHH.

b. **(i)** 7/8.

(ii) 3/4.

(iii) There are 7 outcomes with at least one tail and 3 of these start with H: 3/7.

11.3.10

a. 1/7.

b. 1/4.

c. 1/4.

d. 1/2.

11.3.12

a. 0.20/0.21 = 0.95.

b. 0.20/0.68 = 0.29.

11.3.14

a. $0.65 = P(I|T) = P(I \text{ and } T)/0.21$, so P(I and T) = 0.21 × 0.65 = 0.14.

		Twitter		
		Yes	No	Total
Instagram	Yes	0.14	0.14	0.28
	No	0.07	0.65	0.72
	Total	0.21	0.79	1.00

b. 0.14/0.28 = 0.50.

c. 0.14.

d. 0.65.

11.3.15

No. They would be independent if the proportion of Twitter users in the entire population was the same as the proportion of Twitter users among the Instagram users. In other words, $P(T) = P(T|I)$.

11.3.18

a. (0.61)(0.40) = 0.24.

b. (0.39)(0.30) = 0.12.

c. 0.24 + 0.12 = 0.36.

11.3.20

a. $0.42^5 = 0.013$.

b. $0.58^5 = 0.066$.

c. 1 − 0.066 = 0.934.

11.3.22

a. 0.56 + 0.35 = 0.91.

b. 0.35/0.91 = 0.38.

11.3.24

a.

	Banded	Unbanded	Total
Survived	24	24	48
Died	26	26	52
Total	50	50	100

b. If there is no association, the two conditional proportions of survival must be the same. The only way they can be the same is if they are the same as the overall proportion of survival. So we would need all three values to equal 0.48 in the penguin study. If surviving is independent of being banded, then the probability of surviving given being banded needs to be the same as the probability of surviving. This is what we said had to happen if there was no association and we used the idea of proportion instead of probability. Again, these are both 0.48 in the penguin study.

Section 11.4

11.4.2

D

11.4.3

C

11.4.4

B

11.4.6

a.

x	0	1	2	3
P(x)	1/8	3/8	3/8	1/8

b. The event when exactly 2 coins land heads up.

c. The probability exactly 2 of the 3 coins land heads up is 3/8.

d. The probability 2 or fewer of the 3 coins land heads up is 7/8.

11.4.8

a. The probability that a randomly chosen family household has exactly 4 members is 0.1936.

b. The probability that a randomly chosen family household has more than 4 members is 0.0906 + 0.0341 + 0.0192 = 0.1439.

c. The probability that a randomly chosen family household has 4 or more members is 0.1936 + 0.1439 = 0.3375.

11.4.10

a. 9/24.

b. 15/24.

c. If 3 people draw their own names, then the only name left to draw must be that of the person that hasn't drawn. So if we know 3 people have drawn their own names, we also know all 4 of them must.

11.4.11

a. 3.1149.

b. 1.2633

11.4.13

a. 1.

b. 1.

11.4.15

a. The expected payout of wheel B is $2.33, the same as that of wheel A.

b. The SD of wheel B is $1.1785, much smaller than that of wheel A.

c. Answers will vary. Both will give the same average outcome in the long run, but you are just spinning it once. Those who like taking chances may tend to pick wheel A, as the chance exists to win a larger amount of money than anything on wheel B. Those that are more cautious may pick wheel B as there is a greater chance that you will win something.

11.4.16

a. $1.0017.

b. For wheel A the SD is $6.8475 and the average distance is $3.775. For wheel B the SD is $1.1785 and the average distance is $1.0017. So for wheel A they are not similar (because the $25 payout is an outlier), but for wheel B they are similar because there are no outliers.

11.4.18

a.

x	0	6	10
$P(x)$	25/36	5/36	1/6

b. The expected value is $90/36 = 2.50$, meaning that you can expect to win about $2.40 per game, on average, in the long run.

c. You would have to pay $2.50 per game.

11.4.20

a. 0.477.

b. 0.523.

c. 3.441.

d. 2.462

Section 11.5

11.5.1

B

11.5.2

A

11.5.5

D

11.5.7

a. 7.

b. 2.4152.

c. Mean of 8 and SD of 2.4152.

d. Mean of 14 and SD of 4.8304.

11.5.9

a. 16/36.

b. 20/36.

c. $E(X) = (1)(16/36) + (-1)(20/36) = -4/36$. You can expect to lose $0.11, on average, per game.

11.5.11

a. $-2/38 = -$0.0526$ (you are expected to lose about 5 cents).

b. $5.7626.

c. $-$0.1578.

d. $9.9811.

11.5.13

a.

x	-2	34	70
$P(x)$	0.9481	0.05125	0.000693

b. $-$0.1052.

c. $8.150

11.5.16

Mean of 8.72 and SD of 2.45.

11.5.19

Mean of 36.725°F and SD of 0.388°F.

Section 11.6

11.6.1

A

11.6.3

B. In C, the probability of a yes response presumably differs in the two locations.

11.6.5

(I) would be better modeled with a binomial distribution because the probability of success (picking a female) is much closer to the same value for each student picked because the population size is large compared to the sample size.

11.6.7

a. 0.0548.

b. 0.2516.

c. 0.7712.

d. Not necessarily. The probability that a household in a single neighborhood has Internet access could be much different from what it is nationally.

11.6.9

a. (i) $1 - 0.357 = 0.643$.

(ii) $0.643^4 = 0.1709$.

(iii) $1 - 0.1709 = 0.8291$.

b. $0.8291^{56} = 0.0000276$.

c. The estimate should be larger, as there are many sets of 56 consecutive games in 1941, not just one.

11.6.12

a. Let X represent the number of no-shows. X follows a binomial probability distribution with $n = 44$ and $\pi = 0.05$. We want to find $P(X < 2) = P(X \le 1) = 0.3471$.

b. $P(X \ge 2) = 0.6529$.

c. $E(X) = 44(0.95) = 41.8$ passengers.

11.6.14

a. Let X represent the number of winners in 3 cups. X follows a binomial distribution with $n = 3$ and $\pi = 0.1667$. $P(X = 1) = 0.3473$.

b. $1 - P(X = 0) = 0.4214$.

c. Let Y represent the number of cups before the first winner. Y follows a geometric distribution with $\pi = 0.1667$. $P(Y = 3) = 0.1158$.

d. $P(Y \le 3) = 0.4214$.

11.6.17

a. 0.4043.

b. 0.7293.

c. 0.0809.

d. 0.7293.

11.6.18

a. 1.15.

b. 4.348.

11.6.19

3 years. The probability of getting in exactly once in 1, 2, or 3 years (if you enter until you get in and then stop) is 0.5435.

11.6.22

a. (i) 0.2373.

(ii) 0.9990.

b. (i) 0.0117.

(ii) $P(X < 4) = 0.9844$.

Section 11.7

11.7.1

B

11.7.3

D

11.7.4

B

11.7.6

E

11.7.8

a. 68%.

b. 95%.

c. 95%/2 = 47.5%.

d. 47.5% + 34% = 81.5%.

11.7.10

a. 0.00135.

b. 130.8 and above.

c. No.

11.7.12

a. 0.01066.

b. About 4,547 g and above.

11.7.14

a. 82nd (0.8233),

b. 1,339.1 or above.

11.7.16

a. 0.9.

b. 66.3 in.

11.7.18

a. 0.1841.

b. $P(X = 3) = 4(0.1841)^3(0.8159)^1 = 0.0204$.

c. $P(X = 3) + P(X = 4) = 0.0204 + (0.1841^4) = 0.0215$.

11.7.20

a. 0.3821.

b. 38th.

Section 11.8

11.8.1

B

11.8.3

B

11.8.5

B

11.8.7

0.0918

11.8.8

0.3427

11.8.10

a. 0.7458.

b. Assuming a larger percentage, the distribution will shift to the right. Then the peak of the distribution will no longer be in the middle of our interval, so the area under the curve between 0.17 and 0.21 will decrease (assuming not much change in SD).

11.8.12

a. 0.5708.

b. 0.8253.

c. The probability in (b) is larger because the interval of interest is still centered at the mean of the distribution but is now wider.

11.8.14

a. 0.1333.

b. 0.0065 (with SD = 201.25 g).

11.8.16

a. 0.8491.

b. 0.9982.

11.8.18

a. 0.1265.

b. 0.005296 (with SD = 1.252).

End of chapter exercises

11.CE.1

C

11.CE.3

A

11.CE.5

Each index card would represent a different prize. Shuffle the cards and randomly draw one. Note which prize it is. Repeat this process until you have drawn all four prizes. The number of drawings it took you to get all four prizes is a value in the distribution. Repeat this process many, many times (say, 1,000 or 10,000 total times) to get other values in the distribution. An estimate for the probability that it would take at least 10 purchases to get all four prizes is the proportion of numbers in your distribution that are 10 or more.

11.CE.7

a. P(1st Red or 2nd Red) = P(1st Red) + P(2nd Red) − P(Both Red) = 0.45 + 0.35 − 0.25 = 0.55 by the addition rule. You can also see this in the Venn diagram and table below by adding up 0.20, 0.25, and 0.10.

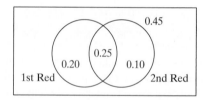

	1st Red	1st Green	Total
2nd Red	**0.25**	**0.10**	0.35
2nd Green	**0.20**	0.45	0.65
Total	0.45	0.55	1

b. The complement to at least one red light is no red lights (or both green). The probability is 0.45.

11.CE.9

a. 0.53.

b. 0.47.

c. 0.17/0.42 = 0.405.

d. No, because P(Speed|Park) = 0.405 ≠ P(Speed) = 0.28.

e. No, because P(Speed and Park) ≠ 0.

f. P(Both|At least one) = 0.17/0.53 = 0.321.